## www.mystatlab.com

**MyStatLab is a text-specific, easily customizable online course that integrates interactive multimedia instruction with content from your Pearson textbook.** As a part of the MyMathLab® series, MyStatLab courses include all of MyMathLab's standard features, plus additional resources designed specifically to help students succeed in statistics, such as Java™ applets, statistical software, and more.

## Features for Instructors

MyStatLab provides you with a rich and flexible set of course materials, along with course-management tools that make it easy to deliver all or a portion of your course online.

### Powerful homework and test manager

Create, import, and manage online homework assignments, quizzes, and tests that are automatically graded, allowing you to spend less time grading and more time teaching. You can choose from a wide range of assignment options, including time limits, proctoring, and maximum number of attempts allowed.

### Custom exercise builder

The MathXL®Exercise Builder (MEB) for MyStatLab lets you create static and algorithmic online exercises for your online assignments. Exercises can include number lines, graphs, and pie charts, and you can create custom feedback that appears when students enter answers.

### Comprehensive gradebook

MyStatLab's online gradebook automatically tracks your students' results on tests, homework, and tutorials. The gradebook provides a number of flexible grading options, including exporting grades to a spreadsheet program such as Microsoft® Excel.

# Features for Students

MyStatLab provides students with a personalized, interactive environment where they can learn at their own pace and measure their progress.

### Interactive tutorial exercises

MyStatLab's homework and practice exercises, correlated to the exercises in the textbook, are generated algorithmically, giving students unlimited opportunity for practice and mastery. Exercises include guided solutions, sample problems, and learning aids for extra help at point-of-use, and they offer helpful feedback when students enter incorrect answers.

### StatCrunch

StatCrunch offers both numerical and data analysis and uses interactive graphics to illustrate the connection between objects selected in a graph and the underlying data. In most MyStatLab courses, all data sets from the textbook are pre-loaded in StatCrunch, and StatCrunch is also available as a tool from all online homework and practice exercises.

### Applets

Applets display statistical concepts in a graphical manner and are suitable as classroom demonstration tools or for independent exploration.

### Student Purchasing Options

There are many ways for students to sign up for MyStatLab:
- Use the access kit bundled with a new textbook
- Purchase a stand-alone access kit from the bookstore
- Register online through www.coursecompass.com

**PEARSON**

www.pearsonhighered.com

David F. Groebner • Patrick W. Shannon
Phillip C. Fry • Kent D. Smith

# CIS 3300 – Business Analytics I
## (Descriptive and Predictive)

Custom Edition for Metropolitan State University of Denver

Taken from:
*Business Statistics: A Decision-Making Approach*, Eighth Edition
by David F. Groebner, Patrick W. Shannon, Phillip C. Fry, and Kent D. Smith

Cover Art: Courtesy of Photodisc/Getty Images.

Taken from:

*Business Statistics: A Decision-Making Approach*, Eighth Edition
by David F. Groebner, Patrick W. Shannon, Phillip C. Fry, and Kent D. Smith
Copyright © 2011, 2008, 2005, 2001 by Pearson Education, Inc.
New York, NY 10013

This special edition published in cooperation with Pearson Education, Inc.

Pearson Education, Inc., 330 Hudson Street, New York, New York 10013
A Pearson Education Company
www.pearsoned.com

Printed in the United States of America

2    16


000200010272051873

AW

ISBN 10: 1-323-45704-6
ISBN 13: 978-1-323-45704-7

# About the **Authors**

**David F. Groebner** is Professor Emeritus of Production Management in the College of Business and Economics at Boise State University. He has bachelor's and master's degrees in engineering and a Ph.D. in business administration. After working as an engineer, he has taught statistics and related subjects for 27 years. In addition to writing textbooks and academic papers, he has worked extensively with both small and large organizations, including Hewlett-Packard, Boise Cascade, Albertson's, and Ore-Ida. He has worked with numerous government agencies, including Boise City and the U.S. Air Force.

**Patrick W. Shannon, Ph.D.** is Dean and Professor of Supply Chain Operations Management in the College of Business and Economics at Boise State University. In addition to his administrative responsibilities, he has taught graduate and undergraduate courses in business statistics, quality management, and production and operations management. In addition, Dr. Shannon has lectured and consulted in the statistical analysis and quality management areas for over 20 years. Among his consulting clients are Boise Cascade Corporation; Hewlett-Packard; PowerBar, Inc.; Potlatch Corporation; Woodgrain Millwork, Inc.; J.R. Simplot Company; Zilog Corporation; and numerous other public- and private-sector organizations. Professor Shannon has co-authored several university-level textbooks and has published numerous articles in such journals as *Business Horizons, Interfaces, Journal of Simulation, Journal of Production and Inventory Control, Quality Progress,* and *Journal of Marketing Research.* He obtained B.S. and M.S. degrees from the University of Montana and a Ph.D. in Statistics and Quantitative Methods from the University of Oregon.

**Phillip C. Fry** is a Professor in the College of Business and Economics at Boise State University, where he has taught since 1988. Phil received his B.A. and M.B.A. degrees from the University of Arkansas, and his M.S. and Ph.D. degrees from Louisiana State University. His teaching and research interests are in the areas of business statistics, production management, and quantitative business modeling. In addition to his academic responsibilities, Phil has consulted with and provided training to small and large organizations, including Boise Cascade Corporation; Hewlett-Packard Corporation; The J.R. Simplot Company; United Water of Idaho; Woodgrain Millwork, Inc.; Boise City; and Micron Electronics.

Phil spends most of his free time with his wife, Susan, and his four children, Phillip Alexander, Alejandra Johanna, and twins Courtney Rene and Candace Marie.

**Kent D. Smith** received a Ph.D. in Applied Statistics from the University of California, Riverside. He holds a master of science degree in Statistics from the University of California, Riverside, and a master of science degree in Systems Analysis from the Air Force Institute of Technology. His bachelor of arts degree in Mathematics was obtained from the University of Utah. Dr. Smith has served as a University Statistical Consultant at the University of California, Riverside, and at California Polytechnic State University, San Luis Obispo. His private consulting has ranged from serving as an expert witness in legal cases, survey sampling for corporations and private researchers, medical and orthodontic research, and assisting graduate students with analysis required for master and doctoral degrees in various disciplines.

Dr. Smith began teaching as a part-time lecturer at California State University, San Bernardino. While completing his doctoral dissertation, he served as a lecturer at University of California, Riverside. Currently, he is Professor Emeritus of Statistics at California Polytechnic State University, San Luis Obispo. Though retired, he still teaches part time at the university. The subjects he teaches include upper-division courses in regression, analysis of variance, linear models, and probability and mathematical statistics, as well as a full array of service courses.

# Brief **Contents**

# Contents

## Chapter 12    Analysis of Variance    475

## Chapters 8–12    Special Review Section    530

# Preface

In today's workplace, students can have an immediate competitive edge over both new graduates and experienced employees if they know how to apply statistical analysis skills to real-world decision-making problems.

Our intent in writing *Business Statistics: A Decision-Making Approach* is to provide an introductory business statistics text for students who do not necessarily have an extensive mathematics background but who need to understand how statistical tools and techniques are applied in business decision making.

This text differs from its competitors in three key ways:

1. Use of a direct approach and concepts and techniques consistently presented in a systematic and ordered way.

2. Presentation of the content at a level that makes it accessible to students of all levels of mathematical maturity. The text features clear, step-by-step explanations that make learning business statistics straightforward.

3. Engaging examples, drawn from our years of experience as authors, educators, and consultants, to show the relevance of the statistical techniques in realistic business decision situations.

Regardless of how accessible or engaging a textbook is, we recognize that many students do not read the chapters from front to back. Instead, they use the text "backward." That is, they go to the assigned exercises and try them, and if they get stuck, they turn to the text to look for examples to help them. Thus, this text features clearly marked, step-by-step examples that students can follow. Each detailed example is linked to a section exercise, which students can use to build specific skills needed to work exercises in the section.

Each chapter begins with a clear set of specific chapter outcomes. The examples and practice exercises are designed to reinforce the objectives and lead students toward the desired outcomes. The exercises are ordered from easy to more difficult and are divided into categories: Conceptual, Skill Development, Business Applications, and Database Exercises.

Another difference is the importance this text places on data and how data are obtained. Many business statistics texts assume that data have already been collected. We have decided to underscore a more modern theme: Data are the starting point. We believe that effective decision making relies on a good understanding of the different types of data and the different data collection options that exist. To highlight our theme, we begin a discussion of data and collecting data in Chapter 1 before any discussion of data analysis is presented. In Chapters 2 and 3, where the important descriptive statistical techniques are introduced, we tie these statistical techniques to the type and level of data for which they are best suited.

Although we know that the role of the computer is important in applying business statistics, it can be overdone at the beginning level to the point where instructors are required to spend too much time teaching the software and too little time teaching statistical concepts. This text features Excel and Minitab but limits the inclusion of software output to those areas where it is of particular advantage to beginning students.

## New to This Edition

- **Textual examples:** More than 50 new examples throughout the text provide step-by-step details, enabling students to follow solution techniques easily. Students can then apply the methodology from each example to solve other problems. These examples are provided in addition to the vast array of business applications to give students a real-world, competitive edge. Featured companies in these new examples include Dove Shampoo and Soap, The Frito-Lay Company, Goodyear Tire Company, Lockheed Martin Corporation, the National Federation of Independent Business, Oakland Raiders NFL Football, Southwest Airlines, and Whole Foods Grocery.
- **Visual summaries:** Each main heading is summarized using a flow diagram, which reminds students of the intended outcomes and leads them to the chapter's conclusion.

## MyStatLab

- **MyStatLab:** This proven book-specific online homework and assessment tool provides a rich and flexible set of course materials, featuring free-response exercises that are algorithmically generated for unlimited practice and mastery. Students can also use a variety of online tools to independently improve their understanding and performance in the course. Instructors can use MyStatLab's homework and test manager to select and assign their own online exercises and can import TestGen tests for added flexibility.
- **Quick prep links:** At the beginning of each chapter, students are supplied with several ways to get ready for the topics discussed in the chapter.
- **Chapter outcomes:** Identifying what is to be gained from completing the chapter helps focus a student's attention. At the beginning of each chapter, every outcome is linked to the corresponding main heading. Throughout the text, the chapter outcomes are recalled at main headings to remind students of the objectives.
- **How to do it:** Associated with the textual examples, lists are provided throughout each chapter to summarize major techniques and reinforce fundamental concepts.
- **Online chapter—Introduction to Decision Analysis:** This chapter discusses the analytic methods used to deal with the wide variety of decision situations a student might encounter.
  - **Appendix B** —Changed from Binomial Distribution Table to Cumulative Binomial Distribution Table.
  - **Appendix C** —Changed from Poisson Probability Distribution Table to Cumulative Poisson Probability Distribution Table.

# Key Pedagogical Features

- **Business applications:** One of the strengths of the previous editions of this textbook has been the emphasis on business applications and decision making. This feature is expanded even more in the eighth edition. Many new applications are included, and all applications are highlighted in the text with special icons, making them easier for students to locate as they use the text.
- **Quick prep links:** Each chapter begins with a list that provides several ways to get ready for the topics discussed in the chapter.
- **Chapter outcomes:** At the beginning of each chapter, outcomes, which identify what is to be gained from completing the chapter, are linked to the corresponding main headings. Throughout the text, the chapter outcomes are recalled at the appropriate main headings to remind students of the objectives.
- **Step-by-step approach:** This edition provides continued and improved emphasis on providing concise, step-by-step details to reinforce chapter material.
  - **How to do it** lists are provided throughout each chapter to summarize major techniques and reinforce fundamental concepts.
  - **Textual examples** throughout the text provide step-by-step details, enabling students to follow solution techniques easily. Students can then apply the methodology from each example to solve other problems. These examples are provided in addition to the vast array of business applications to give students a real-world, competitive edge.
- **Real-world application:** The chapters and cases feature real companies, actual applications, and rich data sets, allowing the authors to concentrate their efforts on addressing how students apply this statistical knowledge to the decision-making process.
  - **McDonald's Corporation video cases** —The authors' relationship with McDonald's provides students with real-world statistical data and integrated video case series.
  - **Chapter cases** —Cases provided in nearly every chapter are designed to give students the opportunity to apply statistical tools. Each case challenges students to define a problem, determine the appropriate tool to use, apply it, and then write a summary report.
- **Special review sections:** For Chapters 1 to 3 and Chapters 8 to 12, special review sections provide a summary and review of the key issues and statistical techniques. Highly effective flow diagrams help students sort out which statistical technique is appropriate to use in a given problem or exercise. These flow diagrams serve as a mini-decision support system that takes the emphasis off memorization and encourages students to seek a

higher level of understanding and learning. Integrative questions and exercises ask students to demonstrate their comprehension of the topics covered in these sections.

- **Problems and exercises:** This edition includes an extensive revision of exercise sections, featuring more than 250 new problems. The exercise sets are broken down into three categories for ease of use and assignment purposes:
    1. **Skill Development**—These problems help students build and expand upon statistical methods learned in the chapter.
    2. **Business Applications**—These problems involve realistic situations in which students apply decision-making techniques.
    3. **Computer Applications**—In addition to the problems that may be worked out manually, many problems have associated data files and can be solved using Excel, Minitab, or other statistical software.

- **Virtual office hours:** The authors appear in three- to five-minute video clips in which they work examples taken directly from the book. Now students can watch and listen to the instructor walk through an example and obtain even greater clarity with respect to how the example is worked and how the results are interpreted.

- **Computer integration:** The text seamlessly integrates computer applications with textual examples and figures, always focusing on interpreting the output. The goal is for students to be able to know which tools to use, how to apply the tools, and how to analyze their results for making decisions.
    - **Minitab 14** is featured, with associated instructions.
    - **Microsoft Excel 2007** integration instructs students in how to use the Excel 2007 user interface for statistical applications.
    - **PHStat2** is a specially developed Excel add-in package that is compatible with the Excel 2007 release. It performs a number of statistical features not included with Excel. The added functions and procedures are useful in the study and application of business statistics. When installed, PHStat2 attaches itself to the Excel menu bar, providing users with a pull-down menu of topics that supplement the Data Analysis add-in tools in Microsoft Excel.

        PHStat2 uses a set of simple and consistent dialog boxes that allow students to specify values and options for almost 50 tools included in the software. PHStat2 produces Excel worksheets organized into areas for input data, intermediate calculations, and the results of analyses. Unlike with some competitors' add-ins, most of these worksheets contain live formulas that allow students to engage immediately in further "what-if" explorations of the data. (Where applicable, these worksheets contain special cell tints that distinguish the cells that contain user-modifiable input values from the cells containing the results, making "what-if" analysis even easier.) Completing the package is an excellent online help system.

## MyStatLab

- **MyStatLab** is a proven book-specific online homework and assessment tool that provides a rich and flexible set of course materials, featuring free-response exercises that are algorithmically generated for unlimited practice and mastery. Students can also use a variety of online tools to independently improve their understanding and performance in the course. Instructors can use MyStatLab's homework and test manager to select and assign their own online exercises and import TestGen tests for added flexibility.

## Student Resources

### Student Solutions Manual

The Student Solutions Manual contains worked-out solutions to odd-numbered problems in the text. It displays the detailed process that students should use to work through the problems. The manual also provides interpretation of the answers and serves as a valuable learning tool for students.

## MyStatLab™

Part of the MyMathLab® and MathXL® product family, MyStatLab™ is a text-specific, easily customizable online course that integrates interactive multimedia instruction with textbook content. MyStatLab gives you the tools you need to deliver all or a portion of your course online, whether your students are in a lab setting or working from home.

- **Interactive tutorial exercises:** A comprehensive set of exercises—correlated to your textbook at the objective level—are algorithmically generated for unlimited practice and mastery. Most exercises are free-response exercises and provide guided solutions, sample problems, and learning aids for extra help at point-of-use.
- **Personalized study plan:** When a student completes a test or quiz in MyStatLab, the program generates a personalized study plan for that student, indicating which topics have been mastered and linking students directly to tutorial exercises for topics they need to study and retest.
- **Multimedia learning aids:** Students can use online learning aids, such as video lectures, animations, and a complete multimedia textbook, to help independently improve their understanding and performance.
- **Statistics tools:** MyStatLab includes built-in tools for statistics, including statistical software called StatCrunch. Students also have access to statistics animations and applets that illustrate key ideas for the course. For those who use technology in their course, technology manual PDFs are included.
- **StatCrunch:** This powerful online tool provides an interactive environment for doing statistics. You can use StatCrunch for both numerical and graphical data analysis, taking advantage of interactive graphics to help you see the connection between objects selected in a graph and the underlying data. In MyStatLab, the data sets from your textbook are preloaded into StatCrunch. StatCrunch is also available as a tool from the online homework and practice exercises in MyStatLab and in MathXL for Statistics. Also available is Statcrunch.com, Web-based software that allows students to perform complex statistical analysis in a simple manner.
- **Pearson Tutor Center (www.pearsontutorservices.com):** Access to the Pearson Tutor Center **is** automatically included with MyStatLab. The Tutor Center is staffed by qualified mathematics instructors who provide textbook-specific tutoring for students via toll-free phone, fax, e-mail, and interactive Web sessions.

MyStatLab is powered by CourseCompass™, Pearson Education's online teaching and learning environment, and by MathXL®, an online homework, tutorial, and assessment system. For more information about MyStatLab, visit www.mystatlab.com.

## Student Videos

Student videos—located at MyStatLab only—feature McDonald's video cases and the virtual office hours videos.

## Student Companion Web Site

The Companion Web Site, www.pearsonhighered.com/groebner, contains valuable online resources for both students and professors, including:

- **Online chapter—Introduction to Decision Analysis:** This chapter discusses the analytic methods used to deal with the wide variety of decision situations a student might encounter.
- **Data files:** The text provides an extensive number of data files for examples, cases, and exercises. These files are also located at MyStatLab.
- **Excel and Minitab tutorials:** Customized PowerPoint tutorials for both Minitab and Excel use data sets from text examples. Separate tutorials for Excel 2003 and Excel 2007 are provided. Students who need additional instruction in Excel or Minitab can access the menu-driven tutorial, which shows exactly the steps needed to replicate all computer examples in the text. These tutorials are also located at MyStatLab.
- **Excel simulations:** Several interactive simulations illustrate key statistical topics and allow students to do "what-if" scenarios. These simulations are also located at MyStatLab.

- **PHStat:** PHStat is a collection of statistical tools that enhance the capabilities of Excel and assist students in learning the concepts of statistics; published by Pearson Education. This tool is also located at MyStatLab.
- **Online study guide:** This guide contains practice or homework quizzes consisting of multiple-choice, true/false, and essay questions that effectively review textual material. It is located on the Companion Web site only.

# Instructor Resources

- **Instructor Resource Center:** The Instructor Resource Center contains the electronic files for the complete Instructor's Solutions Manual, the Test Item File, and Lecture PowerPoint presentations (www.pearsonhighered.com/groebner).
- **Register, Redeem, Login:** At www.pearsonhighered.com/irc, instructors can access a variety of print, media, and presentation resources that are available with this text in downloadable, digital format. For most texts, resources are also available for course management platforms such as Blackboard, WebCT, and Course Compass.
- **It gets better:** Once you register, you will not have additional forms to fill out or multiple usernames and passwords to remember to access new titles and/or editions. As a registered faculty member, you can log in directly to download resource files and receive immediate access and instructions for installing course management content to your campus server.
- **Need help?** Our dedicated technical support team is ready to assist instructors with questions about the media supplements that accompany this text. Visit http://247 .prenhall.com/ for answers to frequently asked questions and toll-free user support phone numbers. The supplements are available to adopting instructors. Detailed descriptions are provided on the Instructor Resource Center.

## Instructor's Solutions Manual

The Instructor's Solutions Manual contains worked-out solutions to all the problems and cases in the text.

## Lecture PowerPoint Presentations

A PowerPoint presentation, created by Angela Mitchell of Wilmington College of Ohio, is available for each chapter. The PowerPoint slides provide instructors with individual lecture outlines to accompany the text. The slides include many of the figures and tables from the text. Instructors can use these lecture notes as is or can easily modify the notes to reflect specific presentation needs.

## Test Item File

The Test Item File, by Jing Quan of Salisbury University, contains a variety of true/false, multiple-choice, and short-answer questions for each chapter.

## TestGen

The computerized TestGen package allows instructors to customize, save, and generate classroom tests. The test program permits instructors to edit, add, or delete questions from the test bank; edit existing graphics and create new graphics; analyze test results; and organize a database of test and student results. This software allows for extensive flexibility and ease of use. It provides many options for organizing and displaying tests, along with search and sort features. The software and the test banks can be downloaded from the Instructor Resource Center, at www.pearsonhighered.com/groebner.

## MyStatLab

- **MathXL® for Statistics:** This powerful online homework, tutorial, and assessment system accompanies Pearson Education textbooks in statistics. With MathXL for Statistics, instructors can create, edit, and assign online homework and tests, using algorithmically generated exercises correlated at the objective level to the textbook. They can also create and assign their own online exercises and import TestGen tests for added flexibility. All student work is tracked in MathXL's online gradebook. Students can take chapter tests in MathXL and receive personalized study plans based on their test results. The study plan diagnoses weaknesses and links students directly to tutorial exercises for the objectives they need to study and retest. Students can also access supplemental animations and video clips directly from selected exercises. MathXL for Statistics is available to qualified adopters. For more information, visit www.mathxl.com or contact your sales representative.

■ **MyStatLab™:** Part of the MyMathLab® and MathXL® product family, MyStatLab™ is a text-specific, easily customizable online course that integrates interactive multimedia instruction with textbook content. MyStatLab gives you the tools you need to deliver all or a portion of your course online, whether your students are in a lab setting or working from home.

■ *Assessment Manager:* An easy-to-use assessment manager lets instructors create online homework, quizzes, and tests that are automatically graded and correlated directly to the textbook. Assignments can be created using a mix of questions from the MyStatLab exercise bank, instructor-created custom exercises, and/or TestGen test items.

■ **Gradebook:** Designed specifically for mathematics and statistics, the MyStatLab gradebook automatically tracks students' results and gives you control over how to calculate final grades. You can also add offline (paper-and-pencil) grades to the gradebook.

■ **Math Exercise Builder:** You can use the MathXL Exercise Builder to create static and algorithmic exercises for your online assignments. A library of sample exercises provides an easy starting point for creating questions, and you can also create questions from scratch.

## Acknowledgments

Publishing this eighth edition of *Business Statistics: A Decision-Making Approach* has been a team effort involving the contributions of many people. At the risk of overlooking someone, we express our sincere appreciation to the many key contributors. Throughout the two years we have worked on this revision, many of our colleagues from colleges and universities around the country have taken time from their busy schedules to provide valuable input and suggestions for improvement. We would like to thank the following people:

Donald I. Bosshardt, *Canisius College*

Sara T. DeLoughy, *Western Connecticut State University*

Nicholas R. Farnum, *California State University—Fullerton*

Kent E. Foster, *Winthrop University*

John Gum, *University of South Florida—St. Petersburg*

Jeffery Guyse, *California State Polytechnic University, Pomona*

Chaiho Kim, *Santa Clara University*

David Knopp, *Chattanooga State Technical Community College*

Linda Leighton, *Fordham University*

Sally A. Lesik, *Central Connecticut State University*

Merrill W. Liechty, *Drexel University*

Robert M. Lynch, *University of Northern Colorado—Monfort College of Business*

Jennifer Martin, *York College of Pennsylvania*

Constance McLaren, *Indiana State University*

Mahour Mellat-Parast, *University of North Carolina—Pembroke*

Carl E. Miller, *Northern Kentucky University*

Tariq Mughal, *David Eccles, School of Business, University of Utah*

Tom Naugler, *Johns Hopkins University*

Kenneth Paetsch, *Cleveland State University*

Ed Pappanastos, *Troy University*

Michael D. Polomsky, *Cleveland State University*

Peter Royce, *University of New Hampshire*

Rose Sebastianelli, *University of Scranton*

Bulent Uyar, *University of Northern Iowa*

Tom Wheeler, *Georgia Southwestern State University*

We also wish to thank Professor Angela Mitchell, who designed and developed the PowerPoint slides that accompany this text. Thanks also to David Stephen for his expert work in developing the PHStat add-ins for Excel that accompany the text.

Thanks, too, to Annie Puciloski, who checked the solutions to every exercise. This is a very time-consuming but extremely important role, and we greatly appreciate her efforts. In addition, we wish to thank Tariq Mughal of The University of Utah for developing the test manual. This, too, requires a huge commitment of time and effort, and we appreciate Dr. Mughal's contributions to the package of materials that accompany the text. Howard Flomberg at the Metropolitan State College of Denver contributed his skills and creative abilities to develop the Excel and Minitab tutorials that are so useful to students, and we thank him for all his contributions. Thanks, too, to Bob Donnelly of Goldey-Beacom College for his development of the Online Study Guide.

Finally, we wish to give our utmost thanks and appreciation to the Prentice Hall publishing team that has assisted us in every way possible to make this eighth edition a reality. Blair Brown was responsible for the text design. Allison Longley oversaw all the media products that accompany this text. Clara Bartunek, in her role as production project manager, guided the development of the book from its initial design all the way through to final printing. Mary Kate Murray, assistant editor, served as our day-to-day contact and expertly facilitated the project in every way imaginable. And finally, we wish to give the highest thanks possible to Chuck Synovec, the senior acquisitions editor for decision sciences, who has provided valuable guidance, motivation, and leadership from beginning to end on this project. It has been a great pleasure to work with Chuck and his team at Prentice Hall.

—David F. Groebner

—Patrick W. Shannon

—Phillip C. Fry

—Kent D. Smith

# The Where, Why, and How of Data Collection

**Outcome 1.** Know the key data collection methods.

**Outcome 2.** Know the difference between a population and a sample.

**Outcome 3.** Understand the similarities and differences between different sampling methods.

**Outcome 4.** Understand how to categorize data by type and level of measurement.

## Why you need to know

Although you may not realize it yet, by taking this business statistics course you will be learning about some of the most useful business procedures available for decision makers. In today's workplace, you can have an immediate competitive edge over other new employees, and even those with more experience, by applying statistical analysis skills to real-world decision making. The purpose of this text is to assist in your learning process and to complement your instructor's efforts in conveying how to apply a variety of important statistical procedures. Each chapter introduces one or more statistical procedure and technique that, regardless of your major, will be useful in your career.

Wal-Mart, the world's largest retail chain, collects and manages massive amounts of data related to the operation of its stores throughout the world. Its highly sophisticated database systems contain sales data, detailed customer data, employee satisfaction data, and much more. Ford Motor Company maintains databases with information on production, quality, customer satisfaction, safety records, and much more. Governmental agencies amass extensive data on such things as unemployment, interest rates, incomes, and education. However, access to data is not limited to large companies. The relatively low cost of computer hard drives with 100-gigabyte or larger capacities makes it possible for small firms, and even individuals, to store vast amounts of data on desktop computers. But without some way to transform the data into useful information, the data any of these companies have gathered are of little value.

Transforming data into information is where business statistics comes in—the statistical procedures introduced in this text are those that are used to help transform data into information. This text focuses on the practical application of statistics; we do not develop the theory you would find in a mathematical statistics course. Will you need to use math in this course? Yes, but mainly the concepts covered in your college algebra course.

Statistics does have its own terminology. You will need to learn various terms that have special statistical meaning. You will also learn certain dos and don'ts related to statistics. But most importantly you will learn specific methods to effectively convert data into information. Don't try to memorize the concepts; rather, go to the next level of learning called *understanding*. Once you understand the underlying concepts, you will be able to *think statistically*.

Because data are the starting point for any statistical analysis, Chapter 1 is devoted to discussing various aspects of data, from how to collect data to the different types of data that you will be analyzing. You need to gain an understanding of the where, why, and how of data and data collection because the remaining chapters deal with the techniques for transforming data into useful information.

# 1.1 What Is Business Statistics?

**Business Statistics**

A collection of procedures and techniques that are used to convert data into meaningful information in a business environment.

Every day, your local newspaper contains stories that report descriptors such as stock prices, crime rates, and government-agency budgets. Such descriptors can be found in many places. However, they are just a small part of the discipline called **business statistics**, which provides a wide variety of methods to assist in data analysis and decision making. Business is one important area of application for these methods.

## Descriptive Statistics

The procedures and techniques that comprise business statistics include those specially designed to *describe data*, such as charts, graphs, and numerical measures. Also included are inferential procedures that help decision makers *draw inferences* from a set of data. Inferential procedures include estimation and hypothesis testing. A brief discussion of these techniques follows. The examples illustrate data that have been entered into the Microsoft Excel and Minitab software packages.

**BUSINESS APPLICATION** **DESCRIBING DATA**

**INDEPENDENT TEXTBOOK PUBLISHING, INC.** The college textbook publishing industry has witnessed a great amount of consolidation in recent years. Large companies have acquired smaller companies. An exception to this consolidation is Independent Text Publishing, Inc. The company currently publishes 15 texts in the business and social sciences areas. Figure 1.1

**FIGURE 1.1** |

Excel 2007 Spreadsheet of Independent Textbook Publishing, Inc.

**Excel 2007 Instructions:**
1. Open File: Independent Textbook.xls.

| | Book | Units Sold | Pages | Competing Books | Advertising Budget | Age of Author | Market Classification |
|---|---|---|---|---|---|---|---|
| 2 | 1 | 15000 | 176 | 5 | 25000 | 49 | Social Sciences |
| 3 | 2 | 140000 | 296 | 10 | 83000 | 57 | Business |
| 4 | 3 | 75000 | 483 | 7 | 40000 | 29 | Business |
| 5 | 4 | 100000 | 811 | 14 | 29000 | 37 | Social Sciences |
| 6 | 5 | 26000 | 302 | 9 | 52000 | 35 | Business |
| 7 | 6 | 33000 | 411 | 15 | 33000 | 43 | Business |
| 8 | 7 | 59000 | 333 | 7 | 19000 | 51 | Social Sciences |
| 9 | 8 | 103000 | 602 | 4 | 37000 | 62 | Business |
| 10 | 9 | 88000 | 504 | 12 | 51000 | 33 | Social Sciences |
| 11 | 10 | 10000 | 204 | 3 | 30000 | 50 | Business |
| 12 | 11 | 9000 | 376 | 4 | 19000 | 26 | Business |
| 13 | 12 | 124000 | 600 | 7 | 41000 | 40 | Business |
| 14 | 13 | 59000 | 400 | 3 | 26000 | 44 | Social Sciences |
| 15 | 14 | 183000 | 597 | 8 | 51000 | 59 | Business |
| 16 | 15 | 16000 | 126 | 1 | 27000 | 38 | Social Sciences |

FIGURE 1.2 |

Histogram Showing the
Copies Sold Distribution

shows an Excel spreadsheet containing data for each of these 15 textbooks. Each column in the spreadsheet corresponds to a different factor for which data were collected. Each row corresponds to a different textbook. Many statistical procedures might help the owners describe these textbook data, including *charts*, *graphs*, and *numerical measures*.

**Charts and Graphs** Chapter 2 will discuss many different charts and graphs—such as the one shown in Figure 1.2, called a *histogram*. This graph displays the shape and spread of the distribution of number of copies sold. The *bar chart* shown in Figure 1.3 shows the total number of textbooks sold broken down by the two markets, business and social sciences.

Bar charts and histograms are only two of the techniques that could be used to graphically analyze the data for the textbook publisher. In Chapter 2 you will learn more about these and other techniques.

**BUSINESS APPLICATION**    **DESCRIBING DATA**

**CROWN INVESTMENTS** During the 1990s and early 2000s, many major changes occurred in the financial services industry. Numerous banks merged. Money flowed into the stock market at rates far surpassing anything the U.S. economy had previously witnessed. The international financial world fluctuated greatly. All these developments have spurred the need for more financial analysts who can critically evaluate and explain financial data to customers.

At Crown Investments, a senior analyst is preparing to present data to upper management on the 100 fastest growing companies on the Hong Kong Stock Exchange. Figure 1.4 shows a Minitab worksheet containing a subset of the data. The columns correspond to the different

FIGURE 1.3 |

Bar Chart Showing Copies
Sold by Sales Category

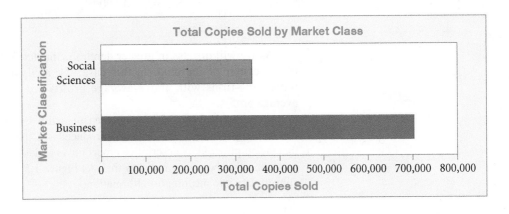

**FIGURE 1.4**

Crown Investment Example

| ↓ | C5 | C6 | C7 | C8 | C9 | C10 | C11 | C12 |
|---|---|---|---|---|---|---|---|---|
| | Growth % | Sales | EPS | Profits | Stk-Price | Last Yr Price | P/E ratio | Stk Market |
| 1 | 256 | 185.3 | -99 | 6.8 | 18.00 | 8.50 | 17 | 1 |
| 2 | 228 | 183.2 | 243 | 43.2 | 42.25 | 12.50 | 31 | 1 |
| 3 | 215 | 187.5 | -99 | 26.5 | 21.25 | 11.13 | 17 | 1 |
| 4 | 209 | 229.8 | 129 | 35.4 | 27.38 | 26.25 | 16 | 1 |
| 5 | 209 | 249.9 | 97 | 8.9 | 23.38 | 15.00 | 53 | 2 |
| 6 | 203 | 399.7 | 18 | 4.2 | 2.31 | 1.13 | 17 | 1 |
| 7 | 200 | 731.4 | 95 | 77.7 | 11.63 | 10.00 | 24 | 2 |
| 8 | 180 | 93.0 | 116 | 8.6 | 6.63 | -99.00 | 21 | 2 |
| 9 | 179 | 440.9 | 72 | 8.4 | 8.25 | -99.00 | 9 | 1 |
| 10 | 167 | 131.8 | -99 | 3.7 | 16.50 | -99.00 | 66 | 1 |

* –99.00 indicates missing data

items of interest (growth percentage, sales, and so on). The data for each company are in a single row. The data file is called "Fast100."

In addition to preparing appropriate graphs, the analyst will compute important numerical measures. One of the most basic and most useful measures in business statistics is one with which you are already familiar: the **arithmetic mean** or **average**.

**Arithmetic Mean or Average**
The sum of all values divided by the number of variables.

---

**Average**

The sum of all the values divided by the number of values. In equation form:

$$\text{Average} = \frac{\sum_{i=1}^{N} x_i}{N} = \frac{\text{Sum of all data values}}{\text{Number of data values}} \qquad (1.1)$$

where:

$$N = \text{Number of data values}$$
$$x_i = i\text{th data value}$$

---

The analyst may be interested in the average profit (that is, the average of the column labeled "Profits") for the 100 companies. The total profit for the 100 companies is $3,193.60, but profits are given in millions of dollars, so the total profit amount is actually $3,193,600,000. The average is found by dividing this total by the number of companies:

$$\text{Average} = \frac{\$3,193,600,000}{100} = \$31,936,000, \text{ or } \$31.936 \text{ million dollars}$$

As we will discuss in greater depth in Chapter 3, the average, or mean, is a measure of the center of the data. In this case, the analyst may use the average profit as an indicator—firms with above-average profits are rated higher than firms with below-average profits.

The graphical and numerical measures illustrated here are only some of the many descriptive procedures that will be introduced in Chapters 2 and 3. The key to remember is that the purpose of any descriptive procedure is to describe data. Your task will be to select the procedure that best accomplishes this. As Figure 1.5 reminds you, the role of statistics is to convert data into meaningful information.

FIGURE 1.5

The Role of Business
Statistics

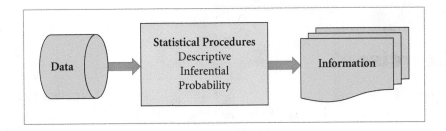

## Inferential Procedures

How do television networks determine which programs people prefer to watch? How does the network that carries the Super Bowl know how many people watched the game? Advertisers pay for television ads based on the audience level, so these numbers are important; millions of dollars are at stake. Clearly, the networks don't check with everyone in the country. Instead, they use **statistical inference procedures** to come up with this information.

There are two primary categories of statistical inference procedures: *estimation* and *hypothesis testing*. These procedures are closely related but serve very different purposes.

**Statistical Inference Procedures**

Procedures that allow a decision maker to reach a conclusion about a set of data based on a subset of that data.

**Estimation**  In situations in which we would like to know about all the data in a large data set but it is impractical to work with all the data, decision makers can use techniques to estimate what the larger data set looks like. The estimates are formed by looking closely at a subset of the larger data set.

---

**BUSINESS APPLICATION**  **STATISTICAL INFERENCE**

---

**TV RATINGS**  The television networks cannot know for sure how many people watched last year's Super Bowl. They cannot possibly ask everyone what he or she saw that day on television. Instead, the networks rely on organizations such as Nielsen Media Research to supply program ratings. For example, Nielsen (www.nielsenmedia.com) surveys people from only a small number of homes across the country asking what shows they watched, and then uses the data from the survey to estimate the number of viewers per show for the entire population.

Advertisers and television networks enter into contracts in which price per ad is based on a certain minimum viewership. If Nielsen Media Research estimate an audience smaller than this minimum, then a network must refund some money to its advertisers.

In Chapter 8 we will discuss the estimating techniques that companies such as Nielsen use.

**Hypothesis Testing**  Television advertising is full of product claims. For example, we might hear that "Goodyear tires will last at least 60,000 miles" or that "more doctors recommend Bayer Aspirin than any other brand." Other claims might include statements like "General Electric lightbulbs last longer than any other brand" or "customers prefer McDonald's over Burger King." Are these just idle boasts, or are they based on actual data? Probably some of both! However, consumer research organizations such as Consumers Union, publisher of *Consumer Reports*, regularly test these types of claims. For example, in the hamburger case, *Consumer Reports* might select a sample of customers who would be asked to blind taste test Burger King's and McDonald's hamburgers, under the hypothesis that there is no difference in customer preferences between the two restaurants. If the sample data show a substantial difference in preferences, then the hypothesis of no difference would be rejected. If only a slight difference in preferences was detected, then *Consumer Reports* could not reject the hypothesis. Chapters 9 and 10 introduce basic hypothesis-testing techniques that are used to test claims about products and services using information taken from samples.

# 1-1: Exercises

## Skill Development

**1-1.** For the following situation indicate whether the statistical application is primarily descriptive or inferential.

"The manager of Anna's Fabric Shop has collected data for 10 years on the number of each type of dress fabric that has been sold at the store. She is interested in making a presentation that will illustrate these data effectively."

**1-2.** Consider the following graph that appeared in a company annual report. What type of graph is this? Explain.

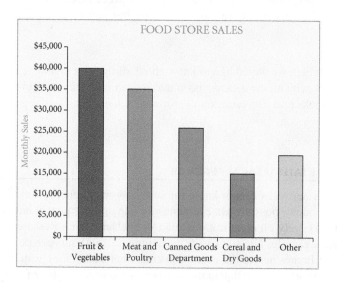

**1-3.** Review Figures 1.2 and 1.3 and discuss any differences you see between the histogram and the bar chart.

**1-4.** Think of yourself as working for an advertising firm. Provide an example of how hypothesis testing can be used to evaluate a product claim.

**1-5.** Define what is meant by hypothesis testing. Provide an example in which you personally have tested a hypothesis (even if you didn't use formal statistical techniques to do so.)

**1-6.** In what situations might a decision maker need to use statistical inference procedures?

**1-7.** Explain under what circumstances you would use hypothesis testing as opposed to an estimation procedure.

**1-8.** Discuss any advantages a graph showing a whole set of data has over a single measure, such as an average.

**1-9.** Discuss any advantages a single measure, such as an average, has over a table showing a whole set of data.

## Business Applications

**1-10.** Describe how statistics could be used by a business to determine if the dishwasher parts it produces last longer than a competitor's brand.

**1-11.** Locate a business periodical such as *Fortune* or *Forbes* or a business newspaper such as *The Wall Street Journal*. Find three examples of the use of a graph to display data. For each graph
 a. Give the name, date, and page number of the periodical in which the graph appeared.
 b. Describe the main point made by the graph.
 c. Analyze the effectiveness of the graphs.

**1-12.** The human resources manager of an automotive supply store has collected the following data showing the number of employees in each of five categories by the number of days missed due to illness or injury during the past year.

| Missed Days | 0–2 days | 3–5 days | 6–8 days | 8–10 days |
|---|---|---|---|---|
| Employees | 159 | 67 | 32 | 10 |

Construct the appropriate chart for these data. Be sure to use labels and to add a title to your chart.

**1-13.** Suppose *Fortune* would like to determine the average age and income of its subscribers. How could statistics be of use in determining these values?

**1-14.** Locate an example from a business periodical or newspaper in which estimation has been used.
 a. What specifically was estimated?
 b. What conclusion was reached using the estimation?
 c. Describe how the data were extracted and how they were used to produce the estimation.
 d. Keeping in mind the goal of the estimation, discuss whether you believe that the estimation was successful and why.
 e. Describe what inferences were drawn as a result of the estimation.

**1-15.** Locate one of the online job Web sites and pick several job listings. For each job type, discuss one or more situations where statistical analyses would be used. Base your answer on research (Internet, business periodicals, personal interviews, etc.). Indicate whether the situations you are describing involve descriptive statistics or inferential statistics or a combination of both.

**1-16.** Suppose Super-Value, a major retail food company, is thinking of introducing a new product line into a market area. It is important to know the age characteristics of the people in the market area.

a. If the executives wish to calculate a number that would characterize the "center" of the age data, what statistical technique would you suggest? Explain your answer.

b. The executives need to know the percentage of people in the market area that are senior citizens. Name the basic category of statistical procedure they would use to determine this information.

c. Describe a hypothesis which the executives might wish to test concerning the percentage of senior citizens in the market area.

**END EXERCISES 1-1**

Chapter Outcome 1. → **1.2  Procedures for Collecting Data**

We have defined business statistics as a set of procedures that are used to transform data into information. Before you learn how to use statistical procedures, it is important that you become familiar with different types of data collection methods.

## Data Collection Methods

There are many methods and procedures available for collecting data. The following are considered some of the most useful and frequently used data collection methods:

- Experiments
- Telephone surveys
- Written questionnaires and surveys
- Direct observation and personal interviews

**BUSINESS APPLICATION   EXPERIMENTS**

**FOOD PROCESSING** A company often must conduct a specific experiment or set of experiments to get the data managers need to make informed decisions. For example, the J. R. Simplot Company in Idaho is a primary supplier of french fries to companies such as McDonald's. At its Caldwell, Idaho, factory, Simplot has a tech center that, among other things, houses a mini french fry plant used to conduct experiments on its potato manufacturing process. McDonald's has strict standards on the quality of the french fries it buys. One important attribute is the color of the fries after cooking. They should be uniformly "golden brown"—not too light or too dark.

French fries are made from potatoes that are peeled, sliced into strips, blanched, partially cooked, and then freeze-dried—not a simple process. Because potatoes differ in many ways (such as sugar content and moisture), blanching time, cooking temperature, and other factors vary from batch to batch.

**Experiment**

A process that produces a single outcome whose result cannot be predicted with certainty.

**Experimental Design**

A plan for performing an experiment in which the variable of interest is defined. One or more factors are identified to be manipulated, changed, or observed so that the impact (or influence) on the variable of interest can be measured or observed.

Simplot tech-center employees start their **experiments** by grouping the raw potatoes into batches with similar characteristics. They run some of the potatoes through the line with blanch time and temperature settings set at specific levels defined by an **experimental design**. After measuring one or more output variables for that run, employees change the settings and run another batch, again measuring the output variables.

Figure 1.6 shows a typical data collection form. The output variable (for example, percentage of fries without dark spots) for each combination of potato category, blanch time, and temperature is recorded in the appropriate cell in the table. Chapter 12 introduces the fundamental concepts related to experimental design and analysis.

**BUSINESS APPLICATION   TELEPHONE SURVEYS**

**PUBLIC ISSUES** One common method of obtaining data about people and their opinions is the telephone survey. Chances are that you have been on the receiving end of one. "Hello. My name is Mary Jane and I represent the XYZ organization. I am conducting a survey on. . . ." Political groups use telephone surveys to poll people about candidates and issues.

**FIGURE 1.6**

Data Layout for the French Fry
Experiment

| Blanch Time | Blanch Temperature | Potato Category 1 | 2 | 3 | 4 |
|---|---|---|---|---|---|
| 10 minutes | 100<br>110<br>120 | | | | |
| 15 minutes | 100<br>110<br>120 | | | | |
| 20 minutes | 100<br>110<br>120 | | | | |
| 25 minutes | 100<br>110<br>120 | | | | |

Telephone surveys are a relatively inexpensive and efficient data collection procedure. Of course, some people will refuse to respond to a survey, others are not home when the calls come, and some people do not have home phones—only have a cell phone—or cannot be reached by phone for one reason or another. Figure 1.7 shows the major steps in conducting a telephone survey. This example survey was run by a Seattle television station to determine public support for using tax dollars to build a new football stadium for the National Football League's Seattle Seahawks. The survey was aimed at property tax payers only.

**FIGURE 1.7**

Major Steps for a Telephone
Survey

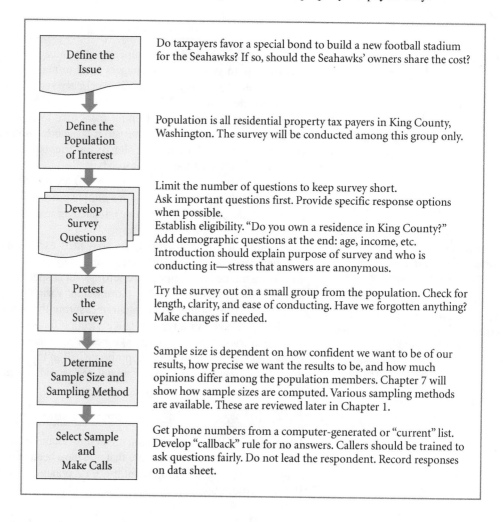

**Define the Issue** — Do taxpayers favor a special bond to build a new football stadium for the Seahawks? If so, should the Seahawks' owners share the cost?

**Define the Population of Interest** — Population is all residential property tax payers in King County, Washington. The survey will be conducted among this group only.

**Develop Survey Questions** — Limit the number of questions to keep survey short.
Ask important questions first. Provide specific response options when possible.
Establish eligibility. "Do you own a residence in King County?"
Add demographic questions at the end: age, income, etc.
Introduction should explain purpose of survey and who is conducting it—stress that answers are anonymous.

**Pretest the Survey** — Try the survey out on a small group from the population. Check for length, clarity, and ease of conducting. Have we forgotten anything? Make changes if needed.

**Determine Sample Size and Sampling Method** — Sample size is dependent on how confident we want to be of our results, how precise we want the results to be, and how much opinions differ among the population members. Chapter 7 will show how sample sizes are computed. Various sampling methods are available. These are reviewed later in Chapter 1.

**Select Sample and Make Calls** — Get phone numbers from a computer-generated or "current" list. Develop "callback" rule for no answers. Callers should be trained to ask questions fairly. Do not lead the respondent. Record responses on data sheet.

Because most people will not stay on the line very long, the phone survey must be short—usually one to three minutes. The questions are generally what are called **closed-end questions**. For example, a closed-end question might be "To which political party do you belong? Republican? Democrat? Or other?"

**Closed-End Questions**
Questions that require the respondent to select from a short list of defined choices.

The survey instrument should have a short statement at the beginning explaining the purpose of the survey and reassuring the respondent that his or her responses will remain confidential. The initial section of the survey should contain questions relating to the central issue of the survey. The last part of the survey should contain **demographic questions** (such as gender, income level, education level) that will allow you to break down the responses and look deeper into the survey results.

**Demographic Questions**
Questions relating to the respondents' characteristics, backgrounds, and attributes.

A survey budget must be considered. For example, if you have $3,000 to spend on calls and each call costs $10 to make, you obviously are limited to making 300 calls. However, keep in mind that 300 calls may not result in 300 usable responses.

The phone survey should be conducted in a short time period. Typically, the prime calling time for a voter survey is between 7:00 P.M. and 9:00 P.M. However, some people are not home in the evening and will be excluded from the survey unless there is a plan for conducting callbacks.

**Written Questionnaires and Surveys**  The most frequently used method to collect opinions and factual data from people is a written questionnaire. In some instances, the questionnaires are mailed to the respondent. In others, they are administered directly to the potential respondents. Written questionnaires are generally the least expensive means of collecting survey data. If they are mailed, the major costs include postage to and from the respondents, questionnaire development and printing costs, and data analysis. Figure 1.8 shows the major steps in conducting a written survey. Note how written surveys are similar to telephone surveys; however, written surveys can be slightly more involved and, therefore, take more time to complete than those used for a telephone survey. However, you must be careful to construct a questionnaire that can be easily completed without requiring too much time.

**FIGURE 1.8**

Written Survey Steps

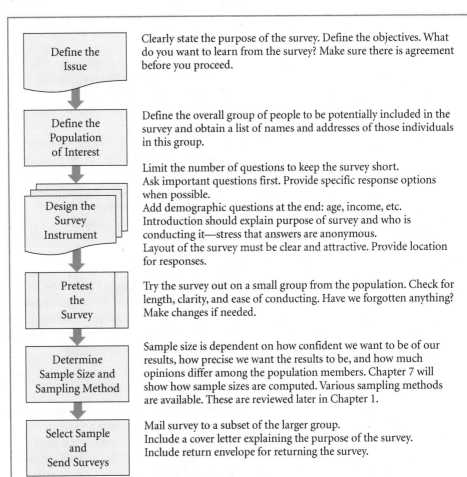

**Define the Issue**
Clearly state the purpose of the survey. Define the objectives. What do you want to learn from the survey? Make sure there is agreement before you proceed.

**Define the Population of Interest**
Define the overall group of people to be potentially included in the survey and obtain a list of names and addresses of those individuals in this group.

**Design the Survey Instrument**
Limit the number of questions to keep the survey short.
Ask important questions first. Provide specific response options when possible.
Add demographic questions at the end: age, income, etc.
Introduction should explain purpose of survey and who is conducting it—stress that answers are anonymous.
Layout of the survey must be clear and attractive. Provide location for responses.

**Pretest the Survey**
Try the survey out on a small group from the population. Check for length, clarity, and ease of conducting. Have we forgotten anything? Make changes if needed.

**Determine Sample Size and Sampling Method**
Sample size is dependent on how confident we want to be of our results, how precise we want the results to be, and how much opinions differ among the population members. Chapter 7 will show how sample sizes are computed. Various sampling methods are available. These are reviewed later in Chapter 1.

**Select Sample and Send Surveys**
Mail survey to a subset of the larger group.
Include a cover letter explaining the purpose of the survey.
Include return envelope for returning the survey.

**Open-End Questions**
Questions that allow respondents the freedom to respond with any value, words, or statements of their own choosing.

A written survey can contain both closed-end and **open-end questions**.

Open-end questions provide the respondent with greater flexibility in answering a question; however, the responses can be difficult to analyze. Note that telephone surveys can use open-end questions, too. However, the caller may have to transcribe a potentially long response and there is risk that the interviewees' comments may be misinterpreted.

Written surveys also should be formatted to make it easy for the respondent to provide accurate and reliable data. This means that proper space must be provided for the responses, and the directions must be clear about how the survey is to be completed. A written survey needs to be pleasing to the eye. How it looks will affect the response rate, so it must look professional.

You also must decide whether to manually enter or scan the data gathered from your written survey. The survey design will be affected by the approach you take. If you are administering a large number of surveys, scanning is preferred. It cuts down on data entry errors and speeds up the data gathering process. However, you may be limited in the form of responses that are possible if you use scanning.

If the survey is administered directly to the desired respondents, you can expect a high response rate. For example, you probably have been on the receiving end of a written survey many times in your college career, when you were asked to fill out a course evaluation form at the end of the term. Most students will complete the form. On the other hand, if a survey is administered through the mail, you can expect a low response rate—typically 5% to 20%. Therefore, if you want 200 responses, you should mail out 1,000 to 4,000 questionnaires.

Overall, written surveys can be a low-cost, effective means of collecting data if you can overcome the problems of low response. Be careful to pretest the survey and spend extra time on the format and look of the survey instrument.

Developing a good written questionnaire or telephone survey instrument is a major challenge. Among the potential problems are the following:

- Leading questions
    Example: "Do you agree with most other reasonably minded people that the city should spend more money on neighborhood parks?"
        Issue: In this case, the phrase "Do you agree" may suggest that you should agree. Also, by suggesting that "most reasonably minded people" already agree, the respondent might be compelled to agree so that he or she can also be considered "reasonably minded."
        Improvement: "In your opinion, should the city increase spending on neighborhood parks?"
    Example: "To what extent would you support paying a small increase in your property taxes if it would allow poor and disadvantaged children to have food and shelter?"
        Issue: The question is ripe with emotional feeling and may imply that if you don't support additional taxes, you don't care about poor children.
        Improvement: "Should property taxes be increased to provide additional funding for social services?"
- Poorly worded questions
    Example: "How much money do you make at your current job?"
        Issue: The responses are likely to be inconsistent. When answering, does the respondent state the answer as an hourly figure or as a weekly or monthly total? Also, many people refuse to answer questions regarding their income.
        Improvement: "Which of the following categories best reflects your weekly income from your current job?

        ———— Under $500          ———— $500–$1,000
        ———— Over $1,000"

    Example: "After trying the new product, please provide a rating from 1 to 10 to indicate how you like its taste and freshness."
        Issue: First, is a low number or a high number on the rating scale considered a positive response? Second, the respondent is being asked to rate two factors, taste and freshness, in a single rating. What if the product is fresh but does not taste good?

Improvement: "After trying the new product, please rate its taste on a 1 to 10 scale with 1 being best. Also rate the product's freshness using the same 1 to 10 scale.

_____ Taste                    _____ Freshness"

The way a question is worded can influence the responses. Consider an example that occurred in September 2008 during the financial crisis that resulted from the sub-prime mortgage crisis and bursting of the real estate bubble. Three surveys were conducted on the same basic issue. The following questions were asked:

"Do you approve or disapprove of the steps the Federal Reserve and Treasury Department have taken to try to deal with the current situation involving the stock market and major financial institutions?" (ABC News/Washington Post) 44% Approve – 42% Disapprove – 14% Unsure

"Do you think the government should use taxpayers' dollars to rescue ailing private financial firms whose collapse could have adverse effects on the economy and market, or is it not the government's responsibility to bail out private companies with taxpayer dollars?" (LA Times/Bloomberg) 31% Use Tax Payers' Dollars – 55% Not Government's Responsibility – 14% Unsure

"As you may know, the government is potentially investing billions to try and keep financial institutions and markets secure. Do you think this is the right thing or the wrong thing for the government to be doing?" (Pew Research Center) 57% Right Thing – 30% Wrong Thing – 13% Unsure

Note the responses to each of these questions. The way the question is worded can affect the responses.

**Direct Observation and Personal Interviews**   _Direct observation_ is another procedure that is often used to collect data. As implied by the name, this technique requires that the process from which the data are being collected is physically observed and the data recorded based on what takes place in the process.

Possibly the most basic way to gather data on human behavior is to watch people. If you are trying to decide whether a new method of displaying your product at the supermarket will be more pleasing to customers, change a few displays and watch customers' reactions. If, as a member of a state's transportation department, you want to determine how well motorists are complying with the state's seat belt laws, place observers at key spots throughout the state to monitor people's seat belt habits. A movie producer, seeking information on whether a new movie will be a success, holds a preview showing and observes the reactions and comments of the movie patrons as they exit the screening. The major constraints when collecting observations are the time and money required to carry out the observations. For observations to be effective, trained observers must be used, which increases the cost. Personal observation is also time-consuming. Finally, personal perception is subjective. There is no guarantee that different observers will see a situation in the same way, much less report it the same way.

_Personal interviews_ are often used to gather data from people. Interviews can be either **structured** or **unstructured**, depending on the objectives, and they can utilize either open-end or closed-end questions.

Regardless of the procedure used for data collection, care must be taken that the data collected are accurate and reliable and that they are the right data for the purpose at hand.

## Other Data Collection Methods

Data collection methods that take advantage of new technologies are becoming more prevalent all the time. For example, many people believe that Wal-Mart is the best company in the world at collecting and using data about the buying habits of its customers. Most of the data are collected automatically as checkout clerks scan the UPC bar codes on the products customers purchase. Not only are Wal-Mart's inventory records automatically updated, but information about the buying habits of customers is recorded. The data help managers organize their stores to increase sales. For instance, Wal-Mart apparently decided to locate beer and disposable diapers close together when it discovered that many male customers also purchase beer when they are sent to the store for diapers.

**Structured Interview**
Interviews in which the questions are scripted.

**Unstructured Interview**
Interviews that begin with one or more broadly stated questions, with further questions being based on the responses.

Bar code scanning is used in many different data collection applications. In a DRAM (dynamic random-access memory) wafer fabrication plant, batches of silicon wafers have bar codes. As the batches travel through the plant's workstations, their progress and quality are tracked through the data that are automatically obtained by scanning.

Every time you use your credit card, data are automatically collected by the retailer and the bank. Computer information systems are developed to store the data and to provide decision makers with procedures to access the data.

In many instances your data collection method will require you to use *physical measurement*. For example, the Andersen Window Company has quality analysts physically measure the width and height of its windows to assure that they meet customer specifications, and a state Department of Weights and Measures will physically test meat and produce scales to determine that customers are being properly charged for their purchases.

## Data Collection Issues

There are several data collection issues of which you need to be aware. When you need data to make a decision, we suggest that you first see if appropriate data have already been collected, because it is usually faster and less expensive to use existing data than to collect data yourself. However, before you rely on data that were collected by someone else for another purpose, you need to check out the source to make sure that the data were collected and recorded properly.

Such organizations as *Value Line* and *Fortune* have built their reputations on providing quality data. Although data errors are occasionally encountered, they are few and far between. You really need to be concerned with data that come from sources with which you are not familiar. This is an issue for many sources on the World Wide Web. Any organization, or any individual, can post data to the Web. Just because the data are there doesn't mean they are accurate. Be careful.

**Bias**
An effect which alters a statistical result by systematically distorting it; different from a random error which may distort on any one occasion but balances out on the average.

**Interviewer Bias** There are other general issues associated with data collection. One of these is the potential for *bias* in the data collection. There are many types of bias. For example, in a personal interview, the interviewer can interject bias (either accidentally or on purpose) by the way she asks the questions, by the tone of her voice, or by the way she looks at the subject being interviewed. We recently allowed ourselves to be interviewed at a trade show. The interviewer began by telling us that he would only get credit for the interview if we answered all of the questions. Next, he asked us to indicate our satisfaction with a particular display. He wasn't satisfied with our less-than-enthusiastic rating and kept asking us if we really meant what we said. He even asked us if we would consider upgrading our rating! How reliable do you think these data will be?

**Nonresponse Bias** Another source of bias that can be interjected into a survey data collection process is called *nonresponse bias*. We stated earlier that mail surveys suffer from a high percentage of unreturned surveys. Phone calls don't always get through, or people refuse to answer. Subjects of personal interviews may refuse to be interviewed. There is a potential problem with nonresponse. Those who respond may provide data that are quite different from the data that would be supplied by those who choose not to respond. If you aren't careful, the responses may be heavily weighted by people who feel strongly one way or another on an issue.

**Selection Bias** Bias can be interjected through the way subjects are selected for data collection. This is referred to as *selection bias*. A study on the virtues of increasing the student athletic fee at your university might not be best served by collecting data from students attending a football game. Sometimes, the problem is more subtle. If we do a telephone survey during the evening hours, we will miss all of the people who work nights. Do they share the same views, income, education levels, and so on as people who work days? If not, the data are biased.

Written and phone surveys and personal interviews can also yield flawed data if the interviewees *lie* in response to questions. For example, people commonly give inaccurate data about such sensitive matters as income. Sometimes, the data errors are not due to lies. The respondents may not know or have accurate information to provide the correct answer.

**Observer Bias** Data collection through personal observation is also subject to problems. People tend to view the same event or item differently. This is referred to as *observer bias*.

One area in which this can easily occur is in safety check programs in companies. An important part of behavioral-based safety programs is the safety observation. Trained data collectors periodically conduct a safety observation on a worker to determine what, if any, unsafe acts might be taking place. We have seen situations in which two observers will conduct an observation on the same worker at the same time, yet record different safety data. This is especially true in areas in which judgment is required on the part of the observer, such as the distance a worker is from an exposed gear mechanism. People judge distance differently.

**Measurement Error** A few years ago we were working with a wood window manufacturer. The company was having a quality problem with one of its saws. A study was developed to measure the width of boards that had been cut by the saw. Two people were trained to use digital calipers and record the data. This caliper is a U-shaped tool that measures distance (in inches) to three decimal places. The caliper was placed around the board and squeezed tightly against the sides. The width was indicated on the display. Each person measured 500 boards during an 8-hour day. When the data were analyzed, it looked like the widths were coming from two different saws; one set showed considerably narrower widths than the other. Upon investigation, we learned that the person with the narrower width measurements was pressing on the calipers much more firmly. The soft wood reacted to the pressure and gave narrower readings. Fortunately, we had separated the data from the two data collectors. Had they been merged, the measurement error might have gone undetected.

**Internal Validity** When data are collected through experimentation, you need to make sure that proper controls have been put in place. For instance, suppose a drug company such as Pfizer is conducting tests on a drug that it hopes will reduce cholesterol. One group of test participants is given the new drug while a second group (a control group) is given a placebo. Suppose that after several months, the group using the drug saw significant cholesterol reduction. For the results to have **internal validity**, the drug company would have had to make sure the two groups were controlled for the many other factors that might affect cholesterol, such as smoking, diet, weight, gender, race, and exercise habits. Issues of internal validity are generally addressed by randomly assigning subjects to the test and control groups. However, if the extraneous factors are not controlled, there could be no assurance that the drug was the factor influencing reduced cholesterol. For data to have internal validity, the extraneous factors must be controlled.

**Internal Validity**
A characteristic of an experiment in which data are collected in such a way as to eliminate the effects of variables within the experimental environment that are not of interest to the researcher.

**External Validity** Even if experiments are internally valid, you will always need to be concerned that the results can be generalized beyond the test environment. For example, if the cholesterol drug test had been performed in Europe, would the same basic results occur for people in North America, South America, or elsewhere? For that matter, the drug company would also be interested in knowing whether the results could be replicated if other subjects are used in a similar experiment. If the results of an experiment can be replicated for groups different from the original population, then there is evidence the results of the experiment have **external validity**.

An extensive discussion of how to measure the magnitude of bias and how to reduce bias and other data collection problems is beyond the scope of this text. However, you should be aware that data may be biased or otherwise flawed. Always pose questions about the potential for bias and determine what steps have been taken to reduce its effect.

**External Validity**
A characteristic of an experiment whose results can be generalized beyond the test environment so that the outcomes can be replicated when the experiment is repeated.

*MyStatLab*

# 1-2: Exercises

## Skill Development

**1-17.** If a pet store wishes to determine the level of customer satisfaction with its services, would it be appropriate to conduct an experiment? Explain.

**1-18.** Define what is meant by a leading question. Provide an example.

**1-19.** Briefly explain what is meant by an experiment and an experimental design.

**1-20.** Refer to the three questions discussed in this section involving the financial crises of 2008 and 2009 and possible government intervention. Note that the questions elicited different responses.

Discuss the way the questions were worded and why they might have produced such different results.

**1-21.** Suppose a survey is conducted using a telephone survey method. The survey is conducted from 9 A.M. to 11 A.M. on Tuesday. Indicate what potential problems the data collectors might encounter.

**1-22.** For each of the following situations, indicate what type of data collection method you would recommend and discuss why you have made that recommendation:

   a. collecting data on the percentage of bike riders who wear helmets
   b. collecting data on the price of regular unleaded gasoline at gas stations in your state
   c. collecting data on customer satisfaction with the service provided by a major U.S. airline

**1-23.** Assume you have received a class assignment to determine the attitude of students in your school toward the school's registration process. What are the validity issues you should be concerned with?

## Business Applications

**1-24.** According to a report issued by the U.S. Department of Agriculture (USDA), the agency estimates that the Southern fire ants spread at a rate of 4 to 5 miles a year. What data collection method do you think was used to collect this data? Explain your answer.

**1-25.** Suppose you are asked to survey students at your university to determine if they are satisfied with the food service choices on campus. What types of biases must you guard against in collecting your data?

**1-26.** Briefly describe how new technologies can assist businesses in their data collection efforts.

**1-27.** Assume you have used an online service such as Orbitz or Travelocity to make an airline reservation. The following day you receive an e-mail containing a questionnaire asking you to rate the quality of the experience. Discuss both the advantages and disadvantages of using this form of questionnaire delivery.

**1-28.** In your capacity as assistant sales manager for a large office products retailer, you have been assigned the task of interviewing purchasing managers for medium and large companies in the San Francisco Bay area. The objective of the interview is to determine the office product buying plans of the company in the coming year. Develop a personal interview form that asks both issue-related questions as well as demographic questions.

**1-29.** The regional manager for Macy's is experimenting with two new end-of-aisle displays of the same product. An end-of-aisle display is a common method retail stores use to promote new products. You have been hired to determine which is more effective. Two measures you have decided to track are which display causes the highest percentage of people to stop and, for those who stop, which causes people to view the display the longest. Discuss how you would gather such data.

**1-30.** In your position as general manager for United Fitness Center, you have been asked to survey the customers of your location to determine whether they want to convert the racquetball courts to an aerobics exercise space. The plan calls for a written survey to be handed out to customers when they arrive at the fitness center. Your task is to develop a short questionnaire with at least three "issue" questions and at least three demographic questions. You also need to provide the finished layout design for the questionnaire.

**1-31.** According to a national CNN/USA/Gallup survey of 1,025 adults, conducted March 14–16, 2008, 63% say they have experienced a hardship because of rising gasoline prices. How do you believe the survey was conducted and what types of bias could occur in the data collection process?

**END EXERCISES 1-2**

---

**Chapter Outcome 2.** ➔ ## 1.3 Populations, Samples, and Sampling Techniques

### Populations and Samples

**Population**
The set of all objects or individuals of interest or the measurements obtained from all objects or individuals of interest.

**Sample**
A subset of the population.

Two of the most important terms in statistics are **population** and **sample**.

The list of all objects or individuals in the population is referred to as the *frame*. Each object or individual in the frame is known as a sampling unit. The choice of the frame depends on what objects or individuals you wish to study and on the availability of the list of these objects or individuals. Once the frame is defined, it forms the list of sampling units. The next example illustrates this concept.

**BUSINESS APPLICATION** **POPULATIONS AND SAMPLES**

**McDONALD'S** We can use McDonald's to illustrate the difference between a population and a sample. McDonald's is very concerned about the time customers spend waiting in the drive-thru line. At a particular McDonald's store, on a given day 566 cars arrived at the drive-thru.

A population includes measurements made on all the items of interest to the data gatherer. In our example, the McDonald's manager would define the population as the waiting time for all 566 cars. The list of these cars, possibly by license number, forms the frame. If she examines the entire population, she is taking a **census**. But suppose 566 cars are too many to track. The McDonald's manager could instead select a subset of these cars, called a *sample*. The manager could use the sample results to make inferences about the population. For example, she might calculate the average waiting time for the sample of cars and then use that to conclude what the average waiting time is for the population. How this inference is drawn will be discussed in later chapters.

**Census**

An enumeration of the entire set of measurements taken from the whole population.

There are trade-offs between taking a census and taking a sample. Usually the main trade-off is whether the information gathered in a census is worth the extra cost. In organizations in which data are stored on computer files, the additional time and effort of taking a census may not be substantial. However, if there are many accounts that must be manually checked, a census may be impractical.

Another consideration is that the measurement error in census data may be greater than in sample data. A person obtaining data from fewer sources tends to be more complete and thorough in both gathering and tabulating the data. As a result, with a sample there are likely to be fewer human errors.

**Parameters and Statistics** Descriptive numerical measures, such as an average or a proportion, that are computed from an entire population are called *parameters*. Corresponding measures for a sample are called *statistics*. Suppose in the previous example the McDonald's manager timed every car that arrived at the drive-thru on a particular day and calculated the average. This population average waiting time would be a parameter. However, if she selected a sample of cars from the population, the average waiting time for the sampled cars would be a statistic. These concepts are more fully discussed in Chapters 3 and 7.

## Sampling Techniques

Once a manager decides to gather information by sampling, he or she can use a sampling technique that falls into one of two categories: **statistical** or **nonstatistical**.

**Statistical Sampling Techniques**

Those sampling methods that use selection techniques based on chance selection.

**Nonstatistical Sampling Techniques**

Those methods of selecting samples using convenience, judgment, or other nonchance processes.

Both nonstatistical and statistical sampling techniques are commonly used by decision makers. Regardless of which technique is used, the decision maker has the same objective—to obtain a sample that is a close representative of the population. There are some advantages to using a statistical sampling technique, as we will discuss many times throughout this text. However, in many cases, nonstatistical sampling represents the only feasible way to sample, as illustrated in the following example.

**BUSINESS APPLICATION**   **NONSTATISTICAL SAMPLING**

**WAGNER ORCHARDS** Wagner Orchards owns and operates a large fruit orchard and fruit-packing plant in Washington State. During harvest time in the cherry orchard, pickers load 20-pound "lugs" with cherries, which are then transported to the packing plant. At the packing plant, the cherries are graded and boxed for shipping nationally and internationally. Because of the volume of cherries involved, it is impossible to assign a quality grade to each individual cherry. Instead, as each lug moves up the conveyor into the packing plant, a quality manager selects a small sample of cherries from the lug; grades these individual cherries as to size, color, and so forth; and then assigns an overall quality grade to the entire lug from which the sample was selected.

**Convenience Sampling**

A sampling technique that selects the items from the population based on accessibility and ease of selection.

Because of the volume of cherries, the quality manager at the orchard uses a nonstatistical sampling method called **convenience sampling**. In doing so, the quality manager is willing to assume that cherry quality (size, color, etc.) is evenly spread throughout the container. That is, the cherries near the top of each lug are the same quality as cherries located anywhere else in the lug.

There are other nonstatistical sampling methods, such as *judgment sampling* and *ratio sampling*, which are not discussed here. Instead, the most frequently used statistical sampling techniques will now be discussed.

**Statistical Sampling** *Statistical sampling* methods (also called *probability sampling*) allow every item in the population to have a known or calculable chance of being included in the sample. The fundamental statistical sample is called a *simple random sample*. Other types of statistical sampling discussed in this text include *stratified random sampling, systematic sampling*, and *cluster sampling*.

Chapter Outcome 3. → **BUSINESS APPLICATION**   **SIMPLE RANDOM SAMPLING**

**CABLE-ONE** A salesperson at Cable-One wishes to estimate the percentage of people in a local subdivision who have satellite television service (such as Direct TV). The result would indicate the extent to which the satellite industry has made inroads into Cable-One's market. The population of interest consists of all families living in the subdivision.

For this example, we simplify the situation by saying that there are only five families in the subdivision: James, Sanchez, Lui, White, and Fitzpatrick. We will let $N$ represent the population size and $n$ the sample size. From the five families ($N = 5$), we select three ($n = 3$) for the sample. There are 10 possible samples of size 3 that could be selected.

| | | |
|---|---|---|
| {James, Sanchez, Lui} | {James, Sanchez, White} | {James, Sanchez, Fitzpatrick} |
| {James, Lui, White} | {James, Lui, Fitzpatrick} | {James, White, Fitzpatrick} |
| {Sanchez, Lui, White} | {Sanchez, Lui, Fitzpatrick} | {Sanchez, White, Fitzpatrick} |
| {Lui, White, Fitzpatrick} | | |

Note that no family is selected more than once in a given sample. This method is called *sampling without replacement* and is the most commonly used method. If the families could be selected more than once, the method would be called *sampling with replacement*.

**Simple random sampling** is the method most people think of when they think of random sampling. In a correctly performed simple random sample, each of these samples would have an equal chance of being selected. For the Cable-One example a simplified way of selecting a simple random sample would be to put each sample of three names on a piece of paper in a bowl and then blindly reach in and select one piece of paper. However, this method would be difficult if the number of possible samples were large. For example, if $N = 50$ and a sample of size $n = 10$ is to be selected, there are more than 10 billion possible samples. Try finding a bowl big enough to hold those!

Simple random samples can be obtained in a variety of ways. We present two examples to illustrate how simple random samples are selected in practice.

**Simple Random Sampling**

A method of selecting items from a population such that every possible sample of a specified size has an equal chance of being selected.

**Excel and Minitab Tutorial**

**BUSINESS APPLICATION**   **RANDOM NUMBERS**

**NORDSTROM'S PAYROLL** Suppose the personnel manager at Nordstrom's Department Store in Seattle is considering changing the payday from once a month to once every two weeks. Before making any decisions, he wants to survey a sample of 10 employees from the store's 300 employees. He first assigns employees a number (001 to 300). He can then use the random number function in either Excel or Minitab to determine which employees to include in the sample. Figure 1.9 shows the results when Excel chooses 10 random numbers. The first employee sampled is number 115, followed by 31, and so forth. The important thing to remember is that assigning each employee a number and then randomly selecting a sample from those numbers gives each possible sample an equal chance of being selected.

**RANDOM NUMBERS TABLE** If you don't have access to computer software such as Excel or Minitab, the items in the population to be sampled can be determined by using the *random numbers table* in Appendix A. Begin by selecting a starting point in the random numbers table (row and digit). Suppose we use row 5, digit 8 as the starting point. Go down 5 rows and over 8 digits. Verify that the digit in this location is 1. Ignoring the blanks between columns that are there only to make the table more readable, the first three-digit number is 149. Employee number 149 is the first one selected in the sample. Each subsequent random number is obtained from the random numbers in the next row down. For instance, the second number is 127. The procedure continues selecting numbers from top to bottom in each subsequent

**FIGURE 1.9**

Excel 2007 Output of Random Numbers for Nordstrom's Example

**Excel 2007 Instructions:**
1. On the **Data** tab, click **Data Analysis**.
2. Select **Random Number Generation** option.
3. Select **Uniform** as the distribution.
4. Define range as between 1 and 300.
5. Indicate where the results are to go.
6. Click **OK**.

To convert numbers to integers, select the data in column A and on the Home tab in the Number group, click the Decrease decimal button several times.

column. Numbers exceeding 300 and duplicate numbers are skipped. When enough numbers are found for the desired sample size, the process is completed. Employees whose numbers are chosen are then surveyed.

**BUSINESS APPLICATION** STRATIFIED RANDOM SAMPLING

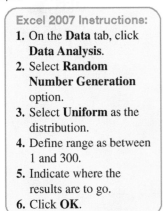

**FEDERAL RESERVE BANK** Sometimes, the sample size required to obtain a needed level of information from a simple random sampling may be greater than our budget permits. At other times, it may take more time to collect than is available. **Stratified random sampling** is an alternative method that has the potential to provide the desired information with a smaller sample size. The following example illustrates how stratified sampling is performed.

**Stratified Random Sampling**

A statistical sampling method in which the population is divided into subgroups called *strata* so that each population item belongs to only one stratum. The objective is to form strata such that the population values of interest within each stratum are as much alike as possible. Sample items are selected from each stratum using the simple random sampling method.

Each year, the Federal Reserve Board asks its staff to estimate the total cash holdings of U.S. financial institutions as of July 1. The staff must base the estimate on a sample. Note that not all financial institutions (banks, credit unions, and the like) are the same size. A majority are small, some are medium-sized, and only a few are large. However, the few large institutions have a substantial percentage of the total cash on hand. To make sure that a simple random sample includes an appropriate number of small, medium, and large institutions, the sample size might have to be quite large.

As an alternative to the simple random sample, the Federal Reserve staff could divide the institutions into three groups called *strata*: small, medium, and large. Staff members could then select a simple random sample of institutions from each stratum and estimate the total cash on hand for all institutions from this combined sample. Figure 1.10 shows the stratified random sampling concept. Note that the combined sample size $(n_1 + n_2 + n_3)$ is the sum of the simple random samples taken from each stratum.

The key behind stratified sampling is to develop a stratum for each characteristic of interest (such as cash on hand) that have items that are quite *homogeneous*. In this example, the size of the financial institution may be a good factor to use in stratifying. Here the combined sample size $(n_1 + n_2 + n_3)$ will be less than the sample size that would have been required if no stratification had occurred. Because sample size is directly related to cost (in both time and money), a stratified sample can be more cost-effective than a simple random sample.

Multiple layers of stratification can further reduce the overall sample size. For example, the Federal Reserve might break the three strata in Figure 1.10 into *substrata* based on type of institution: state bank, interstate bank, credit union, and so on.

**FIGURE 1.10**

Stratified Sampling Example

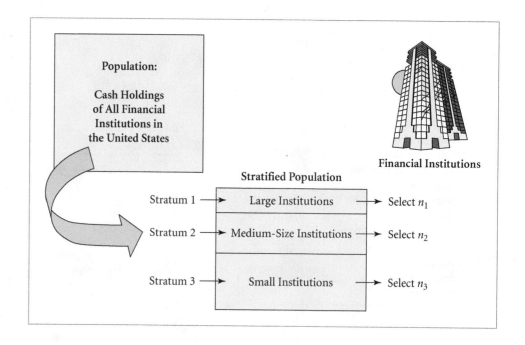

Most large-scale market research studies use stratified random sampling. The well-known political polls, such as the Gallup and Harris polls, use this technique also. For instance, the Gallup poll typically samples between 1,800 and 2,500 people nationwide to estimate how more than 60 million people will vote in a presidential election. We encourage you to go to the Web site www.gallup.com/help/FAQs/poll1.asp to read a very good discussion about how the Gallup polls are conducted. The Web site discusses how samples are selected and many other interesting issues associated with polling.

**BUSINESS APPLICATION** **SYSTEMATIC RANDOM SAMPLING**

**NATIONAL ASSOCIATION OF ACCOUNTANTS** A few years ago, the National Association of Accountants (NAA) considered establishing a code of ethics. To determine the opinion of its 20,000 members, a questionnaire was sent to a sample of 500 members. Although simple random sampling could have been used, an alternative method called **systematic random sampling** was chosen.

The NAA's systematic random sampling plan called for it to send the questionnaire to every 40th member (20,000 / 500 = 40) from the list of members. The list was in alphabetical order. It could have begun by using Excel or Minitab to generate a single random number in the range 1 to 40. Suppose this value was 25. The 25th person in the alphabetic list would be selected. After that, every 40th member would be selected (25, 65, 105, 145, . . .) until there were 500 NAA members.

Systematic sampling is frequently used in business applications. Use it as an alternative to simple random sampling only when you can assume the population is randomly ordered with respect to the measurement being addressed in the survey. In this case, peoples' views on ethics are likely unrelated to the spelling of their last name.

**Systematic Random Sampling**

A statistical sampling technique that involves selecting every $k$th item in the population after a randomly selected starting point between 1 and $k$. The value of $k$ is determined as the ratio of the population size over the desired sample size.

**BUSINESS APPLICATION** **CLUSTER SAMPLING**

**OAKLAND RAIDERS FOOTBALL TEAM** The Oakland Raiders of the National Football League plays its home games at McAfee Coliseum in Oakland, California. Despite their struggles to win in recent years, the team has a passionate fan base. Recently an outside marketing group was retained by the Raiders to interview season ticket holders about the potential for changing how season ticket pricing is structured. The Oakland Raiders Web site www.raiders.com/Tickets/Default.aspx?id=16678 shows the layout of the McAfee Coliseum.

The marketing firm plans to interview season ticket holders just prior to home games during the current season. One sampling technique is to select a simple random sample of size $n$ from the population of all season ticket holders. Unfortunately, this technique would likely require that interviewer(s) go to each section in the stadium. This would prove to be an expensive and time-consuming process. A systematic or stratified sampling procedure also would probably require visiting each section in the stadium. The geographical spread of those being interviewed in this case causes problems.

A sampling technique that overcomes the geographical spread problem is **cluster sampling**. The stadium sections would be the clusters. Ideally, the clusters would each have the same characteristics as the population as a whole.

After the clusters have been defined, a sample of $m$ clusters is selected at random from the list of possible clusters. The number of clusters to select depends on various factors, including our survey budget. Suppose the marketing firm randomly selects eight clusters:

$$104 - 142 - 147 - 218 - 228 - 235 - 307 - 327$$

These are the *primary clusters*. Next, the marketing company can either survey all the ticketholders in each cluster or select a simple random sample of ticketholders from each cluster, depending on time and budget considerations.

**Cluster Sampling**
A method by which the population is divided into groups, or clusters, that are each intended to be mini-populations. A simple random sample of $m$ clusters is selected. The items chosen from a cluster can be selected using any probability sampling technique.

# 1-3: Exercises

## Skill Development

**1-32.** Indicate which sampling method would most likely be used in each of the following situations:
   a. an interview conducted with mayors of a sample of cities in Florida
   b. a poll of voters regarding a referendum calling for a national value-added tax
   c. a survey of customers entering a shopping mall in Minneapolis

**1-33.** A company has 18,000 employees. The file containing the names is ordered by employee number from 1 to 18,000. If a sample of 100 employees is to be selected from the 18,000 using systematic random sampling, within what range of employee numbers will the first employee selected come from?

**1-34.** Describe the difference between a statistic and a parameter.

**1-35.** Why is convenience sampling considered to be a nonstatistical sampling method?

**1-36.** Describe how systematic random sampling could be used to select a random sample of 1,000 customers who have a certificate of deposit at a commercial bank. Assume that the bank has 25,000 customers who own a certificate of deposit.

**1-37.** Explain why a census does not necessarily have to involve a population of people. Use an example to illustrate.

**1-38.** If the manager at First City Bank surveys a sample of 100 customers to determine how many miles they live from the bank, is the mean travel distance for this sample considered a parameter or a statistic? Explain.

**1-39.** Explain the difference between stratified random sampling and cluster sampling.

**1-40.** Use Excel or Minitab to generate five random numbers between 1 and 900.

## Business Applications

**1-41.** According to the U.S. Bureau of Labor Statistics, the annual percentage increase in U.S. college tuition and fees in 1995 was 6.0%, in 1999 it was 4.0%, and in 2004 it was 9.5%. Are these percentages statistics or parameters? Explain.

**1-42.** According to an article in the *Idaho Statesman*, a poll taken the day before elections in Germany showed Chancellor Gerhard Schroeder behind his challenger, Angela Merkel, by 6 to 8 percentage points. Is this a statistic or a parameter? Explain.

**1-43.** Give the name of the kind of sampling that was most likely used in each of the following cases:
   a. a *Wall Street Journal* poll of 2,000 people to determine the president's approval rating
   b. a poll taken of each of the General Motors (GM) dealerships in Ohio in December 2008 to determine an estimate of the average number of 2008-model Chevrolets not yet sold by GM dealerships in the United States
   c. a quality assurance procedure within a Frito-Lay manufacturing plant that tests every 1,000th bag of

Fritos Corn Chips produced to make sure the bag is sealed properly.

d. a sampling technique in which a random sample from each of the tax brackets is obtained by the Internal Revenue Service to audit tax returns

1-44. Your manager has given you an Excel file that contains the names of the company's 500 employees and has asked you to sample 50 employees from the list. You decide to take your sample as follows. First, you assign a random number to each employee using Excel's random number function **Rand**(). Because the random number is volatile (it recalculates itself whenever you modify the file), you freeze the random numbers using the Copy—Paste Special—Values feature. You then sort by the random numbers in ascending order. Finally, you take the first 50 sorted employees as your sample. Does this approach constitute a statistical or a nonstatistical sample?

## Computer **Applications**

1-45. Sysco Foods is a statewide food distributor to restaurants, universities, and other establishments that prepare and sell food. The company has a very large warehouse where the food is stored until it is pulled from the shelves to be delivered to the customers. The warehouse has 64 storage racks numbered 1–64. Each rack is three shelves high, labeled A, B, and C, and each shelf is divided into 80 sections, numbered 1–80. Products are located by rack number, shelf letter, and section number. For example, breakfast cereal is located at 43-A-52 (rack 43, shelf A, section 52).

Each week, employees perform an inventory for a sample of products. Certain products are selected and counted. The *actual count* is compared to the *book count* (the quantity in the records that should be in stock). To simplify things, assume that the company has selected breakfast cereals to inventory. Also for simplicity sake, suppose the cereals occupy racks 1 through 5.

a. Assume that you plan to use simple random sampling to select the sample. Use Excel or Minitab to determine the sections on each of the five racks to be sampled.

b. Assume that you wish to use cluster random sampling to select the sample. Discuss the steps you would take to carry out the sampling.

c. In this case, why might cluster sampling be preferred over simple random sampling? Discuss.

1-46. United Airlines established a discount airline named Ted. The managers were interested in determining how flyers using Ted rate the airline service. They plan to question a random sample of flyers from the November 12 flights between Denver and Fort Lauderdale. A total of 578 people were on the flights that day. United has a list of the travelers together with their mailing addresses. Each traveler is given an identification number (here, from 001 to 578). Use Excel or Minitab to generate a list of 40 flyer identification numbers so that those identified can be surveyed.

1-47. The National Park Service has started charging a user fee to park at selected trailheads and cross-country ski lots. Some users object to this fee, claiming they already pay taxes for these areas. The agency has decided to randomly question selected users at fee areas in Colorado to assess the level of concern.

a. Define the population of interest.

b. Assume a sample of 250 is required. Describe the technique you would use to select a sample from the population. Which sampling technique did you suggest?

c. Assume the population of users is 4,000. Use either Minitab or Excel to generate a list of users to be selected for the sample.

1-48. Mount Hillsdale Hospital has over 4,000 patient files listed alphabetically in its computer system. The office manager wants to survey a statistical sample of these patients to determine how satisfied they were with service provided by the hospital. She plans to use a telephone survey of 100 patients.

a. Describe how you would attach identification numbers to the patient files; for example, how many digits (and which digits) would you use to indicate the first patient file?

b. Describe how the first random number would be obtained to begin a simple random sample method.

c. How many random digits would you need for each random number you selected?

d. Use Excel or Minitab to generate the list of patients to be surveyed.

**END EXERCISES** 1-3

---

**Chapter Outcome 4.** → **1.4 Data Types and Data Measurement Levels**

Chapters 2 and 3 will introduce a variety of techniques for describing data and transforming the data into information. As you will see in those chapters, the statistical techniques deal with different types of data. The level of measurement may vary greatly from application to application. In general, there are four types of data: *quantitative, qualitative, time-series,* and *cross-sectional.* A discussion of each follows.

## Quantitative and Qualitative Data

**Quantitative Data**

Measurements whose values are inherently numerical.

**Qualitative Data**

Data whose measurement scale is inherently categorical.

In some cases, data values are best expressed in purely numerical, or **quantitative** terms, such as in dollars, pounds, inches, or percentages. As an example, a study of college students at your campus might obtain data on the number of hours each week that students work at a paying job and the income level of the students' parents.

In other cases, the observation may signify only the category to which an item belongs. Categorical data are referred to as **qualitative** data.

For example, a study might be interested in the class standings—*freshman, sophomore, junior, senior,* or *graduate*—of college students. The same study also might ask the students to judge the quality of their education as *very good, good, fair, poor,* or *very poor.* Note, even if the students are asked to record a number (1 to 5) to indicate the quality level at which the numbers correspond to a category, the data would still be considered qualitative because the numbers are just codes for the categories.

## Time-Series Data and Cross-Sectional Data

**Time-Series Data**

A set of consecutive data values observed at successive points in time.

**Cross-Sectional Data**

A set of data values observed at a fixed point in time.

Data may also be classified as being either **time-series** or **cross-sectional**.

The data collected from the study of college students about their quality-of-education ratings would be cross-sectional because the data from each student relates to a fixed point in time. In another case, if we sampled 100 stocks from the stock market and determined the closing stock price on March 15, the data would be considered cross-sectional because all measurements corresponded to one point in time.

On the other hand, Ford Motor Company tracks the sales of its Explorer SUVs on a monthly basis. Data values observed at intervals over time are referred to as time-series data. If we determined the closing stock price for a particular stock on a daily basis for a year, the stock prices would be time-series data.

## Data Measurement Levels

Data can also be identified by their *level of measurement*. This is important because the higher the data level, the more sophisticated the analysis that can be performed. This will be clear when you study the material in the remaining chapters of this text.

We shall discuss and give examples of four levels of data measurements: *nominal, ordinal, interval,* and *ratio*. Figure 1.11 illustrates the hierarchy among these data levels, with nominal data being the lowest level.

**Nominal Data**  *Nominal data* are the lowest form of data, yet you will encounter this type of data many times. Assigning codes to categories generates nominal data. For example, a survey question that asks for marital status provides the following responses:

    1. Married      2. Single      3. Divorced      4. Other

**FIGURE 1.11**

Data Level Hierarchy

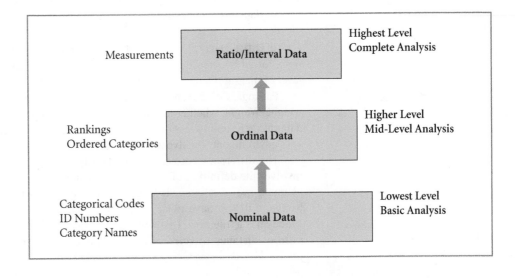

For each person, a code of 1, 2, 3, or 4 would be recorded. These codes are nominal data. Note that the values of the code numbers have no specific meaning, because the order of the categories is arbitrary. We might have shown it this way:

1. Single     2. Divorced     3. Married     4. Other

With nominal data we also have complete control over what codes are used. For example, we could have used

88. Single     11. Divorced     33. Married     55. Other

All that matters is that you know which code stands for which category. Recognize also that the codes need not be numeric. We might use

S = Single     D = Divorced     M = Married     O = Other

**Ordinal Data** *Ordinal*, or *rank data* are one notch above nominal data on the measurement hierarchy. At this level, the data elements can be rank-ordered on the basis of some relationship among them, with the assigned values indicating this order. For example, a typical market research technique is to offer potential customers the chance to use two unidentified brands of a product. The customers are then asked to indicate which brand they prefer. The brand eventually offered to the general public depends on how often it was the preferred test brand. The fact that an ordering of items took place makes this an ordinal measure.

Bank loan applicants are asked to indicate the category corresponding to their household incomes:

————— Under $20,000        ————— $20,000 to $40,000        ————— over $40,000
         (1)                              (2)                              (3)

The codes 1, 2, and 3 refer to the particular income categories, with higher codes assigned to higher incomes.

Ordinal measurement allows decision makers to equate two or more observations or to rank-order the observations. In contrast, nominal data can be compared only for equality. You cannot order nominal measurements. Thus, a primary difference between ordinal and nominal data is that ordinal data can have both an equality ($=$) and a greater than ($>$) relationship, whereas nominal data can have only an equality ($=$) relationship.

**Interval Data** If the distance between two data items can be measured on some scale and the data have ordinal properties ($>$, $<$, or $=$) the data are said to be *interval data*. The best example of interval data is the temperature scale. Both the Fahrenheit and Celsius temperature scales have ordinal properties of "$>$" or "$<$" and "$=$" In addition, the distances between equally spaced points are preserved. For example, $32°F > 30°F$, and $80°C > 78°C$ The difference between $32°F$ and $30°F$ is the same as the difference between $80°F$ and $78°F$, two degrees in each case. Thus, interval data allow us to precisely measure the difference between any two values. With ordinal data this is not possible, because all we can say is that one value is larger than another.

**Ratio Data** Data that have all the characteristics of interval data but also have a true zero point (at which zero means "none") are called *ratio data*. Ratio measurement is the highest level of measurement.

Packagers of frozen foods encounter ratio measures when they pack their products by weight. Weight, whether measured in pounds or grams, is a ratio measurement because it has a unique zero point—zero meaning no weight. Many other types of data encountered in business environments involve ratio measurements, for example, distance, money, and time.

The difference between interval and ratio measurements can be confusing because it involves the definition of a true zero. If you have $5 and your brother has $10, he has twice as much money as you. If you convert the dollars to pounds, euros, yen, or pesos, your brother will still have twice as much. If your money is lost or stolen, you have no dollars. Money has a true zero. Likewise, if you travel 100 miles today and 200 miles tomorrow, the ratio of distance traveled will be 2/1, even if you convert the distance to kilometers. If on the third day you rest, you have traveled no miles. Distance has a true zero. Conversely, if today's temperature is 35°F (1.67°C) and tomorrow's is 70°F (21.11°C) is tomorrow twice as warm as today? The answer is no. One way to see this is to convert the Fahrenheit temperature to Celsius: The ratio will no longer be 2/1 (12.64/1). Likewise, if the temperature reads 0°F (−17.59°C) this does not imply that there is no temperature. It's simply colder than 10°F (−12.22°C) Also, 0°C (32°F) is not the same temperature as 0°F Thus, temperature, measured with either the Fahrenheit or Celsius scale (an interval-level variable), does not have a true zero.

As was mentioned earlier, a major reason for categorizing data by level and type is that the methods you can use to analyze the data are partially dependent on the level and type of data you have available.

---

**EXAMPLE 1-1**    **CATEGORIZING DATA**

For many years *U.S. News and World Report* has published annual rankings based on various data collected from more than 1,300 U.S. colleges and universities. Figure 1.12 shows a portion of the data in the file named "Colleges and Universities." Each column corresponds to a different variable for which data were collected. Before doing any statistical analyses with these data, *U.S. News and World Report* employees need to determine the type and level for each of the factors. Limiting the effort to only those factors that are shown in Figure 1.12, this is done using the following steps:

**Step 1** **Identify each factor in the data set.**
The factors (or variables) in the data set shown in Figure 1.12 are

| College Name | State | Public (1) Private(2) | Math SAT | Verbal SAT | # appli. rec'd. | # appli. accepted. | # new stud. enrolled | # FT under-grad | # PT under-grad |
|---|---|---|---|---|---|---|---|---|---|

Each of the 10 columns represents a different factor. Data might be missing for some colleges and universities.

**Step 2** **Determine whether the data are time-series or cross-sectional.**
Because each row represents a different college or university and the data are for the same year, the data are cross-sectional. Time-series data are measured over time—say, over a period of years.

**Step 3** **Determine which factors are quantitative data and which are qualitative data.**
Qualitative data are codes or numerical values that represent categories. Quantitative data are those that are purely numerical. In this case, the data for the following factors are qualitative:

College Name

State

Code for Public or Private College or University

---

**FIGURE 1.12**

Data for U.S. Colleges and Universities

| | A | B | C | D | E | F | G | H | I | J |
|---|---|---|---|---|---|---|---|---|---|---|
| | | | Public (1)/ Private (2) | Math SAT | Verbal SAT | # appli. rec'd | # appl. accepted | # new stud enrolled | # FT undergrad | # PT undergrad |
| 1 | College Name | State | | | | | | | | |
| 2 | Adelphi University | NY | 2 | 500 | 457 | 2186 | 1924 | 512 | 2683 | 1227 |
| 3 | Alaska Pacific University | AK | 2 | 490 | 482 | 193 | 146 | 55 | 249 | 869 |
| 4 | Albertson College | ID | 2 | 524 | 487 | 587 | 479 | 158 | 678 | 41 |
| 5 | Albertus Magnus College | CT | 2 | 460 | 430 | 353 | 340 | 103 | 416 | 230 |
| 6 | Albright College | PA | 2 | 537 | 486 | 1038 | 839 | 227 | 973 | 306 |
| 7 | Alderson-Broaddus College | WV | 2 | 443 | 394 | 582 | 498 | 172 | 799 | 78 |
| 8 | Allentown Coll. of St. Francis de Sales | PA | 2 | 515 | 470 | 1179 | 780 | 290 | 1130 | 638 |
| 9 | Alvernia College | PA | 2 | 410 | 430 | 707 | 614 | 166 | 801 | 464 |
| 10 | Ambassador University | TX | 2 | 516 | 493 | 397 | 244 | 223 | 1083 | 58 |

A715    Worcester State College

Data for the following factors are considered quantitative:

| Math SAT | Verbal SAT | # new stud. enrolled |
|---|---|---|
| # appl. rec'd. | # appl. accepted | |
| # PT undergrad | # FT undergrad | |

**Step 4   Determine the level of data measurement for each factor.**
The four levels of data are nominal, ordinal, interval, and ratio. This data set has only nominal- and ratio-level data. The three nominal-level factors are

College Name

State

Code for Public or Private College or University

The others are all ratio-level data.

**>> END EXAMPLE**

# 1-4: Exercises

## Skill Development

**1-49.** For each of the following, indicate whether the data are cross-sectional or time-series:
   a. quarterly unemployment rates
   b. unemployment rates by state
   c. monthly sales
   d. employment satisfaction data for a company

**1-50.** What is the difference between qualitative and quantitative data?

**1-51.** For each of the following variables, indicate the level of data measurement:
   a. product rating {1 = excellent, 2 = good, 3 = fair, 4 = poor, 5 = very poor}
   b. home ownership {own, rent, other}
   c. college grade point average
   d. marital status {single, married, divorced, other}

**1-52.** What is the difference between ordinal and nominal data?

**1-53.** *Consumer Reports*, in its rating of cars, indicates repair history with circles. The circles are either white, black, or half-and-half. To which level of data does this correspond? Discuss.

## Business Applications

**1-54.** Verizon has a support center where customers can call to get questions answered about their cell phone account. The manager in charge of the support center has recently conducted a study in which she surveyed 2,300 customers. The customers who called the support center were transferred to a third party who asked the customer a series of questions.

   a. Indicate whether the data generated from this study will be considered cross-sectional or time-series. Explain why.
   b. One of the questions asked customers was approximately how many minutes they had been on hold waiting to get through to a support person. What level of data measurement is obtained from this question? Explain.
   c. Another question asked the customer to rate the service on a scale of 1–7, with 1 being the worst possible service and 7 being the best possible service. What level of data measurement is achieved from this question? Will the data be quantitative or qualitative? Explain.

**1-55.** The following information can be found in the Murphy Oil Corporation Annual Report to Shareholders. For each variable, indicate the level of data measurement.
   a. List of Principal Offices (e.g., El Dorado, Calgary, Houston)
   b. Income (in millions of dollars) from Continuing Operations
   c. List of Principal Subsidiaries (e.g., Murphy Oil USA, Inc., Murphy Exploration & Production Company)
   d. Number of branded retail outlets
   e. Petroleum products sold, in barrels per day
   f. Major Exploration and Production Areas (e.g., Malaysia, Congo, Ecuador)
   g. Capital Expenditures measured in millions of dollars

**1-56.** You have collected the following information on 15 different real estate investment trusts (REITs). Identify whether the data are cross-sectional or time-series.
   a. income distribution by region in 2008

b. per share (diluted) funds from operations (FFO) for the years 2002 to 2008

c. number of properties owned as of December 31, 2008

d. the overall percentage of leased space for the 119 properties in service as of December 31, 2008

e. dividends per share for the years 2002–2008

**1-57.** A loan manager for Bank of the Cascades has the responsibility for approving automobile loans. To assist her in this matter, she has compiled data on 428

cars and trucks. These data are in the file called **Automobiles**.

Indicate the level of data measurement for each of the variables in this data file.

**1-58.** Recently the manager of the call center for a large Internet bank asked his staff to collect data on a random sample of the bank's customers. Data on the following variables were collected and placed in a file called **Bank Call Center**:

| Column A | Column B | Column C | Column D | Column E | Column F |
|---|---|---|---|---|---|
| Account Number | Caller Gender | Account Holder Gender | Past Due Amount | Current Amount Due | Was This a Billing Question? |
| Unique Tracking # | 1 = Male  2 = Female | 1 = Male  2 = Female | Numerical Value | Numerical Value | 3 = Yes  4 = No |

A small portion of the data is as follows:

| Account Number | Caller Gender | Account Holder Gender | Past Due Amount | Current Amount Due | Was This a Billing Question? |
|---|---|---|---|---|---|
| 4348291 | 2 | 2 | 40.35 | 82.85 | 3 |
| 6008516 | 1 | 1 | 0 | −129.67 | 4 |
| 17476479 | 1 | 2 | 0 | 76.38 | 4 |
| 13846306 | 2 | 2 | 0 | 99.24 | 4 |
| 21393711 | 1 | 1 | 0 | 37.98 | 3 |

a. Would you classify these data as time-series or cross-sectional? Explain.

b. Which of the variables are quantitative and which are qualitative?

c. For each of the six variables, indicate the level of data measurement.

**END EXERCISES 1-4**

# Visual Summary

**Chapter 1:** Business statistics is a collection of procedures and techniques used by decision-makers to transform data into useful information. Chapter 1 introduces the subject of business statistics and lays the groundwork for the remaining chapters in the text. Included is a discussion of the different types of data and data collection methods. Chapter 1 also describes the difference between populations and samples.

## 1.1 What Is Business Statistics? (pg. 2–7)

### Summary

The two areas of statistics, **descriptive statistics** and **inferential statistics**, are introduced to set the stage for what is coming in subsequent chapters. Descriptive statistics includes **visual tools** such as charts and graphs and also the **numerical measures** such as the arithmetic average. The role of descriptive statistics is to describe data and help transform data into usable information. Inferential techniques are those that allow decision-makers to draw conclusions about a large body of data by examining a smaller subset of those data. Two areas of inference, **estimation** and **hypothesis testing**, are described.

## 1.2 Procedures for Collecting Data (pg. 7–14)

### Summary

Before data can be analyzed using business statistics techniques, the data must be collected. The types of data collection reviewed are: **experiments**, **telephone surveys**, **written questionnaires** and **direct observation** and **personal interviews**. Data collection issues such as **interviewer bias**, **nonresponse bias**, **selection bias**, **observer bias**, and **measurement error** are covered. The concepts of **internal validity** and **external validity** are defined.

> **Outcome 1.** Know the key data collection methods.

## Conclusion

Statistical analysis begins with data. You need to know how to collect data, how to select samples from a population, and the type and level of data you are using. **Figure 1.13** summarizes the different sampling techniques presented in this chapter. **Figure 1.14** gives a synopsis of the different data collection procedures and **Figure 1.15** shows the different data types and measurement levels.

## 1.3 Populations, Samples, and Sampling Techniques (pg. 14–20)

### Summary

The important concepts of **population** and **sample** are defined and examples of each are provided. Because many statistical applications involve samples, emphasis is placed on how to select samples. Two main sampling categories are presented, **nonstatistical sampling** and **statistical sampling**. The focus is on statistical sampling and four statistical sampling methods are discussed: **simple random sampling**, **stratified random sampling**, **cluster sampling**, and **systematic random sampling**.

> **Outcome 2.** Know the difference between a population and a sample.
>
> **Outcome 3.** Understand the similarities and differences between different sampling methods.

## 1.4 Data Types and Data Measurement Levels (pg. 20–25)

### Summary

This section discusses various ways in which data are classified. For example, data can be classified as being either **quantitative** or **qualitative**. Data can also be **cross-sectional** or **time-series**. Another way to classify data is by the level of measurement. There are four levels from lowest to highest: **nominal**, **ordinal**, **interval**, and **ratio**. Knowing the type of data you have is very important as you will see in Chapters 2 and 3 because the data type influences the type of statistical procedures you can use.

> **Outcome 4.** Understand how to categorize data by type and level of measurement

**FIGURE 1.13**

Sampling Techniques

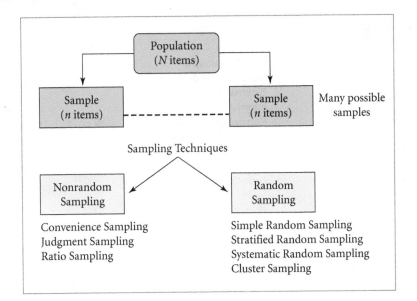

**FIGURE 1.14**

Data Collection Techniques

| Data Collection Method | Advantages | Disadvantages |
|---|---|---|
| Experiments | Provide controls<br>Preplanned objectives | Costly<br>Time-consuming<br>Requires planning |
| Telephone Surveys | Timely<br>Relatively inexpensive | Poor reputation<br>Limited scope and length |
| Mail Questionnaires<br>Written Surveys | Inexpensive<br>Can expand length<br>Can use open-end questions | Low response rate<br>Requires exceptional clarity |
| Direct Observation<br>Personal Interview | Expands analysis opportunities<br>No respondent bias | Potential observer bias<br>Costly |

**FIGURE 1.15**

Data Classification

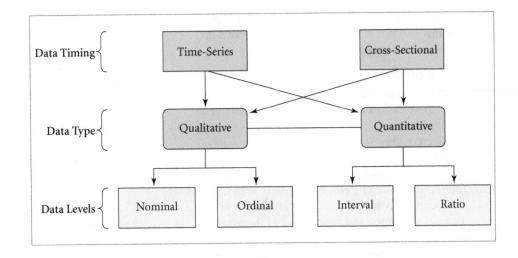

# Key Terms

# Chapter Exercises

MyStatLab

## Conceptual Questions

**1-59.** Several organizations publish the results of presidential approval polls. Movements in these polls are seen as an indication of how the general public views presidential performance. Comment on these polls within the context of what was covered in this chapter.

**1-60.** With what level of data is a bar chart most appropriately used?

**1-61.** With what level of data is a histogram most appropriately used?

**1-62.** Two people see the same movie; one says it was average and the other says it was exceptional. What level of data are they using in these ratings? Discuss how the same movie could receive different reviews.

**1-63.** The University of Michigan publishes a monthly measure of consumer confidence. This is taken as a possible indicator of future economic performance. Comment on this process within the context of what was covered in this chapter.

## Business Applications

**1-64.** In a business publication such as *The Wall Street Journal* or *Business Week*, find a graph or chart representing time-series data. Discuss how the data were gathered and the purpose of the graph or chart.

**1-65.** In a business publication such as *The Wall Street Journal* or *Business Week*, find a graph or chart representing cross-sectional data. Discuss how the data were gathered and the purpose of the graph or chart.

**1-66.** *The Oregonian* newspaper has asked readers to email and respond to the question "Do you believe police officers are using too much force in routine traffic stops?"

a. Would the results of this survey be considered a random sample?

b. What type of bias might be associated with a data collection system such as this? Discuss what options might be used to reduce this bias potential.

**1-67.** The makers of "Mama's Home-Made Salsa" are concerned about the quality of their product. The particular trait of the salsa of concern is the thickness of the salsa in each jar.

a. Discuss a plan by which the managers might determine the percentage of jars of salsa believed to have an unacceptable thickness by potential purchasers. (1) Define the sampling procedure to be used, (2) the randomization method to be used to select the sample, and (3) the measurement to be obtained.

b. Explain why it would or wouldn't be feasible (or, perhaps, possible) to take a census to address this issue.

**1-68.** A maker of energy drinks is considering abandoning can containers and going exclusively to bottles because the sales manager believes customers prefer drinking from bottles. However, the vice president in charge of marketing is not convinced the sales manager is correct.

a. Indicate the data collection method you would use.

b. Indicate what procedures you would follow to apply this technique in this setting.

c. State which level of data measurement applies to the data you would collect. Justify your answer.

d. Is the data qualitative or quantitative? Explain.

# Video Case 1

## Statistical Data Collection @ McDonald's

Think of any well-known, successful business in your community. What do you think has been its secret? Competitive products or services? Talented managers with vision? Dedicated employees with great skills? There's no question these all play an important part in its success. But there's more, lots more. It's "data." That's right, data.

The data collected by a business in the course of running its daily operations form the foundation of every decision made. Those data are analyzed using a variety of statistical techniques to provide decision makers with a succinct and clear picture of the company's activities. The resulting statistical information then plays a key role in decision making, whether those decisions are made by an accountant, marketing manager, or operations specialist. To better understand just what types of business statistics organizations employ, let's take a look at one of the world's most well-respected companies: McDonald's.

McDonald's operates more than 30,000 restaurants in over 118 countries around the world. Total annual revenues recently surpassed the $20 billion mark. Wade Thomas, vice president of U.S. Menu Management for McDonalds, helps drive those sales but couldn't do it without statistics.

"When you're as large as we are, we can't run the business on simple gut instinct. We rely heavily on all kinds of statistical data to help us determine whether our products are meeting customer expectations, when products need to be updated, and much more," says Wade. "The cost of making an educated guess is simply too great a risk."

McDonald's restaurant owner/operators and managers also know the competitiveness of their individual restaurants depends on the data they collect and the statistical techniques used to analyze the data into meaningful information. Each restaurant has a sophisticated cash register system that collects data such as individual customer orders, service times, and methods of payment, to name a few. Periodically, each U.S.–based restaurant undergoes a restaurant operations improvement process, or ROIP, study. A special team of reviewers monitors restaurant activity over a period of several days, collecting data about everything from front-counter service and kitchen efficiency, to drive-thru service times. The data are analyzed by McDonald's U.S. Consumer and Business Insights group at McDonald's headquarters near Chicago to help the restaurant owner/operator and managers better understand what they're doing well and where they have opportunities to grow.

Steve Levigne, vice president of Consumer and Business Insights, manages the team that supports the company's decision-making efforts. Both qualitative and quantitative data are collected and analyzed all the way down to the individual store level. "Depending on the audience, the results may be rolled up to an aggregate picture of operations," says Steve. Software packages such as Microsoft Excel, SAS, and SPSS do most of the number crunching and are useful for preparing the graphical representations of the information so decision makers can quickly see the results.

Not all companies have an entire department staffed with specialists in statistical analysis, however. That's where you come in. The more you know about the procedures for collecting and analyzing data, and how to use them, the better decision maker you'll be, regardless of your career aspirations. So it would seem there's a strong relationship here—knowledge of statistics and your success.

### Discussion Questions:

1. You will recall that McDonald's vice president of U.S. Menu Management, Wade Thomas, indicated that McDonald's relied heavily on statistical data to determine, in part, if its products were meeting customer expectations. The narrative indicated that two important sources of data were the sophisticated register system and the restaurant operations improvement process, ROIP. Describe the types of data that could be generated by these two methods and discuss how these data could be used to determine if McDonald's products were meeting customer expectations.

2. One of McDonald's uses of statistical data is to determine when products need to be updated. Discuss the kinds of data McDonald's would require to make this determination. Also provide how these types of data would be used to determine when a product needed to be updated.

3. This video case presents the types of data collected and used by McDonald's in the course of running its daily operations. For a moment, imagine that McDonald's did not collect this data. Attempt to describe how it might make a decision concerning, for instance, how much its annual advertising budget would be.

4. Visit a McDonald's in your area. While there take note of the different types of data that could be collected using observation only. For each variable you identify, determine the level of data measurement. Select three different variables from your list and outline the specific steps you would use to collect the data. Discuss how each of the variables could be used to help McDonald's manage the restaurant.

# References

Berenson, Mark L., and David M. Levine, *Basic Business Statistics: Concepts and Applications*, 11th ed. (Upper Saddle River, NJ: Prentice Hall, 2009).

Cryer, Jonathan D., and Robert B. Miller, *Statistics for Business: Data Analysis and Modeling*, 2nd ed. (Belmont, CA: Duxbury Press, 1996).

Fowler, Floyd J., *Survey Research Methods*, 4th ed. (Thousand Oaks, CA: Sage Publications, 2008).

Hildebrand, David, and R. Lyman Ott, *Statistical Thinking for Managers*, 4th ed. (Belmont, CA: Duxbury Press, 1998).

John, J. A., D. Whitiker, and D. G. Johnson, *Statistical Thinking for Managers*, 2nd ed. (Boca Raton, FL: CRC Press, 2005).

*Microsoft Excel 2007* (Redmond, WA: Microsoft Corp., 2007).

*Minitab for Windows Version 15* (State College, PA: Minitab, 2007).

Pelosi, Marilyn K., and Theresa M. Sandifer, *Doing Statistics for Business with Excel*, 2nd ed. (New York: John Wiley & Sons, 2002).

Scheaffer, Richard L., William Mendenhall, and Lyman Ott, *Elementary Survey Sampling*, 6th ed. (Brooks/Cole, 2006).

Siegel, Andrew F., *Practical Business Statistics*, 5th ed. (Burr Ridge, IL: Irwin, 2002).

- **Review** the definitions for nominal, ordinal, interval, and ratio data in Section 1-4.
- **Examine** the statistical software, such as Excel or Minitab, that you will be using during this course to make sure you are aware of the

procedures for constructing graphs and tables. For instance, in Excel, look at the Charts group on the Insert tab and the *Pivot Table* feature on the Insert tab. In Minitab, acquaint yourself with the *Graph* menu and the *Tables* command within the *Stat* menu.

- **Look at** popular newspapers such as *USA Today* and business periodicals such as *Fortune, Business Week,* or *The Wall Street Journal* for instances where charts, graphs, or tables are used to convey information.

# Graphs, Charts, and Tables—Describing Your Data

# Why you need to know

We live in an age where we are constantly bombarded with visual images and stimuli. Much of our time is spent watching television, playing video games, or working at a computer. These technologies are advancing rapidly, making the images sharper and more attractive to our eyes. Flat-panel screens, high-resolution monitors, and high-definition televisions represent significant improvements over the original technologies they replaced. However, this phenomenon is not limited to video technology, but has also become an important part of the way businesses communicate with customers, employees, suppliers, and other constituents.

Presentations and reports are expected to include high-quality graphs and charts that effectively transform data into information. Although the written word is still vital, words become even more powerful when coupled with an effective visual illustration of data. The adage that a picture is worth a thousand words is particularly relevant in business decision making.

As a business major, upon graduation you will find yourself on both ends of the data analysis spectrum. On the one hand, regardless of what you end up doing for a career, you will almost certainly be involved in preparing reports and making presentations that require using visual descriptive statistical tools presented in this chapter. You will be on the "do it" end of the data analysis process. Thus, you need to know how to use these statistical tools.

On the other hand, you will also find yourself reading reports or listening to presentations that others have made. In many instances, you will be required to make important decisions, or to reach conclusions, based on the information in those reports or presentations. Thus, you will be on the "use it" end of the data analysis process. You need to be knowledgeable about these tools to effectively screen and critique the work that others do for you.

Charts and graphs are not just tools used internally by businesses. Business periodicals such as *Fortune* and *Business Week* use graphs and charts extensively in articles to help readers better understand key concepts. Many advertisements will even use graphs and charts effectively to convey their message. Virtually every issue of *The Wall Street Journal* contains different graphs, charts, or tables that display data in an informative way.

Thus, you will find yourself to be both a producer and a consumer of the descriptive statistical techniques known as graphs, charts, and tables. You will create a competitive advantage for yourself throughout your career if you obtain a solid understanding of the techniques introduced in Chapter 2.

This chapter introduces some of the most frequently used tools and techniques for describing data with graphs, charts, and tables. Although this analysis can be done manually, we will provide output from Excel and Minitab showing that these software packages can be used as tools for doing the analysis easily, quickly, and with a finished quality that once required a graphic artist.

# 2.1 Frequency Distributions and Histograms

As we discussed in Chapter 1, in today's business climate, companies collect massive amounts of data they hope will be useful for making decisions. Every time a customer makes a purchase at a store like Wal-Mart or Sears, data from that transaction is updated to the store's database. For example, one item of data that is captured is the number of different product categories included in each "market basket" of items purchased. Table 2.1 shows these data for all customer transactions for a single day at one store in Atlanta. A total of 450 customers made purchases on the day in question. The first value in Table 2.1, 4, indicates that the customer's purchase included four different product categories (for example food, sporting goods, photography supplies, and dry goods).

**TABLE 2.1** | **Product Categories per Customer at the Atlanta Retail Store**

| | | | | | | | | | | | | | | |
|---|---|---|---|---|---|---|---|---|---|---|---|---|---|---|
| 4 | 2 | 5 | 8 | 8 | 10 | 1 | 4 | 8 | 3 | 4 | 1 | 1 | 3 | 4 |
| 1 | 4 | 4 | 5 | 4 | 4 | 4 | 9 | 5 | 4 | 4 | 10 | 7 | 11 | 4 |
| 10 | 2 | 6 | 7 | 10 | 5 | 4 | 6 | 4 | 6 | 2 | 3 | 2 | 4 | 5 |
| 5 | 4 | 11 | 1 | 4 | 1 | 9 | 2 | 4 | 6 | 6 | 7 | 6 | 2 | 3 |
| 6 | 5 | 3 | 4 | 5 | 6 | 5 | 3 | 10 | 6 | 5 | 7 | 7 | 4 | 3 |
| 8 | 2 | 2 | 6 | 5 | 11 | 9 | 9 | 5 | 5 | 6 | 5 | 3 | 1 | 7 |
| 6 | 6 | 5 | 3 | 8 | 4 | 3 | 3 | 4 | 4 | 4 | 7 | 6 | 4 | 9 |
| 1 | 6 | 5 | 5 | 4 | 4 | 7 | 5 | 6 | 6 | 9 | 5 | 6 | 10 | 4 |
| 7 | 5 | 8 | 4 | 4 | 7 | 4 | 6 | 6 | 4 | 4 | 2 | 10 | 4 | 5 |
| 4 | 11 | 8 | 7 | 9 | 5 | 6 | 4 | 2 | 8 | 4 | 2 | 6 | 6 | 6 |
| 6 | 4 | 6 | 5 | 7 | 1 | 6 | 9 | 1 | 5 | 9 | 10 | 5 | 5 | 10 |
| 5 | 4 | 7 | 5 | 7 | 6 | 9 | 5 | 3 | 2 | 1 | 5 | 5 | 5 | 5 |
| 5 | 9 | 5 | 3 | 2 | 5 | 7 | 2 | 4 | 6 | 4 | 4 | 4 | 4 | 4 |
| 6 | 5 | 8 | 5 | 5 | 5 | 5 | 5 | 2 | 5 | 5 | 6 | 4 | 6 | 5 |
| 5 | 7 | 10 | 2 | 2 | 6 | 8 | 3 | 1 | 3 | 5 | 6 | 3 | 3 | 6 |
| 5 | 4 | 5 | 3 | 3 | 7 | 9 | 4 | 4 | 5 | 10 | 6 | 10 | 5 | 9 |
| 4 | 3 | 8 | 7 | 1 | 8 | 4 | 3 | 1 | 3 | 6 | 7 | 5 | 5 | 5 |
| 4 | 7 | 4 | 11 | 6 | 6 | 3 | 7 | 9 | 4 | 4 | 2 | 9 | 7 | 5 |
| 1 | 6 | 6 | 8 | 3 | 8 | 4 | 4 | 1 | 9 | 3 | 9 | 3 | 4 | 2 |
| 9 | 5 | 5 | 7 | 10 | 5 | 3 | 4 | 7 | 7 | 6 | 2 | 2 | 4 | 4 |
| 4 | 7 | 3 | 5 | 4 | 9 | 2 | 3 | 4 | 3 | 2 | 1 | 6 | 4 | 6 |
| 1 | 8 | 1 | 4 | 3 | 5 | 5 | 10 | 4 | 4 | 4 | 6 | 9 | 2 | 7 |
| 9 | 4 | 5 | 3 | 6 | 5 | 5 | 3 | 4 | 6 | 5 | 7 | 3 | 6 | 8 |
| 3 | 6 | 1 | 5 | 7 | 7 | 5 | 4 | 6 | 6 | 6 | 3 | 6 | 9 | 5 |
| 4 | 5 | 10 | 1 | 5 | 5 | 7 | 8 | 9 | 1 | 6 | 5 | 6 | 6 | 4 |
| 10 | 6 | 5 | 5 | 5 | 1 | 6 | 5 | 6 | 4 | 7 | 9 | 10 | 2 | 6 |
| 4 | 4 | 6 | 11 | 9 | 5 | 4 | 4 | 3 | 5 | 4 | 6 | 2 | 6 | 7 |
| 3 | 5 | 6 | 7 | 4 | 5 | 4 | 6 | 9 | 4 | 3 | 3 | 6 | 9 | 4 |
| 3 | 7 | 5 | 6 | 11 | 4 | 4 | 8 | 4 | 2 | 8 | 2 | 4 | 2 | 3 |
| 6 | 5 | 1 | 10 | 5 | 9 | 5 | 4 | 5 | 1 | 4 | 9 | 5 | 4 | 4 |

Although the data in Table 2.1 are easy to capture with the technology of today's cash registers, in this form the data provide little or no information that managers could use to determine the buying habits of their customers. However, these data can be converted into useful information through descriptive statistical analysis.

Chapter Outcome 1. ➤ # Frequency Distribution

**Frequency Distribution**
A summary of a set of data that displays the number of observations in each of the distribution's distinct categories or classes.

**Discrete Data**
Data that can take on a countable number of possible values.

**Relative Frequency**
The proportion of total observations that are in a given category. Relative frequency is computed by dividing the frequency in a category by the total number of observations. The relative frequencies can be converted to percentages by multiplying by 100.

One of the first steps would be to construct a **frequency distribution**.

The product data in Table 2.1 take on only a few possible values (1, 2, 3, . . . , 11). The minimum number of product categories is 1 and the maximum number of categories in these data is 11. These data are called **discrete data**.

When you encounter discrete data, where the variable of interest can take on only a reasonably small number of possible values, a frequency distribution is constructed by counting the number of times each possible value occurs in the data set. We organize these counts into a *frequency distribution table*, as shown in Table 2.2. Now, from this frequency distribution we are able to see how the data values are spread over the different number of possible product categories. For instance, you can see that the most frequently occurring number of product categories in a customer's "market basket" is 4, which occurred 92 times. You can also see that the three most common number of product categories are 4, 5, and 6. Only a very few times do customers purchase 10 or 11 product categories in their shopping trip to the store.

Consider another example in which a consulting firm surveyed random samples of residents in two cities, Dallas, Texas, and Knoxville, Tennessee. The firm is investigating the labor markets in these two communities for a client that is thinking of relocating its corporate offices to one of the two locations. Education level of the workforce in the two cities is a key factor in making the relocation decision. The consulting firm surveyed 160 randomly selected adults in Dallas and 330 adults in Knoxville and recorded the number of years of college attended. The responses ranged from zero to eight years. Table 2.3 shows the frequency distributions for each city.

Suppose now we wished to compare the distribution for years of college for Dallas and Knoxville. How do the two cities' distributions compare? Do you see any difficulties in making this comparison? Because the surveys contained different numbers of people, it is difficult to compare the frequency distributions directly. When the number of total observations differs, comparisons are aided if **relative frequencies** are computed. Equation 2.1 is used to compute the relative frequencies.

**TABLE 2.2** | **Atlanta Store Product Categories Frequency Distribution**

| Number of Product Catagories | Frequency |
|---|---|
| 1 | 25 |
| 2 | 29 |
| 3 | 42 |
| 4 | 92 |
| 5 | 83 |
| 6 | 71 |
| 7 | 35 |
| 8 | 19 |
| 9 | 29 |
| 10 | 18 |
| 11 | 7 |
| | Total = 450 |

**TABLE 2.3** | **Frequency Distributions of Years of College Education**

| Dallas | | Knoxville | |
|---|---|---|---|
| Years of College | Frequency | Years of College | Frequency |
| 0 | 35 | 0 | 187 |
| 1 | 21 | 1 | 62 |
| 2 | 24 | 2 | 34 |
| 3 | 22 | 3 | 19 |
| 4 | 31 | 4 | 14 |
| 5 | 13 | 5 | 7 |
| 6 | 6 | 6 | 3 |
| 7 | 5 | 7 | 4 |
| 8 | 3 | 8 | 0 |
| | Total = 160 | | Total = 330 |

**Relative Frequency**

$$\text{Relative frequency} = \frac{f_i}{n} \qquad (2.1)$$

where:

$f_i$ = Frequency of the $i$th value of the discrete variable

$n = \sum_{i=1}^{k} f_i = $ Total number of observations

$k$ = The number of different values for the discrete variable

Table 2.4 shows the relative frequencies for each city's distribution. This makes a comparison of the two much easier. We see that Knoxville has relatively more people without any college (56.7%) or with one year of college (18.8%) than Dallas (21.9% and 13.1%). At all other levels of education, Dallas has relatively more people than Knoxville.

**TABLE 2.4** | **Relative Frequency Distributions of Years of College**

| Years of College | Dallas | | Knoxville | |
|---|---|---|---|---|
| | Frequency | Relative Frequency | Frequency | Relative Frequency |
| 0 | 35 | 35/160 = 0.219 | 187 | 187/330 = 0.567 |
| 1 | 21 | 21/160 = 0.131 | 62 | 62/330 = 0.188 |
| 2 | 24 | 24/160 = 0.150 | 34 | 34/330 = 0.103 |
| 3 | 22 | 22/160 = 0.138 | 19 | 19/330 = 0.058 |
| 4 | 31 | 31/160 = 0.194 | 14 | 14/330 = 0.042 |
| 5 | 13 | 13/160 = 0.081 | 7 | 7/330 = 0.021 |
| 6 | 6 | 6/160 = 0.038 | 3 | 3/330 = 0.009 |
| 7 | 5 | 5/160 = 0.031 | 4 | 4/330 = 0.012 |
| 8 | 3 | 3/160 = 0.019 | 0 | 0/330 = 0.000 |
| Total | 160 | | 330 | |

**TABLE 2.5** | **Marital Status Frequency Distribution**

| Marital Status | Frequency |
|---|---|
| Single | 80 |
| Married | 90 |
| Divorced | 20 |
| Other | 10 |
| | Total = 200 |

The frequency distributions shown in Table 2.2 and Table 2.3 were developed from *quantitative data*. That is, the variable of interest was numerical (number of product categories or number of years of college). However, a frequency distribution can also be developed when the data are *qualitative data*, or nonnumerical data. For instance, if a survey asked individuals for their marital status, the following possible responses could be listed:

Single   Married   Divorced   Other

Table 2.5 shows the frequency distribution from a survey of 200 people.

**How to do it** (Example 2-1)

**Developing Frequency and Relative Frequency Distributions for Discrete Data**

To develop a discrete data frequency distribution, perform the following steps:

1. List all possible values of the variable. If the variable is ordinal level or higher, order the possible values from low to high.

2. Count the number of occurrences at each value of the variable and place this value in a column labeled "frequency."

To develop a relative frequency distribution, do the following:

3. Use Equation 2.1 and divide each frequency count by the total number of observations and place in a column headed "relative frequency."

**EXAMPLE 2-1**   **FREQUENCY AND RELATIVE FREQUENCY DISTRIBUTIONS**

**Real Estate Transactions** In late 2008, the United States experienced a major economic decline thought to be due to the sub-prime loans that many lending institutions made during the previous few years. When the housing bubble burst, many institutions experienced severe problems. As a result, lenders became much more conservative in granting home loans, which in turn made buying and selling homes more challenging. To demonstrate the magnitude of the problem in Kansas City, the Association of Real Estate Brokers conducted a survey of 16 agencies in the area and collected data on the number of real estate transactions closed in December 2008. The following data were observed:

| | | | |
|---|---|---|---|
| 3 | 0 | 0 | 1 |
| 1 | 2 | 2 | 0 |
| 0 | 2 | 1 | 0 |
| 2 | 1 | 4 | 2 |

The real estate analysts wish to construct a frequency distribution and a relative frequency distribution for the number of real estate transactions.

**Step 1**   **List the possible values.**
The possible values for the discrete variable, listed in order, are 0, 1, 2, 3, 4.

**Step 2**   **Count the number of occurrences at each value.**
The frequency distribution follows:

| Transactions | Frequency | Relative Frequency |
|---|---|---|
| 0 | 5 | 5/16 = .3125 |
| 1 | 4 | 4/16 = .2500 |
| 2 | 5 | 5/16 = .3125 |
| 3 | 1 | 1/16 = .0625 |
| 4 | 1 | 1/16 = .0625 |
| Total = 16 | | 1.0000 |

**Step 3**   **Determine the relative frequencies.**
The relative frequencies are determined by dividing each frequency by 16, as shown. Thus, just over 31% of those responding reported no transactions during December 2008.

>> **END EXAMPLE**

**TRY PROBLEM** 2-1 (pg. 50)

**EXAMPLE 2-2** **FREQUENCY DISTRIBUTION FOR QUALITATIVE DATA**

**Vehicle Ownership** The American Automobile Association (AAA) recently surveyed its members about their driving habits. One question asked for the make of vehicle driven by the eldest member in the household. The following data reflect the results for 15 of the respondents:

| Ford | Dodge | Toyota | Ford | Buick |
|------|-------|--------|------|-------|
| Chevy | Toyota | Nissan | Ford | Chevy |
| Ford | Toyota | Chevy | BMW | Honda |

The frequency distribution for this qualitative variable is found as follows:

**Step 1** **List the possible values.**

The possible values for the variable are BMW, Buick, Chevy, Dodge, Ford, Honda, Nissan, Toyota.

**Step 2** **Count the number of occurrences at each value.**

The frequency distribution is

| Car Company | Frequency |
|-------------|-----------|
| BMW | 1 |
| Buick | 1 |
| Chevy | 3 |
| Dodge | 1 |
| Ford | 4 |
| Honda | 1 |
| Nissan | 1 |
| Toyota | 3 |
| Total = | 15 |

**>> END EXAMPLE**

**TRY PROBLEM** 2-8 (pg. 51)

**BUSINESS APPLICATION** **FREQUENCY DISTRIBUTIONS**

**Excel and Minitab Tutorial**

**ATHLETIC SHOE SURVEY** In recent years, a status symbol for many students has been the brand and style of athletic shoes they wear. Companies such as Nike and Adidas compete for the top position in the sport shoe market. A survey was recently conducted in which 100 college students at a southern state school were asked a number of questions, including how many pairs of Nike shoes they currently own. The data are in a file called **SportsShoes**.

The variable *Number of Nike* is a discrete quantitative variable. Figures 2.1 and 2.2 show frequency distributions (Excel and Minitab versions) for the number of Nike shoes owned by those surveyed. These frequency distributions show that, although a few people own more than six pairs of Nike shoes, the bulk of those surveyed own two or fewer pairs.

**Chapter Outcome 1.** → # Grouped Data Frequency Distributions

In the previous examples, the variable of interest was a discrete variable and the number of possible values for the variable was limited to only a few. However, there are many instances in which the variable of interest will be either **continuous** (e.g., weight, time, length) or discrete and will have many possible outcomes (e.g., age, income, stock prices), yet you want to describe the variable using a frequency distribution.

**Continuous Data**

Data whose possible values are uncountable and which may assume any value in an interval.

**BUSINESS APPLICATION** **GROUPED DATA FREQUENCY DISTRIBUTIONS**

**BLOCKBUSTER INC.** Blockbuster is one of the largest video rental and sales companies in the United States. Its stores rent and sell DVD products. Recently, a district manager for Blockbuster in Arkansas conducted a survey of customers in her district. Among the questions

**FIGURE 2.1**

Excel 2007 Output—Nike
Shoes Frequency Distribution

**Excel 2007 Instructions:**
1. Open File: SportsShoes.xls.
2. Enter the Possible Values
   for the Variable; i.e., 0, 1,
   2, 3, 4, etc.
3. Select the cells to contain
   the Frequency values.
4. Select the **formulas** tab.
5. Click on the $f_x$ button.
6. Select the **Statistics—
   FREQUENCY** function.
7. Enter the range of data
   and the bin range (the cells
   containing the possible
   number of shoes).
8. Press **ctrl-shift-enter** to
   determine the frequency
   values.

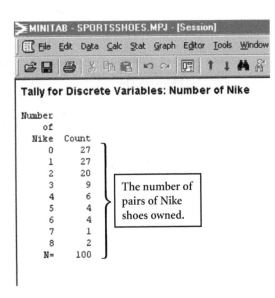

| | A | B | C | D | E | F | G | H | I | J | K | L | M |
|---|---|---|---|---|---|---|---|---|---|---|---|---|---|
| 1 | | Annual | Pairs per | Pairs at | Number of | Number | Brand | | | | | Level of | |
| 2 | Age | Income | Year | This Time | Nike | Adidas | Preference | Comfort | Advertising | Appearance | Price | Activity | Gender |
| 91 | 65 | 27,500 | 1 | 2 | 1 | 0 | 1 | 1 | 2 | 1 | 1 | 1 | 2 |
| 92 | 29 | 21,000 | 5 | 1 | 0 | 1 | 2 | 1 | 2 | 2 | 2 | 2 | 2 |
| 93 | 56 | 63,000 | 2 | 7 | 4 | 2 | 1 | 1 | 1 | 1 | 1 | 1 | 1 |
| 94 | 24 | 13,000 | 2 | 3 | 2 | 1 | 2 | 2 | 1 | 1 | 1 | 1 | 1 |
| 95 | 72 | 80,000 | 2 | 5 | 1 | 4 | 2 | 2 | 2 | 1 | 1 | 1 | 2 |
| 96 | 25 | 23,000 | 1 | 6 | 6 | 0 | 1 | 1 | 2 | 2 | 1 | 3 | 2 |
| 97 | 21 | 32,000 | 3 | 2 | 1 | 0 | 1 | 1 | 2 | 1 | 2 | 1 | 1 |
| 98 | 56 | 51,000 | 2 | 3 | 0 | 1 | 2 | 1 | 1 | 1 | 1 | 1 | 2 |
| 99 | 27 | 26,500 | 6 | 3 | 2 | 0 | 1 | 1 | 2 | 2 | 1 | 3 | 2 |
| 100 | 19 | 11,000 | 1 | 2 | 1 | 1 | 2 | 1 | 2 | 1 | 2 | 1 | 1 |
| 101 | 26 | 32,000 | 1 | 2 | 1 | 0 | 1 | 1 | 2 | 1 | 2 | 2 | 2 |
| 102 | 51 | 90,000 | 2 | 5 | 4 | 1 | 1 | 1 | 2 | 1 | 1 | 2 | 1 |
| 103 | | | | | | | | | | | | | |
| 104 | | | | | Number of | | | | | | | | |
| | | | | | Nikes | | | | | | | | |
| 105 | | | | | 0 | 27 | | | | | | | |
| 106 | | | | | 1 | 27 | | | | | | | |
| 107 | | | | | 2 | 20 | | | | | | | |
| 108 | | | | | 3 | 9 | | | | | | | |
| 109 | | | | | 4 | 6 | | | | | | | |
| 110 | | | | | 5 | 4 | | | | | | | |
| 111 | | | | | 6 | 4 | | | | | | | |
| 112 | | | | | 7 | 1 | | | | | | | |
| 113 | | | | | 8 | 2 | | | | | | | |
| 114 | | | | | | | | | | | | | |

**FIGURE 2.2**

Minitab Output—Nike Shoes
Frequency Distribution

**MINITAB - SPORTSSHOES.MPJ - [Session]**

File  Edit  Data  Calc  Stat  Graph  Editor  Tools  Window

**Tally for Discrete Variables: Number of Nike**

| Number of Nike | Count |
|---|---|
| 0 | 27 |
| 1 | 27 |
| 2 | 20 |
| 3 | 9 |
| 4 | 6 |
| 5 | 4 |
| 6 | 4 |
| 7 | 1 |
| 8 | 2 |
| N= | 100 |

The number of
pairs of Nike
shoes owned.

**Minitab Instructions:**
1. Open file: SportsShoes.MTW.
2. Choose **Stat > Tables >
   Tally Individual Variables**.
3. In **Variables**, enter data
   column.
4. Under **Display**, check
   **Counts**.
5. Click **OK**.

asked on the written survey was "How many DVD movies do you own?" A total of 230 people completed the survey; Table 2.6 shows the responses to the DVD ownership question. These data are discrete, quantitative data. The values range from 0 to 30.

The manager is interested in transforming these data into useful information by constructing a frequency distribution. Table 2.7 shows one approach where the possible values for the number of DVD movies owned is listed from 0 to 30. Although this frequency distribution is a step forward in transforming the data into information, because of the large number of possible values for DVD movies owned, the 230 observations are spread over a large range, making analysis difficult. In this case, the manager might consider forming a *grouped data frequency distribution* by organizing the possible number of DVD movies owned into discrete categories or *classes*.

To begin constructing a grouped frequency distribution, sort the quantitative data from low to high. The sorted data is called a *data array*. Now, define the classes for the variable of interest. Care needs to be taken when constructing these classes to ensure each data point is put into one, and only one, possible class. Therefore, the classes should meet four criteria.

**TABLE 2.6** | **DVD Movies Owned: Blockbuster Survey**

| | | | | | | | | | |
|---|---|---|---|---|---|---|---|---|---|
| 9 | 4 | 13 | 10 | 5 | 10 | 13 | 14 | 10 | 19 |
| 0 | 10 | 16 | 9 | 11 | 14 | 8 | 15 | 7 | 15 |
| 10 | 11 | 9 | 7 | 6 | 12 | 12 | 14 | 15 | 16 |
| 15 | 14 | 10 | 13 | 9 | 12 | 12 | 10 | 10 | 11 |
| 15 | 14 | 9 | 19 | 3 | 9 | 16 | 19 | 15 | 9 |
| 4 | 2 | 4 | 5 | 6 | 2 | 3 | 4 | 7 | 5 |
| 6 | 2 | 2 | 0 | 0 | 8 | 3 | 4 | 3 | 2 |
| 2 | 5 | 2 | 5 | 2 | 2 | 6 | 2 | 5 | 6 |
| 5 | 2 | 7 | 3 | 5 | 1 | 6 | 4 | 3 | 6 |
| 3 | 7 | 7 | 1 | 6 | 2 | 7 | 1 | 3 | 2 |
| 4 | 0 | 2 | 2 | 4 | 6 | 2 | 5 | 3 | 7 |
| 4 | 16 | 9 | 10 | 11 | 7 | 10 | 9 | 10 | 11 |
| 11 | 12 | 9 | 8 | 9 | 7 | 9 | 17 | 8 | 13 |
| 14 | 13 | 10 | 6 | 12 | 5 | 14 | 7 | 13 | 12 |
| 9 | 6 | 10 | 15 | 7 | 7 | 9 | 9 | 13 | 10 |
| 9 | 3 | 17 | 5 | 11 | 9 | 6 | 9 | 15 | 8 |
| 11 | 13 | 4 | 16 | 13 | 9 | 11 | 5 | 12 | 13 |
| 0 | 3 | 3 | 3 | 2 | 1 | 4 | 0 | 2 | 0 |
| 3 | 7 | 1 | 5 | 2 | 2 | 3 | 2 | 1 | 3 |
| 2 | 3 | 3 | 3 | 0 | 3 | 3 | 3 | 1 | 1 |
| 13 | 24 | 24 | 17 | 17 | 15 | 25 | 20 | 15 | 20 |
| 21 | 23 | 25 | 17 | 13 | 22 | 18 | 17 | 30 | 21 |
| 18 | 21 | 17 | 16 | 25 | 14 | 15 | 24 | 21 | 15 |

**TABLE 2.7** | **Frequency Distribution of DVD Movies Owned**

| DVD Movies Owned | Frequency |
|---|---|
| 0 | 8 |
| 1 | 8 |
| 2 | 22 |
| 3 | 22 |
| 4 | 11 |
| 5 | 13 |
| 6 | 12 |
| 7 | 14 |
| 8 | 5 |
| 9 | 19 |
| 10 | 14 |
| 11 | 9 |
| 12 | 8 |
| 13 | 12 |
| 14 | 8 |
| 15 | 12 |
| 16 | 6 |
| 17 | 7 |
| 18 | 2 |
| 19 | 3 |
| 20 | 2 |
| 21 | 4 |
| 22 | 1 |
| 23 | 1 |
| 24 | 3 |
| 25 | 3 |
| 26 | 0 |
| 27 | 0 |
| 28 | 0 |
| 29 | 0 |
| 30 | 1 |
| | Total = 230 |

**Mutually Exclusive Classes**

Classes that do not overlap so that a data value can be placed in only one class.

**All-Inclusive Classes**

A set of classes that contains all the possible data values.

**Equal-Width Classes**

The distance between the lowest possible value and the highest possible value in each class is equal for all classes.

First, they must be **mutually exclusive**.

Second, they must be **all-inclusive**.

Third, if at all possible, they should be of **equal width**.

Fourth, avoid empty classes if possible.

Equal-width classes make analyzing and interpreting the frequency distribution easier. However, there are some instances in which the presence of extreme high or low values makes it necessary to have an open-ended class. For example, annual family incomes in the United States are mostly between \$15,000 and \$200,000. However, there are some families with much higher family incomes. To best accommodate these high incomes, you might consider having the highest income class be "over \$200,000" or "\$200,000 and over" as a catchall for the high-income families.

Empty classes are those for which there are no data values. If this occurs, it may be because you have set up classes that are too narrow.

**Steps for Grouping Data into Classes** There are four steps for grouping data, such as that found in Table 2.6, into classes.

**Step 1** **Determine the number of groups or classes to use.**

Although there is no absolute right or wrong number of classes, one rule of thumb is to have *between 5 and 20 classes*. Another guideline for helping you determine how many classes to use is the $2^k \geq n$ rule, where $k$ = the number of classes and is defined to be the smallest integer so that $2^k \geq n$, where $n$ is the number of data values. For example, for $n = 230$, the $2^k \geq n$ rule would suggest $k = 8$ classes ($2^8 = 256 \geq 230$ while $2^7 = 128 < 230$). This latter method was chosen for our example. Our preliminary step, as specified previously, is to produce a frequency distribution from the data array as in Table 2.7. This will enhance our ability to envision the data structure and the classes.

Remember, these are only guidelines for the number of classes. There is no specific right or wrong number. In general, use fewer classes for smaller data sets; more classes for larger data sets. However, using too few classes tends to condense data too much, and information can be lost. Using too many classes spreads out the data so much that little advantage is gained over the original raw data.

**Step 2** **Establish the class width.**

The minimum **class width** is determined by Equation 2.2.

**Class Width**

The distance between the lowest possible value and the highest possible value for a frequency class.

$$W = \frac{\text{Largest value} - \text{Smallest value}}{\text{Number of classes}} \qquad (2.2)$$

For the Blockbuster data using eight classes, we get

$$W = \frac{\text{Largest value} - \text{Smallest value}}{\text{Number of classes}} = \frac{30 - 0}{8} = 3.75$$

This means we could construct eight classes that are each 3.75 units wide to provide mutually exclusive and all-inclusive classes. However, because our purpose is to make the data more understandable, we suggest that you *round up to a more convenient class width*, such as 4.0. If you do round the class width, always round up.

**Step 3** **Determine the class boundaries for each class.**

The **class boundaries** determine the lowest possible value and the highest possible value for each class. In the Blockbuster example, if we start the first class at 0, we get the class boundaries shown in the first column of the following table. Notice the classes have been formed to be *mutually exclusive* and *all-inclusive*.

**Class Boundaries**

The upper and lower values of each class.

**Step 4** **Determine the class frequency for each class.**

The count for each class is known as a class frequency. As an example, the number of observations in the first class is 60.

| DVD Movies Owned (Classes) | Frequency |
|---|---|
| 0–3 | 60 |
| 4–7 | 50 |
| 8–11 | 47 |
| 12–15 | 40 |
| 16–19 | 18 |
| 20–23 | 8 |
| 24–27 | 6 |
| 28–31 | 1 |
| | Total = 230 |

Another step we can take to help analyze the Blockbuster data is to construct a relative frequency distribution, a **cumulative frequency distribution,** and a **cumulative relative frequency distribution**.

**Cumulative Frequency Distribution**

A summary of a set of data that displays the number of observations with values less than or equal to the upper limit of each of its classes.

**Cumulative Relative Frequency Distribution**

A summary of a set of data that displays the proportion of observations with values less than or equal to the upper limit of each of its classes.

| DVD Movies | Frequency | Relative Frequency | Cumulative Frequency | Cumulative Relative Frequency |
|---|---|---|---|---|
| 0–3 | 60 | 0.261 | 60 | 0.261 |
| 4–7 | 50 | 0.217 | 110 | 0.478 |
| 8–11 | 47 | 0.204 | 157 | 0.683 |
| 12–15 | 40 | 0.174 | 197 | 0.857 |
| 16–19 | 18 | 0.078 | 215 | 0.935 |
| 20–23 | 8 | 0.035 | 223 | 0.970 |
| 24–27 | 6 | 0.026 | 229 | 0.996 |
| 28–31 | 1 | 0.004 | 230 | 1.000 |
| | Total = 230 | | | |

The cumulative frequency distribution is shown in the "Cumulative Frequency" column. We can then form the cumulative relative frequency distribution as shown in the "Cumulative Relative Frequency" column. The cumulative relative frequency distribution indicates, as an example, that 85.7% of the sample own fewer than 16 DVD movies.

**How to do it** (Example 2-3)

**Developing Frequency Distributions for Continuous Variables**

**To develop a continuous data frequency distribution, perform the following steps:**

**1.** Determine the desired number of classes or groups. One rule of thumb is to use 5 to 20 classes. The $2^k \geq n$ rule can also be used.

**2.** Determine the minimum class width using

$$W = \frac{\text{Largest value} - \text{Smallest value}}{\text{Number of classes}}$$

Round the class width up to a more convenient value.

**3.** Define the class boundaries, making sure that the classes that are formed are *mutually exclusive* and *all-inclusive*. Ideally, the classes should have equal widths and should all contain at least one observation.

**4.** Determine the class frequency for each class.

---

**EXAMPLE 2-3    FREQUENCY DISTRIBUTION FOR CONTINUOUS VARIABLES**

**Emergency Response Communication Links** One of the major efforts of the United States Office of Homeland Security has been to improve the communication between emergency responders, like the police and fire departments. The communications have been hampered by problems involving linking divergent radio and computer systems, as well as communication protocols. While most cities have recognized the problem and made efforts to solve it, Homeland Security recently funded practice exercises in 72 cities of different sizes throughout the United States. The resulting data, already sorted but representing seconds before the systems were linked, are as follows:

| | | | | | |
|---|---|---|---|---|---|
| 35 | 339 | 650 | 864 | 1,025 | 1,261 |
| 38 | 340 | 655 | 883 | 1,028 | 1,280 |
| 48 | 395 | 669 | 883 | 1,036 | 1,290 |
| 53 | 457 | 703 | 890 | 1,044 | 1,312 |
| 70 | 478 | 730 | 934 | 1,087 | 1,341 |
| 99 | 501 | 763 | 951 | 1,091 | 1,355 |
| 138 | 521 | 788 | 969 | 1,126 | 1,357 |
| 164 | 556 | 789 | 985 | 1,176 | 1,360 |
| 220 | 583 | 789 | 993 | 1,199 | 1,414 |
| 265 | 595 | 802 | 997 | 1,199 | 1,436 |
| 272 | 596 | 822 | 999 | 1,237 | 1,479 |
| 312 | 604 | 851 | 1,018 | 1,242 | 1,492 |

Homeland Security wishes to construct a frequency distribution showing the times until the communication systems are linked. The frequency distribution is determined as follows:

**Step 1**  **Group the data into classes.**

The number of classes is arbitrary but typically will be between 5 and 20, depending on the volume of data. In this example, we have $n = 72$ data items. Using the $2^k \geq n$ guideline we get $k = 7$ classes ($2^7 = 128 \geq 72$).

**Step 2**  **Determine the class width.**

$$W = \frac{\text{Largest value} - \text{Smallest value}}{\text{Number of classes}} = \frac{1,492 - 35}{7} = 208.1429 \Rightarrow 225$$

Note, we have rounded the class width up from the minimum required value of 208.1429 to the more convenient value of 225.

**Step 3**  **Define the class boundaries.**

| | | |
|---|---|---|
| 0 | and under | 225 |
| 225 | and under | 450 |
| 450 | and under | 675 |
| 675 | and under | 900 |
| 900 | and under | 1,125 |
| 1,125 | and under | 1,350 |
| 1,350 | and under | 1,575 |

These classes are mutually exclusive, all-inclusive, and have equal widths.

**Step 4**  **Determine the class frequency for each class.**

| New Construction Jobs | Frequency |
|---|---|
| 0 and under 225 | 9 |
| 225 and under 450 | 6 |
| 450 and under 675 | 12 |
| 675 and under 900 | 13 |
| 900 and under 1,125 | 14 |
| 1,125 and under 1,350 | 11 |
| 1,350 and under 1,575 | 7 |

This frequency distribution shows that most cities took between 450 and 1,350 seconds (7.5 and 22.5 minutes) to link their communications systems.

**>> END EXAMPLE**

**TRY PROBLEM** 2-5 (pg. 51)

Chapter Outcome 2. ► # Histograms

Although frequency distributions are useful for analyzing large sets of data, they are presented in table format and may not be as visually informative as a graph. If a frequency distribution has been developed from a quantitative variable, a **frequency histogram** can be constructed directly from the frequency distribution. In many cases, the histogram offers a superior format for transforming the data into useful information. (Note: Histograms cannot be constructed from a frequency distribution where the variable of interest is qualitative. However, a similar graph, called a *bar chart*, discussed later in this chapter, is used when qualitative data are involved.)

A histogram shows three general types of information:

1. It provides a visual indication of where the approximate center of the data is. Look for the center point along the horizontal axes in the histograms in Figure 2.3. Even though the shapes of the histograms are the same, there is a clear difference in where the data are centered.

2. We can gain an understanding of the degree of spread (or variation) in the data. The more the data cluster around the center, the smaller the variation in the data. If the data

**Frequency Histogram**

A graph of a frequency distribution with the horizontal axis showing the classes, the vertical axis showing the frequency count, and (for equal class widths) the rectangles having a height equal to the frequency in each class.

**FIGURE 2.3**

Histograms Showing Different
Centers

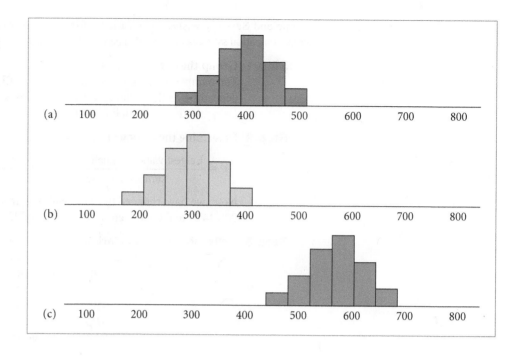

are spread out from the center, the data exhibit greater variation. The examples in
Figure 2.4 all have the same center but are different in terms of spread.
3. We can observe the shape of the distribution. Is it reasonably flat, is it weighted to one
   side or the other, is it balanced around the center, or is it bell-shaped?

**Excel and Minitab Tutorial**

**BUSINESS APPLICATION**   **CONSTRUCTING HISTOGRAMS**

**CAPITAL CREDIT UNION** Even for applications with small amounts of data, such as the
Blockbuster example, constructing grouped data frequency distributions and histograms is a
time-consuming process. Decision makers may hesitate to try different numbers of classes
and different class limits because of the effort involved and because the "best" presentation of
the data may be missed.

**FIGURE 2.4**

Histograms—Same Center,
Different Spread

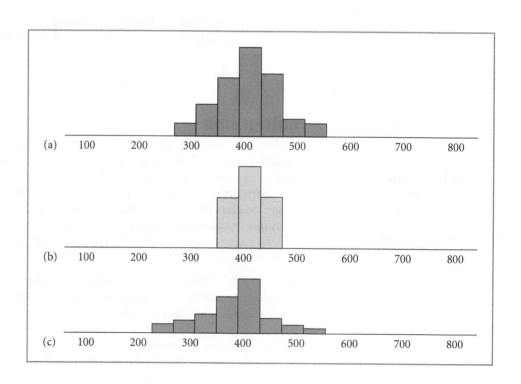

We showed earlier that Excel and Minitab both provide the capability of constructing frequency distributions. Both software packages are also quite capable of generating grouped data frequency distributions and histograms.

Consider Capital Credit Union (CCU) in Mobile, Alabama, which recently began issuing a new credit card. Managers at CCU have been wondering how customers use the card, so a sample of 300 customers was selected. Data on the current credit card balance (rounded to the nearest dollar) and the genders of the cardholders appear in the file **Capital**.

As with the manual process, the first step in Excel or Minitab is to determine the number of classes. Recall that the rule of thumb is to use between 5 and 20 classes, depending on the amount of data. Suppose we decide to use 10 classes.

Next, we determine the class width using Equation 2.2. The highest account balance in the sample is $1,493.00. The minimum is $99.00. Thus, the class width is

$$W = \frac{1,493.00 - 99.00}{10} = 139.40$$

which we round up to $150.00.

Our classes will be

$90–$239.99

$240–$389.99

$390–$539.99

etc.

The resulting histogram in Figure 2.5 shows that the data are centered in the class from $690 to $839.99. The customers vary considerably in their credit card balances, but

**FIGURE 2.5**

Excel 2007 Output of Credit Card Balance Histogram

**Excel 2007 Instructions:**
1. Open file: Capital.xls
2. Set up an area on the worksheet for the bins defined as 239.99, 389.99, etc., up to 1589.99. Be sure to include a label such as "Bins."
3. On the **Data** tab, click **Data Analysis**.
4. Select **Histogram**.
5. Input Range specifies the actual data values as the **Credit Card Account Balance** column and the bin range as the area defined in Step 2.
6. Put on a new worksheet and include the Chart Output.
7. Right-mouse-click on the bars and use the **Format Data Series Options** to set gap width to zero and add lines to the bars.
8. Convert the bins to actual class labels by typing labels in Column A. Note, the bin 239.99 is labeled < 239.99.

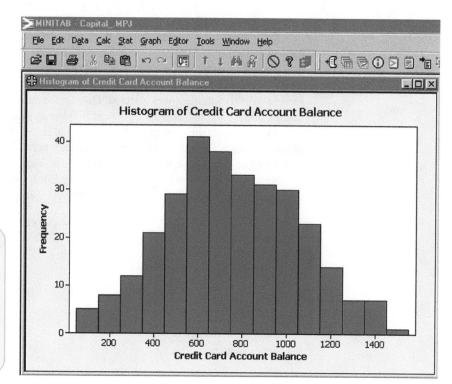

**FIGURE 2.6** | Minitab Output of Credit Card Balance Histogram

**Minitab Instructions:**
1. Open file: Capital.MTW.
2. Choose **Graph > Histogram**.
3. Click **Simple**.
4. Click **OK**.
5. In **Graph variables**, enter data column.
6. Click **OK**.

the distribution is quite symmetrical and somewhat bell-shaped. CCU managers must decide whether the usage rate for the credit card is sufficient to warrant the cost of maintaining the credit card accounts.

**Issues with Excel** If you use Excel to construct a histogram as indicated in the instructions in Figure 2.5, the initial graph will have gaps between the bars. Because histograms illustrate the distribution of data across the range of all possible values for the quantitative variable, *histograms do not have gaps*. Therefore, to get the proper histogram format, you need to close these gaps by setting the gap width to zero, as indicated in the Excel instructions shown in Figure 2.5. Minitab provides no gaps with its default output, as shown in Figure 2.6.

## How to do it (Example 2-4)

### Constructing Frequency Histograms

**To construct a frequency histogram, perform the following steps:**

**1-4.** Follow the steps for constructing a frequency distribution (see Example 2-3).

**5.** Use the horizontal axis to represent classes for the variable of interest. Use the vertical axis to represent the frequency in each class.

**6.** Draw vertical bars for each class or data value so that the heights of the bars correspond to the frequencies. Make sure there are no gaps between the bars. (Note, if the classes do not have equal widths, the bar height should be adjusted to make the area of the bar proportional to the frequency.)

**7.** Label the histogram appropriately.

**EXAMPLE 2-4**    **FREQUENCY HISTOGRAMS**

**Emergency Response Times** The director of emergency responses in Montreal, Canada, is interested in analyzing the time needed for response teams to reach their destinations in emergency situations after leaving their stations. She has acquired the response times for 1,220 calls last month. To develop the frequency histogram, perform the following steps:

**Steps 1-4   Construct a frequency distribution.**

Because response time is a continuous variable measured in seconds, the data should be broken down into classes, and the steps given in Example 2-3 should be used. The following frequency distribution with 10 classes was developed:

| Response Time | Frequency | Response Time | Frequency |
|---|---|---|---|
| 0 and under 30 | 36 | 180 and under 210 | 145 |
| 30 and under 60 | 68 | 210 and under 240 | 80 |
| 60 and under 90 | 195 | 240 and under 270 | 43 |
| 90 and under 120 | 180 | 270 and under 300 | 31 |
| 120 and under 150 | 260 | | |
| 150 and under 180 | 182 | Total = 1,220 | |

**Step 5   Construct the axes for the histogram.**
The horizontal axis will be response time and the vertical axis will be frequency.

**Step 6   Construct bars with heights corresponding to the frequency of each class.**

**Step 7   Label the histogram appropriately.**
This is shown as follows:

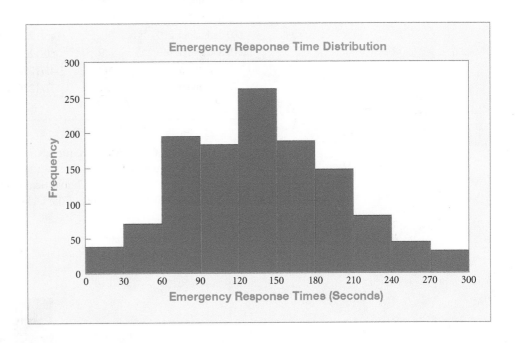

This histogram indicates that the response times vary considerably. The center is somewhere in the range of 120 to 180 seconds.

**>> END EXAMPLE**

**TRY PROBLEM** 2-10 (pg. 51)

## Relative Frequency Histograms and Ogives

**Ogive**
The graphical representation of the cumulative relative frequency. A line is connected to points plotted above the upper limit of each class at a height corresponding to the cumulative relative frequency.

Histograms can also be used to display relative frequency distributions and cumulative relative frequency distributions. A relative frequency histogram is formed in the same manner as a frequency histogram, but relative frequencies, rather than frequencies, are used on the vertical axis. The cumulative relative frequency is presented using a graph called an **ogive**. Example 2-5 illustrates each of these graphical tools.

**EXAMPLE 2-5**    **RELATIVE FREQUENCY HISTOGRAMS AND OGIVES**

Emergency Response Times (*Continued*) Example 2-4 introduced the situation facing the emergency response manager in Montreal. In that example, she formed a frequency distribution for a sample of 1,220 response times. She is now interested in graphing the relative frequencies and the ogive. To do so, use the following steps:

**Step 1**    **Convert the frequency distribution into relative frequencies and cumulative relative frequencies.**

| Response Time | Frequency | Relative Frequency | Cumulative Relative Frequency |
|---|---|---|---|
| 0 and under 30 | 36 | 36/1220 = 0.0295 | 0.0295 |
| 30 and under 60 | 68 | 68/1220 = 0.0557 | 0.0852 |
| 60 and under 90 | 195 | 195/1220 = 0.1598 | 0.2451 |
| 90 and under 120 | 180 | 180/1220 = 0.1475 | 0.3926 |
| 120 and under 150 | 260 | 260/1220 = 0.2131 | 0.6057 |
| 150 and under 180 | 182 | 182/1220 = 0.1492 | 0.7549 |
| 180 and under 210 | 145 | 145/1220 = 0.1189 | 0.8738 |
| 210 and under 240 | 80 | 80/1220 = 0.0656 | 0.9393 |
| 240 and under 270 | 43 | 43/1220 = 0.0352 | 0.9746 |
| 270 and under 300 | 31 | 31/1220 = 0.0254 | 1.0000 |
|  | 1,220 | 1.0000 |  |

**Step 2**    **Construct the relative frequency histogram.**
Place the quantitative variable on the horizontal axis and the relative frequencies on the vertical axis. The vertical bars are drawn to heights corresponding to the relative frequencies of the classes.

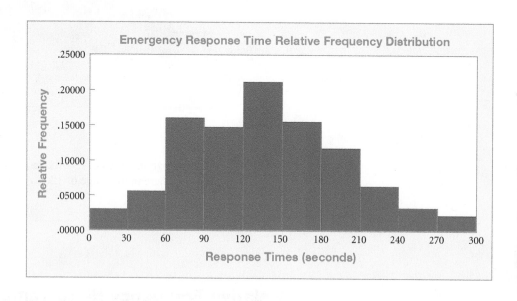

Note the relative frequency histogram has exactly the same shape as the frequency histogram. However, the vertical axis has a different scale.

**Step 3**    **Construct the ogive.**
Place a point above the *upper limit* of each class at a height corresponding to the cumulative relative frequency. Complete the ogive by drawing a line connecting these points.

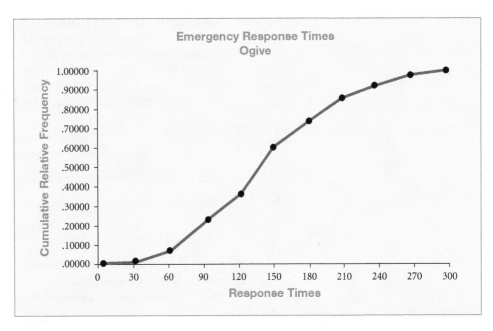

>> END EXAMPLE

**TRY PROBLEM** 2-16 (pg. 53)

Chapter Outcome 3.→ # Joint Frequency Distributions

Frequency distributions are effective tools for describing data. Thus far we have discussed how to develop grouped and ungrouped frequency distributions for one variable at a time. For instance, in the Capital Credit Union example, we were interested in customer credit card balances for all customers. We constructed a frequency distribution and histogram for that variable. However, often we need to examine data that is characterized by more than one variable. This may involve constructing a *joint frequency distribution* for two variables. Joint frequency distributions can be constructed for qualitative or quantitative variables.

**How to do it** (Example 2-6)

**Constructing Joint Frequency Distributions**

A joint frequency distribution is constructed using the following steps:

**1.** Obtain a set of data consisting of paired responses for two variables. The responses can be qualitative or quantitative. If the responses are quantitative, they can be discrete or continuous.

**2.** Construct a table with *r* rows and *c* columns, in which the number of rows represents the number of categories (or numeric classes) of one variable and the number of columns corresponds to the number of categories (or numeric classes) of the second variable.

**3.** Count the number of joint occurrences at each row level and each column level for all combinations of row and column values and place these frequencies in the appropriate cells.

**4.** Compute the row and column totals, which are called the *marginal frequencies.*

**5.** If a joint relative frequency distribution is desired, divide each cell frequency by the total number of paired observations.

| EXAMPLE 2-6 | JOINT FREQUENCY DISTRIBUTION |

**Campus Parking** Parking is typically an issue on college campuses. Problems seem to occur for students, faculty, and staff both in locating a parking spot and in being able to quickly exit a lot at busy times. A particular West Coast campus parking manager has received complaints about the time required to exit lots on her campus. To start analyzing the situation, she has collected a small sample of data from 12 customers showing the type of payment (cash or charge) and the lot number (Lot Number 1, 2, or 3). One possibility is that credit payments increase exit times at the parking lots. The manager wishes to develop a joint frequency distribution to better understand the paying habits of those using her lots. To do this, she can use the following steps:

**Step 1** **Obtain the data.**
The paired data for the two variables for a sample of 12 customers are obtained.

| Customer | Payment Method | Parking Lot |
|----------|----------------|-------------|
| 1 | Charge | 2 |
| 2 | Charge | 1 |
| 3 | Cash | 2 |
| 4 | Charge | 2 |
| 5 | Charge | 1 |
| 6 | Cash | 1 |
| 7 | Cash | 3 |
| 8 | Charge | 1 |
| 9 | Charge | 3 |
| 10 | Cash | 2 |
| 11 | Cash | 1 |
| 12 | Charge | 1 |

Step 2 **Construct the rows and columns of the joint frequency table.**

The row variable will be the payment method, and two rows will be used, corresponding to the two payment methods. The column variable is parking lot number, and it will have three levels, because the data for this variable contain only the values 1, 2, and 3. (Note, if a variable is continuous, classes should be formed using the methods discussed in Example 2-3.)

|  |  | Parking Lot | |  |
|---|---|---|---|---|
|  |  | 1 | 2 | 3 |
| Payment | Cash |  |  |  |

Step 3 **Count the number of joint occurrences at each row level and each column level for all combinations of row and column values and place these frequencies in the appropriate cells.**

|  | Parking Lot | | | |
|---|---|---|---|---|
|  | 1 | 2 | 3 | Total |
| Charge | 4 | 2 | 1 | 7 |
| Cash | 2 | 2 | 1 | 5 |
| Total | 6 | 4 | 2 | 12 |

Step 4 **Calculate the row and column totals (see Step 3).**

The manager can now see that for this sample, most people charged their parking fee (seven people) and Lot number 1 was used by most people in the sample used (six people). Likewise, four people used Lot number 1 and charged their parking fee.

>> **END EXAMPLE**

**TRY PROBLEM** 2-12 (pg. 52)

**BUSINESS APPLICATION** JOINT FREQUENCY DISTRIBUTION

**CAPITAL CREDIT UNION (*CONTINUED*)** Recall that the Capital Credit Union discussed earlier was interested in evaluating the success of its new credit card. Figures 2.5 and 2.6 showed the frequency distribution and histogram for a sample of customer credit card balances. Although this information is useful, the managers would like to know more. Specifically, what does the credit card balance distribution look like for male versus female cardholders?

One way to approach this is to sort the data by the gender variable and develop frequency distributions and histograms for males and females separately. You could then make a visual comparison of the two to determine what, if any, difference exists between males and females. However, an alternative approach is to jointly analyze the two variables: gender and credit card balance.

Although the process is different for Excel and Minitab, both software packages provide methods for analyzing two variables jointly. In Figure 2.5, we constructed the frequency distribution for the 300 credit card balances using 10 classes. The class width was set at $150. Figure 2.7 shows a table that is called a *joint frequency distribution*. This type of table is also called a *cross-tabulation* table.[1]

**Excel and Minitab Tutorial**

---

[1]In Excel, the joint frequency distribution is developed using a tool called Pivot tables. In Minitab, the joint frequency distributions are constructed using the Cross Tabulation option.

**FIGURE 2.7** | Excel 2007 Output of the Capital Credit Union Joint Frequency Distribution

**Excel 2007 Instructions:**

1. Open file: Capital.xls.
2. Place cursor anywhere in the data.
3. On the **Insert** tab, click on **PivotTable** and click **OK**.
4. Drag **Credit Card Account Balance** to "*Drop Row Field Here*" area. (Note, you may need to use Pivot Table **Options** under **Display** and make sure **Classical Pivot Table Layout** is checked.)
5. Right-click in **Credit Card Account Balance** numbers and click **Group**.
6. Change **Start at** to 90. Change **End** to 1589. Change **By** to 150.
7. Drag **Gender** to "*Drop Column Fields Here*" area.
8. Drag **Credit Card Account Balance** to "*Drop Data Items Here*" area.
9. Place cursor in the *Data Item* area, right click, and select **Summarize Data By** and select **Count**.

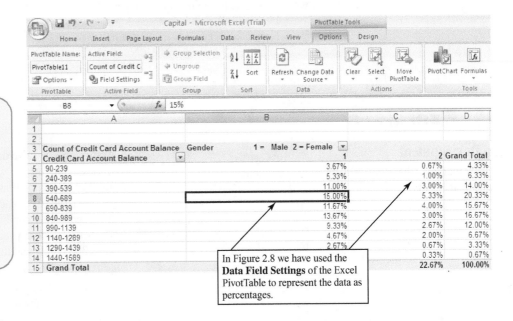

| Count of Credit Card Account Balance | Gender | 1 = Male 2 = Female | | |
|---|---|---|---|---|
| Credit Card Account Balance | | 1 | 2 | Grand Total |
| 90-239 | | 11 | 2 | 13 |
| 240-389 | | 16 | 3 | 19 |
| 390-539 | | 33 | 9 | 42 |
| 540-689 | | 45 | 16 | 61 |
| 690-839 | | 35 | 12 | 47 |
| 840-989 | | 41 | 9 | 50 |
| 990-1139 | | 28 | 8 | 36 |
| 1140-1289 | | 14 | 6 | 20 |
| 1290-1439 | | 8 | 2 | 10 |
| 1440-1589 | | 1 | 1 | 2 |
| Grand Total | | 232 | 68 | 300 |

**Minitab Instructions** (for similar results):

1. Open file: Capital.MTW.
2. Click on **Data > Code > Numeric to Text**.
3. Under **Code data from columns**, select data column.
4. Under **Into columns**, specify destination column: *Classes*.
5. In **Original values**, define each data class range.
6. In **New**, specify code for each class.
7. Click **OK**.
8. Click on **Stat > Tables > Cross Tabulation and Chi-Square**.
9. Under **Categorical Variables For rows** enter *Classes* column and **For columns** enter *Gender* column.
10. Under **Display** check **Counts**.
11. Click **OK**.

The Capital Credit Union managers can use a joint frequency table to analyze the credit card balances for males versus females. For instance, for the 42 customers with balances of $390 to $539, Figure 2.7 shows that 33 were males and 9 were females. Previously, we discussed the concept of relative frequency (proportions, which Excel converts to percentages) as a useful tool for making comparisons between two data sets. In this example, comparisons between males and females would be easier if the frequencies were converted to proportions (or percentages). The result is the *joint relative frequency table* shown in Figure 2.8. Notice that the percentages in each cell are percentages of the total 300 people in the survey. For

**FIGURE 2.8** |

Excel 2007 Output of the Joint Relative Frequencies

**Excel 2007 Instructions:**

1. Place cursor in the **Gender** numbers of the PivotTable.
2. Right-click and select **Value Field Settings**.
3. On the **Show values as** tab, click on the down arrow and select % **of total**.
4. Click **OK**.

| Count of Credit Card Account Balance | Gender | 1 = Male 2 = Female | | |
|---|---|---|---|---|
| Credit Card Account Balance | | 1 | 2 | Grand Total |
| 90-239 | | 3.67% | 0.67% | 4.33% |
| 240-389 | | 5.33% | 1.00% | 6.33% |
| 390-539 | | 11.00% | 3.00% | 14.00% |
| 540-689 | | 15.00% | 5.33% | 20.33% |
| 690-839 | | 11.67% | 4.00% | 15.67% |
| 840-989 | | 13.67% | 3.00% | 16.67% |
| 990-1139 | | 9.33% | 2.67% | 12.00% |
| 1140-1289 | | 4.67% | 2.00% | 6.67% |
| 1290-1439 | | 2.67% | 0.67% | 3.33% |
| 1440-1589 | | 0.33% | 0.33% | 0.67% |
| Grand Total | | | 22.67% | 100.00% |

In Figure 2.8 we have used the **Data Field Settings** of the Excel PivotTable to represent the data as percentages.

**FIGURE 2.9** |

Minitab Relative Frequency
Distribution—Males and
Females

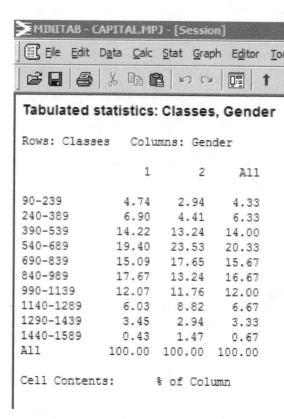

**Tabulated statistics: Classes, Gender**

Rows: Classes    Columns: Gender

|           |   1    |   2    |  All   |
|-----------|--------|--------|--------|
| 90–239    |   4.74 |   2.94 |   4.33 |
| 240–389   |   6.90 |   4.41 |   6.33 |
| 390–539   |  14.22 |  13.24 |  14.00 |
| 540–689   |  19.40 |  23.53 |  20.33 |
| 690–839   |  15.09 |  17.65 |  15.67 |
| 840–989   |  17.67 |  13.24 |  16.67 |
| 990–1139  |  12.07 |  11.76 |  12.00 |
| 1140–1289 |   6.03 |   8.82 |   6.67 |
| 1290–1439 |   3.45 |   2.94 |   3.33 |
| 1440–1589 |   0.43 |   1.47 |   0.67 |
| All       | 100.00 | 100.00 | 100.00 |

Cell Contents:    % of Column

**Minitab Instructions:**
1. Open file: Capital.MTW.
2. Steps 2–7 as in Figure 2.7.
8. Click on **Stat > Tables > Cross Tabulation and Chi-square**.
9. Under **Categorical variables For rows** enter *Classes* column and **For columns** enter *Gender* column.
10. Under **Display**, check **Total Percents**.
11. Click **OK**.

example, the \$540-to-\$689 class had 20.33% (61) of the 300 customers. The male customers with balances in the \$540-to-\$689 range constituted 15% (45) of the 300 customers, whereas females with that balance level made up 5.33% (16) of all 300 customers. On the surface, this result seems to indicate a big difference between males and females at this credit balance level.

Suppose we really wanted to focus on the male versus female issue and control for the fact that there are far more male customers than female. We could compute the percentages differently. Rather than using a base of 300 (the entire sample size), we might instead be interested in the percentages of the males who have balances at each level, and the same measure for females.[2] Figure 2.9 shows the relative frequencies converted to percentages of the column total. In general, there seems to be little difference in the male and female distributions with respect to credit card balances.

There are many options for transferring data into useful information. Thus far, we have introduced frequency distributions, joint frequency tables, and histograms. In the next section, we discuss one of the most useful graphical tools: the bar chart.

---

[2]Such distributions are known as *marginal distributions*.

MyStatLab

## 2-1: **Exercises**

### Skill Development

**2-1.** Given the following data, develop a frequency distribution:

| | | | | |
|---|---|---|---|---|
| 5 | 3 | 2 | 6 | 6 |
| 7 | 3 | 3 | 6 | 7 |
| 7 | 9 | 7 | 5 | 3 |
| 12 | 6 | 10 | 7 | 2 |
| 6 | 8 | 0 | 7 | 4 |

**2-2.** Assuming you have data for a variable with 2,000 values, using the $2^k \geq n$ guideline, what is the least number of groups that should be used in developing a grouped data frequency distribution?

**2-3.** A study is being conducted in which a variable of interest has 1,000 observations. The minimum value in the data set is 300 points and the maximum is 2,900 points.

a. Use the $2^k \geq n$ guideline to determine the minimum number of classes to use in developing a grouped data frequency distribution.

b. Based on the answer to part a, determine the class width that should be used (round up to the nearest 100 points).

**2-4.** Produce the relative frequency distribution from a sample of size 50 that gave rise to the following ogive:

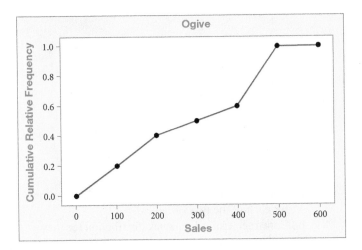

Ogive

**2-5.** You have the following data:

| 8 | 6 | 11 | 14 | 10 |
|---|---|----|----|----|
| 11 | 9 | 7 | 2 | 8 |
| 9 | 5 | 5 | 5 | 12 |
| 7 | 8 | 4 | 17 | 8 |
| 12 | 7 | 8 | 8 | 7 |
| 10 | 8 | 6 | 9 | 9 |
| 11 | 16 | 2 | 7 | 4 |
| 8 | 4 | 4 | 5 | 5 |
| 9 | 9 | 6 | 6 | 7 |
| 7 | 9 | 5 | 4 | 5 |
| 14 | 2 | 9 | 0 | 6 |
| 1 | 1 | 12 | 11 | 4 |

a. Construct a frequency distribution for these data. Use the $2^k \geq n$ guideline to determine the number of classes to use.

b. Develop a relative frequency distribution using the classes you constructed in part a.

c. Develop a cumulative frequency distribution and a cumulative relative frequency distribution using the classes you constructed in part a.

d. Develop a histogram based on the frequency distribution you constructed in part a.

**2-6.** Fill in the missing components of the following frequency distribution constructed for a sample size of 50:

| Class | Frequency | Relative Frequency | Cumulative Relative Frequency |
|-------|-----------|--------------------|-------------------------------|
| 7.85 – < ___ | ___ | ___ | 0.12 |
| ___ – < 8.05 | ___ | | 0.48 |
| 8.05 – < ___ | ___ | ___ | |
| ___ – < 8.25 | ___ | | |
| 8.25 – < ___ | ___ | ___ | |

**2-7.** The following cumulative relative frequency distribution summarizes data obtained in a study of the ending overages (in dollars) for the cash register balance at a business:

| Class | Frequency | Relative Frequency | Cumulative Relative Frequency |
|-------|-----------|--------------------|-------------------------------|
| −60.00 −<−40.00 | 2 | 0.04 | 0.04 |
| −40.00 −<−20.00 | 2 | 0.04 | 0.08 |
| −20.00 −< 00.00 | 8 | 0.16 | 0.24 |
| 00.00 −< 20.00 | 16 | 0.32 | 0.56 |
| 20.00 −< 40.00 | 20 | 0.40 | 0.96 |
| 40.00 −< 60.00 | 2 | 0.04 | 1.00 |

a. Determine the proportion of the days in which there were no shortages

b. Determine the proportion of the days the cash register was less than $20 off.

c. Determine the proportion of the days the cash register was less than $40 over or at most $20 short.

**2-8.** You are given the following data:

| 6 | 10 | 6 | 4 | 9 | 5 |
|---|----|---|---|---|---|
| 5 | 5 | 5 | 7 | 6 | 2 |
| 5 | 5 | 5 | 4 | 5 | 7 |
| 6 | 7 | 8 | 6 | 8 | 4 |
| 7 | 5 | 5 | 5 | 5 | 7 |
| 8 | 7 | 6 | 7 | 5 | 4 |
| 6 | 4 | 4 | 7 | 4 | 6 |
| 6 | 7 | 8 | 6 | 7 | 6 |
| 7 | 8 | 5 | 6 | 5 | 7 |
| 3 | 6 | 4 | 7 | 4 | 4 |

a. Construct a frequency distribution for these data.

b. Based on the frequency distribution, develop a histogram.

c. Construct a relative frequency distribution.

d. Develop a relative frequency histogram.

e. Compare the two histograms. Why do they look alike?

**2-9.** Using the data from Problem 2-8,

a. Construct a grouped data relative frequency distribution of the data. Use the $2^k \geq n$ guideline to determine the number of classes.

b. Construct a cumulative frequency distribution of the data.

c. Construct a relative frequency histogram.

d. Construct an ogive.

## Business **Applications**

**2-10.** Burger King is one of the largest fast-food franchise operations in the world. Recently, the district manager for Burger King in Las Vegas conducted a study in which she selected a random sample of sales receipts. She was interested in the number of line items on the receipts. For instance, if a customer ordered two

1/4-pound hamburgers, one side of fries, and two soft drinks, the number of line items would be five. The following data were observed:

| | | | | | | | | | |
|---|---|---|---|---|---|---|---|---|---|
| 7 | 5 | 7 | 6 | 5 | 5 | 4 | 8 | 6 | 5 |
| 8 | 7 | 6 | 5 | 6 | 2 | 9 | 4 | 4 | 5 |
| 8 | 4 | 9 | 6 | 6 | 5 | 8 | 9 | 9 | 1 |
| 6 | 5 | 10 | 6 | 7 | 6 | 5 | 5 | 5 | 6 |
| 8 | 7 | 6 | 8 | 6 | 6 | 9 | 6 | 12 | 7 |
| 5 | 6 | 7 | 11 | 4 | 4 | 3 | 4 | 1 | 4 |
| 11 | 2 | 5 | 5 | 8 | 2 | 3 | 4 | 9 | 6 |
| 6 | 5 | 8 | 6 | 3 | 6 | 4 | 5 | 8 | 10 |

a. Develop a frequency distribution for these data. Discuss briefly what the frequency distribution tells you about these sample data.
b. Based on the results in part a, construct a frequency histogram for these sample data.

**2-11.** In a survey conducted by AIG, investors were asked to rate how knowledgeable they felt they were as investors. Both online and traditional investors were included in the survey. The survey resulted in the following data:

Of the online investors, 8%, 55%, and 37% responded they were "savvy," "experienced," and "novice," respectively.

Of the traditional investors, the percentages were 4%, 29%, and 67%, respectively.

Of the 600 investors surveyed, 200 were traditional investors.

a. Use the information to construct a joint frequency distribution.
b. Use the information to construct a joint relative frequency distribution.
c. Determine the proportion of investors who were both online investors and rated themselves experienced.
d. Calculate the proportion of investors who were online investors.

**2-12.** The sales manager for the Fox News TV station affiliate in a southern Florida city recently surveyed 20 advertisers and asked each one to rate the service of the station on the following scale:

| Very Good | Good | Fair | Poor | Very Poor |
|---|---|---|---|---|
| 1 | 2 | 3 | 4 | 5 |

He also tracked the general time slot when the advertiser's commercials were shown on the station. The following codes were used:

1 = morning        2 = afternoon
3 = evening        4 = various times

The following sample data were observed:

| Rating | Time Slot | Rating | Time Slot |
|---|---|---|---|
| 2 | 1 | 4 | 3 |
| 1 | 1 | 2 | 2 |
| 3 | 3 | 3 | 3 |
| 2 | 1 | 3 | 3 |
| 1 | 1 | 2 | 1 |
| 4 | 4 | 1 | 1 |
| 2 | 2 | 1 | 1 |
| 1 | 1 | 5 | 3 |
| 2 | 1 | 2 | 4 |
| 2 | 2 | 3 | 4 |

a. Construct separate relative frequency distributions for each of the two variables.
b. Construct a joint frequency distribution for these two variables.
c. Construct a joint relative frequency distribution for these two variables. Write a short paragraph describing what the data imply.

**2-13.** A St. Louis–based shipping company recently selected a random sample of 49 airplane weight slips for crates shipped from an automobile parts supplier. The weights, measured in pounds, for the sampled crates are as follows:

| | | | | | | |
|---|---|---|---|---|---|---|
| 89 | 83 | 97 | 101 | 86 | 89 | 86 |
| 91 | 84 | 89 | 87 | 93 | 86 | 90 |
| 86 | 92 | 92 | 88 | 88 | 92 | 86 |
| 93 | 80 | 93 | 77 | 98 | 94 | 95 |
| 94 | 88 | 95 | 87 | 99 | 98 | 90 |
| 91 | 87 | 89 | 89 | 96 | 88 | 94 |
| 95 | 79 | 94 | 86 | 92 | 94 | 85 |

a. Create a data array of the weights.
b. Develop a frequency distribution using five classes having equal widths.
c. Develop a histogram from the frequency distribution you created in part b.
d. Develop a relative frequency and a cumulative relative frequency distribution for the weights using the same five classes created in part b. What percent of the sampled crates have weights greater than 96 pounds?

**2-14.** The bubble in U.S. housing prices burst in 2008, causing sales of houses to decline in almost every part of the country. Many homes were foreclosed because the owners could not make the payments. Below is a sample of 100 residential properties and the total balance on the mortgage at the time of foreclosure.

| | | | | |
|---|---|---|---|---|
| $172,229 | $211,021 | $159,205 | $247,697 | $247,469 |
| $176,736 | $240,815 | $195,056 | $315,097 | $257,150 |
| $129,779 | $207,451 | $165,225 | $178,970 | $319,101 |
| $ 87,429 | $219,808 | $242,761 | $277,389 | $213,803 |
| $153,468 | $205,696 | $210,447 | $179,029 | $241,331 |
| $117,808 | $188,909 | $376,644 | $185,523 | $168,145 |
| $158,094 | $135,461 | $131,457 | $263,232 | $256,262 |
| $240,034 | $289,973 | $302,341 | $178,684 | $226,998 |
| $176,440 | $268,106 | $181,507 | $118,752 | $251,009 |
| $196,457 | $195,249 | $195,986 | $201,680 | $233,182 |
| $271,552 | $123,262 | $212,411 | $246,462 | $177,673 |
| $103,699 | $252,375 | $192,335 | $265,992 | $232,247 |
| $320,004 | $213,020 | $192,546 | $295,660 | $211,876 |
| $265,787 | $207,443 | $203,043 | $133,014 | $289,645 |
| $251,560 | $302,054 | $185,381 | $284,345 | $184,869 |
| $237,485 | $282,506 | $278,783 | $335,920 | $199,630 |
| $248,272 | $232,234 | $188,833 | $168,905 | $357,612 |
| $241,894 | $186,956 | $114,601 | $301,728 | $251,865 |
| $207,040 | $221,614 | $318,154 | $156,611 | $219,730 |
| $201,473 | $174,840 | $196,622 | $263,686 | $159,029 |

a. Using the $2^k \geq n$ guideline, what is the minimum number of classes that should be used to display these data in a grouped data frequency distribution?

b. Referring to part a, what should the class width be, assuming you round the width up to nearest $1,000?

c. Referring to parts a and b, develop a grouped data frequency distribution for these mortgage balance data.

d. Based on your answer to part c, construct and interpret a frequency histogram for the mortgage balance data.

**2-15.** Wageweb exhibits salary data obtained from surveys. It provides compensation information on over 170 benchmark positions, including finance positions. It recently reported that salaries of Chief Finance Officers (CFOs) ranged from $127,735 to $209,981 (before bonuses). Suppose the following data represent a sample of the annual salaries for 25 CFOs. Assume that data are in thousands of dollars.

| | | | | | | | |
|---|---|---|---|---|---|---|---|
| 173.1 | 171.2 | 141.9 | 112.6 | 211.1 | 156.5 | 145.4 | 134.0 |
| 192.0 | 185.8 | 168.3 | 131.0 | 214.4 | 155.2 | 164.9 | 123.9 |
| 161.9 | 162.7 | 178.8 | 161.3 | 182.0 | 165.8 | 213.1 | 177.4 |
| 159.3 | | | | | | | |

a. Using 11 classes, construct a cumulative frequency distribution.

b. Determine the proportion of CFO salaries that are at least $175,000.

c. Determine the proportion of CFO salaries that are less than $205,000 and at least $135,000.

**2-16.** The *San Diego Union Tribune* reported that the 30-year fixed-rate mortgage rates had risen to an average of 5.74%. A sample of mortgage rates in the San Diego area produced the following interest rates:

| | | | | | | |
|---|---|---|---|---|---|---|
| 5.84 | 5.73 | 5.58 | 5.69 | 5.84 | 5.68 | 5.73 |
| 5.79 | 5.77 | 5.67 | 5.76 | 5.70 | 5.70 | 5.66 |
| 5.71 | 5.80 | 5.81 | 5.75 | 5.81 | 5.78 | 5.79 |
| 5.77 | 5.73 | 5.67 | 5.74 | 5.76 | 5.76 | 5.74 |
| 5.73 | 5.71 | 5.71 | 5.72 | 5.80 | 5.69 | 5.88 |
| 5.70 | 5.75 | 5.75 | 5.68 | 5.72 | 5.70 | 5.67 |
| 5.83 | 5.76 | 5.80 | | | | |

a. Construct a histogram with eight classes beginning at 5.58.

b. Determine the proportion of mortgage rates that are at least 5.74%.

c. Generate an ogive for this data.

### Computer Database Exercises

**2-17.** J.D. Power and Associates' annual customer-satisfaction survey, the Automotive Performance, Execution and Layout (APEAL) Study[SM], in its 13th year, was released on September 22, 2008. The study measures owners' satisfaction with the design, content, layout, and performance of their new vehicles. A file entitled **APEAL2** contains the satisfaction ratings for 2008 for each make of car.

a. Construct a histogram that starts at 710 and has class widths of 20 for the APEAL ratings.

b. The past industry average APEAL rating was 866 for 2005. What does the 2008 data suggest in terms of the relative satisfaction with the 2008 models?

**2-18.** The Franklin Tire Company is interested in demonstrating the durability of its steel-belted radial tires. To do this, the managers have decided to put four tires on 100 different sport utility vehicles and drive them throughout Alaska. The data collected indicate the number of miles (rounded to the nearest 1,000 miles) that each of the SUVs traveled before one of the tires on the vehicle did not meet minimum federal standards for tread thickness. The data file is called **Franklin**.

a. Construct a frequency distribution and histogram using eight classes. Use 51 as the lower limit of the first class.

b. The marketing department wishes to know the tread life of at least 50% of the tires, the 10% that had the longest tread life, and the longest tread life of these tires. Provide this information to the marketing department. Also provide any other significant items that point out the desirability of this line of steel-belted tires.

c. Construct a frequency distribution and histogram using 12 classes, using 51 as the lower limit of the first class. Compare your results with those in parts a and b. Which distribution gives the best information about the desirability of this line of steel-belted tires? Discuss.

**2-19.** The California Golf Association recently conducted a survey of its members. Among other questions, the members were asked to indicate the number of 18-hole rounds that they played last year. Data for a sample of 294 members are provided in the data file called **Golf Survey**.

a. Using the $2^k \geq n$ guideline, what is the minimum number of classes that should be used to display these data in a grouped data frequency distribution?

b. Referring to part a, what should the class width be, assuming you round the width up to the nearest integer?

c. Referring to parts a and b, develop a grouped data frequency distribution for these golf data.

d. Based on your answer to part c, construct and interpret a frequency histogram for the data.

2-20. *Ars Technia* LLD published a news release (Eric Bangeman, "Dell Still King of Market Share") that presented the results of a study concerning the world market share for the major manufacturers of personal computers. It indicated that Dell held 17.9% of this market. The file entitled **PCMarket** contains a sample of the market shares alluded to in the article.

a. Construct a histogram from this set of data and identify the sample shares for each of the listed manufacturers.

b. Excluding the data referred to as "other," determine the total share of the sample for manufacturers that have headquarters in the United States.

2-21. Orlando, Florida, is a well-known, popular vacation destination visited by tourists from around the world. Consequently, the Orlando International Airport is busy throughout the year. Among the variety of data collected by the Greater Orlando Airport Authority is the number of passengers by airline. The file **Orlando Airport** contains passenger data for July 2008. Suppose the airport manager is interested in analyzing the column labeled "Total" for this data.

a. Using the $2^k \geq n$ guideline, what is the minimum number of classes that should be used to display the data in the "Total" column in a grouped data frequency distribution?

b. Referring to part a, what should the class width be, assuming you round the width up to the nearest 1,000 passengers?

c. Referring to parts a and b, develop a grouped data frequency distribution for these airport data.

d. Based on your answer to part c, construct and interpret a frequency histogram for the data.

2-22. The manager of AJ's Fitness Center, a full-service health and exercise club, recently conducted a survey of 1,214 members. The objective of the survey was to determine the satisfaction level of his club's customers. In addition, the survey asked for several demographic factors such as age and gender. The data from the survey are in a file called **AJFitness**.

a. One of the key variables is "Overall Customer Satisfaction." This variable is measured on an ordinal scale as follows:

5 = very satisfied   4 = satisfied   3 = neutral
2 = dissatisfied   1 = very dissatisfied

Develop a frequency distribution for this variable and discuss the results.

b. Develop a joint relative frequency distribution for the variables "Overall Customer Satisfaction" and "Typical Visits Per Week." Discuss the results.

2-23. The file **German Coffee** contains data on individual coffee consumption (in kg) for 144 randomly selected German coffee drinkers.

a. Construct a data array of the coffee consumption data.

b. Construct a frequency distribution of the coffee consumption data. Within what class do more of the observations fall?

c. Construct a histogram of the coffee consumption data. Briefly comment on what the histogram reveals concerning the data.

d. Develop a relative frequency distribution and a cumulative relative frequency distribution of the coffee data. What percentage of the coffee drinkers sampled consume 8.0 kg or more annually?

**END EXERCISES 2-1**

## 2.2 Bar Charts, Pie Charts, and Stem and Leaf Diagrams

Chapter Outcome 4. ➤ **Bar Charts**

**Bar Chart**

A graphical representation of a categorical data set in which a rectangle or bar is drawn over each category or class. The length or height of each bar represents the frequency or percentage of observations or some other measure associated with the category. The bars may be vertical or horizontal. The bars may all be the same color or they may be different colors depicting different categories. Additionally, multiple variables can be graphed on the same bar chart.

Section 2-1 introduced some of the basic tools for describing numerical variables, both discrete and continuous, when the data are in their raw form. However, in many instances, you will be working with categorical data or data that have already been summarized to some extent. In these cases, an effective presentation tool is often a **bar chart**.

**BUSINESS APPLICATION**   DEVELOPING BAR CHARTS

**NEW CAR SALES**   The automobile industry is a significant part of the U.S., Japanese, and German economies. When car sales are up, the economies of these countries are up, and vice-versa. Table 2.8 displays data showing the total number of cars sold in April 2008 by the six

**TABLE 2.8** | **April 2008 New Car Sales for the Top Six Automobile Companies (United States)**

| Car Company | April 2008 Sales |
|---|---|
| General Motors | 282,000 |
| Ford | 206,000 |
| Toyota | 215,000 |
| Chrysler | 160,000 |
| Honda | 138,000 |
| Nissan | 88,000 |

*Source*: *Edmunds Auto Observer,* April 28, 2008.

largest automobile companies in the world. Although the table format is informative, a graphical presentation is often desirable. Because the car sales data are characterized by car company, a bar chart would work well in this instance. The bars on a bar chart can be vertical (called a *column bar chart*) or horizontal (called a *horizontal bar chart*). Figure 2.10 illustrates an example of a column bar chart. The height of the bars corresponds to the number of cars sold by each company. This gives you an idea of the sales advantage held by General Motors in April 2008.

One strength of the bar chart is its capability of displaying multiple variables on the same chart. For instance, a bar chart can conveniently compare new car sales data for April 2008 and sales for the same month the previous year. Figure 2.11 is a horizontal bar chart that does just that. Notice all three U.S. automakers (Ford, GM, and Chrysler) had a decline in sales in April 2008 versus April 2007.

People sometimes confuse histograms and bar charts. Although there are some similarities, they are two very different graphical tools. Histograms are used to represent a frequency distribution associated with a single quantitative (ratio or interval-level) variable. Refer to the histogram illustrations in Section 2-1. In every case, the variable on the horizontal axis was numerical, with values moving from low to high. There are no gaps between the histogram bars. On the other hand, bar charts are used when one or more variables of interest are categorical, as in this case in which the category is "car company."

**FIGURE 2.10** |

Bar Chart Showing April 2008 New Car Sales

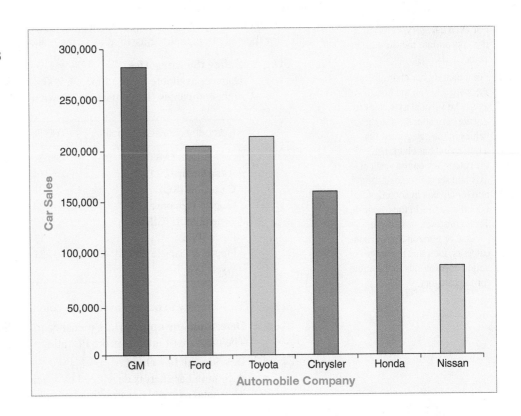

**FIGURE 2.11**

Bar Chart Comparing April
2007 and April 2008 Cars
Sold

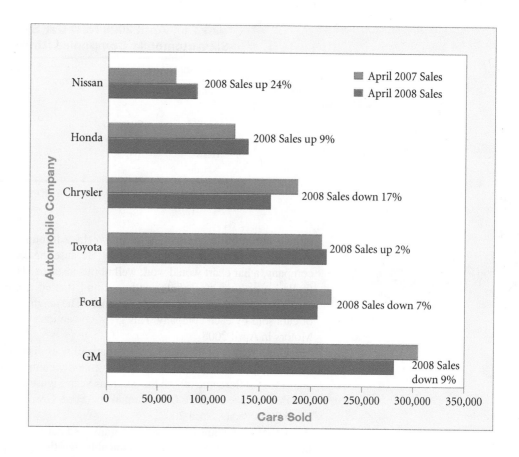

## How to do it (Example 2-7)

**Constructing Bar Charts**

**A bar chart is constructed using the following steps:**

1. Define the categories for the variable of interest.

2. For each category, determine the appropriate measure or value.

3. For a column bar chart, locate the categories on the horizontal axis. The vertical axis is set to a scale corresponding to the values in the categories. For a horizontal bar chart, place the categories on the vertical axis and set the scale of the horizontal axis in accordance with the values in the categories. Then construct bars, either vertical or horizontal, for each category such that the length or height corresponds to the value for the category.

**EXAMPLE 2-7**    **BAR CHARTS**

**Investment Recommendations** In the July 11, 2005, issue of *Fortune*, David Stires authored "The Best Stocks to Buy Now." The article identified 40 companies as good investment opportunities. These companies were divided into five categories: Growth and Income, Bargain Growth, Deep Value, Small Wonders, and Foreign Value. For each company, data for several key variables were reported, including the price/earnings (PE) ratio based on the previous 12 months' reported earnings. We are interested in constructing a bar chart of the PE ratios for the eight companies classified as Growth and Income.

**Step 1    Define the categories.**

Data are available for the June 24, 2005, stock price and PE ratio for each of eight companies. These data are shown as follows:

| Company (Ticker Symbol) | PE Ratio | Stock Price |
|---|---|---|
| Abbott Labs (ABT) | 21 | $49 |
| Altria Group (MO) | 14 | $65 |
| Coca-Cola (KO) | 21 | $42 |
| Colgate-Palmolive (CL) | 20 | $51 |
| General Mills (GIS) | 17 | $51 |
| Pfizer (PFE) | 13 | $29 |
| Procter & Gamble (PG) | 21 | $53 |
| Wyeth (WYE) | 15 | $43 |

The category to be displayed is the company.

**Step 2    Determine the appropriate measure to be displayed.**

The measure of interest is the PE ratio.

**Step 3    Develop the bar chart.**

A column bar chart is developed by placing the eight companies on the horizontal axis and constructing bars whose heights correspond to the value of the company's PE ratio. Each company is assigned a different-colored bar. The resulting bar chart is

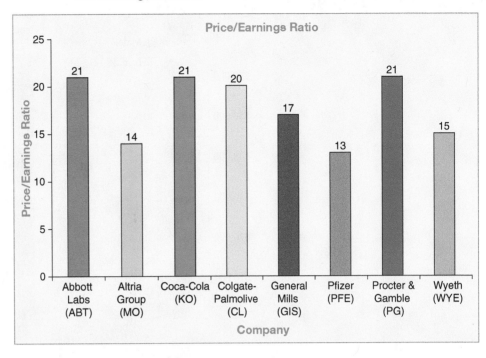

**Step 4** **Interpret the results.**

The bar chart shows three companies with especially low PE ratios. These are Altria Group, Pfizer, and Wyeth. Thus, of the eight recommended companies in the Growth and Income group, these three have the lowest PE ratios.

You might be interested in seeing how these eight companies have done since this article was published in July 2005. Go to one of the online services (for example, Yahoo Finance) to get the current stock prices and PE ratios and compare those with the values listed above.

>> END EXAMPLE

**TRY PROBLEM** 2-27 (pg. 63)

BUSINESS APPLICATION    CONSTRUCTING BAR CHARTS

**BACH, LOMBARD, & WILSON** One of the most useful features of bar charts is that they can display multiple issues. Consider Bach, Lombard, & Wilson, a New England law firm. Recently, the firm handled a case in which a woman was suing her employer, a major electronics firm, claiming the company gave higher starting salaries to men than to women. Consequently, she stated, even though the company tended to give equal-percentage raises to women and men, the gap between the two groups widened.

Attorneys at Bach, Lombard, & Wilson had their staff assemble massive amounts of data. Table 2.9 provides an example of the type of data they collected. A bar chart is a more effective way to convey this information, as Figure 2.12 shows. From this graph we can

**Excel and Minitab Tutorial**

TABLE 2.9 | **Salary Data for Bach, Lombard, & Wilson**

| Year | Males: Average Starting Salaries | Females: Average Starting Salaries |
|------|----------------------------------|------------------------------------|
| 2003 | $44,456 | $41,789 |
| 2004 | $47,286 | $46,478 |
| 2005 | $56,234 | $53,854 |
| 2006 | $57,890 | $58,600 |
| 2007 | $63,467 | $59,070 |
| 2008 | $61,090 | $55,321 |
| 2009 | $67,543 | $64,506 |

**FIGURE 2.12**

Bar Chart of Starting Salaries

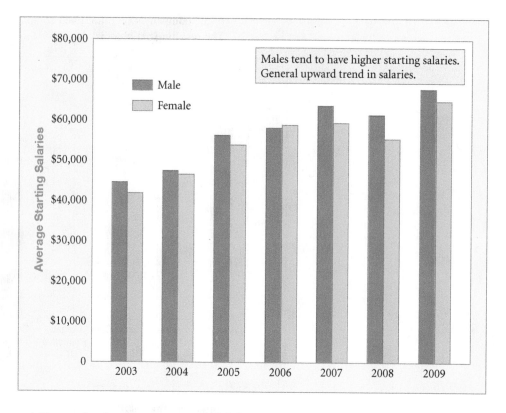

quickly see that in all years except 2006 the starting salaries for males did exceed those for females. The bar chart also illustrates that the general trend in starting salaries for both groups has been increasing, though with a slight downturn in 2008. Do you think the information in Figure 2.12 alone is sufficient to rule in favor of the claimant in this lawsuit? Bar charts like the one in Figure 2.12 that display two or more variables are referred to as *cluster bar charts*.

Suppose other data are available showing the percentage of new hires having master of business administration (MBA) degrees by gender, as illustrated in Table 2.10. The cluster bar chart in Figure 2.13 presents these data clearly. The chart shows that every year the percentage of new hires with MBA degrees was substantially higher for male hires than for female hires. What might this imply about the reason for the difference in starting salaries?

After viewing the bar chart in Figure 2.13, the lead attorney had her staff look at the average starting salary for MBA and non–MBA graduates for the combined seven-year period, broken down by male and female employees. Figure 2.14 shows the bar chart for those data.

Figure 2.14 shows an interesting result. Over the seven-year period, females actually had higher starting salaries than males for those with and without MBA degrees. Then how can Figure 2.12 be correct, when it shows that in almost every year the male average starting salary exceeded the female average starting salary? The answer lies in Figure 2.13, which shows that far more of the newly hired males had MBAs. Because MBAs tend to get substantially higher starting salaries, the overall average male salary was higher. In this case, the initial data looked like the electronics firm had been discriminating against females by paying

**TABLE 2.10** | **Salary Data for the Bach, Lombard, & Wilson Example**

| Year | Males: Average Starting Salaries | Males: Percentage with MBA | Females: Average Starting Salaries | Females: Percentage with MBA |
|------|----------------------------------|----------------------------|------------------------------------|------------------------------|
| 2003 | $44,456 | 35 | $41,789 | 18 |
| 2004 | $47,286 | 39 | $46,478 | 20 |
| 2005 | $56,234 | 49 | $53,854 | 22 |
| 2006 | $57,890 | 40 | $58,600 | 30 |
| 2007 | $63,467 | 46 | $59,070 | 25 |
| 2008 | $61,090 | 32 | $55,321 | 24 |
| 2009 | $67,543 | 48 | $64,506 | 26 |

Excel 2007 Output—Bar
Chart of MBA Hire Data

**Excel 2007 Instructions:**
1. Open file: Bach.xls.
2. Select data for chart.
3. On **Insert** tab, click **Bar Chart**, and then click **2-D Bar** option.
4. Click on **Design** and **Move Chart** to put chart on a separate page.
5. Use the **Layout** tab of the **Axis Titles** to add titles and remove grid lines.
6. Under **Design**, click on **Select Data**.
7. Click on **Edit** under **Horizontal Axis** and specify the location of year variable.

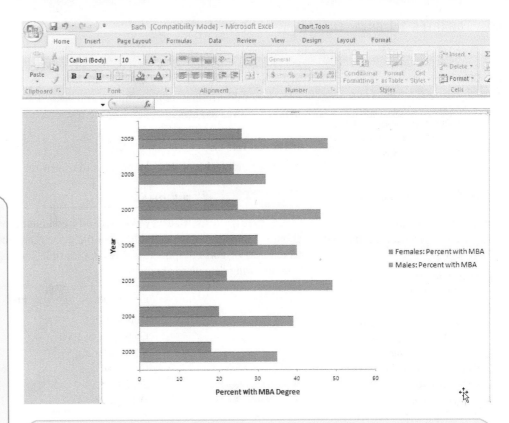

**Minitab Instructions (for similar results):**
(**Create stacked columns** for *Percent Hired*, *Years*, and *Gender, See Tutorial*.)
1. Open file: Bach.MTW.
2. Click on **Graph > Bar Chart**.
3. Under **Bars represent**, select *Values from a table*.
4. Under **One column of values**, select *Cluster*, click **OK**.
5. In **Graph variables**, enter *Percent Hired* column.
6. In **Categorical variables for grouping (1-4 outer-most first)**, enter *Year* and *Gender* columns.
7. Click **OK**.

Excel 2007 Output—Bar
Chart of Average Starting
Salaries by Degree Type and
Gender

**Excel 2007 Instructions:**
1. Open file: Bach.xls.
2. Select data for chart.
3. On **Insert** tab, click **Bar Chart**, and then click **2-D Bar** option.
4. Click on **Design** and **Move Chart** to put chart on a separate page.
5. Use the **Layout** tab of the **Axis Titles** to add titles and remove grid lines.
6. Under **Design**, click on **Select Data**.
7. Click on **Edit** under **Horizontal Axis** and specify the location of x-axis labels.

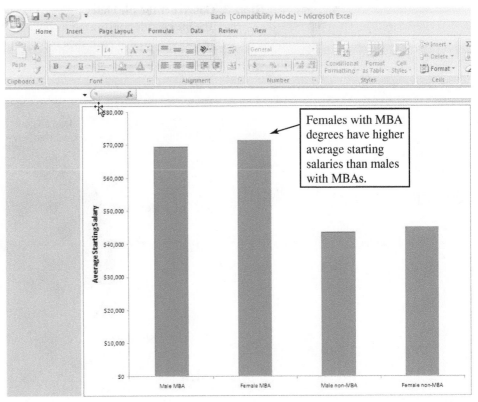

**Pie Chart**

A graph in the shape of a circle. The circle is divided into "slices" corresponding to the categories or classes to be displayed. The size of each slice is proportional to the magnitude of the displayed variable associated with each category or class.

## How to do it (Example 2-8)

### Constructing Pie Charts

**A pie chart is constructed using the following steps:**

1. Define the categories for the variable of interest.

2. For each category, determine the appropriate measure or value. The value assigned to each category is the proportion the category is to the total for all categories.

3. Construct the pie chart by displaying one slice for each category that is proportional in size to the proportion the category value is to the total of all categories.

lower starting salaries. After digging deeper, we see that females actually get the higher starting average salaries with and without MBA degrees. However, does this prove that the company is not discriminating in its hiring practices? Perhaps it purposefully hires fewer female MBAs or fewer females in general. More research is needed.

# Pie Charts

Another graphical tool that can be used to transform data into information is the **pie chart**.

**EXAMPLE 2-8**    **PIE CHARTS**

Gold Equipment A survey was recently conducted of 300 golfers that asked questions about the impact of new technology on the game. One question asked the golfers to indicate which area of golf equipment is most responsible for improving an amateur golfer's game. The following data were obtained:

| Equipment | Frequency |
| --- | --- |
| Golf ball | 81 |
| Club head material | 66 |
| Shaft material | 63 |
| Club head size | 63 |
| Shaft length | 3 |
| Don't know | 24 |

To display these data in pie chart form, use the following steps:

**Step 1**  **Define the categories.**
The categories are the six equipment-response categories.

**Step 2**  **Determine the appropriate measure.**
The appropriate measure is the proportion of the golfers surveyed. The proportion for each category is determined by dividing the number of golfers in a category by the total sample size. For example, for the category "golf ball," the percentage is $81/300 = 0.27 = 27\%$.

**Step 3**  **Construct the pie chart.**
The pie chart is constructed by dividing a circle into six slices (one for each category) such that each slice is proportional to the percentage of golfers in the category.

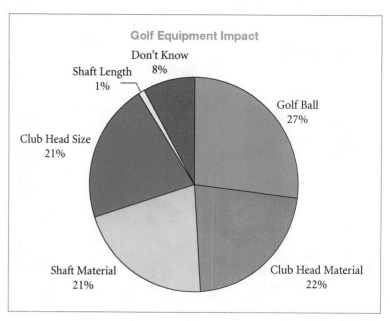

>> **END EXAMPLE**

**TRY PROBLEM** 2-28 (pg. 64)

**FIGURE 2.15**

Pie Chart: Per-Student
Funding for Universities

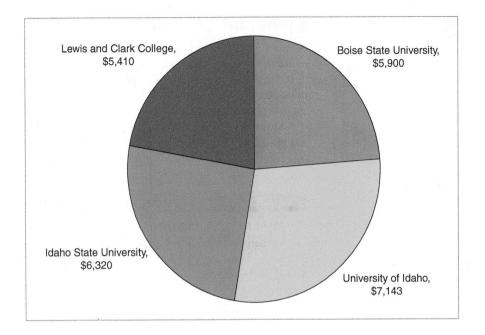

Pie charts are sometimes mistakenly used when a bar chart would be more appropriate. For example, a few years ago the student leaders at Boise State University wanted to draw attention to the funding inequities among the four public universities in Idaho. To do so, they rented a large billboard adjacent to a major thoroughfare through downtown Boise. The billboard contained a large pie chart like the one shown in Figure 2.15, where each slice indicated the funding per student at a given university. However, for a pie chart to be appropriate, the slices of the pie should represent parts of a total. But in the case of the billboard, that was not the case. The amounts merely represented the dollars of state money spent per student at each university. The sum of the four dollar amounts on the pie chart was a meaningless number. In this case, a bar chart like that shown in Figure 2.16 would have been more appropriate.

**FIGURE 2.16**

Bar Chart: Per-Student
Funding for Universities

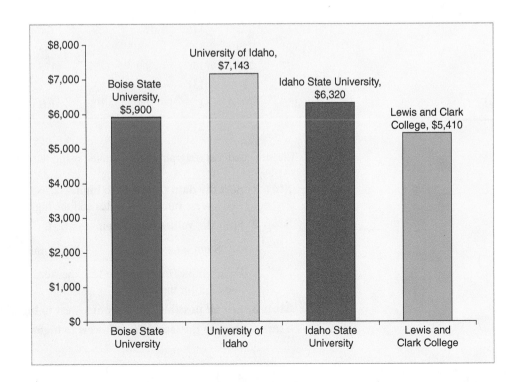

Chapter Outcome 5. → # Stem and Leaf Diagrams

Another graphical technique useful for doing an exploratory analysis of quantitative data is called the *stem and leaf diagram*. The stem and leaf diagram is similar to the histogram introduced in Section 2-1 in that it displays the distribution for the quantitative variable. However, unlike the histogram, in which the individual values of the data are lost if the variable of interest is broken into classes, the stem and leaf diagram shows the individual data values.

Minitab has a procedure for constructing stem and leaf diagrams. Although Excel does not have a stem and leaf procedure, the PHStat add-ins to Excel do have a stem and leaf procedure.

## How to do it (Example 2-9)

### Constructing Stem and Leaf Diagrams

**To construct the stem and leaf diagram for a quantitative variable, use the following steps:**

**1.** Sort the data from low to high.

**2.** Analyze the data for the variable of interest to determine how you wish to split the values into a stem and a leaf.

**3.** List all possible stems in a single column between the lowest and highest values in the data.

**4.** For each stem, list all leaves associated with the stem.

---

**EXAMPLE 2-9    STEM AND LEAF DIAGRAMS**

**Regis Auto Rental** The operations manager for Regis Auto Rental is interested in performing an analysis of the miles driven for the cars the company rents on weekends. One method for analyzing the data for a sample of 200 rentals is the stem and leaf diagram. The following data represent the miles driven in the cars:

| | | | | | | | | | |
|---|---|---|---|---|---|---|---|---|---|
| 113 | 112 | 63 | 127 | 110 | 129 | 142 | 115 | 192 | 94 |
| 165 | 121 | 105 | 140 | 85 | 93 | 105 | 140 | 93 | 126 |
| 183 | 118 | 67 | 104 | 162 | 110 | 76 | 109 | 91 | 132 |
| 88 | 96 | 132 | 80 | 144 | 112 | 57 | 139 | 123 | 124 |
| 172 | 149 | 198 | 114 | 88 | 111 | 133 | 117 | 138 | 134 |
| 53 | 147 | 108 | 109 | 153 | 89 | 159 | 99 | 130 | 93 |
| 161 | 118 | 115 | 117 | 128 | 98 | 125 | 184 | 134 | 132 |
| 117 | 127 | 166 | 72 | 122 | 109 | 124 | 92 | 82 | 69 |
| 110 | 128 | 151 | 67 | 142 | 177 | 135 | 121 | 143 | 89 |
| 160 | 115 | 138 | 79 | 104 | 76 | 89 | 110 | 44 | 140 |
| 117 | 103 | 59 | 109 | 145 | 117 | 162 | 108 | 141 | 139 |
| 148 | 175 | 107 | 117 | 87 | 87 | 150 | 152 | 80 | 168 |
| 88 | 127 | 131 | 85 | 143 | 101 | 137 | 111 | 128 | 147 |
| 110 | 81 | 111 | 149 | 154 | 90 | 150 | 117 | 101 | 116 |
| 153 | 176 | 112 | 147 | 87 | 177 | 190 | 66 | 62 | 154 |
| 143 | 122 | 176 | 153 | 97 | 106 | 86 | 62 | 146 | 98 |
| 134 | 135 | 127 | 118 | 109 | 143 | 146 | 152 | 140 | 95 |
| 102 | 137 | 158 | 69 | 122 | 135 | 136 | 129 | 91 | 136 |
| 135 | 86 | 131 | 154 | 132 | 59 | 136 | 85 | 142 | 137 |
| 155 | 190 | 120 | 154 | 102 | 109 | 97 | 157 | 144 | 149 |

The stem and leaf diagram is constructed using the following steps:

**Step 1    Sort the data from low to high.**
    The lowest value is 44 miles and the highest value is 198 miles.

**Step 2    Split the values into a stem and leaf.**

        Stem = tens place        leaf = units place

    For example, for the value 113, the stem is 11 and the leaf is 3. We are keeping one digit for the leaf.

**Step 3    List all possible stems from lowest to highest.**

**Step 4    Itemize the leaves from lowest to highest and place next to the appropriate stems.**

| | |
|---|---|
| 4 | 4 |
| 5 | 3 7 9 9 |
| 6 | 2 2 3 6 7 7 9 9 |
| 7 | 2 6 6 9 |
| 8 | 0 0 1 2 5 5 5 6 6 7 7 7 8 8 8 9 9 9 |
| 9 | 0 1 1 2 3 3 3 4 5 6 7 7 8 8 9 |
| 10 | 1 1 2 2 3 4 4 5 5 6 7 8 8 9 9 9 9 9 9 |
| 11 | 0 0 0 0 0 1 1 1 2 2 2 3 4 5 5 5 6 7 7 7 7 7 7 7 8 8 8 |
| 12 | 0 1 1 2 2 2 3 4 4 5 6 7 7 7 7 8 8 8 9 9 |
| 13 | 0 1 1 2 2 2 2 3 4 4 4 5 5 5 5 6 6 6 7 7 7 8 8 9 9 |
| 14 | 0 0 0 0 1 2 2 2 3 3 3 3 4 4 5 6 6 7 7 7 8 9 9 9 |
| 15 | 0 0 1 2 2 3 3 3 4 4 4 4 5 7 8 9 |
| 16 | 0 1 2 2 5 6 8 |
| 17 | 2 5 6 6 7 7 |
| 18 | 3 4 |
| 19 | 0 0 2 8 |

The stem and leaf diagram shows that most people drive the rental car between 80 and 160 miles, with the most frequent value in the 110- to 120-mile range.

>> **END EXAMPLE**

**TRY PROBLEM** 2-25 (pg. 63)

# 2-2: Exercises

## Skill Development

**2-24.** The following data reflect the percentages of employees with different levels of education:

| Education Level | Percentage |
|---|---|
| Less than high school graduate | 18 |
| High school graduate | 34 |
| Some college | 14 |
| College graduate | 30 |
| Graduate degree | 4 |
| | Total = 100 |

a. Develop a pie chart to illustrate these data.
b. Develop a horizontal bar chart to illustrate these data.

**2-25.** Given the following data, construct a stem and leaf diagram:

| | | | |
|---|---|---|---|
| 0.7 | 1.7 | 2.8 | 3.8 |
| 0.8 | 1.8 | 3.3 | 4.3 |
| 1.0 | 2.0 | 4.4 | 5.4 |
| 1.1 | 2.1 | 5.3 | 6.3 |
| 1.4 | 2.4 | 5.4 | 6.4 |
| 2.0 | 3.0 | | |

**2-26.** A university has the following number of students at each grade level.

| | |
|---|---|
| Freshman | 3,450 |
| Sophomore | 3,190 |
| Junior | 2,780 |
| Senior | 1,980 |
| Graduate | 750 |

a. Construct a bar chart that effectively displays these data.
b. Construct a pie chart to display these data.
c. Referring to the graphs constructed in parts a and b, indicate which you would favor as the most effective way of presenting these data. Discuss.

**2-27.** Given the following sales data for product category and sales region, construct at least two different bar charts that display the data effectively:

| | | Region | | | |
|---|---|---|---|---|---|
| | | East | West | North | South |
| | XJ-6 Model | 200 | 300 | 50 | 170 |
| Product | X-15-Y Model | 100 | 200 | 20 | 100 |
| Type | Craftsman | 80 | 400 | 60 | 200 |
| | Generic | 100 | 150 | 40 | 50 |

**2-28.** The 2007 Annual Report of Murphy Oil Corporation contains the following information concerning the number of barrels of product sold per day by product category for North America and the United Kingdom.

| North America 2007 | |
|---|---|
| Gasoline | 298,833 |
| Kerosene | 1,685 |
| Diesel & home heating oils | 91,344 |
| Residuals | 15,422 |
| Asphalt, LPG, and other | 9,384 |

| United Kingdom 2007 | |
|---|---|
| Gasoline | 14,356 |
| Kerosene | 4,020 |
| Diesel & home heating oils | 14,785 |
| Residuals | 3,728 |
| Asphalt, LPG, and other | 4,213 |

a. Construct a pie chart to display North American sales by product per day. Display the product sales information as a percentage of total product sales for North America.

b. Construct a pie chart to display United Kingdom sales by product per day. Display the product sales information as a percentage of total product sales for the United Kingdom.

c. Construct a bar chart that effectively compares the daily product sales for North America and the United Kingdom.

**2-29.** Boston Properties is a real estate investment trust (REIT) that owns first-class office properties in selected markets. According to its 2007 annual report, its income distribution by region (in percent) was as follows:

| Region | 2007 Income Distribution |
|---|---|
| Princeton | 4% |
| Washington, D.C. | 21% |
| Boston | 27% |
| New York | 34% |
| San Francisco | 14% |

a. Construct a pie chart to display the income distribution by region for 2007.

b. Construct a bar chart to display the income distribution by region for 2007.

c. Which chart do you think more effectively displays the information?

**2-30.** Hileman Services Company recently released the following data concerning its operating profits (in $billions) for the last five years:

| Year | 2004 | 2005 | 2006 | 2007 | 2008 |
|---|---|---|---|---|---|
| Profit | 0.5 | 0.1 | 0.7 | 0.5 | 0.2 |

a. Construct a bar chart to graphically display these data.

b. Construct a pie chart to graphically display these data.

c. Select the display that most effectively displays the data and provide reasons for your choice.

**2-31.** DaimlerChrysler recently sold its Chrysler division to a private equity firm. Before the sale it reported its first-half revenues (in $billions) as follows:

| Division | Mercedes | Chrysler | Commercial Vehicles | Financial Services | Total |
|---|---|---|---|---|---|
| Revenues | 27.7 | 30.5 | 23.2 | 8.9 | 90.3 |

a. Produce a bar chart for these data.

b. Determine the proportion of first-half revenues accounted for by its vehicle divisions.

## Business Applications

**2-32.** At the March meeting of the board of directors for the Graystone Services Company, one of the regional managers put the following data on the overhead projector to illustrate the ratio of the number of units manufactured to the number of employees at each of Graystone's five manufacturing plants:

| Plant Location | Units Manufactured/Employees |
|---|---|
| Bismarck, ND | 14.5 |
| Boulder, CO | 9.8 |
| Omaha, NE | 13.0 |
| Harrisburg, PA | 17.6 |
| Portland, ME | 5.9 |

a. Discuss whether a pie chart or a bar chart would be most appropriate to present these data graphically.

b. Construct the chart you recommended in part a.

**2-33.** The first few years after the turn of the century saw a rapid increase in housing values, followed by a rapid decline due in part to the sub-prime crisis. The following table indicates the increase in the number of homes valued at more than one million dollars before 2005.

| Year | Number of $1 Million Homes |
|---|---|
| 2000 | 394,878 |
| 2001 | 495,600 |
| 2002 | 595,441 |
| 2003 | 714,467 |
| 2004 | 1,034,386 |

Develop a horizontal bar chart to represent these data in graphical form.

**2-34.** The pharmaceutical industry is a very fast-growing segment of the U.S. and international economies. Recently, there has been controversy over how studies are done to show that drugs are both safe and effective. One drug product, Cymbalta, which is an antidepressant, was purported in a published abstract of an article in a medical journal to be superior to other competing products. Yet, the article itself stated that no studies had actually been done to show such comparisons between Cymbalta and other competing products. In an August 2005 report in an article titled "Reading Fine Print, Insurers Question Drug Studies" in *The Wall Street Journal*, the following data were presented showing the U.S. sales of antidepressant drugs by major brand. The sales data for the first half of 2005 are shown in the following table.

| Antidepressant Drug | Sales (First Half 2005 in Billions) |
|---|---|
| Effexor XR | $1.29 |
| Lexapro | $1.03 |
| Zoloft | $1.55 |
| Cymbalta | $0.27 |
| Other | $0.97 |

Construct an appropriate graph to display these data.

**2-35.** The number of branded retail outlets for Murphy Oil Corporation as of December 31 of each year from 2001 to 2007 are shown below (*Source*: 2007 Annual Report of Murphy Oil Corporation).

| Branded Retail Outlets | 2001 | 2002 | 2003 | 2004 | 2005 | 2006 | 2007 |
|---|---|---|---|---|---|---|---|
| North America (total) | 815 | 914 | 994 | 1,127 | 1,201 | 1,164 | 1,126 |
| United Kingdom | 411 | 416 | 384 | 358 | 412 | 402 | 389 |

Develop a chart that effectively compares the number of branded retail outlets in North America with the number in the United Kingdom.

**2-36.** The 2008 Annual Report of the Procter & Gamble Company reports the following net sales information by global segment:

| Global Segment | 2008 Net Sales ($Millions) |
|---|---|
| Beauty | 19,515 |
| Grooming | 8,254 |
| Health Care | 14,578 |
| Snacks, Coffee, and Pet Care | 4,852 |
| Fabric Care and Home Care | 23,831 |
| Baby Care and Family Care | 13,898 |
| Corporate | (1,425) |

a. Construct a bar chart that displays this information.
b. Construct a pie chart that displays this information. Display each global segment's net sales as a percentage of total company net sales.

**2-37.** A fast-food restaurant monitors its drive-thru service times electronically to ensure that its speed of service is meeting the company's goals. A sample of 28 drive-thru times was recently taken and is shown here.

| Speed of Service (Time in Seconds) | | | |
|---|---|---|---|
| 83 | 138 | 145 | 147 |
| 130 | 79 | 156 | 156 |
| 90 | 85 | 68 | 93 |
| 178 | 76 | 73 | 119 |
| 92 | 146 | 88 | 103 |
| 116 | 134 | 162 | 71 |
| 181 | 110 | 105 | 74 |

a. Construct a stem and leaf diagram of the speed of service times.

b. What range of time might the restaurant say is the most frequent speed of service?

**2-38.** A random sample of 30 customer records for a physician's office showed the following time (in days) to collect insurance payments:

| Number of Days to Collect Payment | | | | |
|---|---|---|---|---|
| 34 | 55 | 36 | 39 | 36 |
| 32 | 35 | 30 | 47 | 31 |
| 60 | 66 | 48 | 43 | 33 |
| 24 | 37 | 38 | 65 | 35 |
| 22 | 45 | 33 | 29 | 41 |
| 38 | 35 | 28 | 56 | 56 |

a. Construct a stem and leaf diagram of these data.
b. Within what range of days are most payments collected?

**2-39.** *USA Today* presented data (Marilyn Adams and Dan Reed, "Difficult Times Battered Airlines," September 16, 2005) to show that major airlines accounting for more than half of capacity were expected to be in bankruptcy court. The total seat capacity of major airlines was 858 billion at the time. For airlines expected to be in bankruptcy court, the following data were presented:

| 2004 Airline Seat Capacity (in Billions) | | | | |
|---|---|---|---|---|
| **Airline** | United | Delta | Northwest | U.S. Airways | ATA |
| **Capacity** | 145 | 130 | 92 | 54 | 21 |

a. Construct a bar graph representing the contribution to the total seat capacity of the major airlines for the five airlines indicated.
b. Produce a pie chart exhibiting the percentage of the total seat capacity for the five major airlines expected to be in bankruptcy court and the combined capacity of all others.
c. Calculate the percentage of the total capacity of the airlines expected to be in bankruptcy court. Was *USA Today* correct in the percentage stated?

**2-40.** Many of the world's most successful companies rely on The NPD Group to provide global sales and marketing information that helps clients make more informed, fact-based decisions to optimize their businesses. These customers need NPD help for insight on what is selling, where, and why so that they can understand and leverage the latest trends. They recently (July 2009) released the following results of a survey intended to determine the market share distribution for the major corporations that make digital music devices:

| Corporation | Apple | SanDisk | Creative Technology | iRiver | Samsung |
|---|---|---|---|---|---|
| Market Share | 74% | 6.4% | 3.9% | 3.6% | 2.6% |

a. Generate a bar chart to display these data.
b. Generate a pie chart to display these data.
c. Which of the two displays most effectively presents the data? Explain your answer.

## Computer Database Exercises

**2-41.** The Honda Ridgeline was among the highest ranked compact pickups in J.D. Power and Associates' annual customer-satisfaction survey. The study also found that models with high ratings have a tendency to stay on dealers' lots a shorter period of time. As an example, the Honda Ridgeline had stayed on dealers' lots an average of 24 days. The file entitled **Honda** contains 50 lengths of stay on dealers' lots for Ridgeline trucks.
   a. Construct a stem and leaf display for these data.
   b. Determine the average length of stay on dealers' lots for the Honda Ridgeline. Does this agree with the average obtained by J.D. Power and Associates? Explain the difference.

**2-42.** The manager for Capital Educators Federal Credit Union has selected a random sample of 300 of the credit union's credit card customers. The data are in a file called **Capital**. The manager is interested in graphically displaying the percentage of card holders of each gender.
   a. Determine the appropriate type of graph to use in this application.
   b. Construct the graph and interpret it.

**2-43.** Recently, a study was conducted in which a random sample of hospitals was selected from each of four categories of hospitals: university related, religious related, community owned, and privately owned. At issue is the hospital charges associated with outpatient gall bladder surgery. The following data are in the file called **Hospitals**:

| University Related | Religious Affiliated | Municipally Owned | Privately Held |
|---|---|---|---|
| $6,120 | $4,010 | $4,320 | $5,100 |
| $5,960 | $3,770 | $4,650 | $4,920 |
| $6,300 | $3,960 | $4,575 | $5,200 |
| $6,500 | $3,620 | $4,440 | $5,345 |
| $6,250 | $3,280 | $4,900 | $4,875 |
| $6,695 | $3,680 | $4,560 | $5,330 |
| $6,475 | $3,350 | $4,610 | $5,415 |

| University Related | Religious Affiliated | Municipally Owned | Privately Held |
|---|---|---|---|
| $6,250 | $3,250 | $4,850 | $5,150 |
| $6,880 | $3,400 | | $5,380 |
| $6,550 | | | |

   a. Compute the average charge for each hospital category.
   b. Construct a bar chart showing the averages by hospital category.
   c. Discuss why a pie chart would not in this case be an appropriate graphical tool.

**2-44.** Amazon.com has become one of the success stories of the Internet age. Its growth can be seen by examining its increasing sales volume (in $billions) and the net income/loss during Amazon's operations. A file entitled **Amazon** contains these data for its first 13 years.
   a. Construct one bar graph illustrating the relationship between sales and income for each separate year of Amazon's existence.
   b. Describe the type of relationship that exists between the years in business and Amazon's sales volume.
   c. Amazon's sales rose sharply. However, its net income yielded losses, which increased during the first few years. In which year did this situation reverse itself and show improvement in the net income balance sheet?

**2-45.** In your capacity as assistant to the administrator at Freedom Hospital, you have been asked to develop a graphical presentation that focuses on the insurance carried by the geriatric patients at the hospital. The data file **Patients** contains data for a sample of geriatric patients. In developing your presentation, please do the following:
   a. Construct a pie chart that shows the percentage of patients with each health insurance payer.
   b. Develop a bar chart that shows total charges for patients by insurance payer.
   c. Develop a stem and leaf diagram for the length-of-stay variable.
   d. Develop a bar chart that shows the number of males and females by insurance carrier.

**END EXERCISES** 2-2

# 2.3 Line Charts and Scatter Diagrams

Chapter Outcome 6. ➤ **Line Charts**

**Line Chart**

A two-dimensional chart showing time on the horizontal axis and the variable of interest on the vertical axis.

**Excel and Minitab Tutorial**

Most of the examples that have been presented thus far have involved *cross-sectional data*, or data gathered from many observations, all taken at the same time. However, if you have *time-series* data that are measured over time (e.g., monthly, quarterly, annually), an effective tool for presenting such data is a **line chart**.

**BUSINESS APPLICATION** CONSTRUCTING LINE CHARTS

**MCGREGOR VINEYARDS** McGregor Vineyards owns and operates a winery in the Sonoma Valley in northern California. At a recent company meeting, the financial manager expressed concern about the company's profit trend over the past 20 weeks. He presented weekly profit and sales data to McGregor management personnel. The data are in the file **McGregor**.

**FIGURE 2.17A**

Excel 2007 Output Showing McGregor Line Charts

**Excel 2007 Instructions:**
1. Open file: McGregor.xls.
2. Select the **Sales (dollars)** data to be graphed.
3. On the **Insert** tab, click the **Line** chart.
4. Click the **Line with Markers** option.
5. Use the **Layout** tab in the **Chart Tools** to remove the Legend, change the Chart Title, add the Axis Titles, and remove the grid lines.
6. Repeat Steps 2–5 for the **Profit** data.

**FIGURE 2.17B**

Minitab Output Showing McGregor Line Charts

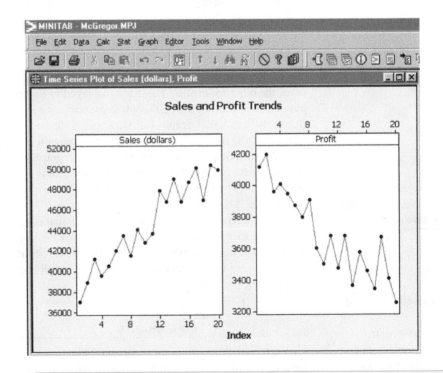

**Minitab Instructions:**
1. Open file: McGregor.MTW.
2. Choose **Graph > Times Series Plot**.
3. Select **Simple**.
4. Click **OK**.
5. In Series enter *Sales* and *Profit* columns.
6. Select **Multiple Graphs**.
7. Under **Show Graph Variables**, select **In separate panels of the same graph**.
8. Click **OK. OK.**

**FIGURE 2.18**

Excel 2007 Line Charts of McGregor Profit and Sales Using Same Value Axis

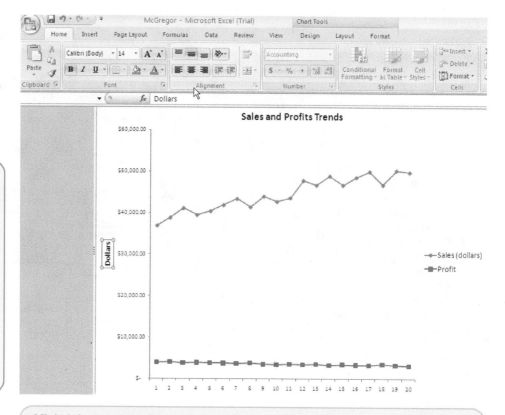

**Excel 2007 Instructions:**
1. Open file: McGregor.xls.
2. Select the two variables, **Sales (dollars)** and **Profit**, to be graphed.
3. On the **Insert** tab, click the **Line** chart.
4. Click the **Line with Markers** option.
5. Use the **Layout** tab in the **Chart Tools** to change the Chart Title, add the Axis Titles, remove the border, and remove the grid lines.

**Minitab Instructions (for similar results):**
1. Open File: McGregor.MTW.
2. Choose **Graph > Times Series Plot**.
3. Select **Multiple**.
4. Click **OK**.
5. In **Series** enter *Sales and Profit* columns.
6. Select **Multiple Graphs**.
7. Under **Show Graph Variables**, select **Overlaid on the same graph**.
8. Click **OK**. **OK**.

Initially, the financial manager developed two separate line charts for this data: one for sales, the other for profits. These are displayed in Figures 2.17a and 2.17b. These line charts provide an indication that, although sales have been increasing, the profit trend is downward. But to fit both Excel graphs on one page, he had to compress the size of the graphs. This "flattened" the lines somewhat, masking the magnitude of the problem.

What the financial manager needed is one graph with both profits and sales. Figure 2.18 shows his first attempt. This is better, but there still is a problem: The sales and profit variables are of different magnitudes. This results in the profit line being flattened out to almost a straight line. The profit trend is hidden.

To overcome this problem, the financial manager needed to construct his graph using two scales, one for each variable. Figure 2.19 shows the improved graph. We can now clearly see that although sales are moving steadily higher, profits are headed downhill. For some reason, costs are rising faster than revenues, and this graph should motivate McGregor Vineyards to look into the problem.

**How to do it** (Example 2-10)

**Constructing Line Charts**

A line chart, also commonly called a *trend chart*, is developed using the following steps:

1. Identify the time-series variable of interest and determine the maximum value and the range of time periods covered in the data.

2. Construct the horizontal axis for the time periods using equal spacing between each time period. Construct the vertical axis with a scale appropriate for the range of values of the time-series variable.

3. Plot the points on the graph and connect the points with straight lines.

**EXAMPLE 2-10** **LINE CHARTS**

**Grogan Builders** Grogan Builders produces mobile homes in Alberta, Canada. The owners are planning to expand the manufacturing facilities. To do so requires additional financing. In preparation for the meeting with the bankers, the owners have assembled data on total annual sales for the past 10 years. These data are shown as follows:

| 2000 | 2001 | 2002 | 2003 | 2004 | 2005 | 2006 | 2007 | 2008 | 2009 |
|------|------|------|------|------|------|------|------|------|------|
| 1,426 | 1,678 | 2,591 | 2,105 | 2,744 | 3,068 | 2,755 | 3,689 | 4,003 | 3,997 |

Excel 2007 Sales and Profits Line
Chart Using Different Value Axes

**Excel 2007 Instructions:**
1. Open file: McGregor.xls.
2. Select data from the profit
   and sales columns.
3. Click on **Insert**.
4. Click on **Line Chart**.
5. Move graph to separate
   page.
6. Select Profit line on graph
   and right click.
7. Click on **Format Data
   Series**.
8. Click on **Secondary Axis**.
9. Click on **Layout** and add
   titles as desired.

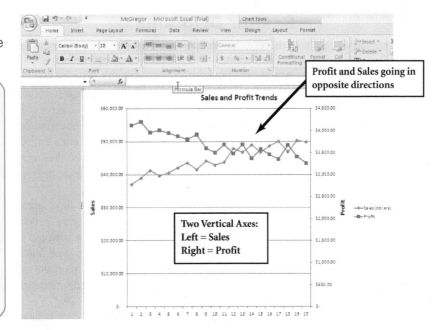

**Minitab Instructions (for similar results):**

1. Open File: McGregor.MTW.
2. Choose **Graph > Times Series Plot**.
3. Select **Multiple**.
4. Click **OK**.

5. In **Series**, enter *Sales* and *Profit* columns.
6. Select **Multiple Graphs**.
7. Click **OK**.

The owners wish to present these data in a line chart to effectively show the company's sales growth over the 10-year period. To construct the line chart, the following steps are used:

**Step 1**   **Identify the time-series variable.**
The time-series variable is units sold measured over 10 years, with a maximum value of 4,003.

**Step 2**   **Construct the horizontal and vertical axes.**
The horizontal axis will have the 10 time periods equally spaced. The vertical axis will start at zero and go to a value exceeding 4,003. We will use 4,500. The vertical axis will also be divided into 500-unit increments.

**Step 3**   **Plot the data values on the graph and connect the points with straight lines.**

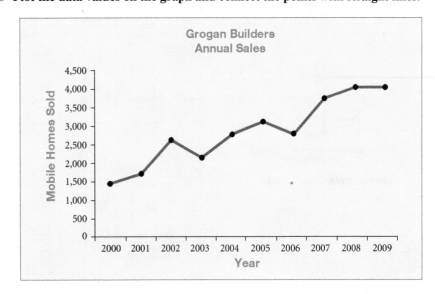

**>> END EXAMPLE**

**TRY PROBLEM** 2-47 (pg. 73)

Chapter Outcome 7.→ **Scatter Diagrams**

In Section 2.1 we introduced a set of statistical procedures known as joint frequency distributions that allow the decision maker to examine two variables at the same time. Another procedure used to study two quantitative variables simultaneously is the **scatter diagram**, or the **scatter plot**.

There are many situations in which we are interested in understanding the *bivariate* relationship between two *quantitative* variables. For example, a company would like to know the relationship between sales and advertising. A bank might be interested in the relationship between savings account balances and credit card balances for its customers. A real estate agent might wish to know the relationship between the selling price of houses and the number of days that the houses have been on the market. The list of possibilities is almost limitless.

Regardless of the variables involved, there are several key relationships we are looking for when we develop a scatter diagram. Figure 2.20 shows scatter diagrams representing some key bivariate relationships that might exist between two quantitative variables.

Chapters 14 and 15 make extensive use of scatter diagrams. They introduce a statistical tool called *regression analysis* that focuses on the relationship between two variables. These variables are known as **dependent** and **independent variables**.

**Scatter Diagram, or Scatter Plot**

A two-dimensional graph of plotted points in which the vertical axis represents values of one quantitative variable and the horizontal axis represents values of the other quantitative variable. Each plotted point has coordinates whose values are obtained from the respective variables.

**Dependent Variable**

A variable whose values are thought to be a function of, or dependent on, the values of another variable called the *independent variable*. On a scatter plot, the dependent variable is placed on the *y* axis and is often called the response variable.

**Independent Variable**

A variable whose values are thought to impact the values of the *dependent variable*. The independent variable, or explanatory variable, is often within the direct control of the decision maker. On a scatter plot, the independent variable, or explanatory variable, is graphed on the *x* axis.

---

**BUSINESS APPLICATION**    **CREATING SCATTER DIAGRAMS**

**PERSONAL COMPUTERS**    Can you think of any product that has increased in quality and capability as rapidly as personal computers? Not that many years ago an 8-MB RAM system with a 486 processor and a 640-KB hard drive sold in the mid-$2500 range. Now the same money would buy a 3.0 GHz or faster machine with a 100+ GB hard drive and 512-MB RAM or more!

In September 2005 we examined various Web sites looking for the best prices on personal computers. The data file called "Personal Computers" contains data on several characteristics, including processor speed, hard drive capacity, RAM, whether a monitor is included, and price for 13 personal computers. Of particular interest is the relationship between the computer price and processing speed. Our objective is to develop a scatter diagram to graphically depict what, if any, relationship exists between these two variables. The dependent variable is price and the independent variable is processor speed. Figure 2.21 shows the Excel scatter diagram output. The relationship between processor speed and price is somewhat curvilinear and positive.

**FIGURE 2.20**

Scatter Diagrams Showing Relationships Between *x* and *y*

**Excel and Minitab Tutorial**

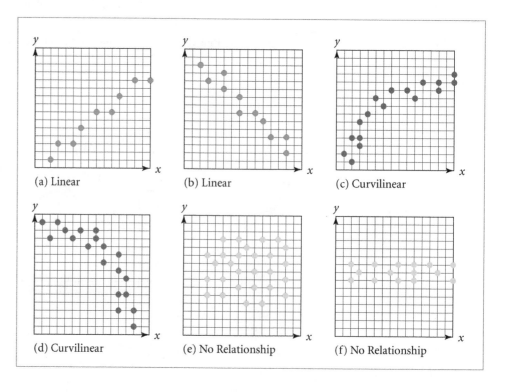

(a) Linear          (b) Linear          (c) Curvilinear

(d) Curvilinear     (e) No Relationship  (f) No Relationship

**FIGURE 2.21** |

Excel 2007 Output of Scatter Diagrams for Personal Computers Data

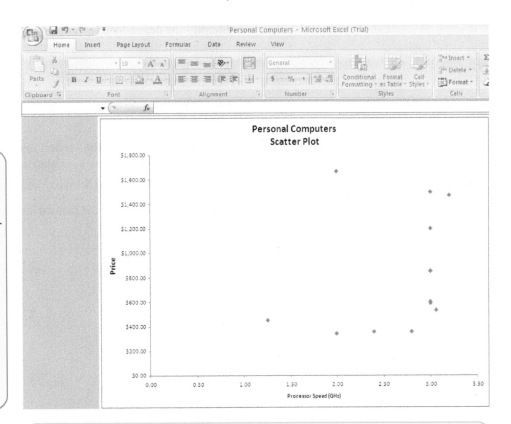

Excel 2007 Instructions:
1. Open file: Personal Computers.xls.
2. Select data for chart (Processor GHz and Price). (Hint, use Ctrl key to select just the two desired columns.)
3. On **Insert** tab, click **XY (Scatter)**, and then click **Scatter with only Markers** option.
4. Move the chart to a separate page.
5. Use the **Layout** tab of the **Chart Tools** to add titles and remove grid lines.

Minitab Instructions (for similar results):
1. Open file: Personal Computers.MTW.
2. Choose **Graph > Scatterplot**.
3. Select **Simple**.
4. Click **OK**.
5. In **Y**, enter *Price* column. In **X**, enter *Processor Speed* column.
6. Click **OK**.

## How to do it (Example 2-11)

**Constructing Scatter Diagrams**
A scatter diagram is a two-dimensional graph showing the joint values for two quantitative variables. It is constructed using the following steps:

1. Identify the two quantitative variables and collect paired responses for the two variables.

2. Determine which variable will be placed on the vertical axis and which variable will be placed on the horizontal axis. Often the vertical axis can be considered the dependent variable (*y*) and the horizontal axis can be considered the independent variable (*x*).

3. Define the range of values for each variable and define the appropriate scale for the *x* and *y* axes.

4. Plot the joint values for the two variables by placing a point in the *x,y* space. Do not connect the points.

**EXAMPLE 2-11    SCATTER DIAGRAMS**

**Fortune's Best Eight Companies** Each year, *Fortune* magazine surveys employees regarding job satisfaction to try to determine which companies are the "best" companies to work for in the United States. *Fortune* also collects a variety of data associated with these companies. For example, the table here shows data for the top eight companies on three variables: number of U.S. employees; number of training hours per year per employee; and total revenue in millions of dollars.

| Company | U.S. Employees | Training Hr/Yr | Revenues ($Millions) |
| --- | --- | --- | --- |
| Southwest Airlines | 24,757 | 15 | $3,400 |
| Kingston Technology | 552 | 100 | $1,300 |
| SAS Institute | 3,154 | 32 | $ 653 |
| Fel-Pro | 2,577 | 60 | $ 450 |
| TD Industries | 976 | 40 | $ 127 |
| MBNA | 18,050 | 48 | $3,300 |
| W.L. Gore | 4,118 | 27 | $1,200 |
| Microsoft | 14,936 | 8 | $8,700 |

To better understand these companies, we might be interested in the relationship between number of U.S. employees and revenue and between training hours and U.S. employees. To construct these scatter diagrams, we can use the following steps:

**Step 1    Identify the two variables of interest.**
In the first case, one variable is U.S. employees and the second is revenue. In the second case, one variable is training hours and the other is U.S. employees.

**Step 2    Identify the dependent and independent variables.**

In each case, think of U.S. employees as the independent ($x$) variable. Thus,

Case 1: $y$ = revenue (vertical axis)        $x$ = U.S. employees
                                                            (horizontal axis)

Case 2: $y$ = training hours              $x$ = U.S. employees
            (vertical axis)                   (horizontal axis)

**Step 3    Establish the scales for the vertical and horizontal axes.**

The maximum value for each variable is

revenue = \$8,700        U.S. employees = 24,757        training hours = 100

**Step 4    Plot the joint values for the two variables by placing a point in the $x, y$ space.**

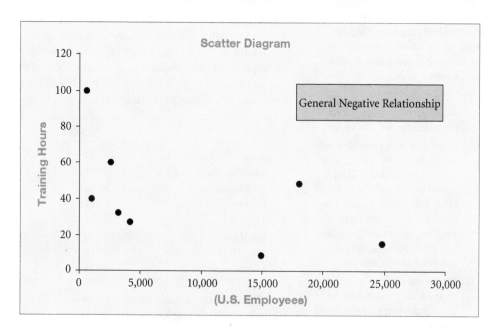

>> END EXAMPLE

**TRY PROBLEM** 2-46 (pg. 73)

## 2-3: Exercises

### Skill Development

**2-46.** The following data represent 11 observations of two quantitative variables:

$x$ = contact hours with client,
$y$ = profit generated from client.

| $x$ | $y$ | $x$ | $y$ | $x$ | $y$ | $x$ | $y$ |
|-----|-----|-----|-----|-----|------|-----|------|
| 45 | 2,345 | 54 | 3,811 | 34 | −700 | 24 | 1,975 |
| 56 | 4,200 | 24 | 2,406 | 45 | 3,457 | 32 | 206 |
| 26 | 278 | 23 | 3,250 | 47 | 2,478 | | |

a. Construct a scatter plot of the data. Indicate whether the plot suggests a linear or nonlinear relationship between the dependent and independent variables.
b. Determine how much influence one data point will have on your perception of the relationship between the independent and dependent variables by deleting the data point with the smallest $x$ value. What appears to be the relationship between the dependent and independent variables?

**2-47.** You have the following sales data for the past 12 months. Develop a line graph for these data.

| Month | Jan | Feb | Mar | Apr | May | Jun |
|-------|-----|-----|-----|-----|-----|-----|
| Sales | 200 | 230 | 210 | 300 | 320 | 290 |
| Month | Jul | Aug | Sep | Oct | Nov | Dec |
| Sales | 300 | 360 | 400 | 410 | 390 | 450 |

**2-48.** The following data have been selected for two variables, $y$ and $x$. Construct a scatter plot for these two variables and indicate what type, if any, relationship appears to be present.

| $y$ | $x$ |
|-----|-----|
| 100 | 23.5 |
| 250 | 17.8 |
| 70 | 28.6 |
| 130 | 19.3 |
| 190 | 15.9 |
| 250 | 19.1 |
| 40 | 35.3 |

**2-49.** The following information shows the year-end dollar value (in millions) of deposits for Bank of the Ozarks, Inc., for the years 1997–2007. (*Source:* Bank of the Ozarks, Inc., 2007 Annual Report.)

| Year | Deposits (in $Millions) |
|------|-------------------------|
| 1997 | 296 |
| 1998 | 529 |
| 1999 | 596 |
| 2000 | 678 |
| 2001 | 678 |
| 2002 | 790 |
| 2003 | 1,062 |
| 2004 | 1,380 |
| 2005 | 1,592 |
| 2006 | 2,045 |
| 2007 | 2,057 |

Prepare a line chart of the data and briefly describe what the chart shows.

**2-50.** VanAuker Properties' controller collected the following data on annual sales and the years of experience of members of his sales staff:

| Sales $K: | 200 | 191 | 135 | 236 | 305 | 183 | 50 | 192 | 184 | 73 |
|-----------|-----|-----|-----|-----|-----|-----|----|-----|-----|-----|
| Years: | 10 | 4 | 5 | 9 | 12 | 6 | 2 | 7 | 6 | 2 |

a. Construct a scatter plot representing these data.
b. Determine the kind of relationship that exists (if any) between years of experience and sales.
c. Approximate the increase in sales that accrues with each additional year of experience for a member of the sales force.

### Business Applications

**2-51.** Amazon.com celebrated its 13th anniversary in July 2007. Its growth can be seen by examining its increasing sales volume (in $billions) as reported by Hoovers Inc.

| Sales | 0.0005 | 0.0157 | 0.1477 | 0.6098 | 1.6398 |
|-------|--------|--------|--------|--------|--------|
| Year | 1995 | 1996 | 1997 | 1998 | 1999 |
| Sales | 2.7619 | 3.1229 | 3.9329 | 5.2637 | 6.9211 |
| Year | 2000 | 2001 | 2002 | 2003 | 2004 |
| Sales | 8.490 | 10.711 | 14.835 | | |
| Year | 2005 | 2006 | 2007 | | |

a. Construct a line plot for Amazon's sales.
b. Describe the type of relationship that exists between the years in business and Amazon's sales volume.
c. In which year does it appear that Amazon had the sharpest increase in sales?

**2-52.** In July 2005, Greg Sandoval of the Associated Press authored a study of the video game industry that focused on the efforts of the industry to interest women in the games. In that study, he cited another report by the Entertainments Software Association that indicated that the percentage of women who played video games in 2004 was 43%, whereas only 12.5% of the software developers were female. Sandoval also presented the following data showing the U.S. computer/video game sales:

| Year | Sales (Billions) |
|------|------------------|
| 1996 | $3.80 |
| 1997 | $4.30 |
| 1998 | $5.70 |
| 1999 | $6.10 |
| 2000 | $6.00 |
| 2001 | $6.30 |
| 2002 | $6.95 |
| 2003 | $7.00 |
| 2004 | $7.30 |

Construct a line chart showing these computer/video game sales data. Write a short statement describing the graph.

2-53. Recent changes in the U.S. federal tax code have increased the popularity of dividend-paying stocks for some investors. Shown here are the diluted net earnings per common share and the dividends per common share for the Procter & Gamble Company (P&G) for the years 1996–2005. (*Source:* 2005 P&G Annual Report.)

| Year | Diluted Net Earnings per Common Share | Dividends per Common Share |
|------|---------------------------------------|----------------------------|
| 1996 | $1.00 | $0.40 |
| 1997 | $1.14 | $0.45 |
| 1998 | $1.28 | $0.51 |
| 1999 | $1.29 | $0.57 |
| 2000 | $1.23 | $0.64 |
| 2001 | $1.03 | $0.70 |
| 2002 | $1.54 | $0.76 |
| 2003 | $1.85 | $0.82 |
| 2004 | $2.32 | $0.93 |
| 2005 | $2.66 | $1.03 |

a. Construct a line chart of diluted net earnings per common share for the years 1996–2005.
b. Construct a line chart of dividends per common share for the years 1996–2005.
c. Construct a chart that can be used to determine whether there is a relationship between the two variables for the years 1996–2005. What relationship, if any, appears to exist between the two variables?

2-54. *Business Week* (Reed, Stanley, et al., "Open Season on Big Oil," September 26, 2005) reported on data provided by A. G. Edwards & Sons concerning the profits ($billions) for 10 of the largest integrated oil and gas companies over the period from 1999 to 2005.

| Year | 1999 | 2000 | 2001 | 2002 | 2003 | 2004 | 2005 |
|------|------|------|------|------|------|------|------|
| Profit ($Billions) | 33.3 | 62.5 | 58.3 | 41.7 | 66.7 | 91.7 | 118.0 |

a. Produce a line plot of the profit versus the year.
b. Describe the types of relationship that exist between years and profits during the specified time period.

c. Which of the relationships would you use to project the companies' profits in the year 2006? Explain your answer.

## Computer Database **Exercises**

2-55. Major League Baseball (MLB) is played in 30 North American cities, including Toronto, Canada. Having a team in a city is generally considered to provide an economic boost to the community. Although winning is the stated goal for all teams, the business side of baseball has to do with attendance. The data file **MLB Attendance-2008** contains data for both home and road game attendance for all 30 MLB teams for 2008. Of interest is the relationship between average home attendance and average road attendance. Using the 2008 attendance data, construct the appropriate graph to help determine the relationship between these two variables and discuss the implications of the graph.

2-56. In the October 17, 2005, issue of *Fortune*, a special advertising section focused on private jets. Included in the section was an article about "fractional" jet ownership, where wealthy individuals and companies share ownership in private jets. The idea is that the expensive airplanes can be better utilized if more than one individual or company has an ownership stake. AvData, Inc., provided data showing the number of fractional ownerships since 1986. These data are in the file called **JetOwnership**. Using these data, develop a line chart that displays the trend in fractional ownership between 1986 and 2004. Discuss.

2-57. Starting in 2005, a chain of events, including the war in Iraq, Hurricane Katrina, and the expanding economies in India and China lead to a sharp increase in fuel costs. As a result, the U.S. airline industry has been hit hard financially, with many airlines declaring bankruptcy. Some airlines are substituting smaller planes on certain routes in an attempt to reduce fuel costs. As an analyst for one of the major airlines, you have been asked to analyze the relationship between passenger capacity and fuel consumption per hour. Data for 19 commonly flown planes is presented in the file called **Airplanes**. Develop the appropriate graph to illustrate the relationship between fuel consumption per hour and passenger capacity. Discuss.

2-58. Japolli Bakery tracks sales of its different bread products on a daily basis. The data at the top of the next page show sales for 22 consecutive days at one of its retail outlets in Nashville. Develop a line chart that displays these data. The data are also located in a data file called **Japolli Bakery**. Discuss what, if any, conclusions you might be able to reach from the line chart.

2-59. Energy prices have been a major source of economic and political debate in the United States and around the world. Consumers have recently seen gasoline prices both rise and fall rapidly, and the impact of fuel prices has been blamed for economic problems in the United

**Japolli Bakery**

| Day of Week | White | Wheat | Multigrain | Black | Cinnamon Raisin | Sourdough French | Light Oat |
|---|---|---|---|---|---|---|---|
| Friday | 436 | 456 | 417 | 311 | 95 | 96 | 224 |
| Saturday | 653 | 571 | 557 | 416 | 129 | 140 | 224 |
| Sunday | 496 | 490 | 403 | 351 | 114 | 108 | 228 |
| Monday | 786 | 611 | 570 | 473 | 165 | 148 | 304 |
| Tuesday | 547 | 474 | 424 | 365 | 144 | 104 | 256 |
| Wednesday | 513 | 443 | 380 | 317 | 100 | 92 | 180 |
| Thursday | 817 | 669 | 622 | 518 | 181 | 152 | 308 |
| Friday | 375 | 390 | 299 | 256 | 124 | 88 | 172 |
| Saturday | 700 | 678 | 564 | 463 | 173 | 136 | 248 |
| Sunday | 597 | 502 | 457 | 383 | 140 | 144 | 312 |
| Monday | 536 | 530 | 428 | 360 | 135 | 112 | 356 |
| Tuesday | 875 | 703 | 605 | 549 | 201 | 188 | 356 |
| Wednesday | 421 | 433 | 336 | 312 | 100 | 104 | 224 |
| Thursday | 667 | 576 | 541 | 438 | 152 | 144 | 304 |
| Friday | 506 | 461 | 406 | 342 | 135 | 116 | 264 |
| Saturday | 470 | 352 | 377 | 266 | 84 | 92 | 172 |
| Sunday | 748 | 643 | 599 | 425 | 153 | 148 | 316 |
| Monday | 376 | 367 | 310 | 279 | 128 | 104 | 208 |
| Tuesday | 704 | 646 | 586 | 426 | 174 | 160 | 264 |
| Wednesday | 591 | 504 | 408 | 349 | 140 | 120 | 276 |
| Thursday | 564 | 497 | 415 | 348 | 107 | 120 | 212 |
| Friday | 817 | 673 | 644 | 492 | 200 | 180 | 348 |

States at different points in time. Although no longer doing so, for years the California Energy Commission published yearly gasoline prices. The data (found in the file called **Gasoline Prices**) reflect the average price of regular unleaded gasoline in the state of California for the years between 1970 and 2005. The first price column is the actual average price of gasoline during each of those years. The second column is the average price adjusted for inflation, with 2005 being the base year.

a. Construct an appropriate chart showing the actual average price of gasoline in California over the years between 1970 and 2005.

b. Add to the graph developed in part a the data for the adjusted gasoline prices.

c. Based on the graph from part b, what conclusions might be reached about the price of gasoline over the years between 1970 and 2005?

2-60. Federal flood insurance underwritten by the federal government was initiated in 1968. This federal flood insurance coverage has, according to *USA Today* ("How You Pay for People to Build in Flood Zones," September 21, 2005), more than tripled in the past 15 years. A file entitled **Flood** contains the amount of federal flood insurance coverage for each of the years from 1990 to 2004.

a. Produce a line plot for these data.

b. Describe the type of relationship between the year and the amount of federal flood insurance.

c. Determine the average increase per year in federal flood insurance.

2-61. The Office of Management and Budget keeps data on many facets of corporations. One item that has become a matter of concern is the number of applications for patents submitted compared to the backlog of applications that have not been processed by the end of the year. A file entitled **Patent** provides data extracted from a *USA Today* article that addresses the problem.

a. Construct the two line plots on the same axes.

b. Determine the types of relationship that exist between the years and the two patent-related variables.

c. During which year(s) did the backlog of applications at the end of the year equal approximately the same number of patent applications?

2-62. The sub-prime mortgage crisis that hit the world economy also impacted the real estate market. Both new and existing home sales were affected. A file entitled **EHSales** contains the number of existing homes sold (in millions) from September of 2007 to September 2008.

a. Construct a line plot for these data.

b. The data file also contains data concerning the median selling price ($thousands). Construct a graph containing the line plot for both the number of sales (*tens* of thousands) and the median ($thousands) price of these sales for the indicated time period.

c. Describe the relationship between the two line plots constructed in part b.

# Visual Summary

**Chapter 2:** The old adage states that a picture is worth a thousand words. In many ways this applies to descriptive statistics. The use of graphs, charts, and tables to display data in a way that helps decision-makers better understand the data is one of the major applications of business statistics. This chapter has introduced many of the most frequently used graphical techniques using examples and business applications.

## 2.1 Frequency Distributions and Histograms (pg. 32–54)
### Summary

A **frequency distribution** is used to determine the number of occurrences in your data that fall at each possible data value or within defined ranges of possible values. It represents a good summary of the data and from a frequency distribution, you can form a graph called a **histogram**. This histogram gives a visual picture showing how the data are distributed. You can use the histogram to see where the data's center is and how spread out the data are. It is often helpful to convert the frequencies in a frequency distribution to **relative frequencies** and to construct a **relative frequency distribution** and a relative frequency histogram. Another option is to convert the frequency distribution to a **cumulative frequency distribution** and then a graph called an ogive. Finally, if you are analyzing two variables simultaneously, you may want to construct a **joint frequency distribution**.

**Outcome 1.** Construct frequency distributions both manually and with your computer.
**Outcome 2.** Construct and interpret a frequency histogram.
**Outcome 3.** Develop and interpret joint frequency distributions.

## 2.2 Bar Charts, Pie Charts and Stem and Leaf Diagrams (pg. 54–66)
### Summary

If your data are **discrete**, or are **nominal** or **ordinal level**, three charts introduced in this section are often considered. These are **bar charts**, **pie charts**, and **stem and leaf diagrams**. A bar chart can be arranged with the bars **vertical** or **horizontal**. A single bar chart can be used to describe two or more variables. In situations where you wish to show how the parts making up a total are distributed, a **pie chart** is often used. The "slices" of the pie are many times depicted as the percentage of the total. A lesser used graphical tool that provides a quick view of how the data are distributed is the **stem and leaf diagram**.

**Outcome 4.** Construct and interpret various types of bar charts.
**Outcome 5.** Build a stem and leaf diagram.

## 2.3 Line Charts and Scatter Diagrams (pg. 66–75)
### Summary

When you are working with **time-series** data and you are interested in displaying the pattern in the data over time, the chart that is used is called a **line chart**. The vertical axis displays the value of the time-series variable while the horizontal axis contains the time increments. The points are plotted and are usually connected by straight lines. In other cases you may be interested in the relationship between two **quantitative** variables; the graphical tool that is used is called a **scatter diagram**. The variable judged to be the **dependent variable** is placed on the vertical axis and **independent variable** goes on the horizontal axis. The joint values are plotted as points in the two-dimensional space. Do not connect the points with lines.

**Outcome 6.** Create a line chart and interpret the trend in the data.
**Outcome 7.** Create a scatter plot and interpret it.

## Conclusion

There are many types of charts, graphs, and tables that can be used to display data. The technique that is used often depends on the type and level of data you have. In cases where multiple graphs or charts can apply, you should select the one that most effectively displays the data for your application. **Figure 2.22** summarizes the different graphical options that are presented in chapter 2.

**FIGURE 2.22**

Summary: Descriptive
Statistical Techniques

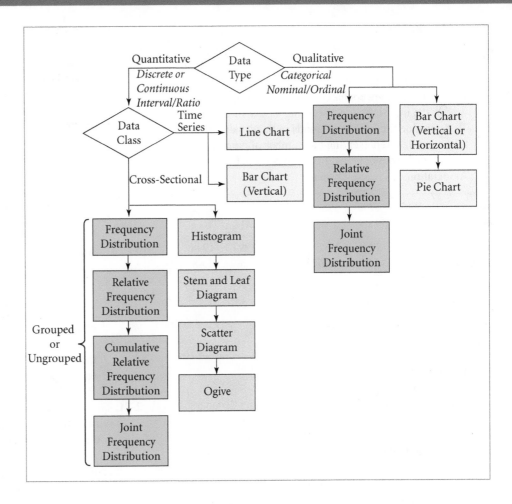

# Equations

**(2.1) Relative Frequency**

$$\text{Relative frequency} = \frac{f_i}{n}$$

**(2.2) Class Width**

$$W = \frac{\text{Largest value} - \text{Smallest value}}{\text{Number of classes}}$$

# Key Terms

All-inclusive classes pg. 39
Bar chart pg. 54
Class boundaries pg. 39
Class width pg. 39
Continuous data pg. 36
Cumulative frequency distribution pg. 40
Cumulative relative frequency distribution pg. 40

Dependent variable pg. 70
Discrete data pg. 33
Equal-width classes pg. 39
Frequency distribution pg. 33
Frequency histogram pg. 41
Independent variable pg. 70
Line chart pg. 66

Mutually exclusive classes pg. 39
Ogive pg. 45
Pie chart pg. 60
Relative frequency pg. 33
Scatter diagram or scatter plot pg. 70

# Chapter Exercises                                             *MyStatLab*

## Conceptual **Questions**

**2-63.** Discuss the advantages of constructing a relative frequency
distribution as opposed to a frequency distribution.

**2-64.** What are the characteristics of a data set that would
lead you to construct a bar chart?

**2-65.** What are the characteristics of a data set that would
lead you to construct a pie chart?

**2-66.** Discuss the differences in data that would lead
you to construct a line chart as opposed to a scatter
plot.

## Business Applications

**2-67.** *USA Today* reported (Anthony Breznican and Gary Strauss, "Where Have All the Moviegoers Gone?" June 23, 2005) that in the summer of 2005 ticket sales to movie theaters had fallen for 17 straight weeks, the industry's longest losing streak since 1985. To determine the long-term trends in ticket sales, the following data representing the number of admissions (in billions) were obtained from the National Association of Theatre Owners:

| Year | 1987 | 1988 | 1989 | 1990 | 1991 | 1992 |
|------|------|------|------|------|------|------|
| Admissions | 1.09 | 1.08 | 1.26 | 1.19 | 1.14 | 1.17 |

| Year | 1993 | 1994 | 1995 | 1996 | 1997 | 1998 |
|------|------|------|------|------|------|------|
| Admissions | 1.24 | 1.28 | 1.26 | 1.34 | 1.39 | 1.48 |

| Year | 1999 | 2000 | 2001 | 2002 | 2003 | 2004 |
|------|------|------|------|------|------|------|
| Admissions | 1.47 | 1.42 | 1.49 | 1.63 | 1.57 | 1.53 |

| Year | 2005 | 2006 | 2007 |
|------|------|------|------|
| Admissions | 1.38 | 1.41 | 1.40 |

    a. Produce a line plot of the data.
    b. Describe any trends that you detect.

**2-68.** The following data represent the commuting distances for employees of the Pay-and-Carry Department store.
    a. The personnel manager for Pay-and-Carry would like you to develop a frequency distribution and histogram for these data.
    b. Develop a stem and leaf diagram for these data.
    c. Break the data into three groups (under 3 miles, 3 and under 6 miles, and 6 and over). Construct a pie chart to illustrate the proportion of employees in each category.

| Commuting Distance (miles) | | | | | | | |
|------|------|------|------|------|------|------|------|
| 3.5 | 2.0 | 4.0 | 2.5 | 0.3 | 1.0 | 12.0 | 17.5 |
| 3.0 | 3.5 | 6.5 | 9.0 | 3.0 | 4.0 | 9.0 | 16.0 |
| 3.5 | 0.5 | 2.5 | 1.0 | 0.7 | 1.5 | 1.4 | 12.0 |
| 9.2 | 8.3 | 1.0 | 3.0 | 7.5 | 3.2 | 2.0 | 1.0 |
| 3.5 | 3.6 | 1.9 | 2.0 | 3.0 | 1.5 | 0.4 | 6.4 |
| 11.0 | 2.5 | 2.4 | 2.7 | 4.0 | 2.0 | 2.0 | 3.0 |

    d. Referring to part c, construct a bar chart to depict the proportion of employees in each category.

**2-69.** Anyone attending college realizes tuition costs have increased rapidly. In fact, tuition had risen at a faster pace than inflation for more than two decades. Data showing costs for both private and public colleges, for selected years, are shown below.

| Year | 1984 | 1989 | 1994 | 1999 | 2004 |
|------|------|------|------|------|------|
| Private College Tuition | $9,202 | $12,146 | $13,844 | $16,454 | $19,710 |
| Public College Tuition | $2,074 | $ 2,395 | $ 3,188 | $ 3,632 | $ 4,694 |

    a. Construct one bar graph illustrating the relationship between private and public university tuition for the displayed years.
    b. Describe the tuition trend for both private and public college tuition.

**2-70.** A recent article in *USA Today* used the following data to illustrate the decline in the percentage of men who receive college and advanced degrees:

| | Bachelor | | | Doctorate | | |
|------|------|------|------|------|------|------|
| | 1989 | 2003 | 2014* | 1989 | 2003 | 2014* |
| Men | 47 | 43 | 40 | 64 | 57 | 49 |
| Women | 53 | 57 | 60 | 36 | 43 | 51 |

*Education Department projection.

    a. Use one graph that contains two bar charts, each of which represents the kind of degree received, to display the relationship between the percentages of men and women receiving each type of degree.
    b. Describe any trends that might be evident.

**2-71.** The Minnesota State Fishing Bureau has contracted with a university biologist to study the length of walleyes (fish) caught in Minnesota lakes. The biologist collected data on a sample of 1,000 fish caught and developed the following relative frequency distribution:

| Class Length (inches) | Relative Frequency $f_i$ |
|------|------|
| 8 to less than 10 | .22 |
| 10 to less than 12 | .15 |
| 12 to less than 14 | .25 |
| 14 to less than 16 | .24 |
| 16 to less than 18 | .06 |
| 18 to less than 20 | .05 |
| 20 to less than 22 | .03 |

    a. Construct a frequency distribution from this relative frequency distribution and then produce a histogram based on the frequency distribution.
    b. Construct a pie chart from the relative frequency distribution. Discuss which of the two graphs, the pie chart or the histogram, you think is more effective in presenting the fish length data.

**2-72.** A computer software company has been looking at the amount of time customers spend on hold after their call is answered by the central switchboard. The company would like to have at most 2% of the callers wait two minutes or more. The company's calling service has provided the following data showing how long each of last month's callers spent on hold:

| Class | Number |
|---|---|
| Less than 15 seconds | 456 |
| 15 to less than 30 seconds | 718 |
| 30 to less than 45 seconds | 891 |
| 45 to less than 60 seconds | 823 |
| 60 to less than 75 seconds | 610 |
| 75 to less than 90 seconds | 449 |
| 90 to less than 105 seconds | 385 |
| 105 to less than 120 seconds | 221 |
| 120 to less than 150 seconds | 158 |
| 150 to less than 180 seconds | 124 |
| 180 to less than 240 seconds | 87 |
| More than 240 seconds | 153 |

a. Develop a relative frequency distribution and ogive for these data.

b. The company estimates it loses an average of $30 in business from callers who must wait two minutes or more before receiving assistance. The company thinks that last month's distribution of waiting times is typical. Estimate how much money the company is losing in business per month because people have to wait too long before receiving assistance.

2-73. The regional sales manager for American Toys, Inc., recently collected data on weekly sales (in dollars) for the 15 stores in his region. He also collected data on the number of salesclerk work hours during the week for each of the stores. The data are as follows:

| Store | Sales | Hours | Store | Sales | Hours |
|---|---|---|---|---|---|
| 1 | 23,300 | 120 | 9 | 27,886 | 140 |
| 2 | 25,600 | 135 | 10 | 54,156 | 300 |
| 3 | 19,200 | 96 | 11 | 34,080 | 254 |
| 4 | 10,211 | 102 | 12 | 25,900 | 180 |
| 5 | 19,330 | 240 | 13 | 36,400 | 270 |
| 6 | 35,789 | 190 | 14 | 25,760 | 175 |
| 7 | 12,540 | 108 | 15 | 31,500 | 256 |
| 8 | 43,150 | 234 | | | |

a. Develop a scatter plot of these data. Determine which variable should be the dependent variable and which should be the independent variable.

b. Based on the scatter plot, what, if any, conclusions might the sales manager reach with respect to the relationship between sales and number of clerk hours worked? Do any stores stand out as being different? Discuss.

## Computer Database **Exercises**

2-74. The Energy Information Administration published a press release on September 26, 2005 (Paula Weir and Pedro Saavedra, "Two Multi-Phase Surveys That Combine Overlapping Sample Cycles at Phase I"). The file entitled **Diesel$** contains the average on-highway diesel prices for each of 53 weeks from September 27, 2004, to September 26, 2005. It also contains equivalent information for the state of California, recognized as having the highest national prices.

a. Construct a chart containing line plots for both the national average and California's diesel prices. Describe the relationship between the diesel prices in California and the national average.

b. In what week did the California average diesel price surpass $3.00 a gallon?

c. Determine the smallest and largest price paid in California for a gallon of diesel. At what weeks did these occur? Use this information to project when California gas prices might exceed $4.00, assuming a linear trend between California diesel prices and the weeks in which they occurred.

2-75. A recent article in *USA Today* reported that Apple had 74% of the digital music device market, according to researcher The NPD Group. The NPD Group provides global sales and marketing information that helps clients make more informed, fact-based decisions to optimize their businesses. The data in the file entitled **Digital** provide the brand of digital devices owned by a sample of consumers that would produce the market shares alluded to in the article. Produce a pie chart that represents the market shares obtained from the referenced sample. Indicate the market shares and the identity of those manufacturers in the pie chart.

2-76. The file **Home-Prices** contains information about single-family housing prices in 100 metropolitan areas in the United States.

a. Construct a frequency distribution and histogram of 1997 median single-family home prices. Use the $2^k \geq n$ guideline to determine the appropriate number of classes.

b. Construct a cumulative relative frequency distribution and ogive for 1997 median single-family home prices.

c. Repeat parts a and b but this time use 1.5 times as many class intervals as recommended by the $2^k \geq n$ guideline. What was the impact of using more class intervals?

2-77. Elliel's Department Store tracks its inventory on a monthly basis. Monthly data for the years 2004–2008 are in the file called **Elliels**.

a. Construct a line chart showing the monthly inventory over the five years. Discuss what this graph implies about inventory.

b. Sum the monthly inventory figures for each year. Then present the sums in bar chart form. Discuss whether you think this is an appropriate graph to describe the inventory situation at Elliels.

2-78. The Energy Information Administration (EIA) surveys the price of diesel fuel. The EIA-888 is a survey of diesel fuel outlet prices from truck stops and service stations across the country. It produces estimates of national and regional prices. The diesel fuel prices that are released are used by the trucking industry to make rate adjustments in hauling contracts. The file entitled "Diesel$" contains the average on-highway diesel prices for each of 53 weeks from September 27, 2004, to September 26, 2005.

a. Construct a histogram with 11 classes beginning at $1.85.
b. Are there any data points that are unusually larger than the rest of the data? In which classes do these points occur? What is the interpretation of this phenomenon?

# Video Case 3

## Drive-Thru Service Times @ McDonald's

When you're on the go and looking for a quick meal, where do you go? If you're like millions of people every day, you make a stop at McDonald's. Known as "quick service restaurants" in the industry (not "fast food"), companies such as McDonald's invest heavily to determine the most efficient and effective ways to provide fast, high-quality service in all phases of their business.

Drive-thru operations play a vital role. It's not surprising that attention is focused on the drive-thru process. After all, over 60% of individual restaurant revenues in the United States come from the drive-thru experience. Yet, understanding the process is more complex than just counting cars. Marla King, professor at the company's international training center Hamburger University, got her start 25 years ago working at a McDonald's drive-thru. She now coaches new restaurant owners and managers. "Our stated drive-thru service time is 90 seconds or less. We train every manager and team member to understand that a quality customer experience at the drive-thru depends on them," says Marla. Some of the factors that affect customers' ability to complete their purchases within 90 seconds include restaurant staffing, equipment layout in the restaurant, training, efficiency of the grill team, and frequency of customer arrivals, to name a few. Also, customer order patterns also play a role. Some customers will just order drinks, whereas others seem to need enough food to feed an entire soccer team. And then there are the special orders. Obviously, there is plenty of room for variability here.

Yet, that doesn't stop the company from using statistical techniques to better understand the drive-thru action. In particular, McDonald's uses graphical techniques to display data and to help transform the data into useful information. For restaurant managers to achieve the goal in their own restaurants, they need training in proper restaurant and drive-thru operations. Hamburger University, McDonald's training center located near Chicago, Illinois, satisfies that need. In the mock-up restaurant service lab, managers go through a "before and after" training scenario. In the "before" scenario, they run the restaurant for 30 minutes as if they were back in their home restaurants. Managers in the training class are assigned to be crew, customers, drive-thru cars, special needs guests (such as hearing impaired, indecisive, clumsy), or observers. Statistical data about the operations, revenues, and service times are collected and analyzed. Without the right training, the restaurant's operations usually start breaking down after 10–15 minutes. After debriefing and analyzing the data collected, the

managers make suggestions for adjustments and head back to the service lab to try again. This time, the results usually come in well within standards. "When presented with the quantitative results, managers are pretty quick to make the connections between better operations, higher revenues, and happier customers," Marla states.

When managers return to their respective restaurants, the training results and techniques are shared with staff who are charged with implementing the ideas locally. The results of the training eventually are measured when McDonald's conducts a restaurant operations improvement process study, or ROIP. The goal is simple: improved operations. When the ROIP review is completed, statistical analyses are performed and managers are given their results. Depending on the results, decisions might be made that require additional financial resources, building construction, staff training, or reconfiguring layouts. Yet one thing is clear: Statistics drive the decisions behind McDonald's drive-through service operations.

## Discussion Questions:

1. After returning from the training session at Hamburger University, a McDonald's store owner selected a random sample of 362 drive-thru customers and carefully measured the time it took from when a customer entered the McDonald's property until the customer received the order at the drive-thru window. These data are in the file called **McDonald's Drive-Thru Waiting Times**. Note, the owner selected some customers during the breakfast period, others during lunch, and others during dinner. Construct any appropriate graphs and charts that will effectively display these drive-thru data. Prepare a short discussion indicating the conclusions that this store owner might reach after reviewing the graphs and charts you have prepared.

2. Referring to question 1, suppose the manager comes away with the conclusion that his store is not meeting the 90-second customer service goal. As a result he plans to dig deeper into the problem by collecting more data from the drive-thru process. Discuss what other measures you would suggest the manager collect. Discuss how these data could be of potential value in helping the store owner understand his problem.

3. Visit a local McDonald's that has a drive-thru facility. Randomly sample 20 drive-thru customers and collect the following data:

a.  the total time from arrival on the property to departure from the drive-thru window
b.  the time from when customers place the order until they receive their order and exit the drive-thru process
c.  the number of cars in the line when the sampled vehicle enters the drive-thru process
d.  Using the data that you have collected, construct appropriate graphs and charts to describe these data. Write a short report discussing the data

# Case 2.1

## Server Downtime

After getting outstanding grades in high school and scoring very high on his ACT and SAT tests, Clayton Haney had his choice of colleges but wanted to follow his parents' legacy and enrolled at Northwestern University. Clayton soon learned that there is a big difference between getting high grades in high school and being a good student. Although he was recognized as being quite bright and very quick to pick up on things, he had never learned how to study. As a result, after slightly more than two years at Northwestern, Clayton was asked to try his luck at another university. To the chagrin of his parents, Clayton decided that college was not for him.

After short stints working for a computer manufacturer and as a manager for a Blockbuster video store, Clayton landed a job working for the EDS company. EDS contracts to support information technology implementation and application for companies in the United States and throughout the world. Clayton had to train himself in virtually all aspects of personal computers and local area networks and was assigned to work for a client in the Chicago area.

Clayton's first assignment was to research the downtime on one of the client's primary network servers. He was asked to study the downtime data for the month of April and to make a short presentation to the company's management. The downtime data are in a file called "Server Downtime." These data are also shown in Table C-2.1-A. Although Clayton is very good at solving computer problems, he has had no training or experience in analyzing data, so he is going to need some help.

### Required Tasks:

1.  Construct a frequency distribution showing the number of times during the month that the server was down for each downtime cause category.
2.  Develop a bar chart that displays the data from the frequency distribution in part a.
3.  Develop a histogram that displays the downtime data.

**TABLE C-2.1-A**

| Date | Problem Experienced | Downtime Minutes |
|------|---------------------|------------------|
| 04/01/06 | Lockups | 25 |
| 04/02/06 | Lockups | 35 |
| 04/05/06 | Memory Errors | 10 |
| 04/07/06 | Lockups | 40 |
| 04/09/06 | Weekly Virus Scan | 60 |
| 04/09/06 | Lockups | 30 |
| 04/09/06 | Memory Errors | 35 |
| 04/09/06 | Memory Errors | 20 |
| 04/12/06 | Slow Startup | 45 |
| 04/12/06 | Weekly Virus Scan | 60 |
| 04/13/06 | Memory Errors | 30 |
| 04/14/06 | Memory Errors | 10 |
| 04/19/06 | Manual Re-start | 20 |
| 04/20/06 | Memory Errors | 35 |
| 04/20/06 | Weekly Virus Scan | 60 |
| 04/20/06 | Lockups | 25 |
| 04/21/06 | Memory Errors | 35 |
| 04/22/06 | Memory Errors | 20 |
| 04/27/06 | Memory Errors | 40 |
| 04/28/06 | Weekly Virus Scan | 60 |
| 04/28/06 | Memory Errors | 15 |
| 04/28/06 | Lockups | 25 |

4.  Develop a pie chart that breaks down the percentage of total downtime that is attributed to each downtime cause during the month.
5.  Prepare a short written report that discusses the downtime data. Make sure you merge the graphs and charts into the report.

# Case 2.2

## Yakima Apples, Inc.

As a rule, Julie Fredrick preferred to work in the field rather than do "office" work in her capacity as a midlevel manager with

Yakima Apples, Inc., a large grower and processor of apples in the state of Washington. However, after just leaving a staff meeting where she was asked to prepare a report of apple consumption in the United States, Julie was actually looking forward to

**TABLE C-2.2-A** | **Apples: Per Capita Consumption in Pounds (fresh weight equivalent)**

| Year | Total | Fresh | Processed Total | Canned | Juice | Frozen | Dried | Other |
|------|-------|-------|------|--------|-------|--------|-------|-------|
| 1970 | 31.4 | 17.0 | 14.4 | 5.6 | 6.4 | 0.8 | 0.9 | 0.7 |
| 1971 | 30.7 | 16.4 | 14.3 | 5.3 | 7.0 | 0.9 | 0.5 | 0.6 |
| 1972 | 28.0 | 15.5 | 12.5 | 4.7 | 5.4 | 1.1 | 0.6 | 0.6 |
| 1973 | 29.5 | 16.1 | 13.3 | 6.0 | 4.6 | 1.0 | 1.1 | 0.6 |
| 1974 | 30.5 | 16.4 | 14.1 | 5.8 | 5.9 | 0.6 | 0.9 | 0.9 |
| 1975 | 33.3 | 19.5 | 13.8 | 4.8 | 6.9 | 0.8 | 1.0 | 0.4 |
| 1976 | 29.7 | 17.1 | 12.6 | 4.3 | 6.3 | 0.6 | 1.1 | 0.3 |
| 1977 | 31.5 | 16.5 | 15.0 | 4.9 | 7.9 | 0.7 | 1.0 | 0.5 |
| 1978 | 35.5 | 17.9 | 17.5 | 5.5 | 9.6 | 0.6 | 1.0 | 0.8 |
| 1979 | 35.9 | 17.1 | 18.8 | 5.9 | 10.6 | 0.6 | 1.1 | 0.6 |
| 1980 | 39.6 | 19.2 | 20.4 | 5.3 | 13.0 | 0.6 | 0.8 | 0.7 |
| 1981 | 34.5 | 16.8 | 17.7 | 4.4 | 11.5 | 0.6 | 0.8 | 0.4 |
| 1982 | 39.5 | 17.5 | 22.0 | 5.4 | 14.6 | 0.7 | 0.9 | 0.5 |
| 1983 | 41.4 | 18.3 | 23.1 | 5.1 | 15.8 | 0.5 | 1.2 | 0.4 |
| 1984 | 44.1 | 18.4 | 25.7 | 5.0 | 18.4 | 0.6 | 1.3 | 0.4 |
| 1985 | 43.0 | 17.3 | 25.7 | 5.3 | 18.4 | 0.6 | 1.2 | 0.3 |
| 1986 | 42.8 | 17.8 | 25.0 | 4.9 | 18.2 | 0.7 | 0.8 | 0.4 |
| 1987 | 48.0 | 20.8 | 27.2 | 5.4 | 19.4 | 0.9 | 1.2 | 0.3 |
| 1988 | 47.0 | 19.8 | 27.2 | 5.7 | 19.1 | 0.8 | 1.2 | 0.3 |
| 1989 | 46.1 | 21.2 | 24.8 | 5.3 | 17.4 | 0.8 | 1.1 | 0.2 |
| 1990 | 47.4 | 19.6 | 27.9 | 5.5 | 20.7 | 0.7 | 0.8 | 0.3 |
| 1991 | 43.3 | 18.1 | 25.2 | 5.1 | 18.1 | 0.8 | 0.8 | 0.4 |
| 1992 | 46.3 | 19.1 | 27.1 | 5.8 | 18.7 | 0.8 | 1.2 | 0.6 |
| 1993 | 47.8 | 19.0 | 28.8 | 5.1 | 21.3 | 0.6 | 1.4 | 0.3 |
| 1994 | 48.5 | 19.3 | 29.1 | 5.3 | 21.3 | 0.5 | 1.5 | 0.5 |
| 1995 | 44.7 | 18.7 | 26.0 | 4.9 | 18.9 | 0.8 | 1.2 | 0.3 |
| 1996 | 46.1 | 18.7 | 27.4 | 4.9 | 20.3 | 0.8 | 1.2 | 0.2 |
| 1997 | 44.5 | 18.1 | 26.5 | 5.6 | 18.5 | 0.8 | 0.9 | 0.7 |
| 1998 | 47.1 | 19.0 | 28.1 | 4.4 | 21.5 | 0.7 | 1.2 | 0.4 |
| 1999 | 46.8 | 18.5 | 28.3 | 4.8 | 21.4 | 0.6 | 1.0 | 0.5 |
| 2000 | 45.3 | 17.5 | 27.9 | 4.4 | 21.4 | 0.9 | 0.8 | 0.5 |
| 2001 | 43.7 | 15.6 | 28.0 | 4.6 | 21.3 | 0.9 | 0.8 | 0.5 |
| 2002 | 43.4 | 16.0 | 27.5 | 4.0 | 21.4 | 0.7 | 0.8 | 0.5 |

*Source:* USDA/Economic Research Service.

spending some time at her computer "crunching some numbers." Arden Golchein, senior marketing manager, indicated that he would e-mail her a data file that contained apple consumption data from 1970 through 2002 and told her that he wanted a very nice report using graphs, charts, and tables to describe apple consumption.

When she got to her desk, the e-mail was waiting and she saved the file under the name "Yakima Apples." These data are also shown in Table C-2.2-A. Julie had done quite a bit of descriptive analysis in her previous job with the Washington State Department of Agriculture, so she had several ideas for types of graphs and tables that she might construct. She began by creating a list of the tasks that she thought would be needed.

**Required Tasks:**

1. Construct a line chart showing the total annual consumption of apples.

2. Construct one line chart that shows two things: the annual consumption of fresh apples and the annual consumption of processed apples.

3. Construct a line chart that shows the annual consumption for each type of processed apples.

4. Construct a histogram for the total annual consumption of apples.

5. Write a short report that discusses the historical pattern of apple consumption. The report will include all pertinent charts and graphs.

# Case 2.3

## Welco Lumber Company—Part A

Gene Denning wears several hats at the Welco Lumber Company, including process improvement team leader, shipping manager, and assistant human resources manager. Welco Lumber makes cedar fencing materials at its Naples, Idaho, facility, employing about 160 people.

Over 75% of the cost of the finished cedar fence boards is in the cedar logs that the company buys on the open market. Therefore, it is very important that the company get as much finished product as possible from each log. One of the most important steps in the manufacturing process is referred to as the head rig. The head rig is a large saw that breaks down the logs into slabs and cants. Figure C-2.3-A shows the concept. From small logs with diameters of 12 inches or less, one cant and four or fewer usable slabs are obtained. From larger logs, multiple cants and four slabs are obtained. Finished fence boards can be produced from both the slabs and the cants.

At some companies, the head rig cutting operation is automated and the cuts are made based on a scanner system and computer algorithms. However, at Welco Lumber, the head rig is operated manually by operators who must look at a log as it arrives and determine how best to break the log down to get the most finished product. In addition, the operators are responsible for making sure that the cants are "centered" so that maximum product can be gained from them.

Recently, Gene Denning headed up a study in which he videotaped 365 logs being broken down by the head rig. All three operators, April, Sid, and Jim, were involved. Each log was marked as to its true diameter. Then Gene observed the way the log was broken down and the degree to which the cants were

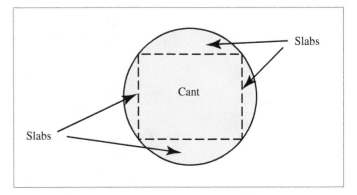

**FIGURE C-2.3-A** | Log Breakdown at the Head Rig

properly centered. He then determined the projected value of the finished product from each log given the way it was actually cut. In addition, he also determined what the value would have been had the log been cut in the optimal way. Data for this study is in a file called "Welco Lumber." A portion of the data is shown in Table C-2.3-A.

You have been asked to assist Gene by analyzing these data using graphs, charts, and tables as appropriate. He wishes to focus on the lost profit to the company and whether there are differences among the operators. Also, do the operators tend to do a better job on small logs than on large logs? In general, he is hoping to learn as much as possible from this study and needs your help with the analysis.

**TABLE C-2.3-A** | **Head Rig Data—Welco Lumber Company**

| 5-Nov-06 | Through | 21-Nov-06 Head Rig Log Study | | | Baseline | | | |
|---|---|---|---|---|---|---|---|---|
| Log # | Operator | Log Size | Large/Small Log | Correct Cut (Yes or No) | Error Category | Actual Value | Potential Value | Potential Gain |
| 1 | Sid | 15 | Large | No | Excessive Log Breakdown | $59.00 | $65.97 | $6.97 |
| 2 | Sid | 17 | Large | No | Excessive Log Breakdown | $79.27 | $85.33 | $6.06 |
| 3 | Sid | 11 | Small | Yes | No Error | $35.40 | $35.40 | $0.00 |
| 4 | Sid | 11 | Small | No | Off Center Cant | $31.61 | $35.40 | $3.79 |
| 5 | Sid | 14 | Large | No | Reduced Value Cut | $47.67 | $58.86 | $11.19 |
| 6 | Sid | 17 | Large | Yes | No Error | $85.33 | $85.33 | $0.00 |
| 7 | Sid | 8 | Small | Yes | No Error | $16.22 | $16.22 | $0.00 |
| 8 | Sid | 11 | Small | Yes | No Error | $35.40 | $35.40 | $0.00 |
| 9 | Sid | 9 | Small | Yes | No Error | $21.54 | $21.54 | $0.00 |
| 10 | Sid | 9 | Small | No | Off Center Cant | $18.92 | $21.54 | $2.62 |
| 11 | Sid | 10 | Small | Yes | No Error | $21.54 | $21.54 | $0.00 |
| 12 | Sid | 8 | Small | Yes | No Error | $16.22 | $16.22 | $0.00 |
| 13 | Sid | 10 | Small | No | Off Center Cant | $25.71 | $28.97 | $3.26 |
| 14 | Sid | 12 | Small | Yes | No Error | $41.79 | $41.79 | $0.00 |
| 15 | Sid | 11 | Small | Yes | No Error | $35.40 | $35.40 | $0.00 |

# References

Berenson, Mark L., and David M. Levine, *Basic Business Statistics: Concepts and Applications*, 11th ed. (Upper Saddle River, NJ: Prentice Hall, 2009).

Cleveland, William S., "Graphs in Scientific Publications," *The American Statistician* 38 (November 1984), pp. 261–269.

Cleveland, William S., and R. McGill, "Graphical Perception: Theory, Experimentation, and Application to the Development of Graphical Methods," *Journal of the American Statistical Association* 79 (September 1984), pp. 531–554.

Cryer, Jonathan D., and Robert B. Miller, *Statistics for Business: Data Analysis and Modeling*, 2nd ed. (Belmont, CA: Duxbury Press, 1996).

*Microsoft Excel 2007* (Redmond, WA: Microsoft Corp., 2007).

*Minitab for Windows Version 15* (State College, PA: Minitab, 2007).

Siegel, Andrew F., *Practical Business Statistics*, 5th ed. (Burr Ridge, IL: Irwin, 2002).

Tufte, Edward R., *Envisioning Information* (Cheshire, CT: Graphics Press, 1990).

Tufte, Edward R., *The Visual Display of Quantitative Information*, 2nd ed. (Cheshire, CT: Graphics Press, 2001).

Tukey, John W., *Exploratory Data Analysis* (Reading, MA: Addison-Wesley, 1977).

- **Review** the definitions for nominal, ordinal, interval, and ratio data in Section 1.4.
- **Examine** the statistical software, such as Excel or Minitab, used during this course to

identify the tools for computing descriptive measures. For instance, in Excel, look at the function wizard and the descriptive statistics tools on the Data tab under Data Analysis. In Minitab acquaint yourself with the *Basic Statistics* menu within the *Stat* menu.

- **Review** the material on frequency histograms in Section 2.1, paying special attention to how histograms help determine where the data are centered and how the data are spread around the center.

# Describing Data Using Numerical Measures

# Why you need to know

Graphs and charts provide effective tools for transforming data into information; however, they are only a starting point. Graphs and charts do not reveal all the information contained in a set of data. To make your descriptive toolkit complete, you need to become familiar with the key descriptive measures that quantify the center of the data and its spread.

Suppose you are an advertising manager for a major tire company and you want to develop an ad campaign touting how much longer your company's tires last than the competition's. You must be careful that your claims are valid. First, the Federal Trade Commission (FTC) is charged with regulating advertising and requires that advertising be truthful. Second, customers who can show that they were misled by an incorrect claim about your tires could sue you and your company. You have no choice. You must use statistical procedures to determine the validity of any claim you might want to make about your tires.

You might start by sampling tires from your company and from the competition. You could measure the number of miles each tire lasts before a specified portion of the tread is depleted. You might graph the data for each company as a histogram, but a clear comparison with this graph might be difficult. Instead, you could compute the summary mileage measures for the various tire brands and show these values side-by-side, perhaps in a bar chart. Thus, to effectively describe data, you will need to combine the graphical tools discussed in Chapter 2 with the numerical measures introduced in this chapter.

## 3.1 Measures of Center and Location

You learned in Chapter 2 that frequency histograms are an effective way of converting quantitative data into useful information. The histogram provides a visual indication of where data are centered and how much spread there is in the data around the center.

However, to fully describe a quantitative variable, we also need to compute measures of its center and spread. These measures can then be coupled with the histogram to give a clear picture of the variable's distribution. This section focuses on measures of the center of data. Section 3.2 introduces measures of the spread of data.

## Parameters and Statistics

**Parameter**

A measure computed from the entire population. As long as the population does not change, the value of the parameter will not change.

**Statistic**

A measure computed from a sample that has been selected from a population. The value of the statistic will depend on which sample is selected.

**Mean**

A numerical measure of the center of a set of quantitative measures computed by dividing the sum of the values by the number of values in the data.

**Population Mean**

The average for all values in the population computed by dividing the sum of all values by the population size.

Depending on whether we are working with a population or a sample, a numerical measure is known as either a **parameter** or a **statistic**.

## Population Mean

There are three important measures of the center of a set of data. The first of these is the **mean**, or average, of the data. To find the mean, we sum the values and divide the sum by the number of data values, as shown in Equation 3.1.

---

**Population Mean**

$$\mu = \frac{\sum_{i=1}^{N} x_i}{N} \tag{3.1}$$

where:

$\mu$ = Population mean (mu)
$N$ = Population size
$x_i$ = $i$th individual value of variable $x$

---

The **population mean** is represented by the Greek symbol $\mu$, pronounced "mu." The formal notation in the numerator for the sum of the $x$ values reads

$$\sum_{i=1}^{N} x_i \rightarrow \text{Sum all } x_i \text{ values where } i \text{ goes from 1 to } N$$

In other words, we are summing all $N$ values in the population.

Because you almost always sum all the data values, to simplify notation in this text, we generally will drop the subscripts after the first time we introduce a formula. Thus, the formula for the population mean will be written as

$$\mu = \frac{\sum x}{N}$$

**Chapter Outcome 1.** ➡ | BUSINESS APPLICATION | **POPULATION MEAN**

**FOSTER CITY HOTEL** The manager of a small hotel in Foster City, California, was asked by the corporate vice president to analyze the Sunday night registration information for the past eight weeks. Data on three variables were collected:

$x_1$ = Total number of rooms rented
$x_2$ = Total dollar revenue from the room rentals
$x_3$ = Number of customer complaints that came from guests each Sunday

These data are shown in Table 3.1. They are a population because they include all data that interest the vice president.

Figure 3.1 shows the frequency histogram for the number of rooms rented. If the manager wants to describe the data further, she can locate the center of the data by finding the balance point for the histogram. Think of the horizontal axis as a plank and the histogram bars as weights proportional to their area. The center of the data would be the point at which the plank would balance. As shown in Figure 3.1, the balance point seems to be about 15 rooms.

**TABLE 3.1** | **Foster City Hotel Data**

| Week | Rooms Rented | Revenue | Complaints |
|------|-------------|---------|-----------|
| 1 | 22 | $1,870 | 0 |
| 2 | 13 | $1,590 | 2 |
| 3 | 10 | $1,760 | 1 |
| 4 | 16 | $2,345 | 0 |
| 5 | 23 | $4,563 | 2 |
| 6 | 13 | $1,630 | 1 |
| 7 | 11 | $2,156 | 0 |
| 8 | 13 | $1,756 | 0 |

Eyeing the histogram might yield a reasonable approximation of the center. However, computing a numerical measure of the center directly from the data is preferable. The most frequently used measure of the center is the mean. The population mean for number of rooms rented is computed using Equation 3.1 as follows:

$$\mu = \frac{\sum x}{N} = \frac{22 + 13 + 10 + 16 + 23 + 13 + 11 + 13}{8}$$

$$= \frac{121}{8}$$

$$\mu = 15.125$$

Thus, the average number of rooms rented on Sunday for the past eight weeks is 15.125. This is the true balance point for the data. Turn to Table 3.2, where we calculate what is called a *deviation* $(x_i - \mu)$ by subtracting the mean from each value, $x_i$.

**FIGURE 3.1**

Balance Point, Rooms Rented at Foster City Hotel

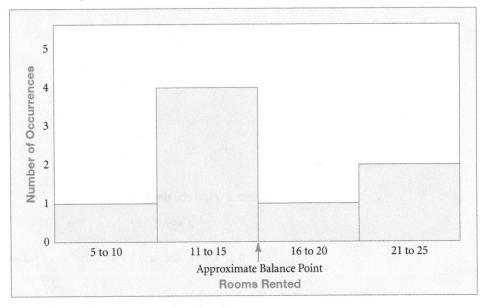

**TABLE 3.2** | **Centering Concept of the Mean Using Hotel Data**

| x | (x − μ) = Deviation |
|---|---------------------|
| 22 | 22 − 15.125 =  6.875 |
| 13 | 13 − 15.125 = −2.125 |
| 10 | 10 − 15.125 = −5.125 |
| 16 | 16 − 15.125 =  0.875 |
| 23 | 23 − 15.125 =  7.875 |
| 13 | 13 − 15.125 = −2.125 |
| 11 | 11 − 15.125 = −4.125 |
| 13 | 13 − 15.125 = −2.125 |
| | $\sum (x - \mu) = $   0.000 ←Sum of deviations equals zero. |

Note that the sum of the deviations of the data from the mean is zero. This is not a coincidence. *For any set of data, the sum of the deviations around the mean will be zero.*

## How to do it (Example 3-1)

### Computing the Population Mean
When the available data constitute the population of interest, the population mean is computed using the following steps:

1. Collect the data for the variable of interest for all items in the population. The data must be quantitative.

2. Sum all values in the population ($\Sigma x_i$).

3. Divide the sum ($\Sigma x_i$) by the number of values ($N$) in the population to get the population mean. The formula for the population mean is

$$\mu = \frac{\Sigma x}{N}$$

**EXAMPLE 3-1    COMPUTING THE POPULATION MEAN**

**United Airlines** To stay competitive, United Airlines, headquartered in Chicago, must update its airplane fleet. Suppose United selects its planes from a list of 17 possible planes, including such models as the Boeing 747-100, Air Bus 300-B4, and the DC 9-10. At a recent meeting, the chief operating officer asked a member of his staff to determine the mean fuel consumption rate per hour of operation for the population of 17 planes.

**Step 1    Collect data for the quantitative variable of interest.**
The manufacturers for each of the 17 planes were asked to provide the hourly fuel consumption in gallons for a flight between Chicago and New York City. These data are recorded as follows:

| Airplane | Fuel Consumption (gal/hr) |
|---|---|
| B747-100 | 3,529 |
| L-1011-100/200 | 2,215 |
| DC-10-10 | 2,174 |
| A300-B4 | 1,482 |
| A310-300 | 1,574 |
| B767-300 | 1,503 |
| B767-200 | 1,377 |
| B757-200 | 985 |
| B727-200 | 1,249 |
| MD-80 | 882 |
| B737-300 | 732 |
| DC-9-50 | 848 |
| B727-100 | 806 |
| B737-100/200 | 1,104 |
| F-100 | 631 |
| DC-9-30-11 | 804 |
| DC-9-10 | 764 |

**Step 2    Add the data values.**

$$\Sigma x = 3,529 + 2,215 + 2,174 + \cdots + 764 = 22,659$$

**Step 3    Divide the sum by the number of values in the population using Equation 3.1.**

$$\mu = \frac{\Sigma x}{N} = \frac{22,659}{17} = 1,332.9$$

The mean number of gallons of fuel consumed per hour on these 17 planes is 1,332.9.

>> **END EXAMPLE**

**BUSINESS APPLICATION    POPULATION MEAN**

**FOSTER CITY HOTEL (*CONTINUED*)** In addition to collecting data on the number of rooms rented on Sunday nights, the Foster City Hotel manager also collected data on the room-rental revenue generated and the number of complaints on Sunday nights. Both Excel and Minitab have procedures for computing numerical measures such as the mean. Because these data are the population of all nights of interest to the hotel manager, she can compute the

**FIGURE 3.2A**

Excel 2007 Output Showing Mean Revenue for the Foster City Hotel

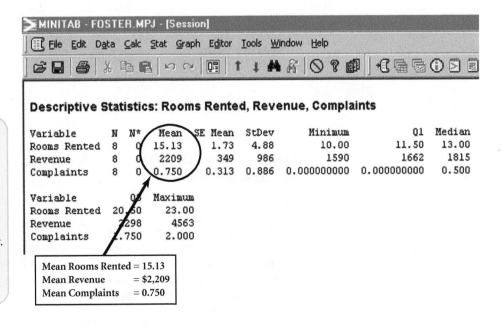

Mean Rooms Rented = 15.13
Mean Revenue     = $2,208.75
Mean Complaints  = 0.75

**Excel 2007 Instructions:**
1. Open File: Foster.xls.
2. On the **Data** tab, click on **Data Analysis**.
3. Click on **Descriptive Statistics**.
4. Define data range for the variables.
5. Check **Summary Statistics**.
6. Name output sheet.
7. On the **Home** tab, adjust decimal point.

**Excel and Minitab Tutorial**

population mean, $\mu$, revenue per night. The population mean is $\mu = \$2{,}208.75$ (rounded to $2,209 in Minitab), as shown in the Excel and Minitab outputs in Figure 3.2a and 3.2b. Likewise, the mean number of complaints is $\mu = 0.75$ per night. (Note, there are other measures shown in the figures. We will discuss several of these later in the chapter.)

Now, for these eight Sunday nights, the manager can report to the corporate vice president that the mean number of rooms rented is 15.13. This level of business generated an average nightly revenue of $2,208.75. The number of complaints averaged 0.75 (less than 1) per night. These values are the true means for the population and are, therefore, called parameters.

Chapter Outcome 1. ➤ ## Sample Mean

**Sample Mean**
The average for all values in the sample computed by dividing the sum of all sample values by the sample size.

The data for the Foster City Hotel constituted the population of interest. Thus, $\mu = 15.13$ nights is the parameter measure. However, if we have a sample rather than a population, the mean for the sample (**sample mean**) is computed using Equation 3.2.

**FIGURE 3.2B**

Minitab Output Showing Mean Revenue for the Foster City Hotel

**Minitab Instructions:**
1. Open file: Foster.MTW.
2. Choose **Stat > Basic Statistics > Display Descriptive Statistics**.
3. In **Variables**, enter columns *Rooms Rented, Revenue,* and *Complaints*.
4. Click **Statistics**.
5. Check required statistics.
6. Click **OK. OK.**

**MINITAB - FOSTER.MPJ - [Session]**

File Edit Data Calc Stat Graph Editor Tools Window Help

**Descriptive Statistics: Rooms Rented, Revenue, Complaints**

| Variable | N | N* | Mean | SE Mean | StDev | Minimum | Q1 | Median |
|---|---|---|---|---|---|---|---|---|
| Rooms Rented | 8 | 0 | 15.13 | 1.73 | 4.88 | 10.00 | 11.50 | 13.00 |
| Revenue | 8 | 0 | 2209 | 349 | 986 | 1590 | 1662 | 1815 |
| Complaints | 8 | 0 | 0.750 | 0.313 | 0.886 | 0.000000000 | 0.000000000 | 0.500 |

| Variable | Q3 | Maximum |
|---|---|---|
| Rooms Rented | 20.50 | 23.00 |
| Revenue | 3298 | 4563 |
| Complaints | 1.750 | 2.000 |

Mean Rooms Rented = 15.13
Mean Revenue     = $2,209
Mean Complaints  = 0.750

**Sample Mean**

$$\bar{x} = \frac{\sum_{i=1}^{n} x_i}{n}$$    (3.2)

where:

$\bar{x}$ = Sample mean (pronounced "x-bar")
$n$ = Sample size

Notice, Equation 3.2 is the same as Equation 3.1 *except* that we sum the sample values, not the population values, and divide by the sample size, not the population size.

The notation for the sample mean is $\bar{x}$. Sample descriptors (statistics) are usually assigned a Roman character. (Recall that population values usually are assigned a Greek character.)

---

**EXAMPLE 3-2    COMPUTING A SAMPLE MEAN**

**Management Salaries** Dominique & Associates is a management search firm that locates qualified management talent for companies looking to fill a position. They have selected a sample of seven recent placements and recorded the starting salaries. The following steps are used to calculate the sample mean salary:

**Step 1  Collect the sample data.**

$\{x_i\}$ = {Management Salaries} = {$144,000; $98,000; $204,000;
$177,000; $155,000; $316,000; $100,000}

**Step 2  Add the values in the sample.**

$\Sigma x$ = $144,000 + $98,000 + $204,000 + $177,000 + $155,000 + $316,000
+ $100,000 = $1,194,000

**Step 3  Divide the sum by the sample size (Equation 3.2).**

$$\bar{x} = \frac{\Sigma x}{n} = \frac{\$1,194,000}{7} = \$170,571.43$$

Therefore, the mean starting salary for the sample of seven managers placed by Dominique & Associates is $170,571.43.

**>>END EXAMPLE**

---

# The Impact of Extreme Values on the Mean

The mean (population or sample) is the balance point for data, so using the mean as a measure of the center generally makes sense. However, the mean does have a potential disadvantage: *The mean can be affected by extreme values.* There are many instances in business when this may occur. For example, in a population or sample of income data, there likely will be extremes on the high end that will pull the mean upward from the center. Example 3-3 illustrates how an extreme value can affect the mean. In these situations, a second measure called the *median* may be more appropriate.

**EXAMPLE 3-3    IMPACT OF EXTREME VALUES**

**Management Salaries** Suppose the sample of management starting salaries (see Example 3-2) had been slightly different. If the salary recorded as $316,000 had actually been $1,000,000, how would the mean be affected? We can see the impact as follows:

**Step 1  Collect the sample data.**

$$\{x_i\} = \{\text{Management Salaries}\} = \{\$144,000; \$98,000; \$204,000;$$
$$\$177,000; \$155,000; \$1,000,000; \$100,000\}$$

extreme value

**Step 2  Add the values.**

$\Sigma x = \$144,000 + 98,000 + 204,000 + 177,000 + 155,000 + 1,000,000 + 100,000$
$= \$1,878,000$

**Step 3  Divide the sum by the number of values in the sample.**

$$\bar{x} = \frac{\Sigma x}{n} = \frac{\$1,878,000}{7} = \$268,285.71$$

Recall, in Example 3-2, the sample mean was $170,571.43.

With only one value in the sample changed, the mean is now substantially higher than before. Because the mean is affected by extreme values, it may be a misleading measure of the data's center. In this case, the mean is larger than all but one of the starting salaries.

**>>END EXAMPLE**

**TRY PROBLEM** 3-15 (pg. 105)

**Chapter Outcome 1.➤ Median**

**Median**

The median is a center value that divides a data array into two halves. We use $\tilde{\mu}$ to denote the population median and $M_d$ to denote the sample median.

Another measure of the center is called the **median**.

The median is found by first arranging data in numerical order from smallest to largest. Data that are sorted in order are referred to as a **data array**.

Equation 3.3 is used to find the index point corresponding to the median value for a set of data placed in numerical order from low to high.

**Data Array**

Data that have been arranged in numerical order.

---

**Median Index**

$$i = \frac{1}{2}n$$    **(3.3)**

where:
  $i$ = The index of the point in the data set corresponding to the median value
  $n$ = Sample size

If $i$ is not an integer, round its value up to the next highest integer. This next highest integer then is the position of the median in the data array.

If $i$ is an integer, the median is the average of the values in position $i$ and position $i + 1$.

---

For instance, suppose a personnel manager has hired 10 new employees. The ages of each of these employees sorted from low to high is listed as follows:

23   25   25   34   35   45   46   47   52   54

Using Equation 3.3 to find the median index, we get

$$i = \frac{1}{2}n = \frac{1}{2}(10) = 5$$

Since the index is an integer, the median value will be the average of the 5th and 6th values in the data set. Thus, the median is

$$M_d = \frac{35 + 45}{2} = 40$$

Consider another case in which customers at a restaurant are asked to rate the service they received on a scale of 1 to 100. A total of 15 customers were asked to provide the ratings. The data, sorted from low to high, are presented as follows:

60   68   75   77   80   80   80   85   88   90   95   95   95   95   99

Using Equation 3.3, we get the median index:

$$i = \frac{1}{2}n = \frac{1}{2}(15) = 7.5$$

Since the index is not an integer, we round 7.5 up to 8. Thus, the median ($M_d$) is the 8th data value from either end. In this case,

$$M_d = 85$$

---

**EXAMPLE 3-4**    **COMPUTING THE MEDIAN**

**Management Salaries** Consider again the example involving the management search firm, Dominique & Associates, and the sample starting salary data in Example 3-2. The median for these data is computed using the following steps:

**Step 1   Collect the sample data.**

$\{x_i\}$ = {Management Salaries} = {$144,000; $98,000; $204,000; $177,000; $155,000; $316,000; $100,000}

**Step 2   Sort the data from smallest to largest, forming a data array.**

$\{x_i\}$ = {$98,000; $100,000; $144,000; $155,000; $177,000; $204,000; $316,000}

**Step 3   Calculate the median index.**

Using Equation 3.3, we get $i = \frac{1}{2}(7) = 3.5$. Rounding up, the median is the fourth value from either end of the data array.

**Step 4   Find the median.**

$\{x_i\}$ = {$98,000; $100,000; $144,000; $155,000; $177,000; $204,000; $316,000}

fourth value = $M_d$

The median salary is $155,000. The notation for the sample median is $M_d$.

Note, if the number of data values in a sample or population is an even number, the median is the average of the two middle values.

>>**END EXAMPLE**

**TRY PROBLEM** 3-2 (pg. 103)

**Symmetric Data**

Data sets whose values are evenly spread around the center. For symmetric data, the mean and median are equal.

**Skewed Data**

Data sets that are not symmetric. For skewed data, the mean will be larger or smaller than the median.

## Skewed and Symmetric Distributions

Data in a population or sample can be either **symmetric** or **skewed**, depending on how the data are distributed around the center.

In the original management salary example (Example 3-2), the mean for the sample of seven managers was $170,571.43. In Example 3-4, the median salary was $155,000. Thus, for

**FIGURE 3.3** |

Skewed and Symmetric
Distributions

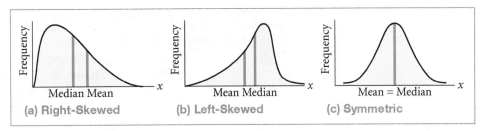

(a) Right-Skewed  (b) Left-Skewed  (c) Symmetric

**Right-Skewed Data**

A data distribution is right skewed if the mean
for the data is larger than the median.

**Left-Skewed Data**

A data distribution is left skewed if the mean for
the data is smaller than the median.

these data the mean and the median are not equal. This sample data set is **right skewed**, because $\bar{x} = \$170{,}571.43 > M_d = \$155{,}000$.

Figure 3.3 illustrates examples of right-skewed, **left-skewed**, and symmetric distributions. The greater the difference between the mean and the median, the more skewed the distribution. *Example 3-5 shows that an advantage of the median over the mean is that the median is not affected by extreme values.* Thus, the median is particularly useful as a measure of the center when the data are highly skewed.[1]

---

**EXAMPLE 3-5**    **IMPACT OF EXTREME VALUES ON THE MEDIAN**

---

Management Salaries (*Continued*) In Example 3-3, when we substituted a $1,000,000 salary for the manager hired at a starting salary of $316,000, the sample mean salary increased from $170,571.43 to $268,285.71. What will happen to the median? The median is determined using the following steps:

Step 1  **Collect the sample data.**
        The sample management salary data (including the extremely high salary) are

$$\{x_i\} = \{\text{Management Salary}\} = \{\$144{,}000; \$98{,}000; \$204{,}000; \$177{,}000;$$
$$\$155{,}000; \$1{,}000{,}000; \$100{,}000\}$$

Step 2  **Sort the data from smallest to largest, forming a data array.**

$$\{x_i\} = \{\$98{,}000; \$100{,}000; \$144{,}000; \$155{,}000; \$177{,}000; \$204{,}000; \$1{,}000{,}000\}$$

Step 3  **Calculate the median index.**
        Using Equation 3.3, we get $i = \frac{1}{2}(7) = 3.5$. Rounding up, the median is the fourth value from either end of the data array.

Step 4  **Find the median.**

$$\{x_i\} = \{\$98{,}000; \$100{,}000; \$144{,}000; \$155{,}000; \$177{,}000; \$204{,}000; \$1{,}000{,}000\}$$

fourth value $= M_d$

The median starting salary is $155,000, the same value as in Example 3-4, when the high starting salary was not included in the data. Thus, the median is not affected by the extreme values in the data.

>>**END EXAMPLE**

**TRY PROBLEM** 3-2 (pg. 103)

Chapter Outcome 1. → **Mode**

**Mode**

The mode is the value in a data set that occurs
most frequently.

The mean is the most commonly used measure of central location, followed closely by the median. However, the **mode** is another measure that is occasionally used as a measure of central location.

A data set may have more than one mode if two or more values tie for the most frequently occurring value. Example 3-6 illustrates this concept and shows how the mode is determined.

---

[1]Both Minitab and Excel will provide a skewness statistic. The sign on the skewness statistic implies the direction of skewness. The higher the absolute value, the more the data are skewed.

**EXAMPLE 3-6**    **DETERMINING THE MODE**

 Smoky Mountain Pizza The owners of Smoky Mountain Pizza are planning to expand their restaurant to include an open-air patio. Before finalizing the design, the managers want to know what the most frequently occurring group size is so they can organize the seating arrangements to best meet demand. They wish to know the mode, which can be calculated using the following steps:

Step 1    **Collect the sample data.**

A sample of 20 groups was selected at random. These data are

$$\{x_i\} = \{\text{people}\} = \{2, 4, 1, 2, 3, 2, 4, 2, 3, 6, 8, 4, 2, 1, 7, 4, 2, 4, 4, 3\}$$

Step 2    **Organize the data into a frequency distribution.**

| $x_i$ | Frequency |
|-------|-----------|
| 1 | 2 |
| 2 | 6 |
| 3 | 3 |
| 4 | 6 |
| 5 | 0 |
| 6 | 1 |
| 7 | 1 |
| 8 | 1 |
| | Total = 20 |

Step 3    **Determine the value(s) that occurs (occur) most frequently.**
In this case, there are two modes, because the values 2 and 4 each occurred six times. Thus the modes are 2 and 4.

**>>END EXAMPLE**

**TRY PROBLEM** 3-2 (pg. 103)

A common mistake is to state the mode as being the frequency of the most frequently occurring value. In Example 3-6, you might be tempted to say that the mode = 6 because that was the highest frequency. Instead, there were two modes, 2 and 4, each of which occurred six times.

If no value occurs more frequently than any other, the data set is said to not have a mode. The mode might be particularly useful in describing the central location value for clothes sizes. For example, shoes come in full and half sizes. Consider the following sample data that have been sorted from low to high:

$$\{x\} = \{7.5, 8.0, 8.5, 9.0, 9.0, 10.0, 10.0, 10.0, 10.5, 10.5, 11.0, 11.5\}$$

The mean for these sample data is

$$\bar{x} = \frac{\sum x}{n} = \frac{7.5 + 8.0 + \cdots + 11.5}{12} = \frac{115.50}{12} = 9.63$$

Although 9.63 is the numerical average, the mode is 10, because more people wore that size shoe than any other. In making purchasing decisions, a shoe store manager would order more shoes at the modal size than at any other size. The mean isn't of any particular use in her purchasing decision.

## Applying the Measures of Central Tendency

The cost of tuition is an important factor that most students and their families consider when deciding where to attend college. The data file **Colleges and Universities** contains data for a sample of 718 colleges and universities in the United States. The cost of out-of-state tuition is

**Excel and Minitab Tutorial**

one of the variables in the data file. Suppose a guidance counselor who will be advising students about college choices wishes to conduct a descriptive analysis for this quantitative variable.

Figure 3.4 shows a frequency histogram generated using Excel. This histogram is a good place to begin the descriptive analysis since it allows the analyst to get a good indication of the center value, the spread around the center, and the general shape of the distribution of out-of-state tuition for these colleges and universities. Given that the file contains 718 colleges and universities, using the $2^k \geq n$ rule introduced in Chapter 2, the guidance counselor used $k = 10$ classes. The least expensive school in the file is CUNY–Medgar Evers College in New York at \$2,600 and the most expensive is Franklin and Marshall in Pennsylvania at \$24,940. Based on this histogram in Figure 3.4 what would you conclude about the distribution of college tuition? Is it skewed right or left?

The analysis can be extended by computing appropriate descriptive measures for the out-of-state tuition variable. Specifically, we want to look at measures of central location. Figure 3.5 shows the Excel output with descriptive measures for out-of-state tuition. First, focus on the primary measures of central location: mean and median. These are

$$\text{Mean} = \$9,933.38 \qquad \text{Median} = \$9,433$$

These statistics provide measures of the center of the out-of-state tuition variable. The mean tuition value was \$9,933.38, whereas the median was \$9,433. Because the mean exceeds the median, we conclude that the data are right skewed—the same conclusion you should have reached by looking at the histogram in Figure 3.4.

**FIGURE 3.4**

Excel 2007 Frequency Histogram of College Tuition Prices

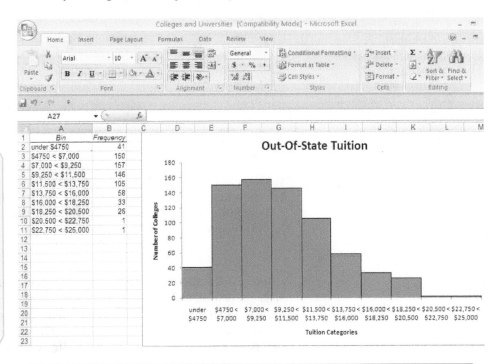

**Minitab Instructions (for similar results):**

1. Open file: Colleges and Universities.MTW.
2. Choose **Graph > Histogram**.
3. Click **Simple**.
4. Click **OK**.
5. In **Graph variables**, enter data column *out-of-state tuition*.
6. Click **OK**.

**Excel 2007 Instructions:**

1. Open file: Colleges and Universities.xls.
2. Set up an area in the worksheet for the bins (upper limits of each class) as 4750, 7000, etc. Be sure to label the column with these values as "Bins."
3. On the **Data** tab, click **Data Analysis**.
4. Select **Histogram**.
5. Input Range specifies the actual data values as the **out-of-state tuition** column and the bin range as the column defined in step 2.
6. Put on a new worksheet and include the **Chart Output**.
7. Right-mouse-click on the bars and use the **Format Data Series Options** to set gap width to zero and add lines to the bars.
8. Convert the bins in column A of the histogram output sheet to actual class labels. Note the bin labeled 4750 is changed to "under \$4,750."
9. Click on **Layout** and set titles as desired.

**FIGURE 3.5**

Excel 2007 Descriptive
Statistics Output

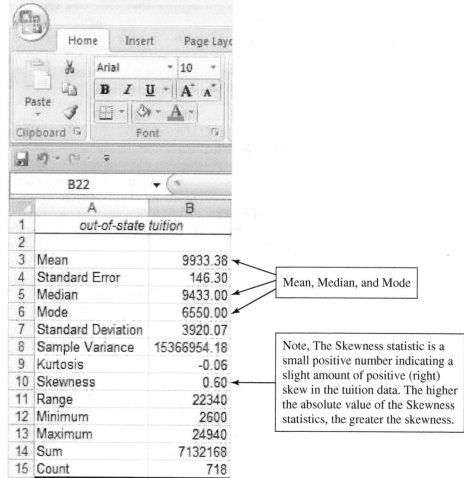

Mean, Median, and Mode

Note, The Skewness statistic is a small positive number indicating a slight amount of positive (right) skew in the tuition data. The higher the absolute value of the Skewness statistics, the greater the skewness.

**Excel 2007 Instructions:**
1. Open file: Colleges and Universities.xls.
2. On the **Data** tab, click on **Data Analysis**.
3. Click on **Descriptive Statistics**.
4. Define data range for the variable.
5. Check **Summary Statistics**.
6. Name output sheet.
7. On the **Home** tab, adjust decimals.

**Minitab Instructions (for similar results):**
1. Open file: Colleges and Universities.MTW.
2. Choose **Stat > Basic Statistics > Display Descriptive Statistics**.
3. In **Variables**, enter columns *out-of-state tuition*.
4. Click **Statistics**.
5. Check required statistics.
6. Click **OK. OK**.

**Issues with Excel** In many instances, data files will have "missing values." That is, the values for one or more variables may not be available for some of the observations. The data may have been lost, or they were not measured when the data were collected. Many times when you receive data like this, the missing values will be coded in a special way. For example, the code "N/A" might be used or a "−99" might be entered to signify that the datum for that observation is missing.

Statistical software packages typically have flexible procedures for dealing with missing data. Minitab provides you with missing data options and properly adjusts the results to account for the missing data. *However, Excel does not contain a missing-value option.* If you attempt to use certain data analysis options in Excel, such as Descriptive Statistics, in the presence of nonnumeric ("N/A") data, you will get an error message. When that happens you must clear the missing values, generally by deleting all rows with missing values. In some instances, you can save the good data in the row by using **Edit-Clear-All** for the cell in question. However, a bigger problem exists when the missing value has been coded as an arbitrary numeric value (−99). In this case, unless you go into the data and clear these values, Excel will use the −99 values in the computations as if they are real values. The result will be incorrect calculations.

Also, if a data set contains more than one mode, Excel will only show the first mode in the list of modes and will not warn you that multiple modes exist. For instance, if you look at

Figure 3.5, Excel has computed a mode = $6,550. If you examine these data, you will see that a tuition of $6,550 occurred 14 times. This is the most frequently occurring value. However, had other tuition values occurred 14 times too, Excel would not have so indicated. Minitab provides the modes and the number of occurrences for the modes in its Display Descriptive Statistics command.

## Chapter Outcome 1. → Other Measures of Location

**Weighted Mean**  The arithmetic mean is the most frequently used measure of central location. Equations 3.1 and 3.2 are used when you have either a population or a sample. For instance, the sample mean is computed using

$$\bar{x} = \frac{\sum x}{n} = \frac{x_1 + x_2 + x_3 + \cdots + x_n}{n}$$

**Weighted Mean**

The mean value of data values that have been weighted according to their relative importance.

In this case, each x value is given an equal weight in the computation of the mean. However, in some applications there is reason to weight the data values differently. In those cases, we need to compute a **weighted mean**.

Equations 3.4 and 3.5 are used to find the weighted mean (or weighted average) for a population and for a sample, respectively.

---

### Weighted Mean for a Population

$$\mu_W = \frac{\sum w_i x_i}{\sum w_i} \tag{3.4}$$

---

### Weighted Mean for a Sample

$$\bar{x}_w = \frac{\sum w_i x_i}{\sum w_i} \tag{3.5}$$

where:

$w_i =$ The weight of the $i$th data value
$x_i =$ The $i$th data value

---

**EXAMPLE 3-7    CALCULATING A WEIGHTED POPULATION MEAN**

**Myers & Associates**  Recently, the law firm of Myers & Associates was involved in litigating a discrimination suit concerning ski instructors at a ski resort in Colorado. One ski instructor from Germany had sued the operator of the ski resort, claiming he had not received equitable pay compared with the other ski instructors from Norway and the United States. In preparing a defense, the Myers attorneys planned to compute the mean annual income for all seven Norwegian ski instructors at the resort. However, because these instructors worked different numbers of days during the ski season, a weighted mean needed to be computed. This was done using the following steps:

**Step 1**  **Collect the desired data and determine the weight to be assigned to each data value.**

In this case, the variable of interest was the income of the ski instructors. The population consisted of seven Norwegian instructors. The weights were the number of days that the instructors worked. The following data and weights were determined:

| $x_i =$ Income: | $7,600 | $3,900 | $5,300 | $4,000 | $7,200 | $2,300 | $5,100 |
|---|---|---|---|---|---|---|---|
| $w_i =$ Days: | 50 | 30 | 40 | 25 | 60 | 15 | 50 |

Step 2    **Multiply each weight by the data value and sum these.**

$$\Sigma w_i x_i = (50)(\$7,600) + (30)(\$3,900) + \cdots + (50)(\$5,100) = \$1,530,500$$

Step 3    **Sum the weights for all values (the weights are the days).**

$$\Sigma w_i = 50 + 30 + 40 + 25 + 60 + 15 + 50 = 270$$

Step 4    **Compute the weighted mean.**
Divide the weighted sum by the sum of the weights. Because we are working with the population, the result will be the population weighted mean.

$$\mu_W = \frac{\Sigma w_i x_i}{\Sigma w_i} = \frac{\$1,530,500}{270} = \$5,668.52$$

Thus, taking into account the number of days worked, the Norwegian ski instructors had a mean income of $5,668.52.

>>**END EXAMPLE**

**TRY PROBLEM** 3-8 (pg. 104)

One weighted-mean example that you are probably very familiar with is your college grade point average (GPA). At most schools, A = 4 points, B = 3 points, and so forth. Each course has a certain number of credits (usually 1 to 5). The credits are the weights. Your GPA is computed by summing the product of points earned in a course and the credits for the course, and then dividing this sum by the total number of credits earned.

**Percentiles**    In some applications, we might wish to describe the location of the data in terms other than the center of the data. For example, prior to enrolling at your university you took the SAT or ACT test and received a **percentile** score in math and verbal skills.

**Percentiles**

The $p$th percentile in a data array is a value that divides the data set into two parts. The lower segment contains at least $p$% and the upper segment contains at least $(100 − p)$% of the data. The 50th percentile is the median.

If you received word that your standardized exam score was at the 90th percentile, it means that you scored as high as or higher than 90% of the other students who took the exam. The score at the 50th percentile would indicate that you were at the median, where at least 50% scored at or below and at least 50% scored at or above your score.[2]

To illustrate how to manually approximate a percentile value, consider a situation in which you have 309 customers enter a bank during the course of a day. The time (rounded to the nearest minute) that each customer spends in the bank is recorded. If we wish to approximate the 10th percentile, we would begin by first sorting the data in order from low to high, then assign each data value a location index from 1 to 309, and next determine the location index that corresponds to the 10th percentile using Equation 3.6.

---

**Percentile Location Index**

$$i = \frac{p}{100}(n) \tag{3.6}$$

where:

$p$ = Desired percent
$n$ = Number of values in the data set

---

If $i$ is not an integer, round up to the next highest integer. The next integer greater than $i$ corresponds to the position of the $p$th percentile in the data set.

If $i$ is an integer, the $p$th percentile is the average of the values in position $i$ and position $i + 1$.

---

[2]More rigorously, the percentile is that value (or set of values) such that at least $p$% of the data is as small or smaller than that value and at least $(100 − p)$% of the data is at least as large as that value. For introductory courses, a convention has been adopted to average the largest and smallest values that qualify as a certain percentile. This is why the median was defined as it was earlier for data sets with an even number of data values.

Thus, the index value associated with the 10th percentile is

$$i = \frac{p}{100}(n) = \frac{10}{100}(309) = 30.90$$

Because $i = 30.90$ is not an integer, we round to the next highest integer, which is 31. Thus, the 10th percentile corresponds to the value in the 31st position from the low end of the sorted data.

---

### How to do it (Example 3-8)

**Calculating Percentiles**
**To calculate a specific percentile for a set of quantitative data, you can use the following steps:**

1. Sort the data in order from the lowest to highest value.

2. Determine the percentile location index, $i$, using Equation 3.6.

$$i = \frac{p}{100}(n)$$

where

$p$ = Desired percent

$n$ = Number of values in the data set

3. If $i$ is not an integer, then round to next highest integer. The $p$th percentile is located at the rounded index position. If $i$ is an integer, the $p$th percentile is the average of the values at location index positions $i$ and $i + 1$.

---

**EXAMPLE 3-8      CALCULATING PERCENTILES**

**Henson Trucking** The Henson Trucking Company is a small company in the business of moving people from one home to another within the Dallas, Texas, area. Historically, the owners have charged the customers on an hourly basis, regardless of the distance of the move within the Dallas city limits. However, they are now considering adding a surcharge for moves over a certain distance. They have decided to base this charge on the 80th percentile. They have a sample of travel-distance data for 30 moves. These data are as follows:

| 13.5 | 8.6 | 16.2 | 21.4 | 21.0 | 23.7 | 4.1 | 13.8 | 20.5 | 9.6 |
| 11.5 | 6.5 | 5.8 | 10.1 | 11.1 | 4.4 | 12.2 | 13.0 | 15.7 | 13.2 |
| 13.4 | 13.1 | 21.7 | 14.6 | 14.1 | 12.4 | 24.9 | 19.3 | 26.9 | 11.7 |

The 80th percentile can be computed using these steps.

**Step 1  Sort the data from lowest to highest**

| 4.1 | 4.4 | 5.8 | 6.5 | 8.6 | 9.6 | 10.1 | 11.1 | 11.5 | 11.7 |
| 12.2 | 12.4 | 13.0 | 13.1 | 13.2 | 13.4 | 13.5 | 13.8 | 14.1 | 14.6 |
| 15.7 | 16.2 | 19.3 | 20.5 | 21.0 | 21.4 | 21.7 | 23.7 | 24.9 | 26.9 |

**Step 2  Determine percentile location index, $i$, using Equation 3.6.**
The 80th percentile location index is

$$i = \frac{p}{100}(n) = \frac{80}{100}(30) = 24$$

**Step 3  Locate the appropriate percentile.**
Because $i = 24$ is an integer value, the 80th percentile is found by averaging the values in the 24th and 25th positions. These are 20.5 and 21.0. Thus, the 80th percentile is $(20.5 + 21.0)/2 = 20.75$; therefore, any distance exceeding 20.75 miles will be subject to a surcharge.

**>>END EXAMPLE**

**TRY PROBLEM** 3-7 (pg. 104)

---

**Quartiles**
Quartiles in a data array are those values that divide the data set into four equal-sized groups. The median corresponds to the second quartile.

**Quartiles** Another location measure that can be used to describe data is **Quartiles**.
The first quartile corresponds to the 25th percentile. That is, it is the value at or below which there is at least 25% (one quarter) of the data and at or above which there is at least 75% of the data. The third quartile is also the 75th percentile. It is the value at or below which there is at least 75% of the data and at or above which there is at least 25% of the data. The second quartile is the 50th percentile and is also the median.

A quartile value can be approximated manually using the same method as for percentiles using Equation 3.6. For the 309 bank customer-service times mentioned earlier, the location of the first-quartile (25th percentile) index is found, after sorting the data, as

$$i = \frac{p}{100}(n) = \frac{25}{100}(309) = 77.25$$

Because 77.25 is not an integer value, we round up to 78. The first quartile is the 78th value from the low end of the sorted data.

**Issues with Excel** The procedure that Excel uses to compute quartiles *is not standard.* Therefore, the quartile and percentile values from Excel will be slightly different from those we found using Equation 3.6 and from what other statistical software packages, including Minitab, will provide. For example, referring to Example 3-8, when Excel is used to compute the 80th percentile for the moving distances, the value returned is 20.58 miles. This is slightly different from the 20.75 we found in Example 3-8. Equation 3.6, the method used by Minitab, is generally accepted by statisticians to be correct. Therefore, if you need precise values for quartiles, use software such as Minitab. However, Excel will give reasonably close percentile and quartile values.

**Chapter Outcome 2.**

**Box and Whisker Plot**
A graph that is composed of two parts: a box and the whiskers. The box has a width that ranges from the first quartile ($Q_1$) to the third quartile ($Q_3$). A vertical line through the box is placed at the median. Limits are located at a value that is 1.5 times the difference between $Q_1$ and $Q_3$ below $Q_1$ and above $Q_3$. The whiskers extend to the left to the lowest value within the limits and to the right to the highest value within the limits.

## Box and Whisker Plots

A descriptive tool that many decision makers like to use is called a **box and whisker plot** (or a box plot). The box and whisker plot incorporates the median and the quartiles to graphically display quantitative data. It is also used to identify *outliers* that are unusually small or large data values that lie mostly by themselves.

**How to do it** (Example 3-9)

**Constructing a Box and Whisker Plot**
**A box and whisker plot is a graphical summary of a quantitative variable. It is constructed using the following steps:**

1. Sort the data values from low to high.

2. Use Equation 3.6 to find the 25th percentile ($Q_1$ = first quartile), the 50th percentile ($Q_2$ = median), and the 75th percentile ($Q_3$ = third quartile).

3. Draw a box so that the ends of the box are at $Q_1$ and $Q_3$. This box will contain the middle 50% of the data values in the population or sample.

4. Draw a vertical line through the box at the median. Half the data values in the box will be on either side of the median.

5. Calculate the *interquartile range (IQR = $Q_3 - Q_1$).* (The interquartile range will be discussed more fully in Section 3.2.) Compute the lower limit for the box and whisker plot as $Q_1 - 1.5(Q_3 - Q_1)$. The upper limit is $Q_3 + 1.5(Q_3 - Q_1)$. Any data values outside these limits are referred to as outliers.

6. Extend dashed lines (called the whiskers) from each end of the box to the lowest and highest value within the limits.

7. Any value outside the limits (outlier) found in step 5 is marked with an asterisk (*).

| EXAMPLE 3-9 | CONSTRUCTING A BOX AND WHISKER PLOT |
|---|---|

**Jackson's Petroleum** A demand analyst for Jackson's Petroleum, a regional operator of gasoline stations and convenience stores in the Southeast, has recently performed a study at one of the company's stores in which he asked customers to set their trip odometer to zero when they filled up. Then, when the customers returned for their next fill-up, he recorded the miles that had been driven. He now plans to make a presentation to the board of directors and wishes to construct a box and whisker plot as part of the presentation as a way to describe the data and identify any outliers. The sorted sample data showing the miles between fill-ups is as follows:

| 231 | 236 | 241 | 242 | 242 | 243 | 243 | 243 | 248 |
|---|---|---|---|---|---|---|---|---|
| 248 | 249 | 250 | 251 | 251 | 252 | 252 | 254 | 255 |
| 255 | 256 | 256 | 257 | 259 | 260 | 260 | 260 | 260 |
| 262 | 262 | 264 | 265 | 265 | 265 | 266 | 268 | 268 |
| 270 | 276 | 277 | 277 | 280 | 286 | 300 | 324 | 345 |

The box and whisker plot is computed using the following steps:

**Step 1  Sort the data from low to high.**

**Step 2  Calculate the 25th percentile ($Q_1$), the 50th percentile (median), and the 75th percentile ($Q_3$).**
The location index for $Q_1$ is

$$i = \frac{p}{100}(n) = \frac{25}{100}(45) = 11.25$$

Thus, $Q_1$ will be the 12th value, which is 250 miles.
    The median location is

$$i = \frac{p}{100}(n) = \frac{50}{100}(45) = 22.5$$

In the sorted data, the median is the 23rd value, which is 259 miles. The third-quartile location is

$$i = \frac{p}{100}(n) = \frac{75}{100}(45) = 33.75$$

Thus, $Q_3$ is the 34th data value. This is 266 miles.

**Step 3**  **Draw the box so the ends correspond to $Q_1$ and $Q_3$.**

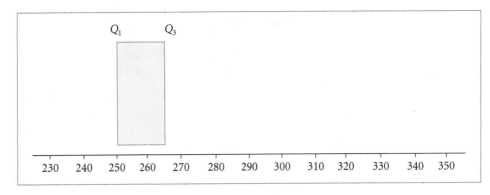

**Step 4**  **Draw a vertical line through the box at the median.**

**Step 5**  **Compute the upper and lower limits.**
The lower limit is computed as $Q_1 - 1.5(Q_3 - Q_1)$. This is

$$\text{Lower Limit} = 250 - 1.5(266 - 250) = 226$$

The upper limit is $Q_3 + 1.5(Q_3 - Q_1)$. This is

$$\text{Upper Limit} = 266 + 1.5(266 - 250) = 290$$

Any value outside these limits is identified as an outlier.

**Step 6**  **Draw the whiskers.**
The whiskers are drawn to the smallest and largest values within the limits.

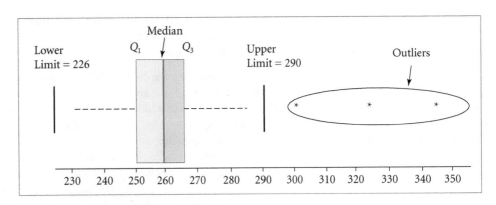

**Step 7**  **Plot the outliers.**
The outliers are plotted as values outside the limits.

>>**END EXAMPLE**

**TRY PROBLEM** 3-5 (pg. 104)

## Data-Level Issues

You need to be very aware of the level of data you are working with before computing the numerical measures introduced in this chapter. A common mistake is to compute means on nominal-level data. For example, a major electronics manufacturer recently surveyed a sample of customers to determine whether they preferred black, white, or colored stereo cases. The data were coded as follows:

$$1 = \text{black}$$
$$2 = \text{white}$$
$$3 = \text{colored}$$

A few of the responses are

Color code = {1, 1, 3, 2, 1, 2, 2, 2, 3, 1, 1, 1, 3, 2, 2, 1, 2}

Using these codes, the sample mean is

$$\bar{x} = \frac{\sum x}{n}$$
$$= \frac{30}{17} = 1.765$$

As you can see, reporting that customers prefer a color somewhere between black and white but closer to white would be meaningless. The mean should not be used with nominal data. This type of mistake tends to happen when people use computer software to perform their calculations. Asking Excel, Minitab, or other statistical software to compute the mean, median, and so on for all the variables in the data set is very easy. Then a table is created and, before long, the meaningless measures creep into your report. Don't let that happen.

There is also some disagreement about whether means should be computed on ordinal data. For example, in market research a 5- or 7-point scale is often used to measure customers' attitudes about products or TV commercials. For example, we might set up the following scale:

$$1 = \text{Strongly agree}$$
$$2 = \text{Agree}$$
$$3 = \text{Neutral}$$
$$4 = \text{Disagree}$$
$$5 = \text{Strongly disagree}$$

Customer responses to a particular question are obtained on this scale from 1 to 5. For a sample of $n = 10$ people, we might get the following responses to a question:

Response = {2, 2, 1, 3, 3, 1, 5, 2, 1, 3}

The mean rating is 2.3. We could then compute the mean for a second issue and compare the means. However, what exactly do we have? First, when we compute a mean for a scaled variable, we are making two basic assumptions:

1. We are assuming the distance between a rating of 1 and 2 is the same as the distance between 2 and 3. We are also saying these distances are exactly the same for the second issue's variable to which you wish to compare it. Although from a numerical standpoint this is true, in terms of what the scale is measuring, is the difference between strongly agree and agree the same as the difference between agree and neutral? If not, is the mean really a meaningful measure?

2. We are also assuming people who respond to the survey have the same definition of what "strongly agree" means or what "disagree" means. When you mark a 4 (disagree) on your survey, are you applying the same criteria as someone else who also marks a 4 on the same issue? If not, then the mean might be misleading.

Although these difficulties exist with ordinal data, we see many examples in which means are computed and used for decision purposes. In fact, we once had a dean who focused on one particular question on the course evaluation survey that was administered in every

**FIGURE 3.6**

Descriptive Measures of the Center

| Descriptive Measure | Computation Method | Data Level | Advantages/Disadvantages |
|---|---|---|---|
| Mean | Sum of values divided by the number of values | Ratio Interval | • Numerical center of the data<br>• Sum of deviations from the mean is zero<br>• Sensitive to extreme values |
| Median | Middle value for data that have been sorted | Ratio Interval Ordinal | • Not sensitive to extreme values<br>• Computed only from the center values<br>• Does not use information from all the data |
| Mode | Value(s) that occur most frequently in the data | Ratio Interval Ordinal Nominal | • May not reflect the center<br>• May not exist<br>• Might have multiple modes |

class each semester. This question was "Considering all factors of importance to you, how would you rate this instructor?"

1 = Excellent    2 = Good    3 = Average    4 = Poor    5 = Very poor

The dean then had his staff compute means for each class and for each professor. He then listed classes and faculty in order based on the mean values, and he based a major part of the performance evaluation on where a faculty member stood with respect to mean score on this one question. By the way, he carried the calculations for the mean out to three decimal places!

In general, the median is the preferred measure of central location for ordinal data instead of the mean.

Figure 3.6 summarizes the three measures of the center that have been discussed in this section.

 MyStatLab

# 3-1: Exercises

## Skill Development

**3-1.** A random sample of 15 articles in a *Fortune* revealed the following word counts per article:

| | | | | |
|---|---|---|---|---|
| 5,176 | 6,005 | 5,052 | 5,310 | 4,188 |
| 4,132 | 5,736 | 5,381 | 4,983 | 4,423 |
| 5,002 | 4,573 | 4,209 | 5,611 | 4,568 |

Compute the mean, median, first quartile, and third quartile for these sample data.

**3-2.** The following data reflect the number of defects produced on an assembly line at the Dearfield Electronics Company for the past 8 days.

| | | | | | | | |
|---|---|---|---|---|---|---|---|
| 3 | 0 | 2 | 0 | 1 | 3 | 5 | 2 |
| 5 | 1 | 3 | 0 | 0 | 1 | 3 | 3 |
| 4 | 3 | 1 | 8 | 4 | 2 | 4 | 0 |

a. Compute the mean number of defects for this population of days.

b. Compute the median number of defects produced for this population of days.

c. Determine if there is a mode number of defects and, if so, indicate the mode value.

**3-3.** A European cereal maker recently sampled 20 of its medium-size oat cereal packages to determine the weights of the cereal in each package. These sample data, measured in ounces, are as follows:

| | | | | | | | | | |
|---|---|---|---|---|---|---|---|---|---|
| 14.7 | 16.3 | 14.3 | 14.2 | 18.7 | 13.2 | 13.1 | 14.4 | 16.2 | 12.8 |
| 13.6 | 17.1 | 14.4 | 11.5 | 15.5 | 15.9 | 13.8 | 14.2 | 15.1 | 13.5 |

Calculate the first and third quartiles for these sample data.

**3-4.** The time (in seconds) that it took for each of 16 vehicles to exit a parking lot in downtown Cincinnati is

| | | | |
|---|---|---|---|
| 106 | 153 | 169 | 116 |
| 135 | 78 | 51 | 129 |
| 100 | 141 | 72 | 101 |
| 130 | 125 | 128 | 139 |

Compute the mean, median, first quartile, and third quartile for the sample data.

**3-5.** A random sample of the miles driven by 20 rental car customers is shown as follows:

| | | | |
|---|---|---|---|
| 90 | 85 | 100 | 150 |
| 125 | 75 | 50 | 100 |
| 75 | 60 | 35 | 90 |
| 100 | 125 | 75 | 85 |
| 50 | 100 | 50 | 80 |

Develop a box and whisker plot for the sample data.

**3-6.** Examine the following data:

| | | | | | | | | | | | |
|---|---|---|---|---|---|---|---|---|---|---|---|
| 23 | 65 | 45 | 19 | 35 | 28 | 39 | 100 | 50 | 26 | 25 | 27 |
| 24 | 17 | 12 | 106 | 23 | 19 | 39 | 70 | 20 | 18 | 44 | 31 |

a. Compute the quartiles.
b. Calculate the 90th percentile.
c. Develop a box and whisker plot.
d. Calculate the 20th and the 30th percentiles.

**3-7.** Consider the following data that represent the commute distances for students who attend Emory University:

| | | | | | | | | | |
|---|---|---|---|---|---|---|---|---|---|
| 3.1 | 4.7 | 8.4 | 11.6 | 12.1 | 13.0 | 13.4 | 16.1 | 17.3 | 20.8 |
| 22.8 | 24.3 | 26.2 | 26.6 | 26.7 | 31.2 | 32.2 | 35.8 | 35.8 | 39.8 |

a. Determine the 80th percentile.
b. Determine numbers that are the 25th and 75th percentiles.
c. Determine a number that qualifies as a median for these data.

**3-8.** A professor wishes to develop a numerical method for giving grades. He intends to base the grade on homework, two midterms, a project, and a final examination. He wishes the final exam to have the largest influence on the grade. He wants the project to have 10%, each midterm to have 20%, and the homework to have 10% of the influence of the semester grade.

a. Determine the weights the professor should use to produce a weighted average for grading purposes.
b. For a student with the following grades during the quarter, calculate a weighted average for the course:

| Instrument | Final | Project | Midterm 1 | Midterm 2 | Homework |
|---|---|---|---|---|---|
| Percentage Grade | 64 | 98 | 67 | 63 | 89 |

c. Calculate an (unweighted) average of these five scores and discuss why the weighted average would be preferable here.

## Business Applications

**3-9.** The manager for the Jiffy Lube in Saratoga, Florida, has collected data on the number of customers who agreed to purchase an air filter when they were also having their oil changed. The sample data are shown as follows:

| | | | | | | | | | | | |
|---|---|---|---|---|---|---|---|---|---|---|---|
| 21 | 19 | 21 | 19 | 19 | 20 | 18 | 12 | 20 | 19 | 17 | 14 |
| 21 | 22 | 25 | 21 | 22 | 23 | 10 | 19 | 25 | 14 | 17 | 18 |

a. Compute the mean, median, and mode for these data.
b. Indicate whether the data are skewed or symmetrical.
c. Construct a box and whisker plot for these data. Referring to your answer in part b, does the box plot support your conclusion about skewness? Discuss.

**3-10.** During the past few years, there has been a lot of discussion about the price of university textbooks. The complaints have come from many places, including students, faculty, parents, and even government officials. The publishing companies have been called on to explain why textbooks cost so much. Recently, one of the major publishing companies was asked to testify before a congressional panel in Washington, D.C. As part of the presentation, the president of the company organized his talk around four main areas: production costs, author royalties, marketing costs, and bookstore markup. He used one of his company's business statistics texts as an example when he pointed out the production costs—including editing, proofing, printing, binding, inventory holding, and distribution—come to about $32 per book sold. Authors receive $12 per copy for the hundreds of hours of creative work in writing the book and supplementary materials. Marketing costs are pegged at about $5 per copy sold and go to pay for the book sales force and examination copies sent to professors. The book is then sold to bookstores for $70 per copy, a markup on costs of about 40% to cover overhead and the publishing costs associated with many upper-division, low-market texts that lose money for the company. Once university bookstores purchase the book, they mark it up, place it on the shelf, and sell it to the student. If books go unsold, they are returned to the publisher for a full refund. The following data reflect the dollar markup on the business statistics text for a sample of 20 college bookstores:

| | | | | |
|---|---|---|---|---|
| $33 | $32 | $42 | $31 | $31 |
| $37 | $37 | $34 | $47 | $31 |
| $42 | $29 | $36 | $32 | $25 |
| $29 | $47 | $26 | $32 | $40 |

a. Compute the mean markup on the business statistics text by university bookstores in the sample.
b. Compute the median markup.
c. Determine the mode markup.
d. Write a short paragraph discussing the statistics computed in parts a–c.

**3-11.** The Xang Corporation operates five clothing suppliers in China to provide merchandise for Nike. Nike recently sought information from the five plants. One variable for which data were collected was the total money (in U.S. dollars) the company spent on medical support for its employees in the first three months of the year. Data on number of employees at the plants are also shown. These data are as follows:

| Medical | $7,400 | $14,400 | $12,300 | $6,200 | $3,100 |
|---------|--------|---------|---------|--------|--------|
| Employees | 123 | 402 | 256 | 109 | 67 |

a. Compute the weighted mean medical payments for these five plants using number of employees as the weights.

b. Explain why Nike would desire that a weighted average be computed in this situation rather than a simple numeric average.

**3-12.** The Tru-Green Lawn Company provides yard care services for customers throughout the Denver area. The company owner recently tracked the time his field employees spent at a sample of customer locations. He was hoping to use these data to help him with his scheduling and to establish billing rates. The following sample data, in minutes, were recorded:

| | | | | | | | | | |
|---|---|---|---|---|---|---|---|---|---|
| 31 | 27 | 29 | 22 | 24 | 30 | 28 | 21 | 29 | 26 |
| 22 | 17 | 17 | 20 | 38 | 10 | 38 | 25 | 27 | 23 |
| 23 | 13 | 17 | 34 | 25 | 29 | 22 | 22 | 14 | 11 |
| 29 | 26 | 29 | 29 | 37 | 32 | 27 | 26 | 18 | 22 |

Describe the central tendency of these data by computing the mean, median, and mode. Based on these measures, can you conclude that the distribution of time spent at customer locations is skewed or symmetric?

**3-13.** Eastern States Bank and Trust monitors its drive-thru service times electronically to ensure that its speed of service is meeting the company's goals. A sample of 28 drive-thru times was recently taken and is shown here.

| Speed of Service (time in seconds) | | | |
|-----|-----|-----|-----|
| 83 | 138 | 145 | 147 |
| 130 | 79 | 156 | 156 |
| 90 | 85 | 68 | 93 |
| 178 | 76 | 73 | 119 |
| 92 | 146 | 88 | 103 |
| 116 | 134 | 162 | 71 |
| 181 | 110 | 105 | 74 |

a. Compute the mean, median, and mode for these sample data.

b. Indicate whether the data are symmetrical or skewed.

c. Construct a box and whisker plot for the sample data. Does the box and whisker plot support your conclusions in part b concerning the symmetry or skewness of these data?

**3-14.** Todd Lindsey & Associates, a commercial real estate company located in Boston, owns six office buildings in the Boston area that it leases to businesses. The lease price per square foot differs by building due to location and building amenities. Currently, all six buildings are fully leased at the prices shown here.

| | Price per Square Foot | Number of Square Feet |
|---|---|---|
| Building 1 | $ 75 | 125,000 |
| Building 2 | $ 85 | 37,500 |
| Building 3 | $ 90 | 77,500 |
| Building 4 | $ 45 | 35,000 |
| Building 5 | $ 55 | 60,000 |
| Building 6 | $110 | 130,000 |

a. Compute the weighted average (mean) price per square foot for these buildings.

b. Why is the weighted average price per square foot preferred to a simple average price per square foot in this case?

**3-15.** *Business Week* recently reported that L. G. Philips LCD Co. would complete a new factory in Paju, South Korea. It will be the world's largest maker of liquid-crystal display panels. The arrival of the plant means that flat-panel LCD televisions would become increasingly affordable. The average retail cost of a 20″ LCD television in 2000 was $5,139. To obtain what the average retail cost of a 37″ LCD was in 2008, a survey yielded the following data (in $U.S.):

| | | | | |
|--------|--------|--------|--------|--------|
| 606.70 | 558.12 | 625.82 | 533.70 | 464.37 |
| 511.15 | 400.56 | 538.20 | 531.64 | 632.14 |
| 474.86 | 567.46 | 588.39 | 528.78 | 610.32 |
| 564.71 | 912.68 | 475.87 | 545.25 | 589.15 |

a. Calculate the mean cost for these data.

b. Examine the data presented. Choose an appropriate measure of the center of the data, justify the choice, and calculate the measure.

c. The influence an observation has on a statistic may be calculated by deleting the observation and calculating the difference between the original statistic and the statistic with the data point removed. The larger the difference, the more influential the data point. Identify the data points that have the most and the least influence in the calculation of the sample mean.

**3-16.** *Wageweb.com* exhibits salary data obtained from surveys. It provides compensation information on over 170 benchmark positions, including finance positions. It reports the salaries of chief finance officers for mid-sized firms. Suppose that a sample is taken of the annual salaries for 25 CFOs. Assume the data are in thousands of dollars.

| | | | | | | | | |
|-------|-------|-------|-------|-------|-------|-------|-------|-------|
| 173.1 | 171.2 | 141.9 | 112.6 | 211.1 | 156.5 | 145.4 | 134.0 | 192.0 |
| 185.8 | 168.3 | 131.0 | 214.4 | 155.2 | 164.9 | 123.9 | 161.9 | 162.7 |
| 178.8 | 161.3 | 182.0 | 165.8 | 213.1 | 177.4 | 159.3 | | |

a. Calculate the mean salary of the CFOs.

b. Based on measures of the center of the data, determine if the CFO salary data are skewed.

c. Construct a box and whisker plot and summarize the characteristics of the CFO salaries that it reveals.

**3-17.** The Federal Deposit Insurance Corporation (FDIC) insures deposits in banks and thrift institutions for up to $250,000. Before the banking crisis of late 2008, there were 8,885 FDIC–insured institutions, with deposits of $6,826,804,000,000. Bank of America had deposits of $681,570,000,000 in nearly 6,000 banking centers during 2004.
   a. Calculate the average deposits per bank for both FDIC–insured institutions and Bank of America.
   b. Describe the relationship between the two averages calculated in part a. Provide a reason for the disparity.
   c. Would the two averages be considered to be parameters or statistics? Explain.

## Computer Database **Exercises**

**3-18.** Each year, *Business Week* publishes information and rankings of master of business administration (MBA) programs. The data file **MBA Analysis** contains data on several variables for eight reputable MBA programs as presented in the October 2, 2000, issue of *Business Week*. The variables include pre– and post–MBA salary, percentage salary increase, undergraduate GPA, average Graduate Management Admission Test (GMAT) score, annual tuition, and expected annual student cost. Compute the mean and median for each of the variables in the database and write a short report that summarizes the data. Include any appropriate charts or graphs to assist in your report.

**3-19.** Dynamic random-access memory (DRAM) memory chips are made from silicon wafers in manufacturing facilities through a very complex process called wafer fabs. The wafers are routed through the fab machines in an order that is referred to as a recipe. The wafers may go through the same machine several times as the chip is created. The data file **DRAM Chips** contains a sample of processing times, measured in fractions of hours, at a particular machine center for one chip recipe.
   a. Compute the mean processing time.
   b. Compute the median processing time.
   c. Determine what the mode processing time is.
   d. Calculate the 80th percentile for processing time.

**3-20.** Japolli Bakery tracks sales of its different bread products on a daily basis. The data for 22 consecutive days at one of its retail outlets in Nashville are in a file called **Japolli Bakery**. Calculate the mean, mode, and median sales for each of the bread categories and write a short report that describes these data. Use any charts or graphs that may be helpful in more fully describing the data.

**3-21.** Before the sub-prime loan crisis and the end of the "housing bubble" in 2008 the value of houses was escalating rapidly, as much as 40% a year in some areas. In an effort to track housing prices the National

Association of Realtors developed the Pending Home Sales Index (PHSI), a new leading indicator for the housing market. An index of 100 is equal to the average level of contract activity during 2001, the first year to be analyzed. The index is based on a large national sample representing about 20% of home sales. The file entitled **Pending** contains the PHSI from January 2004 to August 2005.
   a. Determine the mean and median for the PHSI between January 2004 and August 2005. Specify the shape of the PHSI's distribution.
   b. The PHSI was at 111.0 in January 2004 and it was at 129.5 in August of 2005. Determine the average monthly increase in the PHSI for this period.
   c. Using your answer to part b, suggest a weighting scheme to calculate the weighted mean for the months between January 2004 and August 2005. Use the scheme to produce the weighted average of the PHSI in this time period.
   d. Does the weighted average seem more appropriate here? Explain.

**3-22.** Homeowners and businesses pay taxes on the assessed value of their property. As a result, property taxes can be a problem for elderly homeowners who are on a fixed retirement income. Whereas these retirement incomes remain basically constant, because of rising real estate prices the property taxes in many areas of the country have risen dramatically. In some cases, homeowners are required to sell their homes because they can't afford the taxes. In Phoenix, Arizona, government officials are considering giving certain elderly homeowners a property tax reduction based on income. One proposal calls for all homeowners over the age of 65 with incomes at or below the 20th percentile to get a reduction in property taxes. A random sample of 50 people over the age of 65 was selected, and the household income (as reported on the most current federal tax return) was recorded. These data are also in the file called **Property Tax Incomes**. Use these data to establish the income cutoff point to qualify for the property tax cut.

| $35,303 | $56,855 | $ 7,928 | $26,006 | $28,278 |
| $54,215 | $38,850 | $15,733 | $29,786 | $65,878 |
| $46,658 | $62,874 | $49,427 | $19,017 | $46,007 |
| $32,367 | $31,904 | $35,534 | $66,668 | $37,986 |
| $10,669 | $54,337 | $ 8,858 | $45,263 | $37,746 |
| $14,550 | $ 8,748 | $58,075 | $23,381 | $11,725 |
| $45,044 | $55,807 | $54,211 | $42,961 | $62,682 |
| $32,939 | $38,698 | $11,632 | $66,714 | $31,869 |
| $57,530 | $59,233 | $14,136 | $ 8,824 | $42,183 |
| $58,443 | $34,553 | $26,805 | $16,133 | $61,785 |

**3-23.** Suppose a random sample of 137 households in Detroit was taken as part of a study on annual household spending for food at home. The sample data are contained in the file **Detroit Eats**.
   a. For the sample data, compute the mean and the median and construct a box and whisker plot.

b. Are the data skewed or symmetric?

c. Approximately what percent of the data values are between $2,900 and $3,250?

**3-24.** *USA Today* reported a survey made by Nationwide Mutual Insurance that indicated the average amount of time spent to resolve identity theft cases was 81 hours. The file entitled **Theft** contains data that would produce this statistic.

a. Construct a stem and leaf display. Indicate the shape of data displayed by the stem and leaf display.

b. Use measures that indicate the shape of the distribution. Do these measures give results that agree with the shape shown in part a?

c. Considering your answers to part a and b, indicate which measure you would recommend using to indicate the center of the data.

**END EXERCISES 3-1**

## 3.2 Measures of Variation

BUSINESS APPLICATION    CALCULATING THE RANGE

**BRYCE LUMBER COMPANY** Consider the situation involving two manufacturing facilities for the Bryce Lumber Company. The division vice president asked the two plant managers to record their production output for five days. The resulting sample data are shown in Table 3.3.

Instead of reporting these raw data, the managers reported only the mean and median for their data. The following are the computed statistics for the two plants:

**TABLE 3.3 | Manufacturing Output for Bryce Lumber**

| Plant A | Plant B |
|---------|---------|
| 15 units | 23 units |
| 25 units | 26 units |
| 35 units | 25 units |
| 20 units | 24 units |
| 30 units | 27 units |

| Plant A | Plant B |
|---------|---------|
| $\bar{x} = 25$ units | $\bar{x} = 25$ units |
| $M_d = 25$ units | $M_d = 25$ units |

The division vice president looked at these statistics and concluded the following:

1. Average production is the same at both plants.
2. At both plants, the output is at or more than 25 units half the time and at or fewer than 25 units half the time.
3. Because the mean and median are equal, the distribution of production output at the two plants is symmetrical.
4. Based on these statistics, there is no reason to believe that the two plants are different in terms of their production output.

**Variation**

A set of data exhibits variation if all the data are not the same value.

However, if he had taken a closer look at the raw data, he would have seen there is a very big difference between the two plants. The difference is the production **variation** from day to day. Plant B is very stable, producing almost the same amount every day. Plant A varies considerably, with some high-output days and some low-output days. Thus, looking at only measures of the data's central location can be misleading. To fully describe a set of data, we need a measure of variation or spread.

There is variation in everything that is made by humans or that occurs in nature. The variation may be small, but it is there. Given a fine enough measuring instrument, we can detect the variation. Variation is either a natural part of a process (or inherent to a product) or can be attributed to a special cause that is not considered random.

There are several different measures of variation that are used in business decision making. In this section, we introduce four of these measures: range, interquartile range, variance, and standard deviation.

Chapter Outcome 3. ➤ **Range**

**Range**

The range is a measure of variation that is computed by finding the difference between the maximum and minimum values in a data set.

The simplest measure of variation is the **range**. It is both easy to compute and easy to understand.

The range is computed using Equation 3.7.

---

**Range**

$$R = \text{Maximum Value} - \text{Minimum Value} \qquad \textbf{(3.7)}$$

---

**BRYCE LUMBER (*CONTINUED*)** Table 3.3 showed the production-volume data for the two Bryce Lumber Company plants. The range for each plant is determined using Equation 3.7 as follows:

| Plant A | Plant B |
|---|---|
| $R$ = Maximum − Minimum | $R$ = Maximum − Minimum |
| $R = 35 − 15$ | $R = 27 − 23$ |
| $R = 20$ | $R = 4$ |

We see Plant A has a range that is five times as great as Plant B.

Although the range is quick and easy to compute, it does have some limitations. First, because we use only the high and low values to compute the range, it is very sensitive to extreme values in the data. Second, regardless of how many values are in the sample or population, the range is computed from only two of these values. For these reasons, it is considered a weak measure of variation.

Chapter Outcome 3. ➔ # Interquartile Range

A measure of variation that tends to overcome the range's susceptibility to extreme values is called the **interquartile range**.

Equation 3.8 is used to compute the interquartile range.

**Interquartile Range**

The interquartile range is a measure of variation that is determined by computing the difference between the third and first quartiles.

> **Interquartile Range**
>
> Interquartile Range = Third Quartile − First Quartile        (3.8)

EXAMPLE 3-10   **COMPUTING THE INTERQUARTILE RANGE**

**American Heritage Investments** American Heritage Investments, headquartered in Boston, has a number of individual clients who have recently opened 401(k) investment accounts. Each client must decide how much to contribute on a monthly basis. The manager in charge of 401(k) investments at American Heritage Investments has collected a random sample of 100 clients who make monthly contributions to a 401(k). He has recorded the net dollars, after brokerage fees, which each client deposits into his or her account. He wishes to analyze the variation in these data by computing the range and the interquartile range. He could use the following steps to do so:

**Step 1   Sort the data into a data array from lowest to highest.**
The 100 sorted deposit values, in dollars, are as follows:

| | | | | | | | | | |
|---|---|---|---|---|---|---|---|---|---|
| 33 | 164 | 173 | 184 | 190 | 197 | 207 | 216 | 224 | 237 |
| 53 | 164 | 175 | 186 | 191 | 197 | 207 | 217 | 225 | 240 |
| 150 | 164 | 175 | 186 | 191 | 198 | 208 | 217 | 225 | 240 |
| 152 | 166 | 175 | 186 | 192 | 200 | 208 | 217 | 229 | 240 |
| 157 | 166 | 178 | 187 | 193 | 200 | 208 | 219 | 231 | 250 |
| 160 | 168 | 178 | 188 | 193 | 201 | 210 | 222 | 231 | 251 |
| 161 | 169 | 179 | 188 | 194 | 202 | 211 | 223 | 234 | 259 |
| 162 | 171 | 180 | 188 | 194 | 204 | 212 | 223 | 234 | 270 |
| 162 | 171 | 182 | 190 | 196 | 205 | 213 | 223 | 235 | 379 |
| 163 | 172 | 183 | 190 | 196 | 205 | 216 | 224 | 236 | 479 |

**Step 2   Compute the range using Equation 3.7.**

$$R = \text{Maximum value} - \text{Minimum value}$$
$$R = \$479 - \$33 = \$446$$

Note, the range is sensitive to extreme values. The small value of $33 and the high value of $479 cause the range value to be very large.

**Step 3** **Compute the first and third quartiles.**
Equation 3.6 can be used to find the location of the third quartile (75th percentile) and the first quartile (25th percentile).

For $Q_3$ the location $i = \dfrac{75}{100}(100) = 75$. Thus, $Q_3$ is halfway between the 75th and 76th data values, which is found as follows:

$$Q_3 = (219 + 222)/2 = 220.50$$

For $Q_1$, the location is $i = \dfrac{25}{100}(100) = 25$. Then $Q_1$ is halfway between the 25th and 26th data values.

$$Q_1 = (178 + 178)/2 = 178$$

**Step 4** **Compute the interquartile range.**
The interquartile range overcomes the range's problem of sensitivity to extreme values. It is computed using Equation 3.8:

$$\text{Interquartile range} = Q_3 - Q_1$$
$$= 220.50 - 178 = 42.50$$

Note, the interquartile range would be unchanged even if the values on the high or low end of the distribution were even more extreme than those shown in these sample data.

>>**END EXAMPLE**

**TRY PROBLEM** 3-30 (pg. 116)

**Chapter Outcome 3.** ➞ # Population Variance and Standard Deviation

Although the range is easy to compute and understand and the interquartile range is designed to overcome the range's sensitivity to extreme values, neither measure uses all the available data in its computation. Thus, both measures ignore potentially valuable information in data.

**Variance**
The population variance is the average of the squared distances of the data values from the mean.

**Standard Deviation**
The standard deviation is the positive square root of the variance.

Two measures of variation that incorporate all the values in a data set are the **variance** and the **standard deviation**.

These two measures are closely related. The standard deviation is the square root of the variance. The standard deviation is in the original units (dollars, pounds, etc.), whereas the units of measure in the variance are squared. Because dealing with original units is easier than dealing with the square of the units, we usually use the standard deviation to measure variation in a population or sample.

**BUSINESS APPLICATION**    **CALCULATING THE VARIANCE AND STANDARD DEVIATION**

**BRYCE LUMBER (*CONTINUED*)** Recall the Bryce Lumber application, in which we compared the production output for two of the company's plants. Table 3.3 showed the data, which are considered a population for our purposes here.

Previously we examined the variability in the output from these two plants by computing the ranges. Although those results gave us some sense of how much more variable Plant A is than Plant B, we also pointed out some of the deficiencies of the range. The variance and standard deviation offer alternatives to the range for measuring variation in data.

Equation 3.9 is the formula for the population variance. Like the population mean, the population variance and standard deviation are assigned a Greek symbol.

---

### Population Variance

$$\sigma^2 = \frac{\sum\limits_{i=1}^{N}(x_i - \mu)^2}{N} \qquad\qquad (3.9)$$

where:

$\mu$ = Population mean
$N$ = Population size
$\sigma^2$ = Population variance (sigma squared)

---

We begin by computing the variance for the output data from Plant A. The first step in manually calculating the variance is to find the mean using Equation 3.1.

$$\mu = \frac{\sum x}{N} = \frac{15 + 25 + 35 + 20 + 30}{5} = \frac{125}{5} = 25$$

Next, subtract the mean from each value, as shown in Table 3.4. Notice the sum of the deviations from the mean is 0. Recall from Section 3.1 that this will be true for any set of data. The positive differences are cancelled out by the negative differences. To overcome this fact when computing the variance, we square each of the differences and then sum the squared differences. These calculations are also shown in Table 3.4.

The final step in computing the population variance is to divide the sum of the squared differences by the population size, $N = 5$.

$$\sigma^2 = \frac{\sum(x - \mu)^2}{N} = \frac{250}{5} = 50$$

The population variance is 50 *products squared*.

Manual calculations for the population variance may be easier if you use an alternative formula for $\sigma^2$ that is the algebraic equivalent. This is shown as Equation 3.10.

---

### Population Variance Shortcut

$$\sigma^2 = \frac{\sum x^2 - \dfrac{(\sum x)^2}{N}}{N} \qquad\qquad (3.10)$$

---

Example 3-11 will illustrate using Equation 3.10 to find a population variance.

Because we squared the deviations to keep the positive values and negative values from canceling, the units of measure were also squared, but the term *products squared* doesn't have a meaning. To get back to the original units of measure, take the square root of the variance.

**TABLE 3.4** | **Computing the Population Variance: Squaring the Deviations**

| $x_i$ | $(x_i - \mu)$ | $(x_i - \mu)^2$ |
|-------|---------------|-----------------|
| 15 | $15 - 25 = -10$ | 100 |
| 25 | $25 - 25 = 0$ | 0 |
| 35 | $35 - 25 = 10$ | 100 |
| 20 | $20 - 25 = -5$ | 25 |
| 30 | $30 - 25 = 5$ | 25 |
| | $\sum(x_i - \mu) = 0$ | $\sum(x_i - \mu)^2 = 250$ |

The result is the standard deviation. Equation 3.11 shows the formula for the population standard deviation.

**Population Standard Deviation**

$$\sigma = \sqrt{\sigma^2} = \sqrt{\frac{\sum\limits_{i=1}^{N}(x_i - \mu)^2}{N}}$$

(3.11)

Therefore, the population standard deviation of Plant A's production output is

$$\sigma = \sqrt{50}$$
$$\sigma = 7.07 \text{ products}$$

The population standard deviation is a parameter and will not change unless the population values change.

We could repeat this process using the data for Plant B, which also had a mean output of 25 products. You should verify that the population variance is

$$\sigma^2 = \frac{\sum(x - \mu)^2}{N} = \frac{10}{5} = 2 \text{ products squared}$$

The standard deviation is found by taking the square root of the variance.

$$\sigma = \sqrt{2}$$
$$\sigma = 1.414 \text{ products}$$

Thus, Plant A has an output standard deviation that is five times larger than Plant B's. The fact that Plant A's range was also five times larger than the range for Plant B is merely a coincidence.

---

**How to do it** (Example 3-11)

**Computing the Population Variance and Standard Deviation**
The population variance and standard deviation are computed using the following steps:

1. Collect quantitative data for the variable of interest for the entire population.

2. Use either Equation 3.9 or Equation 3.10 to compute the variance.

3. If Equation 3.10 is used, find the sum of the $x$-values ($\Sigma x$) and then square this sum ($\Sigma x)^2$.

4. Square each $x$ value and sum these squared values ($\Sigma x^2$).

5. Compute the variance using

$$\sigma^2 = \frac{\Sigma x^2 - \dfrac{(\Sigma x)^2}{N}}{N}$$

6. Compute the standard deviation by taking the square root of the variance:

$$\sigma = \sqrt{\sigma^2}$$

**EXAMPLE 3-11**    **COMPUTING A POPULATION VARIANCE AND STANDARD DEVIATION**

**Boydson Shipping Company** Boydson Shipping Company owns and operates a fleet of tanker ships that carry commodities between the countries of the world. In the past six months, the company has had seven contracts that called for shipments between Vancouver, Canada, and London, England. For many reasons, the travel time varies between these two locations. The scheduling manager is interested in knowing the variance and standard deviation in shipping times for these seven shipments. To find these values, he can follow these steps:

**Step 1**  **Collect the data for the population.**
The shipping times are shown as follows:
$$x = \text{shipping weeks}$$
$$= \{5, 7, 5, 9, 7, 4, 6\}$$

**Step 2**  **Select Equation 3.10 to find the population variance.**

$$\sigma^2 = \frac{\Sigma x^2 - \dfrac{(\Sigma x)^2}{N}}{N}$$

**Step 3**  **Add the $x$ values and square the sum.**
$$\Sigma x = 5 + 7 + 5 + 9 + 7 + 4 + 6 = 43$$
$$(\Sigma x^2) = (43)^2 = 1,849$$

Step 4   **Square each of the $x$ values and sum these squares.**

$$\Sigma x^2 = 5^2 + 7^2 + 5^2 + 9^2 + 7^2 + 4^2 + 6^2 = 281$$

Step 5   **Compute the population variance.**

$$\sigma^2 = \frac{\Sigma x^2 - \dfrac{(\Sigma x)^2}{N}}{N} = \frac{281 - \dfrac{1,849}{7}}{7} = 2.4082$$

The variance is in units squared, so in this example the population variance is 2.4082 weeks squared.

Step 6   **Calculate the standard deviation as the square root of the variance.**

$$\sigma = \sqrt{\sigma^2} = \sqrt{2.4082} = 1.5518 \text{ weeks}$$

Thus, the standard deviation for the number of shipping weeks between Vancouver and London for the seven shipments is 1.5518 weeks.

**>>END EXAMPLE**

**TRY PROBLEM** 3-27 (pg. 116)

# Sample Variance and Standard Deviation

Equations 3.9, 3.10, and 3.11 are the equations for the population variance and standard deviation. Any time you are working with a population, these are the equations that are used. However, in most instances, you will be describing sample data that have been selected from the population. In addition to using different notations for the sample variance and sample standard deviation, the equations are also slightly different. Equations 3.12 and 3.13 can be used to find the sample variance. Note that Equation 3.13 is considered the shortcut formula for manual computations.

---

**Sample Variance**

$$s^2 = \frac{\displaystyle\sum_{i=1}^{n} (x_i - \overline{x})^2}{n - 1}$$

(3.12)

---

**Sample Variance Shortcut**

$$s^2 = \frac{\Sigma x^2 - \dfrac{(\Sigma x)^2}{n}}{n - 1}$$

(3.13)

where:

$$n = \text{Sample size}$$
$$\overline{x} = \text{Sample mean}$$
$$s^2 = \text{Sample variance}$$

---

The sample standard deviation is found by taking the square root of the sample variance, as shown in Equation 3.14.

**Sample Standard Deviation**

$$s = \sqrt{s^2} = \sqrt{\frac{\displaystyle\sum_{i=1}^{n} (x_i - \overline{x})^2}{n - 1}}$$

(3.14)

Take note in Equations 3.12, 3.13, and 3.14 that the denominator is $n - 1$ (sample size minus 1). This may seem strange, given that the denominator for the population variance and the standard deviation is simply $N$, the population size. The mathematical justification for the $n - 1$ divisor is outside the scope of this text. However, the general reason for this is that we want the average sample variance to equal the population variance. If we were to select all possible samples of size $n$ from a given population and for each sample we computed the sample variance using Equation 3.12 or Equation 3.13, the average of all the sample variances would equal $\sigma^2$ (the population variance), provided we used $n - 1$ as the divisor. Using $n$ instead of $n - 1$ in the denominator would produce an average sample variance that would be smaller than $\sigma^2$, the population variance. Because we want an estimator on average to equal the population variance, we use $n - 1$ in the denominator of $s^2$.

| **EXAMPLE 3-12** | **COMPUTING A SAMPLE VARIANCE AND STANDARD DEVIATION** |
|---|---|

**Zenith Systems** The quality control manager at Zenith Systems, a manufacturer of equipment used in the oil and gas drilling business, recently performed 10 independent tests on parts attached to the equipment the company makes. In each test, 100 parts were examined and the number of defective parts recorded. The tests can be considered to be samples of all possible tests on 100 parts that could be conducted. To fully analyze the data, the manager can calculate the sample variance and sample standard deviation using the following steps:

**Step 1**  **Select the sample and record the data for the variable of interest.**

| Test | Defects = x | Test | Defects = x |
|---|---|---|---|
| 1 | 4 | 6 | 0 |
| 2 | 7 | 7 | 3 |
| 3 | 1 | 8 | 2 |
| 4 | 0 | 9 | 6 |
| 5 | 5 | 10 | 2 |

**Step 2**  **Select either Equation 3.12 or Equation 3.13 to compute the sample variance.**
If we use Equation 3.12,

$$s^2 = \frac{\Sigma(x - \bar{x})^2}{n - 1}$$

**Step 3**  **Compute $\bar{x}$.**
The sample mean number of defectives is

$$\bar{x} = \frac{\Sigma x}{n} = \frac{30}{10} = 3.0$$

**Step 4**  **Determine the sum of the squared deviations of each $x$ value from $\bar{x}$.**

| Test | Defectives = x | $(x - \bar{x})$ | $(x - \bar{x})^2$ |
|---|---|---|---|
| 1 | 4 | 1 | 1 |
| 2 | 7 | 4 | 16 |
| 3 | 1 | −2 | 4 |
| 4 | 0 | −3 | 9 |
| 5 | 5 | 2 | 4 |
| 6 | 0 | −3 | 9 |
| 7 | 3 | 0 | 0 |
| 8 | 2 | −1 | 1 |
| 9 | 6 | 3 | 9 |
| 10 | 2 | −1 | 1 |
| | $\Sigma = 30$ | $\Sigma = 0$ | $\Sigma = 54$ |

Step 5 **Compute the sample variance using Equation 3.12.**

$$s^2 = \frac{\Sigma(x-\bar{x})^2}{n-1} = \frac{54}{9} = 6$$

The sample variance is measured in squared units. Thus, the variance in this example is 6 defectives squared.

Step 6 **Compute the sample standard deviation by taking the square root of the variance (see Equation 3.14).**

$$s = \sqrt{\frac{\Sigma(x-\bar{x})^2}{n-1}} = \sqrt{\frac{54}{9}} = \sqrt{6}$$
$$s = 2.4495 \text{ defects}$$

This sample standard deviation measures the variation in the sample data for number of defects per sample.

>>**END EXAMPLE**

**TRY PROBLEM** 3-25 (pg. 115)

---

**BUSINESS APPLICATION** CALCULATING MEASURES OF VARIATION USING EXCEL

**COLLEGES AND UNIVERSITIES (*CONTINUED*)** In Section 3.1, the guidance counselor was interested in describing the data representing the cost of out-of-state tuition for a large number of colleges and universities in the United States. The data for 718 schools are in the file called **Colleges and Universities**. Previously we determined the following descriptive measures of the center for the variable, out-of-state tuition:

Mean = $9,933.38

Median = $9,433.00

Mode = $6,550

**Excel and Minitab Tutorial**

Next, the analyst will turn her attention to measures of variability. The range (maximum − minimum) is one measure of variability. Both Excel and Minitab can compute the range. Both software packages can also be used to compute the standard deviation of tuition, which is a more powerful measure of variation than the range. Figure 3.7 shows the Excel descriptive statistics results. We find the following measures of variation:

Range = $22,340.00

Standard Deviation = $3,920.07

These values are measures of the spread in the data. You should know that outlier values in a data set will increase both the range and standard deviation. One guideline for identifying outliers is the ±3 standard deviation rule. That is, if a value falls outside ±3 standard deviations from the mean, it is considered an outlier. Also, as shown in section 3.1, outliers can be identified using box and whisker plots.

**FIGURE 3.7**

Excel 2007 Descriptive Statistics Output—Colleges and Universities

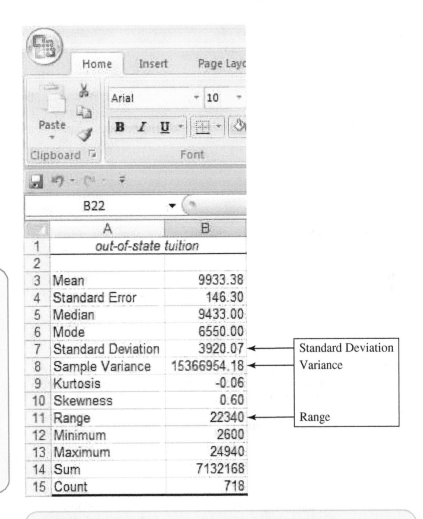

**Excel 2007 Instructions:**
1. Open file: Colleges and Universities.xls.
2. On the **Data** tab, click on **Data Analysis**.
3. Click on **Descriptive Statistics**.
4. Define data range for the variable.
5. Check **Summary Statistics**.
6. Name output sheet.
7. On the **Home** tab, adjust decimals.

| | A | B |
|---|---|---|
| 1 | out-of-state tuition | |
| 2 | | |
| 3 | Mean | 9933.38 |
| 4 | Standard Error | 146.30 |
| 5 | Median | 9433.00 |
| 6 | Mode | 6550.00 |
| 7 | Standard Deviation | 3920.07 |
| 8 | Sample Variance | 15366954.18 |
| 9 | Kurtosis | -0.06 |
| 10 | Skewness | 0.60 |
| 11 | Range | 22340 |
| 12 | Minimum | 2600 |
| 13 | Maximum | 24940 |
| 14 | Sum | 7132168 |
| 15 | Count | 718 |

Standard Deviation
Variance

Range

**Minitab Instructions (for similar results):**
1. Open file: Colleges and Universities.MTW.
2. Choose **Stat > Basic Statistics > Display Descriptive Statistics**.
3. In **Variables**, enter columns *out-of-state tuition*.
4. Click **Statistics**.
5. Check required statistics.
6. Click **OK. OK.**

# MyStatLab

# 3-2: Exercises

## Skill Development

**3-25.** Google is noted for its generous employee benefits. The following data reflect the number of vacation days that a sample of employees at Google have left to take before the end of the year:

| | | | | | | | |
|---|---|---|---|---|---|---|---|
| 3 | 0 | 2 | 0 | 1 | 3 | 5 | 2 |
| 5 | 1 | 3 | 0 | 0 | 1 | 3 | 3 |
| 4 | 3 | 1 | 8 | 4 | 2 | 4 | 0 |

a. Compute the range for these sample data.
b. Compute the variance for these sample data.

c. Compute the standard deviation for these sample data.

**3-26.** The following data reflect the number of times a population of business executives flew on business during the previous month:

$$4 \quad 6 \quad 9 \quad 4 \quad 5 \quad 7$$

a. Compute the range for these data.
b. Compute the variance and standard deviation.
c. Assuming that these data represent a sample rather than a population, compute the variance and standard deviation. Discuss the difference between the values computed here and in part b.

**3-27.** The following data are the population of ages of students who have recently purchased a sports video game:

| 16 | 15 | 17 | 15 | 15 | 15 |
|----|----|----|----|----|----|
| 14 | 9  | 16 | 15 | 13 | 10 |
| 8  | 18 | 20 | 17 | 17 | 17 |
| 18 | 23 | 7  | 15 | 20 | 10 |
| 14 | 14 | 12 | 12 | 24 | 21 |

a. Compute the population variance.
b. Compute the population standard deviation.

**3-28.** A county library in Minnesota reported the following number of books checked out in 15 randomly selected months:

| 5,176 | 6,005 | 5,052 | 5,310 | 4,188 |
|-------|-------|-------|-------|-------|
| 4,132 | 5,736 | 5,381 | 4,983 | 4,423 |
| 5,002 | 4,573 | 4,209 | 5,611 | 4,568 |

Determine the range, variance, and standard deviation for the sample data.

**3-29.** The following data show the number of hours spent watching television for 12 randomly selected freshmen attending a liberal arts college in the Midwest:

| Hours of Television Viewed Weekly | | | |
|------|------|------|-----|
| 7.5  | 11.5 | 14.4 | 7.8 |
| 13   | 10.3 | 5.4  | 12  |
| 12.2 | 8.9  | 8.5  | 6.6 |

Calculate the range, variance, standard deviation, and interquartile range for the sample data.

**3-30.** Consider the following two separate samples:

| 27 | 27 | 25 | 12 | 15 | 10 | 20 | 37 | 31 | 35 |
|----|----|----|----|----|----|----|----|----|----|

and

| 1 | 3 | 2 | 16 | 18 | 16 | 16 | 4 | 16 | 118 |
|---|---|---|----|----|----|----|---|----|-----|

a. Calculate the range, variance, standard deviation, and interquartile range for each data set.
b. Which data set is most spread out based on these statistics?
c. Now remove the largest number from each data set and repeat the calculations called for in part a.
d. Compare the results of parts a and c. Which statistic seems to be most affected by outliers?

**3-31.** The following set of data shows the number of alcoholic drinks that students at a Kansas university reported they had consumed in the past month:

| 24 | 16 | 23 | 26 | 30 | 21 | 15 | 9 |
|----|----|----|----|----|----|----|---|
| 18 | 27 | 14 | 6  | 14 | 10 | 12 |   |

a. Assume the data set is a sample. Calculate the range, variance, standard deviation, and interquartile range for the data set.
b. Assume the data set is a population. Calculate the range, variance, standard deviation, and interquartile range for the data set.

c. Indicate the relationship between the statistics and the respective parameters calculated in parts a and b.

## Business Applications

**3-32.** Easy Connect, Inc., provides access to computers for business uses. The manager monitors computer use to make sure that the number of computers is sufficient to meet the needs of the customers. Recently, the manager collected data on a sample of customers and tracked the time the customers started working at a computer until they were finished. The elapsed times, in minutes, are shown as follows:

| 40 | 42 | 18 | 32 | 43 | 35 | 11 | 39 | 36 | 37 |
|----|----|----|----|----|----|----|----|----|----|
| 8  | 34 | 34 | 50 | 20 | 39 | 31 | 75 | 33 | 17 |

Compute appropriate measures of the center and variation to describe the time customers spend on the computer.

**3-33.** A random sample of 20 pledges to a public radio fund-raiser revealed the following dollar pledges:

| 90  | 85  | 100 | 150 |
|-----|-----|-----|-----|
| 125 | 75  | 50  | 100 |
| 75  | 60  | 35  | 90  |
| 100 | 125 | 75  | 85  |
| 50  | 100 | 50  | 80  |

a. Compute the range, variance, standard deviation, and interquartile range for these sample data.
b. Briefly explain the difference between the range and the interquartile range as a measure of dispersion.

**3-34.** Gold's Gym selected a random sample of 10 customers and monitored the number of times each customer used the workout facility in a one-month period. The following data were collected:

| 10 | 19 | 17 | 19 | 12 | 20 | 20 | 15 | 16 | 13 |
|----|----|----|----|----|----|----|----|----|----|

Gold's managers are considering a promotion in which they reward frequent users with a small gift. They have decided that they will only give gifts to those customers whose number of visits in a one-month period is 1 standard deviation above the mean. Find the minimum number of visits required to receive a gift.

**3-35.** The registrar at Whitworth College has been asked to prepare a report about the graduate students. Among other things, she wants to analyze the ages of the students. She has taken a sample of 10 graduate students and has found the following ages:

| 32 | 22 | 24 | 27 | 27 | 33 | 28 | 23 | 24 | 21 |
|----|----|----|----|----|----|----|----|----|----|

a. Compute the range, interquartile range, and the standard deviation for these data.
b. An earlier study showed that the mean age of graduate students in U.S. colleges and universities is 37.8 years. Based on your calculations in part a, what might you conclude about the age of students in Whitworth's programs?

**3-36.** The branch manager for the D. L. Evens Bank has been asked to prepare a presentation for next week's board meeting. At the presentation, she will discuss the status of her branch's loans issued for recreation vehicles (RVs). In particular, she will analyze the loan balances for a sample of 10 RV loans. The following data were collected:

| | | | | |
|---|---|---|---|---|
| $11,509 | $8,088 | $13,415 | $17,028 | $16,754 |
| $18,626 | $4,917 | $11,740 | $16,393 | $ 8,757 |

a. Compute the mean loan balance.
b. Compute the loan balance standard deviation.
c. Write a one-paragraph statement that uses the statistics computed in parts a and b to describe the RV loan data at the branch.

**3-37.** A parking garage in Memphis monitors the time it takes customers to exit the parking structure from the time they get in their car until they are on the streets. A sample of 28 exits was recently taken and is shown here.

| Garage Exit (time in seconds) | | | |
|---|---|---|---|
| 83 | 138 | 145 | 147 |
| 130 | 79 | 156 | 156 |
| 90 | 85 | 68 | 93 |
| 178 | 76 | 73 | 119 |
| 92 | 146 | 88 | 103 |
| 116 | 134 | 162 | 71 |
| 181 | 110 | 105 | 74 |

a. Calculate the range, interquartile range, variance, and standard deviation for these sample data.
b. If the minimum time and the maximum time in the sample data are both increased by 10 seconds, would this affect the value for the interquartile range that you calculated in part a? Why or why not?
c. Suppose the clock that electronically recorded the times was not working properly when the sample was taken and each of the sampled times needs to be increased by 10 seconds. How would adding 10 seconds to each of the sampled speed of service times change the sample variance of the data?

**3-38.** Nielsen Monitor-Plus, a service of Nielsen Media Research, is one of the leaders in advertising information services in the United States, providing advertising activity for 16 media, including television tracking, in all 210 Designated Market Areas (DMAs). One of the issues it has researched is the increasing amount of "clutter"—nonprogramming minutes in an hour of prime time—including network and local commercials and advertisements for other shows. Recently it found the average nonprogramming minutes in an hour of prime-time broadcasting for network television was 15:48 minutes. For cable television, the average was 14:55 minutes.
a. Calculate the difference in the average clutter between network and cable television.
b. Suppose the standard deviation in the amount of clutter for both the network and cable television

was either 5 minutes or 15 seconds. Which standard deviation would lead you to conclude that there was a major difference in the two clutter averages? Comment.

**3-39.** The Bureau of Labor Statistics in its *Monthly Labor Review* published the "over-the-month" percent change in the price index for imports from April 2004 to April 2005. These data are reproduced next.

| Month | Apr | May | Jun | Jul | Aug | Sep | Oct |
|---|---|---|---|---|---|---|---|
| ΔIndex | 0.2 | 1.5 | −0.2 | 0.4 | 1.5 | 0.5 | 1.6 |
| Month | Nov | Dec | Jan | Feb | Mar | Apr | |
| ΔIndex | −0.3 | −1.4 | 0.6 | 0.9 | 2.0 | 0.8 | |

a. Calculate the mean, standard deviation, and the interquartile range for the nine months of 2004 and the four months of 2005.
b. Compare the two averages that were calculated in part a. What do these two measurements indicate about the price index in each time period?
c. Compare the two standard deviations that were calculated in part a. What do these two measurements indicate about the price index in each time period?

**3-40.** The U.S. Government Accountability Office recently indicated the price of college textbooks has been rising an average of 6% annually since the academic year 1987–1988. The report estimated that the average cost of books and supplies for first-time, full-time students at four-year public universities for the academic year had reached $898. A data set that would produce this average follows:

| | | | | | | |
|---|---|---|---|---|---|---|
| 537.51 | 1032.52 | 1119.17 | 877.27 | 856.87 | 739.91 | 963.79 |
| 847.92 | 1393.81 | 524.68 | 1012.91 | 1176.46 | 944.60 | 708.26 |
| 1074.35 | 778.87 | 967.91 | 562.55 | 789.50 | 1051.65 | |

a. Calculate the mean and standard deviation.
b. Determine the number of standard deviations the most extreme cost is away from the mean. If you were to advise a prospective student concerning the money the student should save to afford the cost of books and supplies for at least 90% of the colleges, determine the amount you would suggest. (*Hint*: Don't forget the yearly inflation of the cost of books and supplies.)

## Computer Database **Exercises**

**3-41.** The manager of a phone kiosk in the Valley Mall recently collected data on a sample of 50 customers who purchased a cell phone and a monthly call plan. The data she recorded are in the data file called **Phone Survey**.
a. The manager is interested in describing the difference between male and female customers with respect to the price of the phone purchased. She wants to compute mean and standard deviation of phone purchase price for each group of customers.
b. The manager is also interested in an analysis of the phone purchase price based on whether the use will be for home or business. Again, she wants to

compute mean and standard deviation of phone purchase price for each group of customers.

**3-42.** Each year, *Business Week* publishes information and rankings of MBA programs. The data file **MBA Analysis** contains data on several variables for eight reputable MBA programs as presented in the October 2, 2000, issue of *Business Week*. The variables include pre– and post–MBA salary, percentage salary increase, undergraduate GPA, average GMAT score, annual tuition, and expected annual student cost. Compute the mean, median, range, variance, and the standard deviation for each of the variables in the database and write a short report that summarizes the data using these measures. Include any appropriate charts or graphs to assist in your report.

**3-43.** The First City Real Estate Company lists and sells residential real estate property in and around Yuma, Arizona. At a recent company meeting, the managing partner asked the office administrator to provide a descriptive analysis of the asking prices of the homes the company currently has listed. This list includes 319 homes; the price data, along with other home characteristics, are included in the data file called **First City Real Estate**. These data constitute a population.
  a. Compute the mean listing price.
  b. Compute the median listing price.
  c. Compute the range in listing prices.
  d. Compute the standard deviation in listing prices.
  e. Write a short report using the statistics computed in parts a–d to describe the prices of the homes currently listed by First City Real Estate.

**3-44.** Suppose an investigation to determine whether the increased availability of generic drugs, Internet drug purchases, and cost controls have reduced out-of-pocket drug expenses. As a part of the investigation, a random sample of 196 privately insured adults with incomes above 200% of the poverty level was taken,

and their 2005 out-of-pocket medical expenses for prescription drugs were collected. The data are in the file **Drug Expenses**.
  a. Calculate the mean and median for the sample data.
  b. Calculate the range, variance, standard deviation, and interquartile range for the sample data.
  c. Construct a box and whisker plot for the sample data.
  d. Write a short report that describes out-of-pocket drug expenses for privately insured adults whose incomes are greater than 200% of the poverty level.

**3-45.** Executive MBA programs have become increasingly popular. In an article entitled "The Best Executive MBAs," *Business Week* provided data concerning the top 25 executive MBA programs. The tuition for each of the schools selected was given. A file entitled **EMBA** contains this data.
  a. Calculate the 20th, 40th, 60th, and 80th percentile among the ranks.
  b. Calculate the mean and standard deviation of the tuition for the five subgroups defined by the rank percentiles in part a. (*Hint*: For this purpose, are the data subgroups samples or populations?)
  c. Do the various subgroups' descriptive statistics echo their standing among the listed programs? Comment.

**3-46.** When PricewaterhouseCoopers Saratoga released its 2005/2006 Human Capital Index Report it indicated that the average hiring cost for an American company to fill a job vacancy in 2004 was $3,270. Sample data for recent job hires is in a file entitled **Hired**.
  a. Calculate the variance and standard deviation for the sample data.
  b. Construct a box and whisker plot. Does this plot indicate that extreme values (outliers) may be inflating the measures of spread calculated in part a?
  c. Suggest and calculate a measure of spread that is not affected by outliers.

**END EXERCISES** 3-2

## 3.3 Using the Mean and Standard Deviation Together

In the previous sections, we introduced several important descriptive measures that are useful for transforming data into meaningful information. Two of the most important of these measures are the mean and the standard deviation. In this section, we discuss several statistical tools that combine these two.

**Chapter Outcome 4.** ➤ **Coefficient of Variation**

The standard deviation measures the variation in a set of data. For decision makers, the standard deviation indicates how spread out a distribution is. For distributions having the same mean, the distribution with the largest standard deviation has the greatest relative spread. When two or more distributions have different means, the relative spread cannot be determined by merely comparing standard deviations.

**Coefficient of Variation**

The ratio of the standard deviation to the mean expressed as a percentage. The coefficient of variation is used to measure variation relative to the mean.

The **coefficient of variation** (*CV*) is used to measure the relative variation for distributions with different means.

The coefficient of variation for a population is computed using Equation 3.15, whereas Equation 3.16 is used for sample data.

---

**Population Coefficient of Variation**

$$CV = \frac{\sigma}{\mu}(100)\%$$

(3.15)

---

**Sample Coefficient of Variation**

$$CV = \frac{s}{\bar{x}}(100)\%$$

(3.16)

---

When the coefficients of variation for two or more distributions are compared, the distribution with the largest *CV* is said to have the greatest relative spread.

In finance, the *CV* measures the relative risk of a stock portfolio. Assume portfolio A has a collection of stocks that average a 12% return with a standard deviation of 3% and portfolio B has an average return of 6% with a standard deviation of 2%. We can compute the *CV* values for each as follows:

$$CV(A) = \frac{3}{12}(100)\% = 25\%$$

and

$$CV(B) = \frac{2}{6}(100)\% = 33\%$$

Even though portfolio B has a lower standard deviation, it would be considered more risky than portfolio A because B's *CV* is 33% and A's *CV* is 25%.

---

**EXAMPLE 3-13**    **COMPUTING THE COEFFICIENT OF VARIATION**

**Agra-Tech Industries** Agra-Tech Industries has recently introduced feed supplements for both cattle and hogs that will increase the rate at which the animals gain weight. Three years of feedlot tests indicate that steers fed the supplement will weigh an average of 125 pounds more than those not fed the supplement. However, not every steer on the supplement has the same weight gain; results vary. The standard deviation in weight-gain advantage for the steers in the three-year study has been 10 pounds.

Similar tests with hogs indicate those fed the supplement average 40 additional pounds compared with hogs not given the supplement. The standard deviation for the hogs was also 10 pounds. Even though the standard deviation is the same for both cattle and hogs, the mean weight gains differ. Therefore, the coefficient of variation is needed to compare relative variability. The coefficient of variation for each is computed using the following steps:

**Step 1**   **Collect the sample (or population) data for the variable of interest.**
In this case, we have two samples: weight gain for cattle and weight gain for hogs.

**Step 2**   **Compute the mean and the standard deviation.**
For the two samples in this example, we get

Cattle: $\bar{x} = 125$ lb and $s = 10$ lb
Hogs: $\bar{x} = 40$ lb  and $s = 10$ lb

**Step 3**   **Compute the coefficient of variation using Equation 3.15 (for populations) or Equation 3.16 (for samples).**
Because the data in this example are from samples, the *CV* is computed using

$$CV = \frac{s}{\bar{x}}(100)\%$$

For each data set, we get

$$CV(\text{cattle}) = \frac{10}{125}(100)\% = 8\%$$

$$CV(\text{hogs}) = \frac{10}{40}(100)\% = 25\%$$

These results indicate that hogs exhibit much greater relative variability in weight gain compared with cattle.

**>>END EXAMPLE**

**TRY PROBLEM** 3-50 (pg. 124)

**Chapter Outcome 5.** ➤ **The Empirical Rule** A tool that is helpful in describing data in certain circumstances is called the **Empirical Rule**. For the Empirical Rule to be used, the frequency distribution must be bell-shaped, such as the one shown in Figure 3.8.

**Empirical Rule**

If the data distribution is bell-shaped, then the interval

$\mu \pm 1\sigma$ contains approximately 68% of the values

$\mu \pm 2\sigma$ contains approximately 95% of the values

$\mu \pm 3\sigma$ contains virtually all of the data values

**Excel and Minitab Tutorial**

| BUSINESS APPLICATION | EMPIRICAL RULE |
| --- | --- |

**BURGER N' BREW** The standard deviation can be thought of as a measure of distance from the mean. Consider the Phoenix Burger n' Brew restaurant chain, which records the number of each hamburger option it sells each day at each location. The numbers of chili burgers sold each day for the past 365 days are in the file called **Burger N' Brew**. Figure 3.9 shows the frequency histogram for those data. The distribution is nearly *symmetrical* and is approximately *bell-shaped*. The mean number of chili burgers sold was 15.1, with a standard deviation of 3.1.

The Empirical Rule is a very useful statistical concept for helping us understand the data in a bell-shaped distribution. In the Burger N' Brew example, with $\bar{x} = 15.1$ and $s = 3.1$, if we move 1 standard deviation in each direction from the mean, approximately 68% of the data should lie within the following range:

$$15.1 \pm 1(3.1)$$
$$12.0 \text{ --------------------------- } 18.2$$

**FIGURE 3.8**

Illustrating the Empirical Rule for the Bell-Shaped Distribution

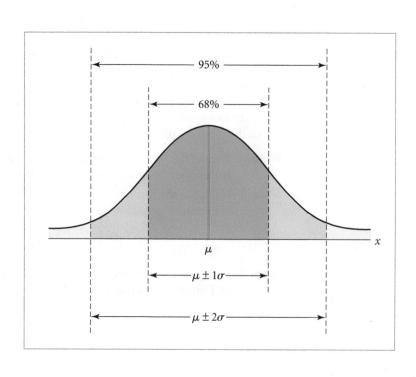

**FIGURE 3.9**

Excel 2007 Histogram for
Burger n' Brew Data

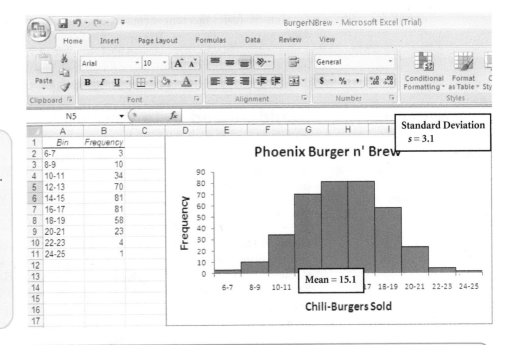

**Minitab Instructions (for similar results):**

1. Open file: BurgerNBrew. MTW.
2. Choose **Graph > Histogram**.
3. Click **Simple**.
4. Click **OK**.
5. In **Graph variables**, enter data column *Chili-Burgers Sold*.
6. Click **OK**.

**Excel 2007 Instructions:**

1. Open file: BurgerNBrew.xls.
2. Set up Bins (upper limit of each class).
3. On the **Data** tab, click on **Data Analysis—Histogram**.
4. Supply data range and bin range.
5. Put on a new worksheet and include the **Chart Output**.
6. Right-mouse-click on the bars and use the **Format Data Series Options** to set gap width to zero and add lines to the bars.
7. Convert the bins to actual class labels by typing labels in column A. Note, bin 1 is labeled 6-7.

The actual number of days Burger n' Brew sold between 12 and 18 chili burgers is 262. Thus, out of 365 days, 72% of the days Burger n' Brew sold between 12 and 18 chili burgers. (The reason that we didn't get exactly 68% is that the distribution in Figure 3.9 is not perfectly bell-shaped.)

If we look at the interval 2 standard deviations from either side of the mean, we would expect approximately 95% of the data. The interval is

$$15.1 \pm 2(3.1)$$
$$15.1 \pm 6.2$$
$$8.9 \text{ ------------------------ } 21.30$$

Counting the values between these limits, we find 353 of the 365 values, or 97%. Again this is close to what the Empirical Rule predicted. Finally, according to the Empirical Rule, we would expect almost all of the data to fall within 3 standard deviations. The interval is

$$15.1 \pm 3(3.1)$$
$$15.1 \pm 9.3$$
$$5.80 \text{ ------------------------ } 24.40$$

Looking at the data in Figure 3.9, we find that in fact all the data do fall within this interval.

Therefore, if we know only the mean and the standard deviation for a set of data, the Empirical Rule gives us a tool for describing how the data are distributed if the distribution is bell-shaped.

**Tchebysheff's Theorem**

Regardless of how data are distributed, *at least* $(1 - 1/k^2)$ of the values will fall within $k$ standard deviations of the mean. For example:

At least $\left(1 - \dfrac{1}{1^2}\right) = 0 = 0\%$ of the values will fall within $k = 1$ standard deviation of the mean.

At least $\left(1 - \dfrac{1}{2^2}\right) = \dfrac{3}{4} = 75\%$ of the values will lie within $k = 2$ standard deviations of the mean.

At least $\left(1 - \dfrac{1}{3^2}\right) = \dfrac{8}{9} = 89\%$ of the values will lie within $k = 3$ standard deviations of the mean.

**Chapter Outcome 5.** →

# Tchebysheff's Theorem

The Empirical Rule applies when a distribution is bell-shaped. But what about the many situations when a distribution is skewed and not bell-shaped? In these cases, we can use **Tchebysheff's theorem**.

Tchebysheff's theorem is conservative. It tells us nothing about the data within 1 standard deviation of the mean. Tchebysheff indicates that *at least* 75% of the data will fall within 2 standard deviations—it could be more. If we applied Tchebysheff's theorem to bell-shaped distributions, the percentage estimates are very low. The thing to remember is that Tchebysheff's theorem applies to *any distribution*. This gives it great flexibility.

**Chapter Outcome 4.** → # Standardized Data Values

**Standardized Data Values**

The number of standard deviations a value is from the mean. Standardized data values are sometimes referred to as *z* scores.

When you are dealing with quantitative data, you will sometimes want to convert the measures to a form called **standardized data values**. This is especially useful when we wish to compare data from two or more distributions when the data scales for the two distributions are substantially different.

**BUSINESS APPLICATION**    STANDARDIZING DATA

**HUMAN RESOURCES**    Consider a company that uses placement exams as part of its hiring process. The company currently will accept scores from either of two tests: AIMS Hiring and BHS-Screen. The problem is that the AIMS Hiring test has an average score of 2,000 and a standard deviation of 200, whereas the BHS-Screen test has an average score of 80 with a standard deviation of 12. (These means and standard deviations were developed from a large number of people who have taken the two tests.) How can the company compare applicants when the average scores and measures of spread are so different for the two tests? One approach is to *standardize* the test scores.

Suppose the company is considering two applicants, John and Mary. John took the AIMS Hiring test and scored 2,344, whereas Mary took the BHS-Screen and scored 95. Their scores can be standardized using Equation 3.17.

---

**Standardized Population Data**

$$z = \frac{x - \mu}{\sigma}$$    (3.17)

where:

$x$ = Original data value
$\mu$ = Population mean
$\sigma$ = Population standard deviation
$z$ = Standard score (number of standard deviations $x$ is from $\mu$)

---

If you are working with sample data rather than a population, Equation 3.18 can be used to standardize the values.

---

**Standardized Sample Data**

$$z = \frac{x - \overline{x}}{s}$$    (3.18)

where:

$x$ = Original data value
$\overline{x}$ = Sample mean
$s$ = Sample standard deviation
$z$ = The standard score

---

We can standardize the test scores for John and Mary using

$$z = \frac{x - \mu}{\sigma}$$

For the AIMS Hiring test, the mean, $\mu$, is 2,000 and the standard deviation, $\sigma$, equals 200. John's score of 2,344 converts to

$$z = \frac{2,344 - 2,000}{200}$$
$$z = 1.72$$

The BHS-Screen's $\mu = 80$ and $\sigma = 12$. Mary's score of 95 converts to

$$z = \frac{95 - 80}{12}$$
$$z = 1.25$$

Compared to the average score on the AIMS Hiring test, John's score is 1.72 standard deviations higher. Mary's score is only 1.25 standard deviations higher than the average score on the BHS-Screen test. Therefore, even though the two tests used different scales, standardizing the data allows us to conclude John scored relatively better on his test than Mary did on her test.

**How to do it** (Example 3-14)

**Converting Data to Standardized Values**

For a set of quantitative data, each data value can be converted to a corresponding standardized value by determining how many standard deviations the value is from the mean. Here are the steps to do this.

1. Collect the population or sample values for the quantitative variable of interest.

2. Compute the population mean and standard deviation or the sample mean and standard deviation.

3. Convert the values to standardized z-values using Equation 3.17 or Equation 3.18. For populations,

$$z = \frac{x - \mu}{\sigma}$$

For samples,

$$z = \frac{x - \bar{x}}{s}$$

**EXAMPLE 3-14    CONVERTING DATA TO STANDARDIZED VALUES**

**SAT and ACT Exams** Many colleges and universities require students to submit either SAT or ACT scores or both. One eastern university requires both exam scores. However, in assessing whether to admit a student, the university uses whichever exam score favors the student among all the applicants. Suppose the school receives 4,000 applications for admission. To determine which exam will be used for each student, the school will standardize the exam scores from both tests. To do this, it can use the following steps:

**Step 1  Collect data.**
The university will collect the data for the 4,000 SAT scores and the 4,000 ACT scores for those students who applied for admission.

**Step 2  Compute the mean and standard deviation.**
Assuming that these data reflect the population of interest for the university, the population mean is computed using

$$\text{SAT:} \quad \mu = \frac{\sum x}{N} = 1,255 \qquad \text{ACT:} \quad \mu = \frac{\sum x}{N} = 28.3$$

The standard deviation is computed using

$$\text{SAT:} \quad \sigma = \sqrt{\frac{\sum (x - \mu)^2}{N}} = 72 \qquad \text{ACT:} \quad \sigma = \sqrt{\frac{\sum (x - \mu)^2}{N}} = 2.4$$

**Step 3  Standardize the data.**
Convert the x values to z values using

$$z = \frac{x - \mu}{\sigma}$$

Suppose a particular applicant has an SAT score of 1,228 and an ACT score of 27. These test scores can be converted to standardized scores.

$$\text{SAT:} \quad z = \frac{x - \mu}{\sigma} = \frac{1,228 - 1,255}{72} = -0.375$$

$$\text{ACT:} \quad z = \frac{x - \mu}{\sigma} = \frac{27 - 28.3}{2.4} = -0.542$$

The negative $z$ values indicate that this student is below the mean on both the SAT and ACT exams. Because the university wishes to use the score that most favors the student, it will use the SAT score. The student is only 0.375 standard deviations below the SAT mean, compared with 0.542 standard deviations below the ACT mean.

>>END EXAMPLE

TRY PROBLEM 3-52 (pg. 124)

*MyStatLab*

# 3-3: Exercises

## Skill Development

**3-47.** A population of unknown shape has a mean of 3,000 and a standard deviation of 200.
  a. Find the minimum proportion of observations in the population that are in the range 2,600 to 3,400.
  b. Determine the maximum proportion of the observations that are above 3,600.
  c. What statement could you make concerning the proportion of observations that are smaller than 2,400?

**3-48.** The mean time that a certain model of light bulb will last is 400 hours, with a standard deviation equal to 50 hours.
  a. Calculate the standardized value for a light bulb that lasts 500 hours.
  b. Assuming that the distribution of hours that light bulbs last is bell-shaped, what percentage of bulbs could be expected to last longer than 500 hours?

**3-49.** Consider the following set of sample data:

| 78 | 121 | 143 | 88 | 110 | 107 | 62 | 122 | 130 | 95 | 78 | 139 | 89 | 125 |

  a. Compute the mean and standard deviation for these sample data.
  b. Calculate the coefficient of variation for these sample data and interpret its meaning.
  c. Using Tchebysheff's theorem, determine the range of values that should include at least 89% of the data. Count the number of data values that fall into this range and comment on whether your interval range was conservative or not.

**3-50.** You are given the following parameters for two populations:

| Population 1 | Population 2 |
|---|---|
| $\mu = 700$ | $\mu = 29,000$ |
| $\sigma = 50$ | $\sigma = 5,000$ |

  a. Compute the coefficient of variation for each population.
  b. Based on the answers to part a, which population has data values that are more variable relative to the size of the population mean?

**3-51.** Two distributions of data are being analyzed. Distribution A has a mean of 500 and a standard deviation equal to 100. Distribution B has a mean of 10 and a standard deviation equal to 4.0. Based on this information, use the coefficient of variation to determine which distribution has greater relative variation.

**3-52.** Given two distributions with the following characteristics:

| Distribution A | Distribution B |
|---|---|
| $\mu = 45,600$ | $\mu = 33.40$ |
| $\sigma = 6,333$ | $\sigma = 4.05$ |

If a value from distribution A is 50,000 and a value from distribution B is 40.0, convert each value to a standardized $z$ value and indicate which one is relatively closer to its respective mean.

**3-53.** If a sample mean is 1,000 and the sample standard deviation is 250, determine the standardized value for
  a. $x = 800$
  b. $x = 1,200$
  c. $x = 1,000$

**3-54.** The following data represent random samples taken from two different populations, A and B:

| A | 31 | 10 | 69 | 25 | 62 | 61 | 46 | 74 | 57 |
|---|---|---|---|---|---|---|---|---|---|
| B | 1,030 | 1,111 | 1,155 | 978 | 943 | 983 | 932 | 1,067 | 1,013 |

  a. Compute the mean and standard deviation for the sample data randomly selected from population A.
  b. Compute the mean and standard deviation for the sample data randomly selected from population B.
  c. Which sample has the greater spread when measured by the standard deviation?
  d. Compute the coefficient of variation for the sample data selected from population A and from population B. Which sample exhibits the greater relative variation?

**3-55.** Consider the following sample:

| 22 | 46 | 25 | 37 | 35 | 84 | 33 | 54 | 80 | 37 |
|---|---|---|---|---|---|---|---|---|---|
| 76 | 34 | 48 | 86 | 41 | 13 | 49 | 45 | 62 | 47 |
| 72 | 70 | 91 | 51 | 91 | 43 | 56 | 25 | 12 | 65 |

a. Calculate the mean and standard deviation for this data.

b. Determine the percentage of data values that fall in each of the following intervals: $\bar{x} \pm s, \bar{x} \pm 2s, \bar{x} \pm 3s$.

c. Compare these with the percentages that should be expected from a bell-shaped distribution. Does it seem plausible that these data came from a bell-shaped population? Explain.

**3-56.** Consider the following population:

| 71 | 89 | 65 | 97 | 46 | 52 | 99 | 41 | 62 | 88 |
|----|----|----|----|----|----|----|----|----|----|
| 73 | 50 | 91 | 71 | 52 | 86 | 92 | 60 | 70 | 91 |
| 73 | 98 | 56 | 80 | 70 | 63 | 55 | 61 | 40 | 95 |

a. Determine the mean and variance.

b. Determine the percentage of data values that fall in each of the following intervals: $\bar{x} \pm 2s, \bar{x} \pm 3s, \bar{x} \pm 4s$.

c. Compare these with the percentages specified by Tchebysheff's theorem.

## Business **Applications**

**3-57.** Pfizer, Inc., a major U.S. pharmaceutical company, is developing a new drug aimed at reducing the pain associated with migraine headaches. Two drugs are currently under development. One consideration in the evaluation of the medication is how long the pain-killing effects of the drugs last. A random sample of 12 tests for each drug revealed the following times (in minutes) until the effects of the drug were neutralized. The random samples are as follows:

| **Drug A** | 258 214 243 227 235 222 240 245 245 234 243 211 |
|----|----|
| **Drug B** | 219 283 291 277 258 273 289 260 286 265 284 266 |

a. Calculate the mean and standard deviation for each of the two drugs.

b. Based on the sample means calculated in part a, which drug appears to be effective longer?

c. Based on the sample standard deviations calculated in part a, which drug appears to have the greater variability in effect time?

d. Calculate the sample coefficient of variation for the two drugs. Based on the coefficient of variation, which drug has the greater variability in its time until the effect is neutralized?

**3-58.** Wells Fargo Bank's call center has representatives that speak both English and Spanish. A random sample of 11 calls to English-speaking service representatives and a random sample of 14 calls to Spanish-speaking service representatives was taken and the time to complete the calls was measured. The results (in seconds) are as follows:

| **Time to Complete the Call (in seconds)** | |
|----|----|
| English-Speaking | 131 80 140 118 79 94 103 145 113 100 122 |
| Spanish-Speaking | 170 177 150 208 151 127 147 140 109 184 119 149 129 152 |

a. Compute the mean and standard deviation for the time to complete calls to English-speaking service representatives.

b. Compute the mean and standard deviation for the time to complete calls to Spanish-speaking service representatives.

c. Compute the coefficient of variation for the time to complete calls to English-speaking and Spanish-speaking service representatives. Which group has the greater relative variability in the time to complete calls?

d. Construct box and whisker plots for the time required to complete the two types of calls and briefly discuss.

**3-59.** Lockheed-Martin is a supplier for the aerospace industry. Recently, the company was considering switching to Cirus Systems, Inc., a new supplier for one of the component parts it needs for an assembly. At issue is the variability of the components supplied by Cirus Systems, Inc., compared to that of the existing supplier. The existing supplier makes the desired part with a mean diameter of 3.75 inches and a standard deviation of 0.078 inches. Unfortunately, Lockheed-Martin does not have any of the exact same parts from the new supplier. Instead, the new supplier has sent a sample of 20 parts of a different size that it claims are representative of the type of work it can do. These sample data are shown here and in the data file called **Cirus**.

| **Diameters (in inches)** | | | | | |
|----|----|----|----|----|----|
| 18.018 | 17.856 | 18.095 | 17.992 | 18.086 | 17.812 |
| 17.988 | 17.996 | 18.129 | 18.003 | 18.214 | 18.313 |
| 17.983 | 18.153 | 17.996 | 17.908 | | |
| 17.948 | 18.219 | 18.079 | 17.799 | | |

Prepare a short letter to Lockheed-Martin indicating which supplier you would recommend based on relative variability.

**3-60.** A recent article in *The Washington Post Weekly Edition* indicated that about 80% of the estimated $200 billion of federal housing subsidies consists of tax breaks (mainly deductions for mortgage interest payments and preferential treatment for profits on home sales). Federal housing benefits average $8,268 for those with incomes between $50,000 and $200,000 and $365 for those with income of $40,000 to $50,000. Suppose the standard deviations of the housing benefits in these two categories were equal to $2,750 and $120, respectively.

a. Examine the two standard deviations. What do these indicate about the range of benefits enjoyed by the two groups?

b. Repeat part a using the coefficient of variation as the measure of relative variation.

**3-61.** Anaheim Human Resources, Inc., performs employment screening for large companies in southern California. It usually follows a two-step process. First, potential applicants are given a test that covers basic knowledge and intelligence. If applicants score between a certain range, they are called in for an interview. If they score below a certain point, they are sent a rejection letter. If applicants score above a certain point, they are sent directly to the client's human resources office without the interview. Recently, Anaheim Human Resources began working with a new client and formulated a new test just for this company. Thirty people were given the test, which is supposed to produce scores that are distributed according to a bell-shaped distribution. The following data reflect the scores of those 30 people:

| 76 | 75 | 74 | 56 | 61 | 76 |
|----|----|----|----|----|----|
| 62 | 96 | 68 | 62 | 78 | 76 |
| 84 | 67 | 60 | 96 | 77 | 59 |
| 67 | 81 | 66 | 71 | 69 | 65 |
| 58 | 77 | 82 | 75 | 76 | 67 |

Anaheim Human Resources has in the past issued a rejection letter with no interview to the lower 16% taking the test. They also send the upper 2.5% directly to the company without an interview. Everyone else is interviewed. Based on the data and the assumption of a bell-shaped distribution, what score should be used for the two cutoffs?

**3-62.** The College Board's Annual Survey of Colleges provides up-to-date information on tuition and other expenses associated with attending public and private nonprofit institutions of postsecondary education in the United States. Each fall, the College Board releases the survey results on how much colleges and universities are charging undergraduate students in the new academic year. The survey indicated that the average published tuition and fees for 2005–2006 were $5,491 at public four-year colleges and universities and $21,235 at private, nonprofit four-year colleges and universities. The standard deviation was approximately $3,000 at public four-year colleges and universities and approximately $10,000 for private colleges and universities.

a. Do the private, nonprofit four-year colleges and universities have the larger relative variability? Provide statistical evidence to support your answer.

b. If the data on published tuition and fees were bell-shaped, determine the largest and smallest amount paid at the four-year private, nonprofit colleges and universities.

c. Based on your answer to part b, do you believe that the data are bell-shaped? Support your answer using statistical reasoning.

### Computer Database **Exercises**

**3-63.** April 15 of every year is a day that most adults in the United States can relate to—the day that federal and state income taxes are due. Although there have been several attempts by Congress and the Internal Revenue Service over the past few years to simplify the income tax process, many people still have a difficult time completing their tax returns properly. To draw attention

to this problem, a West Coast newspaper has asked 50 certified public accountant (CPA) firms to complete the same tax return for a hypothetical head of household. The CPA firms have their tax experts complete the return with the objective of determining the total federal income tax liability. The data in the file called **Taxes** show the taxes owed as figured by each of the 50 CPA firms. Theoretically, they should all come up with the same taxes owed.

Based on these data, write a short article for the paper that describes the results of this experiment. Include in your article such descriptive statistics as the mean, median, and standard deviation. You might consider using percentiles, the coefficient of variation, and Tchebysheff's theorem to help describe the data.

**3-64.** Nike ONE Black is one of the golf balls Nike, Inc., produces. It must meet the specifications of the United States Golf Association (USGA). The USGA mandates that the diameter of the ball shall not be less than 1.682 inches (42.67 mm). To verify that this specification is met, sample golf balls are taken from the production line and measured. These data are found in the file entitled **Diameter**.

a. Calculate the mean and standard deviation of this sample.

b. Examine the specification for the diameter of the golf ball again. Does it seem that the data could possibly be bell-shaped? Explain.

c. Determine the proportion of diameters in the following intervals: $\bar{x} \pm 2s, \bar{x} \pm 3s, \bar{x} \pm 4s$. Compare these with the percentages specified by Tchebysheff's theorem.

**3-65.** The Centers for Disease Control and Prevention (CDC) started the Vessel Sanitation Program (VSP) in the early 1970s because of several disease outbreaks on cruise ships. The VSP was established to protect the health of passengers and crew by minimizing the risk of gastrointestinal illness on cruise ships. Inspections are scored on a point system of maximum 100, and cruise ships earn a score based on the criteria. Ships that score an 86 or higher have a satisfactory sanitation level. Data from a recent inspection are contained in a file entitled **Cruiscore**.

a. Calculate the mean, standard deviation, median, and interquartile range. Which of these measures would seem most appropriate to characterize this data set?

b. Produce a box and whisker plot of the data. Would the Empirical Rule or Tchebysheff's theorem be appropriate for describing this data set? Explain.

c. If you wished to travel only on those ships that are at the 90th percentile or above in terms of sanitation, what would be the lowest sanitation score you would find acceptable?

**3-66.** Airfare prices were collected for a round-trip from Los Angeles (LAX) to San Francisco (SFO). Airfare prices were also collected for a round-trip from Los Angeles (LAX) to Barcelona, Spain (BCN). Airfares were obtained for the designated and nearby airports. The passenger was to fly coach class round-trip, staying seven days. The data are contained in a file entitled **Airfare**.

a. Calculate the mean and standard deviation for each of the flights.

b. Calculate an appropriate measure of the relative variability of these two flights.

c. A British friend of yours is currently in Barcelona and wishes to fly to Los Angeles. If the flight fares are the same but priced in English pounds, determine his mean, standard deviation, and measure of relative dispersion for that data. (*Note*: $1 = 0.566 GBP.)

**3-67.** Doing business internationally is no longer something reserved for the largest companies. In fact, medium-size and, in some cases, even small companies are finding themselves with the opportunity to do business internationally. One factor that will be important for world trade is the growth rate of the population of the world's countries. The data file called **Countries** contains data on the 2000 population and the growth rate between 1990 and 2000 for 74 countries throughout the world. Based on these data, which countries had growth rates that exceeded 2 standard deviations higher than the mean growth rate? Which countries had growth rates more than 2 standard deviations below the mean growth rate?

**END EXERCISES** 3-3

# Visual Summary

**Chapter 3:** To fully describe your data, not only do you need to use the graphs, charts and tables introduced in Chapter 2, you need to provide the measures of the center and measures of variations in the data that are presented in this chapter. Together, the numeric measures and the graphs and charts can paint a complete picture of the data that transform it from just data to useful information for decision-making purposes.

## 3.1 Measures of Center and Location (pg. 85–107)

### Summary

The three numerical measures of the center for a set of data are the **mean**, **median** and the **mode**. The mean is the **arithmetic average** and is the most frequently used measure. However, if the data are **skewed** or are **ordinal** level, the median is suggested. Unlike the mean which is sensitive to extreme values in the data, the median is unaffected by extremes. The mode is less frequently used as a measure of the center since it is simply the value in the data that occurs most frequently. When one of these measures is computed from a **population**, the measure is said to be a **parameter**, but if the measure is computed from **sample** data, the measure is called a **statistic**. Other measures of location that are commonly used are **percentiles** and **quartiles**. Finally, many decision makers prefer to construct a **box and whisker plot** which uses a box to display the range of the middle 50 percent of the data. The limits of whiskers are calculated based on the numerical distance between the first and third quartiles.

**Outcome 1.** Compute the mean, median, mode and weighted average for a set of data and understand what these values represent.

**Outcome 2.** Construct a box and whisker graph and interpret it.

## 3.2 Measures of Variation (pg. 107–118)

### Summary

One of the major issues that business decision makers face every day is the **variation** that exists in their operations, processes, and people. Because virtually all data exhibit variation, it is important to measure it. The simplest measure of variation is the **range** which is the difference between the highest value and the lowest value in the data. An alternative to the range that ignores the extremes in the data is the **interquartile range** which measures the numerical distance between the 3rd and 1st quartiles. But the two most frequently used measures of variation are the **variance** and the **standard deviation**. The equations for these two measures differ slightly depending on whether you are working with a population or a sample. The standard deviation is measured in the same units as the variable of interest and is a measure of the average deviation of the individual data items around the mean.

**Outcome 3.** Compute the range, variance, and standard deviation and know what these values mean.

## 3.3 Using the Mean and Standard Deviation Together (pg. 118–127)

### Summary

The real power of statistical measures of the center and variation come when they are used together to fully describe the data. One particular measure that is used a great deal in business, especially in financial analysis, is the **coefficient of variation**. When comparing two or more data sets, the larger the coefficient of variation, the greater the relative variation of the data. Another very important way in which the mean and standard deviation are used together is evident in the **empirical rule** which allows decision makers to better understand the data from a **bell-shaped** distribution. In cases where the data are not bell-shaped, the data can be described using **Tchebysheff's Theorem**. The final way discussed in this chapter in which the mean and standard deviation are used together is the **z-value**. Z-values for each individual data point measure the number of standard deviations a data value is from the mean.

**Outcome 4.** Compute a z score and the coefficient of variation and understand how they are applied in decision-making situations.

**Outcome 5.** Understand the Empirical Rule and Tchebysheff's Theorem

## Conclusion

A very important part of the descriptive tools in statistics is the collection of numerical measures that can be computed. When these measures of the center and variation in the data are combined with charts and graphs, you can fully describe the data. **Figure 3.10** presents a summary of the key numerical measures that are discussed in Chapter 3. Remember, measures computed from a population are called parameters while measures computed from a sample are called statistics.

**FIGURE 3.10** | Summary of Numerical Statistical Measures

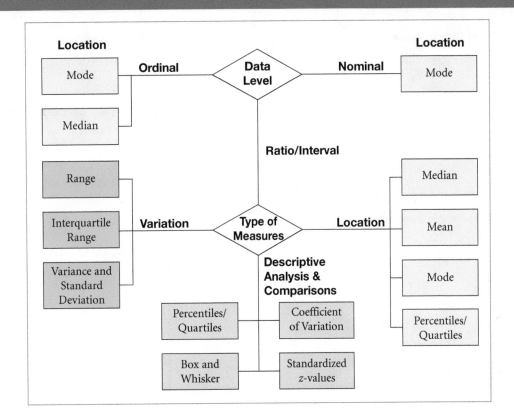

# Equations

**(3.1) Population Mean** pg. 86

$$\mu = \frac{\displaystyle\sum_{i=1}^{N} x_i}{N}$$

**(3.2) Sample Mean** pg. 90

$$\bar{x} = \frac{\displaystyle\sum_{i=1}^{n} x_i}{n}$$

**(3.3) Median Index** pg. 91

$$i = \frac{1}{2}n$$

**(3.4) Weighted Mean for a Population** pg. 97

$$\mu_w = \frac{\sum w_i x_i}{\sum w_i}$$

**(3.5) Weighted Mean for a Sample** pg. 97

$$\bar{x}_w = \frac{\sum w_i x_i}{\sum w_i}$$

**(3.6) Percentile Location Index** pg. 98

$$i = \frac{p}{100}(n)$$

**(3.7) Range** pg. 107

$$R = \text{Maximum value} - \text{Minimum value}$$

**(3.8) Interquartile Range** pg. 108

$$\text{Interquartile range} = \text{Third quartile} - \text{First quartile}$$

**(3.9) Population Variance** pg. 110

$$\sigma^2 = \frac{\displaystyle\sum_{i=1}^{N} (x_i - \mu)^2}{N}$$

**(3.10) Population Variance Shortcut** pg. 110

$$\sigma^2 = \frac{\sum x^2 - \frac{(\sum x)^2}{N}}{N}$$

**(3.11) Population Standard Deviation** pg. 111

$$\sigma = \sqrt{\sigma^2} = \sqrt{\frac{\displaystyle\sum_{i=1}^{N} (x_i - \mu)^2}{N}}$$

**(3.12)** Sample Variance  pg. 112

$$s^2 = \frac{\sum_{i=1}^{n}(x_i - \bar{x})^2}{n-1}$$

**(3.13)** Sample Variance Shortcut  pg. 112

$$s^2 = \frac{\sum x^2 - \dfrac{\left(\sum x\right)^2}{n}}{n-1}$$

**(3.14)** Sample Standard Deviation  pg. 112

$$s = \sqrt{s^2} = \sqrt{\frac{\sum_{i=1}^{n}(x_i - \bar{x})^2}{n-1}}$$

**(3.15)** Population Coefficient of Variation  pg. 119

$$CV = \frac{\sigma}{\mu}(100)\%$$

**(3.16)** Sample Coefficient of Variation  pg. 119

$$CV = \frac{s}{\bar{x}}(100)\%$$

**(3.17)** Standardized Population Data  pg. 122

$$z = \frac{x - \mu}{\sigma}$$

**(3.18)** Standardized Sample Data  pg. 122

$$z = \frac{x - \bar{x}}{s}$$

# Key Terms

**Box and whisker plot** pg. 100
**Coefficient of variation** pg. 119
**Data array** pg. 91
**Empirical Rule** pg. 120
**Interquartile range** pg. 108
**Left-skewed data** pg. 93
**Mean** pg. 86
**Median** pg. 91
**Mode** pg. 93

**Parameter** pg. 86
**Percentiles** pg. 98
**Population mean** pg. 86
**Quartiles** pg. 99
**Range** pg. 107
**Right-skewed data** pg. 93
**Sample mean** pg. 89
**Skewed data** pg. 92
**Standard deviation** pg. 109

**Standardized data values** pg. 122
**Statistic** pg. 86
**Symmetric data** pg. 92
**Tchebysheff's theorem** pg. 121
**Variance** pg. 109
**Variation** pg. 107
**Weighted mean** pg. 97

# Chapter Exercises

*MyStatLab*

## Conceptual Questions

**3-68.** Consider the following questions concerning the sample variance:
  a. Is it possible for a variance to be negative? Explain.
  b. What is the smallest value a variance can be? Under what conditions does the variance equal this smallest value?
  c. Under what conditions is the sample variance smaller than the corresponding sample standard deviation?

**3-69.** For a continuous variable that has a bell-shaped distribution, determine the percentiles associated with the endpoints of the intervals specified in the Empirical Rule.

**3-70.** Consider that the Empirical Rule stipulates that virtually all of the data values are within the interval $\mu \pm 3\sigma$. Use this stipulation to determine an approximation for the standard deviation involving the range.

**3-71.** At almost every university in the United States, the university computes student grade point averages (GPAs). The following scale is typically used by universities:

| | | |
|---|---|---|
| A = 4 points | B = 3 points | C = 2 points |
| D = 1 point | F = 0 points | |

Discuss what, if any, problems might exist when GPAs for two students are compared? What about comparing GPAs for students from two different universities?

**3-72.** Since the standard deviation of a set of data requires more effort to compute than the range does, what advantages does the standard deviation have when discussing the spread in a set of data?

**3-73.** The mode seems like a very simple measure of the location of a distribution. When would the mode be preferred over the median or the mean?

## Business Applications

**3-74.** Home Pros sells supplies to "do-it-yourselfers." One of the things the company prides itself on is fast service. It uses a number system and takes customers in the order they arrive at the store. Recently, the assistant manager tracked the time customers spent in the store from the time they took a number until they left. A sample of 16 customers was selected and the following data (measured in minutes) were recorded:

| 15 | 14 | 16 | 14 | 14 | 14 | 13 | 8 |
| 12 | 9 | 7 | 17 | 10 | 15 | 16 | 16 |

a. Compute the mean, median, mode, range, interquartile range, and standard deviation.
b. Develop a box and whisker plot for these data.

**3-75.** Over 221 million computer and video games were sold in 2002—nearly two games for every U.S. household according to the *Detroit News* (February 15, 2004). Of Americans age 6 or older 60%—about 145 million people—play computer and video games. Gamers spend an average of 3 to 4 hours playing games online every day. The average age of players is 28. Video games and gamers have even created a new form of marketing—called "advergaming." "Advergaming is taking games—something that people do for recreation—and inserting a message," said Julie Roehm, director of marketing communications for the Chrysler Group, which sells Chrysler, Jeep, and Dodge brand vehicles. "It's important we go to all the places our consumers are." Suppose it is possible to assume the standard deviation of the ages of video game users is 9 years and that the distribution is bell-shaped. To assist the marketing department in obtaining demographics to increase sales, determine the proportion of players who are
a. between 19 and 28
b. between 28 and 37
c. older than 37

**3-76.** Travelers are facing increased costs for both driving and flying to chosen destinations. With rising costs for both modes of transportation, what really weighs on the decision to drive or to fly? To gain a better understanding of the "fly or drive" decision, Runzheimer International reviewed ("The 'Fly or Drive' Decision: Runzheimer International Analyzes Costs," October 21, 2005) costs for trips between Los Angeles to San Francisco, 425 miles one way. Los Angeles to San Francisco round-trip costs $617.90 by car and $407.00 by plane. Cost flexibility is greater with the flying trips because of greater airfare choices. The driving trip costs, except for the on-road lunches, are pretty much set in place. Assume the standard deviation for the cost of flying trips is approximately $100.
a. If a flight to San Francisco from Los Angeles was chosen at random, determine the proportion of the time that the cost would be smaller than $507. Assume the flight costs are bell-shaped.
b. Determine a flight cost that would qualify as the 25th percentile.
c. If nothing can be assumed about the distribution of the flight costs, determine the largest percentile that could be attributed to an airfare of $250.

**3-77.** With the ups and downs in the economy since 2008, many discount airline fares are available if a customer knows how to obtain the discount. Many travelers complain that they get a different price every time they call. The American Consumer Institute recently priced tickets between Spokane, Washington, and St. Louis, Missouri. The passenger was to fly coach class round-trip, staying seven days. Calls were made directly to airlines and to travel agents with the following results. Note that the data reflect round-trip airfare.

| $229.00 | $345.00 | $599.00 | $229.00 | $429.00 | $605.00 |
| $339.00 | $339.00 | $229.00 | $279.00 | $344.00 | $407.00 |

a. Compute the mean quoted airfare.
b. Compute the variance and standard deviation in airfares quoted. Treat the data as a sample.

**3-78.** The manager of the Cottonwood Grille recently selected a random sample of 18 customers and kept track of how long the customers were required to wait from the time they arrived at the restaurant until they were actually served dinner. This study resulted from several complaints the manager had received from customers saying that their wait time was unduly long and that it appeared that the objective was to keep people waiting in the lounge for as long as possible to increase the lounge business. The following data were recorded, with time measured in minutes:

| 34 | 24 | 43 | 56 | 74 | 20 | 19 | 33 | 55 |
| 43 | 54 | 34 | 27 | 34 | 36 | 24 | 54 | 39 |

a. Compute the mean waiting time for this sample of customers.
b. Compute the median waiting time for this sample of customers.
c. Compute the variance and standard deviation of waiting time for this sample of customers.
d. Develop a frequency distribution using six classes, each with a class width of 10. Make the lower limit of the first class 15.
e. Develop a frequency histogram for the frequency distribution.
f. Construct a box and whisker plot of these data.
g. The manager is considering giving a complementary drink to customers whose waiting time is

longer than the third quartile. Determine the minimum number of minutes a customer would have to wait in order to receive a complementary drink.

**3-79.** Simplot Agri-Chemical has decided to implement a new incentive system for the managers of its three plants. The plan calls for a bonus to be paid next month to the manager whose plant has the greatest relative improvement over the average monthly production volume. The following data reflect the historical production volumes at the three plants:

| Plant 1 | Plant 2 | Plant 3 |
|---------|---------|---------|
| $\mu = 700$ | $\mu = 2,300$ | $\mu = 1,200$ |
| $\sigma = 200$ | $\sigma = 350$ | $\sigma = 30$ |

At the close of next month, the monthly output for the three plants was

| Plant 1 = 810 | Plant 2 = 2,600 | Plant 3 = 1,320 |
|---------------|-----------------|-----------------|

Suppose the division manager has awarded the bonus to the manager of Plant 2 since her plant increased its production by 300 units over the mean, more than that for any of the other managers. Do you agree with the award of the bonus for this month? Explain, using the appropriate statistical measures to support your position.

**3-80.** According to the annual report issued by Wilson & Associates, an investment firm in Bowling Green, the stocks in its Growth Fund have generated an average return of 8% with a standard deviation of 2%. The stocks in the Specialized Fund have generated an average return of 18% with a standard deviation of 6%.

a. Based on the data provided, which of these funds has exhibited greater relative variability? Use the proper statistical measure to make your determination.

b. Suppose an investor who is very risk-averse is interested in one of these two funds. Based strictly on relative variability, which fund would you recommend? Discuss.

c. Suppose the distributions for the two stock funds had a bell-shaped distribution with the means and standard deviations previously indicated. Which fund appears to be the best investment, assuming future returns will mimic past returns? Explain.

**3-81.** The Dakota Farm Cooperative owns and leases prime farmland in the upper Midwest. Most of its 34,000 acres are planted in grain. The cooperative performs a substantial amount of testing to determine what seed types produce the greatest yields. Recently, the cooperative tested three types of corn seed on test plots. The following values were observed after the first test year:

| | Seed Type A | Seed Type B | Seed Type C |
|---|-----|-----|-----|
| Mean Bushels/Acre | 88 | 56 | 100 |
| Standard Deviation | 25 | 15 | 16 |

a. Based on the results of this testing, which seed seems to produce the greatest average yield per acre? Comment on the type of testing controls that should have been used to make this study valid.

b. Suppose the company is interested in consistency. Which seed type shows the least relative variability?

c. Assuming the Empirical Rule applies, describe the production distribution for each of the three seed types.

d. Suppose you were a farmer and had to obtain at least 135 bushels per acre to escape bankruptcy. Which seed type would you plant? Explain your choice.

e. Rework your answer to part d assuming the farmer needed 115 bushels per acre instead.

**3-82.** The Hillcrest Golf and Country Club manager selected a random sample of the members and recorded the number of rounds of golf they played last season. The reason for his interest in this data is that the club is thinking of applying a discount to members who golf more than a specified number of rounds per year. The sample of eight people produced the following number of rounds played:

| 13 | 32 | 12 | 9 | 16 | 17 | 16 | 12 |
|----|----|----|---|----|----|----|----|

a. Compute the mean for these sample data.

b. Compute the median for these sample data.

c. Compute the mode for these sample data.

d. Calculate the variance and standard deviation for these sample data.

e. Note that one person in the sample played 32 rounds. What effect, if any, does this large value have on each of the three measures of location? Discuss.

f. For these sample data, which measure of location provides the best measure of the center of the data? Discuss.

g. Given this sample data, suppose the manager wishes to give discounts to golfers in the top quartile. What should the minimum number of rounds played be to receive a discount?

**3-83.** Stock investors often look to beat the performance of the S&P 500 Index, which generally serves as a yardstick for the market as a whole. The following table shows a comparison of the five-year cumulative total shareholder returns for IDACORP common stock, the S&P 500 Index, and the Edison Electric Institute (EEI) Electric Utilities Index. The data assumes that $100 was invested on December 31, 2002, with beginning-of-period weighting of the peer group indices (based on market capitalization) and monthly compounding of returns (*Source:* IDACORP 2007 Annual Report).

| Year | IDACORP ($) | S&P 500 ($) | EEI Electric Utilities Index ($) |
|------|-------------|-------------|----------------------------------|
| 2002 | 100.00 | 100.00 | 100.00 |
| 2003 | 128.86 | 128.67 | 123.48 |
| 2004 | 137.11 | 142.65 | 151.68 |
| 2005 | 136.92 | 149.66 | 176.02 |
| 2006 | 186.71 | 173.27 | 212.56 |
| 2007 | 176.26 | 182.78 | 247.76 |

Using the information provided, construct appropriate statistical measures that illustrate the performance of the three investments. How well has IDACORP performed over the time periods compared to the S&P 500? How well has it performed relative to its industry as measured by the returns of the EEI Electric Utilities Index?

3-84. When the Zagat Survey®, a leading provider of leisure-based survey results, released its San Francisco Restaurants Survey, it marked the 25th year that Zagat Survey reported on diners and the 19th year that the company has covered San Francisco. The participants dined out an average of 3.2 times per week, with the average price per meal falling from the previous year from $34.07 to $33.75.

   a. If the standard deviation of the price of meals in San Francisco was $10, determine the largest proportion of meal prices that could be larger than $50.

   b. If the checks were paid in Chinese currency ($1 USD = 8.0916 Chinese yuan), determine the mean and standard deviation of meal prices in San Francisco. How would this change of currency affect your answer to part a?

## Computer Database Exercises

3-85. The data in the file named **Fast100** was collected by D. L. Green & Associates, a regional investment management company that specializes in working with clients who wish to invest in smaller companies with high growth potential. To aid the investment firm in locating appropriate investments for its clients, Sandra Williams, an assistant client manager, put together a database on 100 fast-growing companies. The database consists of data on eight variables for each of the 100 companies. Note that in some cases data are not available. A code of −99 has been used to signify missing data. These data will have to be omitted from any calculations.

   a. Select the variable Sales. Develop a frequency distribution and histogram for Sales.

   b. Compute the mean, median, and standard deviation for the Sales variable.

   c. Determine the interquartile range for the Sales variable.

   d. Construct a box and whisker plot for the Sales variable. Identify any outliers. Discard the outliers and recalculate the measures in part b.

   e. Each year a goal is set for sales. Next year's goal will be to have average sales that are at this year's 65th percentile. Identify next year's sales goal.

3-86. The Environmental Protection Agency (EPA) tests all new cars and provides a mileage rating for both city and highway driving conditions. Thirty cars were tested and are contained in the data file **Automobiles**. The file contains data on several variables. In this problem, focus on the city and highway mileage data.

   a. Calculate the sample mean miles per gallon (mpg) for both city and highway driving for the 30 cars. Also calculate the sample standard deviation for the two mileage variables. Do the data tend to support the premise that cars get better mileage on the highway than around town? Discuss.

   b. Referring to part a, what can the EPA conclude about the relative variability between car models for highway versus city driving? (*Hint*: Compute the appropriate measure to compare relative variability.)

   c. Assume that mileage ratings are approximately bell-shaped. Approximately what proportion of cars gets at least as good mileage in city driving conditions as the mean mileage for highway driving for all cars?

3-87. According to the National Retail Federation (NRF), the NRF 2005 Halloween Consumer Intentions and Actions Survey, conducted by BIGresearch, found that consumer spending ($3.29 billion) for 2005 was expected to be 5.4% above the amount for 2004. Much of the increase in spending was expected to come from young adults. Consumers in the 18–24 age group expected to spend an overall average of $50.75. On costumes alone they expect to spend an average of $22.00. A file entitled **Costumes** contains similar data.

   a. Calculate the mean and standard deviation of these data.

   b. Determine the following intervals for this data set: $\bar{x} \pm 1s, \bar{x} \pm 2s, \bar{x} \pm 3s$.

   c. Suppose your responsibility as an assistant manager was to determine the price of costumes to be sold. The manager has informed you to set the price of one costume so that it was beyond the budget of only 2.5% of the customers. Assume that the data set has a bell-shaped distribution.

3-88. PayScale is a source of online compensation information, providing access to accurate compensation data for both employees and employers. PayScale allows users to obtain compensation information providing a snapshot of the job market. Recently, it published statistics for the salaries of MBA graduates. The file entitled **Payscale** contains data with the same characteristics as those obtained by PayScale for California and Florida.

   a. Calculate the standard deviations of the salaries for both states' MBA graduates. Which state seems to have the widest spectrum of salaries for MBA graduates?

b. Calculate the average and median salary for each state's MBA graduates.

c. Examining the averages calculated in part b, determine which state's MBA graduates have the largest relative dispersion.

**3-89.** *Yahoo! Finance* makes available historical stock prices. It lists the opening, high, and low stock prices for each stock available on NYSE and NASDAQ. A file entitled **GEstock** gives this data for General Electric (GE) for a recent 99-day period.

a. Calculate the difference between the opening and closing stock prices for GE over this time period. Then calculate the mean, median, and standard deviation of these differences.

b. Indicate what the mean in part a indicates about the relative prices of the opening and closing stock prices for GE.

c. Compare the dispersion of the opening stock prices with the difference between the opening and closing stock prices.

**3-90.** Zepolle's Bakery makes a variety of bread types that it sells to supermarket chains in the area. One of Zepolle's problems is that the number of loaves of each type of bread sold each day by the chain stores varies considerably, making it difficult to know how many loaves to bake. A sample of daily demand data is contained in the file called **Bakery**.

a. Which bread type has the highest average daily demand?

b. Develop a frequency distribution for each bread type.

c. Which bread type has the highest standard deviation in demand?

d. Which bread type has the greatest relative variability? Which type has the lowest relative variability?

e. Assuming that these sample data are representative of demand during the year, determine how many loaves of each type of bread should be made such that demand would be met on at least 75% of the days during the year.

f. Create a new variable called Total Loaves Sold. On which day of the week is the average for total loaves sold the highest?

**3-91.** The Internal Revenue Service (IRS) has come under a great deal of criticism in recent years for various actions it is purported to have taken against U.S. citizens related to collecting federal income taxes. The IRS is also criticized for the complexity of the tax code, although the tax laws are actually written by congressional staff and passed by

Congress. For the past few years, one of the country's biggest tax-preparing companies has sponsored an event in which 50 certified public accountants from all sizes of CPA firms are asked to determine the tax owed for a fictitious citizen. The IRS is also asked to determine the "correct" tax owed. Last year, the "correct" figure stated by the IRS was $11,560. The file **Taxes** contains the data for the 50 accountants.

a. Compute a new variable that is the difference between the IRS number and the number determined by each accountant.

b. For this new variable computed in part a, develop a frequency distribution.

c. For the new variable computed in part a, determine the mean, median, and standard deviation.

d. Determine the percentile that would correspond to the "correct" tax figure if the IRS figure were one of the CPA firms' estimated tax figures. Describe what this implies about the agreement between the IRS and consultants' calculated tax.

**3-92.** The Cozine Corporation operates a garbage hauling business. Up to this point, the company has been charged a flat fee for each of the garbage trucks that enters the county landfill. The flat fee is based on the assumed truck weight of 45,000 pounds. In two weeks, the company is required to appear before the county commissioners to discuss a rate adjustment. In preparation for this meeting, Cozine has hired an independent company to weigh a sample of Cozine's garbage trucks just prior to their entering the landfill. The data file **Cozine** contains the data the company has collected.

a. Based on the sample data, what percentile does the 45,000-pound weight fall closest to?

b. Compute appropriate measures of central location for the data.

c. Construct a frequency histogram based on the sample data. Use the $2^k \geq n$ guideline (see Chapter 2) to determine the number of classes. Also, construct a box and whisker plot for these data. Discuss the relative advantages of histograms and box and whisker plots for presenting these data.

d. Use the information determined in parts a–c to develop a presentation to the county commissioners. Make sure the presentation attempts to answer the question of whether Cozine deserves a rate reduction.

# Video Case 3

## Drive-Thru Service Times @ McDonalds

When you're on the go and looking for a quick meal, where do you go? If you're like millions of people every day, you make a stop at McDonald's. Known as "quick service restaurants" in the industry (not "fast food"), companies such as McDonald's invest heavily to determine the most efficient and effective ways to provide fast, high-quality service in all phases of their business.

Drive-thru operations play a vital role. It's not surprising that attention is focused on the drive-thru process. After all, over 60% of individual restaurant revenues in the United States come from the drive-thru experience. Yet, understanding the process is more complex than just counting cars. Marla King, professor at the company's international training center, Hamburger University, got her start 25 years ago working at a McDonald's drive-thru. She now coaches new restaurant owners and managers. "Our stated drive-thru service time is 90 seconds or less. We train every manager and team member to understand that a quality customer experience at the drive-thru depends on them," says Marla. Some of the factors that affect a customers' ability to complete their purchases within 90 seconds include restaurant staffing, equipment layout in the restaurant, training, efficiency of the grill team, and frequency of customer arrivals, to name a few. Also, customer order patterns play a role. Some customers will just order drinks, whereas others seem to need enough food to feed an entire soccer team. And then there are the special orders. Obviously, there is plenty of room for variability here.

Yet that doesn't stop the company from using statistical techniques to better understand the drive-thru action. In particular, McDonald's utilizes numerical measures of the center and spread in the data to help transform the data into useful information. For restaurant managers to achieve the goal in their own restaurants, they need training in proper restaurant and drive-thru operations. Hamburger University, McDonald's training center located near Chicago, Illinois, satisfies that need. In the mock-up restaurant service lab, managers go through a "before and after" training scenario. In the "before" scenario, they run the restaurant for 30 minutes as if they were back in their home restaurants. Managers in the training class are assigned to be crew, customers, drive-thru cars, special needs guests (such as hearing impaired, indecisive, clumsy), or observers. Statistical data about the operations, revenues, and service times are collected and analyzed. Without the right training, the restaurant's operations usually start breaking down after 10–15 minutes. After debriefing and analyzing the data collected, the managers make suggestions for adjustments and head back to the service lab

to try again. This time, the results usually come in well within standards. "When presented with the quantitative results, managers are pretty quick to make the connections between better operations, higher revenues, and happier customers," Marla states.

When managers return to their respective restaurants, the training results and techniques are shared with staff charged with implementing the ideas locally. The results of the training eventually are measured when McDonald's conducts a restaurant operations improvement process study, or ROIP. The goal is simple: improved operations. When the ROIP review is completed, statistical analyses are performed and managers are given their results. Depending on the results, decisions might be made that require additional financial resources, building construction, staff training, or layout reconfiguration. Yet one thing is clear: Statistics drive the decisions behind McDonald's drive-thru service operations.

### Discussion Questions:

1. After returning from the training session at Hamburger University, a McDonald's store owner selected a random sample of 362 drive-thru customers and carefully measured the time it took from when a customer entered the McDonald's property until the customer had received the order at the drive-thru window. These data are in the file called "McDonald's Drive-Thru Waiting Times." Note, the owner selected some customers during the breakfast period, others during lunch, and others during dinner. For the overall sample, compute the key measures of central tendency. Based on these measures, what conclusion might the owner reach with respect to how well his store is doing in meeting the 90-second customer service goal? Discuss.

2. Referring to question 1, compute the key measures of central tendency for drive-thru times broken down by breakfast, lunch, and dinner time periods. Based on these calculations, does it appear that the store is doing better at one of these time periods than the others in providing shorter drive-thru waiting times? Discuss.

3. Referring to questions 1 and 2, compute the range and standard deviation for drive-thru times for the overall sample and for the three different times of the day. Also calculate the appropriate measure of relative variability for each time period. Discuss these measures of variability and what they might imply about what customers can expect at this McDonald's drive-thru.

4. Determine the 1st and 3rd quartiles for drive-thru times and develop a box and whisker diagram for the overall sample data. Are there any outliers identified in these sample data? Discuss.

# Case 3.1

## WGI—Human Resources

WGI is a large international construction company with operations in 43 countries. The company has been a major player in the recon-

struction efforts in Iraq, with a number of subcontracts under the major contractor, Haliburton, Inc. However, the company is also involved in many small projects both in the United States and around the world. One of these is a sewer line installation project in Madison, Wisconsin. The contract is what is called a "cost plus" contract, meaning that the city of Madison will pay for all direct costs, including materials and labor, of the project plus an additional fee to WGI. Roberta Bernhart is the human resources (HR) manager for the Madison project and is responsible for overseeing all aspects of employee compensation and HR issues.

WGI is required to produce a variety of reports to the Madison city council on an annual basis. Recently, the council asked WGI to prepare a report showing the current hourly rates for the non-salaried work crew on the project. Specifically, the council is interested in any proposed pay increases to the work crew that will ultimately be passed along to the city of Madison. In response to the city's request, Roberta put together a data file for all 19 non-salaried work crew members, called "WGI," which shows their current hourly pay rate and the proposed increase to take place the first of next month. These data are as follows:

| Name | Current Rate | New Rate |
|------|------|------|
| Jody | $20.55 | $22.55 |
| Tim | $22.15 | $23.81 |
| Thomas | $14.18 | $15.60 |
| Shari | $14.18 | $15.60 |
| John | $18.80 | $20.20 |
| Jared | $18.98 | $20.20 |
| Loren | $25.24 | $26.42 |
| Mike | $18.36 | $19.28 |
| Patrick | $17.20 | $18.06 |
| Sharon | $16.99 | $17.84 |
| Sam | $16.45 | $17.27 |
| Susan | $18.90 | $19.66 |

| Name | Current Rate | New Rate |
|------|------|------|
| Chris | $18.30 | $19.02 |
| Steve F | $27.45 | $28.12 |
| Kevin | $16.00 | $16.64 |
| Larry | $17.47 | $18.00 |
| MaryAnn | $23.99 | $24.47 |
| Mark | $22.62 | $23.08 |
| Aaron | $15.00 | $15.40 |

The city council expects the report to contain both graphic and numerical descriptive analyses. Roberta has outlined the following tasks and has asked you to help her.

### Required Tasks:

1. Develop, and interpret, histograms showing the distributions of current hourly rates and proposed new hourly rates for the crew members.
2. Compute and interpret key measures of central tendency and variation for the current and new hourly rates. Determine the coefficient of variation for each.
3. Compute a new variable called Pay Increase that reflects the difference between the proposed new pay rate and the current rate. Develop a histogram for this variable, and then compute key measures of the center and variation for the new variable.
4. Compute a new variable that is the percentage increase in hourly pay rate. Prepare a graphical and numerical description of this new variable.
5. Prepare a report to the city council that contains the results from tasks 1–4.

# Case 3.2

## National Call Center

Candice Worthy and Philip Hanson are day shift supervisors at National Call Center's Austin, Texas, facility. National provides contract call center services for a number of companies, including banks and major retail companies. Candice and Philip have both been with the company for slightly over five years, having joined National right after graduating with bachelor degrees from the University of Texas. As they walked down the hall together after the weekly staff meeting, the two friends were discussing the assignment they were just handed by Mark Gonzales, the division manager. The assignment came out of a discussion at the meeting in which one of National's clients wanted a report describing the calls being handled for them by National. Mark had asked Candice and Philip to describe the data in a file called "National Call Center" and produce a report that would both graphically and numerically analyze the data. The data are for a sample of 57 calls and for the following variables:

Account Number

Caller Gender

Account Holder Gender

Past Due Amount

Current Account Balance

Nature of Call (Billing Question or Other)

By the time they reached their office Candice and Philip had outlined some of the key tasks that they needed to do.

### Required Tasks:

1. Develop bar charts showing the mean and median current account balance by gender of the caller.
2. Develop bar charts showing the mean and median current account balance by gender of the account holder.
3. Construct a scatter diagram showing current balance on the horizontal axis and past due amount on the vertical axis.
4. Compute the key descriptive statistics for the center and for the variation in current account balance broken down by gender of the caller, gender of the account holder, and by the nature of the call.
5. Repeat task 4 but compute the statistics for the past due balances.
6. Compute the coefficient of variation for current account balances for male and female account holders.
7. Develop frequency and relative frequency distributions for the gender of callers, gender of account holders, and nature of the calls.
8. Develop joint frequency and joint relative frequency distributions for the account holder gender by whether or not the account has a past due balance.
9. Write a report to National's client that contains the results for tasks 1–8 along with a discussion of these statistics and graphs.

# Case 3.3

## Welco Lumber Company—Part B

Case 2.3 in Chapter 2 introduced you to the Welco Lumber Company and to Gene Denning, Welco Lumber Company's process improvement team leader. Welco Lumber makes cedar fencing materials at its Naples, Idaho, facility, employing about 160 people.

In Case 2.3 you were asked to help Gene develop a graphical descriptive analysis for data collected from the head rig. The head rig is a large saw that breaks down the logs into slabs and cants. Refer to Case 2.3 for more details involving a study that Gene recently conducted in which he videotaped 365 logs being broken down by the head rig. All three operators, April, Sid, and Jim, were involved. Each log was marked as to its true diameter. Then Gene observed the way the log was broken down and the degree to which the cants were properly centered. He then determined the projected value of the finished product from each log given the way it was actually cut. In addition, he also determined what the value would have been had the log been cut in the optimal way. Data for this study are in a file called "Welco Lumber."

In addition to the graphical analysis that you helped Gene perform in Case 2.3, you have been asked to assist Gene by analyzing these data using appropriate measures of the center and variation. He wishes to focus on the lost profit to the company and whether there are differences among the operators. Also, do the operators tend to perform better on small logs than on large logs? In general, he is hoping to learn as much as possible from this study and needs your help with the analysis.

# Case 3.4

## AJ's Fitness Center

When A. J. Reeser signed papers to take ownership of the fitness center previously known as the Park Center Club, he realized that he had just taken the biggest financial step in his life. Every asset he could pull together had been pledged against the mortgage. If the new AJ's Fitness Center didn't succeed, he would be in really bad shape financially. But A. J. didn't plan on failing. After all, he had never failed at anything.

As a high school football All-American, A. J. had been heavily recruited by major colleges around the country. Although he loved football, he and his family had always put academics ahead of sports. Thus, he surprised almost everyone other than those who knew him best when he chose to attend an Ivy League university not particularly noted for its football success. Although he excelled at football and was a member of two winning teams, he also succeeded in the classroom and graduated in four years. He spent six years working for McKinsey & Company, a major consulting firm, at which he gained significant experience in a broad range of business situations.

He was hired away from McKinsey & Company by the Dryden Group, a management services company that specializes in running health and fitness operations and recreational resorts throughout the world. After eight years of leading the Fitness Center section at Dryden, A. J. found that earning a high salary and the perks associated with corporate life were not satisfying him. Besides, the travel was getting old now that he had married and had two young children. When the opportunity to purchase the Park Center Club came, he decided that the time was right to control his own destiny.

A key aspect of the deal was that AJ's Fitness Club would keep its existing clientele, consisting of 1,833 memberships. One of the things A. J. was very concerned about was whether these members would stay with the club after the sale or move on to other fitness clubs in the area. He knew that keeping existing customers is a lot less expensive than attracting new customers.

Within days of assuming ownership, A. J. developed a survey that was mailed to all 1,833 members. The letter that accompanied the survey discussed A. J.'s philosophy and asked several key questions regarding the current level of satisfaction. Survey respondents were eligible to win a free lifetime membership in a drawing—an inducement that was no doubt responsible for the 1,214 usable responses.

To get help with the analysis of the survey data, A. J. approached the College of Business at a local university with the idea of having a senior student serve as an intern at AJ's Fitness Center. In addition to an hourly wage, the intern would get free use of the fitness facilities for the rest of the academic year.

The intern's first task was to key the data from the survey into a file that could be analyzed using a spreadsheet or a statistical software package. The survey contained eight questions that were keyed into eight columns, as follows:

Column 1:  Satisfaction with the club's weight- and exercise-equipment facilities

Column 2:  Satisfaction with the club's staff

Column 3:  Satisfaction with the club's exercise programs (aerobics, etc.)

Column 4:  Satisfaction with the club's overall service

Note, columns 1 through 4 were coded on an ordinal scale as follows:

| 1 | 2 | 3 | 4 | 5 |
|---|---|---|---|---|
| Very unsatisfied | Unsatisfied | Neutral | Satisfied | Very satisfied |

Column 5:  Number of years that the respondent had been a member at this club

Column 6:  Gender (1 = Male, 2 = Female)

Column 7:     Typical number of visits to the club per week

Column 8:     Age

The data, saved in the file "AJFitness," were clearly too much for anyone to comprehend in raw form. At yesterday's meeting, A. J. asked the intern to "make some sense of the data." When the intern asked for some direction, A. J.'s response was, "That's what I'm paying you the big bucks for. I just want you to develop a descriptive analysis of these data. Use whatever charts, graphs, and tables that will help us understand our customers. Also, use any pertinent numerical measures that will help in the analysis. For right now, give me a report that discusses the data. Why don't we set a time to get together next week to review your report?"

# References

Berenson, Mark L., and David M. Levine, *Basic Business Statistics: Concepts and Applications,* 11th ed. (Upper Saddle River, NJ: Prentice Hall, 2009).

*Microsoft Excel 2007* (Redmond, WA: Microsoft Corp., 2007).

*Minitab for Windows Version 15* (State College, PA: Minitab, 2007).

Siegel, Andrew F., *Practical Business Statistics*, 5th ed. (Burr Ridge, IL: Irwin, 2003).

Tukey, John W., *Exploratory Data Analysis* (Reading, MA: Addison-Wesley, 1977).

# Special Review Section

This is the first of two special review sections in this text. The material in these sections, which is presented using block diagrams and flowcharts, is intended to help you tie together the material from several key chapters. These sections are not a substitute for reading and studying the chapters covered by the review. However, you can use this review material to add to your understanding of the individual topics in the chapters.

## Chapters 1–3

Chapters 1 to 3 introduce data, data collection, and statistical tools for describing data. The steps needed to gather "good" statistical data, transform it to usable information, and present the information in a manner that allows good decisions are outlined in the following figures.

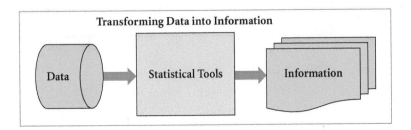

# A Typical Application Sequence

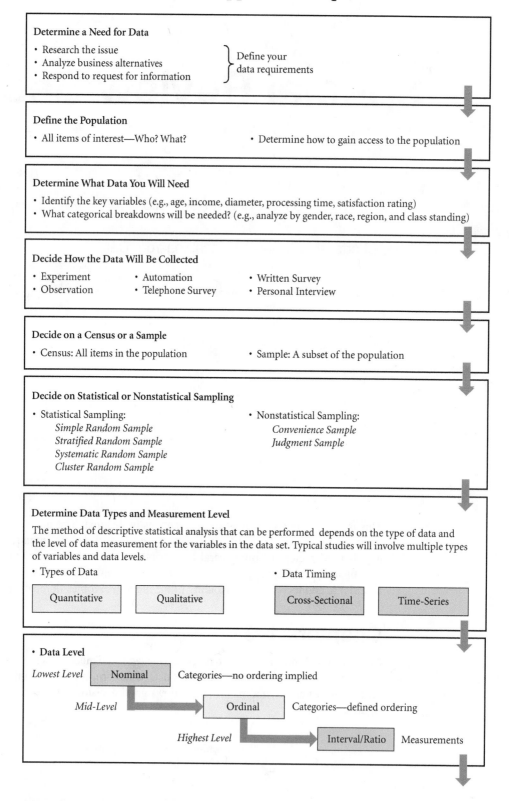

**Determine a Need for Data**

- Research the issue
- Analyze business alternatives
- Respond to request for information

} Define your
data requirements

**Define the Population**

- All items of interest—Who? What?
- Determine how to gain access to the population

**Determine What Data You Will Need**

- Identify the key variables (e.g., age, income, diameter, processing time, satisfaction rating)
- What categorical breakdowns will be needed? (e.g., analyze by gender, race, region, and class standing)

**Decide How the Data Will Be Collected**

- Experiment
- Observation
- Automation
- Telephone Survey
- Written Survey
- Personal Interview

**Decide on a Census or a Sample**

- Census: All items in the population
- Sample: A subset of the population

**Decide on Statistical or Nonstatistical Sampling**

- Statistical Sampling:
  - *Simple Random Sample*
  - *Stratified Random Sample*
  - *Systematic Random Sample*
  - *Cluster Random Sample*
- Nonstatistical Sampling:
  - *Convenience Sample*
  - *Judgment Sample*

**Determine Data Types and Measurement Level**

The method of descriptive statistical analysis that can be performed depends on the type of data and the level of data measurement for the variables in the data set. Typical studies will involve multiple types of variables and data levels.

- Types of Data

| Quantitative | | Qualitative |

- Data Timing

| Cross-Sectional | | Time-Series |

- Data Level

*Lowest Level*　| Nominal |　Categories—no ordering implied

*Mid-Level*　| Ordinal |　Categories—defined ordering

*Highest Level*　| Interval/Ratio |　Measurements

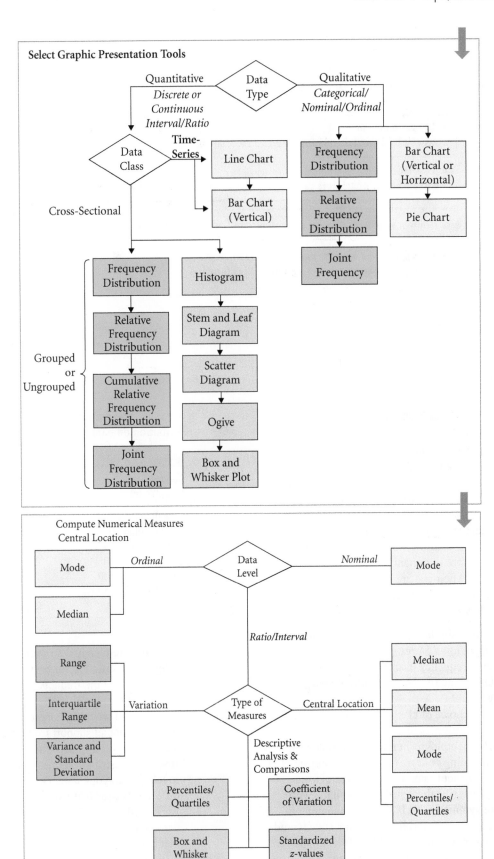

**Select Graphic Presentation Tools**

The choice of numerical descriptive analysis depends on the level of data measurement. If the data are ratio or interval, you have the widest range of numerical tools available.

**Write the Statistical Report**

There is no one set format for writing a statistical report. However, there are a few suggestions you may find useful.

- *Lay the foundation*:
  Provide background and motivation for the analysis.

- *Describe the data collection methodology*:
  Explain how the data were gathered and the sampling techniques were used.

- *Use a logical sequence*:
  Follow a systematic plan for presenting your findings and analysis.

- *Label figures and tables by number*:
  Employ a consistent numbering and labeling format.

# Exercises

## Integrative Application Exercises

Chapters 1 to 3 have introduced you to the basics of descriptive statistics. Many of the business application problems, advanced business application problems, and cases in these chapters will give you practice in performing descriptive statistical analysis. However, too often you are told which procedure you should use, or you can surmise which to use by the location of the exercise. It is important that you learn to identify the appropriate procedure on your own in order to solve problems for test purposes. But more important, this ability is essential throughout your career when you are required to select procedures for the tasks you will undertake. The following exercises will provide you with identification practice.

**SR.1.** Go to your university library and obtain the *Statistical Abstract of the United States*.
  a. Construct a frequency distribution for unemployment rate by state for the most current year available.
  b. Justify your choice of class limits and number of classes.
  c. Locate the unemployment rate for the state in which you are attending college. (1) What proportion of the unemployment rates are below that of your state? (2) Describe the distribution's shape with respect to symmetry. (3) If you were planning to build a new manufacturing plant, what state would you choose in which to build? Justify your answer. (4) Are there any unusual features of this distribution? Describe them.

**SR.2.** The State Industrial Development Council is presently working on a financial services brochure to send to out-of-state companies. It is hoped that the brochure will be helpful in attracting companies to relocate to your state. You are given the following frequency distribution on banks in your state:

| Deposit Size (in millions) | Number of Banks | Total Deposits (in millions) |
|---|---|---|
| Less than 5 | 2 | 7.2 |
| 5 to less than 10 | 7 | 52.1 |
| 10 to less than 25 | 6 | 111.5 |
| 25 to less than 50 | 3 | 95.4 |
| 50 to less than 100 | 2 | 166.6 |
| 100 to less than 500 | 2 | 529.8 |
| Over 500 | 2 | 1663.0 |

  a. Does this frequency distribution violate any of the rules of construction for frequency distributions? If so, reconstruct the frequency distribution to remedy this violation.
  b. The Council wishes to target companies that would require financial support from banks that have at least $25 million in deposits. Reconstruct the frequency distribution to attract such companies to relocate to your state. Do this by considering different classes that would accomplish such a goal.
  c. Reconstruct the frequency distribution to attract companies that require financial support from banks that have between $5 million and $25 million in deposits.
  d. Present an eye-catching, two-paragraph summary of what the data would mean to a company that is considering moving to the state. Your boss has said you need to include relative frequencies in this presentation.

**SR.3.** As an intern for Intel Corporation, suppose you have been asked to help the vice president prepare a newsletter to the shareholders. You have been given access to the data in a file called **Intel** that contains Intel Corporation financial data for the years 1987–1996. Go to the Internet or to Intel's annual report and update the file to include the same variables for the years 1997 to the present. Then, use graphs to effectively present the data in a format that would be usable for the vice president's newsletter. Write a short article that discusses the information shown in your graphs.

**SR.4.** The Woodmill Company makes windows and door trim products. The first step in the process is to rip dimension ($2 \times 8$, $2 \times 10$, etc.) lumber into narrower pieces. Currently, the company uses a manual process in which an experienced operator quickly looks at a board and determines what rip widths to use. The decision is based on the knots and defects in the wood.

A company in Oregon has developed an optical scanner that can be used to determine the rip widths. The scanner is programmed to recognize defects and to determine rip widths that will "optimize" the value of the board. A test run of 100 boards was put through the scanner and the rip widths were identified. However, the boards were not actually ripped. A lumber grader determined the resulting values for each of the 100 boards assuming that the rips determined by the scanner had been made. Next, the same 100 boards were manually ripped using the normal process. The grader then determined the value for each board after the manual rip process was completed. The resulting data, in the file **Woodmill**, consist of manual rip values and scanner rip values for each of the 100 boards.

a. Develop a frequency distribution for the board values for the scanner and the manual process.

b. Compute appropriate descriptive statistics for both manual and scanner values. Use these data along with the frequency distribution developed in part a

to prepare a written report that describes the results of the test. Be sure to include in your report a conclusion regarding whether the scanner outperforms the manual process.

c. Which process, scanner or manual, generated the most values that were more than 2 standard deviations from the mean?

d. Which of the two processes has the least relative variability?

**SR.5.** The commercial banking industry is undergoing rapid changes due to advances in technology and competitive pressures in the financial services sector. The data file **Banks** contains selected information tabulated by *Fortune* concerning the revenues, profitability, and number of employees for the 51 largest U.S. commercial banks in terms of revenues. Use the information in this file to complete the following:

a. Compute the mean, median, and standard deviation for the three variables revenues, profits, and number of employees.

b. Convert the data for each variable to a z-value. Consider Mellon Bank Corporation headquartered in Pittsburgh. How does it compare to the average bank in the study on the three variables? Discuss.

c. As you can see by examining the data and by looking at the statistics computed in part a, not all banks had the same revenue, same profit, or the same number of employees. Which variable had the greatest relative variation among the banks in the study?

d. Calculate a new variable: profits per employee. Develop a frequency distribution and a histogram for this new variable. Also compute the mean, median, and standard deviation for the new variable. Write a short report that describes the profits per employee for the banks.

e. Referring to part d, how many banks had a profit per employee ratio which exceeded 2 standard deviations from the mean?

**END EXERCISES 3-1**

Here is an integrative case study designed to give you more experience. In addition, we have included several term project assignments that require you to collect and analyze data.

# Review Case 1

## State Department of Insurance

This case study describes the efforts undertaken by the director of the Insurance Division to assess the magnitude of the uninsured motorist problem in a western state. The objective of the case study is to introduce you to a data collection application and show how one organization developed a database. The database **Liabins** contains a subset of the data actually collected by the state department.

The impetus for the case came from the legislative transportation committee, which heard much testimony during the recent legislative session about the problems that occur when an uninsured motorist is involved in a traffic accident where damages to individuals and property occur. The state's law enforcement officers also testified that a large number of vehicles are not covered by liability insurance.

Because of both political pressure and a sense of duty to do what is right, the legislative committee spent many hours wrestling with what to do about drivers who do not carry the mandatory liability insurance. Because the actual magnitude of the problem was unknown, the committee finally arrived at a compromise plan, which required the state Insurance Division to perform random audits of vehicles to determine whether the vehicle was covered by liability insurance. The audits are to be performed on approximately 1% of the state's 1 million registered vehicles each month. If a vehicle is found not to have liability insurance, the vehicle license and the owner's driver's license will be revoked for three months and a $250 fine will be imposed.

However, before actually implementing the audit process, which is projected to cost $1.5 million per year, Herb Kriner, director of the Insurance Division, was told to conduct a preliminary study of the uninsured motorists problem in the state and to report back to the legislative committee in six months.

### The Study

A random sample of 12 counties in the state was selected in a manner that gave the counties with higher numbers of registered vehicles proportionally higher chances of being selected. Two locations were selected in each county and the state police set up roadblocks on a randomly selected day. Vehicles with in-state license plates were stopped at random until approximately 100 vehicles had been stopped at each location. The target total was about 2,400 vehicles statewide.

The issue of primary interest was whether the vehicle was insured. This was determined by observing whether the vehicle was carrying the required certificate of insurance. If so, the officer took down the insurance company name and address and the policy number. If the certificate was not in the car, but the owner stated that insurance was carried, the owner was given a postcard to return within five days supplying the required information. A vehicle was determined to be uninsured if no postcard was returned or if, subsequently, the insurance company reported that the policy was not valid on the day of the survey.

In addition to the issue of insurance coverage, Herb Kriner wanted to collect other information about the vehicle and the owner. This was done using a personal interview during which the police officer asked a series of questions and observed certain things such as seat belt usage and driver's and vehicle license expiration status. Also, the owners' driving records were obtained through the Transportation Department's computer division and added to the information gathered by the state police.

### The Data

The data are contained in the file **Liabins**. The sheet titled "Description" contains an explanation of the data set and the variables.

### Issues to Address

Herb Kriner has two weeks before making a presentation to the legislative subcommittee that has been dealing with the liability insurance issue. As Herb's chief analyst, your job is to perform a comprehensive analysis of the data and to prepare the report that Herb will deliver to the legislature. Remember, this report will go a long way in determining whether the state should spend the $1.5 million to implement a full liability insurance audit system.

# Term Project Assignments

For the project selected, you are to devise a sampling plan, collect appropriate data, and carry out a full descriptive analysis aimed at shedding light on the key issues for the project. The finished project will include a written report of a length and format specified by your professor.

## Project A

*Issue:* Your College of Business and Economics seeks input from business majors regarding class scheduling. Some potential issues are

- Day or evening
- Morning or afternoon
- One-day, two-day, or three-day schedules
- Weekend
- Location (on or off campus)

## Project B

*Issue:* Intercollegiate athletics is a part of most major universities. Revenue from attendance at major sporting events is one key to financing the athletic program. Investigate the drivers of attendance at your university's men's basketball and football games. Some potential issues:

- Game times
- Game days (basketball)

- Ticket prices
- Athletic booster club memberships
- Competition for entertainment dollars

## Project C

*Issue:* The department of your major is interested in surveying department alumni. Some potential issues are

- Satisfaction with degree
- Employment status
- Job satisfaction
- Suggestions for improving course content

## Capstone Project

### Project Objective

The objective of this business statistics capstone project is to provide you with an opportunity to integrate the statistical tools and concepts that you have learned thus far in your business statistics course. Like all real-world applications, completing this project will not require you to utilize every statistical technique covered in the first three chapters. Rather, an objective of the assignment is for you to determine which of the statistical tools and techniques are appropriate for the situation you have selected.

### Project Description

Assume that you are working as an intern for a financial management company. Your employer has a large number of clients who trust the company managers to invest their funds. In your position, you are responsibile for producing reports for clients when they request information. Your company has two large data files with financial information for a large number of U.S. companies. The first is called **US Companies 2003**, which contains financial information for the companies' 2001 or 2002 fiscal year-end. The second file is called US **Companies 2005**, which has data for the fiscal 2003 or 2004 year-end. The 2003 file has data for 7,098 companies. The 2005 file has data for 6,992 companies. Thus, many companies are listed in both files but some are just in one or the other.

The two files have many of the same variables, but the 2003 file has a larger range of financial variables than the

2005 file. For some companies, the data for certain variables are not available and a code of NA is used to so indicate. The 2003 file has a special worksheet that contains the description of each variable. These descriptions apply to the 2005 data file as well.

You have been given access to these two data files for use in preparing your reports. Your role will be to perform certain statistical analyses that can be used to help convert these data into useful information in order to respond to the clients' questions.

This morning, one of the partners of your company received a call from a client who asked for a report that would compare companies in the financial services industry (SIC codes in the 6000s) to companies in production-oriented businesses (SIC codes in the 2000s and 3000s). There are no firm guidelines on what the report should entail, but the partner has suggested the following:

- Start with the 2005 data file. Pull the data for all companies with the desired SIC codes into a new worksheet.
- Prepare a complete descriptive analysis of key financial variables using appropriate charts and graphs to help compare the two types of businesses.
- Determine whether there are differences between the two classes of companies in terms of key financial measures.
- Using data from the 2003 file for companies that have these SIC codes and that are also in the 2005 file, develop a comparison that shows the changes over the time span both within SIC code grouping and between SIC code groupings.

### Project Deliverables

To successfully complete this capstone project, you are required to deliver a management report that addresses the partner's requests (listed above) and also contains at least one other substantial type of analysis not mentioned by the partner. This latter work should be set off in a special section of the report.

The final report should be presented in a professional format using the style or format suggested by your instructor.

**Chapter 5** Quick Prep Links

- **Review** the concepts of simple random sampling discussed in Chapter 1.

- **Review** the discussion of weighted averages in Chapter 3.

- **Review** the basic rules of probability in Chapter 4, including the Addition and Multiplication rules.

chapter **5**

# Discrete Probability Distributions

## Why you need to know

Each day, Hewlett-Packard (HP), the computer manufacturer, receives component parts such as disk drives, motherboards, and internal modems from suppliers. When a batch of parts arrives, the quality assurance section randomly samples a fixed number of parts and tests them to see if any are defective. Suppose in one such test a sample of 20 parts is selected from a supplier whose contract calls for at most 5% defective parts. How many defective parts in the sample of 20 should HP expect if the contract is being satisfied? What should be concluded if the sample contains 3 defects? Answers to these questions require calculations based on a probability distribution known as the *binomial distribution*.

How many teller stations should Wells Fargo Bank construct in a new bank branch? If there are four teller stations, will customers have to wait too long or will there be excess capacity and wasted space? To help answer these questions, decision makers use a probability distribution known as the *Poisson distribution*.

A personnel manager has a chance to promote 3 people from 10 equally qualified candidates. Suppose none of 6 women are selected by the manager. Is this evidence of gender bias or would we expect to see this type of result? A distribution known as the *hypergeometric distribution* would be very helpful in addressing this issue.

The *binomial, Poisson,* and *hypergeometric* distributions are three *discrete* probability distributions used in business decision making. This chapter introduces discrete probability distributions and shows how they are used in business settings. As you learned in Chapter 4, probability is the way decision makers express their uncertainty about outcomes and events. Through the use of well-established discrete probability distributions like those introduced in Chapter 5, you will be better prepared for making decisions in an uncertain environment.

# 5.1 Introduction to Discrete Probability Distributions

## Random Variables

As discussed in Chapter 4, when a random experiment is performed, some outcome must occur. When the experiment has a quantitative characteristic, we can associate a number with each outcome. For example, an inspector who examines three plasma flat panel televisions can judge each television as "acceptable" or "unacceptable." The outcome of the experiment defines the specific number of acceptable televisions. The possible outcomes are

$$x = \{0, 1, 2, 3\}$$

**Random Variable**

A variable that takes on different numerical values based on chance.

The value $x$ is called a **random variable** since the numerical values it takes on are random and vary from trial to trial. Although the inspector knows these are the possible values for the variable before she samples, she does not know which value will occur in any given trial. Further, the value of the random variable may be different each time three plasma televisions are inspected.

**Discrete Random Variable**

A random variable that can only assume a finite number of values or an infinite sequence of values such as 0, 1, 2....

Two classes of random variables exist: **discrete random variables** and **continuous random variables**. For instance, if a bank auditor randomly examines 15 accounts to verify the accuracy of the balances, the number of inaccurate account balances can be represented by a discrete random variable with the following values:

$$x = \{0, 1, \ldots, 15\}$$

**Continuous Random Variables**

Random variables that can assume an uncountably infinite number of values.

In another situation, 10 employees were recently hired by a major electronics company. The number of females in that group can be described as a discrete random variable with possible values equal to

$$x = \{0, 1, 2, 3, \ldots, 10\}$$

Notice that the value for a discrete random variable is often determined by counting. In the bank auditing example, the value of variable $x$ is determined by counting the number of accounts with errors. In the hiring example, the value of variable $x$ is determined by counting the number of females hired.

In other situations, the random variable is said to be continuous. For example, the exact time it takes a city bus to complete its route may be any value between two points, say 30 minutes to 35 minutes. If $x$ is the time required, then $x$ is continuous because, if measured precisely enough, the possible values, $x$, can be any value in the interval 30 to 35 minutes. Other examples of continuous variables include measures of distance and measures of weight when measured precisely. A continuous random variable is generally defined by measuring, which is contrasted with a discrete random variable, whose value is typically determined by counting. Chapter 6 focuses on some important probability distributions for continuous random variables.

**Displaying Discrete Probability Distributions Graphically** The probability distribution for a discrete random variable is composed of the values the variable can assume and the probabilities for each of the possible values. For example, if three parts are tested to determine if they are defective, the probability distribution for the number of defectives might be

| $x$ = Number of Defectives | $P(x)$ |
|:---:|:---:|
| 0 | 0.10 |
| 1 | 0.30 |
| 2 | 0.40 |
| 3 | 0.20 |
| | $\Sigma = 1.00$ |

Graphically, the discrete probability distribution associated with these defectives can be represented by the areas of rectangles in which the base of each rectangle is one unit wide and the height corresponds to the probability. The areas of the rectangles sum to 1. Figure 5.1 illustrates two examples of discrete probability distributions. Figure 5.1(a) shows a discrete

**FIGURE 5.1** |

Discrete Probability
Distributions

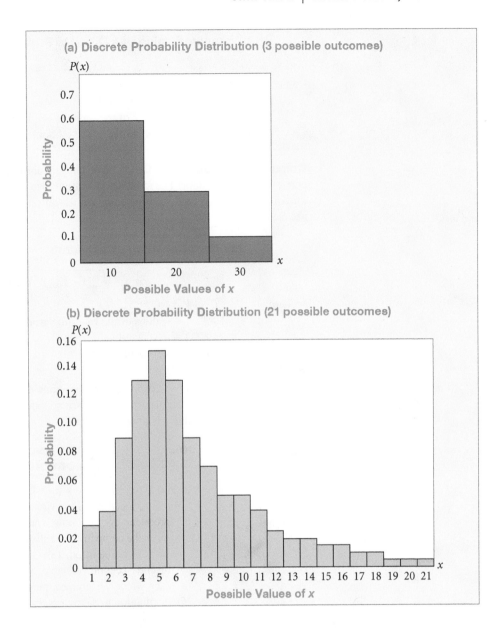

(a) Discrete Probability Distribution (3 possible outcomes)

(b) Discrete Probability Distribution (21 possible outcomes)

random variable with only three possible outcomes. Figure 5.1(b) shows the probability distribution for a discrete variable that has 21 possible outcomes. Note, as the number of possible outcomes increases, the distribution becomes smoother and the individual probability of any particular value tends to be reduced. In all cases, the sum of the probabilities is 1.

Discrete probability distributions have many applications in business decision-making situations. In the remainder of this section, we discuss several important issues that are of particular importance to discrete probability distributions.

**Expected Value**

The mean of a probability distribution. The average value when the experiment that generates values for the random variable is repeated over the long run.

# Mean and Standard Deviation of Discrete Distributions

A probability distribution, like a frequency distribution, can be only partially described by a graph. To aid in a decision situation, you may need to calculate the distribution's *mean* and *standard deviation*. These values measure the central location and spread, respectively, of the probability distribution.

**Chapter Outcome 1.** ➡ Calculating the Mean  The mean of a discrete probability distribution is also called the **expected value** of the random variable from an experiment. The expected value is actually a *weighted average* of the random variable values, in which the weights are the probabilities assigned to the values. The expected value is given in Equation 5.1.

## Expected Value of a Discrete Probability Distribution

$$E(x) = \Sigma xP(x) \tag{5.1}$$

where:

$E(x)$ = Expected value of $x$
$x$ = Values of the random variable
$P(x)$ = Probability of the random variable taking on the value $x$

**Calculating the Standard Deviation**  The standard deviation measures the spread, or dispersion, in a set of data. The standard deviation also measures the spread in the values of a random variable. To calculate the standard deviation for a discrete probability distribution, use Equation 5.2.

## Standard Deviation of a Discrete Probability Distribution

$$\sigma_x = \sqrt{\Sigma[x - E(x)]^2\, P(x)} \tag{5.2}$$

where:

$x$ = Values of the random variable
$E(x)$ = Expected value of $x$
$P(x)$ = Probability of the random variable taking on the value $x$

Equation 5.2 is different in form than the previous equations given for standard deviation, Equations 3.9 and 3.12. This is because we are now dealing with a discrete probability distribution rather than population or sample values.

> **EXAMPLE 5-1**   **COMPUTING THE MEAN AND STANDARD DEVIATION OF A DISCRETE RANDOM VARIABLE**

**Clifton Windows and Glass Company** Clifton Windows and Glass, located in Des Moines, Iowa, makes and distributes window products for new home constructions throughout the Midwest. Each week the company's quality manager examines one randomly selected window to see whether the window contains one or more defects. The discrete random variable, $x$, is the number of defects observed on each window examined, ranging from 0 to 3. The following frequency distribution was developed:

| $x$ | Frequency |
|---|---|
| 0 | 150 |
| 1 | 110 |
| 2 | 50 |
| 3 | 90 |
| | $\Sigma = 400$ |

Assuming that these data reflect typical production at the company, the manager wishes to develop a discrete probability distribution and compute the mean and standard deviation for the distribution. This can be done using the following steps:

**Step 1**  **Convert the frequency distribution into a probability distribution using the relative frequency assessment method.**

| $x$ | Frequency |
|---|---|
| 0 | 150/400 = 0.375 |
| 1 | 110/400 = 0.275 |
| 2 | 50/400 = 0.125 |
| 3 | 90/400 = 0.225 |
| | $\Sigma = 1.000$ |

Step 2  **Compute the expected value using Equation 5.1.**

$$E(x) = \sum x P(x)$$

$$E(x) = (0)(0.375) + (1)(0.275) + (2)(0.125) + (3)(0.225)$$

$$E(x) = 1.20$$

The expected value is 1.20 defects per window. Thus, assuming the distribution of the number of defects is representative of that of each individual window, the long-run average number of defects per window will be 1.20.

Step 3  **Compute the standard deviation using Equation 5.2.**

$$\sigma_x = \sqrt{\sum [x - E(x)]^2 P(x)}$$

| $x$ | $P(x)$ | $[x - E(x)]$ | $[x - E(x)]^2$ | $[x - E(x)]^2 P(x)$ |
|---|---|---|---|---|
| 0 | 0.375 | $0 - 1.2 = -1.20$ | 1.44 | 0.540 |
| 1 | 0.275 | $1 - 1.2 = -.20$ | 0.04 | 0.011 |
| 2 | 0.125 | $2 - 1.2 = .80$ | 0.64 | 0.080 |
| 3 | 0.225 | $3 - 1.2 = 1.80$ | 3.24 | 0.729 |
| | | | | $\Sigma = 1.360$ |

$$\sigma_x = \sqrt{1.36} = 1.17$$

The standard deviation of the discrete probability distribution is 1.17 defects per window.

>>**END EXAMPLE**

**TRY PROBLEM** 5-4 (pg. 196)

---

**BUSINESS APPLICATION**    **EXPECTED VALUES**

**TABLE 5.1** | **Probability Distribution—Defect Rate for Supplier B**

| Defect Rate $x$ | Probability $P(x)$ |
|---|---|
| 0.01 | 0.3 |
| 0.05 | 0.4 |
| 0.10 | 0.2 |
| 0.15 | 0.1 |

**GUGLIANA & SONS** Gugliana & Sons in New York City imports Halloween masks from China and other Far East countries for distribution in the United States and Canada. For one particular product line, Gugliana currently has two suppliers. Both suppliers have a poor record when it comes to quality. Gugliana is planning to purchase 100,000 of a particular Halloween mask and wants to use the least-cost supplier for the entire purchase. Supplier A is less expensive by $0.12 per mask and has an ongoing record of supplying 10% defects. Supplier B is more expensive but may be a higher quality supplier. Gugliana records indicate that the rate of defects from supplier B varies. Table 5.1 shows the probability distributions for the defect percentages for supplier B. Each defect is thought to cost the company $0.95.

Looking first at supplier A, at a defect rate of 0.10, out of 100,000 units the number of defects is expected to be 10,000. The cost of these is $0.95 \times 10,000 = $9,500. For supplier B, the expected defect rate is found using Equation 5.1 as follows:

$$E(\text{Defect rate}) = \sum x P(x)$$

$$E(\text{Defect rate}) = (0.01)(0.3) + (0.05)(0.4) + (0.10)(0.2) + (0.15)(0.1)$$

$$E(\text{Defect rate}) = 0.058$$

Thus, supplier B is expected to supply 5.8% defects, or 5,800 out of the 100,000 units ordered, for an expected cost of $0.95 \times 5,800 = $5,510. Based on defect cost alone, supplier B is less expensive ($5,510 versus $9,500). However, recall that supplier B's product sells for $0.12 per unit more. Thus, on a 100,000-unit order, supplier B costs an extra $0.12 \times 100,000 = $12,000 more than supplier A. The relative costs are

Supplier A = $9,500          Supplier B = $5,510 + $12,000 = $17,510

Therefore, based on expected costs, supplier A should be selected to supply the 100,000 Halloween masks.

*MyStatLab*

# 5-1: Exercises

## Skill Development

**5-1.** An economics quiz contains six multiple-choice questions. Let $x$ represent the number of questions a student answers correctly.
a. Is $x$ a continuous or discrete random variable?
b. What are the possible values of $x$?

**5-2.** Two numbers are randomly drawn without replacement from a list of five. If the five numbers are 2, 2, 4, 6, 8, what is the probability distribution of the sum of the two numbers selected? Show the probability distribution graphically.

**5-3.** If the Prudential Insurance Company surveys its customers to determine the number of children under age 22 living in each household,
a. What is the random variable for this survey?
b. Is the random variable discrete or continuous?

**5-4.** Given the following discrete probability distribution,

| $x$ | $P(x)$ |
|------|--------|
| 50 | 0.375 |
| 65 | 0.15 |
| 70 | 0.225 |
| 75 | 0.05 |
| 90 | 0.20 |

a. Calculate the expected value of $x$.
b. Calculate the variance of $x$.
c. Calculate the standard deviation of $x$.

**5-5.** Because of bad weather, the number of days next week that the captain of a charter fishing boat can leave port is uncertain. Let $x$ = number of days that the boat is able to leave port per week. The following probability distribution for the variable, $x$, was determined based on historical data when the weather was poor:

| $x$ | $P(x)$ |
|------|--------|
| 0 | 0.05 |
| 1 | 0.10 |
| 2 | 0.10 |
| 3 | 0.20 |
| 4 | 0.20 |
| 5 | 0.15 |
| 6 | 0.15 |
| 7 | 0.05 |

Based on the probability distribution, what is the expected number of days per week the captain can leave port?

**5-6.** Consider the following discrete probability distribution:

| $x$ | $P(x)$ |
|------|--------|
| 3 | 0.13 |
| 6 | 0.12 |
| 9 | 0.15 |
| 12 | 0.60 |

a. Calculate the variance and standard deviation of the random variable.
b. Let $y = x + 7$. Calculate the variance and standard deviation of the random variable $y$.
c. Let $z = 7x$. Calculate the variance and standard deviation of the random variable $z$.
d. From your calculations in part a and part b, indicate the effect that adding a constant to a random variable has on its variance and standard deviation.
e. From your calculations in part a and part c, indicate the effect that multiplying a random variable with a constant has on the variance and the standard deviation of the random variable.

**5-7.** Given the following discrete probability distribution,

| $x$ | $P(x)$ |
|------|--------|
| 100 | 0.25 |
| 125 | 0.30 |
| 150 | 0.45 |

a. Calculate the expected value of $x$.
b. Calculate the variance of $x$.
c. Calculate the standard deviation of $x$.

**5-8.** The roll of a pair of dice has the following probability distribution, where the random variable $x$ is the sum of the values produced by each die:

| $x$ | $P(x)$ | $x$ | $P(x)$ |
|------|--------|------|--------|
| 2 | 1/36 | 8 | 5/36 |
| 3 | 2/36 | 9 | 4/36 |
| 4 | 3/36 | 10 | 3/36 |
| 5 | 4/36 | 11 | 2/36 |
| 6 | 5/36 | 12 | 1/36 |
| 7 | 6/36 | | |

a. Calculate the expected value of $x$.
b. Calculate the variance of $x$.
c. Calculate the standard deviation of $x$.

**5-9.** Consider the following discrete probability distribution:

| x | P(x) |
|----|------|
| 5 | 0.10 |
| 10 | 0.15 |
| 15 | 0.25 |
| 20 | 0.50 |

a. Calculate the expected value of the random variable.
b. Let $y = x + 5$. Calculate the expected value of the new random variable $y$.
c. Let $z = 5x$. Calculate the expected value of the new random variable $z$.
d. From your calculations in part a and part b, indicate the effect that adding a constant to a random variable has on the expected value of the random variable.
e. From your calculations in part a and part c, indicate the effect that multiplying a random variable by a constant has on the expected value of the random variable.

**5-10.** Examine the following probability distribution:

| x | 5 | 10 | 15 | 20 | 25 | 30 | 35 | 40 | 45 | 50 |
|------|------|------|------|------|------|------|------|------|------|------|
| P(x) | 0.01 | 0.05 | 0.14 | 0.20 | 0.30 | 0.15 | 0.05 | 0.04 | 0.01 | 0.05 |

a. Calculate the expected value and standard deviation for this random variable.
b. Denote the expected value as $\mu$. Calculate $\mu - \sigma$ and $\mu + \sigma$.
c. Determine the proportion of the distribution that is contained within the interval $\mu \pm \sigma$.
d. Repeat part c for (1) $\mu \pm 2\sigma$ and (2) $\mu \pm 3\sigma$.

## Business **Applications**

**5-11.** The U.S. Census Bureau (Annual Social & Economic Supplement) collects demographics concerning the number of people in families per household. Assume the distribution of the number of people per household is shown in the following table:

| x | P(x) |
|----|------|
| 2 | 0.27 |
| 3 | 0.25 |
| 4 | 0.28 |
| 5 | 0.13 |
| 6 | 0.04 |
| 7 | 0.03 |

a. Calculate the expected number of people in families per household in the United States.
b. Compute the variance and standard deviation of the number of people in families per household.

**5-12.** Jennings Assembly in Hartford, Connecticut, uses a component supplied by a company in Brazil. The component is expensive to carry in inventory and consequently is not always available in stock when requested. Furthermore, shipping schedules are such that the lead time for transportation of the component is not a constant. Using historical records, the manufacturing firm has developed the following probability distribution for the product's lead time. The distribution is shown here, where the random variable $x$ is the number of days between the placement of the replenishment order and the receipt of the item.

| x | P(x) |
|----|------|
| 2 | 0.15 |
| 3 | 0.45 |
| 4 | 0.30 |
| 5 | 0.075 |
| 6 | 0.025 |

a. What is the average lead time for the component?
b. What is the coefficient of variation for delivery lead time?
c. How might the manufacturing firm in the United States use this information?

**5-13.** Marque Electronics is a family-owned electronics repair business in Kansas City. The owner has read an advertisement from a local competitor that guarantees all high-definition television (HDTV) repairs within four days. Based on his company's past experience, he wants to know if he can offer a similar guarantee. His past service records are used to determine the following probability distribution:

| Number of Days | Probability |
|----------------|-------------|
| 1 | 0.15 |
| 2 | 0.25 |
| 3 | 0.30 |
| 4 | 0.18 |
| 5 | 0.12 |

a. Calculate the mean number of days his customers wait for an HDTV repair.
b. Also calculate the variance and standard deviation.
c. Based on the calculations in parts a and b, what conclusion should the manager reach regarding his company's repair times?

**5-14.** Cramer's Bar and Grille in Dallas can seat 130 people at a time. The manager has been gathering data on the number of minutes a party of four spends in the restaurant from the moment they are seated to when they pay the check. What is the mean number of minutes for a dinner party of four? What is the variance and standard deviation?

| Number of Minutes | Probability |
|-------------------|-------------|
| 60 | 0.05 |
| 70 | 0.15 |
| 80 | 0.20 |
| 90 | 0.45 |
| 100 | 0.10 |
| 110 | 0.05 |

**5-15.** Rossmore Brothers, Inc., sells plumbing supplies for commercial and residential applications. The company currently has only one supplier for a particular type of faucet. Based on historical data that the company has maintained, the company has assessed the following probability distribution for the proportion of defective faucets that it receives from this supplier:

| Proportion Defective | Probability |
|:---:|:---:|
| 0.01 | 0.4 |
| 0.02 | 0.3 |
| 0.05 | 0.2 |
| 0.10 | 0.1 |

This supplier charges Rossmore Brothers, Inc., $29.00 per unit for this faucet. Although the supplier will replace any defects free of charge, Rossmore managers figure the cost of dealing with the defects is about $5.00 each.

a. Assuming that Rossmore Brothers is planning to purchase 2,000 of these faucets from the supplier, what is the total expected cost to Rossmore Brothers for the deal?

b. Suppose that Rossmore Brothers has an opportunity to buy the same faucets from another supplier at a cost of $28.50 per unit. However, based on its investigations, Rossmore Brothers has assessed the following probability distribution for the proportion of defective faucets that will be delivered by the new supplier:

| Proportion Defective $x$ | Probability $P(x)$ |
|:---:|:---:|
| 0.01 | 0.1 |
| 0.02 | 0.1 |
| 0.05 | 0.7 |
| 0.10 | 0.1 |

Assuming that the defect cost is still $5.00 each and based on total expected cost for an order of 2,000 faucets, should Rossmore buy from the new supplier or stick with its original supplier?

**5-16.** Radio Shack stocks four alarm clock radios. If it has fewer than four clock radios available at the end of a week, the store restocks the item to bring the in-stock level up to four. If weekly demand is greater than the four units in stock, the store loses the sale. The radio sells for $25 and costs the store $15. The Radio Shack manager estimates that the probability distribution of weekly demand for the radio is as follows:

| $x$ (Weekly Demand) | $P(x)$ |
|:---:|:---:|
| 0 | 0.05 |
| 1 | 0.05 |
| 2 | 0.10 |
| 3 | 0.20 |
| 4 | 0.40 |
| 5 | 0.10 |
| 6 | 0.05 |
| 7 | 0.05 |

a. What is the expected weekly demand for the alarm clock radio?

b. What is the probability that weekly demand will be greater than the number of available radios?

c. What is the expected weekly profit from the sale of the alarm clock radio? (Remember: There are only four clock radios available in any week to meet demand.)

d. On average, how much profit is lost each week because the radio is not available when demanded?

**5-17.** Fiero Products, LTD, of Bologna, Italy, makes a variety of footwear, including indoor slippers, children's shoes, and flip-flops. To keep up with increasing demand, it is considering three expansion plans: (1) a small factory with yearly costs of $150,000 that will increase the production of flip-flops by 400,000; (2) a mid-sized factory with yearly costs of $250,000 that will increase the production of flip-flops by 600,000; and (3) a large factory with yearly costs of $350,000 that will increase the production of flip-flops by 900,000. The profit per flip-flop is projected to be $0.75. The probability distribution of demand for flip-flops is considered to be

| Demand | 300,000 | 700,000 | 900,000 |
|:---|:---:|:---:|:---:|
| Probability | 0.2 | 0.5 | 0.3 |

a. Compute the expected profit for each of the expansion plans.

b. Calculate the standard deviation for each of the expansion plans.

c. Which expansion plan would you suggest? Provide the statistical reasoning behind your selection.

**5-18.** A large corporation in search of a CEO and a CFO has narrowed the fields for each position to a short list. The CEO candidates graduated from Chicago (C) and three Ivy League universities: Harvard (H), Princeton (P), and Yale (Y). The four CFO candidates graduated from MIT (M), Northwestern (N), and two Ivy League universities, Dartmouth (D) and Brown (B). The personnel director wishes to determine the distribution of the number of Ivy League graduates who could fill these positions.

a. Assume the selections were made randomly. Construct the probability distribution of the number of Ivy League graduates who could fill these positions.

b. Would it be surprising if both positions were filled with Ivy League graduates?

c. Calculate the expected value and standard deviation of the number of Ivy League graduates who fill these positions.

## Computer Database **Exercises**

**5-19.** Starbucks has entered into an agreement with a publisher to begin selling a food and beverage magazine on a trial basis. The magazine retails for $3.95 in other stores. Starbucks bought it for $1.95 and sold it for $3.49. During the trial period, Starbucks placed 10 copies of the magazine in each of 150 stores throughout the country. The file entitled **Sold** contains the number of magazines sold in each of the stores.

a. Produce a frequency distribution for these data. Convert the frequency distribution into a probability distribution using the relative frequency assessment method.

b. Calculate the expected profit from the sale of these 10 magazines.

c. Starbucks is negotiating returning all unsold magazines for a salvage price. Determine the salvage price Starbucks will need to obtain to yield a positive expected profit from selling 10 magazines.

**5-20.** Pfizer Inc. is the manufacturer of Revolution (Selamectin), a topical parasiticide used for the treatment, control, and prevention of flea infestation, heartworm, and ear mites for dogs and cats. One of its selling points is that it provides protection for an entire month. Such claims are made on the basis of research and statistical studies. The file entitled **Fleafree** contains data similar to those obtained in Pfizer's research. It presents the number of days Revolution could remain effective when applied to mature cats.

a. Produce a frequency distribution for these data. Convert the frequency distribution into a probability distribution using the relative frequency assessment method.

b. Calculate the expected value and standard deviation for the number of days Revolution could remain effective.

c. If the marketing department wished to advertise the number of days that 90% of the cats remain protected while using Revolution, what would this number of days be?

**5-21.** Fiber Systems makes boat tops for a number of boat manufacturers. Its fabric has a limited two-year warranty. Periodic testing is done to determine if the warranty policy should be changed. One such study may have examined those covers that became unserviceable while still under warranty. Data that could be produced by such a study are contained in the file entitled **Covers**. The data represent assessment of the number of months a cover was used until it became unserviceable.

a. Produce a frequency distribution for these data. Convert the frequency distribution into a probability distribution using the relative frequency assessment method.

b. Calculate the expected value and standard deviation for the time until the covers became unserviceable.

c. The quality control department thinks that among those covers that do become unserviceable while still under warranty the majority last longer than 19 months. Produce the relevant statistic to verify this assumption.

**END EXERCISES 5-1**

---

Chapter Outcome 2.→ ## 5.2 The Binomial Probability Distribution

In Section 5.1 you learned that random variables can be classified as either *discrete* or *continuous*. In most instances, the value of a discrete random variable is determined by counting. For instance, the number of customers who arrive at a store each day is a discrete variable. Its value is determined by counting the customers.

Several theoretical discrete distributions have extensive application in business decision making. A probability distribution is called *theoretical* when the mathematical properties of its random variable are used to produce its probabilities. Such distributions are different from the distributions that are obtained subjectively or from observation. Sections 5.2 and 5.3 focus on theoretical discrete probability distributions. Chapter 6 will introduce important theoretical continuous probability distributions.

### The Binomial Distribution

The first theoretical probability distribution we will consider is the **binomial distribution** that describes processes whose trials have only two possible outcomes. The physical events described by this type of process are widespread. For instance, a quality control system in a manufacturing plant labels each tested item as either defective or acceptable. A firm bidding for a contract either will or will not get the contract. A marketing research firm may receive responses to a questionnaire in the form of "Yes, I will buy" or "No, I will not buy." The personnel manager in an organization is faced with two possible outcomes each time he offers a job—either the applicant accepts the offer or rejects it.

### Characteristics of the Binomial Distribution

The binomial distribution requires that the experiment's trials be independent. This can be assured if the sampling is performed with replacement from a finite population. This means that an item is sampled from a population and returned to the population, after its characteristic(s)

**Binomial Probability Distribution Characteristics**

A distribution that gives the probability of $x$ successes in $n$ trials in a process that meets the following conditions:

1. A trial has only two possible outcomes: a success or a failure.
2. There is a fixed number, $n$, of identical trials.
3. The trials of the experiment are independent of each other. This means that if one outcome is a success, this does not influence the chance of another outcome being a success.
4. The process must be consistent in generating successes and failures. That is, the probability, $p$, associated with a success remains constant from trial to trial.
5. If $p$ represents the probability of a success, then $(1 - p) = q$ is the probability of a failure.

have been recorded, before the next item is sampled. However, sampling with replacement is the exception rather than the rule in business applications. Most often, the sampling is performed without replacement. Strictly speaking, when sampling is performed without replacement, the conditions for the binomial distribution cannot be satisfied. However, the conditions are approximately satisfied if the sample selected is quite small relative to the size of the population from which the sample is selected. A commonly used rule of thumb is that the binomial distribution can be applied if the sample size is at most 5% of the population size.

---

**BUSINESS APPLICATION**    **USING THE BINOMIAL DISTRIBUTION**

**HOUSEHOLD SECURITY** Household Security produces and installs 300 custom-made home security units every week. The units are priced to include one-day installation service by two technicians. A unit with either a design or production problem must be modified on site and will require more than one day to install.

Household Security has completed an extensive study of its design and manufacturing systems. The information shows that if the company is operating at standard quality, 10% of the security units will have problems and will require more than one day to install. The binomial distribution applies to this situation because the following conditions exist:

1. There are only two possible outcomes when a unit is installed: It is good or it is defective (will take more than one day to install). Finding a defective unit in this application will be considered a success. A success occurs when we observe the outcome of interest.
2. Each unit is designed and made in the same way.
3. The outcome of a security unit (good or defective) is independent of whether the preceding unit was good or defective.
4. The probability of a defective unit, $p = 0.10$, remains constant from unit to unit.
5. The probability of a good unit, $q = 1 - p = 0.90$, remains constant from unit to unit.

To determine the likely cause of defects—design or manufacturing—the quality assurance group at Household Security developed a plan for dismantling a random sample of four security units each week. Because the sample size is small ($4/300 = 0.0133$ or 1.33%) relative to the size of the population (300 units per week), the conditions of independence and constant probability will be approximately satisfied because the sample is less than 5% of the population.

We let the number of defective units be the random variable of interest. The number of defectives is limited to discrete values, $x = 0, 1, 2, 3,$ or 4. We can determine the probability that the random variable will have any of the discrete values. One way is to list the sample space, as shown in Table 5.2. We can find the probability of zero defectives, for instance, by employing the Multiplication Rule for Independent Events.

$$P(x = 0 \text{ defectives}) = P(G \text{ and } G \text{ and } G \text{ and } G)$$

where:

$$G = \text{Unit is good (not defective)}$$

Here,

$$P(G) = 0.90$$

and we have assumed the units are independent. Using the Multiplication Rule for Independent Events introduced in Chapter 4 (Rule 9),

$$P(G \text{ and } G \text{ and } G \text{ and } G) = P(G)P(G)P(G)P(G) = (0.90)(0.90)(0.90)(0.90)$$
$$= 0.90^4$$
$$= 0.6561$$

We can also find the probability of exactly one defective in a sample of four. This is accomplished using both the Multiplication Rule for Independent Events and the Addition Rule for Mutually Exclusive Events, which was also introduced in Chapter 4 (Rule 5):

$$P(1 \text{ defective}) = P(G \text{ and } G \text{ and } G \text{ and } D) + P(G \text{ and } G \text{ and } D \text{ and } G)$$
$$+ P(G \text{ and } D \text{ and } G \text{ and } G) + P(D \text{ and } G \text{ and } G \text{ and } G)$$

**TABLE 5.2** | **Sample Space for Household Security**

| Results | No. of Defectives | No. of Ways |
|---|---|---|
| G,G,G,G | 0 | 1 |
| G,G,G,D | 1 | |
| G,G,D,G | | 4 |
| G,D,G,G | | |
| D,G,G,G | | |
| G,G,D,D | 2 | |
| G,D,G,D | | |
| D,G,G,D | | 6 |
| G,D,D,G | | |
| D,G,D,G | | |
| D,D,G,G | | |
| D,D,D,G | 3 | |
| D,D,G,D | | 4 |
| D,G,D,D | | |
| G,D,D,D | | |
| D,D,D,D | 4 | 1 |

where:

$$P(G \text{ and } G \text{ and } G \text{ and } D) = P(G)P(G)P(G)P(D) = (0.90)(0.90)(0.90)(0.10)$$
$$= (0.90^3)(0.10)$$

Likewise:

$$P(G \text{ and } G \text{ and } D \text{ and } G) = (0.90^3)(0.10)$$
$$P(G \text{ and } D \text{ and } G \text{ and } G) = (0.90^3)(0.10)$$
$$P(D \text{ and } G \text{ and } G \text{ and } G) = (0.90^3)(0.10)$$

Then:

$$P(1 \text{ defective}) = (0.90^3)(0.10) + (0.90^3)(0.10) + (0.90^3)(0.10) + (0.90^3)(0.10)$$
$$= (4)(0.90^3)(0.10)$$
$$= 0.2916$$

Note that each of the four possible ways of finding one defective unit has the same probability $[(0.90^3)(0.10)]$. We determine the probability of one of the ways to obtain one defective unit and multiply this value by the number of ways (four) of obtaining one defective unit. This produces the overall probability of one defective unit.

**Combinations** In this relatively simple application, we can fairly easily list the sample space and from that count the number of ways that each possible number of defectives can occur. However, for examples with larger sample sizes, this approach is inefficient. A more effective method exists for counting the number of ways binomial events can occur. This method is called the **counting rule for combinations**. This rule is used to find the number of outcomes from an experiment in which $x$ objects are to be selected from a group of $n$ objects. Equation 5.3 is used to find the combinations.

**Counting Rule for Combinations**

$$C_x^n = \frac{n!}{x!(n-x)!} \tag{5.3}$$

where:

$C_x^n$ = Number of combinations of $x$ objects selected from $n$ objects
$n!$ = $n(n-1)(n-2)\ldots(2)(1)$
$0!$ = 1 by definition

Using Equation 5.3, we find the number of ways that $x = 2$ defectives can occur in a sample of $n = 4$ as

$$C_x^n = \frac{n!}{x!(n-x)!} = \frac{4!}{2!(4-2)!} = \frac{(4)(3)(2)(1)}{(2)(1)(2)(1)} = \frac{24}{4} = 6 \text{ ways}$$

Refer to Table 5.2 to see that this is the same value for two defects in a sample of four that was obtained by listing the sample space.

Now we can find the probabilities of two defectives.

$$P(2 \text{ defectives}) = (6)(0.90^2)(0.10^2)$$
$$= 0.0486$$

Use this method to verify the following:

$$P(3 \text{ defectives}) = (4)(0.90)(0.10^3)$$
$$= 0.0036$$
$$P(4 \text{ defectives}) = (1)(0.10^4)$$
$$= 0.0001$$

**TABLE 5.3** | **Binomial Distribution for Household Security: $n = 4$, $p = 0.10$**

| $x$ = # of Defects | $P(x)$ |
|---|---|
| 0 | 0.6561 |
| 1 | 0.2916 |
| 2 | 0.0486 |
| 3 | 0.0036 |
| 4 | 0.0001 |
| | $\Sigma = 1.0000$ |

The key to developing the probability distribution for a binomial process is first to determine the probability of any one way the event of interest can occur and then to multiply this probability by the number of ways that event can occur. Table 5.3 shows the binomial probability distribution for the number of defective security units in a sample size of four when the probability of any individual unit being defective is 0.10. The probability distribution is graphed in Figure 5.2. Most samples would contain zero or one defective unit when the production system is functioning as designed.

**Binomial Formula**  The steps that we have taken to develop this binomial probability distribution can be summarized through a formula called the *binomial formula*, shown as Equation 5.4. Note, this formula is composed of two parts: the combinations of $x$ items selected from $n$ items and the probability of one of the ways that $x$ items can occur.

**Binomial Formula**

$$P(x) = \frac{n!}{x!(n-x)!} p^x q^{n-x} \tag{5.4}$$

where:

$n$ = Random sample size
$x$ = Number of successes (when a success is defined as what we are looking for)
$n - x$ = Number of failures
$p$ = Probability of a success
$q = 1 - p$ = Probability of a failure
$n! = n(n-1)(n-2)(n-3)\ldots(2)(1)$
$0! = 1$ by definition

Applying Equation 5.4 to the security system example for $n = 4$, $p = 0.10$, and $x = 2$ defects, we get

$$P(x) = \frac{n!}{x!(n-x)!} p^x q^{n-x}$$

$$P(2) = \frac{4!}{2!2!}(0.10^2)(0.90^2) = 6(0.10^2)(0.90^2) = 0.0486$$

This is the same value we calculated earlier when we listed out the sample space above.

**FIGURE 5.2**

Binomial Distribution for
Household Security

| EXAMPLE 5-2 | **USING THE BINOMIAL FORMULA** |

**Creative Style and Cut** Creative Style and Cut, an upscale beauty salon in San Francisco, offers a full refund to anyone who is not satisfied with the way his or her hair looks after it has been cut and styled. The owners believe the hair style satisfaction from customer to customer is independent and that the probability a customer will ask for a refund is 0.20. Suppose a random sample of six customers is observed. In four instances, the customer has asked for a refund. The owners might be interested in the probability of four refund requests from six customers. If the binomial distribution applies, the probability can be found using the following steps:

**Step 1    Define the characteristics of the binomial distribution.**
In this case, the characteristics are

$$n = 6, \qquad p = 0.20, \qquad q = 1 - p = 0.80$$

**Step 2    Determine the probability of $x$ successes in $n$ trials using the binomial formula, Equation 5.4.**
In this case, $n = 6$, $p = 0.20$, $q = 0.80$, and we are interested in the probability of $x = 4$ successes.

$$P(x) = \frac{n!}{x!(n-x)!} p^x q^{n-x}$$
$$P(4) = \frac{6!}{4!(6-4)!} (0.20^4)(0.80^{6-4})$$
$$P(4) = 15(0.20^4)(0.80^2)$$
$$P(4) = 0.0154$$

There is only a 0.0154 chance that exactly four customers will want a refund in a sample of six if the chance that any one of the customers will want a refund is 0.20.

**>>END EXAMPLE**

**TRY PROBLEM** 5-24 (pg. 209)

**Using the Binomial Distribution Table** Using Equation 5.4 to develop the binomial distribution is not difficult, but it can be time-consuming. To make binomial probabilities easier to find, you can use the binomial table in Appendix B. This table is constructed to give *cumulative* probabilities for different sample sizes and probabilities of success. Each column is headed by a probability, *p*, which is the probability associated with a success. The column headings correspond to probabilities of success ranging from 0.01 to 1.00. Down the left side of the table are integer values that correspond to the number of successes, *x*, for the specified sample size, *n*. The values in the body of the table are the cumulative probabilities of *x* or fewer successes in a random sample of size *n*.

---

**BUSINESS APPLICATION**    **BINOMIAL DISTRIBUTION TABLE**

**U.S. BIO** U.S. Bio, a pharmaceutical company, has developed a drug to restore hair growth in men. Like most drugs, this product has potential side effects. One of these is increased blood pressure. The company is willing to market the drug if there are blood-pressure increases in 2% or fewer of the men using the drug.

The company plans to conduct a clinical test with 10 randomly selected men. The number of men with increased blood pressure will be $x = 0, 1, 2, \ldots 10$. We can use the binomial table in Appendix B to develop the probability distribution. Go to the column for $p = 0.02$. The values of *x* are listed down the left side of the table. For example, the probability of $x \leq 2$ occurrences is 0.9991. This means that it is extremely likely that 2 or fewer men, in a sample of 10, would exhibit increased blood pressure if the overall fraction having this side effect is 0.02. The probability of 3 or more men in the sample of $n = 10$ having high blood pressure as a result of the hair growth drug is

$$P(x \geq 3) = 1 - P(x \leq 2) = 1 - 0.9991 = 0.0009$$

There are about 9 chances in 10,000 that we would find 3 or more men with increased blood pressure if the probability of it happening for any one person is $p = 0.02$. If the test did show that 3 men had elevated blood pressure after taking the new drug, the true rate of high blood pressure likely exceeds 2%, and the company should have serious doubts about marketing the drug.

---

**EXAMPLE 5-3**    **USING THE BINOMIAL TABLE**

Nielsen Television Ratings The Nielsen Media Group is the best-known television ratings company. On Tuesday after the 2002 Masters Golf Tournament in Augusta, Georgia, which Tiger Woods won, the company announced that slightly more than 9% of all televisions were tuned to the final round on Sunday. Assuming that the 9% rating is correct, what is the probability that in a random sample of 20 television sets, 2 or fewer would have been tuned to the Masters? This question can be answered, assuming that the binomial distribution applies, using the following steps:

Step 1   **Define the characteristics of the binomial distribution.**
In this case, the characteristics are

$$n = 20, \qquad p = 0.09, \qquad q = 1 - p = 0.91$$

Step 2   **Define the event of interest.**
We are interested in knowing

$$P(x \leq 2) = P(0) + P(1) + P(2)$$

Step 3   **Go to the binomial table in Appendix B to find the desired probability.**
Locate the appropriate column for *p* and the appropriate section in the table for the sample size, *n*. In this case, we locate the section of the table corresponding to sample size equal to $n = 20$ and go to the column headed $p = 0.09$ and the row labeled $x = 2$. The cumulative, $P(x \leq 2)$, listed in the table is 0.7334. Thus, there is a 0.7334 chance that 2 or fewer sets in a random sample of 20 were tuned to the Masters.

>>**END EXAMPLE**

**TRY PROBLEM** 5-28 (pg. 209)

| EXAMPLE 5-4 | **USING THE BINOMIAL DISTRIBUTION** |

**Clearwater Research** Clearwater Research is a full-service marketing research consulting firm. Recently it was retained to do a project for a major U.S. airline. The airline was considering changing from an assigned-seating reservation system to one in which fliers would be able to take any seat they wished on a first-come, first-served basis. The airline believes that 80% of its fliers would like this change if it was accompanied with a reduction in ticket prices. Clearwater Research will survey a large number of customers on this issue, but prior to conducting the full research, it has selected a random sample of 20 customers and determined that 12 like the proposed change. What is the probability of finding 12 or fewer who like the change if the probability is 0.80 that a customer will like the change?

If we assume the binomial distribution applies, we can use the following steps to answer this question:

**Step 1  Define the characteristics of the binomial distribution.**
In this case, the characteristics are

$$n = 20, \qquad p = 0.80, \qquad q = 1 - p = 0.20$$

**Step 2  Define the event of interest.**
We are interested in knowing

$$P(x \leq 12)$$

**Step 3  Go to the binomial table in Appendix B to find the desired probability.**
Locate the appropriate column for $p$ and the appropriate section in the table for the sample size, $n$. Locate the column for $p = 0.80$. Go to the row corresponding to $x = 12$ and the column for $p = 0.80$ in the section of the table for $n = 20$ to get

$$P(x \leq 12) = 0.0321$$

Thus, it is quite unlikely that if 80% of customers like the new seating plan 12 or fewer in a sample of 20 would like it. The airline may want to rethink its plan.

>>**END EXAMPLE**

**TRY PROBLEM** 5-29 (pg. 209)

**Mean and Standard Deviation of the Binomial Distribution**  In Section 5.1 we stated the mean of a discrete probability distribution is also referred to as the *expected value*. The expected value of a discrete random variable, $x$, is found using Equation 5.1.

$$\mu_x = E(x) = \Sigma x P(x)$$

**MEAN OF A BINOMIAL DISTRIBUTION**  This equation for the expected value can be used with any discrete probability distribution, including the binomial. However, if we are working with a binomial distribution, the expected value can be found more easily by using Equation 5.5.

---

**Expected Value of a Binomial Distribution**

$$\mu_x = E(x) = np \qquad \qquad \textbf{(5.5)}$$

where:

$n$ = Sample size
$p$ = Probability of a success

**Excel and Minitab Tutorial**

**CATALOG SALES** Catalog sales have been a part of the U.S. economy for many years, and companies such as Lands' End, L.L. Bean, and Eddie Bauer have enjoyed increased business. One feature that has made mail-order buying so popular is the ease with which customers can return merchandise. Nevertheless, one mail-order catalog has the goal of no more than 11% of all purchased items returned.

The binomial distribution can describe the number of items returned. For instance, in a given hour the company shipped 300 items. If the probability of an item being returned is $p = 0.11$, the expected number of items (mean) to be returned is

$$\mu_x = E(x) = np$$
$$\mu_x = E(x) = (300)(0.11) = 33$$

Thus, the average number of returned items for each 300 items shipped is 33.

Suppose the company sales manager wants to know if the return rate is stable at 11%. To test this, she monitors a random sample of 300 items and finds that 44 have been returned. This return rate exceeds the mean of 33 units, which concerns her. However, before reaching a conclusion, she will be interested in the probability of observing 44 or more returns in a sample of 300.

$$P(x \geq 44) = 1 - P(x \leq 43)$$

The binomial table in Appendix B does not contain sample sizes as large as 300. Instead, we can use Excel's BINOMDIST function or the binomial command in Minitab's Calc— Probability Distribution menu to find the probability. The Excel and Minitab outputs in Figure 5.3a and Figure 5.3b show the cumulative probability of 43 or fewer is equal to

$$P(x \leq 43) = 0.97$$

Then the probability of 44 or more returns is

$$P(x \geq 44) = 1 - 0.97 = 0.03$$

There is only a 3% chance of 44 or more items being returned if the 11% return rate is still in effect. This low probability suggests that the return rate may have increased above 11% because we would not expect to see 44 returned items. The probability is very small.

**FIGURE 5.3A**

Excel 2007 Output for Mail-order Sales Returns

**FIGURE 5.3B**

Minitab Output for Mail-order Sales Returns

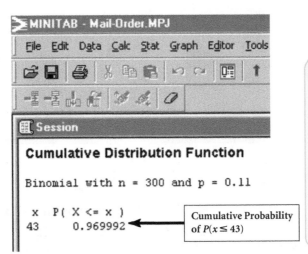

> **MINITAB - Mail-Order.MPJ**
>
> File  Edit  Data  Calc  Stat  Graph  Editor  Tools
>
> **Session**
>
> **Cumulative Distribution Function**
>
> Binomial with n = 300 and p = 0.11
>
> x    P( X <= x )
> 43      0.969992

Cumulative Probability of $P(x \le 43)$

**Minitab Instructions:**
1. Choose **Calc > Probability Distribution > Binomial**.
2. Choose **Cumulative probability**.
3. In **Number of trials** enter sample size.
4. In **Probability of success** enter $p$.
5. In **Input constant** enter the number of successes: $x$.
6. Click **OK**.

---

**EXAMPLE 5-5**    **FINDING THE MEAN OF THE BINOMIAL DISTRIBUTION**

**Clearwater Research** In Example 5-4, Clearwater Research had been hired to do a study for a major airline that is planning to change from a designated-seat assignment plan to an open-seating system. The company believes that 80% of its customers approve of the idea. Clearwater Research interviewed a sample of $n = 20$ and found 12 who like the proposed change. If the airline is correct in its assessment of the probability, what is the expected number of people in a sample of $n = 20$ who will like the change? We can find this using the following steps:

**Step 1**  **Define the characteristics of the binomial distribution.**
In this case, the characteristics are

$$n = 20, \qquad p = 0.80, \qquad q = 1 - p = 0.20$$

**Step 2**  **Use Equation 5.5 to find the expected value.**

$$\mu_x = E(x) = np$$
$$E(x) = 20(0.80) = 16$$

The average number who would say they like the proposed change is 16 in a sample of 20.

**>>END EXAMPLE**

**TRY PROBLEM** 5-33a (pg. 209)

---

**STANDARD DEVIATION OF A BINOMIAL DISTRIBUTION** The standard deviation for any discrete probability distribution can be calculated using Equation 5.2. We show this again as

$$\sigma_x = \sqrt{\sum [x - E(x)]^2 P(x)}$$

If a discrete probability distribution meets the binomial distribution conditions, the standard deviation is more easily computed by Equation 5.6.

| **Standard Deviation of the Binomial Distribution** |
| :---: |
| $$\sigma = \sqrt{npq}$$    (5.6) |

where:
$n$ = Sample size
$p$ = Probability of a success
$q = 1 - p$ = Probability of a failure

**FIGURE 5.4**

The Binomial Distribution with Varying Sample Sizes ($p = 0.50$)

(a) Number of Successes (x)   (b) Number of Successes (x)   (c) Number of Successes (x)

---

**EXAMPLE 5-6**   **FINDING THE STANDARD DEVIATION OF A BINOMIAL DISTRIBUTION**

**Clearwater Research** Refer to Examples 5-4 and 5-5, in which Clearwater Research surveyed a sample of $n = 20$ airline customers about changing the way seats are assigned on flights. The airline believes that 80% of its customers approve of the proposed change. Example 5-5 showed that if the airline is correct in its assessment, the expected number in a sample of 20 who would like the change is 16. However, there are other possible outcomes if 20 customers are surveyed. What is the standard deviation of the random variable, $x$, in this case? We can find the standard deviation for the binomial distribution using the following steps:

**Step 1   Define the characteristics of the binomial distribution.**
In this case, the characteristics are

$$n = 20, \quad p = 0.80, \quad q = 1 - p = 0.20$$

**Step 2   Use Equation 5.6 to calculate the standard deviation.**

$$\sigma = \sqrt{npq} = \sqrt{20(0.80)(0.20)} = 1.7889$$

>>**END EXAMPLE**

**TRY PROBLEM** 5-33 (pg. 209)

---

**Additional Information about the Binomial Distribution** At this point, several comments about the binomial distribution are worth making. If $p$, the probability of a success, is 0.50, the binomial distribution is *symmetrical* and bell-shaped, regardless of the sample size. This is illustrated in Figure 5.4, which shows frequency histograms for samples of $n = 5$, $n = 10$, and $n = 50$. Notice that all three distributions are centered at the expected value, $E(x) = np$.

When the value of $p$ differs from 0.50 in either direction, the binomial distribution is skewed. The skewness will be most pronounced when $n$ is small and $p$ approaches 0 or 1. However, the binomial distribution becomes more bell-shaped as $n$ increases. The frequency histograms shown in Figure 5.5 bear this out.

**FIGURE 5.5**

The Binomial Distribution with Varying Sample Sizes ($p = 0.05$)

(a) Number of Successes (x)   (b) Number of Successes (x)   (c) Number of Successes (x)

# 5-2: Exercises

## Skill Development

**5-22.** The manager for State Bank and Trust has recently examined the credit card account balances for the customers of her bank and found that 20% have an outstanding balance at the credit card limit. Suppose the manager randomly selects 15 customers and finds 4 that have balances at the limit. Assume that the properties of the binomial distribution apply.

a. What is the probability of finding 4 customers in a sample of 15 who have "maxed out" their credit cards?

b. What is the probability that 4 or fewer customers in the sample will have balances at the limit of the credit card?

**5-23.** For a binomial distribution with a sample size equal to 10 and a probability of a success equal to 0.30, what is the probability that the sample will contain exactly three successes? Use the binomial formula to determine the probability.

**5-24.** Use the binomial formula to calculate the following probabilities for an experiment in which $n = 5$ and $p = 0.4$:

a. the probability that $x$ is at most 1

b. the probability that $x$ is at least 4

c. the probability that $x$ is less than 1

**5-25.** If a binomial distribution applies with a sample size of $n = 20$, find

a. the probability of 5 successes if the probability of a success is 0.40

b. the probability of at least 7 successes if the probability of a success is 0.25

c. the expected value, $n = 20$, $p = 0.20$

d. the standard deviation, $n = 20$, $p = 0.20$

**5-26.** A report issued by the American Association of Building Contractors indicates that 40% of all home buyers will do some remodeling to their home within the first five years of home ownership. Assuming this is true, use the binomial distribution to determine the probability that in a random sample of 20 homeowners, 2 or fewer will remodel their homes. Use the binomial table.

**5-27.** Find the probability of exactly 5 successes in a sample of $n = 10$ when the probability of a success is 0.70.

**5-28.** Assuming the binomial distribution applies with a sample size of $n = 15$, find

a. the probability of 5 or more successes if the probability of a success is 0.30

b. the probability of fewer than 4 successes if the probability of a success is 0.75

c. the expected value of the random variable if the probability of success is 0.40

d. the standard deviation of the random variable if the probability of success is 0.40

**5-29.** A random variable follows a binomial distribution with a probability of success equal to 0.65. For a sample size of $n = 7$, find

a. the probability of exactly 3 successes

b. the probability of 4 or more successes

c. the probability of exactly 7 successes

d. the expected value of the random variable

**5-30.** A random variable follows a binomial distribution with a probability of success equal to 0.45. For $n = 11$, find

a. the probability of exactly 1 success

b. the probability of 4 or fewer successes

c. the probability of at least 8 successes

**5-31.** Use the binomial distribution table to determine the following probabilities:

a. $n = 6$, $p = 0.08$; find $P(x = 2)$

b. $n = 9$, $p = 0.80$; determine $P(x < 4)$

c. $n = 11$, $p = 0.65$; calculate $P(2 < x \le 5)$

d. $n = 14$, $p = 0.95$; find $P(x \ge 13)$

e. $n = 20$, $p = 0.50$; compute $P(x > 3)$

**5-32.** Use the binomial distribution in which $n = 6$ and $p = 0.3$ to calculate the following probabilities:

a. $x$ is at most 1.

b. $x$ is at least 2.

c. $x$ is more than 5.

d. $x$ is less than 6.

**5-33.** Given a binomial distribution with $n = 8$ and $p = 0.40$, obtain the following:

a. the mean

b. the standard deviation

c. the probability that the number of successes is larger than the mean

d. the probability that the number of successes is within 2 standard deviations of the mean

## Business Applications

**5-34.** Magic Valley Memorial Hospital administrators have recently received an internal audit report that indicates that 15% of all patient bills contain an error of one form or another. After spending considerable effort to improve the hospital's billing process, the administrators are convinced that things have improved. They believe that the new error rate is somewhere closer to 0.05.

a. Suppose that recently the hospital randomly sampled 10 patient bills and conducted a thorough study to determine whether an error exists. It found 3 bills with errors. Assuming that managers are correct that they have improved the error rate to 0.05, what is the probability that they would find 3 or more errors in a sample of 10 bills?

b. Referring to part a, what conclusion would you reach based on the probability of finding 3 or more errors in the sample of 10 bills?

**5-35.** The Committee for the Study of the American Electorate indicated that 60.7% of the voting-age voters cast ballots in the 2004 presidential election. It also indicated 30.8% of voting-age voters cast ballots for President Bush. A start-up company in San Jose, California, has 10 employees.

   a. How many of the employees would you expect to have voted for President Bush?

   b. All of the employees indicated that they voted in the 2004 presidential election. Determine the probability of this assuming they followed the national trend.

   c. Eight of the employees voted for President Bush. Determine the probability that at least 8 of the employees would vote for President Bush if they followed the national trend.

   d. Based on your calculations in parts b and c, do the employees reflect the national trend? Support your answer with statistical calculations and reasoning.

**5-36.** Dell Computers receives large shipments of microprocessors from Intel Corp. It must try to ensure the proportion of microprocessors that are defective is small. Suppose Dell decides to test five microprocessors out of a shipment of thousands of these microprocessors. Suppose that if at least one of the microprocessors is defective, the shipment is returned.

   a. If Intel Corp.'s shipment contains 10% defective microprocessors, calculate the probability the entire shipment will be returned.

   b. If Intel and Dell agree that Intel will not provide more than 5% defective chips, calculate the probability that the entire shipment will be returned even though only 5% are defective.

   c. Calculate the probability that the entire shipment will be kept by Dell even though the shipment has 10% defective microprocessors.

**5-37.** In his article entitled "Acceptance Sampling Solves Drilling Issues: A Case Study," published in *Woodworking Magazine*, author Ken Wong discusses a problem faced by furniture manufacturing companies dealing with the quality of the drilling of dowel holes. Wong states, "Incorrect sizing and distances with respect to dowel holes can cause many problems for the rest of the process especially when drilling is conducted early in the production process."

   Consider the case of Dragon Wood Furniture in Bismarck, North Dakota, which believes that when the drilling process is operating at an acceptable rate, the upper limit on the percentage of incorrectly drilled dowel holes is 4%. To monitor its drilling process, Dragon Wood Furniture randomly samples 20 products each hour and determines if the dowel hole in each product is correctly drilled or not. If, in the sample of 20 holes, 1 or more incorrectly drilled holes is discovered, the production process is stopped and the drilling process is recalibrated.

   a. If the process is really operating correctly ($p = 0.04$), what is the probability that the sampling effort will produce $x = 0$ defective holes and thus the process will properly be left to continue running?

   b. Suppose the true defect rate has risen to 0.10, what is the probability the sample will produce results that properly tell the managers to halt production to recalibrate the drilling machine?

   c. Prepare a short letter to the manufacturing manager at Dragon Wood Furniture discussing the effectiveness of the sampling process that her company is using. Base your response on the results to parts a and b.

**5-38.** Mooney, Hileman & Jones, a marketing agency located in Cleveland, has created an advertising campaign for a major retail chain, which the agency's executives believe is a winner. For an ad campaign to be successful, at least 80% of those seeing a television commercial must be able to recall the name of the company featured in the commercial one hour after viewing the commercial. Before distributing the ad campaign nationally, the company plans to show the commercial to a random sample of 20 people. It will also show the same people two additional commercials for different products or businesses.

   a. Assuming that the advertisement will be successful (80% will be able to recall the name of the company in the ad), what is the expected number of people in the sample who will recall the company featured in the Mooney, Hileman & Jones commercial one hour after viewing the three commercials?

   b. Suppose that in the sample of 20 people, 11 were able to recall the name of the company in the Mooney, Hileman & Jones commercial one hour after viewing. Based on the premise that the advertising campaign will be successful, what is the probability of 11 or fewer people being able to recall the company name?

   c. Based on your responses to parts a and b, what conclusion might Mooney, Hileman & Jones executives make about this particular advertising campaign?

**5-39.** A survey by KRC Research for *U.S. News* reported that 37% of people plan to spend more on eating out after they retire. If eight people are randomly selected, then determine the

   a. expected number of people who plan to spend more on eating out after they retire

   b. standard deviation of the individuals who plan to spend more on eating out after they retire

   c. probability that two or fewer in the sample indicate that they actually plan to spend more on eating out after retirement

**5-40.** The Nielsen Media Group is the major media ratings company and conducts surveys on a weekly basis to determine household viewing choices. The following table shows the top 10 broadcast television programs for the week of September 29, 2008.

| Rank* | Program | Network | Rating** | Viewers*** |
|---|---|---|---|---|
| 1 | *Dancing with the Stars* | ABC | 12.2 | 18.883 |
| 2 | *NCIS* | CBS | 11 | 17.47 |
| 3 | *60 Minutes* | CBS | 10.5 | 16.648 |
| 4 | *Dancing W/Stars Results* | ABC | 10.2 | 15.491 |
| 5 | *Desperate Housewives* | ABC | 10 | 15.685 |
| 6 | *Mentalist, The* | CBS | 9.8 | 15.484 |
| 7 | *CSI: NY* | CBS | 9.6 | 14.878 |
| 8 | *Criminal Minds* | CBS | 9.5 | 14.78 |
| 9 | *CSI: Miami* | CBS | 9.2 | 14.345 |
| 10 | *NBC Sunday Night Football* | NBC | 8.8 | 14.207 |

*Rank is based on U.S. Household Rating % from Nielsen Media Research's National People Meter Sample.
**A household rating is the estimate of the size of a television audience relative to the total universe, expressed as a percentage. As of September 24, 2007, there are an estimated 112,800,000 television households in the United States. A single national household ratings point represents 1%, or 1,128,000 households.
***Measured in millions; includes all persons over the age of two.
Source: www.nielsenmedia.com

a. Suppose that the producers of *NCIS* commissioned a study that called for the consultants to randomly call 25 people immediately after the *NCIS* time slot and interview those who said that they had just watched *NCIS*. Suppose the consultant submits a report saying that it found no one in the sample of 25 homes who claimed to have watched the program and therefore did not do any surveys. What is the probability of this happening, assuming that the Nielsen ratings for the show are accurate?

b. Assume the producers for *Desperate Housewives* planned to survey 1,000 people on the day following the broadcast of the program. The purpose of the survey was to determine what the reaction would be if one of the leading characters was murdered on the show. Based on the Nielsen ratings, what would be the expected number of people who would end up being included in the analysis, assuming that all 1,000 people could be reached?

**5-41.** A small hotel in a popular resort area has 20 rooms. The hotel manager estimates that 15% of all confirmed reservations are "no-shows." Consequently, the hotel accepts confirmed reservations for as many as 25 rooms. If more confirmed reservations arrive than there are rooms, the overbooked guests are sent to another hotel and given a complementary dinner. If the hotel currently has 25 confirmed reservations, find
a. the probability that no customers will be sent to another hotel
b. the probability that exactly 2 guests will be sent to another hotel
c. the probability that 3 or more guests will be sent to another hotel

**5-42.** A manufacturing firm produces a product that has a ceramic coating. The coating is baked on to the product, and the baking process is known to produce 15% defective items (for example, cracked or chipped finishes). Every hour, 20 products from the thousands that are baked hourly are sampled from the ceramic-coating process and inspected.
a. What is the probability that 5 defective items will be found in the next sample of 20?
b. On average, how many defective items would be expected to occur in each sample of 20?
c. How likely is it that 15 or more nondefective (good) items would occur in a sample due to chance alone?

**5-43.** The Employee Benefit Research Institute reports that 69% of workers reported that they and/or their spouse had saved some money for retirement.
a. If a random sample of 30 workers is taken, what is the probability that fewer than 17 workers and/or their spouses have saved some money for retirement?
b. If a random sample of 50 workers is taken, what is the probability that more than 40 workers and/or their spouses have saved some money for retirement?

**5-44.** Radio frequency identification (RFID) is an electronic scanning technology that can be used to identify items in a number of ways. One advantage of RFID is that it can eliminate the need to manually count inventory, which can help improve inventory management. The technology is not infallible, however, and sometimes errors occur when items are scanned. If the probability that a scanning error occurs is 0.0065, use either Excel or Minitab to find
a. the probability that exactly 20 items will be scanned incorrectly from the next 5,000 items scanned
b. the probability that more than 20 items will be scanned incorrectly from the next 5,000 items scanned
c. the probability that the number of items scanned incorrectly is between 10 and 25 from the next 5,000 items scanned
d. the expected number of items scanned incorrectly from the next 5,000 items scanned

**5-45.** Peter S. Kastner, director of the consulting firm Vericours Inc., reported that 40% of all rebates are not redeemed because consumers either fail to apply for them or their applications are rejected. TCA Fulfillment Services published its redemption rates: 50% for a $30 rebate on a $100 product, 10% for a $10 rebate on a $100 product, and 35% for a $50 rebate on a $200 product.
a. Calculate the weighted average proportion of redemption rates for TCA Fulfillment using the size of the rebate to establish the weights. Does it appear that TCA Fulfillment has a lower rebate rate than that indicated by Vericours? Explain.

b. To more accurately answer the question posed in part a, a random sample of 20 individuals who purchased an item accompanied by a rebate could be asked if they submitted their rebate. Suppose 4 of the questioned individuals said they did redeem their rebate. If Vericours' estimate of the redemption rate is correct, determine the expected number of rebates that would be redeemed. Does it appear that Vericours' estimate may be too high?

c. Determine the likelihood that such an extreme sample result as indicated in part b or something more extreme would occur if the weighted average proportion provides the actual rebate rate.

d. Repeat the calculations of part c assuming that Vericours' estimate of the redemption rate is correct.

e. Are you convinced that the redemption rate is smaller than that indicated by Vericours? Explain.

5-46. *Business Week* reported that business executives want to break down the obstacles that keep them from communicating directly with stock owners. Ms. Borrus reports that 80% of shareholders hold stock in "street names," which are registered with their bank or brokerage. If the brokerage doesn't furnish these names to the corporations, executives cannot communicate with their shareholders. To determine if the percent reported by Ms. Borrus is correct, a sample of 20 shareholders were asked if they held their stock in "street names." Seventeen responded that they did.

a. Supposing the true proportion of shareholders that hold stock under street names is 0.80, calculate the probability that 17 or more of the sampled individuals hold their stock under street names.

b. Repeat the calculation in part a using proportions of 0.70 and 0.90.

c. Based on your calculations in parts a and b, which proportion do you think is most likely true? Support your answer.

## Computer Database **Exercises**

5-47. *USA Today* has reported (Ginny Graves, "As Women Rise in Society, Many Married Couples Still Don't Do 'Equal,'" June 30, 2005) on the gender gap that exists between married spouses. One of the measures of the progress that has been made in that area is the number of women who outearn their husbands. According to the 2003 census conducted by the Bureau of Labor Statistics, 32.5% of female spouses outearn their male counterparts. The file entitled **Gendergap** contains the incomes of 150 married couples in Utah.

a. Determine the number of families in which the female outearns her husband.

b. Calculate the expected number of female spouses who outearn their male counterparts in the sample of 150 married couples based on the Bureau of Labor Statistics study.

c. If the percentage of married women in Utah who outearn their male spouses is the same as that indicated by the Bureau of Labor Statistics, determine the probability that at least the number found in part a would occur.

d. Based on your calculation in part c, does the Bureau of Labor Statistics' percentage seem plausible if Utah is not different than the rest of the United States?

5-48. Tony Hsieh is CEO of e-tailer Zappos.com. His company sells shoes online. It differentiates itself by its selection of shoes and a devotion to customer service. It offers free shipping and free return shipping. An area where costs could be cut back is the shipping charges for return shipping, specifically those that result from the wrong size of shoes being sent. Zappos may try to keep the percentage of returns due to incorrect size to no more than 5%. The file entitled **Shoesize** contains a sample of 125 shoe sizes that were sent to customers and the sizes that were actually ordered.

a. Determine the number of pairs of wrong-size shoes that were delivered to customers.

b. Calculate the probability of obtaining at least that many pairs of wrong-sized shoes delivered to customers if the proportion of incorrect sizes is actually 0.05.

c. On the basis of your calculation, determine whether Zappos has kept the percentage of returns due to incorrect size to no more than 5%. Support your answer with statistical reasoning.

d. If Zappos sells 5 million pairs of shoes in one year and it costs an average of $4.75 a pair to return them, calculate the expected cost associated with wrong-sized shoes being returned using the probability calculated from the sample data.

5-49. International Data Corp. (IDC) has shown that the average return on business analytics projects was almost four-and-a-half times the initial investment. Analytics consists of tools and applications that present better metrics to the user and to the probable future outcome of an event. IDC looked at how long it takes a typical company to recoup its investment in analytics. It determined that 29% of the U.S. corporations that adopted analytics took six months or less to recoup their investment. The file entitled **Analytics** contains a sample of the time it might have taken 35 corporations to recoup their investment in analytics.

a. Determine the number of corporations that recovered their investment in analytics in six months or less.

b. Calculate the probability of obtaining at most the number of corporations that you determined in part a if the percent of those recovering their investment is as indicated by IDC.

c. Determine the 70th percentile of the number of the 35 corporations that recovered their investment in analytics in six months or less. (*Hint*: Recall and use the definition of percentiles from Section 3.1.)

# 5.3 Other Discrete Probability Distributions

The binomial distribution is very useful in many business situations, as indicated by the examples and applications presented in the previous section. However, as we pointed out, there are several requirements that must hold before we can use the binomial distribution to determine probabilities. If those conditions are not satisfied, there may be other theoretical probability distributions that could be employed. In this section we introduce two other very useful discrete probability distributions: the Poisson distribution and the hypergeometric distribution.

Chapter Outcome 3. → ## The Poisson Distribution

To use the binomial distribution, we must be able to count the number of successes and the number of failures. Although in many situations you may be able to count the number of successes, you often cannot count the number of failures. For example, suppose a company builds freeways in Vermont. The company could count the number of potholes that develop per mile (here a pothole is referred to as a success because it is what we are looking for), but how could it count the number of nonpotholes? Or what about a hospital supplying emergency medical services in Los Angeles? It could easily count the number of emergencies its units respond to in one hour, but how could it determine how many calls it did not receive? Obviously, in these cases the number of possible outcomes (successes + failures) is difficult, if not impossible, to determine. If the total number of possible outcomes cannot be determined, the binomial distribution cannot be applied. In these cases you may be able to use the Poisson distribution.

**Characteristics of the Poisson Distribution** The **Poisson distribution**[1] describes a process that extends over time, space, or any well-defined unit of inspection. The outcomes of interest, such as emergency calls or potholes, occur at random, and we count the number of outcomes that occur in a given segment of time or space. We might count the number of emergency calls in a one-hour period or the number of potholes in a two-mile stretch of freeway. As we did with the binomial distribution, we will call these outcomes *successes* even though (like potholes) they might be undesirable.

The possible counts are the integers 0, 1, 2, . . . , and we would like to know the probability of each of these values. For example, what is the chance of getting exactly four emergency calls in a particular hour? What is the chance that a chosen two-mile stretch of freeway will contain zero potholes?

We can use the Poisson probability distribution to answer these questions if we make the following assumptions:

1. We know $\lambda$, the average number of successes in one segment. For example, we know that there is an average of 8 emergency calls per hour ($\lambda = 8$) or an average of 15 potholes per mile of freeway ($\lambda = 15$).
2. The probability of $x$ successes in a segment is the same for all segments of the same size. For example, the probability distribution of emergency calls is the same for any one-hour period of time at the hospital.
3. What happens in one segment has no influence on any nonoverlapping segment. For example, the number of calls arriving between 9:30 P.M. and 10:30 P.M. has no influence on the number of calls between 11:00 P.M. and 12:00 midnight.
4. We imagine dividing time or space into tiny subsegments. Then the chance of *more* than one success in a subsegment is negligible and the chance of exactly one success in a tiny subsegment of length $t$ is $\lambda t$. For example, the chance of two emergency calls in the same second is essentially 0, and if $\lambda = 8$ calls per hour, the chance of a call in any given second is $(8)(1/3,600) \approx 0.0022$.

---

[1]The Poisson distribution can be derived as the limiting distribution of the binomial distribution as the number of trials, $n$, tends to infinity and the probability of success decreases to zero. It serves as a good approximation to the binomial when $n$ is large.

Once $\lambda$ has been determined, we can calculate the average occurrence rate for any number of segments ($t$). This is $\lambda t$. Note that $\lambda$ and $t$ must be in compatible units. If we have $\lambda = 20$ arrivals per hour, the segments must be in hours or fractional parts of an hour. That is, if we have $\lambda = 20$ per hour and we wish to work with half-hour time periods, the segment would be

$$t = \frac{1}{2} \text{hour}$$

not $t = 30$ minutes.

Although the Poisson distribution is often used to describe situations such as the number of customers who arrive at a hospital emergency room per hour or the number of calls the Hewlett-Packard LaserJet printer service center receives in a 30-minute period, the segments need not be time intervals. Poisson distributions are also used to describe such random variables as the number of knots in a sheet of plywood or the number of contaminants in a gallon of lake water. The segments would be the sheet of plywood and the gallon of water.

Another important point is that $\lambda t$, the average number in $t$ segments, is not necessarily the number we will see if we observe the process for $t$ segments. We might expect an average of 20 people to arrive at a checkout stand in any given hour, but we do not expect to find exactly that number arriving every hour. The actual arrivals will form a distribution with an expected value, or mean, equal to $\lambda t$. So, for the Poisson distribution,

$$E[x] = \mu_x = \lambda t$$

Once $\lambda$ and $t$ have been specified, the probability for any discrete value in the Poisson distribution can be found using Equation 5.7.

---

### Poisson Probability Distribution

$$P(x) = \frac{(\lambda t)^x \, e^{-\lambda t}}{x!}$$
(5.7)

where:

$t$ = Number of segments of interest
$x$ = Number of successes in $t$ segments
$\lambda$ = Expected number of successes in one segment
$e$ = Base of the natural logarithm system (2.71828 . . .)

---

**BUSINESS APPLICATION**   **POISSON DISTRIBUTION**

**WHOLE FOODS GROCERY** A study conducted at Whole Foods Grocery shows that the average number of arrivals to the checkout section of the store per hour is 16. Further, the distribution for the number of arrivals is considered to be Poisson distributed. Figure 5.6 shows the shape of the Poisson distribution for $\lambda = 16$. The probability of each possible number of customers arriving can be computed using Equation 5.7. For example, we can find the probability of $x = 12$ customers in one hour ($t = 1$) as follows:

$$P(x = 12) = \frac{(\lambda t)^x \, e^{-\lambda t}}{x!} = \frac{16^{12} e^{-16}}{12!} = 0.0661$$

**Poisson Probability Distribution Table** As was the case with the binomial distribution, a table of probabilities exists for the Poisson distribution. (The Poisson table appears in Appendix C.) The Poisson table shows the cumulative probabilities for $x$ or fewer occurrences for different $\lambda t$ values. We can use the following business application to illustrate how to use the Poisson table.

**FIGURE 5.6**

Poisson Distribution for Whole Foods Checkout Arrivals with $\lambda = 16$

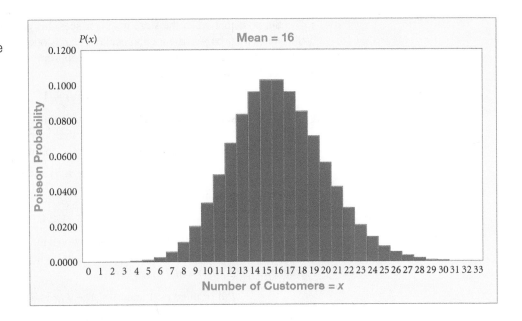

---

**BUSINESS APPLICATION** **USING THE POISSON DISTRIBUTION TABLE**

**WHOLE FOODS GROCERY (*CONTINUED*)** At Whole Foods Grocery, customers are thought to arrive at the checkout section according to a Poisson distribution with $\lambda = 16$ customers per hour. (See Figure 5.6.) Based on previous studies, the store manager believes that the service time for each customer is quite constant at six minutes. Suppose, during each six-minute time period, the store has three checkers available. This means that three customers can be served during each six-minute segment. The manager is interested in the probability that one or more customers will have to wait for service during a six-minute period.

To determine this probability, you will need to convert the mean arrivals from $\lambda = 16$ customers per hour to a new average for a six-minute segment. Six minutes corresponds to 0.10 hours, so you will change the segment size, $t = 0.10$. Then the mean number of arrivals in six minutes is $\lambda t = 16(0.10) = 1.6$ customers.

Now, because there are three checkers, any time four or more customers arrive in a six-minute period, at least one customer will have to wait for service. Thus,

$$P(1 \text{ or more customers wait}) = P(4) + P(5) + P(6) + \ldots$$

or you can use the *Complement Rule*, discussed in Chapter 4, as follows:

$$P(1 \text{ or more customers wait}) = 1 - P(x \leq 3)$$

The Poisson table in Appendix C can be used to find the necessary probabilities. To use the table, first go across the top of the table until you find the desired value of $\lambda t$. In this case, look for $\lambda t = 1.6$. Next, go down the left-hand side to find the value of $x$ corresponding to the number of occurrences of interest. For example, consider $x = 3$ customer arrivals. The probability of $x \leq 3$ is given as 0.9212. (Note, the Poisson table in Appendix C provides the cumulative probability of $x$ or fewer successes.) Thus,

$$P(x \leq 3) = 0.9212$$

Then the probability of four or more customers arriving is

$$P(4 \text{ or more customers}) = 1 - P(x \leq 3)$$
$$P(4 \text{ or more customers}) = 1 - 0.9212 = 0.0788$$

Given the store's capacity to serve three customers in a six-minute period, the probability of one or more customers having to wait is 0.0778.

Suppose that when the store manager sees this probability, she is somewhat concerned. She states that she wants enough checkout stands open so that the chance of a customer waiting does not exceed 0.05. To determine the appropriate number of checkers, you can use the Poisson table to find the following:

$$P(4 \text{ or more customers}) = 1 - P(x \le ?) \le 0.05$$

In other words, a customer will have to wait if more customers arrive than there are checkers. As long as the number of arrivals, $x$, is less than or equal to the number of checkers, no one will wait. Then what value of $x$ will provide the following?

$$1 - P(x \le ?) \le 0.05$$

Therefore, you want

$$P(x \le ?) \ge 0.95$$

You can go to the table for $\lambda t = 1.6$ and scan down the column starting with $P(x = 0) = 0.2019$ until the cumulative probability listed is 0.95 or higher. When you reach $x = 4$, the cumulative probability, $P(x \le 4) \ge 0.9763$. Then,

$$P(4 \text{ or more customers}) = 1 - P(x \le 4) = 1 - 0.9763 = 0.0237$$

Because 0.0237 is less than or equal to the 0.05 limit imposed by the manager, she would have to schedule four checkers.

## How to do it (Example 5-7)

### Using the Poisson Distribution

**The following steps are used to find probabilities using the Poisson distribution:**

1. Define the segment units. The segment units are usually blocks of time, areas of space, or volume.

2. Determine the mean of the random variable. The mean is the parameter that defines the Poisson distribution and is referred to as $\lambda$. It is the average number of successes in a segment of unit size.

3. Determine $t$, the number of the segments to be considered, and then calculate $\lambda t$.

4. Define the event of interest and use the Poisson formula or the Poisson table to find the probability.

---

**EXAMPLE 5-7** **USING THE POISSON DISTRIBUTION**

**Grogan Fabrics** Grogan Fabrics, headquartered in Auckland, New Zealand, makes wool fabrics for export to many other countries around the world. Before shipping, fabric quality tests are performed. The industry standards call for the average number of defects per fabric bolt to not exceed five. During a recent test, the inspector selected a 30-yard bolt at random and carefully examined the first 3 yards, finding three defects. To determine the probability of this event occurring if the fabric meets the industry standards, assuming that the Poisson distribution applies, the company can perform the following steps:

**Step 1 Define the segment unit.**
Because the mean was stated as five defects per fabric bolt, the segment unit in this case is one 30-yard fabric bolt.

**Step 2 Determine the mean of the random variable.**
In this case if the company meets the industry standards, the mean will be

$$\lambda = 5$$

**Step 3 Determine the segment size $t$.**
The company quality inspectors analyzed 3 yards from a 30-yard bolt, which is equal to 0.1 units. So $t = 0.1$. Then,

$$\lambda t = 5(0.1) = 0.50$$

When looking at 3 yards, the company would expect to find 0.5 defects if the industry standards are being met.

**Step 4 Define the event of interest and use the Poisson formula or the Poisson tables to find the probability.**
In this case, three defects were observed. Because 3 exceeds the expected number ($\lambda t = 0.5$) the company would want to find

$$P(x \ge 3) = P(x = 3) + P(x = 4) + \ldots$$

The Poisson table in Appendix C is used to determine these probabilities. Locate the desired probability under the column headed $\lambda t = 0.50$. Then find the values of $x$ down the left-hand column.

$$P(x \ge 3) = 1 - P(x \le 2)$$
$$= 1 - 0.9856$$
$$= 0.0144$$

This low probability may cause the company some concern about whether it is actually meeting the quality standards.

**>>END EXAMPLE**

**TRY PROBLEM** 5-50 (pg. 223)

**The Mean and Standard Deviation of the Poisson Distribution** The mean of the Poisson distribution is $\lambda t$. This is the value we use to specify which Poisson distribution we are using. We must know the mean before we can find probabilities for a Poisson distribution.

Figure 5.6 illustrated that the outcome of a Poisson distributed variable is subject to variation. Like any other discrete probability distribution, the standard deviation for the Poisson can be computed using Equation 5.2:

$$\sigma_x = \sqrt{\sum [x - E(x)]^2 \, P(x)}$$

However, for a Poisson distribution, the standard deviation also can be found using Equation 5.8.

---

**Standard Deviation of the Poisson Distribution**

$$\sigma = \sqrt{\lambda t} \tag{5.8}$$

---

The standard deviation of the Poisson distribution is simply the square root of the mean. Therefore, if you are working with a Poisson process, reducing the mean will reduce the variability also.

**Excel and Minitab Tutorial**

**BUSINESS APPLICATION**    **THE POISSON PROBABILITY DISTRIBUTION**

**HERITAGE TILE** To illustrate the importance of the relationship between the mean and standard deviation of the Poisson distribution, consider Heritage Tile in New York City. The company makes ceramic tile for kitchens and bathrooms. The quality standards call for the number of imperfections in a tile to average 3 or fewer. The distribution of imperfections is thought to be Poisson. Both Minitab and Excel generate Poisson probabilities in much the same way as for the binomial distribution, which was discussed in Section 5.2. If we assume that the company is meeting the standard, Figure 5.7a and Figure 5.7b show the Poisson probability distribution generated using Excel and Minitab when $\lambda t = 3.0$. Even though the average number of defects is 3, the manager is concerned about the high probabilities associated with the number of imperfections equal to 4, 5, 6, or more on a tile. The variability is too great. Using Equation 5.5, the standard deviation for this distribution is

$$\sigma = \sqrt{3.0} = 1.732$$

This large standard deviation means that although some tiles will have few if any imperfections, others will have several, causing problems for installers and unhappy customers.

A quality improvement effort directed at reducing the average number of imperfections to 2.0 would also reduce the standard deviation to

$$\sigma = \sqrt{2.0} = 1.414$$

Further reductions in the average would also reduce variation in the number of imperfections between tiles. This would mean more consistency for installers and higher customer satisfaction.

**Chapter Outcome 3.** ➤ **The Hypergeometric Distribution**

Although the binomial and Poisson distributions are very useful in many business decision-making situations, they both require that the trials be independent. For instance, in binomial applications the probability of a success in one trial must be the same as the probability of a success in any other trial. Although there are certainly times when this assumption can be satisfied, or at least approximated, in instances in which the population is fairly small and we

**FIGURE 5.7A** | Excel 2007 Output for Heritage Tile Example

**Excel 2007 Instructions:**
1. Open a blank worksheet.
2. Enter values for *x* ranging from 0 to 10.
3. Place the cursor in the first blank cell in the next column.
4. Click on *fx* (**Function wizard**) and then select the **Statistical** category.
5. Select the **Poisson** function.
6. Reference the cell with the desired *x* value and enter the mean. Enter **False** to choose noncumulative probabilities.
7. Copy function down for all values of *x*.
8. Graph using **Insert > Column** and label axes and title appropriately.

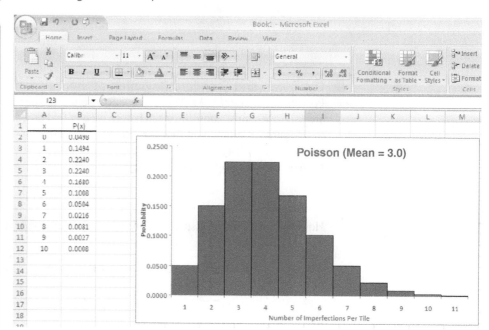

**FIGURE 5.7B**

Minitab Output for Heritage Tile Example

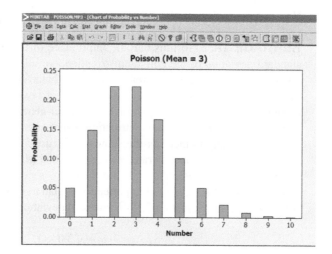

**Minitab Instructions:**
1. Create column *Number* with integers from 0 to 10.
2. Choose **Calc > Probability Distributions > Poisson**.
3. Select **Probability**.
4. In **Mean**, enter 3.
5. Select **Input column**.
6. In **Input column**, enter the column of integers.
7. In **Optional storage**, enter column *Probability*.
8. Click **OK**.
9. Choose **Graph > Bar Chart**.
10. In **Bars represent**, select **Values from a Table**, select **Simple**.
11. Click **OK**.
12. In **Graph variables**, Insert *Probability*.
13. In **Categorical variable**, insert *Number*.
14. Click **OK**.

are sampling without replacement, the condition of independence will not hold. In these cases, a discrete probability distribution referred to as the *hypergeometric distribution* can be useful.

---

**BUSINESS APPLICATION**    **THE HYPERGEOMETRIC PROBABILITY DISTRIBUTION**

**H.J. WOLCOTT CORPORATION** The H.J. Wolcott Corporation manufactures luggage for the travel industry. Because of the intense competition in the marketplace for luggage, Wolcott has made every attempt to make high-quality luggage. However, a recent production run of 20 pieces of a particular luggage model contained 2 units that tested out as defective. The problem was traced to a shipment of defective latches that Wolcott received shortly before the production run started.

The production manager ordered that the entire batch of 20 luggage pieces be isolated from other production output until further testing could be completed. Unfortunately, a new shipping clerk packaged 10 of these isolated luggage pieces and shipped them to a California retailer to fill an order that was already overdue. By the time the production manager noticed what had happened, the luggage was already in transit.

The immediate concern was whether one or more of the defectives had been included in the shipment. The new shipping clerk thought there was a good chance that no defectives were included. Short of reinspecting the remaining luggage pieces, how might the Wolcott Corporation determine the probability that no defectives were actually shipped?

At first glance, it might seem that the question could be answered by employing the binomial distribution with $n = 10$, $p = 2/20 = 0.10$, and $x = 0$. Using the binomial distribution table in Appendix B, we get

$$P(x = 0) = 0.3487$$

There is a 0.3487 chance that no defectives were shipped, assuming the selection process satisfied the requirements of a binomial distribution. However, for the binomial distribution to be applicable, the trials must be independent, and the probability of a success, $p$, must remain constant from trial to trial. In order for this to occur when the sampling is from a "small," *finite* population, the sampling must be performed with *replacement*. This means that after each item is selected, it is returned to the population and, therefore, may be selected again later in the sampling.

In the Wolcott example, the sampling was performed without replacement because each piece of luggage could only be shipped one time. Also, the population of luggage pieces is finite with size $N = 20$, which is a "small" population. Thus, $p$, the probability of a defective luggage unit, does not remain equal to 0.10 on each trial. The value of $p$ on any particular trial depends on what has already been selected on previous trials.

The event of interest is

$$G\ G\ G\ G\ G\ G\ G\ G\ G\ G$$

The probability that the first item selected for shipment would be good would be 18/20, because there were 18 good luggage units in the batch of 20. Now, assuming the first unit selected was good, the probability the second unit was good is 17/19, because we then had only 19 luggage units to select from and 17 of those would be good. The probability that all 10 items selected were good is

$$\frac{18}{20} \times \frac{17}{19} \times \frac{16}{18} \times \frac{15}{17} \times \frac{14}{16} \times \frac{13}{15} \times \frac{12}{14} \times \frac{11}{13} \times \frac{10}{12} \times \frac{9}{11} = 0.2368$$

This value is not the same as the 0.3847 probability we got when the binomial distribution was used. This demonstrates that when sampling is performed without replacement from finite populations, the binomial distribution produces inaccurate probabilities. To protect against large inaccuracies, the binomial distribution should only be used when the sample is small relative to the size of the population. Under that circumstance, the value of $p$ will not change very much as the sample is selected, and the binomial distribution will be a reasonable approximation to the actual probability distribution.

## Hypergeometric Distribution

The hypergeometric distribution is formed by the ratio of the number of ways an event of interest can occur over the total number of ways any event can occur.

In cases in which the sample is large relative to the size of the population, a discrete probability distribution, called the **hypergeometric distribution**, is the correct distribution for computing probabilities for the random variable of interest.

$$C_x^n = \frac{n!}{x!(n-x)!}$$

We then use Equation 5.3 for counting combinations (see Section 5.2) to form the equation for computing probabilities for the hypergeometric distribution. When each trial has two possible outcomes (success and failure), hypergeometric probabilities are computed using Equation 5.9.

---

**Hypergeometric Distribution (Two Possible Outcomes per Trial)**

$$P(x) = \frac{C_{n-x}^{N-X} \cdot C_x^X}{C_n^N} \tag{5.9}$$

where:

$N$ = Population size
$X$ = Number of successes in the population
$n$ = Sample size
$x$ = Number of successes in the sample
$n - x$ = Number of failures in the sample

---

Notice that the numerator of Equation 5.9 is the product of the number of ways you can select $x$ successes in a random sample out of the $X$ successes in the population and the number of ways you can select $n - x$ failures in a sample from the $N - X$ failures in the population. The denominator in the equation is the number of ways the sample can be selected from the population.

In the Wolcott example, the probability of zero defectives being shipped ($x = 0$) is

$$P(x=0) = \frac{C_{10-0}^{20-2} \cdot C_0^2}{C_{10}^{20}}$$

$$P(x=0) = \frac{C_{10}^{18} \cdot C_0^2}{C_{10}^{20}}$$

Carrying out the arithmetic, we get

$$P(x=0) = \frac{(43,758)(1)}{184,756} = 0.2368$$

As we found before, the probability that zero defectives were included in the shipment is 0.2368, or approximately 24%.

The probabilities of $x = 1$ and $x = 2$ defectives can also be found by using Equation 5.9, as follows:

$$P(x=1) = \frac{C_{10-1}^{20-2} \cdot C_1^2}{C_{10}^{20}} = 0.5264$$

and

$$P(x=2) = \frac{C_{10-2}^{20-2} \cdot C_2^2}{C_{10}^{20}} = 0.2368$$

Thus, the hypergeometric probability distribution for the number of defective luggage units in a random selection of 10 is

| $x$ | $P(x)$ |
|---|---|
| 0 | 0.2368 |
| 1 | 0.5264 |
| 2 | 0.2368 |
| | $\Sigma P(x) = 1.0000$ |

Recall that when we introduced the hypergeometric distribution, we said that it is used in situations when we are sampling without replacement from a finite population. However, when the population size is large relative to the sample size, decision makers typically use the binomial distribution as an approximation of the hypergeometric. This eases the computational burden and provides useful approximations in those cases. Although there is no exact rule for when the binomial approximation can be used, we suggest that the sample should be less than 5% of the population size. Otherwise, use the hypergeometric distribution when sampling is done without replacement from the finite population.

---

**EXAMPLE 5-8**    **THE HYPERGEOMETRIC DISTRIBUTION (ONE OF TWO POSSIBLE OUTCOMES PER TRIAL)**

---

Gender Equity One of the biggest changes in U.S. business practice in the past few decades has been the inclusion of women in the management ranks of companies. Tom Peters, management consultant and author of such books as *In Search of Excellence,* has stated that one of the reasons the Middle Eastern countries have suffered economically compared with countries such as the United States is that they have not included women in their economic system. However, there are still issues in U.S. business. Consider a situation in which a Maryland company needed to downsize one department having 30 people—12 women and 18 men. Ten people were laid off, and upper management said the layoffs were done randomly. By chance alone, 40% (12/30) of the layoffs would be women. However, of the 10 laid off, 8 were women. This is 80%, not the 40% due to chance. A labor attorney is interested in the probability of 8 or more women being laid off by chance alone. This can be determined using the following steps:

**Step 1  Determine the population size and the combined sample size.**

The population size and sample size are

$$N = 30 \quad \text{and} \quad n = 10$$

**Step 2  Define the event of interest.**

The attorney is interested in the event:

$$P(x \geq 8) = ?$$

What are the chances that 8 or more women would be selected?

**Step 3  Determine the number of successes in the population and the number of successes in the sample.**

In this situation, a success is the event that a woman is selected. There are $X = 12$ women in the population and $x \geq 8$ in the sample. We will break this down as $x = 8, x = 9, x = 10$.

**Step 4  Compute the desired probabilities using Equation 5.9.**

$$P(x) = \frac{C_{n-x}^{N-X} \cdot C_x^X}{C_n^N}$$

We want[2]:

$$P(x \geq 8) = P(x = 8) + P(x = 9) + P(x = 10)$$

$$P(x = 8) = \frac{C_{10-8}^{30-12} \cdot C_8^{12}}{C_{10}^{30}} = \frac{C_2^{18} \cdot C_8^{12}}{C_{10}^{30}} = 0.0025$$

$$P(x = 9) = \frac{C_1^{18} \cdot C_9^{12}}{C_{10}^{30}} = 0.0001$$

$$P(x = 10) = \frac{C_0^{18} \cdot C_{10}^{12}}{C_{10}^{30}} \approx 0.0000$$

Therefore, $P(x \geq 8) = 0.0025 + 0.0001 + 0.0000 = 0.0026$

The chances that 8 or more women would have been selected among the 10 people chosen for layoff strictly due to chance is 0.0026. The attorney will likely wish to challenge the layoffs based on this extremely low probability.

>>**END EXAMPLE**

**TRY PROBLEM** 5-53 (pg. 223)

**The Hypergeometric Distribution with More Than Two Possible Outcomes per Trial** Equation 5.9 assumes that on any given sample selection or trial only one of two possible outcomes will occur. However, the hypergeometric distribution can easily be extended to consider any number of possible categories of outcomes on a given trial by employing Equation 5.10.

---

**Hypergeometric Distribution ($k$ Possible Outcomes per Trial)**

$$P(x_1, x_2, \ldots, x_k) = \frac{C_{x_1}^{X_1} \cdot C_{x_2}^{X_2} \cdot C_{x_3}^{X_3} \cdot \ldots \cdot C_{x_k}^{X_K}}{C_n^N} \qquad (5.10)$$

where:

$$\sum_{i=1}^{k} X_i = N$$

$$\sum_{i=1}^{k} x_i = n$$

$N$ = Population size
$n$ = Total sample size
$X_i$ = Number of items in the population with outcome $i$
$x_i$ = Number of items in the sample with outcome $i$

---

**EXAMPLE 5-9** **THE HYPERGEOMETRIC DISTRIBUTION FOR MULTIPLE OUTCOMES**

Brand Preference Study Consider a marketing study that involves placing toothpaste made by four different companies in a basket at the exit to a drugstore. A sign on the basket invites customers to take one tube free of charge. At the beginning of the study, the basket contains the following:

5 brand A tubes
4 brand B tubes
6 brand C tubes
4 brand D tubes

The researchers were interested in the brand selection patterns for customers who could select without regard to price. Suppose six customers were observed and three selected brand B, two selected brand D, and one selected brand C. No one selected brand A. The probability of

---
[2]Note, you can use Excel's HYPGEOMDIST function to compute these probabilities.

this selection mix, assuming the customers were selecting entirely at random without replacement from a finite population, can be found using the following steps:

**Step 1** **Determine the population size and the combined sample size.**

The population size and sample size are

$$N = 19 \quad \text{and} \quad n = 6$$

**Step 2** **Define the event of interest.**

The event of interest is

$$P(x_1 = 0; x_2 = 3; x_3 = 1; x_4 = 2) = ?$$

**Step 3** **Determine the number in each category in the population and the number in each category in the sample.**

| $X_1 = 5$ | (brand A) | $x_1 = 0$ |
|---|---|---|
| $X_2 = 4$ | (brand B) | $x_2 = 3$ |
| $X_3 = 6$ | (brand C) | $x_3 = 1$ |
| $X_4 = 4$ | (brand D) | $x_4 = 2$ |
| $N = 19$ | | $n = 6$ |

**Step 4** **Compute the desired probability using Equation 5.10.**

$$P(x_1, x_2, x_3, \ldots, x_k) = \frac{C_{x_1}^{X_1} \cdot C_{x_2}^{X_2} \cdot C_{x_3}^{X_3} \cdot \ldots \cdot C_{x_k}^{X_k}}{C_n^N}$$

$$P(0,3,1,2) = \frac{C_0^5 \cdot C_3^4 \cdot C_1^6 \cdot C_2^4}{C_6^{19}}$$

$$= \frac{(1)(4)(6)(6)}{27,132} = \frac{144}{27,132}$$

$$= 0.0053$$

There are slightly more than 5 chances in 1,000 of this exact selection occurring by random chance.

>>**END EXAMPLE**

**TRY PROBLEM** 5-52 (pg. 223)

 MyStatLab

# 5-3: Exercises

## Skill Development

**5-50.** The mean number of errors per page made by a member of the word processing pool for a large company is thought to be 1.5 with the number of errors distributed according to a Poisson distribution. If three pages are examined, what is the probability that more than 3 errors will be observed?

**5-51.** Arrivals to a bank automated teller machine (ATM) are distributed according to a Poisson distribution with a mean equal to three per 15 minutes.
a. Determine the probability that in a given 15-minute segment no customers will arrive at the ATM.
b. What is the probability that fewer than four customers will arrive in a 30-minute segment?

**5-52.** Consider a situation in which a used-car lot contains five Fords, four General Motors (GM) cars, and five Toyotas. If five cars are selected at random to be placed on a special sale, what is the probability that three are Fords and two are GMs?

**5-53.** A population of 10 items contains 3 that are red and 7 that are green. What is the probability that in a random sample of 3 items selected without replacement, 2 red and 1 green items are selected?

**5-54.** If a random variable follows a Poisson distribution with $\lambda = 20$ and $t = \frac{1}{2}$, find the
a. expected value, variance, and standard deviation of this Poisson distribution
b. probability of exactly 8 successes

**5-55.** A corporation has 11 manufacturing plants. Of these, 7 are domestic and 4 are located outside the United States. Each year a performance evaluation is conducted for 4 randomly selected plants.
a. What is the probability that a performance evaluation will include exactly 1 plant outside the United States?
b. What is the probability that a performance evaluation will contain 3 plants from the United States?

c. What is the probability that a performance evaluation will include 2 or more plants from outside the United States?

**5-56.** Determine the following values associated with a Poisson distribution with $\lambda t$ equal to 3:
   a. $P(x \le 3)$
   b. $P(x > 3)$
   c. $P(2 < x \le 5)$
   d. Find the smallest $x'$ so that $P(x \le x') > 0.50$.

**5-57.** A random variable, $x$, has a hypergeometric distribution with $N = 10$, $X = 7$, and $n = 4$. Calculate the following quantities:
   a. $P(x = 3)$
   b. $P(x = 5)$
   c. $P(x \ge 4)$
   d. Find the largest $x'$ so that $P(x > x') > 0.25$.

## Business Applications

**5-58.** A new phone answering system installed by the Ohio Power Company is capable of handling five calls every 10 minutes. Prior to installing the new system, company analysts determined that the incoming calls to the system are Poisson distributed with a mean equal to two every 10 minutes. If this incoming call distribution is what the analysts think it is, what is the probability that in a 10-minute period more calls will arrive than the system can handle? Based on this probability, comment on the adequacy of the new answering system.

**5-59.** The Weyerhauser Lumber Company headquartered in Tacoma, Washington, is one of the largest timber and wood product companies in the world. Weyerhauser manufactures plywood at one of its Oregon plants. Plywood contains minor imperfections that can be repaired with small "plugs." One customer will accept plywood with a maximum of 3.5 plugs per sheet on average. Suppose a shipment was sent to this customer and when the customer inspected two sheets at random, 10 plugged defects were counted. What is the probability of observing 10 or more plugged defects if in fact the 3.5 average per sheet is being satisfied? Comment on what this probability implies about whether you think the company is meeting the 3.5 per sheet defect rate.

**5-60.** When things are operating properly, E-Bank United, an Internet bank, can process a maximum of 25 electronic transfers every minute during the busiest periods of the day. If it receives more transfer requests than this, then the bank's computer system will become so overburdened that it will slow to the point that no electronic transfers can be handled. If during the busiest periods of the day requests for electronic transfers arrive at the rate of 170 per 10-minute period on average, what is the probability that the system will be overwhelmed by requests? Assume that the process can be described using a Poisson distribution.

**5-61.** A stock portfolio contains 20 stocks. Of these stocks, 10 are considered "large-cap" stocks, 5 are "mid-cap," and 5 are "small cap." The portfolio manager has been asked by his client to develop a report that highlights

7 randomly selected stocks. When she presents her report to the client, all 7 of the stocks are large-cap stocks. The client is very suspicious that the manager has not randomly selected the stocks. She believes that the chances of all 7 of the stocks being large cap must be very low. Compute the probability of all 7 being large cap and comment on the concerns of the client.

**5-62.** College-Pro Painting does home interior and exterior painting. The company uses inexperienced painters that do not always do a high-quality job. It believes that its painting process can be described by a Poisson distribution with an average of 4.8 defects per 400 square feet of painting.
   a. What is the probability that a 400-square-foot painted section will have fewer than 6 blemishes?
   b. What is the probability that six randomly sampled sections of size 400 square feet will each have 7 or fewer blemishes?

**5-63.** Masters-at-Work was founded by two brothers in Atlanta to provide in-home computer and electronic installation services as well as tech support to solve hardware, software, or computer peripheral crises. Masters-at-Work became highly successful with branches throughout the South and was purchased by Best Buy but continued to operate under the Masters-at-Work name. A shipment of 20 Intel® Pentium® 4 processors was sent to Masters-at-Work. Four of them were defective. One of the Masters-at-Work technicians selected 5 of the processors to put in his parts inventory and went on three service calls.
   a. Determine the probability that only 1 of the 5 processors is defective.
   b. Determine the probability that 3 of the 5 processors are not defective.
   c. Determine the probability that the technician will have enough processors to replace 3 defective processors at the repair sites.

**5-64.** John Thurgood founded a company that translates Chinese books into English. His company is currently testing a computer-based translation service. Since Chinese symbols are difficult to translate, John assumes the computer program will make some errors, but then so do human translators. The computer error rate is supposed to be an average of 3 per 400 words of translation. Suppose John randomly selects a 1,200-word passage. Assuming that the Poisson distribution applies, if the computer error rate is actually 3 errors per 400 words,
   a. determine the probability that no errors will be found.
   b. calculate the probability that more than 14 errors will be found.
   c. find the probability that fewer than 9 errors will be found.
   d. If 15 errors are found in the 1,200-word passage, what would you conclude about the computer company's claim? Why?

**5-65.** Beacon Hill Trees & Shrubs currently has an inventory of 10 fruit trees, 8 pine trees, and 14 maple trees. It plans to give 4 trees away at next Saturday's lawn and garden show in the city park. The 4 winners can select which type of tree they want. Assume they select randomly.

a. What is the probability that all 4 winners will select the same type of tree?

b. What is the probability that 3 winners will select pine trees and the other tree will be a maple?

c. What is the probability that no fruit trees and 2 of each of the others will be selected?

**5-66.** Fasteners used in a manufacturing process are shipped by the supplier to the manufacturer in boxes that contain 20 fasteners. Because the fasteners are critical to the production process, their failure will cause the product to fail. The manufacturing firm and the supplier have agreed that a random sample of 4 fasteners will be selected from every box and tested to see if the fasteners meet the manufacturer's specifications. The nature of the testing process is such that tested fasteners become unusable and must be discarded. The supplier and the manufacturer have agreed that if 2 or more fasteners fail the test, the entire box will be selected as being defective. Assume that a new box has just been received for inspection. If the box has 5 defective fasteners, what is the probability that a random sample of 4 will have 2 or more defective fasteners? What is the probability the box will be accepted?

**5-67.** Lucky Dogs sells spicy hot dogs from a pushcart. The owner of Lucky Dogs is open every day between 11:00 A.M. and 1:00 P.M. Assume the demand for spicy hot dogs follows a Poisson distribution with a mean of 50 per hour.

a. What is the probability the owner will run out of spicy dogs over the two-hour period if he stocks his cart with 115 spicy dogs every day?

b. How many spicy hot dogs should the owner stock if he wants to limit the probability of being out of stock to less than 2.5%?

(*Hint*: Students will have to use Excel's **Statistics > Poisson** or Minitab's **Calc > Probability Distributions > Poisson** option.)

**5-68.** *USA Today* recently reported that about one third of eligible workers haven't enrolled in their employers' 401(k) plans. Costco has been contemplating new incentives to encourage more participation from its employees. Of the 12 employees in one of Costco's automotive departments, 5 have enrolled in Costco's 401(k) plan. The store manager has randomly selected 7 of the automotive department employees to receive investment training.

a. Calculate the probability that all of the employees currently enrolled in the 401(k) program are selected for the investment training.

b. Calculate the probability that none of the employees currently enrolled in the 401(k) program is selected for the investment training.

c. Compute the probability that more than half of the employees currently enrolled in the 401(k) program are selected for the investment training.

**5-69.** The Small Business Administration's Center for Women's Business Research indicated 30% of private firms had female owners, 52% had male owners, and 18% had male and female co-owners. In one community, there are 50 privately owned firms. Ten privately owned firms are selected to receive assistance in marketing their products. Assume the percentages indicated by the Small Business Administration apply to this community.

a. Calculate the probability that one half of the firms selected will be solely owned by a woman, 3 owned by men, and the rest co-owned by women and men.

b. Calculate the probability that all of the firms selected will be solely owned by women.

c. Calculate the probability that 6 will be owned by a woman and the rest co-owned.

## Computer Database **Exercises**

**5-70.** The National Federation of Independent Business (NFIB) survey contacted 130 small firms. One of the many inquiries was to determine the number of employees the firms had. The file entitled **Employees** contains the responses by the firms. The number of employees was grouped into the following categories: (1) fewer than 20; (2) 20–99; (3) 100–499; and (4) 500 or more.

a. Determine the number of firms in each of these categories.

b. If the NFIB contacts 25 of these firms to gather more information, determine the probability that it will choose the following number of firms in each category: (1) 22, (2) 2, (3) 1, and (4) 0.

c. Calculate the probability that it will choose all of the firms from those businesses with fewer than 20 workers.

**5-71.** Cliff Summey is the quality assurance engineer for Sticks and Stones Billiard Supply, a manufacturer of billiard supplies. One of the items that Sticks and Stones produces is sets of pocket billiard balls. Cliff has been monitoring the finish of the pocket billiard balls. He is concerned that sets of billiard balls have been shipped with an increasing number of scratches. The company's goal is to have no more than an average of one scratch per set of pocket billiard balls. A set contains 16 balls. Over the last week, Cliff selected a sample of 48 billiard balls and inspected them to determine the number of scratches. The data collected by Cliff are displayed in the file called **Poolball**.

a. Determine the number of scratches in the sample.

b. Calculate the average number of scratches for 48 pocket billiard balls if Sticks and Stones has met its goal.

c. Determine the probability that there would be at least as many scratches observed per set of pocket billiard balls if Sticks and Stones has met its goal.

d. Based on the sample evidence, does it appear that Sticks and Stones has met its goal? Provide statistical reasons for your conclusion.

# Visual Summary

**Chapter 5:** A **random variable** can take on values that are either discrete or continuous. This chapter has focused on discrete random variables where the potential values are usually integer values. Examples of discrete random variables include the number of defects in a sample of twenty parts, the number of customers who purchase Coca-Cola rather than Pepsi when 100 customers are observed, the number of days late a shipment will be when the product is shipped from India to the United States, or the number of female managers who are promoted from a pool of 30 females and 60 males at a Fortune 500 company. The probabilities associated with the individual values of a random variable form the probability distribution. The most frequently used discrete probability distributions are the **binomial distribution** and the **Poisson distribution**.

 **5.1** Introduction to Discrete Probability Distributions (pg. 192–199)

Summary

A **discrete random** variable can assume only a finite number of values or an infinite sequence of values such as 0, 1, 2,…. The mean of a discrete random variable is called the **expected value** and represents the long-run average value for the random variable. The graph of a discrete random variable looks like a histogram with the values of the random variable presented on the horizontal axis and the bars above the values having heights corresponding to the probability of the outcome occurring. The sum of the individual probabilities sum to one.

**Outcome 1.** Be able to calculate and interpret the expected value of a discrete random variable

 **5.2** The Binomial Probability Distribution (pg. 199–212)

Summary

The **binomial distribution** applies when an experimental trial has only two possible outcomes called *success* and *failure*, the probability of success remains constant from trial to trial, the trials are **independent**, and there are a fixed number of identical trials being considered. The probabilities for a binomial distribution can be calculated using **Equation 5.4**, derived from the **binomial table** in the appendix, or found using Excel or Minitab. The expected value of the binomial distribution is found by multiplying $n$, the number of trials, by $p$, the probability of a success on any one trial. The shape of a binomial distribution depends on the sample size (number of trials) and p, the probability of a success. When $p$ is close to .50, the binomial distribution will be fairly symmetric and bell shaped. Even when $p$ is near 0 or 1, if $n$, the sample size, is large, the binomial distribution will still be fairly symmetric and bell shaped.

**Outcome 2.** Be able to apply the binomial distribution to business decision-making situations

**5.3** Other Discrete Probability Distributions (pg. 213–225)

Summary

Although the **binomial distribution** may be the most often applied discrete distribution for business decision makers, the **Poisson distribution** and the **hypergeometric distribution** are also frequently employed. The Poisson distribution is used in situations where the value of the random variable is found by counting the number of occurrences within a defined segment of time or space. If you know the mean number of occurrences per segment, you can use the Poisson formula, the Poisson tables in the appendix, or software such as Excel or Minitab to find the probability of any specific number of occurrences within the segment. The Poisson distribution is often used to describe the number of customers who arrive at a service facility in a specific amount of time. The **hypergeometric** distribution is used in situations where the sample size is large relative to the size of the population and the sampling is done without replacement.

**Outcome 3.** Be able to compute probabilities for the Poisson and hypergeometric distributions and apply these distributions to decision-making situations

## Conclusion

Business applications involving discrete random variables are very common in business situations. The probabilities for each possible outcome of the discrete random variable form the discrete probability distribution. The expected value of a discrete probability distribution is the mean and represents the long-run average value of the random variable. Chapter 5 has introduced three specific discrete random variables that are frequently used in business situations: binomial distribution, Poisson distribution, and the hypergeometric distribution.

# Equations

**(5.1)** Expected Value of a Discrete Probability Distribution pg. 194

$$E(x) = \Sigma x P(x)$$

**(5.2)** Standard Deviation of a Discrete Probability Distribution pg. 194

$$\sigma_x = \sqrt{\Sigma[x - E(x)]^2\, P(x)}$$

**(5.3)** Counting Rule for Combinations pg. 201

$$C_x^n = \frac{n!}{x!(n-x)!}$$

**(5.4)** Binomial Formula pg. 202

$$P(x) = \frac{n!}{x!(n-x)!}\, p^x q^{n-x}$$

**(5.5)** Expected Value of a Binomial Distribution pg. 205

$$\mu_x = E(x) = np$$

**(5.6)** Standard Deviation of the Binomial Distribution pg. 207

$$\sigma = \sqrt{npq}$$

**(5.7)** Poisson Probability Distribution pg. 214

$$P(x) = \frac{(\lambda t)^x\, e^{-\lambda t}}{x!}$$

**(5.8)** Standard Deviation of the Poisson Distribution pg. 217

$$\sigma = \sqrt{\lambda t}$$

**(5.9)** Hypergeometric Distribution (Two Possible Outcomes per Trial) pg. 220

$$P(x) = \frac{C_{n-x}^{N-X} \cdot C_x^X}{C_n^N}$$

**(5.10)** Hypergeometric Distribution (k Possible Outcomes per Trial) pg. 222

$$P(x_1, x_2, x_3, \ldots, x_k) = \frac{C_{x_1}^{X_1} \cdot C_{x_2}^{X_2} \cdot C_{x_3}^{X_3} \cdot \ldots \cdot C_{x_k}^{X_k}}{C_n^N}$$

# Key Terms

Binomial Probability Distribution
  Characteristics pg. 199
Continuous random variable pg. 192

Counting rule for combinations pg. 201
Discrete random variable pg. 192
Expected value pg. 193

Random variable pg. 192
Hypergeometric distribution pg. 220

# Chapter Exercises     MyStatLab

## Conceptual Questions

**5-72.** Three discrete distributions were discussed in this chapter. Each was defined by a random variable that measured the number of successes. To apply these distributions, you must know which one to use. Describe the distinguishing characteristics for each distribution.

**5-73.** How is the shape of the binomial distribution changed for a given value of $p$ as the sample size is increased? Discuss.

**5-74.** Discuss the basic differences and similarities between the binomial distribution and the Poisson distribution.

**5-75.** Beginning statistics students are often puzzled by two characteristics of distributions in this chapter: (1) The trials are independent, and (2) the probability of a success remains constant from trial to trial. Students often think these two characteristics are the same.

The questions in this exercise point out the difference. Consider a hypergeometric distribution where $N = 3$, $X = 2$, and $n = 2$.

a. Mathematically demonstrate that the trials for this experiment are dependent by calculating the probability of obtaining a success on the second trial if the first trial resulted in a success. Repeat this calculation if the first trial was a failure. Use these two probabilities to prove that the trials are dependent.

b. Now calculate the probability that a success is obtained on each of the three respective trials and, therefore, demonstrate that the trials are dependent but that the probability of a success is constant from trial to trial.

**5-76.** Consider an experiment in which a sample of size $n = 5$ is taken from a binomial distribution.

a. Calculate the probability of each value of the random variable for the probability of a success equal to (1) 0.1, (2) 0.25, (3) 0.50, (4) 0.75, and (5) 0.9.

b. Which probabilities produced a right-skewed distribution? Why?

c. Which probability of a success yielded a symmetric distribution? Why?

d. Which probabilities produced a left-skewed distribution? Discuss why.

## Business Applications

**5-77.** The McMillanNewspaper Company sometimes makes printing errors in its advertising and is forced to provide corrected advertising in the next issue of the paper. The managing editor has done a study of this problem and found the following data:

| No. of Errors x | Relative Frequency |
|---|---|
| 0 | 0.56 |
| 1 | 0.21 |
| 2 | 0.13 |
| 3 | 0.07 |
| 4 | 0.03 |

a. Using the relative frequencies as probabilities, what is the expected number of errors? Interpret what this value means to the managing editor.

b. Compute the variance and standard deviation for the number of errors and explain what these values measure.

**5-78.** The Ziteck Corporation buys parts from international suppliers. One part is currently being purchased from a Malaysian supplier under a contract that calls for at most 5% of the 10,000 parts to be defective. When a shipment arrives, Ziteck randomly samples 10 parts. If it finds 2 or fewer defectives in the sample, it keeps the shipment; otherwise, it returns the entire shipment to the supplier.

a. Assuming that the conditions for the binomial distribution are satisfied, what is the probability that the sample will lead Ziteck to keep the shipment if the defect rate is actually 0.05?

b. Suppose the supplier is actually sending Ziteck 10% defects. What is the probability that the sample will lead Ziteck to accept the shipment anyway?

c. Comment on this sampling plan (sample size and accept/reject point). Do you think it favors either Ziteck or the supplier? Discuss.

**5-79.** California-based Wagner Foods, Inc., has a process that inserts fruit juice into 24-ounce containers. When the process is in control, half the cans actually contain more than 24 ounces and half contain less. Suppose a quality inspector has just randomly sampled nine cans and found that all nine had more than 24 ounces. Calculate the probability that this result would occur

if the filling process was actually still in control. Based on this probability, what conclusion might be reached? Discuss.

**5-80.** Your company president has told you that the company experiences product returns at the rate of two per month with the number of product returns distributed as a Poisson random variable. Determine the probability that next month there will be

a. no returns

b. one return

c. two returns

d. more than two returns

e. In the last three months your company has had only one month in which the number of returns was at most two. Calculate the probability of this event occurring. What will you tell the president of your company concerning the return rate? Make sure you support your statement with something other than opinion.

**5-81.** The Defense Department has recently advertised for bids for producing a new night-vision binocular. Vista Optical has decided to submit a bid for the contract. The first step was to supply a sample of binoculars for the army to test at its Kentucky development grounds. Vista makes a superior night-vision binocular. However, the 4 sent to the army for testing were taken from a development-lab project of 20 units that contained 4 defectives. The army has indicated it will reject any manufacturer that submits 1 or more defective binoculars. What is the probability that this mistake has cost Vista any chance for the contract?

**5-82.** VERCOR provides merger and acquisition consultants to assist corporations when owners decide to offer their business for sale. One of its news releases, "Tax Audit Frequency Is Rising," written by David L. Perkins Jr., a VERCOR partner and which originally appeared in *The Business Owner*, indicated that the proportion of the largest businesses, those corporations with assets of $10 million and over, that were audited was 0.17.

a. One member of VERCOR's board of directors is on the board of directors of four other large corporations. Calculate the expected number of these five corporations that should get audited, assuming selection is random.

b. Three of the five corporations were actually audited. Determine the probability that at least three of the five corporations would be audited if 17% of large corporations are audited. (Assume random selection.)

c. The board member is concerned that the corporations have been singled out to be audited by the Internal Revenue Service (IRS). Respond to these thoughts using probability and statistical logic.

**5-83.** Stafford Production, Inc., is concerned with the quality of the parts it purchases that will be used in the end items it assembles. Part number 34-78D is used in the company's new laser printer. The parts are sensitive to dust and can easily be damaged in shipment even if they are acceptable when they leave the vendor's plant. In a shipment of four parts, the purchasing agent has assessed the following probability distribution for the number of defective products:

| x | P(x) |
|---|------|
| 0 | 0.20 |
| 1 | 0.20 |
| 2 | 0.20 |
| 3 | 0.20 |
| 4 | 0.20 |

a. What is the expected number of defectives in a shipment of four parts? Discuss what this value really means to Stafford Production, Inc.
b. Compute and interpret the standard deviation of the number of defective parts in a shipment of four.
c. Examine the probabilities as assessed and indicate why this probability distribution might be called a uniform distribution. Provide some reasons why the probabilities might all be equal, as they are in this case.

**5-84.** Bach Photographs takes school pictures and charges only $0.99 for a sitting, which consists of six poses. The company then makes up three packages that are offered to the parents, who have a choice of buying 0, 1, 2, or all 3 of the packages. Based on his experience in the business, Bill Bach has assessed the following probabilities of the number of packages that might be purchased by a parent:

| No. of Packages x | P(x) |
|-------------------|------|
| 0 | 0.30 |
| 1 | 0.40 |
| 2 | 0.20 |
| 3 | 0.10 |

a. What is the expected number of packages to be purchased by each parent?
b. What is the standard deviation for the random variable, x?
c. Suppose all of the picture packages are to be priced at the same level. How much should they be priced if Bach Photographs wants to break even? Assume that the production costs are $3.00 per package. Remember that the sitting charge is $0.99.

**5-85.** The managing partner for Westwood One Investment Managers, Inc., gave a public seminar in which she discussed a number of issues, including investment risk analysis. In that seminar, she reminded people that the coefficient of variation often can be used as a measure of risk of an investment. (See Chapter 3 for a review of the coefficient of variation.) To demonstrate her point, she used two hypothetical stocks as examples. She let

x equal the change in assets for a $1,000.00 investment in stock 1 and y reflect the change in assets for a $1,000.00 investment in stock 2. She showed the seminar participants the following probability distributions:

| x | P(x) | y | P(y) |
|---|------|---|------|
| −$1,000.00 | 0.10 | −$1,000.00 | 0.20 |
| 0.00 | 0.10 | 0.00 | 0.40 |
| 500.00 | 0.30 | 500.00 | 0.30 |
| 1,000.00 | 0.30 | 1,000.00 | 0.05 |
| 2,000.00 | 0.20 | 2,000.00 | 0.05 |

a. Compute the expected values for random variables x and y.
b. Compute the standard deviations for random variables x and y.
c. Recalling that the coefficient of variation is determined by the ratio of the standard deviation over the mean, compute the coefficient of variation for each random variable.
d. Referring to part c, suppose the seminar director said that the first stock was riskier since its standard deviation was greater than the standard deviation of the second stock. How would you respond? (*Hint*: What do the coefficients of variation imply?)

**5-86.** Simmons Market Research conducted a national consumer study of 13,787 respondents in the spring of 2009. The respondents were asked to indicate the primary source of the vitamins or mineral supplements they consume. Thirty-five percent indicated a multiple formula was their choice. A subset of 20 respondents who used multiple vitamins was selected for further questioning. Half of them used a One A Day vitamin; the rest used generic brands. Of this subset, 4 were asked to fill out a more complete health survey.
a. Calculate the probability that the final selection of 4 subset members were all One A Day multiple vitamin users.
b. Compute the number of One A Day users expected to be selected.
c. Calculate the probability that fewer than half of the final selection were One A Day users.

**5-87.** The 700-room Westin Charlotte offers a premiere uptown location in the heart of the city's financial district. On a busy weekend, the hotel has 20 rooms that are not occupied. Suppose that smoking is allowed in 8 of the rooms. A small tour group arrives, which has four smokers and six nonsmokers. The desk clerk randomly selects 10 rooms and gives the keys to the tour guide to distribute to the travelers.
a. Compute the probability that the tour guide will have the correct mix of rooms so that all members of the tour group will receive a room that accommodates their smoking preferences.
b. Determine the probability that the tour guide will have to assign at least one nonsmoker to a smoking room.

c. Determine the probability that the tour guide will have to assign at least one smoker to a nonsmoking room.

## Computer Database **Exercises**

**5-88.** A 23-mile stretch of a two-lane highway east of Paso Robles, California, was once considered a "death trap" by residents of San Luis Obispo County. Formerly known as "Blood Alley," Highway 46 gained notoriety for the number of fatalities (29) and crashes over a 240-week period. More than two-thirds involved head-on collisions. The file entitled **Crashes** contains the simulated number of fatal crashes during this time period.

a. Determine the average number of crashes in the 240 weeks.

b. Calculate the probability that at least 19 crashes would occur over the 240-week period if the average number of crashes per week was as calculated in part a.

c. Calculate the probability that at least 19 crashes would occur over a five-year period if the average number of crashes per week was as calculated in part a.

d. A coalition of state, local, and private organizations devised a coordinated and innovative approach to dramatically reduce deaths and injuries on this road. During the 16 months before and after completion of the project, fatal crashes were reduced to zero. Calculate the probability that there would be no fatal crashes if the mean number of fatal crashes was not changed by the coalition. Does it appear that the average number of fatal accidents has indeed decreased?

**5-89.** American Household, SM Inc., produces a wide array of home safety and security products. One of its products is the First Alert SA302 Dual Sensor Remote Control Smoke Alarm. As part of its quality control program, it constantly tests to assure that the alarms work. A change in the manufacturing process requires the company to determine the proportion of alarms that fail the quality control tests. Each day, 20 smoke alarms are taken from the production line and tested, and the number of defectives is recorded. A file

entitled **Smokeless** contains the possible results from the last 90 days of testing.

a. Compute the proportion of defective smoke alarms.

b. Calculate the expected number and the standard deviation of defectives for each day's testing. Assume the proportion of defectives is what was computed in part a. (*Hint*: Recall the formulas for the mean and the standard deviation for a binomial distribution.)

c. To make sure that the proportion of defectives does not change, the quality control manager wants to establish control limits that are 3 standard deviations above the mean and 3 standard deviations below the mean. Calculate these limits.

d. Determine the probability that a randomly chosen set of 20 smoke alarms would have a number of defectives that was beyond the control limits established in part c.

**5-90.** Covercraft manufactures covers to protect automobile interiors and finishes. Its Block-It 200 Series fabric has a limited two-year warranty. Periodic testing is done to determine if the warranty policy should be changed. One such study examined those covers that became unserviceable while still under warranty. Data that could be produced by such a study are contained in the file entitled **Covers**. The data represent the number of months a cover was used until it became unserviceable. Covercraft might want to examine more carefully the covers that became unserviceable while still under warranty. Specifically, it wants to examine those that became unserviceable before they had been in use one year.

a. Determine the number of covers that became unserviceable before they had been in use less than a year and a half.

b. If Covercraft quality control staff selects 20 of the covers at random, determine the probability that none of them will have failed before they had been in service a year and a half.

c. If Covercraft quality control staff needs to examine at least 5 of the failed covers, determine the probability that they will obtain this many.

# Case 5.1

## SaveMor Pharmacies

A common practice now is for large retail pharmacies to buy the customer base from smaller, independent pharmacies. The way this works is that the buyer requests to see the customer list along with the buying history. The buyer then makes an offer based on its projection of how many of the seller's customers will move their business to the buyer's pharmacy and on how many dollars of new business will come to the buyer as a result of the purchase. Once

the deal is made, the buyer and seller usually send out a joint letter to the seller's customers explaining the transaction and informing them that their prescription files have been transferred to the purchasing company.

The problem is that there is no guarantee regarding what proportion of the existing customers will make the switch to the buying company. That is the issue facing Heidi Fendenand, acquisitions manager for SaveMor Pharmacies. SaveMor has the opportunity to purchase the 6,780-person customer base from Hubbard Pharmacy in San Jose, California. Based on previous acquisitions, Heidi believes that if 70% or more of the customers will make the switch, then the deal is favorable to SaveMor. However, if 60% or less make the move to SaveMor, then the deal will be a bad one and she would recommend against it.

Quincy Kregthorpe, a research analyst who works for Heidi, has suggested that SaveMor take a new approach to this acquisition decision. He has suggested that SaveMor contact a random sample of 20 Hubbard customers telling them of the proposed sale and asking them if they will be willing to switch their business to SaveMor. Quincy has suggested that if 15 or more of the 20 customers indicate that they would make the switch, then SaveMor should go ahead with the purchase. Otherwise, it should decline the deal or negotiate a lower purchase price.

Heidi liked this idea and contacted Cal Hubbard, Hubbard's owner, to discuss the idea of surveying 20 randomly selected customers. Cal was agreeable as long as only these 20 customers would be told about the potential sale.

Before taking the next step, Heidi met with Quincy to discuss the plan one more time. She was concerned that the proposed sampling plan might have too high a probability of rejecting the purchase deal even if it was a positive one from SaveMor's viewpoint.

On the other hand, she was concerned that the plan might also have a high probability of accepting the purchase deal when in fact it would be unfavorable to SaveMor. After discussing these concerns for over an hour, Quincy finally offered to perform an evaluation of the sampling plan.

### Required Tasks:

1. Compute the probability that the sampling plan will provide a result that suggests that SaveMor should reject the deal even if the true proportion of all customers who would switch is actually 0.70.
2. Compute the probability that the sampling plan will provide a result that suggests that SaveMor should accept the deal even if the true proportion of all customers who would switch is actually only 0.60.
3. Write a short report to Heidi outlining the sampling plan, the assumptions on which the evaluation of the sampling plan has been based, and the conclusions regarding the potential effectiveness of the sampling plan. The report should make a recommendation about whether Heidi should go through with the idea of using the sampling plan.

# Case 5.2

## Arrowmark Vending

Arrowmark Vending has the contract to supply pizza at all home football games for a university in the Big 12 athletic conference. It is a constant challenge at each game to determine how many pizzas to have available at the games. Tom Kealey, operations manager for Arrowmark, has determined that his fixed cost of providing pizzas, whether he sells 1 pizza or 4,000 pizzas, is $1,000. This cost includes hiring employees to work at the concession booths, hiring extra employees to cook the pizzas the day of the game, delivering them to the game, and advertising during the game. He believes that this cost should be equally allocated between two types of pizzas.

Tom has determined that he will supply only two types of pizzas: plain cheese and pepperoni and cheese combo. His cost to make a plain cheese pizza is $4.50 each, and his cost to make pepperoni and cheese combo is $5.00 each. Both pizzas will sell for $9.00 at the game. Unsold pizzas have no value and are donated to a local shelter for the homeless.

Past experience has shown the following demand distributions for the two types of pizza at home games:

| Plain Cheese Demand | Probability | Pepperoni and Cheese Demand | Probability |
|---|---|---|---|
| 200 | 0.10 | 300 | 0.10 |
| 300 | 0.15 | 400 | 0.20 |
| 400 | 0.15 | 500 | 0.25 |
| 500 | 0.20 | 600 | 0.25 |
| 600 | 0.20 | 700 | 0.15 |
| 700 | 0.10 | 800 | 0.05 |
| 800 | 0.05 | | |
| 900 | 0.05 | | |

### Required Tasks:

1. For each type of pizza, determine the profit (or loss) associated with producing at each possible demand level. For instance, determine the profit if 200 plain cheese pizzas are produced and 200 are demanded. What is the profit if 200 plain cheese pizzas are produced but 300 were demanded, and so on?

2. Compute the expected profit associated with each possible production level (assuming Tom will only produce at one of the possible demand levels) for each type of pizza.
3. Prepare a short report that provides Tom with the information regarding how many of each type of pizza he should produce if he wants to achieve the highest expected profit from pizza sales at the game.

# Case 5.3

## Boise Cascade Corporation

At the Boise Cascade Corporation, lumber mill logs arrive by truck and are scaled (measured to determine the number of board feet) before they are dumped into a log pond. Figure C-5.3 illustrates the basic flow. The mill manager must determine how many scale stations to have open during various times of the day. If he has too many stations open, the scalers will have excessive idle time and the cost of scaling will be unnecessarily high. On the other hand, if too few scale stations are open, some log trucks will have to wait.

The manager has studied the truck arrival patterns and has determined that during the first open hour (7:00 A.M.–8:00 A.M.), the trucks randomly arrive at 12 per hour on average. Each scale station can scale 6 trucks per hour (10 minutes each). If the manager knew how many trucks would arrive during the hour, he would know how many scale stations to have open.

| | |
|---|---|
| 0 to 6 trucks: | open 1 scale station |
| 7 to 12 trucks: | open 2 scale stations |
| etc. | |

However, the number of trucks is a random variable and is uncertain. Your task is to provide guidance for the decision.

**FIGURE C-5.3**

Truck Flow for Boise Cascade Mill Example

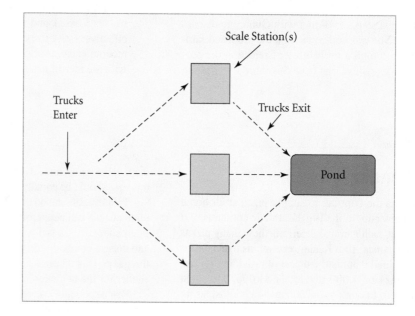

# References

Hogg, R. V., and Elliot A. Tanis, *Probability and Statistical Inference*, 8th ed. (Upper Saddle River, NJ: Prentice Hall, 2009).

Larsen, Richard J., and Moriss L. Marx, *An Introduction to Mathematical Statistics and Its Applications*, 4th ed. (Upper Saddle River, NJ: Prentice Hall, 2005).

*Microsoft Excel 2007* (Redmond, WA: Microsoft Corp., 2007).

*Minitab for Windows Version 15* (State College, PA: Minitab, 2007).

Siegel, Andrew F., *Practical Business Statistics*, 5th ed. (Burr Ridge, IL: Irwin, 2002).

**Chapter 6 Quick Prep Links**
- **Review** the methods for determining the probability for a discrete random variable in Chapter 5.

- **Review** the discussion of the mean and standard deviation in Sections 3.1 and 3.2.

- **Review** the concept of *z*-scores outlined in Section 3.3.

chapter **6**

# Introduction to Continuous Probability Distributions

**6.1** The Normal Probability Distribution (pg. 234–249) ←——— **Outcome 1.** Convert a normal distribution to a standard normal distribution.

**Outcome 2.** Determine probabilities using the standard normal distribution.

**Outcome 3.** Calculate values of the random variable associated with specified probabilities from a normal distribution.

**6.2** Other Continuous Probability Distributions (pg. 249–257) ←——— **Outcome 4.** Calculate probabilities associated with a uniformly distributed random variable.

**Outcome 5.** Determine probabilities using an exponential probability distribution.

# Why you need to know

As shown in Chapter 5, you will encounter many business situations where the random variable of interest is discrete and where probability distributions such as the binomial, Poisson, or the hypergeometric will be useful for analyzing decision situations. However, you will also deal with applications where the random variable of interest is *continuous* rather than discrete. For instance, Honda managers are interested in a measure called cycle time, which is the time between cars coming off the assembly line. Their factory is designed to produce a car every 55 seconds, and the operations managers would be interested in determining the probability the actual time between cars will exceed 60 seconds. A pharmaceutical company may be interested in the probability that a new drug will reduce blood pressure by more than 20 points for patients. The Post Cereal company could be interested in the probability that cereal boxes labeled as containing 16 ounces will actually contain at least that much cereal.

In each of these examples, the value of the variable of interest is determined by measuring (measuring the time between cars, measuring the blood pressure reading, measuring the weight of cereal in a box). In every instance, the number of possible values for the variable is limited only by the capacity of the measuring device. The constraints imposed by the measuring devices produce a finite number of outcomes. In these and similar situations, a continuous probability distribution can be used to approximate the distribution of possible outcomes for the random variables. The approximation is appropriate when the number of possible outcomes is large. Chapter 6 introduces three specific continuous probability distributions of particular importance for decision making and the study of business statistics. The first of these, the *normal distribution*, is by far the most important because a great many applications involve random variables that possess the characteristics of the normal distribution. In addition, many of the topics in the remaining chapters of this textbook dealing with statistical estimation and hypothesis testing are based on the normal distribution.

In addition to the normal distribution, you will be introduced to the uniform distribution and the exponential distribution. Both are important continuous probability distributions and have many applications in business decision making. You need to have a firm understanding and working knowledge of all three continuous probability distributions introduced in this chapter.

# 6.1 The Normal Probability Distribution

Chapter 5 introduced three important discrete probability distributions: the binomial distribution, the Poisson distribution, and the hypergeometric distribution. For each distribution, the random variable of interest is discrete and its value is determined by *counting*. In other instances, you will encounter applications in which the value of the random variable is determined by *measuring* rather than by counting. In these cases, the random variable is said to be approximately *continuous* and can take on any value along some defined continuum. For instance, a Pepsi-Cola can that is supposed to contain 12 ounces might actually contain any amount between 11.90 and 12.10 ounces, such as 11.9853 ounces. When the variable of interest is approximately continuous, the probability distribution associated with the random variable is called a *continuous probability distribution*.

One important difference between discrete and continuous probability distributions involves the calculation of probabilities associated with specific values of the random variable. For instance, in a market research example in which 100 people are surveyed and asked whether they have a positive view of a product, we could use the binomial distribution to find the probability of any specific number of positive reviews, such as $P(x = 75)$ or $P(x = 76)$. Although these individual probabilities may be small values, they can be computed because the random variable is discrete. However, if the random variable is continuous, as in the Pepsi-Cola example, there is an uncountably infinite number of possible outcomes for the random variable. Theoretically, the probability of any one of these individual outcomes is zero. That is, $P(x = 11.92) = 0$ or $P(x = 12.05) = 0$. Thus, when you are working with continuous distributions, you will need to find the probability for a range of possible values such as $P(x \leq 11.92)$ or $P(11.92 \leq x \leq 12.0)$. Likewise, you can conclude that

$$P(x \leq 11.92) = P(x < 11.92)$$

because we assume that $P(x = 11.92) = 0$.

There are many different continuous probability distributions, but the most important of these is the *normal distribution*.

## The Normal Distribution

You will encounter many business situations in which the random variable of interest will be treated as a continuous variable. There are several continuous distributions that are frequently used to describe physical situations. The most useful continuous probability distribution is the **normal distribution**.[1] The reason is that the output from a great many processes (both man-made and natural) is normally distributed.

Figure 6.1 illustrates a typical normal distribution and highlights the normal distribution's characteristics. All normal distributions have the same general shape as the one shown in Figure 6.1. However, they can differ in their mean value and their variation, depending on the situation being considered. The process being represented determines the scale of the

**Normal Distribution**

The normal distribution is a bell-shaped distribution with the following properties:

1. It is *unimodal*; that is, the normal distribution peaks at a single value.
2. It is *symmetrical*; this means that the two areas under the curve between the mean and any two points equidistant on either side of the mean are identical. One side of the distribution is the mirror image of the other side.
3. The mean, median, and mode are equal.
4. The normal approaches the horizontal axis on either side of the mean toward plus and minus infinity ($\infty$). In more formal terms, the normal distribution is *asymptotic* to the *x* axis.
5. The amount of variation in the random variable determines the height and spread of the normal distribution.

**FIGURE 6.1**

Characteristics of the Normal Distribution

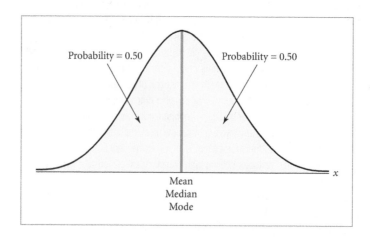

---

[1]It is common to refer to the very large family of normal distributions as "*the* normal distribution."

**FIGURE 6.2** |

Difference between Normal
Distributions

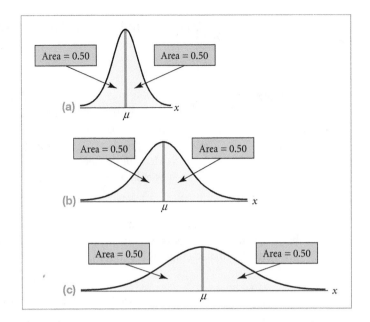

horizontal axis. It may be pounds, inches, dollars, or any other attribute with a continuous measurement. Figure 6.2 shows several normal distributions with different centers and different spreads. Note that the total area (probability) under each normal curve equals 1.

The normal distribution is described by the rather complicated-looking probability density function, shown in Equation 6.1.

---

**Normal Probability Density Function**

$$f(x) = \frac{1}{\sigma\sqrt{2\pi}} e^{-(x-\mu)^2/2\sigma^2}$$

**(6.1)**

where:

$x$ = Any value of the continuous random variable
$\sigma$ = Population standard deviation
$\pi$ = 3.14159
$e$ = Base of the natural log = 2.71828 . . .
$\mu$ = Population mean

---

To graph the normal distribution, we need to know the mean, $\mu$, and the standard deviation, $\sigma$. Placing $\mu$, $\sigma$, and a value of the variable, $x$, into the probability density function, we can calculate a height, $f(x)$, of the density function. If we could try enough $x$ values, we could construct curves like those shown in Figures 6.1 and 6.2.

The area under the normal curve corresponds to probability. Because $x$ is a continuous random variable, the probability, $P(x)$, is equal to 0 for any particular $x$. However, we can find the probability for a range of values between $x_1$ and $x_2$ by finding the area under the curve between these two values. A special normal distribution called the *standard normal distribution* is used to find areas (probabilities) for all normal distributions.

**Chapter Outcome 1.**

**Standard Normal Distribution**

A normal distribution that has a mean = 0.0 and a standard deviation = 1.0. The horizontal axis is scaled in $z$-values that measure the number of standard deviations a point is from the mean. Values above the mean have positive $z$-values. Values below the mean have negative $z$-values.

# The Standard Normal Distribution

The trick to finding probabilities for a normal distribution is to convert the normal distribution to a **standard normal distribution**.

To convert a normal distribution to a standard normal distribution, the values ($x$) of the random variable are standardized as outlined previously in Chapter 3. The conversion formula is shown as Equation 6.2.

### Standardized Normal z-Value

$$z = \frac{x - \mu}{\sigma}$$

(6.2)

where:

$z$ = Scaled value (the number of standard deviations a point $x$ is from the mean)

$x$ = Any point on the horizontal axis

$\mu$ = Mean of the specific normal distribution

$\sigma$ = Standard deviation of the specific normal distribution

Equation 6.2 *scales* any normal distribution axis from its true units (time, weight, dollars, barrels, and so forth) to the standard measure referred to as a *z-value*. Thus, any value of the normally distributed continuous random variable can be represented by a unique *z*-value.

---

**BUSINESS APPLICATION**   STANDARD NORMAL DISTRIBUTION

---

**REAL ESTATE SALES** Before the sub-prime mortgage crisis and slowdown in home sales, an article in the *Washington Post* by Kirstin Downey and Sandra Fleishman entitled "D.C. Area Housing Market Cools Off" stated that the average time that a home remained on the market before selling in Fairfax County is 16 days. Suppose that further analysis performed by Metropolitan Regional Information Systems Inc., which runs the local multiple-listing service, shows the distribution of days that homes stay on the market before selling is approximated by a normal distribution with a standard deviation of 4 days. Figure 6.3 shows this normal distribution with $\mu = 16$ and $\sigma = 4$.

Three homes sold in Fairfax County were selected from the multiple-listing inventory. The days that these homes spent on the market were

Home 1: $x = 16$ days

Home 2: $x = 18.5$ days

Home 3: $x = 9$ days

Equation 6.2 is used to convert these values from a normally distributed population with $\mu = 16$ and $\sigma = 4$ to corresponding *z*-values in a standard normal distribution. For Home 1, we get

$$z = \frac{x - \mu}{\sigma} = \frac{16 - 16}{4} = 0$$

Note, Home 1 was on the market 16 days, which happens to be equal to the population mean. The standardized *z*-value corresponding to the population mean is zero. This indicates that the population mean is 0 standard deviations from itself.

**FIGURE 6.3**

Distribution of Days Homes Stay on the Market until They Sell

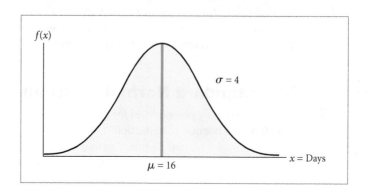

**FIGURE 6.4**

Standard Normal Distribution

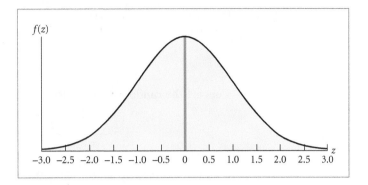

For Home 2, we get

$$z = \frac{x - \mu}{\sigma} = \frac{18.5 - 16}{4} = 0.63$$

Thus, for this population, a home that stays on the market 18 days is 0.63 standard deviations higher than the mean. The standardized $z$-value for Home 3 is

$$z = \frac{x - \mu}{\sigma} = \frac{9 - 16}{4} = -1.75$$

This means a home from this population that stays on the market for only 9 days has a value that is 1.75 standard deviations below the population mean. Note, a negative $z$-value always indicates the $x$-value is less than the mean, $\mu$.

**Chapter Outcome 2.**

The $z$-value represents the number of standard deviations a point is above or below the population mean. Equation 6.2 can be used to convert any specified value, $x$, from the population distribution to a corresponding $z$-value. If the population distribution is normally distributed as shown in Figure 6.3, then the distribution of $z$-values will also be normally distributed and is called the *standard normal distribution*. Figure 6.4 shows a standard normal distribution.

**How to do it** (Example 6-1)

**Using the Normal Distribution**

**If a continuous random variable is distributed as a normal distribution, the distribution is symmetrically distributed around the mean, and is described by the mean and standard deviation. To find probabilities associated with a normally distributed random variable, use the following steps:**

1. Determine the mean, $\mu$, and the standard deviation, $\sigma$.

2. Define the event of interest, such as $P(x \geq x_1)$.

3. Convert the normal distribution to the standard normal distribution using Equation 6.2:

$$z = \frac{x - \mu}{\sigma}$$

4. Use the standard normal distribution table to find the probability associated with the calculated $z$-value. The table gives the probability between the $z$-value and the mean.

5. Determine the desired probability using the knowledge that the probability of a value being on either side of the mean is 0.50 and the total probability under the normal distribution is 1.0.

You can convert the normal distribution to a standard normal distribution and use the standard normal table to find the desired probability. Example 6-1 shows the steps required to do this.

**Using the Standard Normal Table** The *standard normal table* in Appendix D provides probabilities (or areas under the normal curve) associated with many different $z$-values. The standard normal table is constructed so that the probabilities provided represent the chance of a value being between a positive $z$-value and its population mean, 0.

The standard normal table is also reproduced in Table 6.1. This table provides probabilities for $z$-values between $z = 0.00$ and $z = 3.09$. Note, because the normal distribution is symmetric, the probability of a value being between a positive $z$-value and its population mean, 0, is the same as that of a value being between a negative $z$-value and its population mean, 0. So we can use one standard normal table for both positive and negative $z$-values.

**EXAMPLE 6-1    USING THE STANDARD NORMAL TABLE**

**Airline Passenger Loading Times** After completing a study, the Chicago O'Hare Airport managers have concluded that the time needed to get passengers loaded onto an airplane is normally distributed with a mean equal to 15 minutes and a standard deviation equal to 3.5 minutes. Recently one airplane required 22 minutes to get passengers on board and ready for take off. To find the probability that a flight will take 22 or more minutes to get passengers loaded, you can use the following steps:

**Step 1    Determine the mean and standard deviation for the random variable.**
The parameters of the probability distribution are

$$\mu = 15 \quad \text{and} \quad \sigma = 3.5$$

Step 2 **Define the event of interest.**

The flight load time is 22 minutes. We wish to find

$$P(x \geq 22) = ?$$

Step 3 **Convert the random variable to a standardized value using Equation 6.2.**

$$z = \frac{x - \mu}{\sigma} = \frac{22 - 15}{3.5} = 2.00$$

Step 4 **Find the probability associated with the $z$-value in the standard normal distribution table (Table 6-1 or Appendix D).**

To find the probability associated with $z = 2.00$, [i.e., $P(0 \leq z \leq 2.00)$], do the following:

1. Go down the left-hand column of the table to $z = 2.0$.
2. Go across the top row of the table to the column 0.00 for the second decimal place in $z = 2.00$.
3. Find the value where the row and column intersect.

The value, 0.4772, is the probability that a value in a normal distribution will lie between the mean and 2.00 standard deviations above the mean.

Step 5 **Determine the probability for the event of interest.**

$$P(x \geq 22) = ?$$

We know that the area on each side of the mean under the normal distribution is equal to 0.50. In Step 4 we computed the probability associated with $z = 2.00$ to be 0.4772, which is the probability of a value falling between the mean and 2.00 standard deviations above the mean. Then, the probability we are looking for is

$$P(x \geq 22) = P(z \geq 2.00) = 0.5000 - 0.4772 = 0.0228$$

**>>END EXAMPLE**

**TRY PROBLEM** 6-2 (pg. 246)

---

**BUSINESS APPLICATION**    **THE NORMAL DISTRIBUTION**

**REAL ESTATE SALES (*CONTINUED*)** Earlier, we discussed the situation involving real estate sales in Fairfax County near Washington, D.C., in which a report showed that the mean days a home stays on the market before it sells is 16 days. We assumed the distribution for days on the market before a home sells was normally distributed with $\mu = 16$ and $\sigma = 4$. A local D.C. television station interviewed an individual whose home had recently sold after 14 days on the market. Contrary to what the reporter had anticipated, this homeowner was mildly disappointed in how long her home took to sell. She said she thought it should have sold quicker given the fast-paced real estate market, but the reporter countered that he thought the probability was quite high that a home would require 14 or more days to sell. Specifically, we want to find

$$P(x \geq 14) = ?$$

This probability corresponds to the area under a normal distribution to the right of $x = 14$ days. This will be the sum of the area between $x = 14$ and $\mu = 16$ plus the area to the right of $\mu = 16$. Refer to Figure 6.5.

**TABLE 6.1** | **Standard Normal Distribution Table**

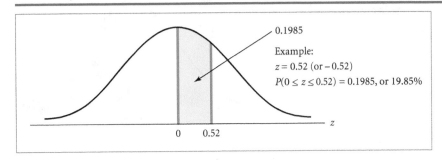

| z | .00 | .01 | .02 | .03 | .04 | .05 | .06 | .07 | .08 | .09 |
|---|-----|-----|-----|-----|-----|-----|-----|-----|-----|-----|
| **0.0** | .0000 | .0040 | .0080 | .0120 | .0160 | .0199 | .0239 | .0279 | .0319 | .0359 |
| **0.1** | .0398 | .0438 | .0478 | .0517 | .0557 | .0596 | .0636 | .0675 | .0714 | .0753 |
| **0.2** | .0793 | .0832 | .0871 | .0910 | .0948 | .0987 | .1026 | .1064 | .1103 | .1141 |
| **0.3** | .1179 | .1217 | .1255 | .1293 | .1331 | .1368 | .1406 | .1443 | .1480 | .1517 |
| **0.4** | .1554 | .1591 | .1628 | .1664 | .1700 | .1736 | .1772 | .1808 | .1844 | .1879 |
| **0.5** | .1915 | .1950 | .1985 | .2019 | .2054 | .2088 | .2123 | .2157 | .2190 | .2224 |
| **0.6** | .2257 | .2291 | .2324 | .2357 | .2389 | .2422 | .2454 | .2486 | .2517 | .2549 |
| **0.7** | .2580 | .2611 | .2642 | .2673 | .2704 | .2734 | .2764 | .2794 | .2823 | .2852 |
| **0.8** | .2881 | .2910 | .2939 | .2967 | .2995 | .3023 | .3051 | .3078 | .3106 | .3133 |
| **0.9** | .3159 | .3186 | .3212 | .3238 | .3264 | .3289 | .3315 | .3340 | .3365 | .3389 |
| **1.0** | .3413 | .3438 | .3461 | .3485 | .3508 | .3531 | .3554 | .3577 | .3599 | .3621 |
| **1.1** | .3643 | .3665 | .3686 | .3708 | .3729 | .3749 | .3770 | .3790 | .3810 | .3830 |
| **1.2** | .3849 | .3869 | .3888 | .3907 | .3925 | .3944 | .3962 | .3980 | .3997 | .4015 |
| **1.3** | .4032 | .4049 | .4066 | .4082 | .4099 | .4115 | .4131 | .4147 | .4162 | .4177 |
| **1.4** | .4192 | .4207 | .4222 | .4236 | .4251 | .4265 | .4279 | .4292 | .4306 | .4319 |
| **1.5** | .4332 | .4345 | .4357 | .4370 | .4382 | .4394 | .4406 | .4418 | .4429 | .4441 |
| **1.6** | .4452 | .4463 | .4474 | .4484 | .4495 | .4505 | .4515 | .4525 | .4535 | .4545 |
| **1.7** | .4554 | .4564 | .4573 | .4582 | .4591 | .4599 | .4608 | .4616 | .4625 | .4633 |
| **1.8** | .4641 | .4649 | .4656 | .4664 | .4671 | .4678 | .4686 | .4693 | .4699 | .4706 |
| **1.9** | .4713 | .4719 | .4726 | .4732 | .4738 | .4744 | .4750 | .4756 | .4761 | .4767 |
| **2.0** | .4772 | .4778 | .4783 | .4788 | .4793 | .4798 | .4803 | .4808 | .4812 | .4817 |
| **2.1** | .4821 | .4826 | .4830 | .4834 | .4838 | .4842 | .4846 | .4850 | .4854 | .4857 |
| **2.2** | .4861 | .4864 | .4868 | .4871 | .4875 | .4878 | .4881 | .4884 | .4887 | .4890 |
| **2.3** | .4893 | .4896 | .4898 | .4901 | .4904 | .4906 | .4909 | .4911 | .4913 | .4916 |
| **2.4** | .4918 | .4920 | .4922 | .4925 | .4927 | .4929 | .4931 | .4932 | .4934 | .4936 |
| **2.5** | .4938 | .4940 | .4941 | .4943 | .4945 | .4946 | .4948 | .4949 | .4951 | .4952 |
| **2.6** | .4953 | .4955 | .4956 | .4957 | .4959 | .4960 | .4961 | .4962 | .4963 | .4964 |
| **2.7** | .4965 | .4966 | .4967 | .4968 | .4969 | .4970 | .4971 | .4972 | .4973 | .4974 |
| **2.8** | .4974 | .4975 | .4976 | .4977 | .4977 | .4978 | .4979 | .4979 | .4980 | .4981 |
| **2.9** | .4981 | .4982 | .4982 | .4983 | .4984 | .4984 | .4985 | .4985 | .4986 | .4986 |
| **3.0** | .4987 | .4987 | .4987 | .4988 | .4988 | .4989 | .4989 | .4989 | .4990 | .4990 |

To illustrate: 19.85% of the area under a normal curve lies between the mean, $\mu$, and a point 0.52 standard deviation units away.

**FIGURE 6.5** |

Probabilities from the Normal
Curve for Fairfax Real Estate

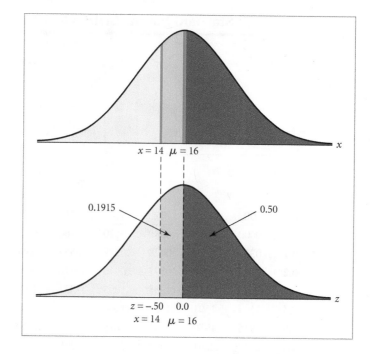

To find this probability, you first convert $x = 14$ days to its corresponding $z$-value. This is equivalent to determining the number of standard deviations $x = 14$ is from the population mean of $\mu = 16$. Equation 6.2 is used to do this as follows:

$$z = \frac{x - \mu}{\sigma} = \frac{14 - 16}{4} = -0.50$$

Because the normal distribution is symmetrical, even though the $z$-value is –0.50, we find the desired probability by going to the standard normal distribution table for a positive $z = 0.50$. The probability in the table for $z = 0.50$ corresponds to the probability of a $z$-value occurring between $z = 0.50$ and $z = 0.0$. This is the same as the probability of a $z$-value falling between $z = -0.50$ and $z = 0.00$. Thus, from the standard normal table (Table 6.1 or Appendix D), we get

$$P(-0.50 \le z \le 0.00) = 0.1915$$

This is the area between $x = 14$ and $\mu = 16$ in Figure 6.5. We now add 0.1915 to 0.5000 [$P(x > 16 = .5000$]. Therefore, the probability that a home will require 14 or more days to sell is

$$P(x \ge 14) = 0.1915 + 0.5000 = 0.6915$$

This is illustrated in Figure 6.5. Thus, there is nearly a 70% chance that a home will require at least 14 days to sell.

---

**BUSINESS APPLICATION** | **USING THE NORMAL DISTRIBUTION**

---

**GENERAL ELECTRIC COMPANY** Several states, including California, have passed legislation requiring automakers to sell a certain percentage of zero-emissions cars within their borders. One current alternative is battery-powered cars. The major problem with battery-operated cars is the limited time they can be driven before the batteries must be recharged. Suppose that General Electric (GE) has developed a Longlife battery pack it claims will power a car at a sustained speed of 45 miles per hour for an average of 8 hours. But of course there will be variations: Some battery packs will last longer and some less than 8 hours. Current data indicate that the standard deviation of battery operation time before a charge is needed is 0.4 hours. Data show a normal distribution of uptime on these battery packs. Automakers are concerned that batteries may run short. For example, drivers might find

**FIGURE 6.6** |

Longlife Battery

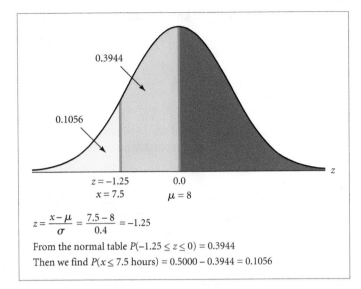

$$z = \frac{x - \mu}{\sigma} = \frac{7.5 - 8}{0.4} = -1.25$$

From the normal table $P(-1.25 \le z \le 0) = 0.3944$

Then we find $P(x \le 7.5 \text{ hours}) = 0.5000 - 0.3944 = 0.1056$

an "8-hour" battery that lasts 7.5 hours or less unacceptable. What are the chances of this happening with the Longlife battery pack?

To calculate the probability the batteries will last 7.5 hours or less, find the appropriate area under the normal curve shown in Figure 6.6. There is approximately 1 chance in 10 that a battery will last 7.5 hours or less when the vehicle is driven at 45 miles per hour.

Suppose this level of reliability is unacceptable to the automakers. Instead of a 10% chance of an "8-hour" battery lasting 7.5 hours or less, the automakers will accept no more than a 2% chance. GE managers ask what the mean uptime would have to be to meet the 2% requirement.

Assuming that uptime is normally distributed, we can answer this question by using the standard normal distribution. However, instead of using the standard normal table to find a probability, we use it in reverse to find the $z$-value that corresponds to a known probability. Figure 6.7 shows the uptime distribution for the battery packs. Note, the 2% probability is shown in the left tail of the distribution. This is the allowable chance of a battery lasting 7.5 hours or less. We must solve for $\mu$, the mean uptime that will meet this requirement.

1. Go to the body of the standard normal table, where the probabilities are located, and find the probability as close to 0.48 as possible. This is 0.4798.
2. Determine the $z$-value associated with 0.4798. This is $z = 2.05$. Because we are below the mean, the $z$ is negative. Thus, $z = -2.05$.
3. The formula for $z$ is

$$z = \frac{x - \mu}{\sigma}$$

**FIGURE 6.7** |

Longlife Battery, Solving for the Mean

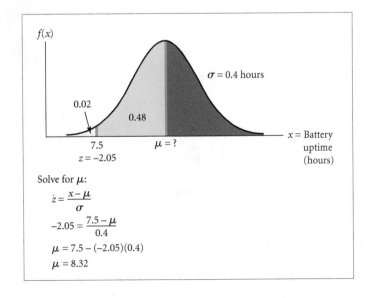

Solve for $\mu$:

$$z = \frac{x - \mu}{\sigma}$$

$$-2.05 = \frac{7.5 - \mu}{0.4}$$

$$\mu = 7.5 - (-2.05)(0.4)$$

$$\mu = 8.32$$

4. Substituting the known values, we get

$$-2.05 = \frac{7.5 - \mu}{0.4}$$

5. Solve for $\mu$:

$$\mu = 7.5 - (-2.05)(0.4) = 8.32 \text{ hours}$$

General Electric will need to increase the mean life of the battery pack to 8.32 hours to meet the automakers' requirement that no more than 2% of the batteries fail in 7.5 hours or less.

**Chapter Outcome 3.** → | BUSINESS APPLICATION | **USING THE NORMAL DISTRIBUTION**

**Excel and Minitab Tutorial**

**STATE BANK AND TRUST** The director of operations for the State Bank and Trust recently performed a study of the time bank customers spent from when they walk into the bank until they complete their banking. The data file **State Bank** contains the data for a sample of 1,045 customers randomly observed over a four-week period. The customers in the survey were limited to those who were there for basic bank business, such as making a deposit or a withdrawal or cashing a check. The histogram in Figure 6.8 shows that the banking times are distributed as an approximate normal distribution.[2]

The mean service time for the 1,045 customers was 22.14 minutes, with a standard deviation equal to 6.09 minutes. On the basis of these data, the manager assumes that the service

**FIGURE 6.8**

Excel 2007 Output for State Bank and Trust Service Times

**Excel 2007 Instructions:**
1. Open file: State Bank.xls.
2. Create bins (upper limit of each class).
3. Select **Data > Data Analysis**.
4. Select **Histogram**.
5. Define data and bin ranges.
6. Check **Chart Output**.
7. Define Output Location.
8. Select the chart and right click.
9. Click on **Format Data Series** and set gap width to zero.

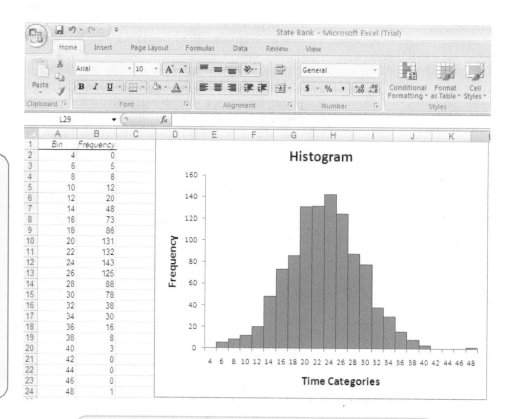

**Minitab Instructions (for similar results):**
1. Open file: State Bank. MTW.
2. Choose **Graph > Histogram**.
3. Click **Simple**.
4. Click **OK**.
5. In **Graph Variables**, enter data column **Service Time**.
6. Click **OK**.

---

[2]A statistical technique known as the chi-square goodness-of-fit test, introduced in Chapter 13, can be used to determine statistically whether the data follow a normal distribution.

**FIGURE 6.9**

Normal Distribution for the State Bank and Trust Example

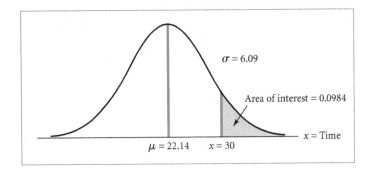

times are normally distributed with $\mu = 22.14$ and $\sigma = 6.09$. Given these assumptions, the manager is considering providing a gift certificate to a local restaurant to any customer who is required to spend more than 30 minutes to complete basic bank business. Before doing this, she is interested in the probability of having to pay off on this offer.

Figure 6.9 shows the theoretical distribution, with the area of interest identified. The manager is interested in finding

$$P(x > 30 \text{ minutes})$$

This can be done manually or with Excel or Minitab. Figure 6.10a and Figure 6.10b show the computer output. The cumulative probability is

$$P(x \leq 30) = 0.9016$$

Then to find the probability of interest, we subtract this value from 1.0, giving

$$P(x \leq 30 \text{ minutes}) = 1.0 - 0.9016 = 0.0984$$

Thus, there are just under 10 chances in 100 that the bank would have to give out a gift certificate. Suppose the manager believes this policy is too liberal. She wants to set the time limit so that the chance of giving out the gift is at most only 5%. You can use the standard normal table, the Probability Distribution command in Minitab, or the NORMDIST function in Excel

**FIGURE 6.10A**

Excel 2007 Output for State Bank and Trust

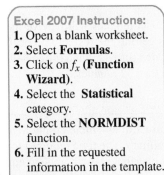

**Excel 2007 Instructions:**
1. Open a blank worksheet.
2. Select **Formulas**.
3. Click on $f_x$ (**Function Wizard**).
4. Select the **Statistical** category.
5. Select the **NORMDIST** function.
6. Fill in the requested information in the template.
7. **True** indicates cumulative probabilities.
8. Click **OK**.

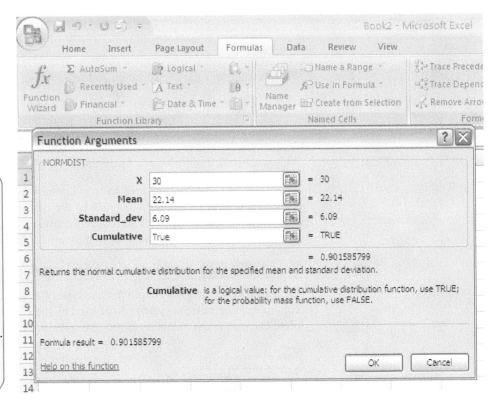

**FIGURE 6.10B**

Minitab Output for State Bank
and Trust

to find the new limit.[3] To use the table, we first consider that the manager wants a 5% area in the upper tail of the normal distribution. This will leave

$$0.50 - 0.05 = 0.45$$

between the new time limit and the mean. Now go to the body of the standard normal table, where the probabilities are, and locate the value as close to 0.45 as possible (0.4495 or 0.4505). Next, determine the $z$-value that corresponds to this probability. Because 0.45 lies midway between 0.4495 and 0.4505, we interpolate halfway between $z = 1.64$ and $z = 1.65$ to get

$$z = 1.645$$

Now, we know

$$z = \frac{x - \mu}{\sigma}$$

We then substitute the known values and solve for $x$:

$$1.645 = \frac{x - 22.14}{6.09}$$
$$x = 22.14 + 1.645(6.09)$$
$$x = 32.158 \text{ minutes}$$

Therefore, any customer required to spend more than 32.158 minutes will receive the gift. This should result in no more than 5% of the customers getting the restaurant certificate. Obviously, the bank will work to reduce the average service time or standard deviation so even fewer customers will have to be in the bank for more than 32 minutes.

**EXAMPLE 6-2** | **USING THE NORMAL DISTRIBUTION**

**Delphi Technologies** Delphi Technologies has a contract to assemble components for communication satellite systems to be used by the U.S. military. The time required to complete one part of the assembly is thought to be normally distributed, with a mean equal to

---

[3]The function is =NORMSINV(.95) in Excel. This will return the $z$-value corresponding to the area to the left of the upper tail equaling .05.

30 hours and a standard deviation equal to 4.7 hours. To keep the assembly flow moving on schedule, this assembly step needs to be completed in 26 to 35 hours. To determine the probability of this happening, use the following steps:

**Step 1    Determine the mean, $\mu$, and the standard deviation, $\sigma$.**
The mean assembly time for this step in the process is thought to be 30 hours, and the standard deviation is thought to be 4.7 hours.

**Step 2    Define the event of interest.**
We are interested in determining the following:

$$P(26 \leq x \leq 35) = ?$$

**Step 3    Convert values of the specified normal distribution to corresponding values of the standard normal distribution using Equation 6.2:**

$$z = \frac{x - \mu}{\sigma}$$

We need to find the $z$-value corresponding to $x = 26$ and to $x = 35$.

$$z = \frac{x - \mu}{\sigma} = \frac{26 - 30}{4.7} = -0.85 \quad \text{and} \quad z = \frac{35 - 30}{4.7} = 1.06$$

**Step 4    Use the standard normal table to find the probabilities associated with each $z$ value.**
For $z = -0.85$, the probability is 0.3023.
For $z = 1.06$, the probability is 0.3554.

**Step 5    Determine the desired probability for the event of interest.**

$$P(26 \leq x \leq 35) = 0.3023 + 0.3554 = 0.6577$$

Thus, there is a 0.6577 chance that this step in the assembly process will stay on schedule.

>>**END EXAMPLE**

**TRY PROBLEM** 6-13 (pg. 246)

**Approximate Areas under the Normal Curve**  In Chapter 3 we introduced the Empirical Rule for probabilities with bell-shaped distributions. For the normal distribution we can make this rule more precise. Knowing the area under the normal curve between $\pm 1\sigma$, $\pm 2\sigma$, and $\pm 3\sigma$ provides a useful benchmark for estimating probabilities and checking reasonableness of results. Figure 6.11 shows these benchmark areas for any normal distribution.

**FIGURE 6.11**

Approximate Areas under the Normal Curve

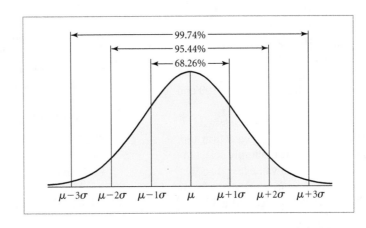

*MyStatLab*

# 6-1: Exercises

## Skill Development

**6-1.** For a normally distributed population with $\mu = 200$ and $\sigma = 20$, determine the standardized $z$-value for each of the following:
   a. $x = 225$
   b. $x = 190$
   c. $x = 240$

**6-2.** For a standardized normal distribution, calculate the following probabilities:
   a. $P(z < 1.5)$
   b. $P(z \geq 0.85)$
   c. $P(-1.28 < z < 1.75)$

**6-3.** For a standardized normal distribution, calculate the following probabilities:
   a. $P(0.00 < z \leq 2.33)$
   b. $P(-1.00 < z \leq 1.00)$
   c. $P(1.78 < z < 2.34)$

**6-4.** For a standardized normal distribution, determine a value, say $z_0$, so that
   a. $P(0 < z < z_0) = 0.4772$
   b. $P(-z_0 \leq z < 0) = 0.45$
   c. $P(-z_0 \leq z \leq z_0) = 0.95$
   d. $P(z > z_0) = 0.025$
   e. $P(z \leq z_0) = 0.01$

**6-5.** Consider a random variable, $z$, that has a standardized normal distribution. Determine the following probabilities:
   a. $P(0 < z < 1.96)$
   b. $P(z > 1.645)$
   c. $P(1.28 < z \leq 2.33)$
   d. $P(-2 \leq z \leq 3)$
   e. $P(z > -1)$

**6-6.** A random variable, $x$, has a normal distribution with $\mu = 13.6$ and $\sigma = 2.90$. Determine a value, $x_0$, so that
   a. $P(x > x_0) = 0.05$.
   b. $P(x \leq x_0) = 0.975$.
   c. $P(\mu - x_0 \leq x \leq \mu + x_0) = 0.95$.

**6-7.** For the following normal distributions with parameters as specified, calculate the required probabilities:
   a. $\mu = 5, \sigma = 2$; calculate $P(0 < x < 8)$.
   b. $\mu = 5, \sigma = 4$; calculate $P(0 < x < 8)$.
   c. $\mu = 3, \sigma = 2$; calculate $P(0 < x < 8)$.
   d. $\mu = 4, \sigma = 3$; calculate $P(x > 1)$.
   e. $\mu = 0, \sigma = 3$; calculate $P(x > 1)$.

**6-8.** A population is normally distributed with $\mu = 100$ and $\sigma = 20$.
   a. Find the probability that a value randomly selected from this population will have a value greater than 130.
   b. Find the probability that a value randomly selected from this population will have a value less than 90.
   c. Find the probability that a value randomly selected from this population will have a value between 90 and 130.

**6-9.** A random variable is known to be normally distributed with the following parameters:

$$\mu = 5.5 \quad \text{and} \quad \sigma = 0.50$$

   a. Determine the value of $x$ such that the probability of a value from this distribution exceeding $x$ is at most 0.10.
   b. Referring to your answer in part a, what must the population mean be changed to if the probability of exceeding the value of $x$ found in part a is reduced from 0.10 to 0.05?

**6-10.** A randomly selected value from a normal distribution is found to be 2.1 standard deviations above its mean.
   a. What is the probability that a randomly selected value from the distribution will be greater than 2.1 standard deviations above the mean?
   b. What is the probability that a randomly selected value from the distribution will be less than 2.1 standard deviations from the mean?

**6-11.** Assume that a random variable is normally distributed with a mean of 1,500 and a variance of 324.
   a. What is the probability that a randomly selected value will be greater than 1,550?
   b. What is the probability that a randomly selected value will be less than 1,485?
   c. What is the probability that a randomly selected value will be either less than 1,475 or greater than 1,535?

**6-12.** A random variable is normally distributed with a mean of 25 and a standard deviation of 5. If an observation is randomly selected from the distribution,
   a. What value will be exceeded 10% of the time?
   b. What value will be exceeded 85% of the time?
   c. Determine two values of which the smallest has 25% of the values below it and the largest has 25% of the values above it.
   d. What value will 15% of the observations be below?

**6-13.** A random variable is normally distributed with a mean of 60 and a standard deviation of 9.
   a. What is the probability that a randomly selected value from the distribution will be less than 46.5?
   b. What is the probability that a randomly selected value from the distribution will be greater than 78?
   c. What is the probability that a randomly selected value will be between 51 and 73.5?

## Business Applications

**6-14.** A global financial institution transfers a large data file every evening from offices around the world to its London headquarters. Once the file is received, it must be cleaned and partitioned before being stored in the company's data warehouse. Each file is the same size and the time required to transfer, clean, and partition a file is normally distributed, with a mean of 1.5 hours and a standard deviation of 15 minutes.

a. If one file is selected at random, what is the probability that it will take longer than 1 hour and 55 minutes to transfer, clean, and partition the file?

b. If a manager must be present until 85% of the files are transferred, cleaned, and partitioned, how long will the manager need to be there?

c. What percentage of the data files will take between 63 minutes and 110 minutes to be transferred, cleaned, and partitioned?

**6-15.** Canine Crunchies Inc. (CCI) sells large bags of dog food to warehouse clubs. CCI uses an automatic filling process to fill the bags. Weights of the filled bags are approximately normally distributed with a mean of 50 kilograms and a standard deviation of 1.25 kilograms.

a. What is the probability that a filled bag will weigh less than 49.5 kilograms?

b. What is the probability that a randomly sampled filled bag will weigh between 48.5 and 51 kilograms?

c. What is the minimum weight a bag of dog food could be and remain in the top 15% of all bags filled?

d. CCI is unable to adjust the mean of the filling process. However, it is able to adjust the standard deviation of the filling process. What would the standard deviation need to be so that no more than 2% of all filled bags weigh more than 52 kilograms?

**6-16.** LaCrosse Technology is one of many manufacturers of atomic clocks. It makes an atomic digital watch that is radio-controlled and that maintains its accuracy by reading a radio signal from a WWVB radio signal from Colorado. It neither loses nor gains a second in 20 million years. It is powered by a 3-volt lithium battery expected to last three years. Suppose the life of the battery has a standard deviation of 0.3 years and is normally distributed.

a. Determine the probability that the watch's battery will last longer than 3.5 years.

b. Calculate the probability that the watch's battery will last more than 2.75 years.

c. Compute the length-of-life value for which 10% of the watch's batteries last longer.

**6-17.** The average number of acres burned by forest and range fires in a large Wyoming county is 4,300 acres per year, with a standard deviation of 750 acres. The distribution of the number of acres burned is normal.

a. Compute the probability that more than 5,000 acres will be burned in any year.

b. Determine the probability that fewer then 4,000 acres will be burned in any year.

c. What is the probability that between 2,500 and 4,200 acres will be burned?

d. In those years when more than 5,500 acres are burned, help is needed from eastern-region fire teams. Determine the probability help will be needed in any year.

**6-18.** An Internet retailer stocks a popular electronic toy at a central warehouse that supplies the eastern United States. Every week the retailer makes a decision about how many units of the toy to stock. Suppose that weekly demand for the toy is approximately normally distributed with a mean of 2,500 units and a standard deviation of 300 units.

a. If the retailer wants to limit the probability of being out of stock of the electronic toy to no more than 2.5% in a week, how many units should the central warehouse stock?

b. If the retailer has 2,750 units on hand at the start of the week, what is the probability that weekly demand will be greater than inventory?

c. If the standard deviation of weekly demand for the toy increases from 300 units to 500 units, how many more toys would have to be stocked to ensure that the probability of weekly demand exceeding inventory is no more than 2.5%?

**6-19.** C&C Industries manufactures a wash-down motor that is used in the food processing industry. The motor is marketed with a warranty that guarantees it will be replaced free of charge if it fails within the first 13,000 hours of operation. On average, C&C wash-down motors operate for 15,000 hours with a standard deviation of 1,250 hours before failing. The number of operating hours before failure is approximately normally distributed.

a. What is the probability that a wash-down motor will have to be replaced free of charge?

b. What percentage of C&C wash-down motors can be expected to operate for more than 17,500 hours?

c. If C&C wants to design a wash-down motor so that no more than 1% are replaced free of charge, what would the average hours of operation before failure have to be if the standard deviation remains at 1,250 hours?

**6-20.** A private equity firm is evaluating two alternative investments. Although the returns are random, each investment's return can be described using a normal distribution. The first investment has a mean return of $2,000,000 with a standard deviation of $125,000. The second investment has a mean return of $2,275,000 with a standard deviation of $500,000.

a. How likely is it that the first investment will return $1,900,000 or less?

b. How likely is it that the second investment will return $1,900,000 or less?

c. If the firm would like to limit the probability of a return being less than $1,750,000, which investment should it make?

**6-21.** J.J. Kettering & Associates is a financial planning group in Fresno, California. The company specializes in financial planning for schoolteachers in the Fresno area. As such, it administers a 403(b) tax shelter annuity program in which public schoolteachers can participate. The teachers can contribute up to $20,000 per year on a pretax basis to the 403(b) account. Very few teachers have incomes sufficient to allow them to make the maximum contribution. The lead analyst at J.J. Kettering & Associates has recently analyzed the company's 403(b) clients and determined that the annual contribution is approximately normally distributed with a mean equal to $6,400. Further, he has determined that the probability a customer will contribute over $13,000 is 0.025. Based on this information, what is the standard deviation of contributions to the 403(b) program?

**6-22.** No Leak Plumbing and Repair provides customers with firm quotes for a plumbing repair job before actually starting the job. To be able to do this, No Leak has been very careful to maintain time records over the years. For example, it has determined that the time it takes to remove a broken sink disposal and to install a new unit is normally distributed with a mean equal to 47 minutes and a standard deviation equal to 12 minutes. The company bills at $75.00 for the first 30 minutes and $2.00 per minute for anything beyond 30 minutes.

Suppose the going rate for this procedure by other plumbing shops in the area is $85.00, not including the cost of the new equipment. If No Leak bids the disposal job at $85, on what percentage of such jobs will the actual time required exceed the time for which it will be getting paid?

**6-23.** According to *Business Week*, Maternity Chic, a purveyor of designer maternity wear, sells dresses and pants priced around $150 each for an average total sale of $1,200. The total sale has a normal distribution with a standard deviation of $350.

a. Calculate the probability that a randomly selected customer will have a total sale of more than $1,500.

b. Compute the probability that the total sale will be within 2 standard deviations of the mean total sales.

c. Determine the median total sale.

**6-24.** The Aberdeen Coca-Cola Bottling plant located in Aberdeen, North Carolina, is the bottler and distributor for Coca-Cola products in the Aberdeen area. The company's product line includes 12-ounce cans of Coke products. The cans are filled by an automated filling process that can be adjusted to any mean fill volume and that will fill cans according to a normal distribution. However, not all cans will contain the same volume due to variation in the filling process. Historical records show that regardless of what the mean is set at, the standard deviation in fill will be 0.035 ounces. Operations managers at the plant know that if they put too much Coke in a can, the company loses money. If too little is put in the can, customers are short-changed and the North Carolina Department of Weights and Measures may fine the company.

a. Suppose the industry standards for fill volume call for each 12-ounce can to contain between 11.98 and

12.02 ounces. Assuming that the Aberdeen manager sets the mean fill at 12 ounces, what is the probability that a can will contain a volume of Coke product that falls in the desired range?

b. Assume that the Aberdeen manager is focused on an upcoming audit by the North Carolina Department of Weights and Measures. She knows the process is to select one Coke can at random and that if it contains less than 11.97 ounces, the company will be reprimanded and potentially fined. Assuming that the manager wants at most a 5% chance of this happening, at what level should she set the mean fill level? Comment on the ramifications of this step, assuming that the company fills tens of thousands of cans each week.

**6-25.** MP-3 players, and most notably the Apple iPod, have become an industry standard for people who want to have access to their favorite music and videos in a portable format. The iPod can store massive numbers of songs and videos with its 120-GB hard drive. Although owners of the iPod have the potential to store lots of data, a recent study showed that the actual disk storage being used is normally distributed with a mean equal to 1.95 GB and a standard deviation of 0.48 GB. Suppose a competitor to Apple is thinking of entering the market with a low-cost iPod clone that has only 1.0 GB of storage. The marketing slogan will be "Why Pay for Storage Capacity that You Don't Need?"

Based on the data from the study of iPod owners, what percentage of owners, based on their current usage, would have enough capacity with the new 1-GB player?

**6-26.** According to the Federal Reserve Board, the average credit card debt per U.S. household was $8,565 in 2008. Assume that the distribution of credit card debt per household has a normal distribution with a standard deviation of $3,000.

a. Determine the percentage of households that have a credit card debt of more than $13,000.

b. One household has a credit card debt that is at the 95th percentile. Determine its credit card debt.

c. If four households were selected at random, determine the probability that at least half of them would have credit card debt of more than $13,000.

**6-27.** Georgia-Pacific is a major forest products company in the United States. In addition to timberlands, the company owns and operates numerous manufacturing plants that make lumber and paper products. At one of their plywood plants, the operations manager has been struggling to make sure that the plywood thickness meets quality standards. Specifically, all sheets of their ¾-inch plywood must fall within the range 0.747 to 0.753 inches in thickness. Studies have shown that the current process produces plywood that has thicknesses that are normally distributed with a mean of 0.751 inches and a standard deviation equal to 0.004 inches.

a. Use either Excel or Minitab to determine the proportion of plywood sheets that will meet quality specifications (0.747 to 0.753), given how the current process is performing.

b. Referring to part a, suppose the manager is unhappy with the proportion of product meeting specifications. Assuming that he can get the mean adjusted to 0.75 inches, what must the standard deviation be if he is going to have 98% of his product meet specifications?

**6-28.** A senior loan officer for Whitney National Bank has recently studied the bank's real estate loan portfolio and found that the distribution of loan balances is approximately normally distributed with a mean of $155,600 and a standard deviation equal to $33,050. As part of an internal audit, bank auditors recently randomly selected 100 real estate loans from the portfolio of all loans and found that 80 of these loans had balances below $170,000. The senior loan officer is concerned that the sample selected by the auditors is not representative of the overall portfolio. In particular, he is interested in knowing the expected proportion of loans in the portfolio that would have balances below $170,000. You are asked to conduct an appropriate analysis and write a short report to the senior loan officers with your conclusion about the sample.

## Computer Database **Exercises**

**6-29.** The PricewaterhouseCoopers Human Capital Index Report indicated that the average cost for an American company to fill a job vacancy during the study period was $3,270. Sample data similar to that used in the study are in a file entitled **Hired**.

a. Produce a relative frequency histogram for these data. Does it seem plausible the data were sampled from a normally distributed population?

b. Calculate the mean and standard deviation of the cost of filling a job vacancy.

c. Determine the probability that the cost of filling a job vacancy would be between $2,000 and $3,000.

d. Given that the cost of filling a job vacancy was between $2,000 and $3,000, determine the probability that the cost would be more than $2,500.

**6-30.** A recent article in *USA Today* discussed prices for the 200 brand-name drugs most commonly used by Americans over age 50. Atrovent, a treatment for lung conditions such as emphysema, was one of the drugs. The file entitled **Drug$** contains daily cost data similar to those obtained in the research.

a. Produce a relative frequency histogram for these data. Does it seem plausible the data were sampled from a population that was normally distributed?

b. Compute the mean and standard deviation for the sample data in the file **Drug$**.

c. Assuming the sample came from a normally distributed population and the sample standard deviation is a good approximation for the population standard deviation, determine the probability that a randomly chosen transaction would yield a price of $2.12 or smaller even though the population mean was $2.51.

**6-31.** *USA Today*'s annual survey of public flagship universities (Arienne Thompson and Breanne Gilpatrick, "Double-Digit Hikes Are Down," October 5, 2005) indicates that the median increase in in-state tuition was 7% for the 2005–2006 academic year. A file entitled **Tuition** contains the percentage change for the 67 flagship universities.

a. Produce a relative frequency histogram for these data. Does it seem plausible that the data are from a population that has a normal distribution?

b. Suppose the decimal point of the three largest numbers had inadvertently been moved one place to the right in the data. Move the decimal point one place to the left and reconstruct the relative frequency histogram. Now does it seem plausible that the data have an approximate normal distribution?

c. Use the normal distribution of part b to approximate the proportion of universities that raised their in-state tuition more than 10%. Use the appropriate parameters obtained from this population.

d. Use the normal distribution of part b to approximate the fifth percentile for the percent of tuition increase.

**END EXERCISES 6-1**

# 6.2 Other Continuous Probability Distributions

The normal distribution is the most frequently used continuous probability distribution in statistics. However, there are other continuous distributions that apply to business decision making. This section introduces two of these: the uniform distribution and the exponential distribution.

Chapter Outcome 4. → **Uniform Probability Distribution**

The *uniform distribution* is sometimes referred to as the *distribution of little information*, because the probability over any interval of the continuous random variable is the same as for any other interval of the same width.

**FIGURE 6.12**

Uniform Distributions

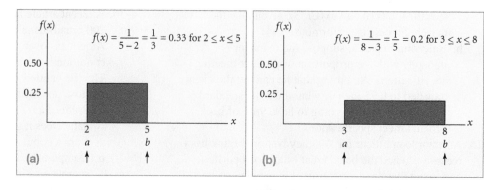

Equation 6.3 defines the *continuous uniform density function*.

---

**Continuous Uniform Density Function**

$$f(x) = \begin{cases} \dfrac{1}{b-a} & \text{if } a \leq x \leq b \\[2mm] 0 & \text{otherwise} \end{cases}$$

(6.3)

where:

$f(x)$ = Value of the density function at any $x$-value

$a$ = The smallest value assumed by the uniform random variable of interest

$b$ = The largest value assumed by the uniform random variable of interest

---

Figure 6.12 illustrates two examples of uniform probability distributions with different $a$ to $b$ intervals. Note the height of the probability density function is the same for all values of $x$ between $a$ and $b$ for a given distribution. The graph of the uniform distribution is a rectangle.

**EXAMPLE 6-3    USING THE UNIFORM DISTRIBUTION**

**Weyerhaeuser Tree Farms** The Weyerhaeuser Company owns and operates several tree farms in Washington State. The lead botanist for the company has stated that fir trees on one parcel of land will increase in diameter between one and four inches per year according to a uniform distribution. Suppose the company is interested in the probability that a given tree will have an increased diameter of more than 2 inches. The probability can be determined using the following steps:

**Step 1   Define the density function.**
The height of the probability rectangle, $f(x)$, for the tree growth interval of one to four inches is determined using Equation 6.3, as follows:

$$f(x) = \frac{1}{b-a}$$
$$f(x) = \frac{1}{4-1} = \frac{1}{3} = 0.33$$

**Step 2   Define the event of interest.**
The botanist is specifically interested in a tree that has increased by more than two inches in diameter. This event of interest is $x > 2.0$.

**Step 3  Calculate the required probability.**

We determine the probability as follows:

$$P(x > 2.0) = 1 - P(x \le 2.0)$$
$$= 1 - f(x)(2.0 - 1.0)$$
$$= 1 - 0.33(1.0)$$
$$= 1 - 0.33$$
$$= 0.67$$

Thus, there is a 0.67 probability that a tree will increase by more than two inches in diameter.

**>>END EXAMPLE**

**TRY PROBLEM** 6-32 (pg. 254)

Like the normal distribution, the uniform distribution can be further described by specifying the mean and the standard deviation. These values are computed using Equations 6.4 and 6.5.

---

**Mean and Standard Deviation of a Uniform Distribution**

Mean (Expected Value):

$$E(x) = \mu = \frac{a+b}{2} \qquad \text{(6.4)}$$

Standard Deviation:

$$\sigma = \sqrt{\frac{(b-a)^2}{12}} \qquad \text{(6.5)}$$

where:

$a$ = The smallest value assumed by the uniform random variable of interest

$b$ = The largest value assumed by the uniform random variable of interest

---

**EXAMPLE 6-4**    **THE MEAN AND STANDARD DEVIATION OF A UNIFORM DISTRIBUTION**

 **Austrian Airlines** The service manager for Austrian Airlines is uncertain about the time needed for the ground crew to turn an airplane around from the time it lands until it is ready to take off. He has been given information from the operations supervisor indicating that the times seem to range between 15 and 45 minutes. Without any further information, the service manager will apply a uniform distribution to the turnaround. Based on this, he can determine the mean and standard deviation for the airplane turnaround times using the following steps:

**Step 1  Define the density function.**

Equation 6.3 can be used to define the distribution:

$$f(x) = \frac{1}{b-a} = \frac{1}{45-15} = \frac{1}{30} = 0.0333$$

**Step 2  Compute the mean of the probability distribution using Equation 6.4.**

$$\mu = \frac{a+b}{2} = \frac{15+45}{2} = 30$$

Thus, the mean turnaround time is 30 minutes.

**Step 3** Compute the standard deviation using Equation 6.5.

$$\sigma = \sqrt{\frac{(b-a)^2}{12}} = \sqrt{\frac{(45-15)^2}{12}} = \sqrt{75} = 8.66$$

The standard deviation is 8.66 minutes.

>>END EXAMPLE

TRY PROBLEM 6-34 (pg. 255)

Chapter Outcome 5. → **The Exponential Probability Distribution**

Another continuous probability distribution that is frequently used in business situations is the *exponential distribution*. The exponential distribution is used to measure the time that elapses between two occurrences of an event, such as the time between "hits" on an Internet home page. The exponential distribution might also be used to describe the time between arrivals of customers at a bank drive-in teller window or the time between failures of an electronic component. Equation 6.6 shows the probability density function for the exponential distribution.

---

### Exponential Density Function

A continuous random variable that is exponentially distributed has the probability density function given by

$$f(x) = \lambda e^{-\lambda x}, \qquad x \geq 0 \qquad \text{(6.6)}$$

where:

$$e = 2.71828\ldots$$
$$1/\lambda = \text{The mean time between events } (\lambda > 0)$$

---

Note, the parameter that defines the exponential distribution is $\lambda$ (lambda). You should recall from Chapter 5 that $\lambda$ is the mean value for the Poisson distribution. If the number of occurrences per time period is known to be Poisson distributed with a mean of $\lambda$, then the time between occurrences will be exponentially distributed with a mean time of $1/\lambda$.

If we select a value for $\lambda$, we can graph the exponential distribution by substituting $\lambda$ and different values for $x$ into Equation 6.6. For instance, Figure 6.13 shows exponential density functions for $\lambda = 0.5$, $\lambda = 1.0$, $\lambda = 2.0$, and $\lambda = 3.0$. Note in Figure 6.13 that for any exponential density function, $f(x)$, $f(0) = \lambda$, as $x$ increases, $f(x)$ approaches zero. It can also be shown that *the standard deviation of any exponential distribution is equal to the mean*, $1/\lambda$.

**FIGURE 6.13**

Exponential Distributions

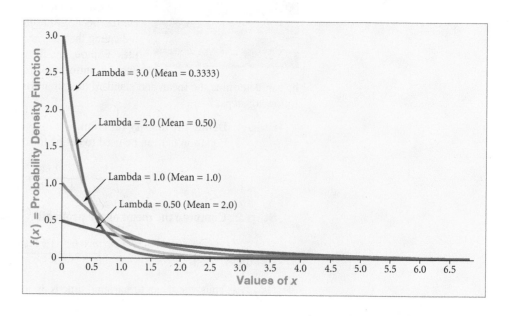

As with any continuous probability distribution, the probability that a value will fall within an interval is the area under the graph between the two points defining the interval. Equation 6.7 is used to find the probability that a value will be equal to or less than a particular value for an exponential distribution.

---

**Exponential Probability**

$$P(0 \leq x \leq a) = 1 - e^{-\lambda a}$$    **(6.7)**

where:

$a$ = the value of interest

$1/\lambda$ = mean

$e$ = natural number $\simeq 2.71828$

---

Appendix E contains a table of $e^{-\lambda a}$ values for different values of $\lambda a$. You can use this table and Equation 6.7 to find the probabilities when the $\lambda a$ of interest is contained in the table. You can also use Minitab or Excel to find exponential probabilities, as the following application illustrates.

**Excel and Minitab Tutorial**

BUSINESS APPLICATION    **USING EXCEL AND MINITAB TO CALCULATE EXPONENTIAL PROBABILITIES**

**HAINES INTERNET SERVICES** The Haines Internet Services Company has determined that the number of customers who attempt to connect to the Internet per hour is Poisson distributed with $\lambda = 30$ per hour. The time between connect requests is exponentially distributed with a mean time between requests of 2.0 minutes, computed as follows:

$$\lambda = 30 \text{ attempts per 60 minutes} = 0.50 \text{ attempts per minute}$$

The mean time between attempted connects, then, is

$$1/\lambda = \frac{1}{0.50} = 2.0 \text{ minutes}$$

Because of the system that Haines uses, if customer requests are too close together— 45 seconds (0.75 minutes) or less—the connection will fail. The managers at Haines are analyzing whether they should purchase new equipment that will eliminate this problem. They need to know the probability that a customer will fail to connect. Thus, they want

$$P(x \leq 0.75 \text{ minutes}) = ?$$

To find this probability using a calculator, we need to first determine $\lambda a$. In this example, $\lambda = 0.50$ and $a = 0.75$. Then,

$$\lambda a = (0.50)(0.75) = 0.3750$$

We find that the desired probability is

$$1 - e^{-\lambda a} = 1 - e^{-0.3750}$$
$$= 0.3127$$

The managers can also use the EXPONDIST function in Excel or the Probability Distribution command in Minitab to compute the precise value for the desired probability.[4] Figure 6.14a and Figure 6.14b show that the chance of failing to connect is 0.3127. This means that nearly one third of the customers will experience a problem with the current system.

---

[4]The Excel EXPONDIST function requires that $\lambda$ be inputted rather than $1/\lambda$.

**FIGURE 6.14A**

Excel 2007 Exponential
Probability Output for Haines
Internet Services

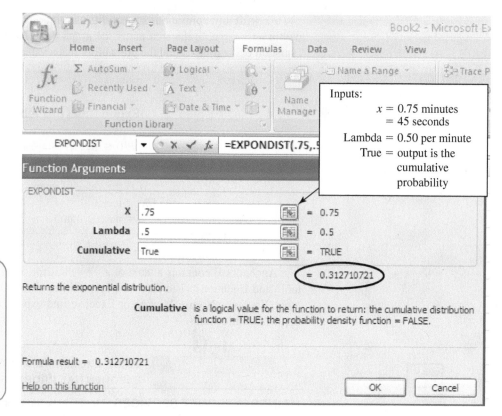

Inputs:

$x = 0.75$ minutes
$= 45$ seconds
Lambda $= 0.50$ per minute
True $=$ output is the cumulative probability

**Excel 2007 Instructions:**
1. Open blank worksheet.
2. Select **Formulas** tab.
3. Select **More Functions**.
4. Select **Statistical >
   EXPONDIST**.
5. Enter values for *x*, lambda
   and "true" for cumulative.
6. Click **OK**.

**FIGURE 6.14B**

Minitab Exponential
Probability Output for Haines
Internet Services

**Minitab Instructions:**
1. Choose **Calc > Probability
   Distributions >
   Exponential**.
2. Choose **Cumulative
   probability**.
3. In **Scale**, enter μ.
4. In **Input constant**, enter
   value for *x*.
5. Click **OK**.

*MyStatLab* ▲

# 6-2: Exercises

## Skill Development

**6-32.** A continuous random variable is uniformly distributed
between 100 and 150.
  a. What is the probability a randomly selected value
     will be greater than 135?
  b. What is the probability a randomly selected value
     will be less than 115?
  c. What is the probability a randomly selected value
     will be between 115 and 135?

**6-33.** Determine the following:
  a. the probability that a uniform random variable
     whose range is between 10 and 30 assumes
     a value in the interval (10 to 20) or (15 to 25)
  b. the quartiles for a uniform random variable
     whose range is from 4 to 20
  c. the mean time between events for an
     exponential random variable that has a
     median equal to 10

d. the 90th percentile for an exponential random variable that has the mean time between events equal to 0.4.

**6-34.** Suppose a random variable, $x$, has a uniform distribution with $a = 5$ and $b = 9$.

a. Calculate $P(5.5 \le x \le 8)$.

b. Determine $P(x > 7)$.

c. Compute the mean, $\mu$, and standard deviation, $\sigma$, of this random variable.

d. Determine the probability that $x$ is in the interval $(\mu \pm 2\sigma)$.

**6-35.** Let $x$ be an exponential random variable with $\lambda = 0.5$. Calculate the following probabilities:

a. $P(x < 5)$

b. $P(x > 6)$

c. $P(5 \le x \le 6)$

d. $P(x \ge 2)$

e. the probability that $x$ is at most 6

**6-36.** The useful life of an electrical component is exponentially distributed with a mean of 2,500 hours.

a. What is the probability the circuit will last more than 3,000 hours?

b. What is the probability the circuit will last between 2,500 and 2,750 hours?

c. What is the probability the circuit will fail within the first 2,000 hours?

**6-37.** The time between telephone calls to a cable television payment processing center follows an exponential distribution with a mean of 1.5 minutes.

a. What is the probability that the time between the next two calls will be 45 seconds or less?

b. What is the probability that the time between the next two calls will be greater than 112.5 seconds?

## Business Applications

**6-38.** Suppose you are traveling on business to a foreign country for the first time. You do not have a bus schedule or a watch with you. However, you have been told that buses stop in front of your hotel every 20 minutes throughout the day. If you show up at the bus stop at a random moment during the day, determine the probability that

a. you will have to wait for more than 10 minutes

b. you will only have to wait for 6 minutes or less

c. you will have to wait between 8 and 15 minutes

**6-39.** When only the value-added time is considered, the time it takes to build a laser printer is thought to be uniformly distributed between 8 and 15 hours.

a. What are the chances that it will take more than 10 value-added hours to build a printer?

b. How likely is it that a printer will require less than 9 value-added hours?

c. Suppose a single customer orders two printers. Determine the probability that the first and second printer each will require less than 9 value-added hours to complete.

**6-40.** The time required to prepare a dry cappuccino using whole milk at the Daily Grind Coffee House is uniformly distributed between 25 and 35 seconds.

Assuming a customer has just ordered a whole-milk dry cappuccino,

a. What is the probability that the preparation time will be more than 29 seconds?

b. What is the probability that the preparation time will be between 28 and 33 seconds?

c. What percentage of whole-milk dry cappuccinos will be prepared within 31 seconds?

d. What is the standard deviation of preparation times for a dry cappuccino using whole milk at the Daily Grind Coffee House?

**6-41.** The time to failure for a power supply unit used in a particular brand of personal computer (PC) is thought to be exponentially distributed with a mean of 4,000 hours as per the contract between the vendor and the PC maker. The PC manufacturer has just had a warranty return from a customer who had the power supply fail after 2,100 hours of use.

a. What is the probability that the power supply would fail at 2,100 hours or less? Based on this probability, do you feel the PC maker has a right to require that the power supply maker refund the money on this unit?

b. Assuming that the PC maker has sold 100,000 computers with this power supply, approximately how many should be returned due to failure at 2,100 hours or less?

**6-42.** A delicatessen located in the heart of the business district of a large city serves a variety of customers. The delicatessen is open 24 hours a day every day of the week. In an effort to speed up take-out orders, the deli accepts orders by fax. If, on the average, 20 orders are received by fax every two hours throughout the day, find the

a. probability that a faxed order will arrive within the next 9 minutes

b. probability that the time between two faxed orders will be between 3 and 6 minutes

c. probability that 12 or more minutes will elapse between faxed orders

**6-43.** Dennis Cauchon and Julie Appleby reported in *USA Today* that the average patient cost per stay in American hospitals was $8,166. Assume that this cost is exponentially distributed.

a. Determine the probability that a randomly selected patient's stay in an American hospital will cost more than $10,000.

b. Calculate the probability that a randomly selected patient's stay in an American hospital will cost less than $5,000.

c. Compute the probability that a randomly selected patient's stay in an American hospital will cost between $8,000 and $12,000.

**6-44.** During the busiest time of the day customers arrive at the Daily Grind Coffee House at an average of 15 customers per 20-minute period.

a. What is the probability that a customer will arrive within the next 3 minutes?

b. What is the probability that the time between the arrivals of customers is 12 minutes or more?

c. What is the probability that the next customer will arrive within 4 and 6 minutes?

**6-45.** The average amount spent on electronics each year in U.S. households is $1,250 according to an article in *USA Today* (Michelle Kessler, "Gadget Makers Make Mad Dash to Market," January 4, 2006). Assume that the amount spent on electronics each year has an exponential distribution.

a. Calculate the probability that a randomly chosen U.S. household would spend more than $5,000 on electronics.

b. Compute the probability that a randomly chosen U.S. household would spend more than the average amount spent by U.S. households.

c. Determine the probability that a randomly chosen U.S. household would spend more than 1 standard deviation below the average amount spent by U.S. households.

**6-46.** Charter Southeast Airlines states that the flight between Fort Lauderdale, Florida, and Los Angeles takes 5 hours and 37 minutes. Assume that the actual flight times are uniformly distributed between 5 hours and 20 minutes and 5 hours and 50 minutes.

a. Determine the probability that the flight will be more than 10 minutes late.

b. Calculate the probability that the flight will be more than 5 minutes early.

c. Compute the average flight time between these two cities.

d. Determine the variance in the flight times between these two cities.

**6-47.** A corrugated container company is testing whether a computer decision model will improve the uptime of its box production line. Currently, knives used in the production process are checked manually and replaced when the operator believes the knives are dull. Knives are expensive, so operators are encouraged not to change the knives early. Unfortunately, if knives are left running for too long, the cuts are not made properly, which can jam the machines and require that the entire process be shut down for unscheduled maintenance. Shutting down the entire line is costly in terms of lost production and repair work, so the company would like to reduce the number of shutdowns that occur daily. Currently, the company experiences an average of 0.75 knife-related shutdowns per shift, exponentially distributed. In testing, the computer decision model reduced the frequency of knife-related shutdowns to an average of 0.20 per shift, exponentially distributed. The decision model is expensive but the company will install it if it can help achieve the target of four consecutive shifts without a knife-related shutdown.

a. Under the current system, what is the probability that the plant would run four or more consecutive shifts without a knife-related shutdown?

b. Using the computer decision model, what is the probability that the plant could run four or more

consecutive shifts without a knife-related shutdown? Has the decision model helped the company achieve its goal?

c. What would be the maximum average number of shutdowns allowed per day such that the probability of experiencing four or more consecutive shifts without a knife-related shutdown is greater than or equal to 0.70?

## Computer Database **Exercises**

**6-48.** Rolls-Royce PLC provides forecasts for the business jet market and covers the regional and major aircraft markets. In a recent release, Rolls-Royce indicated that in both North America and Europe the number of delayed departures has declined since a peak in 1999/2000. This is partly due to a reduction in the number of flights at major airports and the younger aircraft fleets, but also results from improvements in air traffic management capacity, especially in Europe. Comparing January–April 2003 with the same period in 2001 (for similar traffic levels), the average en route delay per flight was reduced by 65%, from 2.2 minutes to 0.7 minutes. The file entitled **Delays** contains a possible sample of the en route delay times in minutes for 200 flights.

a. Produce a relative frequency histogram for this data. Does it seem plausible the data come from a population that has an exponential distribution?

b. Calculate the mean and standard deviation of the en route delays.

c. Determine the probability that this exponential random variable will be smaller than its mean.

d. Determine the median time in minutes for the en route delays assuming they have an exponential distribution with a mean equal to that obtained in part b.

e. Using only the information obtained in parts c and d, describe the shape of this distribution. Does this agree with the findings in part a?

**6-49.** Although some financial institutions do not charge fees for using ATMs, many do. A recent study found the average fee charged by banks to process an ATM transaction was $2.91. The file entitled **ATM Fees** contains a list of ATM fees that might be required by banks.

a. Produce a relative frequency histogram for these data. Does it seem plausible the data came from a population that has an exponential distribution?

b. Calculate the mean and standard deviation of the ATM fees.

c. Assume that the distribution of ATM fees is exponentially distributed with the same mean as that of the sample. Determine the probability that a randomly chosen bank's ATM fee would be greater than $3.00.

**6-50.** The San Luis Obispo, California, Transit Program provides daily fixed-route transit service to the general public within the city limits and to Cal Poly State

University's staff and students. The most heavily traveled route schedules a city bus to arrive at Cal Poly at 8:54 A.M. The file entitled **Late** lists plausible differences between the actual and scheduled time of arrival rounded to the nearest minute for this route.

a. Produce a relative frequency histogram for these data. Does it seem plausible the data came from a population that has a uniform distribution?

b. Provide the density for this uniform distribution.

c. Classes start 10 minutes after the hour and classes are a 5-minute walk from the drop-off point. Determine the probability that a randomly chosen bus on this route would cause the students on board to be late for class. Assume the differences form a continuous uniform distribution with a range the same as the sample.

d. Determine the median difference between the actual and scheduled arrival times.

**END EXERCISES 6-2**

# Visual Summary

**Chapter 6:** A **random variable** can take on values that are either discrete or continuous. This chapter has focused on continuous random variables where the potential values of the variable can be any value on a continuum. Examples of continuous random variables include the time it takes a worker to assemble a part, the weight of a potato, the distance it takes to stop a car once the brakes have been applied, and the volume of waste water emitted from a food processing facility. Values of a continuous random variable are generally determined by measuring. One of the most frequently used continuous probability distributions is called the **normal distribution**.

## 6.1 The Normal Probability Distribution (pg. 234–249)

### Summary

The **normal distribution** is a symmetric, bell-shaped probability distribution. Half the probability lies to the right and half lies to the left of the mean. To find probabilities associated with a normal distribution, you will want to convert to a **standard normal distribution** by first converting values of the random variables to **standardized z-values**. The probabilities associated with a range of values for the random variable are found using the **normal distribution table** in the appendix or by using Excel or Minitab.

> **Outcome 1.** Convert a normal distribution to a standard normal distribution.
> **Outcome 2.** Determine probabilities using the standard normal distribution.
> **Outcome 3.** Calculate values of the random variable associated with specified probabilities from a normal distribution.

## 6.2 Other Continuous Probability Distributions (pg. 249–257)

### Summary

Although the normal distribution is by far the most frequently used continuous probability distribution, two other continuous distributions are introduced in this section. These are the *uniform distribution* and the **exponential distribution**. With the uniform distribution, the probability over any interval is the same as any other interval of the same width. The probabilities for the uniform distribution are computed using Equation 6.3. The exponential distribution is based on a single parameter, lambda, and is often used to describe random service times or the time between customer arrivals in waiting line applications. The probability over a range of values for an exponential distribution can be computed using Equation 6.7 or by using the exponential table in the appendix. Also, Excel and Minitab have functions for calculating the exponential probabilities.

> **Outcome 4.** Calculate probabilities associated with a uniformly distributed random variable.
> **Outcome 5.** Determine probabilities for an exponential probability distribution.

## Conclusion

The normal distribution has wide application throughout the study of business statistics. You will be making use of the normal distribution in subsequent chapters. The normal distribution has very special properties. It is a symmetric, bell-shaped distribution. To find probabilities for a normal distribution, you will first standardize the distribution by converting values of the random variable to standardized z-values. Other continuous distributions introduced in this chapter are the exponential distribution and the uniform distribution. **Figure 6.15** summarizes the discrete probability distributions introduced in Chapter 5 and the continuous probability distributions introduced in this chapter.

**FIGURE 6.15** |

Probability Distribution
Summary

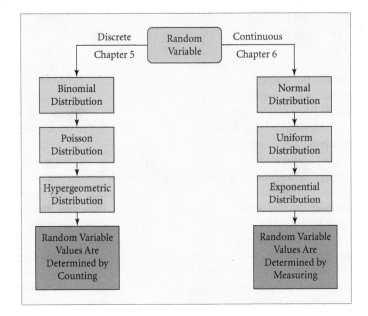

# Equations

**(6.1)** Normal Probability Density Function pg. 235

$$f(x) = \frac{1}{\sigma\sqrt{2\pi}}\, e^{-(x-\mu)^2/2\sigma^2}$$

**(6.2)** Standardized Normal z-Value pg. 236

$$z = \frac{x - \mu}{\sigma}$$

**(6.3)** Continuous Uniform Density Function pg. 250

$$f(x) = \begin{cases} \dfrac{1}{b-a} & \text{if } a \le x \le b \\[2mm] 0 & \text{otherwise} \end{cases}$$

**(6.4)** Mean of the Uniform Distribution pg. 251

$$E(x) = \mu = \frac{a+b}{2}$$

**(6.5)** Standard Deviation of the Uniform Distribution pg. 251

$$\sigma = \sqrt{\frac{(b-a)^2}{12}}$$

**(6.6)** Exponential Density Function pg. 252

$$f(x) = \lambda\, e^{-\lambda x}, \qquad x \ge 0$$

**(6.7)** Exponential Probability pg. 253

$$P(0 \le x \le a) = 1 - e^{-\lambda a}$$

# Key Terms

Normal distribution pg. 234          Standard normal distribution pg. 235

# Chapter Exercises                    *MyStatLab*

## Conceptual Questions

**6-51.** Discuss the difference between discrete and continuous probability distributions. Discuss two situations where a variable of interest may be considered either continuous or discrete.

**6-52.** Recall the Empirical Rule from Chapter 3. It states that if the data distribution is bell-shaped, then the interval

$\mu \pm \sigma$ contains approximately 68% of the values, $\mu \pm 2\sigma$ contains approximately 95%, and $\mu \pm 3\sigma$ contains virtually all of the data values. The bell-shaped distribution referenced is the normal distribution.

a. Verify that a standard normal distribution contains approximately 68% of the values in the interval $\mu \pm \sigma$.

b. Verify that a standard normal distribution contains approximately 95% of the values in the interval $\mu \pm 2\sigma$.

c. Verify that a standard normal distribution contains virtually all of the data in the interval $\mu \pm 3\sigma$.

**6-53.** The probability that a value from a normally distributed random variable will exceed the mean is 0.50. The same is true for the uniform distribution. Why is this not necessarily true for the exponential distribution? Discuss and show examples to illustrate your point.

**6-54.** Suppose you tell one of your fellow students that when working with a continuous distribution, it does not make sense to try to compute the probability of any specific value since it will be zero. She says that, when the experiment is performed some value must occur, the probability can't be zero. Your task is to respond to her statement and in doing so explain why it is appropriate to find the probability for specific ranges of values for a continuous distribution.

**6-55.** The exponential distribution has a characteristic that is called the "memoryless" property. This means $P(X > x) = P(X > x + x_0 | X > x_0)$. To illustrate this, consider the calls coming into 911. Suppose that the distribution of the time between occurrences has an exponential distribution with a mean of one half hour ($= 0.5$).

a. Calculate the probability that no calls come in during the first hour.

b. Now suppose that you are monitoring the call frequency and you note that a call does not come in during the first two hours. Determine the probability that no calls will come in during the next hour.

**6-56.** Revisit Problem 6-55, but examine whether it would matter when you started monitoring the 911 calls if the time between occurrences had a uniform distribution with a mean of 2 and a range of 4.

a. Calculate the probability that no call comes in during the first hour.

b. Now suppose that you are monitoring the call frequency and you note that no call comes in during the first two hours. Determine the probability that no calls will arrive during the next hour.

## Business Applications

**6-57.** The manager for Select-a-Seat, a company that sells tickets to athletic games, concerts, and other events, has determined that the number of people arriving at the Broadway location on a typical day is Poisson distributed with a mean of 12 per hour. It takes approximately four minutes to process a ticket request. Thus, if customers arrive in intervals that are less than four minutes, they will have to wait. Assuming that a customer has just arrived and the ticket agent is starting to serve that customer, what is the probability that the next customer who arrives will have to wait in line?

**6-58.** The Three Sisters Lumber Company is considering buying a machine that planes lumber to the correct thickness. The machine is advertised to produce

"6-inch lumber" having a thickness that is normally distributed, with a mean of 6 inches and a standard deviation of 0.1 inch.

a. If building standards in the industry require a 99% chance of a board being between 5.85 and 6.15 inches, should Three Sisters purchase this machine? Why or why not?

b. To what level would the company that manufactures the machine have to reduce the standard deviation for the machine to conform to industry standards?

**6-59.** Two automatic dispensing machines are being considered for use in a fast-food chain. The first dispenses an amount of liquid that has a normal distribution with a mean of 11.9 ounces and a standard deviation of 0.07 ounces. The second dispenses an amount of liquid that has a normal distribution with a mean of 12.0 ounces and a standard deviation of 0.05 ounces. Acceptable amounts of dispensed liquid are between 11.9 and 12.0 ounces. Calculate the relevant probabilities and determine which machine should be selected.

**6-60.** A small private ambulance service in Kentucky has determined that the time between emergency calls is exponentially distributed with a mean of 41 minutes. When a unit goes on call, it is out of service for 60 minutes. If a unit is busy when an emergency call is received, the call is immediately routed to another service. The company is considering buying a second ambulance. However, before doing so, the owners are interested in determining the probability that a call will come in before the ambulance is back in service. Without knowing the costs involved in this situation, does this probability tend to support the need for a second ambulance? Discuss.

**6-61.** An online article (http://beauty.about.com) by Julyne Derrick, "Shelf Lives: How Long Can You Keep Makeup," suggests that eye shadow and eyeliner each have a shelf life of up to three years. Suppose the shelf lives of these two products are exponentially distributed with an average shelf life of one year.

a. Calculate the probability that the shelf life of eye shadow will be longer than three years.

b. Determine the probability that at least one of these products will have a shelf life of more than three years.

c. Determine the probability that a purchased eyeliner that is useful after one year will be useful after three years.

**6-62.** The Sea Pines Golf Course is preparing for a major LPGA golf tournament. Since parking near the course is extremely limited (room for only 500 cars), the course officials have contracted with the local community to provide parking and a bus shuttle service. Sunday, the final day of the tournament, will have the largest crowd, and the officials estimate there will be between 8,000 and 12,000 cars needing parking spaces but think no value is more likely than another.

The tournament committee is discussing how many parking spots to contract from the city. If they want to limit the chance of not having enough provided parking to 10%, how many spaces do they need from the city on Sunday?

6-63. One of the products of Pittsburg Plate Glass Industries (PPG) is laminated safety glass. It is made up of two pieces of glass 0.125 inch thick, with a thin layer of vinyl sandwiched between them. The average thickness of the laminated safety glass is 0.25 inch. The thickness of the glass does not vary from the mean by more than 0.10 inch. Assume the thickness of the glass has a uniform distribution.
   a. Provide the density for this uniform distribution.
   b. If the glass has a thickness that is more than 0.05 inch below the mean, it must be discarded for safety considerations. Determine the probability that a randomly selected automobile glass is discarded due to safety considerations.
   c. If the glass is more than 0.075 above the mean, it will create installation problems and must be discarded. Calculate the probability that a randomly selected automobile glass will be rejected due to installation concerns.
   d. Given that a randomly selected automobile glass is not rejected for safety considerations, determine the probability that it will be rejected for installation concerns.

6-64. The St. Maries plywood plant is part of the Potlatch Corporation's Northwest Division. The plywood superintendent organized a study of the tree diameters that are being shipped to the mill. After collecting a large amount of data on diameters, he concluded that the distribution is approximately normally distributed with a mean of 14.25 inches and a standard deviation of 2.92 inches. Because of the way plywood is made, there is a certain amount of waste on each log because the peeling process leaves a core that is approximately 3 inches thick. For this reason, he feels that any log less than 10 inches in diameter is not profitable for making plywood.
   a. Based on the data the superintendent has collected, what is the probability that a log will be unprofitable?
   b. An alternative is to peel the log and then sell the core as "peeler logs." These peeler logs are sold as fence posts and for various landscape projects. There is not as much profit in these peeler logs, however. The superintendent has determined that he can make a profit if the peeler log's diameter is not more than 32% of the diameter of the log. Using this additional information, calculate the proportion of logs that will be unprofitable.

6-65. The personnel manager for a large company is interested in the distribution of sick-leave hours for employees of her company. A recent study revealed the distribution to be approximately normal, with a mean of 58 hours per year and a standard deviation of 14 hours.

An office manager in one division has reason to believe that during the past year, two of his employees have taken excessive sick leave relative to everyone else. The first employee used 74 hours of sick leave, and the second used 90 hours. What would you conclude about the office manager's claim and why?

## Computer Database **Exercises**

6-66. The Cozine Corporation runs the landfill operation outside Little Rock, Arkansas. Each day, each of the company's trucks makes several trips from the city to the landfill. On each entry the truck is weighed. The data file **Cozine** contains a sample of 200 truck weights. Determine the mean and standard deviation for the garbage truck weights. Assuming that these sample values are representative of the population of all Cozine garbage trucks, and assuming that the distribution is normally distributed,
   a. Determine the probability that a truck will arrive at the landfill weighing in excess of 46,000 pounds.
   b. Compare the probability in part a to the proportion of trucks in the sample that weighed over 46,000 pounds. What does this imply to you?
   c. Suppose the managers are concerned that trucks are returning to the landfill before they are fully loaded. If they have set a minimum weight of 38,000 pounds before the truck returns to the landfill, what is the probability that a truck will fail to meet the minimum standard?

6-67. The Hydronics Company is in the business of developing health supplements. Recently, the company's research and development department came up with two weight-loss products that included products produced by Hydronics. To determine whether these products are effective, the company has conducted a test. A total of 300 people who were 30 pounds or more overweight were recruited to participate in the study. Of these, 100 people were given a placebo supplement, 100 people were given product 1, and 100 people were given product 2. As might be expected, some people dropped out of the study before the four-week study period was completed. The weight loss (or gain) for each individual is listed in the data file called **Hydronics**. Note, positive values indicate that the individual actually gained weight during the study period.
   a. Develop a frequency histogram for the weight loss (or gain) for those people on product 1. Does it appear from this graph that weight loss is approximately normally distributed?
   b. Referring to part a, assuming that a normal distribution does apply, compute the mean and standard deviation weight loss for the product 1 subjects.
   c. Referring to parts a and b, assume that the weight-change distribution for product 1 users is normally distributed and that the sample mean and standard deviation are used to directly represent the

population mean and standard deviation. Then, what is the probability that a plan 1 user will lose over 12 pounds in a four-week period?

d. Referring to your answer in part c, would it be appropriate for the company to claim that plan 1 users can expect to lose as much as 12 pounds in four weeks? Discuss.

**6-68.** Midwest Fan Manufacturing Inc. was established in 1986 as a manufacturer and distributor of quality ventilation equipment. Midwest Fan's products include the AXC range hood exhaust fans. The file entitled **Fan Life** contains the length of life of 125 randomly chosen AXC fans that were used in an accelerated life-testing experiment.

a. Produce a relative frequency histogram for the data. Does it seem plausible the data came from a population that has an exponential distribution?

b. Calculate the mean and standard deviation of the fans' length of life.

c. Calculate the median length of life of the fans.

d. Determine the probability that a randomly chosen fan will have a life of more than 25,000 hours.

**6-69.** Team Marketing Report (TMR) produces the Fan Cost Index™ (FCI) survey, now in its 16th year, which tracks the cost of attendance for a family of four at National Football League (NFL) games. The FCI includes four average-price tickets, four small soft drinks, two small beers, four hot dogs, two game programs, parking, and two adult-size caps. The league's average FCI in 2008 was $396.36. The file entitled **NFL Price** is a sample of 175 randomly chosen fans' FCIs.

a. Produce a relative frequency histogram for these data. Does it seem plausible the data were sampled from a population that was normally distributed?

b. Calculate the mean and standard deviation of the league's FCI.

c. Calculate the 90th percentile of the league's fans' FCI.

d. The San Francisco 49ers had an FCI of $376.71. Determine the percentile of the FCI of a randomly chosen family whose FCI is the same as that of the 49ers' average FCI.

**6-70.** The Future-Vision Cable TV Company recently surveyed its customers. A total of 548 responses were received. Among other things, the respondents were asked to indicate their household income. The data from the survey are found in a file named **Future-Vision**.

a. Develop a frequency histogram for the income variable. Does it appear from the graph that income is approximately normally distributed? Discuss.

b. Compute the mean and standard deviation for the income variable.

c. Referring to parts a and b and assuming that income is normally distributed and the sample mean and standard deviation are good substitutes for the population values, what is the probability that a Future-Vision customer will have an income exceeding $40,000?

d. Suppose that Future-Vision managers are thinking about offering a monthly discount to customers who have a household income below a certain level. If the management wants to grant discounts to no more than 7% of the customers, what income level should be used for the cutoff?

**6-71.** Championship Billiards, owned by D & R Industries, in Lincolnwood, Illinois, provides some of the finest billiard fabrics, cushion rubber, and component parts in the industry. It sells billiard cloth in bolts and half-bolts. A half-bolt of billiard cloth has an average length of 35 yards with widths of either 62 or 66 inches. The file entitled **Half Bolts** contains the lengths of 120 randomly selected half-bolts.

a. Produce a relative frequency histogram for these data. Does it seem plausible the data came from a population that has a uniform distribution?

b. Provide the density, $f(x)$, for this uniform distribution.

c. A billiard retailer, Sticks & Stones Billiard Supply, is going to recover the pool tables in the local college pool hall, which has eight tables. It takes approximately 3.8 yards per table. If Championship ships a randomly chosen half-bolt, determine the probability that it will contain enough cloth to recover the eight tables.

# Case 6.1

## State Entitlement Programs

Franklin Joiner, director of health, education, and welfare, had just left a meeting with the state's newly elected governor and several of the other recently appointed department heads. One of the governor's campaign promises was to try to halt the rising cost of a certain state entitlement program. In several speeches, the governor indicated the state of Idaho should allocate funds only to those individuals ranked in the bottom 10% of the state's income distribution. Now the governor wants to know how much one could earn before being disqualified from the program and he also wants to know the range of incomes for the middle 95% of the state's income distribution.

Frank had mentioned in the meeting that he thought incomes in the state could be approximated by a normal distribution and that mean per capita income was about $33,000 with a standard deviation of nearly $9,000. The governor was expecting a memo in his office by 3:00 P.M. that afternoon with answers to his questions.

### Required Tasks:

1. Assuming that incomes can be approximated using a normal distribution with the specified mean and standard deviation, calculate the income that cut off the bottom 10% of incomes.

2. Assuming that incomes can be approximated using a normal distribution with the specified mean and standard deviation, calculate the middle 95% of incomes. *Hint*: This requires calculating two values.

3. Write a short memo describing your results and how they were obtained. Your memo should clearly state the income that would disqualify people from the program, as well as the range of incomes in the middle 95% of the state's income distribution.

# Case 6.2

## Credit Data, Inc.

Credit Data, Inc., has been monitoring the amount of time its bill collectors spend on calls that produce contacts with consumers. Management is interested in the distribution of time a collector spends on each call in which they initiate contact, inform a consumer about an outstanding debt, discuss a payment plan, and receive payments by phone. Credit Data is mostly interested in how quickly a collector can initiate and end a conversation to move on to the next call. For employees of Credit Data, time is money in the sense that one account may require one call and 2 minutes to collect, whereas another account may take five calls and 10 minutes per call to collect. The company has discovered that the time collectors spend talking to consumers about accounts is approximated by a normal distribution with a mean of 8 minutes and a standard deviation of 2.5 minutes. The managers believe that the mean is too high and should be reduced by more efficient phone call methods. Specifically, they wish to have no more than 10% of all calls require more than 10.5 minutes.

### Required Tasks:

1. Assuming that training can affect the average time but not the standard deviation, the managers are interested in knowing to what level the mean call time needs to be reduced in order to meet the 10% requirement.
2. Assuming that the standard deviation can be affected by training but the mean time will remain at 8 minutes, to what level must the standard deviation be reduced in order to meet the 10% requirement?
3. If nothing is done, what percent of all calls can be expected to require more than 10.5 minutes?

# Case 6.3

## American Oil Company

Chad Williams, field geologist for the American Oil Company, settled into his first-class seat on the Sun-Air flight between Los Angeles and Oakland, California. Earlier that afternoon, he had attended a meeting with the design engineering group at the Los Angeles New Product Division. He was now on his way to the home office in Oakland. He was looking forward to the one-hour flight because it would give him a chance to reflect on a problem that surfaced during the meeting. It would also give him a chance to think about the exciting opportunities that lay ahead in Australia.

Chad works with a small group of highly trained people at American Oil who literally walk the earth looking for new sources of oil. They make use of the latest in electronic equipment to take a wide range of measurements from many thousands of feet below the earth's surface. It is one of these electronic machines that is the source of Chad's current problem. Engineers in Los Angeles have designed a sophisticated enhancement that will greatly improve the equipment's ability to detect oil. The enhancement requires 800 capacitors, which must operate within ±0.50 microns from the specified standard of 12 microns.

The problem is that the supplier can provide capacitors that operate according to a normal distribution, with a mean of 12 microns and a standard deviation of 1 micron. Thus, Chad knows that not all capacitors will meet the specifications required by the new piece of exploration equipment. This will mean that to have at least 800 usable capacitors, American Oil will have to order more than 800 from the supplier. However, these items are very expensive, so he wants to order as few as possible to meet their needs. At the meeting, the group agreed that they wanted a 98% chance that any order of capacitors would contain the sufficient number of usable items. If the project is to remain on schedule, Chad must place the order by tomorrow. He wants the new equipment ready to go by the time he leaves for an exploration trip in Australia. As he reclined in his seat, sipping a cool lemonade, he wondered whether a basic statistical technique could be used to help determine how many capacitors to order.

# References

Albright, Christian S., Wayne L. Winston, and Christopher Zappe, *Data Analysis for Managers with Microsoft Excel* (Pacific Grove, CA: Duxbury, 2003).

Hogg, R. V., and Elliot A. Tanis, *Probability and Statistical Inference*, 8th ed. (Upper Saddle River, NJ: Prentice Hall, 2009).

Marx, Morris L., and Richard J. Larsen, *An Introduction to Mathematical Statistics and Its Applications*, 4th ed. (Upper Saddle River, NJ: Prentice Hall, 2005).

*Microsoft Excel 2007* (Redmond, WA: Microsoft Corp., 2007).

*Minitab for Windows Version 15* (State College, PA: Minitab, 2007).

Siegel, Andrew F., *Practical Business Statistics*, 5th ed. (Burr Ridge, IL: Irwin, 2002).

chapter 7

**Chapter 7** Quick Prep Links

- **Review** the discussion of random sampling in Chapter 1.
- **Review** the steps for computing means and standard deviations in Chapter 3.

- **Make sure** you are familiar with the normal distribution and how to compute standardized $z$-values as introduced in Chapter 6.

- **Review** the concepts associated with finding probabilities with a standard normal distribution as discussed in Chapter 6.

# Introduction to Sampling Distributions

## Why you need to know

A restaurant executive receives a summary report from her analyst that indicates the mean dollars spent by adults on fine dining per year is $302.45. As she reads further, she learns that the mean value is based on a statistical sample of 540 adults in New Mexico. The $302.45 is a *statistic*, not a *parameter*, because it is based on a sample rather than an entire population. If you were this marketing executive, you might have several questions:

- Is the actual population mean equal to $302.45?
- If the population mean is not $302.45, how close is $302.45 to the true population mean?
- Is a sample of 540 taken from a population of nearly 2 million sufficient to provide a "good" estimate of the population mean?

A manufacturer of do-it-yourself plumbing repair kits selects a random sample of kits boxed and ready for shipment to customers. These repair kits are unboxed and inspected to see whether what is in the box matches exactly what is supposed to be in the box. This past week, 233 kits were sampled and 18 had one or more discrepancies. This is a 7.7% defect rate. Should the quality engineer conclude that exactly 7.7% of the 13,300 repair kits made this week reached the customer with one or more order discrepancies? Is the actual percentage higher or lower than 7.7% and, if so, by how much? Should the quality engineer request that more repair kits be sampled?

The questions facing the restaurant executive and the quality engineer are common to those faced by people in business everywhere. You will almost assuredly find yourself in a similar situation many times in the future. To help answer these questions, you need to have an understanding of *sampling distributions*. Whenever decisions are based on samples rather than an entire population, questions about the sample results exist. Anytime we sample from a population, there are many, many possible samples that could have been selected. Each sample will contain different items. Because of this, the sample means for each possible sample can be different, or the sample percentages can be different. The sampling distribution describes the distribution of possible sample outcomes. Knowing what this distribution looks like will help you understand the specific result you obtained from the one sample you selected.

This chapter introduces you to the important concepts of sampling error and sampling distributions and discusses how you can use this knowledge to help answer the questions facing the marketing executive and the quality engineer. The information presented here provides an essential building block to understanding statistical estimation and hypothesis testing, which will be covered in upcoming chapters.

# 7.1 Sampling Error: What It Is and Why It Happens

As discussed in previous chapters, you will encounter many situations in business in which a sample will be taken from a population and you will be required to analyze the sample data. Chapter 1 introduced several different statistical sampling techniques. Chapters 2 and 3 introduced a variety of descriptive tools that are useful in analyzing sample data. The objective of random sampling is to gather data that reflect a population. Then when analysis is performed on the sample data, the results will be as though we had worked with all the population data. However, we very rarely know if our objective has been achieved. To be able to determine if a sample replicates the population, we must know the entire population, and if that is the case, we do not need to sample. We can just census the population. Because we do not know the population, we require that our sample be random so that bias is not introduced into an already difficult task.

Chapter Outcome 1. ➡ **Calculating Sampling Error**

Regardless of how careful we are in using random sampling methods, the sample may not be a perfect reflection of the population. For example a *statistic* such as $\bar{x}$ might be computed for sample data. Unless the sample is a perfect replication of the population, the statistic will likely not equal the *parameter*, $\mu$. In this case, the difference between the sample mean and the population mean is called **sampling error**. In the case in which we are interested in the mean value, the sampling error is computed using Equation 7.1.

**Sampling Error**

The difference between a measure computed from a sample (a statistic) and the corresponding measure computed from the population (a parameter).

---

**Sampling Error of the Sample Mean**

$$\text{Sampling error} = \bar{x} - \mu \qquad \text{(7.1)}$$

where:

$\bar{x}$ = Sample mean
$\mu$ = Population mean

---

**BUSINESS APPLICATION**  SAMPLING ERROR

**HUMMEL DEVELOPMENT CORPORATION** The Hummel Development Corporation has built 12 office complexes. Table 7.1 shows a list of the 12 projects and the total square footage of each project.

Because these 12 projects are all the office complexes the company has worked on, the square-feet area for all 12 projects, shown in Table 7.1, is a population. Equation 7.2 is used to compute the mean square feet in the population of projects.

---

**Population Mean**

$$\mu = \frac{\sum x}{N} \qquad \text{(7.2)}$$

where:

$\mu$ = Population mean
$x$ = Values in the population
$N$ = Population size

---

**TABLE 7.1 | Square Feet for Office Complex Projects**

| Complex | Square Feet |
|---------|-------------|
| 1 | 114,560 |
| 2 | 202,300 |
| 3 | 78,600 |
| 4 | 156,700 |
| 5 | 134,600 |
| 6 | 88,200 |
| 7 | 177,300 |
| 8 | 155,300 |
| 9 | 214,200 |
| 10 | 303,800 |
| 11 | 125,200 |
| 12 | 156,900 |

The mean square feet for the 12 office complexes is

$$\mu = \frac{114{,}560 + 202{,}300 + \cdots + 125{,}200 + 156{,}900}{12}$$

$$\mu = 158{,}972 \text{ square feet}$$

**Parameter**

A measure computed from the entire population. As long as the population does not change, the value of the parameter will not change.

**Simple Random Sample**

A sample selected in such a manner that each possible sample of a given size has an equal chance of being selected.

The average square footage of the offices built by the firm is 158,972 square feet. This value is a **parameter**. No matter how many times we compute the value, assuming no arithmetic mistakes, we will get the same value for the population mean.

Hummel is a finalist to be the developer of a new office building in Madison, Wisconsin. The client who will hire the firm plans to select a **simple random sample** of $n = 5$ projects from those the finalists have completed. The client plans to travel to these office buildings to see the quality of the construction and to interview owners and occupants. (You may want to refer to Chapter 1 to review the material on simple random samples.)

Refer to the office complex data in Table 7.1, and suppose the client randomly selects the following five Hummel projects from the population:

| Complex | Square Feet |
|---------|-------------|
| 5 | 134,600 |
| 4 | 156,700 |
| 1 | 114,560 |
| 8 | 155,300 |
| 9 | 214,200 |

Key in the selection process is the finalists' past performance on large projects, so the client might be interested in the mean size of the office buildings that the finalists have developed. Equation 7.3 is used to compute the sample mean.

**Sample Mean**

$$\bar{x} = \frac{\sum x}{n} \tag{7.3}$$

where:

$\bar{x}$ = Sample mean
$x$ = Sample values selected from the population
$n$ = Sample size

The sample mean is

$$\bar{x} = \frac{134{,}600 + 156{,}700 + 114{,}560 + 155{,}300 + 214{,}200}{5} = \frac{775{,}360}{5} = 155{,}072$$

The average number of square feet in the random sample of five office buildings selected by the client is 155,072. This value is a *statistic* based on the sample.

Recall the mean for the population:

$$\mu = 158{,}972 \text{ square feet}$$

The sample mean is

$$\bar{x} = 155{,}072 \text{ square feet}$$

As you can see, the sample mean does not equal the population mean. This difference is called the *sampling error*. Using Equation 7.1, we compute the sampling error as follows.

$$\text{Sampling error} = \bar{x} - \mu$$
$$= 155{,}072 - 158{,}972 = -3{,}900 \text{ square feet}$$

The sample mean for the random sample of $n = 5$ office buildings is 3,900 square feet less than the population mean. Regardless of how carefully you construct your sampling plan, you can expect to see sampling error. A random sample will almost never be a perfect image of its population. The sample value and the population value will most likely be different.

Suppose the client who selected the random sample throws these five projects back into the stack and selects a second random sample of five as follows:

| Complex | Square Feet |
|---------|-------------|
| 9 | 214,200 |
| 6 | 88,200 |
| 5 | 134,600 |
| 12 | 156,900 |
| 10 | 303,800 |

The mean for this sample is

$$\bar{x} = \frac{214,200 + 88,200 + 134,600 + 156,900 + 303,800}{5} = \frac{897,700}{5} = 179,540 \text{ square feet}$$

This time, the sample mean is larger than the population mean. This time the sampling error is

$$\bar{x} - \mu = 179,540 - 158,972$$
$$= 20,568 \text{ square feet}$$

This illustrates some useful fundamental concepts:

- The size of the sampling error depends on which sample is selected.
- The sampling error may be positive or negative.
- There is potentially a different $\bar{x}$ for each possible sample.

If the client wanted to use the sample mean to estimate the population mean, in one case they would be 3,900 square feet too small, and in the other they would be 20,568 square feet too large.

---

**EXAMPLE 7-1**    **COMPUTING THE SAMPLING ERROR**

**Southwest Airlines** Southwest Airlines is one of the most successful airlines in the United States. The company started as a short-distance, discount airline with service primarily in Texas. It now offers coast-to-coast service between certain airports. The prices from Portland, Oregon, to the 10 eastern cities that can be reached on Southwest from Portland are listed as follows:

| $479 | $569 | $599 | $649 | $649 | $699 | $699 | $749 | $799 | $799 |
|------|------|------|------|------|------|------|------|------|------|

Suppose a Southwest manager wished to do a quick analysis of the Portland ticket prices and randomly sampled $n = 4$ prices from the population of $N = 10$. The selected ticket prices were

| $569 | $649 | $799 | $799 |
|------|------|------|------|

The sampling error can be computed using the following steps:

**Step 1**  **Determine the population mean using Equation 7.2.**

$$\mu = \frac{\sum x}{N} = \frac{479 + 569 + 599 + \cdots + 799 + 799}{10} = \frac{6,690}{10} = \$669$$

**Step 2**  **Compute the sample mean using Equation 7.3.**

$$\bar{x} = \frac{\sum x}{n} = \frac{569 + 649 + 799 + 799}{4} = \frac{2,816}{4} = \$704$$

**Step 3**  **Compute the sampling error using Equation 7.1.**

$$\bar{x} - \mu = 704 - 669 = \$35$$

This sample of four has a sampling error of $35. The sample of ticket prices has a slightly larger mean price than the mean for the population.

>>**END EXAMPLE**

**TRY PROBLEM** 7-1 (pg. 270)

### The Role of Sample Size in Sampling Error

**BUSINESS APPLICATION** SAMPLING ERROR

**HUMMEL DEVELOPMENT CORPORATION (*CONTINUED*)** Previously, we selected random samples of 5 office complexes from the 12 projects Hummel Development Corporation has built. We then computed the resulting sampling error. There are actually 792 possible samples of size 5 taken from 12 projects. This value is found using the counting rule for combinations, which was discussed in Chapter 5.[1]

In actual situations, only one sample is selected, and the decision maker uses the sample measure to estimate the population measure. A "small" sampling error may be acceptable. However, if the sampling error is too "large," conclusions about the population could be misleading.

We can look at the extremes on either end to evaluate the potential for extreme sampling error. The population of square feet for the 12 projects is

| Complex | Square Feet | Complex | Square Feet |
|---------|-------------|---------|-------------|
| 1 | 114,560 | 7 | 177,300 |
| 2 | 202,300 | 8 | 155,300 |
| 3 | 78,600 | 9 | 214,200 |
| 4 | 156,700 | 10 | 303,800 |
| 5 | 134,600 | 11 | 125,200 |
| 6 | 88,200 | 12 | 156,900 |

Suppose, by chance, the developers ended up with the five smallest office complexes in their sample. These would be

| Complex | Square Feet |
|---------|-------------|
| 3 | 78,600 |
| 6 | 88,200 |
| 1 | 114,560 |
| 11 | 125,200 |
| 5 | 134,600 |

The mean of this sample is

$$\bar{x} = 108,232 \text{ square feet}$$

Of all the possible random samples of 5, this one provides the smallest sample mean. The sampling error is

$$\bar{x} - \mu = 108,232 - 158,972 = -50,740 \text{ square feet}$$

Thus, if this sample is selected, the sampling error would be −50,740 square feet.

On the other extreme, suppose the sample contained the five largest office complexes, as follows:

| Complex | Square Feet |
|---------|-------------|
| 10 | 303,800 |
| 9 | 214,200 |
| 2 | 202,300 |
| 7 | 177,300 |
| 12 | 156,900 |

---

[1]The number of combinations of $x$ items from a sample of $n$ is $\dfrac{n!}{x!\,(n-x)!}$ .

**TABLE 7.2** | **Hummel Office Building Example for *n* = 3 (Extreme Samples)**

| Smallest Office Buildings | | Largest Office Buildings | |
|---|---|---|---|
| Complex | Square Feet | Complex | Square Feet |
| 3 | 78,600 | 10 | 303,800 |
| 6 | 88,200 | 9 | 214,200 |
| 1 | 114,560 | 2 | 202,300 |
| $\bar{x}$ = 93,786.67 sq. feet | | $\bar{x}$ = 240,100 sq. feet | |
| Sampling Error: | | Sampling Error: | |
| 93,786.67 − 158,972 = −65,185.33 square feet | | 240,100 − 158,972 = 81,128 square feet | |

The mean for this sample is $\bar{x}$ = 210,900. This is the largest possible sample mean from all the possible samples. The sampling error in this case would be

$$\bar{x} - \mu = 210,900 - 158,972 = 51,928 \text{ square feet}$$

The potential for extreme sampling error ranges from

$$-50,740 \text{ to } +51,928 \text{ square feet}$$

The remaining possible random samples of 5 will provide sampling errors between these limits.

What happens if the sample size is larger or smaller? Suppose the client scales back his sample size to *n* = 3 office complexes. Table 7.2 shows the extremes. By reducing the sample size from 5 to 3, the range of potential sampling error has increased from

$$(-50,740 \text{ to } +51,928 \text{ square feet})$$

to

$$(-65,185.33 \text{ to } +81,128 \text{ square feet})$$

This illustrates that the potential for extreme sampling error is greater when smaller-sized samples are used.

Although larger sample sizes reduce the potential for extreme sampling error, there is no guarantee that the larger sample size will always give the smallest sampling error. For example, Table 7.3 shows two further applications of the office complex data. As illustrated, this random sample of three had a sampling error of −2,672 square feet, whereas this random sample of five had a sampling error of 16,540 square feet. In this case, the smaller sample was "better" than the larger sample. However, in Section 7-2, you will learn that, on average, the sampling error produced by large samples will be less than the sampling error from small samples.

**TABLE 7.3** | **Hummel Office Building Example with Different Sample Sizes**

| *n* = 5 | | *n* = 3 | |
|---|---|---|---|
| Complex | Square Feet | Complex | Square Feet |
| 4 | 156,700 | 12 | 156,900 |
| 1 | 114,560 | 8 | 155,300 |
| 7 | 177,300 | 4 | 156,700 |
| 11 | 125,200 | | |
| 10 | 303,800 | | |
| $\bar{x}$ = 175,512 sq. feet | | $\bar{x}$ = 156,300 sq. feet | |
| Sampling Error: | | Sampling Error: | |
| 175,512 − 158,972 = 16,540 square feet | | 156,300 − 158,972 = −2,672 square feet | |

# 7-1: Exercises

## Skill Development

**7-1.** A population has a mean of 125. If a random sample of 8 items from the population results in the following sampled values, what is the sampling error for the sample?

| 103 | 123 | 99 | 107 | 121 | 100 | 100 | 99 |
|---|---|---|---|---|---|---|---|

**7-2.** The following data are the 16 values in a population:

| 10 | 5 | 19 | 20 | 10 | 8 | 10 | 2 |
|---|---|---|---|---|---|---|---|
| 14 | 18 | 7 | 8 | 14 | 2 | 3 | 10 |

a. Compute the population mean.
b. Suppose a simple random sample of 5 values from the population is selected with the following results:

| 5 | 10 | 20 | 2 | 3 |
|---|---|---|---|---|

Compute the mean of this sample.
c. Based on the results for parts a and b, compute the sampling error for the sample mean.

**7-3.** The following population is provided:

| 17 | 15 | 8 | 12 | 9 | 7 | 9 | 11 |
|---|---|---|---|---|---|---|---|
| 12 | 14 | 16 | 9 | 5 | 10 | 14 | 13 |
| 12 | 12 | 11 | 9 | 14 | 8 | 14 | 12 |

Further, a simple random sample from this population gives the following values:

| 12 | 9 | 5 | 10 | 14 | 11 |
|---|---|---|---|---|---|

Compute the sampling error for the sample mean in this situation.

**7-4.** Consider the following population:

| 18 | 26 | 32 | 17 | 34 | 17 | 17 | 22 |
|---|---|---|---|---|---|---|---|
| 29 | 24 | 24 | 35 | 13 | 29 | 38 | |

The following sample was drawn from this population:

| 35 | 18 | 24 | 17 | 24 | 32 | 17 | 29 |
|---|---|---|---|---|---|---|---|

a. Determine the sampling error for the sample mean.
b. Determine the largest possible sampling error for this sample of $n = 8$.

**7-5.** Assume that the following represent a population of $N = 24$ values:

| 10 | 14 | 32 | 9 | 34 | 19 | 31 | 24 |
|---|---|---|---|---|---|---|---|
| 33 | 11 | 14 | 30 | 6 | 27 | 33 | 32 |
| 28 | 30 | 10 | 31 | 19 | 13 | 6 | 35 |

a. If a random sample of $n = 10$ items includes the following values, compute the sampling error for the sample mean:

| 32 | 19 | 6 | 11 | 10 |
|---|---|---|---|---|
| 19 | 28 | 9 | 13 | 33 |

b. For a sample of size $n = 6$, compute the range for the possible sampling error. (*Hint*: Find the sampling error for the 6 smallest sample values and the 6 largest sample values.)
c. For a sample of size $n = 12$, compute the range for the possible sampling error. How does sample size affect the potential for extreme sampling error?

**7-6.** Assume that the following represent a population of $N = 16$ values.

| 25 | 12 | 21 | 13 | 19 | 17 | 15 | 18 |
|---|---|---|---|---|---|---|---|
| 23 | 16 | 18 | 15 | 22 | 14 | 23 | 17 |

a. Compute the population mean.
b. If a random sample of $n = 9$ includes the following values

| 12 | 18 | 13 | 17 | 23 | 14 | 16 | 25 | 15 |
|---|---|---|---|---|---|---|---|---|

compute the sample mean and calculate the sampling error for this sample.
c. Determine the range of extreme sampling error for a sample of size $n = 4$. (*Hint*: Calculate the lowest possible sample mean and highest possible sample mean.)

**7-7.** Consider the following population:

| 3 | 6 | 9 |
|---|---|---|

a. Calculate the population mean.
b. Select, with replacement, and list each possible sample of size 2. Also, calculate the sample mean for each sample.
c. Calculate the sampling error associated with each sample mean.
d. Assuming that each sample is equally likely, produce the distribution of the sampling errors.

## Business **Applications**

**7-8.** Hillman Management Services manages apartment complexes in Tulsa, Oklahoma. They currently have 30 units available for rent. The monthly rental prices (in dollars) for this population of 30 units are

| | | | | | | | | | |
|---|---|---|---|---|---|---|---|---|---|
| 455 | 690 | 450 | 495 | 550 | 780 | 800 | 395 | 500 | 405 |
| 675 | 550 | 490 | 495 | 700 | 995 | 650 | 550 | 400 | 750 |
| 600 | 780 | 650 | 905 | 415 | 600 | 600 | 780 | 575 | 750 |

a. What is the range of possible sampling error if a random sample of size $n = 6$ is selected from the population?
b. What is the range of possible sampling error if a random sample of size $n = 10$ is selected? Compare your answers to parts a and b and explain why the difference exists.

**7-9.** A previous report from the Centers for Disease Control and Prevention (CDC) indicates that smokers, on average, miss 6.16 days of work per year due to sickness (including smoking-related acute and chronic conditions). Nonsmokers miss an average of 3.86 days of work per year. If two years later the CDC believes that the average days of work missed by smokers has not changed, it could confirm this by sampling. Consider the following sample:

| | | | | | | | | | |
|---|---|---|---|---|---|---|---|---|---|
| 13 | 4 | 4 | 5 | 12 | 8 | 9 | 11 | 1 | 5 |
| 6 | 9 | 14 | 6 | 3 | 5 | 10 | 7 | 0 | 14 |
| 6 | 15 | 0 | 2 | 5 | 3 | 10 | 8 | 6 | 7 |
| 0 | 0 | 15 | 14 | 6 | 2 | 2 | 1 | 4 | 15 |
| 10 | 12 | 3 | 0 | 14 | 10 | 0 | 1 | 9 | 14 |

Determine the sampling error of this sample, assuming that the CDC supposition is correct.

**7-10.** An Internet service provider states that the average number of hours its customers are online each day is 3.75. Suppose a random sample of 14 of the company's customers is selected and the average number of hours that they are online each day is measured. The sample results are

| | | | | | | |
|---|---|---|---|---|---|---|
| 3.11 | 1.97 | 3.52 | 4.56 | 7.19 | 3.89 | 7.71 |
| 2.12 | 4.68 | 6.78 | 5.02 | 4.28 | 3.23 | 1.29 |

Based on the sample of 14 customers, how much sampling error exists? Would you expect the sampling error to increase or decrease if the sample size was increased to 40?

**7-11.** The Anasazi Real Estate Company has 20 listings for homes in Santa Fe, New Mexico. The number of days each house has been on the market without selling is as follows:

| | | | | | | | | | |
|---|---|---|---|---|---|---|---|---|---|
| 26 | 45 | 16 | 77 | 33 | 50 | 19 | 23 | 55 | 107 |
| 88 | 15 | 7 | 19 | 30 | 60 | 80 | 66 | 31 | 17 |

a. Considering these 20 values to be the population of interest, what is the mean of the population?
b. The company is making a sales brochure and wishes to feature 5 homes selected at random from the list. The number of days the 5 sampled homes have been on the market is

| | | | | |
|---|---|---|---|---|
| 77 | 60 | 15 | 31 | 23 |

If these 5 houses were used to estimate the mean for all 20, what would the sampling error be?
c. What is the range of possible sampling error if 5 homes are selected at random from the population?

**7-12.** The administrator at Saint Frances Hospital is concerned about the amount of overtime the nursing staff is incurring and wonders whether so much overtime is really necessary. The hospital employs 60 nurses. Following is the number of hours of overtime reported by each nurse last week. These data are the population of interest.

| Nurse | Overtime | Nurse | Overtime | Nurse | Overtime |
|---|---|---|---|---|---|
| 1 | 2 | 21 | 4 | 41 | 3 |
| 2 | 1 | 22 | 2 | 42 | 3 |
| 3 | 7 | 23 | 3 | 43 | 2 |
| 4 | 0 | 24 | 5 | 44 | 1 |
| 5 | 4 | 25 | 5 | 45 | 3 |
| 6 | 2 | 26 | 6 | 46 | 3 |
| 7 | 6 | 27 | 2 | 47 | 3 |
| 8 | 4 | 28 | 2 | 48 | 3 |
| 9 | 2 | 29 | 7 | 49 | 4 |
| 10 | 5 | 30 | 4 | 50 | 6 |
| 11 | 5 | 31 | 4 | 51 | 0 |
| 12 | 4 | 32 | 3 | 52 | 3 |
| 13 | 5 | 33 | 3 | 53 | 4 |
| 14 | 0 | 34 | 4 | 54 | 6 |
| 15 | 6 | 35 | 5 | 55 | 0 |
| 16 | 0 | 36 | 5 | 56 | 3 |
| 17 | 2 | 37 | 0 | 57 | 3 |
| 18 | 4 | 38 | 0 | 58 | 7 |
| 19 | 2 | 39 | 4 | 59 | 5 |
| 20 | 5 | 40 | 3 | 60 | 7 |

Using the random numbers table in Appendix A with a starting point in column (digit) 14 and row 10, select a random sample of 6 nurses. Go down the table from the starting point. Determine the mean hours of overtime for these 6 nurses and calculate the sampling error associated with this particular sample mean.

**7-13.** Princess Cruises recently offered a 16-day voyage from Beijing to Bangkok during the time period from May to August. The announced price, excluding airfare, for a room with an ocean view or a balcony was listed as $3,475. Cruise fares usually are quite variable due to discounting by the cruise line and travel agents. A sample of 20 passengers who purchased this cruise paid the following amounts (in dollars):

| | | | | | | | | | |
|---|---|---|---|---|---|---|---|---|---|
| 3,559 | 3,005 | 3,389 | 3,505 | 3,605 | 3,545 | 3,529 | 3,709 | 3,229 | 3,419 |
| 3,439 | 3,375 | 3,349 | 3,559 | 3,419 | 3,569 | 3,559 | 3,575 | 3,449 | 3,119 |

a. Calculate the sample mean cruise fare.
b. Determine the sampling error for this sample.
c. Would the results obtained in part b indicate that the average cruise fare during this period for this cruise is different from the listed price? Explain your answer from a statistical point of view.

**7-14.** An investment advisor has worked with 24 clients for the past five years. Following are the percentage rates of average five-year returns that these 24 clients experienced over this time frame on their investments:

| | | | | | | | | | | | |
|---|---|---|---|---|---|---|---|---|---|---|---|
| 11.2 | 11.2 | 15.9 | 2.7 | 4.6 | 7.6 | 15.6 | 1.3 | 3.3 | 4.8 | 12.8 | 14.9 |
| 10.1 | 10.9 | 4.9 | −2.1 | 12.5 | 3.7 | 7.6 | 4.9 | 10.2 | 0.4 | 9.6 | −0.5 |

This investment advisor plans to introduce a new investment program to a sample of his customers this year. Because this is experimental, he plans to randomly select 5 of the customers to be part of the program. However, he would like those selected to have a mean return rate close to the population mean for the 24 clients. Suppose the following 5 values represent the average five-year annual return for the clients that were selected in the random sample:

| | | | | |
|---|---|---|---|---|
| 11.2 | −2.1 | 12.5 | 1.3 | 3.3 |

Calculate the sampling error associated with the mean of this random sample. What would you tell this advisor regarding the sample he has selected?

**7-15.** A computer lab at a small college has 25 computers. Twice during the day a full scan for viruses is performed on each computer. Because of differences in the configuration of the computers, the times required to complete the scan are different for each machine. Records for the scans are kept and indicate that the time (in seconds) required to perform the scan for each machine is as shown here.

**Time in Seconds to Complete Scan**

| | | | | |
|---|---|---|---|---|
| 1,500 | 1,347 | 1,552 | 1,453 | 1,371 |
| 1,362 | 1,447 | 1,362 | 1,216 | 1,378 |
| 1,647 | 1,093 | 1,350 | 1,834 | 1,480 |
| 1,522 | 1,410 | 1,446 | 1,291 | 1,601 |
| 1,365 | 1,575 | 1,134 | 1,532 | 1,534 |

a. What is the mean time required to scan all 25 computers?
b. Suppose a random sample of 5 computers is taken and the scan times for each are as follows: 1,534, 1,447, 1,371, 1,410, and 1,834. If these 5 randomly

sampled computers are used to estimate the mean scan time for all 25 computers, what would the sampling error be?
c. What is the range of possible sampling error if a random sample size of 7 computers is taken to estimate the mean scan time for all 25 machines?

## Computer Database **Exercises**

**7-16.** *USA Today* reports salaries for National Football League (NFL) teams. The file **Jaguars** contains the salaries for the 2007 Jacksonville Jaguars.
a. Calculate the average total salary for the Jacksonville Jaguars for 2007.
b. Calculate the smallest sample mean for total salary and the largest sample mean for total salary using a sample size of 10. Calculate the sampling error for each sample mean.
c. Repeat the calculations in part b for samples of size 5 and 2.
d. What effect does a change in the sample size appear to have on the dispersion of the sampling errors?

**7-17.** The file entitled **Clothing** contains the monthly retail sales ($millions) of U.S. women's clothing stores for 70 months. A sample taken from this population to estimate the average sales in this time period follows:

| | | | | | | |
|---|---|---|---|---|---|---|
| 2,942 | 2,574 | 2,760 | 2,939 | 2,642 | 2,905 | 2,568 |
| 2,677 | 2,572 | 3,119 | 2,697 | 2,884 | 2,632 | 2,742 |
| 2,671 | 2,884 | 2,946 | 2,825 | 2,987 | 2,729 | 2,676 |
| 2,846 | 3,112 | 2,924 | 2,676 | | | |

a. Calculate the population mean.
b. Calculate the sample mean.
c. How much sampling error is present in this sample?
d. Determine the range of possible sampling error if 25 sales figures are sampled at random from this population.

**7-18.** The Dow-Jones Industrial Average (DJIA) Index is a well-known stock index. The index was originally developed in 1884 and has been in place ever since as a gauge of how the U.S. stock market is performing. The file **Dow Jones** contains date, open, high, low, close, and volume for the DJIA for the trading days between January 2, 2002, and October 31, 2008.
a. Assuming that the data in the file **Dow Jones** constitute the population of interest, what is the population mean closing value for the DJIA?
b. Using Excel or Minitab, select a random sample of 10 days' closing values (make certain not to include duplicate days) and calculate the sample mean and the sampling error for the sample.
c. Repeat part b with a sample size of 50 days' closing values.
d. Repeat part b with a sample size of 100 days' closing values.
e. Write a short statement describing your results. Were they as expected? Explain.

**7-19.** Welco Lumber Company is based in Shelton, Washington, and is a privately held company that makes cedar siding, cedar lumber, and cedar fencing products for sale and distribution throughout North America. The major cost of production is the cedar logs that are the raw material necessary to make the finished cedar products. Thus, it is very important to the company to get the maximum yield from each log. Of course, the dollar value to be achieved from a log depends initially on the diameter of the log. Each log is 8 feet long when it reaches the mill. The file called **Welco** contains a random sample of logs of various diameters and the potential value of the finished products that could be developed from the log if it is made into fence boards.

a. Calculate the sample mean potential value for each diameter of logs in the sample.

b. Discuss whether there is a way to determine how much sampling error exists for a given diameter log based on the sample. Can you determine whether the sampling error will be positive or negative? Discuss.

**7-20.** Maher, Barney, and White LLC is a legal firm with 40 employees. All of the firm's employees are eligible to participate in the company's 401(k) plan, and the firm is proud of its 100% participation rate. The file **MBW 401** contains the most recent year-end 401(k) account balance for each of the firm's 40 employees.

a. Compute the population mean and population standard deviation for the most recent year-end 401(k) account balances at Maher, Barney, and White.

b. Suppose that an audit of the firm's 401(k) plan is being conducted and 12 randomly selected employee account balances are to be examined. If the following employees (indicated by employee number) are randomly selected to be included in the study, what is the estimate for the most recent

year-end mean 401(k) account balance? How much sampling error is present in this estimate?

| Employee # | | | | | | | | | | | |
| --- | --- | --- | --- | --- | --- | --- | --- | --- | --- | --- | --- |
| 26 | 8 | 31 | 3 | 38 | 30 | 17 | 9 | 21 | 39 | 18 | 11 |

c. Calculate the range of possible sampling error if a random sample of 15 employees is used to estimate the most recent year-end mean 401(k) account balance.

**7-21.** The Badke Foundation was set up by the Fred Badke family following his death in 2001. Fred had been a very successful heart surgeon and real estate investor in San Diego, and the family wanted to set up an organization that could be used to help less fortunate people. However, one of the concepts behind the Badke Foundation is to use the Badke money as seed money for gathering contributions from middle-class families. To help in the solicitation of contributions, the foundation was considering the idea of hiring a consulting company that specialized in this activity. Leaders of the consulting company maintained in their presentation that the mean contribution from families who actually contribute after receiving a specially prepared letter would be $20.00.

Before actually hiring the company, the Badke Foundation sent out the letter and request materials to many people in the San Diego area. They received contributions from 166 families. The contribution amounts are in the data file called **Badke**.

a. Assuming that these data reflect a random sample of the population of contributions that would be received, compute the sampling error based on the claim made by the consulting firm.

b. Comment on any issues you have with the assumption that the data represent a random sample. Does the calculation of the sampling error matter if the sample is not a random sample? Discuss.

**END EXERCISES 7-1**

# 7.2 Sampling Distribution of the Mean

Section 7.1 introduced the concept of sampling error. A random sample selected from a population will not perfectly match the population. Thus the sample statistic likely will not equal the population parameter. If this difference arises because the random sample is not a perfect representation of the population, it is called sampling error.

In business applications, decision makers select a single random sample from a population. They compute a sample measure and use it to make decisions about the entire population. For example, Nielsen Media Research takes a single random sample of television viewers to determine the percentage of the population who are watching a particular program during a particular week. Of course, the sample selected is only one of many possible samples that could have been selected from the same population. The sampling error will differ depending on which sample is selected. If, in theory, you were to select all possible random samples of a given size and compute the sample means for each one, these means would vary above and below the true population mean. If we graphed these values as a histogram, the graph would be the **sampling distribution**.

**Sampling Distribution**

The distribution of all possible values of a statistic for a given sample size that has been randomly selected from a population.

In this section, we introduce the basic concepts of sampling distributions. We will use an Excel tool to select repeated samples from the same population for demonstration purposes only. The same thing can be done using Minitab.

**Chapter Outcome 2.** → # Simulating the Sampling Distribution for $\bar{x}$

**Excel and Minitab Tutorial**

**BUSINESS APPLICATION** **SAMPLING DISTRIBUTIONS**

**AIMS INVESTMENT COMPANY** Aims Investment Company handles employee retirement funds, primarily for small companies. The file called **AIMS** contains data on the number of mutual funds in each client's portfolio. The file contains data for all 200 Aims customers, so it is considered a population. Figure 7.1 shows a histogram for the population.

The mean number of mutual funds in a portfolio is 2.505 funds. The standard deviation is 1.507 funds. The graph in Figure 7.1 indicates that the population is spread between zero and six funds, with more customers owning two funds than any other number.

Suppose the controller at Aims plans to select a random sample of 10 accounts. In Excel, we can use the Sampling tool to generate the random sample.[2] Figure 7.2 shows the number of mutual funds owned for a random sample of 10 clients. The sample mean of 1.8 is also shown. To illustrate the concept of a sampling distribution, we repeat this process 500 times, generating 500 different random samples of 10. For each sample, we compute the sample mean. Figure 7.3 shows the frequency histogram for these sample means. Note that the horizontal axis represents the $\bar{x}$-values. The graph in Figure 7.3 is not a complete sampling distribution because it is based on only 500 samples out of the many ($1.6236 \times 10^{27}$) possible samples that could be selected. However, this simulation gives us an idea of what the sampling distribution looks like.

Look again at the population distribution in Figure 7.1 and compare it with the shape of the frequency histogram in Figure 7.3. Although the population distribution is somewhat skewed, the distribution of sample means is taking the shape of a normal distribution.

Note also that the population mean for the 200 individual customers in the population is 2.505 mutual funds. If we average the 500 sample means in Figure 7.3, we get 2.41. This value is the *mean of the 500 sample means*. It is reasonably close to the population mean.

**FIGURE 7.1** |

Distribution of Mutual Funds for the Aims Investment Company

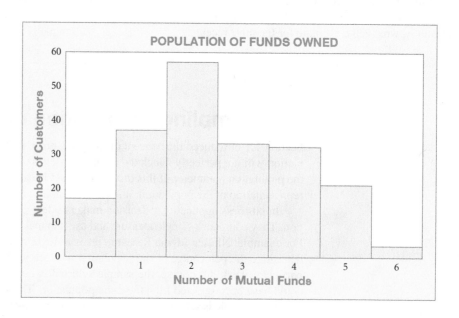

---

[2]The same thing can be achieved in Minitab by using the Sample from Columns option under the Calc > Probability Data command.

FIGURE 7.2

Excel 2007 Output for the Aims Investment Company First Sample Size $n = 10$

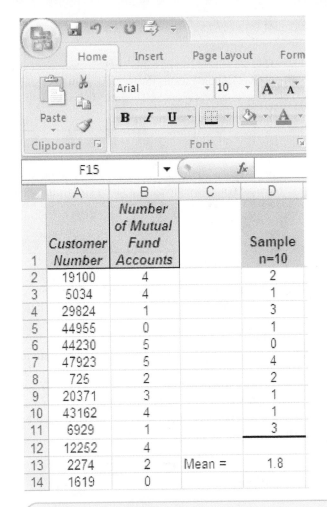

| | A | B | C | D |
|---|---|---|---|---|
| 1 | Customer Number | Number of Mutual Fund Accounts | | Sample n=10 |
| 2 | 19100 | 4 | | 2 |
| 3 | 5034 | 4 | | 1 |
| 4 | 29824 | 1 | | 3 |
| 5 | 44955 | 0 | | 1 |
| 6 | 44230 | 5 | | 0 |
| 7 | 47923 | 5 | | 4 |
| 8 | 725 | 2 | | 2 |
| 9 | 20371 | 3 | | 1 |
| 10 | 43162 | 4 | | 1 |
| 11 | 6929 | 1 | | 3 |
| 12 | 12252 | 4 | | |
| 13 | 2274 | 2 | Mean = | 1.8 |
| 14 | 1619 | 0 | | |

**Excel 2007 Instructions:**
1. Open File: AIMS.xls.
2. Select **Data tab**.
3. Select **Data Analysis**.
4. Select **Sampling**.
5. Define the population data range [B2:B201].
6. Select **Random Sampling**.
7. Select **Output Option**.
8. Compute sample mean using Excel Equation = average(D2:D11).

**Minitab Instructions (for similar results):**
1. Open file: AIMS.MTW.
2. Choose **Calc > Random Data > Sample From Columns**.
3. In **Number of rows to Sample**, enter the sample size.
4. In box following **From column(s)**, enter data column: *Number of Mutual Fund Accounts*.
5. In **Store Samples in**, enter sample's storage column.
6. Click **OK**.
7. Choose **Calc > Calculator**.
8. In **Store Result in Variable** enter column to store mean.
9. Choose **Mean** from **Functions**. **Expression: Mean (Sample Column)**.
10. Repeat steps 3–10 to form sample.
11. Click **OK**.

FIGURE 7.3

Aims Investment Company, Histogram of 500 Sample Means from Sample Size $n = 10$

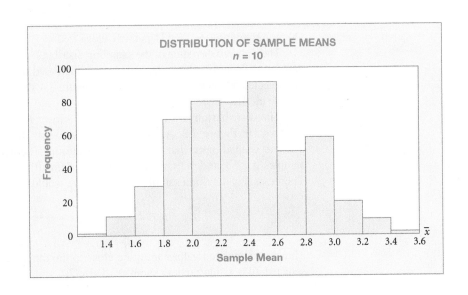

Had we selected all possible random samples of size 10 from the population and computed all possible sample means, the average sample mean would be equal to the population mean. This concept is expressed as Theorem 1.

---

### Theorem 1

For any population, the average value of all possible sample means computed from all possible random samples of a given size from the population will equal the population mean. This is expressed as

$$\mu_{\bar{x}} = \mu$$

---

When the average of all possible values of the sample statistic equals the corresponding parameter, no matter the value of the parameter, we call that statistic an **unbiased estimator** of the parameter.

Also, the population standard deviation is 1.507 mutual funds. This measures the variation in the number of mutual funds between individual customers. When we compute the standard deviation of the 500 sample means, we get 0.421, which is considerably smaller than the population standard deviation. If all possible random samples of size $n$ are selected from the population, the distribution of possible sample means will have a standard deviation that is equal to the population standard deviation divided by the square root of the sample size, as Theorem 2 states.

**Unbiased Estimator**

A characteristic of certain statistics in which the average of all possible values of the sample statistic equals a parameter, no matter the value of the parameter.

---

### Theorem 2

For any population, the standard deviation of the possible sample means computed from all possible random samples of size $n$ is equal to the population standard deviation divided by the square root of the sample size. This is shown as

$$\sigma_{\bar{x}} = \frac{\sigma}{\sqrt{n}}$$

---

Recall the population standard deviation is $\sigma = 1.507$. Then, based on Theorem 2, had we selected all possible random samples of size $n = 10$ rather than only 500 samples, the standard deviation for the possible sample means would be

$$\sigma_{\bar{x}} = \frac{\sigma}{\sqrt{n}} = \frac{1.507}{\sqrt{10}} = 0.477$$

Our simulated value of 0.421 is fairly close to 0.477.

The standard deviation of the sampling distribution will be less than the population standard deviation. To further illustrate, suppose we increased the sample size from $n = 10$ to $n = 20$ and selected 500 new samples of size 20. Figure 7.4 shows the distribution of the 500 different sample means.

The distribution in Figure 7.4 is even closer to a normal distribution than what we observed in Figure 7.3. As sample size increases, the distribution of sample means will become shaped more like a normal distribution. The average sample mean for these 500 samples is 2.53, and the standard deviation of the different sample means is 0.376. Based on Theorems 1 and 2, for a sample size of 20, we would expect the following:

$$\mu_{\bar{x}} = \mu = 2.505 \quad \text{and} \quad \sigma_{\bar{x}} = \frac{\sigma}{\sqrt{n}} = \frac{1.507}{\sqrt{20}} = 0.337$$

Thus, our simulated values are quite close to the theoretical values we would expect had we selected all possible random samples of size 20.

**FIGURE 7.4**

Aims Investment Company, Histogram of Sample Means from Sample Size $n = 20$

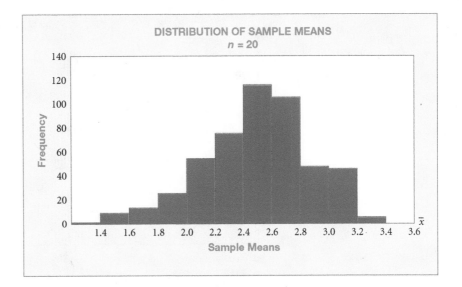

**Sampling from Normal Populations** The previous discussion began with the population of mutual funds shown in Figure 7.1. The population was not normally distributed, but as we increased the sample size, the sampling distribution of possible sample means began to approach a normal distribution. We will return to this situation shortly, but what happens if the population itself is normally distributed? To help answer this question, we can again use Excel to generate a normally distributed population.[3]

Figure 7.5 shows a simulated population that is approximately normally distributed with a mean equal to 1,000 and a standard deviation equal to 200. The data range is from 250 to 1,800.

Next, we simulate the selection of 2,000 random samples of size 10 from the population and compute the sample mean for each sample. These sample means can then be graphed as a frequency histogram, as shown in Figure 7.6. This histogram represents the sampling distribution. Note that it, too, is approximately normally distributed.

We next compute the average of the 2,000 sample means and use it to approximate $\mu_{\bar{x}}$, as follows:

$$\mu_{\bar{x}} \approx \frac{\sum \bar{x}}{2,000} = \frac{2,000,178}{2,000} \approx 1,000$$

**FIGURE 7.5**

Simulated Normal Population Distribution

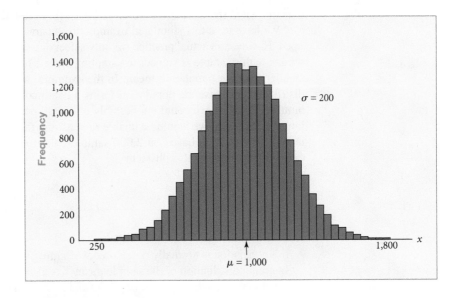

---

[3]The same task can be performed in Minitab using the Calc. > Random Data command. However, you will have to generate each sample individually, which will take time.

**FIGURE 7.6**

Approximated Sampling Distribution (*n* = 10)

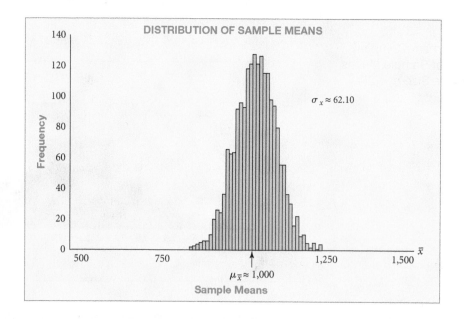

The mean of these sample means is approximately 1,000. This is the same value as the population mean.

We also approximate the standard deviation of the sample means as follows:

$$\sigma_{\bar{x}} \approx \sqrt{\frac{\sum(\bar{x} - \mu_{\bar{x}})^2}{2{,}000}} = 62.10$$

We see the standard deviation of the sample means is 62.10. This is much smaller than the population standard deviation, which is 200. The largest sample mean was just more than 1,212, and the smallest sample mean was just less than 775. Recall, however, that the population ranged from 250 to 1,800. The variation in the sample means always will be less than the variation for the population as a whole. Using Theorem 2, we would expect the sample means to have a standard deviation equal to

$$\sigma_{\bar{x}} = \frac{\sigma}{\sqrt{n}} = \frac{200}{\sqrt{10}} = 63.25$$

Our simulated standard deviation of 62.10 is fairly close to the theoretical value of 63.25.

We have used this simulated example to illustrate how a sampling distribution is developed. However, in actual practice we only select one random sample from the population, and we know this sample is subject to sampling error. The sample mean may be either larger or smaller than the population mean. In the example, we assumed the population is normally distributed. Because the population forms a continuous distribution and has an uncountable number of values, we could not possibly obtain all possible random samples from this population. As a result, we would be unable to construct the true sampling distribution. Figure 7.6 is an approximation based on 2,000 samples. Fortunately, an important statistical theorem exists that overcomes this obstacle:

### Theorem 3

If a population is normally distributed, with mean $\mu$ and a standard deviation $\sigma$, the sampling distribution of the sample mean $\bar{x}$ is also normally distributed with a mean equal to the population mean ($\mu_{\bar{x}} = \mu$) and a standard deviation equal to the population standard deviation divided by the square root of the sample size ($\sigma_{\bar{x}} = \sigma/\sqrt{n}$).

In Theorem 3, the quantity $(\sigma_{\bar{x}} = \sigma/\sqrt{n})$ is the *standard deviation of the sampling distribution*. Another term that is given to this is the *standard error of $\bar{x}$*, because it is the measure of the standard deviation of the potential sampling error.

Suppose we again use the simulated population shown in Figure 7.5, with $\mu = 1,000$ and $\sigma = 200$. We are interested in seeing what the sampling distribution will look like for different size samples. For a sample size of 5, Theorem 3 indicates that the sampling distribution will be normally distributed and have a mean equal to 1,000 and a standard deviation equal to

$$\sigma_{\bar{x}} = \frac{200}{\sqrt{5}} = 89.44$$

If we were to take a random sample of 10 (as simulated earlier), Theorem 3 indicates the sampling distribution would be normal, with a mean equal to 1,000 and a standard deviation equal to

$$\sigma_{\bar{x}} = \frac{200}{\sqrt{10}} = 63.25$$

For a sample size of 20, the sampling distribution will be centered at $\mu_{\bar{x}} = 1,000$, with a standard deviation equal to

$$\sigma_{\bar{x}} = \frac{200}{\sqrt{20}} = 44.72$$

Notice, as the sample size is increased, the standard deviation of the sampling distribution is reduced. This means the potential for extreme sampling error is reduced when larger sample sizes are used. Figure 7.7 shows sampling distributions for sample sizes of 5, 10, and 20. When the population is normally distributed, the sampling distribution of $\bar{x}$ will always be normal and centered at the population mean. Only the spread in the distribution will change as the sample size changes.

**FIGURE 7.7**

Theorem 3 Examples

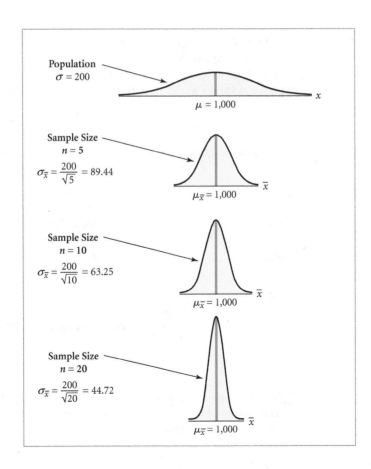

This illustrates a very important statistical concept referred to as *consistency*. Earlier we defined a statistic as *unbiased* if the average value of the statistic equals the parameter to be estimated. Theorem 1 asserted that the sample mean is an *unbiased* estimator of the population mean no matter the value of the parameter. However, just because a statistic is unbiased does not tell us whether the statistic will be close in value to the parameter. But if, as the sample size is increased, we can expect the value of the statistic to become closer to the parameter, then we say that the statistic is a **consistent estimator** of the parameter. Figure 7.7 illustrates that the sample mean is a consistent estimator of the population mean.

The sampling distribution is composed of all possible sample means of the same size. Half the sample means will lie above the center of the sampling distribution and half will lie below. The relative distance that a given sample mean is from the center can be determined by *standardizing* the sampling distribution. As discussed in Chapter 6, a standardized value is determined by converting the value from its original units into a *z*-value. A *z*-value measures the number of standard deviations a value is from the mean. This same concept can be used when working with a sampling distribution. Equation 7.4 shows how the *z*-values are computed.

**Consistent Estimator**

An unbiased estimator is said to be a consistent estimator if the difference between the estimator and the parameter tends to become smaller as the sample size becomes larger.

---

### *z*-Value for Sampling Distribution of $\bar{x}$

$$z = \frac{\bar{x} - \mu}{\frac{\sigma}{\sqrt{n}}}$$

(7.4)

where:

$\bar{x}$ = Sample mean
$\mu$ = Population mean
$\sigma$ = Population standard deviation
$n$ = Sample size

---

Note, if the sample being selected is large relative to the size of the population (greater than 5% of the population size), and the sampling is being done without replacement, we need to modify how we compute the standard deviation of the sampling distribution and *z*-value using what is known as the *finite population correction factor*, as shown in Equation 7.5.

---

### *z*-Value Adjusted for the Finite Population Correction Factor

$$z = \frac{\bar{x} - \mu}{\frac{\sigma}{\sqrt{n}} \sqrt{\frac{N-n}{N-1}}}$$

(7.5)

where:

$N$ = Population size
$n$ = Sample size
$\sqrt{\dfrac{N-n}{N-1}}$ = Finite population correction factor

---

The finite population correction factor is used to calculate the standard deviation of the sampling distribution when the sampling is performed without replacement or when the sample size is greater than 5% of the population size.

**EXAMPLE 7-2**   **FINDING THE PROBABILITY THAT $\bar{x}$ IS IN A GIVEN RANGE**

**Harmony Systems** Harmony Systems manufactures supplies for the healthcare industry. One item they make is a round bandage. When the production process is operating according to specifications, the diameter of these bandages is normally distributed with a mean equal to 1.5 inches and a standard deviation of 0.05 inches. Before shipping a large batch of these bandages, Harmony quality analysts have selected a random sample of eight bandages with the following diameters:

| 1.57 | 1.59 | 1.48 | 1.60 | 1.59 | 1.62 | 1.55 | 1.52 |
|------|------|------|------|------|------|------|------|

The analysts want to use these measurements to determine if the process is no longer operating within the specifications. The following steps can be used:

**Step 1  Determine the mean for this sample.**

$$\bar{x} = \frac{\Sigma x}{n} = \frac{12.52}{8} = 1.565 \text{ inches}$$

**Step 2  Define the sampling distribution for $\bar{x}$ using Theorem 3.**

Theorem 3 indicates that if the population is normally distributed, the sampling distribution for $\bar{x}$ will also be normally distributed, with

$$\mu_{\bar{x}} = \mu \quad \text{and} \quad \sigma_{\bar{x}} = \frac{\sigma}{\sqrt{n}}$$

Thus, in this case, the mean of the sampling distribution should be 1.50 inches, and the standard deviation should be $0.05/\sqrt{8} = 0.0177$ inches.

**Step 3  Define the probability statement of interest.**

Because the sample mean is $\bar{x} = 1.565$, which is greater than the mean of the sampling distribution, we want to find

$$P(\bar{x} \geq 1.565 \text{ inches}) = ?$$

**Step 4  Convert the sample mean to a standardized $z$-value, using Equation 7.4.**

$$z = \frac{\bar{x} - \mu}{\frac{\sigma}{\sqrt{n}}} = \frac{1.565 - 1.50}{\frac{0.05}{\sqrt{8}}} = \frac{0.065}{0.0177} = 3.67$$

**Step 5  Use the standard normal distribution table to determine the desired probability.**

$$P(z \geq 3.67) = ?$$

The standard normal distribution table in Appendix D does not show $z$-values as high as 3.67. This implies that $P(z \geq 3.67) \approx 0.00$. So, if the production process is working properly, there is virtually no chance that a random sample of eight bandages will have a mean diameter of 1.565 inches or greater. Because the analysts at Harmony Systems did find this sample result, there is a very good chance that something is wrong with the process.

>>**END EXAMPLE**

**TRY PROBLEM** 7-26 (pg. 286)

**FIGURE 7.8**

Simulated Nonnormal
Population

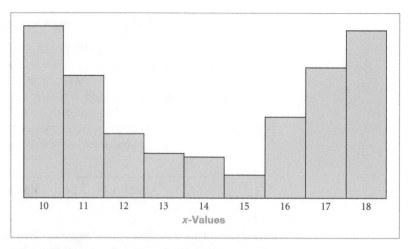

x-Values

Chapter Outcome 3. →**The Central Limit Theorem**

Theorem 3 applies when the population is normally distributed. Although there are many situations in business when this will be the case, there are also many situations when the population is not normal. For example, incomes in a region tend to be right skewed. Some distributions, such as people's weight, are bimodal (a peak weight group for males and another peak weight group for females).

What does the sampling distribution of $\bar{x}$ look like when a population is not normally distributed? The answer is . . . it depends. It depends on what the shape of the population is and what size sample is selected. To illustrate, suppose we have a U-shaped population, such as the one in Figure 7.8, with mean = 14.00 and standard deviation = 3.00. Now, we select 3,000 simple random samples of size 3 and compute the mean for each sample. These $\bar{x}$-values are graphed in the histogram shown in Figure 7.9.

The average of these 3,000 sample means is

$$\frac{\sum \bar{x}}{3,000} \approx \mu_{\bar{x}} = 14.02$$

Notice this value is approximately equal to the population mean of 14.00, as Theorem 1 would suggest.[4]

Next we compute the standard deviation as

$$\sigma_{\bar{x}} \approx \sqrt{\frac{\sum(\bar{x} - \mu_{\bar{x}})^2}{3,000}} = 1.82$$

The standard deviation of the sampling distribution is less than the standard deviation for the population, which was 3.00. This will always be the case.

**FIGURE 7.9**

Frequency Histogram
of $\bar{x}$ $(n = 3)$

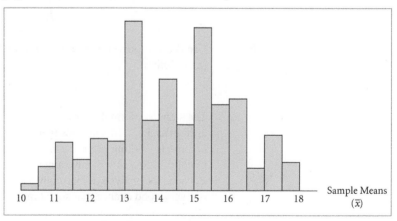

Sample Means
$(\bar{x})$

14.02 = Average of sample means

1.82 = Standard deviation of sample means

---

[4]Note, if we had selected all possible samples of three, the average of the samples means would have been equal to the population mean.

**FIGURE 7.10**

Frequency Histogram of $\bar{x}$ ($n = 10$)

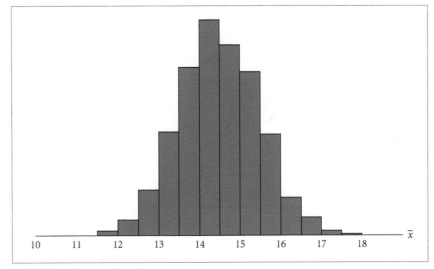

14.02 = Average of sample means
0.97 = Standard deviation of sample means

The frequency histogram of $\bar{x}$-values for the 3,000 samples of 3 looks different than the population distribution, which is U-shaped. Suppose we increase the sample size to 10 and take 3,000 samples from the same U-shaped population. The resulting frequency histogram of $\bar{x}$-values is shown in Figure 7.10. Now the frequency distribution looks much like a normal distribution. The average of the sample means is still equal to 14.02, which is virtually equal to the population mean. The standard deviation for this sampling distribution is now reduced to 0.97.

This example is not a special case. Instead, it illustrates a very important statistical concept called the **Central Limit Theorem**.

---

### Theorem 4: The Central Limit Theorem

For simple random samples of $n$ observations taken from a population with mean $\mu$ and standard deviation $\sigma$, regardless of the population's distribution, provided the sample size is sufficiently large, the distribution of the sample means, $\bar{x}$, will be approximately normal with a mean equal to the population mean ($\mu_{\bar{x}} = \mu$) and a standard deviation equal to the population standard deviation divided by the square root of the sample size ($\sigma_{\bar{x}} = \sigma/\sqrt{n}$). The larger the sample size, the better the approximation to the normal distribution.

---

The Central Limit Theorem is very important because with it we know the shape of the sampling distribution even though we may not know the shape of the population distribution. The one catch is that the sample size must be "sufficiently large." What is a sufficiently large sample size?

The answer depends on the shape of the population. If the population is quite symmetric, then sample sizes as small as 2 or 3 can provide a normally distributed sampling distribution. If the population is highly skewed or otherwise irregularly shaped, the required sample size will be larger. Recall the example of the U-shaped population. The frequency distribution obtained from samples of 3 was shaped differently than the population, but not like a normal distribution. However, for samples of 10, the frequency distribution was a very close approximation to a normal distribution. Figures 7.11, 7.12, and 7.13 show some examples of the Central Limit Theorem concept. Simulation studies indicate that even for very strange-looking populations, samples of 25 to 30 produce sampling distributions that are approximately normal. Thus, *a conservative definition of a sufficiently large sample size is $n \geq 30$*. The Central Limit Theorem is illustrated in the following example.

**FIGURE 7.11**

Central Limit Theorem with
Uniform Population
Distribution

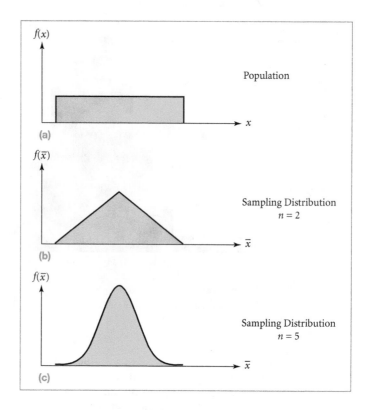

**FIGURE 7.12**

Central Limit Theorem with
Triangular Population

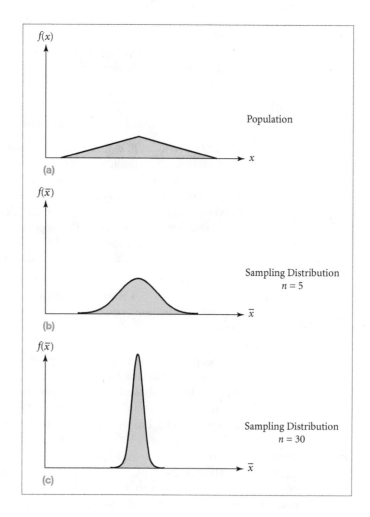

**FIGURE 7.13**

Central Limit Theorem with a Skewed Population

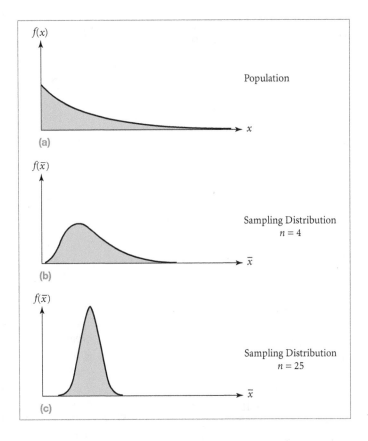

(a) Population

(b) Sampling Distribution $n = 4$

(c) Sampling Distribution $n = 25$

## How to do it (Example 7-3)

**Sampling Distribution of $\bar{x}$**

To find probabilities associated with a sampling distribution of $\bar{x}$ for samples of size $n$ from a population with mean $\mu$ and standard deviation $\sigma$, use the following steps.

1. Compute the sample mean using

$$\bar{x} = \frac{\sum x}{n}$$

2. Define the sampling distribution.

   If the population is normally distributed, the sampling distribution also will be normally distributed for any size sample. If the population is not normally distributed but the sample size is sufficiently large, the sampling distribution will be approximately normal. In either case, the sampling distribution will have

$$\mu_{\bar{x}} = \mu \quad \text{and} \quad \sigma_{\bar{x}} = \frac{\sigma}{\sqrt{n}}$$

3. Define the probability statement of interest.

   We are interested in finding the probability of some range of sample means, such as

$$P(\bar{x} \geq 25) = ?$$

4. Use the standard normal distribution to find the probability of interest, using Equation 7.4 or 7.5 to convert the sample mean to a corresponding $z$-value.

$$z = \frac{\bar{x} - \mu}{\frac{\sigma}{\sqrt{n}}} \quad \text{or} \quad z = \frac{\bar{x} - \mu}{\frac{\sigma}{\sqrt{n}}\sqrt{\frac{N-n}{N-1}}}$$

   Then use the standard normal table to find the probability associated with the calculated $z$-value.

---

**EXAMPLE 7-3**    **FINDING THE PROBABILITY THAT $\bar{x}$ IS IN A GIVEN RANGE**

**Fairway Stores, Inc.** Past sales records indicate that sales at the store are right skewed, with a population mean of $12.50 per customer and a standard deviation of $5.50. The store manager has selected a random sample of 100 sales receipts. She is interested in determining the probability of getting a sample mean between $12.25 and $13.00 from this population. To find this probability, she can use the following steps.

**Step 1** **Determine the sample mean.**

In this case, two sample means are being considered:

$$\bar{x} = \$12.25 \quad \text{and} \quad \bar{x} = \$13.00$$

**Step 2** **Define the sampling distribution.**

The Central Limit Theorem can be used because the sample size is large enough ($n = 100$) to determine that the sampling distribution will be approximately normal (even though the population is right skewed), with

$$\mu_{\bar{x}} = \$12.50 \quad \text{and} \quad \sigma_{\bar{x}} = \frac{\$5.50}{\sqrt{100}} = \$0.55$$

**Step 3** **Define the probability statement of interest.**

The manager is interested in

$$P(\$12.25 \leq \bar{x} \leq \$13.00) = ?$$

**Step 4** **Use the standard normal distribution to find the probability of interest.**

Assuming the population of sales records is quite large, we use Equation 7.4 to convert the sample means to corresponding $z$-values.

$$z = \frac{\bar{x} - \mu}{\frac{\sigma}{\sqrt{n}}} = \frac{12.25 - 12.50}{\frac{5.50}{\sqrt{100}}} = -0.46 \quad \text{and} \quad z = \frac{\bar{x} - \mu}{\frac{\sigma}{\sqrt{n}}} = \frac{13.00 - 12.50}{\frac{5.50}{\sqrt{100}}} = 0.91$$

From the standard normal table in Appendix D, the probability associated with $z = -0.46$ is 0.1772, and the probability for $z = 0.91$ is 0.3186. Therefore,

$$P(\$12.25 \le \bar{x} \le \$13.00) = P(-0.46 \le z \le 0.91) = 0.1772 + 0.3186 = 0.4958$$

There is nearly a 0.50 chance that the sample mean will fall in the range $12.25 to $13.00.

>>**END EXAMPLE**

**TRY PROBLEM** 7-30 (pg. 286)

 MyStatLab

# 7-2: Exercises

## Skill Development

**7-22.** A population with a mean of 1,250 and a standard deviation of 400 is known to be highly skewed to the right. If a random sample of 64 items is selected from the population, what is the probability that the sample mean will be less than 1,325?

**7-23.** Suppose that a population is known to be normally distributed with $\mu = 2,000$ and $\sigma = 230$. If a random sample of size $n = 8$ is selected, calculate the probability that the sample mean will exceed 2,100.

**7-24.** A normally distributed population has a mean of 500 and a standard deviation of 60.
  a. Determine the probability that a random sample of size 16 selected from this population will have a sample mean less than 475.
  b. Determine the probability that a random sample of size 25 selected from the population will have a sample mean greater than or equal to 515.

**7-25.** If a population is known to be normally distributed with $\mu = 250$ and $\sigma = 40$, what will be the characteristics of the sampling distribution for $\bar{x}$ based on a random sample of size 25 selected from the population?

**7-26.** Suppose nine items are randomly sampled from a normally distributed population with a mean of 100 and a standard deviation of 20. The nine randomly sampled values are

| | | | | |
|---|---|---|---|---|
| 125 | 95 | 66 | 116 | 99 |
| 91 | 102 | 51 | 110 | |

Calculate the probability of getting a sample mean that is smaller than the sample mean for these nine sampled values.

**7-27.** A random sample of 100 items is selected from a population of size 350. What is the probability that the sample mean will exceed 200 if the population mean is 195 and the population standard deviation equals 20? (*Hint*: Use the finite correction factor since the sample size is more than 5% of the population size.)

**7-28.** Given a distribution that has a mean of 40 and a standard deviation of 13, calculate the probability that a sample of 49 has a sample mean that is
  a. greater than 37
  b. at most 43
  c. between 37 and 43
  d. between 43 and 45
  e. no more than 35

**7-29.** Consider a normal distribution with mean = 12 and standard deviation = 90. Calculate $P(\bar{x} > 36)$ for each of the following sample sizes:
  a. $n = 1$
  b. $n = 9$
  c. $n = 16$
  d. $n = 25$

## Business Applications

**7-30.** SeeClear Windows makes windows for use in homes and commercial buildings. The standards for glass thickness call for the glass to average 0.375 inches with a standard deviation equal to 0.050 inches. Suppose a random sample of $n = 50$ windows yields a sample mean of 0.392 inches.
  a. What is the probability of $\bar{x} \ge 0.392$ if the windows meet the standards?
  b. Based on your answer to part a, what would you conclude about the population of windows? Is it meeting the standards?

**7-31.** Many Happy Returns is a tax preparation service with offices located throughout the western United States. Suppose the average number of returns processed by employees of Many Happy Returns during tax season is 12 per day with a standard deviation of 3 per day. A random sample of 36 employees taken during tax season revealed the following number of returns processed daily:

| | | | | | | | | |
|---|---|---|---|---|---|---|---|---|
| 11 | 17 | 13 | 9 | 13 | 13 | 13 | 12 | 15 |
| 15 | 13 | 15 | 10 | 15 | 13 | 13 | 15 | 13 |
| 9 | 9 | 9 | 15 | 13 | 14 | 9 | 14 | 11 |
| 11 | 17 | 16 | 9 | 8 | 10 | 15 | 12 | 11 |

a. What is the probability of having a sample mean equal to or smaller than the sample mean for this sample if the population mean is 12 processed returns daily with a standard deviation of 3 returns per day?

b. What is the probability of having a sample mean larger than the one obtained from this sample if the population mean is 12 processed returns daily with a standard deviation of 3 returns per day?

c. Explain how it is possible to answer parts a and b when the population distribution of daily tax returns at Many Happy Returns is not known.

**7-32.** SeaFair Fashions relies on its sales force of 220 to do an initial screening of all new fashions. The company is currently bringing out a new line of swimwear and has invited 40 salespeople to its Orlando home office. An issue of constant concern to the SeaFair sales office is the volume of orders generated by each salesperson. Last year, the overall company average was $417,330 with a standard deviation of $45,285. (*Hint*: The finite population correction factor, Equation 7.5, is required.)

a. Determine the probability the sample of 40 will have a sales average less than $400,000.

b. What shape do you think the distribution of all possible sample means of 40 will have? Discuss.

c. Determine the value of the standard deviation of the distribution of the sample mean of all possible samples of size 40.

d. How would the answers to parts a, b, and c change if the home office brought 60 salespeople to Orlando? Provide the respective answers for this sample size.

e. Each year SeaFair invites the sales personnel with sales above the 85th percentile to enjoy a complementary vacation in Hawaii. Determine the smallest average salary for the sales personnel that were in Hawaii last year. (Assume the distribution of sales was normally distributed last year.)

**7-33.** Suppose the life of a particular brand of calculator battery is approximately normally distributed with a mean of 75 hours and a standard deviation of 10 hours.

a. What is the probability that a single battery randomly selected from the population will have a life between 70 and 80 hours?

b. What is the probability that 16 randomly sampled batteries from the population will have a sample mean life of between 70 and 80 hours?

c. If the manufacturer of the battery is able to reduce the standard deviation of battery life from 10 to 9 hours, what would be the probability that 16 batteries randomly sampled from the population will have a sample mean life of between 70 and 80 hours?

**7-34.** Sands, Inc., makes particleboard for the building industry. Particleboard is built by mixing wood chips and resins together and pressing the sheets under extreme heat and pressure to form a 4-feet × 8-feet sheet that is used as a substitute for plywood.

The strength of the particleboards is tied to the board's weight. Boards that are too light are brittle and do not meet the quality standard for strength. Boards that are too heavy are strong but are difficult for customers to handle. The company knows that there will be variation in the boards' weight. Product specifications call for the weight per sheet to average 10 pounds with a standard deviation of 1.75 pounds. During each shift, Sands employees select and weigh a random sample of 25 boards. The boards are thought to have a normally distributed weight distribution.

If the average of the sample slips below 9.60 pounds, an adjustment is made to the process to add more moisture and resins to increase the weight (and, Sands hopes, the strength).

a. Assuming that the process is operating correctly according to specifications, what is the probability that a sample will indicate that an adjustment is needed?

b. Assume the population mean weight per sheet slips to 9 pounds. Determine the probability that the sample will indicate an adjustment is not needed.

c. Assuming that 10 pounds is the mean weight, what should the cutoff be if the company wants no more than a 5% chance that a sample of 25 boards will have an average weight less than 9.6 lbs?

**7-35.** The branch manager for United Savings and Loan in Seaside, Virginia, has worked with her employees in an effort to reduce the waiting time for customers at the bank. Recently, she and the team concluded that average waiting time is now down to 3.5 minutes with a standard deviation equal to 1.0 minute. However, before making a statement at a managers' meeting, this branch manager wanted to double-check that the process was working as thought. To make this check, she randomly sampled 25 customers and recorded the time they had to wait. She discovered that mean wait time for this sample of customers was 4.2 minutes. Based on the team's claims about waiting time, what is the probability that a sample mean for $n = 25$ people would be as large or larger than 4.2 minutes? What should the manager conclude based on these data?

**7-36.** In an article entitled "Fuel Economy Calculations to Be Altered," James R. Healey indicated that the government planned to change how it calculates fuel economy for new cars and trucks. This is the first modification since 1985. It is expected to lower average mileage for city driving in conventional cars from 10% to 20%. AAA has forecast that the 2008 Ford F-150 would achieve 15.7 mile per gallon (mpg). The 2005 Ford F-150 was tested by AAA members driving the vehicle themselves and was found to have an average of 14.3 mpg.

a. Assume that the mean obtained by AAA members is the true mean for the population of 2008 Ford F-150 trucks and that the population standard deviation is 5 mpg. Suppose 100 AAA members were to test the 2008 F-150. Determine the probability that the average mpg would be at least 15.7.

b. The current method of calculating the mpg forecasts that the 2008 F-150 will average 16.8 mpg. Determine the probability that these same 100 AAA members would average more than 16.8 mpg while testing the 2008 F-150.

c. The new method is expected to lower the average mileage by somewhere between 10% and 20%. Calculate the probability that the average obtained by the 100 AAA members will be somewhere between 10% and 20% smaller than the 14.3 mpg obtained during the 2005 trials even if the new method is not employed.

**7-37.** Airlines have recently toughened their standards for the weight of checked baggage, limiting the weight of a bag to 50 pounds on domestic U.S. flights. Heavier bags will be carried but at an additional fee. Suppose that one major airline has stated in an internal memo to employees that the mean weight for bags checked last year on the airline was 34.3 pounds with a standard deviation of 5.7 pounds. Further, it stated that the distribution of weights was approximately normally distributed. This memo was leaked to a consumers group in Atlanta. This group had selected and weighed a random sample of 14 bags to be checked on a flight departing from Atlanta. The following data (pounds) were recorded:

| 29 | 27 | 40 | 34 | 30 | 30 | 35 |
|----|----|----|----|----|----|----|
| 44 | 33 | 28 | 36 | 33 | 30 | 40 |

What is the probability that a sample mean as small or smaller than the one for this sample would occur if the airline's claims about the population of baggage weight is accurate? Comment on the results.

**7-38.** ACNielsen is a New York–based corporation and a member of the modern marketing research industry. One of the items that ACNielsen tracks is the expenditure on over-the-counter (OTC) cough medicines. ACNielsen recently indicated that consumers spent $620 million on OTC cough medicines in the United States. The article also indicated that nearly 30 million visits for coughs were made to doctors' offices in the United States.

a. Determine the average cost of OTC cough medicines per doctor's office visit based on 30 million purchases.

b. Assuming that the average cost indicated in part a is the true average cost of OTC cough medicines per doctor's visit and the standard deviation is $10, determine the probability that the average cost for a random selection of 30 individuals will result in an average expenditure of more than $25 in OTC cough medicines.

c. Determine the 90th percentile for the average cost of OTC cough medicines for a sample of 36 individuals, all of whom have visited a doctor's office for cough symptoms.

## Computer Database **Exercises**

**7-39.** One of the top-selling video games continues to be *Madden NFL 09* published by Electronic Arts. While prices vary widely depending on store, the suggested retail price for this video game is $46. The file entitled **Madden** contains a random sample of the retail prices paid for *Madden NFL 09*.

a. Calculate the sample mean and standard deviation of retail prices paid for *Madden NFL 09*.

b. To determine if the average retail price has fallen, assume the population mean is $46, calculate the probability that a sample of size 200 would result in a sample mean no larger than the one calculated in part a. Assume that the sample standard deviation is representative of the population standard deviation.

c. In part b you used $46 as the population mean. Calculate the probability required in part b assuming that the population mean is $45.75.

d. On the basis of your calculations in parts b and c, does it seem likely that the average retail price for *Madden NFL 09* has decreased? Explain.

**7-40.** Acee Bottling and Distributing bottles and markets Pepsi-Cola products in southwestern Montana. The average fill volume for Pepsi cans is supposed to be 12 ounces. The filling machine has a known standard deviation of 0.05 ounces. Each week, the company selects a simple random sample of 60 cans and carefully measures the volume in each can. The results of the latest sample are shown in the file called **Acee Bottling**. Based on the data in the sample, what would you conclude about whether the filling process is working as expected? Base your answer on the probability of observing the sample mean you compute for these sample data.

**7-41.** Bruce Leichtman is president of Leichtman Research Group, Inc. (LRG), which specializes in research and consulting on broadband, media, and entertainment industries. In a recent survey, the company determined the cost of extra high-definition (HD) gear needed to watch television in HD. The costs ranged from $5 a month for a set-top box to $200 for a new satellite. The file entitled **HDCosts** contains a sample of the cost of the extras whose purchase was required to watch television in HD. Assume that the population average cost is $150 and the standard deviation is $50.

a. Create a box and whisker plot and use it and the sample average to determine if the population from which this sample was obtained could be normally distributed.

b. Determine the probability that the mean of a random sample of size 150 costs for HD extras would be more than $5 away from the mean of the sample described above.

c. Given your response to part a, do you believe the results obtained in part b are valid? Explain.

**7-42.** The highly respected financial magazine *Forbes* publishes data on CEO salaries each year. At the end of 2005, *Forbes* posted CEO compensation data to its

Web site (www.forbes.com/2005/04/20/05ceoland. html). These data reflect the total compensation for CEOs for 496 of the nation's 500 largest companies and are listed in a file called **CEO Compensation**.

a. Treating the data in the file as the population of interest, compute the population mean and standard deviation for CEO compensation.

b. Use either Excel or Minitab to select a simple random sample of $n = 100$ executive compensation amounts. Compute the sample mean for this sample. Find the probability of getting a sample mean as extreme or more extreme than the one you got. (*Hint*: Use the finite population correction factor because the sample is large relative to the size of the population.)

**7-43.** The data file called **CEO Compensation** contains data for the CEOs of 496 of the nation's top 500 companies in 2005. These data are published by the Forbes organization and are available on its Web site (www. forbes.com/2005/04/20/05ceoland.html).

a. Treating these data as the population of interest, compute the population mean and standard deviation for CEO age.

b. Select a random sample of $n = 12$ CEOs and calculate the sample mean age for this sample. Also compute the sampling error.

c. Based on your result in part b, compute the probability of getting a sample mean as large or larger than the one you obtained.

**7-44.** The file **Salaries** contains the annual salary for all faculty at a small state college in the Midwest. Assume that these faculty salaries represent the population of interest.

a. Compute the population mean and population standard deviation.

b. Develop a frequency distribution of these data using 10 classes. Do the population data appear to be normally distributed?

c. What is the probability that a random sample of 16 faculty selected from the population would have a sample mean annual salary greater than or equal to $56,650?

d. Suppose the following 25 faculty were randomly sampled from the population and used to estimate the population mean annual salary:

| Faculty ID Number | | | | |
|---|---|---|---|---|
| 137 | 040 | 054 | 005 | 064 |
| 134 | 013 | 199 | 168 | 027 |
| 095 | 065 | 193 | 059 | 192 |
| 084 | 176 | 029 | 143 | 182 |
| 009 | 033 | 152 | 068 | 044 |

What would the sampling error be?

e. Referring to part d, what is the probability of obtaining a sample mean smaller than the one obtained from this sample?

**END EXERCISES 7-2**

## 7.3 Sampling Distribution of a Proportion
### Working with Proportions

In many instances, the objective of sampling is to estimate a population proportion. For instance, an accountant may be interested in determining the proportion of accounts payable balances that are correct. A production supervisor may wish to determine the percentage of product that is defect-free. A marketing research department might want to know the proportion of potential customers who will purchase a particular product. In all these instances, the decision makers could select a sample, compute the sample proportion, and make their decision based on the sample results.

Sample proportions are subject to sampling error, just as are sample means. The concept of sampling distributions provides us a way to assess the potential magnitude of the sampling error for proportions in given situations.

**BUSINESS APPLICATION**  SAMPLING DISTRIBUTIONS FOR PROPORTIONS

**STRONG & ASSOCIATES** Consider Strong & Associates, a market research firm that surveyed every customer who purchased a new or used car from the Ford dealers in the Seattle area during one day of the second week of March last year. The key question in the survey was "Are you satisfied with the service received?"

The population size was 80 customers. The number of customers who answered "Yes" to the question was 72. The value of interest in this example is the **population proportion**. Equation 7.6 is used to compute a population proportion.

**Population Proportion**

The fraction of values in a population that have a specific attribute.

---

### Population Proportion

$$\pi = \frac{X}{N} \tag{7.6}$$

where:

$\pi$ = Population proportion
$X$ = Number of items in the population having the attribute of interest
$N$ = Population size

---

The proportion of customers in the population who are satisfied with the service at the Ford dealerships is

$$\pi = \frac{72}{80} = 0.90$$

Therefore, 90% of the population responded "Yes" to the survey question. This is the *parameter*. It is a measurement taken from the population. It is the "true value."

Now, suppose that the market research firm wishes to do a follow-up survey for a simple random sample of $n = 20$ of the customers. What fraction of this sample will be people who had previously responded "Yes" to the satisfaction question?

The answer depends on which sample is selected. There are many ($3.5353 \times 10^{18}$ to be precise) possible random samples of 20 that could be selected from 80 people. However, the marketing research firm will select only one of these possible samples. At one extreme, suppose the 20 people selected for the sample included all 8 who answered "No" to the satisfaction question and 12 others who answered "Yes." The **sample proportion** is computed using Equation 7.7.

**Sample Proportion**

The fraction of items in a sample that have the attribute of interest.

---

### Sample Proportion

$$p = \frac{x}{n} \tag{7.7}$$

where:

$p$ = Sample proportion
$x$ = Number of items in the sample with the attribute of interest
$n$ = Sample size

---

For the Ford dealerships example, the sample proportion of "Yes" responses is

$$p = \frac{12}{20} = 0.60$$

The sample proportion of "Yes" responses is 0.60, whereas the population proportion is 0.90. The difference between the sample value and the population value is sampling error. Equation 7.8 is used to compute the sampling error involving a single proportion.

---

### Single-Proportion Sampling Error

$$\text{Sampling error} = p - \pi \tag{7.8}$$

where:

$\pi$ = Population proportion
$p$ = Sample proportion

---

Then for this extreme situation we get

$$\text{Sampling error} = 0.60 - 0.90 = -0.30$$

If a sample on the other extreme had been selected and all 20 people came from the original list of 72 who had responded "Yes" the sample proportion would be

$$p = \frac{20}{20} = 1.00$$

For this sample, the sampling error is

$$\text{Sampling error} = 1.00 - 0.90 = 0.10$$

Thus, the range of sampling error in this example is from $-0.30$ to $0.10$. As with any sampling situation, you can expect some sampling error. The sample proportion will probably not equal the population proportion because the sample selected will not be a perfect replica of the population.

---

**EXAMPLE 7-4**    **SAMPLING ERROR FOR A PROPORTION**

**Hewlett-Packard–Compaq Merger** In 2002 a proxy fight took place between the management of Hewlett-Packard (HP) and Walter Hewlett, the son of one of HP's founders, over whether the merger between HP and Compaq should be approved. Each outstanding share of common stock was allocated one vote. After the vote in March 2002, the initial tally showed that the proportion of shares in the approval column was 0.51. After the vote, a lawsuit was filed by a group led by Walter Hewlett, which claimed improprieties by the HP management team. Suppose the attorneys for the Hewlett faction randomly selected 40 shares from the millions of total shares. The intent was to interview the owners of these shares to determine whether they had voted for the merger. Of the shares in the sample, 26 carried an "Approval" vote. The attorneys can use the following steps to assess the sampling error:

**Step 1    Determine the population proportion.**

In this case, the proportion of votes cast in favor of the merger is

$$\pi = 0.51$$

This is the number of approval votes divided by the total number of shares.

**Step 2    Compute the sample proportion using Equation 7.7.**

The sample proportion is

$$p = \frac{x}{n} = \frac{26}{40} = 0.65$$

**Step 3    Compute the sampling error using Equation 7.8.**

$$\text{Sampling error} = p - \pi = 0.65 - 0.51 = 0.14$$

The proportion of "Approval" votes from the shares in this sample exceeds the population proportion by 0.14.

>>**END EXAMPLE**

**TRY PROBLEM** 7-47 (pg. 295)

---

**Chapter Outcome 4.** → **Sampling Distribution of _p_**

In many applications you will be interested in determining the proportion ($\pi$) of all items in a population that possess a particular attribute. The best estimate of this population proportion will be $p$, the sample proportion. However, any inference about how close your estimate is to the true population value will be based on the distribution of this sample proportion, $p$, whose underlying distribution is the binomial. However, if the sample size is sufficiently large such that

$$n\pi \geq 5 \quad \text{and} \quad n(1-\pi) \geq 5$$

then the normal distribution can be used as a reasonable approximation to the discrete binomial distribution.[5] Providing we have a large enough sample size, the distribution of all possible sample proportions will be approximately normally distributed. In addition to being normally distributed, the sampling distribution will have a mean and standard error as indicated in Equations 7.9 and 7.10.

---

### Mean and Standard Error of the Sampling Distribution of $p$

$$\text{Mean} = \mu_p = \pi \tag{7.9}$$

and

$$\text{Standard error} = \sigma_p = \sqrt{\frac{\pi(1-\pi)}{n}} \tag{7.10}$$

where:

$\pi$ = Population proportion
$n$ = Sample size
$p$ = Sample proportion

---

In Section 7.2, we introduced Theorem 4, the Central Limit Theorem, which indicates that regardless of the shape of the population distribution, the distribution of possible sample means will be approximately normal as long as the sample size is sufficiently large. Theorem 5 is similar but pertains to the sampling distribution for the sample proportion.

---

### Theorem 5: Sampling Distribution of $p$

Regardless of the value of the population proportion, $\pi$, (with the obvious exceptions of $\pi = 0$ and $\pi = 1$) the sampling distribution for the sample proportion, $p$, will be approximately normally distributed with $\mu_p = \pi$ and

$$\sigma_p = \sqrt{\frac{\pi(1-\pi)}{n}},$$

providing $n\pi \geq 5$ and $n(1 - \pi) \geq 5$. The approximation to the normal distribution improves as the sample size increases and $\pi$ approaches 0.50.

---

BUSINESS APPLICATION    SAMPLING DISTRIBUTION FOR PROPORTIONS

**FUSES UNLIMITED** Fuses Unlimited makes fuses for automobile signal systems and distributes them to retailers throughout the United States. Recently Fuses Unlimited executives have observed that 15% of the fuses do not work properly during final test. There appears to be no particular pattern to the defects. Whether one fuse works or doesn't work seems independent of whether any other fuse works or does not work.

Suppose that the company recently received an e-mail from a customer who claimed that 18% of the 500 fuses purchased failed to work properly when they ran a test at their store. Assume the general damage rate of

$$\pi = 0.15$$

---

[5]An application of the Central Limit Theorem provides the rationale for this statement. Recall that $p = x/n$, where $x$ is the sum of random variables ($x_i$) whose values are 0 and 1. Therefore, $p$ is in reality just a sample mean. Each of these $x_i$ can be thought of as binomial random variables from a sample of size $n = 1$. Thus, they each have a mean of $\mu = n\pi = \pi$ and a variance of $\sigma^2 = n\pi(1 - \pi) = \pi(1 - \pi)$. As we have seen from the Central Limit Theorem, the sample mean has an expected value of $\mu$ and a variance of $\sigma^2/n$. Thus, the sample proportion has an expected value of $\mu = \pi$ and a variance of $\sigma^2 = \dfrac{\pi(1 - \pi)}{n}$.

holds for the population of all fuses. How likely is it that a sample of

$$n = 500$$

units will contain 18% or more defective items? To answer this question, we first check to determine if the sample size is sufficiently large. Because both

$$n(\pi) = 500(0.15) = 75 \geq 5 \quad \text{and} \quad n(1 - \pi) = 500(0.85) = 425 \geq 5$$

we can safely conclude that the sampling distribution of sample proportions will be approximately normal. Using Equations 7.9 and 7.10, we can compute the mean and standard error for the sampling distribution as follows:

$$\mu_p = 0.15$$

and

$$\sigma_p = \sqrt{\frac{(0.15)(0.85)}{500}} = 0.016$$

Equation 7.11 is used to convert the sample proportion to a standardized $z$-value.

---

### $z$-Value for Sampling Distribution of $p$

$$z = \frac{p - \pi}{\sigma_p} \tag{7.11}$$

where:

$z$ = Number of standard errors $p$ is from $\pi$

$p$ = Sample proportion

$\sigma_p = \sqrt{\dfrac{\pi(1 - \pi)}{n}}$ = Standard error of the sampling distribution[6]

$\pi$ = Population proportion

---

From Equation 7.11, we get

$$z = \frac{p - \pi}{\sigma_p} = \frac{0.18 - 0.15}{\sqrt{\dfrac{(0.15)(0.85)}{500}}} = 1.88$$

Therefore, the 0.18 defect rate reported by the customer is 1.88 standard errors above the population mean of 0.15. Figure 7.14 illustrates that the chances of a defect rate of 0.18 or more is

$$P(p \geq 0.18) = 0.0301$$

Because this is a very low probability, the Fuses Unlimited managers might want to see if there was something unusual about this shipment of fuses.

**FIGURE 7.14**

Standard Normal Distribution for Fuses Unlimited

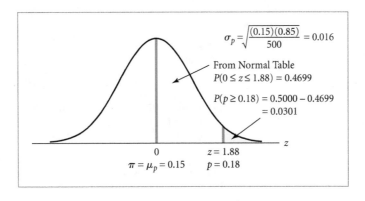

---

[6]If the sample size $n$ is greater than 5% of the population size, the standard error of the sampling distribution should be computed using the finite population correction factor as $\sigma_p = \sqrt{\dfrac{\pi(1 - \pi)}{n}} \sqrt{\dfrac{N - n}{N - 1}}$.

## How to do it (Example 7-5)

### Sampling Distribution of $p$

To find probabilities associated with a sampling distribution for a single-population proportion, the following steps can be used.

1. Determine the population proportion, $\pi$, using

$$\pi = \frac{X}{N}$$

2. Calculate the sample proportion using

$$p = \frac{x}{n}$$

3. Determine the mean and standard deviation of the sampling distribution using

$$\mu_p = \pi \quad \text{and} \quad \sigma_p = \sqrt{\frac{\pi(1-\pi)}{n}}$$

4. Define the event of interest. For example:

$$P(p \geq 0.30) = ?$$

5. If $n\pi$ and $n(1 - \pi)$ are both $\geq 5$, then convert $p$ to a standardized $z$-value using

$$z = \frac{p - \pi}{\sigma_p}$$

6. Use the standard normal distribution table in Appendix D to determine the required probability.

---

**EXAMPLE 7-5**   **FINDING THE PROBABILITY THAT $P$ IS IN A GIVEN RANGE**

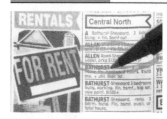

**The Daily Statesman** The classified-advertisement manager for the *Daily Statesman* newspaper believes that the proportion of "apartment for rent" ads placed in the paper that results in a rental within two weeks is 0.80 or higher. She would like to make this claim as part of the paper's promotion of its classified section. Before doing this, she has selected a simple random sample of 100 "apartment for rent" ads. Of these, 73 resulted in a rental within the two-week period. To determine the probability of this result or something more extreme, she can use the following steps:

**Step 1**   **Determine the population proportion, $\pi$.**
The population proportion is believed to be $\pi = 0.80$, based on the manager's experience.

**Step 2**   **Calculate the sample proportion.**
In this case, a random sample of $n = 100$ ads was selected, with 73 having the attribute of interest. Thus,

$$p = \frac{x}{n} = \frac{73}{100} = 0.73$$

**Step 3**   **Determine the mean and standard deviation of the sampling distribution.**
The mean of the sampling distribution is equal to $p$, the population proportion. So

$$\mu_p = \pi = 0.80$$

The standard deviation of the sampling distribution for $p$ is computed using

$$\sigma_p = \sqrt{\frac{\pi(1-\pi)}{n}} = \sqrt{\frac{0.80(1-0.80)}{100}} = 0.04$$

**Step 4**   **Define the event of interest.**
In this case, because 0.73 is less than 0.80, we are interested in

$$P(p \leq 0.73) = ?$$

**Step 5**   **If $\pi p$ and $n(1 - \pi)$ are both $\geq 5$, then convert $p$ to a standardized $z$-value.**
Checking, we get

$$n\pi = 100(0.80) = 80 \geq 5 \quad \text{and} \quad n(1 - \pi) = 100(0.20) = 20 \geq 5$$

Then we convert to a standardized $z$-value using

$$z = \frac{p - \pi}{\sigma_p} = \frac{0.73 - 0.80}{\sqrt{\dfrac{0.80(1-0.80)}{100}}} = -1.75$$

**Step 6**   **Use the standard normal distribution table in Appendix D to determine the probability for the event of interest.**
We want

$$P(p \leq 0.73) \quad \text{or} \quad P(z \leq -1.75)$$

From the normal distribution table for $z = -1.75$, we get 0.4599, which corresponds to the probability of a $z$-value between $-1.75$ and $0.0$. To get the probability of interest, we subtract 0.4599 from 0.5000, giving 0.0401. There is only a 4% chance that a random sample of $n = 100$ would produce a sample proportion of $p \leq 0.73$ if the population proportion is 0.80. She might want to use caution before making this claim.

**>>END EXAMPLE**

**TRY PROBLEM** 7-45 (pg. 295)

## 7-3: Exercises

### Skill Development

**7-45.** A population has a proportion equal to 0.30. Calculate the following probabilities with $n = 100$:
    a. $P(p \leq 0.35)$
    b. $P(p > 0.40)$
    c. $P(0.25 < p \leq 0.40)$
    d. $P(p \geq 0.27)$.

**7-46.** If a random sample of 200 items is taken from a population in which the proportion of items having a desired attribute is $\pi = 0.30$, what is the probability that the proportion of successes in the sample will be less than or equal to 0.27?

**7-47.** The proportion of items in a population that possess a specific attribute is known to be 0.70.
    a. If a simple random sample of size $n = 100$ is selected and the proportion of items in the sample that contain the attribute of interest is 0.65, what is the sampling error?
    b. Referring to part a, what is the probability that a sample of size 100 would have a sample proportion of 0.65 or less if the population proportion is 0.70?

**7-48.** Given a population where the proportion of items with a desired attribute is $\pi = 0.25$, if a sample of 400 is taken,
    a. What is the standard deviation of the sampling distribution of $p$?
    b. What is the probability the proportion of successes in the sample will be greater than 0.22?

**7-49.** Given a population in which the probability of success is $\pi = 0.20$, if a sample of 500 items is taken, then
    a. Calculate the probability the proportion of successes in the sample will be between 0.18 and 0.23.
    b. Calculate the probability the proportion of successes in the sample will be between 0.18 and 0.23 if the sample size is 200.

**7-50.** Given a population where the proportion of items with a desired attribute is $\pi = 0.50$, if a sample of 200 is taken,
    a. Find the probability the proportion of successes in the sample will be between 0.47 and 0.51.
    b. Referring to part a, what would the probability be if the sample size were 100?

**7-51.** Given a population where the probability of a success is $\pi = 0.40$, if a sample of 1,000 is taken,
    a. Calculate the probability the proportion of successes in the sample will be less than 0.42.
    b. What is the probability the proportion of successes in the sample will be greater than 0.44?

**7-52.** A random sample of size 100 is to be taken from a population that has a proportion equal to 0.35. The sample proportion will be used to estimate the population proportion.

    a. Calculate the probability that the sample proportion will be within $\pm 0.05$ of the population proportion.
    b. Calculate the probability that the sample proportion will be within $\pm 1$ standard error of the population proportion.
    c. Calculate the probability that the sample proportion will be within $\pm 0.10$ of the population proportion.

**7-53.** A survey is conducted from a population of people of whom 40% have a college degree. The following sample data were recorded for a question asked of each person sampled, "Do you have a college degree?"

| | | | | |
|---|---|---|---|---|
| YES | NO | NO | YES | YES |
| YES | YES | YES | YES | YES |
| YES | NO | NO | NO | YES |
| NO | YES | YES | NO | NO |
| NO | YES | YES | YES | NO |
| YES | NO | YES | NO | NO |
| YES | NO | NO | NO | YES |
| YES | NO | NO | NO | NO |
| NO | NO | YES | NO | NO |
| NO | YES | NO | YES | YES |
| NO | NO | NO | YES | NO |
| NO | NO | NO | YES | YES |

    a. Calculate the sample proportion of respondents who have a college degree.
    b. What is the probability of getting a sample proportion as extreme or more extreme than the one observed in part a if the population has 40% with college degrees?

### Business Applications

**7-54.** United Manufacturing and Supply makes sprinkler valves for use in residential sprinkler systems. United supplies these valves to major companies such as Rain Bird and Nelson, who in turn sell sprinkler products to retailers. United recently entered into a contract to supply 40,000 sprinkler valves. The contract called for at least 97% of the valves to be free of defects. Before shipping the valves, United managers tested 200 randomly selected valves and found 190 defect-free valves in the sample. The managers wish to know the probability of finding 190 or fewer defect-free valves if in fact the population of 40,000 valves is 97% defect-free. Discuss how they could use this information to determine whether to ship the valves to the customer.

**7-55.** The J R Simplot Company is one of the world's largest privately held agricultural companies, employing over 10,000 people in the United States, Canada, China,

Mexico, and Australia. More information can be found at the company's Web site: www.Simplot.com. One of its major products is french fries that are sold primarily on the commercial market to customers such as McDonald's and Burger King. French fries have numerous quality attributes that are important to customers. One of these is called "dark ends," which are the dark-colored ends that can occur when the fries are cooked. Suppose a major customer will accept no more than 0.06 of the fries having dark ends.

Recently, the customer called the Simplot Company saying that a recent random sample of 300 fries was tested from a shipment and 27 fries had dark ends. Assuming that the population does meet the 0.06 standard, what is the probability of getting a sample of 300 with 27 or more dark ends? Comment on this result.

7-56. The National Association of Realtors released a survey indicating that a surprising 43% of first-time home buyers purchased their homes with no-money-down loans during 2005. The fear is that house prices will decline and leave homeowners owing more than their homes are worth. PMI Mortgage Insurance estimated that there existed a 50% risk that prices would decline within two years in major metro areas such as San Diego, Boston, Long Island, New York City, Los Angeles, and San Francisco.
   a. A survey taken by realtors in the San Francisco area found that 12 out of the 20 first-time home buyers sampled purchased their home with no-money-down loans. Calculate the probability that at least 12 in a sample of 20 first-time buyers would take out no-money-down loans if San Francisco's proportion is the same as the nationwide proportion of no-money-down loans.
   b. Determine the probability requested in part a if the nationwide proportion is 0.53.
   c. Determine the probability that between 8 and 12 of a sample of 20 first-time home buyers would take out no-money-down loans if the 43% value applies.

7-57. According to the most recent Labor Department data, 10.5% of engineers (electrical, mechanical, civil, and industrial) were women. Suppose a random sample of 50 engineers is selected.
   a. How likely is it that the random sample of 50 engineers will contain 8 or more women in these positions?
   b. How likely is it that the random sample will contain fewer than 5 women in these positions?
   c. If the random sample included 200 engineers, how would this change your answer to part b?

7-58. TransUnion is a leading global provider of business intelligence services. Transunion reported that 33% of the mortgages in the year previous to the sub-prime mortgage crisis were adjustable-rate mortgages (ARMs).
   a. In samples of mortgages of size 75, what proportion of the samples would you expect to produce sample proportions equal to or larger than 0.25?

   b. If a sample of size 75 produced a sample proportion of 0.45, what would you infer that the population proportion of mortgages with ARMs really is?
   c. In a sample of 90 mortgages, what would the probability be that the number of mortgages with ARMS would be between 25 and 35?

7-59. Airgistics provides air consolidation and freight-forwarding services for companies that ship their products internationally. As a part of its commitment to continuous process improvement, Airgistics monitors the performance of its partner carriers to ensure that high standards of on-time delivery are met. Airgistics currently believes that it achieves a 96% on-time performance for its customers. Recently, a random sample of 200 customer shipments was selected for study, and 188 of them were found to have met the on-time delivery promise.
   a. What is the probability that a random sample of 200 customer shipments would contain 188 or fewer on-time deliveries if the true population of on-time deliveries is 96%?
   b. Would you be surprised if the random sample of 200 customer shipments had 197 on-time deliveries?
   c. Suppose the random sample of 200 customer shipments revealed that 178 were on time. Would such a finding cause you to question Airgistics' claim that its on-time performance is 96%? Support your answer with a probability calculation.

## Computer Database **Exercises**

7-60. Procter & Gamble (P&G) merged with Gillette in 2005. One of the concerns the new, larger company has is the increasing burden of retirement expenditures. An effort is being made to encourage employees to participate in 401(k) accounts. Nationwide, 66% of eligible workers participate in these accounts. The file entitled **Gillette** contains responses of 200 P&G workers when asked if they were currently participating in a 401(k) account.
   a. Determine the sample proportion of P&G workers who participate in 401(k) accounts.
   b. Determine the sampling error if in reality P&G workers have the same proportion of participants in 401(k) accounts as does the rest of the nation.
   c. Determine the probability that a sample proportion at least as large as that obtained in the sample would be obtained if P&G workers have the same proportion of participants in 401(k) accounts as does the rest of the nation.
   d. Does it appear that a larger proportion of P&G workers participate in 401(k) accounts than do the workers of the nation as a whole? Support your response.

7-61. The Bureau of Transportation Statistics releases information concerning the monthly percentage of U.S. airline flights that land no later than 15 minutes after scheduled arrival. The average of these percentages for the 12 months in 2004 was 78.08%. These data become available as soon as feasible. However, the airlines can provide preliminary results by obtaining a sample. The file entitled **Ontime** contains the sample data indicating the number of minutes after scheduled arrival time that the aircraft arrived. Note that a negative entry indicates the minutes earlier than the scheduled arrival time that the aircraft arrived.

a. Calculate the proportion of sampled airline flights that landed within 15 minutes of scheduled arrival.

b. Calculate the probability that a sample proportion of on-time flights would be within ±0.06 of a population proportion equal to 0.7808.

c. If the airlines' goal was to attain the same proportion of on-time arrivals as in 2004, do the preliminary results indicate that they have met this goal? Support your assertions.

7-62. The Bureau of Labor Statistics, U.S. Office of Personnel Management, indicated that the average hourly compensation (salary plus benefits) for federal workers (not including military or postal service employees) was $44.82. The rates for private industry and state and local government workers are believed to be considerably less than that. The file entitled **Paychecks** contains a random sample of the hourly amounts paid to state and local government workers.

a. If the hourly compensation for federal workers was normally distributed, determine the median hourly compensation.

b. Calculate the sample proportion of the state and local government workers whose hourly compensation is less than $44.82.

c. If a sample of size 150 was obtained from a population whose population proportion was equal to your answer to part a, determine the probability that the sample proportion would be equal to or greater than the answer obtained in part b.

d. On the basis of your work in parts a, b, and c, would you conclude that the proportion of state and local workers whose hourly compensation is less than $44.82 is the same as that of the federal workers? Explain.

7-63. *Driven*, a recently released magazine targeted to young professionals, states that 65% of its subscribers have an annual income greater than $100,000. The sales staff at *Driven* uses this high proportion of subscribers earning more than $100,000 as a selling point when trying to get companies to place advertisements with the magazine. *Driven* is currently trying to sell a large

amount of advertising to Meuscher, an upscale chocolatier, for a special year-end issue on fine foods and wines. Before committing to advertise in *Driven*, Meuscher's market research staff has decided to randomly sample 201 of *Driven*'s subscribers to verify *Driven*'s claim that 65% of its subscribers earn more than $100,000 annually.

a. The file **Driven** contains the responses of 201 randomly sampled subscribers of the magazine. The responses are coded "Yes" if the subscriber earns over $100,000 annually and "No" if the subscriber does not earn over $100,000 annually. Open the file **Driven** and create a new variable that has a value of 1 for "yes" and 0 for "no."

b. Calculate the sample proportion of subscribers who have annual incomes greater than $100,000.

c. How likely is it that a sample proportion greater than the one calculated in part b would be obtained if the population proportion of subscribers earning over $100,000 annually is 65%?

d. Based on the probability you calculated in part c, should Meuscher advertise in *Driven*?

7-64. A study conducted by Watson Wyatt Worldwide, a human resources consulting firm, revealed that 13% of Fortune 1000 companies either terminated or froze their defined-benefit pension plans. As part of a study to evaluate how well its benefits package compares to other Fortune 1000 companies, a retail firm randomly samples 36 Fortune 1000 companies in odd-numbered years and asks them to complete a benefits questionnaire. One question asked is whether the company has changed its defined-benefits pension plan by either freezing it or terminating it during the survey year. The results of the survey are contained in the file **Pension Survey**.

a. Open the file **Pension Survey**. Create a new variable that has a value equal to 1 if the firm has either terminated or frozen its defined-benefits pension plan and equal to 0 if the firm has not significantly altered its pension plan.

b. Determine the sample proportion of companies that either terminated or froze their defined-benefits pension plan.

c. How likely is it that a sample proportion greater than or equal to the one found in the survey would occur if the true population of firms who have terminated or frozen their defined-benefits pension plan is as reported by Watson Wyatt Worldwide?

# Visual Summary

**Chapter 7:** Many business situations require that a sample be selected from a population and an analysis performed on the sample data. The objective of random sampling is to select data that mirror the population. Then when the sampled data are analyzed the results will be as if we had worked with all the population data. Whenever decisions are based on samples rather than a population, questions about the sample results exist. Chapter 7 introduces the important concepts associated with making decisions based on samples. Included is a discussion of sampling error, as well as the sampling distribution of the mean and the sampling distribution of a proportion.

  **7.1** Sampling Error: What It Is and Why It Happens (pg. 265–273)

Summary

Regardless of how careful we are in selecting a random sample the sample may not perfectly represent the population. In such cases the sample statistic will likely not equal the population parameter. If this difference arises because the random sample is not a perfect representation of the population, it is called **sampling error**. **Sampling error** refers to the difference between a measure computed from a sample (**a statistic**) and the corresponding measure computed from the population (**a parameter**). Some fundamental concepts associated with sampling errors include the following:

The size of the sampling error depends on which sample is selected.

The sampling error may be positive or negative.

There is potentially a different statistic for each sample selected.

**Outcome 1.** Understand the concept of sampling error.

  **7.2** Sampling Distribution of the Mean (pg. 273–289)

Summary

In business applications, decision makers select a single random sample from a population. A sample measure is then computed from the sample and used to make decisions about the population. The selected sample is, of course, only one of many that could have been drawn from the population. If all possible random samples of a given sample size were selected and the sample mean was computed for each sample taken, the sample means would vary above and below the true population mean. If these values were graphed as a histogram, the graph would be a **sampling distribution**. Therefore, the **sampling distribution** is the distribution of all possible values of a statistic for a given sample size that has been randomly selected from a population. When the average of all possible values of the sample statistic equals the corresponding parameter, the statistic is said to be an **unbiased estimator** of the parameter. An unbiased estimator is **consistent** if the difference between the estimator and the parameter tends to become smaller as the sample size becomes larger. An important statistical concept called the **Central Limit Theorem** tells us that for a sufficiently large sample size the distribution of the sample means will be approximately normal with a mean equal to the population mean and a standard deviation equal to the population standard deviation divided by the square root of the sample size. The larger the sample size the better the approximation to the normal distribution.

**Outcome 2.** Determine the mean and standard deviation for the sampling distribution of the sample mean $\bar{x}$.

**Outcome 3.** Understand the importance of the Central Limit Theorem.

  **7.3** Sampling Distribution of a Proportion (pg. 289–297)

Summary

In many situations the objective of sampling will be to estimate a **population proportion**. Sample proportions are subject to sampling error, just as sample means. Again, the concept of sampling distributions provides a way to assess the potential magnitude of the sampling error for proportions in a given situation.

In those situations where you are interested in determining the proportion of all items that possess a particular attribute, the sample proportion will be the best estimate of the true population proportion. The distribution of the sample proportion is binomial; however, if the sample size is sufficiently large then the **Central Limit Theorem** tells us that normal distribution can be used as an approximation.

**Outcome 4.** Determine the mean and standard deviation for the sampling distribution of the sample proportion.

## Conclusion

When a sample is taken it is one of many that could have been chosen. Consequently, the sample statistic is only one of many that could have been calculated. There is no reason to believe that the sample statistic will equal the population parameter. The difference between the two is called sampling error. Because sampling error exists, decision makers must be aware of how sample statistics are distributed in order to understand the potential for extreme sampling error. The **Central Limit Theorem** tells us that no matter how the population is distributed, if the sample size is large enough then the sampling distribution will be approximately normally distributed.

# Equations

**(7.1)** Sampling Error of the Sample Mean pg. 265

$$\text{Sampling error} = \bar{x} - \mu$$

**(7.2)** Population Mean pg. 265

$$\mu = \frac{\sum x}{N}$$

**(7.3)** Sample Mean pg. 266

$$\bar{x} = \frac{\sum x}{n}$$

**(7.4)** z-Value for Sampling Distribution of $\bar{x}$ pg. 280

$$z = \frac{\bar{x} - \mu}{\dfrac{\sigma}{\sqrt{n}}}$$

**(7.5)** z-Value Adjusted for the Finite Population Correction Factor pg. 280

$$z = \frac{\bar{x} - \mu}{\dfrac{\sigma}{\sqrt{n}}\sqrt{\dfrac{N-n}{N-1}}}$$

**(7.6)** Population Proportion pg. 290

$$\pi = \frac{X}{N}$$

**(7.7)** Sample Proportion pg. 290

$$p = \frac{x}{n}$$

**(7.8)** Single-Proportion Sampling Error pg. 290

$$\text{Sampling error} = p - \pi$$

**(7.9)** Mean of the Sampling Distribution of $p$ pg. 292

$$\text{Mean} = \mu_p = \pi$$

**(7.10)** Standard Error of the Sampling Distribution of $p$ pg. 292

$$\text{Standard error} = \sigma_p = \sqrt{\frac{\pi(1-\pi)}{n}}$$

**(7.11)** z-Value for Sampling Distribution of $p$ pg. 293

$$z = \frac{p - \pi}{\sigma_p}$$

# Key Terms

Central Limit Theorem pg. 283
Consistent estimator pg. 280
Parameter pg. 266

Population proportion pg. 289
Sample proportion pg. 290
Sampling distribution pg. 273

Sampling error pg. 265
Simple random sample pg. 266
Unbiased estimator pg. 276

# Chapter Exercises                    *MyStatLab*

## Conceptual **Questions**

**7-65.** Under what conditions should the finite population correction factor be used in determining the standard error of a sampling distribution?

**7-66.** A sample of size 30 is obtained from a population that has a proportion of 0.34. Determine the range of sampling errors possible when the sample proportion is used to estimate the population proportion.
(*Hint*: Review the Empirical Rule.)

**7-67.** Discuss why the sampling distribution will be less variable than the population distribution. Give a short example to illustrate your answer.

**7-68.** Discuss the similarities and differences between a standard deviation and a standard error.

**7-69.** A researcher has collected all possible samples of a size of 150 from a population and listed the sample means for each of these samples.

a. If the average of the sample means is 450.55, what would be the numerical value of the true population mean? Discuss.

b. If the standard deviation of the sample means is 12.25, determine the standard deviation of the model from which the samples came. To perform this calculation, assume the population has a size of 1,250.

**7-70.** Consider the standard error of a sample proportion obtained from a sample of size 100.

a. Determine the standard error obtained from a population with $\pi = 0.1$.

b. Repeat part a for a population proportion equal to (1) 0.5 and (2) 0.9.

c. Which population proportion results in the largest standard error?

d. Given your responses to parts a, b, and c, which value of a population proportion would produce the largest sampling error?

**7-71.** If a population is known to be normally distributed, what size sample is required to ensure that the sampling distribution of $\bar{x}$ is normally distributed?

**7-72.** Suppose we are told the sampling distribution developed from a sample of size 400 has a mean of 56.78 and a standard error of 9.6. If the population is known to be normally distributed, what are the population mean and population standard deviation? Discuss how these values relate to the values for the sampling distribution.

## Business Applications

**7-73.** The Baily Hill Bicycle Shop sells mountain bikes and offers a maintenance program to its customers. The manager has found the average repair bill during the maintenance program's first year to be $15.30 with a standard deviation of $7.00.
   a. What is the probability a random sample of 40 customers will have a mean repair cost exceeding $16.00?
   b. What is the probability the mean repair cost for a sample of 100 customers will be between $15.10 and $15.80?
   c. The manager has decided to offer a Spring special. He is aware of the mean and standard deviation for repair bills last year. Therefore, he has decided to randomly select and repair the first 50 bicycles for $14.00 each. He notes this is not even 1 standard deviation below the mean price to make such repairs. He asks your advice. Is this a risky thing to do? Based upon the probability of a repair bill being $14.00 or less, what would you recommend? Discuss.

**7-74.** When its ovens are working properly, the time required to bake fruit pies at Ellardo Bakeries is normally distributed with a mean of 45 minutes and a standard deviation of 5 minutes. Yesterday, a random sample of 16 pies had an average baking time of 50 minutes.
   a. If Ellardo's ovens are working correctly, how likely is it that a sample of 16 pies would have an average baking time of 50 minutes or more?
   b. Would you recommend that Ellardo inspect its ovens to see if they are working properly? Justify your answer.

**7-75.** An analysis performed by Hewitt Associates indicated the median amount saved in a 401(k) plan by people 50 to 59 years old was $53,440. The average saved is $115,260 for that age group. Assume the standard deviation is $75,000.
   a. Examining these statements, would it be possible to use a normal distribution to determine the proportion of workers who have saved more than $115,260? Support your assertions.
   b. If it is possible to determine the probability that a sample of size 5 has an average amount saved in a 401(k) plan that is more than $115,260, do so. If not, explain why you are unable to do so.

   c. Repeat the instructions in part b with a sample size of 35.

**7-76.** Suppose at your university some administrators believe that the proportion of students preferring to take classes at night exceeds 0.30. The president is skeptical and so has an assistant take a simple random sample of 200 students. Of these, 66 indicate that they prefer night classes. What is the probability of finding a sample proportion equal to or greater than that found if the president's skepticism is justified? Assume $n \leq 5$ percent of $N$.

**7-77.** A year-old study found that the service time for all drive-thru customers at the Stardust Coffee Shop is uniformly distributed between 3 and 6 minutes. Assuming the service time distribution has not changed, a random sample of 49 customers is taken and the service time for each is recorded.
   a. Calculate the mean and standard deviation of service times for all drive-thru customers at the Stardust Coffee Shop. (*Hint*: Review the uniform distribution from Chapter 6.)
   b. What is the probability that a sample of 49 customers would have a sample mean of 4.25 minutes or more if the true population mean and standard deviation for service times are as calculated in part a?
   c. How can the probability in part b be determined when the population of service times is not normally distributed?

**7-78.** The time it takes a mechanic to tune an engine is known to be normally distributed with a mean of 45 minutes and a standard deviation of 14 minutes.
   a. Determine the mean and standard error of a sampling distribution for a sample size of 20 tune-ups. Draw a picture of the sampling distribution.
   b. Calculate the largest sampling error you would expect to make in estimating the population mean with the sample size of 20 tune-ups.

**7-79.** Frito-Lay is one of the world's largest makers of snack foods. One of the final steps in making products like Cheetos and Doritos is to package the product in sacks or other containers. Suppose Frito-Lay managers set the fill volume on Cheetos to an average volume of 16 ounces. The filling machine is known to fill with a standard deviation of 0.25 ounces with a normal distribution around the mean fill level.
   a. What is the probability that a single bag of Cheetos will have a fill volume that exceeds 16.10 ounces?
   b. What is the probability that a random sample of 12 bags of Cheetos will have a mean fill volume that exceeds 16.10 ounces?
   c. Compare your answers to parts a and b and discuss why they are different.

**7-80.** Frank N. Magid Associates conducted a telephone survey of 1,109 consumers to obtain the number of cell phones in houses. The survey obtained the following results:

| Cell phones | 0 | 1 | 2 | 3 | ≥ 4 |
|---|---|---|---|---|---|
| Percent | 19 | 26 | 33 | 13 | 9 |

a. Determine the sample proportion of households that own two or more cell phones.

b. If the proportion of households that own two or more cell phones is equal to 0.50, determine the probability that in a sample of 1,109 consumers at least 599 would own two or more cell phones.

c. The margin of error of the survey was ±3 percentage points. This means that the sample proportion would be within 3 percentage points of the population proportion. If the population proportion of households that had two or more cell phones was 0.50, determine the probability that the margin of error would be ±3 percentage points.

7-81. The Bendbo Corporation has a total of 300 employees in its two manufacturing locations and the headquarters office. A study conducted five years ago showed the average commuting distance to work for Bendbo employees was 6.2 miles with a standard deviation of 3 miles. Recently, a follow-up study based on a random sample of 100 employees indicated an average travel distance of 5.9 miles.

a. Assuming that the mean and standard deviation of the original study hold, what is the probability of obtaining a sample mean of 5.9 miles or less?

b. Based on this probability, do you think the average travel distance may have decreased?

c. A second random sample of 40 was selected. This sample produced a mean travel distance of 5.9 miles. If the mean for all employees is 6.2 miles and the standard deviation is 3 miles, what is the probability of observing a sample mean of 5.9 miles or less?

d. Discuss why the probabilities differ even though the sample results were the same in each case.

7-82. MPC makes personal computers that are then sold directly over the phone and over the Internet. One of the most critical factors in the success of PC makers is how fast they can turn their inventory of parts. Faster inventory turns mean lower average inventory cost. Recently at a meeting, the vice president (VP) of manufacturing said that there is no reason to continue offering hard disk drives that have less than a 100-GB storage capacity since only 10% of MPC customers ask for the smaller hard disks. After much discussion and debate about the accuracy of the VP's figure, it was decided to sample 100 orders from the past week's sales. This sample revealed 14 requests for drives with less than 100-GB capacity.

a. Determine the probability of finding 14 or more requests like this if the VP's assertion is correct.

Do you believe that the proportion of customers requesting hard drives with storage capacity is as small as 0.10? Explain.

b. Suppose a second sample of 100 customers was selected. This sample again yielded 14 requests for a hard drive with less than 100 GB of storage. Combining this sample information with that found in part a, what conclusion would you now reach regarding the VP's 10% claim? Base your answer on probability.

7-83. Dave Wilson, president of the Graduate Management Admissions Council (GMAC), reported the results of a recent GMAC survey of 5,829 MBA graduates. The average annual base salary increased to $88,626. The high annual base salary was set in 2001 at approximately $92,500 after adjusting for inflation.

a. Assuming that the standard deviation of the salary and bonus for new MBAs was $40,000, calculate the probability that a randomly selected sample of size 5,829 graduates would yield a sample mean of at most $88,626 if the population mean equaled $92,500.

b. Is it plausible that the average annual base salaries for both 2001 and recent graduates were actually the same? Support your assertions.

c. Determine the probability that at least half of 5 MBA students who graduated in 2001 would get annual base salaries of at least $92,500.

7-84. A major video rental chain recently decided to allow customers to rent movies for three nights rather than one. The marketing team that made this decision reasoned that at least 70% of the customers would return the movie by the second night anyway. A sample of 500 customers found 68% returned the movie prior to the third night.

a. Given the marketing team's estimate, what would be the probability of a sample result with 68% or fewer returns prior to the third night?

b. Based on your calculations, would you recommend the adoption of the new rental policy? Support your answer with statistical reasoning and calculations.

## Computer Database Exercises

7-85. The **Patients** file contains information for a random sample of geriatric patients. During a meeting, one hospital administrator indicated that 70% of the geriatric patients are males.

a. Based on the data contained in the **Patients** file, would you conclude the administrator's assertion concerning the proportion of male geriatric patients is correct? Justify your answer.

b. The administrator also believes 80% of all geriatric patients are covered by Medicare (Code = CARE). Again, based on the data contained in the file, what conclusion should the hospital administrator reach concerning the proportion of geriatric patients covered by Medicare? Discuss.

**7-86.** *USA Today* reported the results of a survey conducted by HarrisInteractive to determine the percentage of adults who use a computer to access the Internet (from work, home, or other locations). The newspaper indicated the survey revealed that 74% of adults use a computer to access the Internet. The file entitled **Online** produces a representative sample of the data collected by *USA Today*.

a. Calculate the sample proportion of adults who connect to the Internet using a computer.

b. If the Harris poll's estimate of the proportion of adults using the Internet is correct, determine the sampling error for the sample in the **Online** file.

c. Determine the probability that a sample proportion would be at most as far away as the **Online** sample if the Harris poll's estimate was correct.

d. The Harris poll indicated that its sample had a margin of error of ±2%. The sample size used by the Harris poll was 2,022. Calculate the probability that the sample proportion from a sample size of 2,022 would be at most as far away from the population proportion as suggested by the margin of error.

**7-87.** The file **High Desert Banking** contains information regarding consumer, real estate, and small commercial loans made last year by the bank. Use your computer software to do the following:

a. Construct a frequency histogram using eight classes for dollar value of loans made last year. Does the population distribution appear to be normally distributed?

b. Compute the population mean for all loans made last year.

c. Compute the population standard deviation for all loans made last year.

d. Select a simple random sample of 36 loans. Compute the sample mean. By how much does the sample mean differ from the population mean? Use the Central Limit Theorem to determine the probability that you would have a sample mean this small or smaller and the probability that you would have a sample mean this large or larger.

**7-88.** Analysis by American Express found high fuel prices and airline losses resulted in increasing fares for business travelers. The average fare paid for business travel rose during the second quarter of 2008 to $260, up from $236 in the second quarter of 2007. However, fuel prices started declining in the fall of 2008. The file entitled **Busfares** contains sample prices paid by business travelers in the first quarter of 2009.

a. Determine the sample average fare for business travelers in the first quarter of 2009.

b. If the average has not changed since the second quarter of 2008, determine the sampling error.

c. If this data were normally distributed, determine the probability that the sample mean would be as far away from the population mean or more so.

d. Does it appear that the average business traveler's fare has changed since 2008's second quarter? Explain.

**7-89.** Covercraft manufactures covers to protect automobile interiors and finishes. Its Block-It 200 Series fabric has a limited two-year warranty. Periodic testing is done to determine if the warranty policy should be changed. One such study may have examined those covers that became unserviceable while still under warranty. Data that could be produced by such a study are contained in the file entitled **Covers**." The data represent the number of months a cover was used until it became unserviceable. Covercraft might want to examine more carefully the covers that became unserviceable while still under warranty. Specifically, it wants to examine those that became unserviceable before they had been in use one year.

a. Covercraft has begun to think that it should lower its warranty period to perhaps 20 months. It believes that in doing this, 20% of the covers that now fail before the warranty is up will have surpassed the 20-month warranty rate. Calculate the proportion of the sample that became unserviceable after 20 months of service.

b. Determine the probability of obtaining a sample proportion at least as large as that calculated in part a if the true proportion was equal to 0.20.

c. Based on your calculation in part b, should Covercraft lower its warranty period to 20 months? Support your answer.

**7-90.** The data file **Trucks** contains data on a sample of 200 trucks that were weighed on two scales. The WIM (weigh-in-motion) scale weighs the trucks as they drive down the highway. The POE scale weighs the trucks while they are stopped at the port-of-entry station. The maker of the WIM scale believes that its scale will weigh heavier than the POE scale 60% of the time when gross weight is considered.

a. Create a new variable that has a value = 1 when the WIM gross weight > POE gross weight, and 0 otherwise.

b. Determine the sample proportion of times the WIM gross weight exceeds POE gross weight.

c. Based on this sample, what is the probability of finding a proportion less than that found in part b? For this calculation, assume the WIM maker's assertion is correct.

d. Based on the probability found in part c, what should the WIM maker conclude? Is his 60% figure reasonable?

# Case 7.1

## Carpita Bottling Company

Don Carpita owns and operates Carpita Bottling Company in Lakeland, Wisconsin. The company bottles soda and beer and distributes the products in the counties surrounding Lakeland.

The company has four bottling machines, which can be adjusted to fill bottles at any mean fill level between 2 ounces and 72 ounces. The machines exhibit some variation in actual fill from the mean setting. For instance, if the mean setting is 16 ounces, the actual fill may be slightly more or less than that amount.

Three of the four filling machines are relatively new, and their fill variation is not as great as that of the older machine. Don has observed that the standard deviation in fill for the three new machines is about 1% of the mean fill level when the mean fill is set at 16 ounces or less, and it is 0.5% of the mean at settings exceeding 16 ounces. The older machine has a standard deviation of about 1.5% of the mean setting regardless of the mean fill setting. However, the older machine tends to under fill bottles more than over fill, so the older machine is set at a mean fill slightly in excess of the desired mean to compensate for the propensity to under fill. For example, when 16-ounce bottles are to be filled, the machine is set at a mean fill level of 16.05 ounces.

The company can simultaneously fill bottles with two brands of soda using two machines, and it can use the other two machines to bottle beer. Although each filling machine has its own warehouse and the products are loaded from the warehouse directly onto a truck, products from two or more filling machines may be loaded on the same truck. However, an individual store almost always receives bottles on a particular day from just one machine.

On Saturday morning Don received a call at home from the J. R. Summers grocery store manager. She was very upset because the shipment of 16-ounce bottles of beer received yesterday contained several bottles that were not adequately filled. The manager wanted Don to replace the entire shipment at once.

Don gulped down his coffee and prepared to head to the store to check out the problem. He started thinking how he could determine which machine was responsible for the problem. If he could at least determine whether it was the old machine or one of the new ones, he could save his maintenance people a lot of time and effort checking all the machines.

His plan was to select a sample of 64 bottles of beer from the store and measure the contents. Don figures that he might be able to determine, on the basis of the average contents, whether it is more likely that the beer was bottled by a new machine or by the old one.

The results of the sampling showed an average of 15.993 ounces. Now Don needs some help in determining whether a sample mean of 15.993 ounces or less is more likely to come from the new machines or the older machine.

# Case 7.2

## Truck Safety Inspection

The Idaho Department of Law Enforcement, in conjunction with the federal government, recently began a truck inspection program in Idaho. The current inspection effort is limited to an inspection of only those trucks that visually appear to have some defect when they stop at one of the weigh stations in the state. The proposed inspection program will not be limited to the trucks with visible defects, but will potentially subject all trucks to a comprehensive safety inspection.

Jane Lund of the Department of Law Enforcement is in charge of the new program. She has stated that the ultimate objective of the new truck inspection program is to reduce the number of trucks with safety defects operating in Idaho. Ideally, all trucks passing through, or operating within Idaho would be inspected once a month, and substantial penalties would be applied to operators if safety defects were discovered. Ms. Lund is confident that such an inspection program would, without fail, reduce the number of defective trucks operating on Idaho's highways. However, each safety inspection takes about an hour, and because of limited money to hire inspectors, she realizes that all trucks cannot be inspected. She also knows it is unrealistic to have trucks wait to be inspected until trucks ahead of them have been checked. Such delays would cause problems with the drivers.

In meetings with her staff, Jane has suggested that before the inspection program begins, the number of defective trucks currently operating in Idaho should be estimated. This estimate can be compared with later estimates to see if the inspection program has been effective. To arrive at this initial estimate, Jane thinks that some sort of sampling plan to select representative trucks from the population for all trucks in the state must be developed. She has suggested that this sampling be done at the eight weigh stations near Idaho's borders, but she is unsure how to establish a statistically sound sampling plan that is practical to implement.

# References

Berenson, Mark L., and David M. Levine, *Basic Business Statistics: Concepts and Applications*, 11th ed. (Upper Saddle River, NJ: Prentice Hall, 2009).

Cochran, William G., *Sampling Techniques*, 3rd ed. (New York: Wiley, 1977).

Hogg, R. V., and Elliot A. Tanis, *Probability and Statistical Inference*, 8th ed. (Upper Saddle River, NJ: Prentice Hall, 2009).

Johnson, Richard A., and Dean W. Wichern, *Business Statistics: Decision Making with Data* (New York City: Wiley, 1997).

Larsen, Richard J., and Moriss L. Marx, *An Introduction to Mathematical Statistics and Its Applications*, 4th ed. (Upper Saddle River, NJ: Prentice Hall, 2005).

*Microsoft Excel 2007* (Redmond, WA: Microsoft Corp., 2007).

*Minitab for Windows Version 15* (State College, PA: Minitab, 2007).

**Chapter 8 Quick Prep Links**

- **Review** material on calculating and interpreting sample means and standard deviations in Chapter 3.

- **Review** the normal distribution in Section 6.1.

- **Make sure** you understand the concepts associated with sampling distributions for $\bar{x}$ and $p$ by reviewing Sections 7.1, 7.2, and 7.3.

**8**

chapter

# Estimating Single Population Parameters

## Why you need to know

Wherever you find yourself working, you may need to know population values (*parameters*) to help you make decisions. A bank manager needs to know the percentage of loan accounts that are past due. A human resources manager might wish to know the average hourly wage for skilled labor in the company's hiring area. A manufacturing manager needs to know the average machine downtime in his plant. The programming manager at a major television network needs to know the percentage of people watching each of his shows so he can cancel the poor performers. A restaurant manager needs to know the percentage of customers who will order the daily special so she will know how many orders to have available.

In these cases and many others like them, decision makers need to know a population parameter. However, gaining access to an entire population is extremely expensive and time-consuming and, in many cases, infeasible. Therefore, an alternative approach is to select a sample from the population. The sample data are used to compute a desired statistic that forms an estimate of the corresponding population parameter.

Chapter 1 discussed various sampling techniques, including statistical and nonstatistical methods. Chapter 7 introduced the concepts of sampling error and sampling distributions. Chapter 8 builds on these concepts and introduces the steps needed to develop and interpret statistical estimations of various population values. The concepts introduced here will be very useful. You will undoubtedly need to estimate population parameters as a regular part of your managerial decision-making activities. In addition, you will receive estimates that other people have developed that you will need to evaluate before relying on them as inputs to your decision-making process. Was the sample size large enough to provide valid estimates of the population parameter? How confident can you be that the estimate matches the population parameter of interest? These and similar questions can all be answered using the concepts and procedures presented in this chapter.

# 8.1 Point and Confidence Interval Estimates for a Population Mean

Chapter Outcome 1.➞ ## Point Estimates and Confidence Intervals

Every election year, political parties and news agencies conduct polls. These polls attempt to determine the percentage of voters who will favor a particular candidate or a particular issue. For example, suppose a poll indicates that 62% of the people older than 18 in your state favor limiting property taxes to 1% of the market value of the property. The pollsters have not contacted every person in the state; rather, they have sampled only a relatively few people to arrive at the 62% figure. In statistical terminology, the 62% is the **point estimate** of the true population percentage of people who favor the property-tax limitation.

The Environmental Protection Agency (EPA) tests the mileage of automobiles sold in the United States. The resulting EPA mileage rating is actually a point estimate for the true average mileage of all cars of a given model.

Production managers study their companies' manufacturing processes to determine product costs. They typically select a sample of items and follow each sampled item through a complete production process. The costs at each step in the process are measured and summed to determine the total cost. They then divide the sum by the sample size to get the mean cost. This figure is the point estimate for the true mean cost of all the items produced. The point estimate is used in assigning a selling price to the finished product.

Which point estimator the decision maker uses depends on the population characteristic the decision maker wishes to estimate. However, regardless of the population value being estimated, we always expect **sampling error**.

Chapter 7 discussed sampling error. We cannot eliminate sampling error, but we can deal with it in our decision process. For example, when production managers use $\bar{x}$, the average cost of a sample of items, to establish the average cost of production, the point estimate, $\bar{x}$, will most likely not equal the population mean, $\mu$. In fact, the probability of $\bar{x} = \mu$ is essentially zero. With $\bar{x}$ as their only information, the cost accountants will have no way of determining exactly how far $\bar{x}$ is from $\mu$.

To overcome this problem with point estimates, the most common procedure is to calculate an interval estimate known as a **confidence interval**.

An application will help to make this definition clear.

**Point Estimate**

A single statistic, determined from a sample, that is used to estimate the corresponding population parameter.

**Sampling Error**

The difference between a measure (a statistic) computed from a sample and the corresponding measure (a parameter) computed from the population.

**Confidence Interval**

An interval developed from sample values such that if all possible intervals of a given width were constructed, a percentage of these intervals, known as the confidence level, would include the true population parameter.

Lower confidence limit          Point estimate          Upper confidence limit

**Excel and Minitab Tutorial**

---

**BUSINESS APPLICATION**    CALCULATING A CONFIDENCE INTERVAL ESTIMATE

**NAGEL BEVERAGE COMPANY** The Nagel Beverage Company has recently installed a new soft-drink filling machine that allows the operator to adjust the mean fill quantity. However, no matter what the mean setting, the actual volume of the liquid in each soft-drink can will vary. The machine has been carefully tested and is known to fill cans with an amount of liquid that has a standard deviation of $\sigma = 0.2$ ounce.

The filling machine has been adjusted to fill cans at an average of 12 ounces. After running the machine for several hours, a simple random sample of 100 cans is selected, and the volume of soda in each can is measured in the company's quality lab. Figure 8.1 shows the frequency histogram of the sample data. (The data are in a file called **Nagel-Beverage**.) Notice that the distribution seems to be centered at a point larger than 12 ounces. The manager wishes to use the sample data to estimate the mean fill amount for all cans filled by this machine.

The sample mean computed from 100 cans is $\bar{x} = 12.09$ ounces. This is the *point estimate* of the population mean, $\mu$. Because of the potential for sampling error, the manager should not expect a particular $\bar{x}$ to equal $\mu$. However, as discussed in Chapter 7, the Central Limit Theorem indicates that the distribution of all possible sample means of 100 will be approximately normally distributed around the population mean with its spread measured by $\sigma/\sqrt{n}$, as illustrated in Figure 8.2.

**FIGURE 8.1**

Excel 2007 Histogram for Nagel Beverage

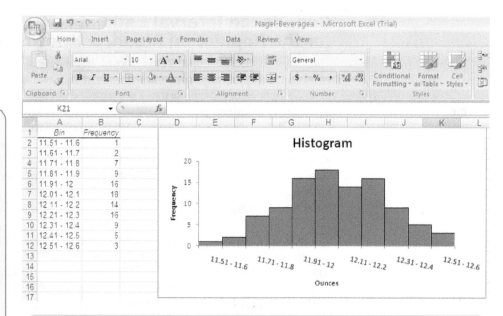

**Excel 2007 Instructions:**
1. Open File: Nagel Beverage.xls.
2. Create bins (upper limit of each class).
3. Select **Data > Data Analysis**.
4. Select **Histogram**.
5. Define data and bin ranges.
6. Check **Chart Output**.
7. Modify bin definitions.
8. Select chart and right click.
9. Click on **Format Data Series** and close gap width to zero.
10. Label Axes using **Layout > Axis Titles**.

**Minitab Instructions (for similar results):**
1. **Open file:** Nagel Beverage MTW.
2. Choose **Graph > Histogram**.
3. Click **Simple**.
4. Click **OK**.
5. In **Graph** variables, enter data Column: *Ounces*.
6. Click **OK**.

Although the sample mean is 12.09 ounces, the manager knows the true population mean may be larger or smaller than this number. To account for the potential for sampling error, the manager can develop a *confidence interval estimate* for $\mu$. This estimate will take the following form:

Lower confidence limit          Upper confidence limit

$$\bar{x} = 12.09$$

The key now is to determine the upper and lower limits of the interval. The specific method for computing these values depends on whether the population standard deviation, $\sigma$, is known or unknown. We first take up the case in which $\sigma$ is known.

**FIGURE 8.2**

Sampling Distribution of $\bar{x}$

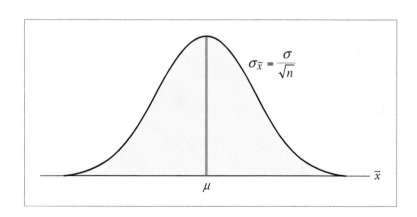

# Confidence Interval Estimate for the Population Mean, $\sigma$ Known

**Standard Error**

A value that measures the spread of the sample means around the population mean. The standard error is reduced when the sample size is increased.

There are two cases that must be considered. In the case in which the simple random sample is drawn from a normal distribution with a mean of $\mu$ and a standard deviation of $\sigma$, the sampling distribution of the sample mean is a normal distribution with a mean of $\mu$ and a standard deviation (or **standard error**) of $\sigma/\sqrt{n}$. This is true for any sample size.

The second case is where the population does not have a normal distribution or the distribution of the population is not known. Chapter 7 addressed these specific circumstances. Recall that in such cases the Central Limit Theorem can be invoked if the sample size is sufficiently large ($n \geq 30$). In such cases, the sampling distribution is an approximately normal distribution, with a mean of $\mu$ and a standard deviation of $\sigma/\sqrt{n}$. The approximation becomes more precise as the sample size increases. The standard deviation, $\sigma/\sqrt{n}$, is known as the *standard error* of the sample mean.

In both these cases, the sampling distribution for $\bar{x}$ is assumed to be normally distributed. Looking at the sampling distribution in Figure 8.2, it is apparent that the probability that $\bar{x}$ will exceed $\mu$ is the same as the probability that $\bar{x}$ will be less than $\mu$. We also know from our discussion in Chapter 7 that we can calculate the percentage of sample means in the interval formed by a specified distance above and below $\mu$. This percentage corresponds to the probability that the sample mean will be in the specified interval. For example, the probability of obtaining a value for $\bar{x}$ that is within 1.96 standard errors either side of $\mu$ is 0.95. To verify this, recall from Chapter 7 that the standardized $z$-value measures the number of standard errors $\bar{x}$ is from $\mu$. The probability from the standard normal distribution table corresponding to $z = 1.96$ is 0.4750. Likewise, the probability corresponding to $z = -1.96$ is equal to 0.4750. Therefore,

$$P(-1.96 \leq z \leq 1.96) = 0.4750 + 0.4750 = 0.95$$

This is illustrated in Figure 8.3.

Because the standard error is $\sigma/\sqrt{n}$, then 95% of all sample means will fall in the range

$$\mu - 1.96\frac{\sigma}{\sqrt{n}} \quad\text{------------}\quad \mu + 1.96\frac{\sigma}{\sqrt{n}}$$

This is illustrated in Figure 8.4.

In a like manner, we can determine that 80% of all sample means will fall in the range

$$\mu - 1.28\frac{\sigma}{\sqrt{n}} \quad\text{------------}\quad \mu + 1.28\frac{\sigma}{\sqrt{n}}$$

Also, we can determine that 90% of all sample means will fall in the range

$$\mu - 1.645\frac{\sigma}{\sqrt{n}} \quad\text{------------}\quad \mu + 1.645\frac{\sigma}{\sqrt{n}}$$

**FIGURE 8.3**

Critical Value for a 95% Confidence Interval

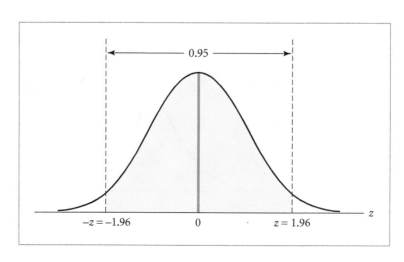

**FIGURE 8.4** |

95% Confidence Intervals from Selected Random Samples

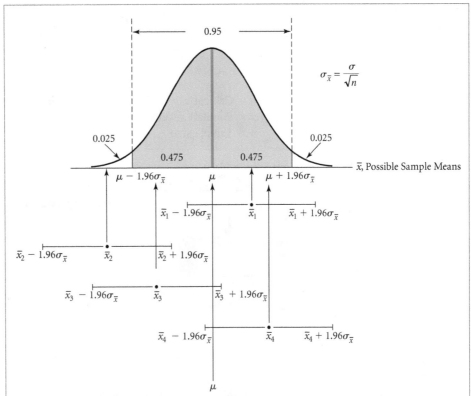

*Note*: Most intervals include $\mu$ and some do not. Those intervals that do not contain the population mean are developed from sample means that fall in either tail of the sampling distribution. If all possible intervals were constructed from a given sample size, 95% would include $\mu$.

This concept can be generalized to any probability by substituting the appropriate $z$-value from the standard normal distribution.

Now, given that our objective is to estimate $\mu$ based on a random sample of size $n$, if we form an interval estimate using

$$\bar{x} \pm z \frac{\sigma}{\sqrt{n}}$$

**Confidence Level**
The percentage of all possible confidence intervals that will contain the true population parameter.

the proportion of all possible intervals containing $\mu$ will equal the probability associated with the specified $z$-value. In estimation terminology, the $z$-value is referred to as the *critical value*.

**Chapter Outcome 2.** → **Confidence Interval Calculation** Confidence interval estimates can be constructed using the general format shown in Equation 8.1.

**TABLE 8.1** | **Critical Values for Commonly Used Confidence Levels**

| Confidence Level | Critical Value |
|---|---|
| 80% | $z = 1.28$ |
| 90% | $z = 1.645$ |
| 95% | $z = 1.96$ |
| 99% | $z = 2.575$ |

*Note*: Instead of using the standard normal table, you can also find the critical $z$-value using Excel's NORMSINV function or Minitab's Calc > Probability Distribution command.

| **Confidence Interval General Format** | |
|---|---|
| Point estimate $\pm$ (Critical value)(Standard error) | **(8.1)** |

The first step in developing a confidence interval estimate is to specify the **confidence level** that is needed to determine the critical value.

Once you decide on the confidence level, the next step is to determine the critical value. If the population standard deviation is known and the population is normally distributed, or if the sample size is large enough to comply with the Central Limit Theorem requirements, the critical value is a $z$-value from the standard normal table. Table 8.1 shows several of the most frequently used critical values.

The next step is to compute the standard error for the sampling distribution, shown in Chapter 7 and also earlier in this chapter to be $\sigma_{\bar{x}} = \sigma/\sqrt{n}$. Then, Equation 8.2 is used to compute the confidence interval estimate for $\mu$.

---

**Confidence Interval Estimate for $\mu$, $\sigma$ Known**

$$\bar{x} \pm z \frac{\sigma}{\sqrt{n}} \qquad\qquad (8.2)$$

where:

$z$ = Critical value from the standard normal table for a specified confidence level
$\sigma$ = Population standard deviation
$n$ = Sample size

---

**BUSINESS APPLICATION**  **CONFIDENCE INTERVAL ESTIMATE FOR $\mu$**

**NAGEL BEVERAGE COMPANY (*CONTINUED*)**  Recall that the sample of 100 cans produced a sample mean of $\bar{x} = 12.09$ ounces and the Nagel manager knows that $\sigma = 0.2$ ounce. Thus, the 95% confidence interval estimate for the population mean is

$$\bar{x} \pm z \frac{\sigma}{\sqrt{n}}$$

$$12.09 \pm 1.96 \frac{0.2}{\sqrt{100}}$$

$$12.09 \pm 0.039$$

$$12.051 \text{ ounces} \text{——————} 12.129 \text{ ounces}$$

Based on this sample information, the Nagel manager believes that the true mean fill for all cans is within the following interval:

12.051 ounces                                    12.129 ounces

$\bar{x} = 12.09$ ounces

Because this interval does not contain the target mean of 12 ounces, the manager should conclude that the filling equipment is out of adjustment and is putting in too much soda, on average.

---

**EXAMPLE 8-1**  **CONFIDENCE INTERVAL ESTIMATE FOR $\mu$, $\sigma$ KNOWN**

**Tampa, Florida, Property Tax** City officials in Tampa, Florida, wish to know the mean amount of dollars that home owners in Tampa pay annually for property taxes on personal residences. To do this, they could use the following steps:

**Step 1**  **Define the population of interest and select a simple random sample of size $n$.**
The population is the amount of dollars paid annually for property tax for all single-family personal residences in the city of Tampa. A simple random sample of 200 tax bills will be selected, and the amount of property taxes paid will be recorded.

**Step 2**  **Specify the confidence level.**
The officials want to develop a 90% confidence interval estimate. Thus, 90% of all possible intervals will contain the population mean.

**Step 3**  **Compute the sample mean.**
After the sample has been selected and the dollars spent on property taxes last year have been recorded for each of the 200 tax bills sampled, the sample mean is computed using

$$\bar{x} = \frac{\sum x}{n}$$

Assume the sample mean is $5,230.

---

**How to do it (Example 8-1)**

**Confidence Interval Estimate for $\mu$ with $\sigma$ Known**

Use the following steps to compute a confidence interval estimate for the population mean when the population standard deviation is assumed known and either the population distribution is normal or the sample size $n$ is $\geq 30$.

**1.** Define the population of interest and select a simple random sample of size $n$.

**2.** Specify the confidence level.

**3.** Compute the sample mean using

$$\bar{x} = \frac{\sum x}{n}$$

**4.** Determine the standard error of the sampling distribution using

$$\sigma_{\bar{x}} = \frac{\sigma}{\sqrt{n}}$$

**5.** Determine the critical value, $z$, from the standard normal table.

**6.** Compute the confidence interval estimate using

$$\bar{x} \pm z \frac{\sigma}{\sqrt{n}}$$

Step 4   **Determine the standard error of the sampling distribution.**
Suppose past studies have indicated that the population standard deviation is

$$\sigma = \$500$$

Then the standard error of the sampling distribution is computed using

$$\sigma_{\bar{x}} = \frac{\sigma}{\sqrt{n}} = \frac{\$500}{\sqrt{200}} = \$35.36$$

Step 5   **Determine the critical value, z, from the standard normal table.**
Because the sample size is large, the Central Limit Theorem applies. The sampling distribution will be normally distributed, and the critical value will be a $z$-value from the standard normal distribution. The officials want a 90% confidence level, so the $z$-value is 1.645.

Step 6   **Compute the confidence interval estimate.**
The 90% confidence interval estimate for the population mean is

$$\bar{x} \pm z \frac{\sigma}{\sqrt{n}}$$

$$\$5,230 \pm 1.645 \frac{500}{\sqrt{200}}$$

$$\$5,230 \pm \$58.16$$

$$\$5,171.84 \text{ ——— } \$5,288.16$$

Thus, based on the sample results, with 90% confidence, the officials in Tampa believe that the true population mean for dollars spent on property taxes on single-family residences last year is between \$5,171.84 and \$5,288.16.

>>**END EXAMPLE**

**TRY PROBLEM** 8-1 (pg. 320)

---

**Special Message about Interpreting Confidence Intervals**

There is a subtle distinction to be made here. Beginning students often wonder if it is permissible to say, "There is a 0.90 probability that the population mean is between \$5,171.84 and \$5,288.16." This may seem to be the logical consequence of constructing a confidence interval. However, we must be very careful to attribute probability only to random events or variables. Because the population mean is a fixed value, there can be no probability statement about the population mean. The confidence interval we have computed will either contain the population mean or it will not. If you were to produce all the possible confidence intervals using the mean of each possible sample of a given size from the population, 90% of these intervals would contain the population mean.

### Impact of the Confidence Level on the Interval Estimate

BUSINESS APPLICATION   **MARGIN OF ERROR**

**NAGEL BEVERAGE (CONTINUED)**  In the Nagel Beverage example, the manager specified a 95% confidence level. The resulting confidence interval estimate for the population mean was

$$\bar{x} \pm z \frac{\sigma}{\sqrt{n}}$$

$$12.09 \pm 1.96 \frac{0.2}{\sqrt{100}}$$

$$12.09 \pm 0.04$$

$$12.05 \text{ ounces ——— } 12.13 \text{ ounces}$$

**Margin of Error**
The amount that is added and subtracted to the point estimate to determine the endpoints of the confidence interval. Also, a measure of how close we expect the point estimate to be to the population parameter with the specified level of confidence.

The quantity, 0.04, on the right of the $\pm$ sign is called the **margin of error**. This is illustrated in Equation 8.3. The margin of error defines the relationship between the sample mean and the population mean.

---

**Margin of Error for Estimating $\mu$, $\sigma$ Known**

$$e = z \frac{\sigma}{\sqrt{n}}$$

(8.3)

where:

$e$ = Margin of error
$z$ = Critical value
$\dfrac{\sigma}{\sqrt{n}}$ = Standard error of the sample distibution

---

Now suppose the manager at Nagel is willing to settle for 80% confidence. This will impact the critical value. To determine the new value, divide 0.80 by 2, giving 0.40. Go to the standard normal table and locate a probability value (area under the curve) that is as close to 0.40 as possible. The corresponding $z$-value is 1.28.[1] The 80% confidence interval estimate is

$$\bar{x} \pm z \frac{\sigma}{\sqrt{n}}$$

$$12.09 \pm (1.28) \frac{0.2}{\sqrt{100}}$$

$$12.09 \pm 0.03$$

$$12.06 \text{ ounces} \text{ ———— } 12.12 \text{ ounces}$$

Based on this sample information and the 80% confidence interval, we believe that the true average fill level is between 12.06 ounces and 12.12 ounces.

By lowering the confidence level, we are likely to obtain an interval that contains the population mean. However, on the positive side, the margin of error has been reduced from $\pm 0.04$ ounces to $\pm 0.03$ ounces. For equivalent samples from a population:

1. If the confidence level is decreased, the margin of error is reduced.
2. If the confidence level is increased, the margin of error is increased.

The Nagel manager will need to decide which is more important, a higher confidence level or a lower margin of error.

---

**EXAMPLE 8-2**    **IMPACT OF CHANGING THE CONFIDENCE LEVEL**

**National Recycling** National Recycling operates a garbage hauling company in a southern Maine city. Each year, the company must apply for a new contract with the state. The contract is in part based on the pounds of recycled materials collected. Part of the analysis that goes into contract development is an estimate of the mean pounds of recycled material submitted by each customer in the city on a quarterly basis. The city has asked for both 99% and 90% confidence interval estimates for the mean. If, after the contract has been signed, the actual mean pounds deviates from the estimate over time, an adjustment will be made (up or down) in the amount National Recycling receives. The steps used to generate these estimates follow.

**Step 1**  **Define the population of interest and select a simple random sample of size $n$.**
The population is the collection of all of National Recycling's customers, and a simple random sample of $n = 100$ customers is selected.

**Step 2**  **Specify the confidence level.**
The city requires 99% and 90% confidence interval estimates.

**Step 3**  **Compute the sample mean.**
After the sample has been selected and the pounds of recycled materials have been determined for each of the 100 customers sampled, the sample mean is computed using

$$\bar{x} = \frac{\sum x}{n}$$

Suppose the sample mean is 40.78 pounds.

---

[1] You can also use Excel's NORMSINV function = NORMSINV(.90) = 1.281.

**Step 4**  **Determine the standard error of the sampling distribution.**

Suppose, from past years, the population standard deviation is known to be $\sigma = 12.6$ pounds. Then the standard error of the sampling distribution is computed using

$$\sigma_{\bar{x}} = \frac{\sigma}{\sqrt{n}} = \frac{12.6}{\sqrt{100}} = 1.26 \text{ pounds}$$

**Step 5**  **Determine the critical value, $z$, from the standard normal table.**

First, the state wants a 99% confidence interval estimate, so the $z$-value is determined by finding a probability in Appendix D corresponding to $0.99/2 = 0.495$. The correct $z$-value is between $z = 2.57$ and $z = 2.58$. We split the difference to get the critical value: $z = 2.575$. For 90% confidence, the critical $z$ is determined to be 1.645.

**Step 6**  **Compute the confidence interval estimate.**

The 99% confidence interval estimate for the population mean is

$$\bar{x} \pm z\frac{\sigma}{\sqrt{n}}$$

$$40.78 \pm 2.575\frac{12.6}{\sqrt{100}}$$

$$40.78 \pm 3.24$$

37.54 pounds ———— 44.02 pounds

The margin of error at 99% confidence is $\pm 3.24$ pounds.
The 90% confidence interval estimate for the population mean is

$$\bar{x} \pm z\frac{\sigma}{\sqrt{n}}$$

$$40.78 \pm 1.645\frac{12.6}{\sqrt{100}}$$

$$40.78 \pm 2.07$$

38.71 pounds ———— 42.85 pounds

The margin of error is only 2.07 pounds when the confidence level is reduced from 99% to 90%. The margin of error will be smaller when the confidence level is smaller.

>>**END EXAMPLE**

**TRY PROBLEM** 8-5 (pg. 320)

---

Lowering the confidence level is one way to reduce the margin of error. However, by examining Equation 8.3, you will note there are two other values that affect the margin of error. One of these is the population standard deviation. The more the population's standard deviation, $\sigma$, can be reduced, the smaller the margin of error will be. In a business environment, large standard deviations for measurements related to the quality of a product are not desired. In fact, corporations spend considerable effort to decrease the variation in their products either by changing their process or by controlling variables that cause the variation. Typically, all avenues for reducing the standard deviation should be pursued before thoughts of reducing the confidence level are entertained.

Unfortunately, there are many situations in which reducing the population standard deviation is not possible. In these cases, another step that can be taken to reduce the margin of error is to increase the sample size. As you learned in Chapter 7, an increase in sample size reduces the standard error of the sampling distribution. This can be the most direct way of reducing the margin of error as long as obtaining an increased sample is not prohibitively costly or unattainable for other reasons.

### Impact of the Sample Size on the Interval Estimate

**BUSINESS APPLICATION**    **UNDERSTANDING THE VALUE OF A LARGER SAMPLE SIZE**

**NAGEL BEVERAGE (*CONTINUED*)** Suppose the Nagel Beverage Company production manager decided to increase the sample to 400 cans. This is a four-fold increase over the original sample size. We learned in Chapter 7 that an increase in sample size reduces the standard error of the sampling distribution because the standard error is computed as $\sigma/\sqrt{n}$, Thus, without adversely affecting his confidence level, the manager can reduce the margin of error by increasing his sample size.

Assume that the sample mean for the larger sample size also happens to be $\bar{x} = 12.09$ ounces. The new 95% confidence interval estimate is

$$12.09 \pm 1.96 \frac{0.2}{\sqrt{400}}$$

$$12.09 \pm 0.02$$

$$12.07 \text{ ounces} \text{ ———— } 12.11 \text{ ounces}$$

Notice that by increasing the sample size to 400 cans, the margin of error is reduced from the original 0.04 ounces to 0.02 ounces. The production manager now believes that his sample mean is within ±0.02 ounces of the true population mean.

The production manager was able to reduce the margin of error without reducing the confidence level. However, the downside is that sampling 400 cans instead of 100 cans will cost more money and take more time. That's the trade-off. Absent the possibility of reducing the population standard deviation, if he wants to reduce the margin of error, he must either reduce the confidence level or increase the sample size, or some combination of each. If he is unwilling to do so, he will have to accept the larger margin of error.

## Confidence Interval Estimates for the Population Mean, σ Unknown

In the Nagel Beverage Company application, the manager was dealing with a filling machine that had a known standard deviation in fill volume. You may encounter situations in which the standard deviation is known. However, in most cases, if you do not know the population mean, you also will not know the population standard deviation. When this occurs, you need to make a minor, but important, modification to the confidence interval estimation process.

## Student's *t*-Distribution

When the population standard deviation is known, the sampling distribution of the mean has only one unknown parameter: its mean, $\mu$. This is estimated by $\bar{x}$. However, when the population standard deviation is unknown, there are two unknown parameters, $\mu$ and $\sigma$, which can be estimated by $\bar{x}$ and $s$, respectively. This estimation doesn't affect the general format for a confidence interval, as shown earlier in Equation 8.1:

Point estimate ± (Critical value)(Standard error)

However, not knowing the population standard deviation does affect the critical value. Recall that when $\sigma$ is known and the population is normally distributed or the Central Limit Theorem applies, the critical value is a *z*-value taken from the standard normal table. But when $\sigma$ is not known, the critical value is a *t*-value taken from a family of distributions called the **Student's *t*-distributions**.

Because the specific *t*-distribution chosen is based on its *degrees of freedom*, it is important to understand what degrees of freedom means. Recall that the sample standard deviation is an estimate of the population's standard deviation and is defined as

$$s = \sqrt{\frac{\Sigma(x - \bar{x})^2}{n - 1}}$$

**Student's *t*-Distributions**

A family of distributions that is bell-shaped and symmetric like the standard normal distribution but with greater area in the tails. Each distribution in the *t*-family is defined by its degrees of freedom. As the degrees of freedom increase, the *t*-distribution approaches the normal distribution.

Therefore, if we wish to estimate the population standard deviation, we must first calculate the sample mean. The sample mean is itself an estimator of a parameter, namely, the population mean. The sample mean is obtained from a sample of $n$ randomly and independently chosen data values. Once the sample mean has been obtained, there are only $n - 1$ independent pieces of data information left in the sample.

To illustrate, examine a sample of size $n = 3$ in which the sample mean is calculated to be 12. This implies that the sum of the three data values equals 36 ($3 \times 12$). If you know that the first two data values are 10 and 8, respectively, then the third data value is determined to be 18. Similarly, if you know that the first two data values are 18 and 7, respectively, the third data value must be 11. You are free to choose any two of the three data values. In general, if you must estimate $k$ parameters before you are able to estimate the population's standard deviation from a sample of $n$ data values, you have the freedom to choose any $n - k$ data values before the remaining $k$-values are determined. This value, $n - k$, is called the **degrees of freedom**.

When the population is normally distributed, the $t$-value represents the number of standard errors $\bar{x}$ is from $\mu$, as shown in Equation 8.4. Appendix F contains a table of standardized $t$-values that correspond to specified tail areas and different degrees of freedom. The $t$-table is used to determine the critical value when we do not know the population standard deviation. The $t$-table is reproduced in the inside front cover of your text and also in Table 8.2. Note, in Equation 8.4 we use the sample standard deviation, $s$, to estimate the population standard deviation, $\sigma$. The fact that we are estimating $\sigma$ is the reason the $t$-distribution is more spread out (i.e., has a larger standard deviation) than the normal distribution (see Figure 8.5). By estimating $\sigma$, we are introducing more uncertainty into the estimation process; therefore, achieving the same level of confidence requires a $t$-value larger than the $z$-value for the same confidence

**Degrees of Freedom**

The number of independent data values available to estimate the population's standard deviation. If $k$ parameters must be estimated before the population's standard deviation can be calculated from a sample of size $n$, the degrees of freedom are equal to $n - k$.

---

**$t$-Value for $\bar{x}$**

$$t = \frac{\bar{x} - \mu}{\dfrac{s}{\sqrt{n}}} \qquad (8.4)$$

where:

$$\bar{x} = \text{Sample mean}$$
$$\mu = \text{Population mean}$$
$$s = \text{Sample standard deviation}$$
$$n = \text{Sample size}$$

---

**Assumption**

The $t$-distribution is based on the assumption that the population is normally distributed. Although beyond the scope of this text, it can be shown that as long as the population is reasonably symmetric, the $t$-distribution can be used.

---

**FIGURE 8.5**

*t*-Distribution and Normal Distribution

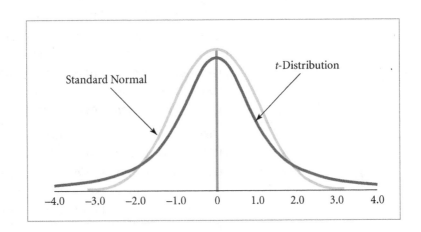

**TABLE 8.2  Values of *t* for Selected Probabilities**

| | Probabilities (or Areas under *t*-Distribution Curve) | | | | | | | | |
|---|---|---|---|---|---|---|---|---|---|
| Conf. Level | 0.1 | 0.3 | 0.5 | 0.7 | 0.8 | 0.9 | 0.95 | 0.98 | 0.99 |
| One Tail | 0.45 | 0.35 | 0.25 | 0.15 | 0.1 | 0.05 | 0.025 | 0.01 | 0.005 |
| Two Tails | 0.9 | 0.7 | 0.5 | 0.3 | 0.2 | 0.1 | 0.05 | 0.02 | 0.01 |
| *d.f.* | | | | | *Values of t* | | | | |
| 1 | 0.1584 | 0.5095 | 1.0000 | 1.9626 | 3.0777 | 6.3137 | 12.7062 | 31.8210 | 63.6559 |
| 2 | 0.1421 | 0.4447 | 0.8165 | 1.3862 | 1.8856 | 2.9200 | 4.3027 | 6.9645 | 9.9250 |
| 3 | 0.1366 | 0.4242 | 0.7649 | 1.2498 | 1.6377 | 2.3534 | 3.1824 | 4.5407 | 5.8408 |
| 4 | 0.1338 | 0.4142 | 0.7407 | 1.1896 | 1.5332 | 2.1318 | 2.7765 | 3.7469 | 4.6041 |
| 5 | 0.1322 | 0.4082 | 0.7267 | 1.1558 | 1.4759 | 2.0150 | 2.5706 | 3.3649 | 4.0321 |
| 6 | 0.1311 | 0.4043 | 0.7176 | 1.1342 | 1.4398 | 1.9432 | 2.4469 | 3.1427 | 3.7074 |
| 7 | 0.1303 | 0.4015 | 0.7111 | 1.1192 | 1.4149 | 1.8946 | 2.3646 | 2.9979 | 3.4995 |
| 8 | 0.1297 | 0.3995 | 0.7064 | 1.1081 | 1.3968 | 1.8595 | 2.3060 | 2.8965 | 3.3554 |
| 9 | 0.1293 | 0.3979 | 0.7027 | 1.0997 | 1.3830 | 1.8331 | 2.2622 | 2.8214 | 3.2498 |
| 10 | 0.1289 | 0.3966 | 0.6998 | 1.0931 | 1.3722 | 1.8125 | 2.2281 | 2.7638 | 3.1693 |
| 11 | 0.1286 | 0.3956 | 0.6974 | 1.0877 | 1.3634 | 1.7959 | 2.2010 | 2.7181 | 3.1058 |
| 12 | 0.1283 | 0.3947 | 0.6955 | 1.0832 | 1.3562 | 1.7823 | 2.1788 | 2.6810 | 3.0545 |
| 13 | 0.1281 | 0.3940 | 0.6938 | 1.0795 | 1.3502 | 1.7709 | 2.1604 | 2.6503 | 3.0123 |
| 14 | 0.1280 | 0.3933 | 0.6924 | 1.0763 | 1.3450 | 1.7613 | 2.1448 | 2.6245 | 2.9768 |
| 15 | 0.1278 | 0.3928 | 0.6912 | 1.0735 | 1.3406 | 1.7531 | 2.1315 | 2.6025 | 2.9467 |
| 16 | 0.1277 | 0.3923 | 0.6901 | 1.0711 | 1.3368 | 1.7459 | 2.1199 | 2.5835 | 2.9208 |
| 17 | 0.1276 | 0.3919 | 0.6892 | 1.0690 | 1.3334 | 1.7396 | 2.1098 | 2.5669 | 2.8982 |
| 18 | 0.1274 | 0.3915 | 0.6884 | 1.0672 | 1.3304 | 1.7341 | 2.1009 | 2.5524 | 2.8784 |
| 19 | 0.1274 | 0.3912 | 0.6876 | 1.0655 | 1.3277 | 1.7291 | 2.0930 | 2.5395 | 2.8609 |
| 20 | 0.1273 | 0.3909 | 0.6870 | 1.0640 | 1.3253 | 1.7247 | 2.0860 | 2.5280 | 2.8453 |
| 21 | 0.1272 | 0.3906 | 0.6864 | 1.0627 | 1.3232 | 1.7207 | 2.0796 | 2.5176 | 2.8314 |
| 22 | 0.1271 | 0.3904 | 0.6858 | 1.0614 | 1.3212 | 1.7171 | 2.0739 | 2.5083 | 2.8188 |
| 23 | 0.1271 | 0.3902 | 0.6853 | 1.0603 | 1.3195 | 1.7139 | 2.0687 | 2.4999 | 2.8073 |
| 24 | 0.1270 | 0.3900 | 0.6848 | 1.0593 | 1.3178 | 1.7109 | 2.0639 | 2.4922 | 2.7970 |
| 25 | 0.1269 | 0.3898 | 0.6844 | 1.0584 | 1.3163 | 1.7081 | 2.0595 | 2.4851 | 2.7874 |
| 26 | 0.1269 | 0.3896 | 0.6840 | 1.0575 | 1.3150 | 1.7056 | 2.0555 | 2.4786 | 2.7787 |
| 27 | 0.1268 | 0.3894 | 0.6837 | 1.0567 | 1.3137 | 1.7033 | 2.0518 | 2.4727 | 2.7707 |
| 28 | 0.1268 | 0.3893 | 0.6834 | 1.0560 | 1.3125 | 1.7011 | 2.0484 | 2.4671 | 2.7633 |
| 29 | 0.1268 | 0.3892 | 0.6830 | 1.0553 | 1.3114 | 1.6991 | 2.0452 | 2.4620 | 2.7564 |
| 30 | 0.1267 | 0.3890 | 0.6828 | 1.0547 | 1.3104 | 1.6973 | 2.0423 | 2.4573 | 2.7500 |
| 40 | 0.1265 | 0.3881 | 0.6807 | 1.0500 | 1.3031 | 1.6839 | 2.0211 | 2.4233 | 2.7045 |
| 50 | 0.1263 | 0.3875 | 0.6794 | 1.0473 | 1.2987 | 1.6759 | 2.0086 | 2.4033 | 2.6778 |
| 60 | 0.1262 | 0.3872 | 0.6786 | 1.0455 | 1.2958 | 1.6706 | 2.0003 | 2.3901 | 2.6603 |
| 70 | 0.1261 | 0.3869 | 0.6780 | 1.0442 | 1.2938 | 1.6669 | 1.9944 | 2.3808 | 2.6479 |
| 80 | 0.1261 | 0.3867 | 0.6776 | 1.0432 | 1.2922 | 1.6641 | 1.9901 | 2.3739 | 2.6387 |
| 90 | 0.1260 | 0.3866 | 0.6772 | 1.0424 | 1.2910 | 1.6620 | 1.9867 | 2.3685 | 2.6316 |
| 100 | 0.1260 | 0.3864 | 0.6770 | 1.0418 | 1.2901 | 1.6602 | 1.9840 | 2.3642 | 2.6259 |
| 250 | 0.1258 | 0.3858 | 0.6755 | 1.0386 | 1.2849 | 1.6510 | 1.9695 | 2.3414 | 2.5956 |
| 500 | 0.1257 | 0.3855 | 0.6750 | 1.0375 | 1.2832 | 1.6479 | 1.9647 | 2.3338 | 2.5857 |
| ∞ | 0.1257 | 0.3853 | 0.6745 | 1.0364 | 1.2816 | 1.6449 | 1.9600 | 2.3264 | 2.5758 |

**Excel and Minitab Tutorial**

**HERITAGE SOFTWARE** Heritage Software, a maker of educational and business software, operates a service center in Tulsa, Oklahoma, where employees respond to customer calls about questions and problems with the company's software packages. Recently, a team of Heritage employees was asked to study the average length of time service representatives spend with customers. The team decided that a simple random sample of 25 calls would be collected and the population mean call time would be estimated based on the sample data. Not only did the team not know the average length of time, $\mu$, but it also didn't know the standard deviation of length of the service time, $\sigma$.

Table 8.3 shows the sample data for 25 calls. (These data are in a file called **Heritage**.) The managers at Heritage Software are willing to assume the population of call times is approximately normal.[2]

Heritage's sample mean and standard deviation are

$$\bar{x} = 7.088 \text{ minutes}$$
$$s = 4.64 \text{ minutes}$$

If the managers need a single-valued estimate of the population mean, they would use the point estimate, $\bar{x} = 7.088$ minutes. However, they should realize that this point estimate is subject to sampling error. To take the sampling error into account, the managers can construct a confidence interval estimate. Equation 8.5 shows the formula for the confidence interval estimate for the population mean when the population standard deviation is unknown.

**TABLE 8.3** | **Sample Call Times for Heritage Software**

| | | | | |
|---|---|---|---|---|
| 7.1 | 11.6 | 12.4 | 8.5 | 0.4 |
| 13.6 | 1.7 | 11.0 | 6.1 | 11.0 |
| 1.4 | 16.9 | 3.7 | 3.3 | 0.8 |
| 3.6 | 2.6 | 14.6 | 6.1 | 6.4 |
| 1.9 | 7.7 | 8.8 | 6.9 | 9.1 |

**Chapter Outcome 2.** →

**Confidence Interval Estimate for $\mu$, $\sigma$ Unknown**

$$\bar{x} \pm t\frac{s}{\sqrt{n}} \qquad (8.5)$$

where:

$\bar{x}$ = Sample mean
$t$ = Critical value from the $t$-distribution with $n-1$ degrees of freedom for the desired confidence level
$s$ = Sample standard deviation
$n$ = Sample size

The first step is to specify the desired confidence level. For example, suppose the Heritage team specifies a 95% confidence level. To get the critical $t$-value from the $t$-table in Appendix F, go to the top of the table to the row labeled "Conf. Level." Locate the column headed "0.95." Next, go to the row corresponding to

$$n - 1 = 25 - 1 = 24 \text{ degrees of freedom}$$

The critical $t$-value for 95% confidence and 24 degrees of freedom is

$$t = 2.0639*$$

The Heritage team can now compute the 95% confidence interval estimate using Equation 8.5 as follows:

$$\bar{x} \pm t\frac{s}{\sqrt{n}}$$
$$7.088 \pm 2.0639\frac{4.64}{\sqrt{25}}$$
$$7.088 \pm 1.915$$
$$5.173 \text{ min.} \text{———} 9.003 \text{ min.}$$

---

[2]Chapter 13 introduces a statistical technique called the goodness-of-fit test that can be used to test whether the sample data could have come from a normally distributed population. PHStat and Minitab contain box and whisker plot features, and you could also use Excel or Minitab to construct a histogram.

*You can get the $t$ critical value by using Excel's **TINV** function. For this example, enter **TINV**(0.05,24) to get 2.0639. (*Note:* The **TINV** function requires that $1 -$ confidence level = 0.95 be used, whereas the **NORMSINV** function requires 0.025.) You can also insert the cumulative probability 0.975 into Minitab's **Calc > Probability Distribution > t** command.

**FIGURE 8.6**

Excel 2007 Output for the
Heritage Example

**Excel 2007 Instructions:**
1. Open file: Heritage.xls.
2. Select **Data** tab.
3. Select **Data Analysis**.
4. Select **Descriptive Statistics**.
5. Specify data range for the data.
6. Define **Output Location**.
7. Check **Summary Statistics**.
8. Click **OK**.

Therefore, based on the random sample of 25 calls and the 95% confidence interval, the Heritage Software team has estimated the true average time per call to be between 5.173 minutes and 9.003 minutes.

Excel and Minitab have procedures for computing the confidence interval estimate of the population mean. The Excel output is shown in Figure 8.6. Note, the margin of error is printed. You will have to use it and the sample mean to compute the upper and lower limits. Figure 8.7 shows the results when Minitab is used to compute the 95% confidence interval estimate for the Heritage Company.

**FIGURE 8.7**

Minitab Output for the
Heritage Example

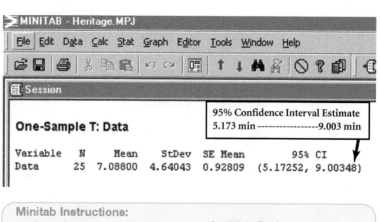

**Minitab Instructions:**
1. Open file: Heritage.MTW.
2. Choose **Stat > Basic Statistics > 1–sample t**.
3. In **Samples in column**, enter data column.
4. Click **Options**.
5. In **Confidence level**, enter confidence level.
6. Click **OK. OK**.

## How to do it (Example 8-3)

**EXAMPLE 8-3**   **CONFIDENCE INTERVAL ESTIMATE FOR $\mu$, $\sigma$ UNKNOWN**

### Confidence Interval Estimates for a Single Population Mean

A confidence interval estimate for a single population mean can be developed using the following steps.

1. Define the population of interest and the variable for which you wish to estimate the population mean.

2. Determine the sample size and select a simple random sample.

3. Compute the confidence interval as follows, depending on the conditions that exist:

   - If $\sigma$ is known, and the population is normally distributed, use

     $$\bar{x} \pm z \frac{\sigma}{\sqrt{n}}$$

   - If $\sigma$ is unknown and we can assume that the population distribution is approximately normal, use

     $$\bar{x} \pm t \frac{s}{\sqrt{n}}$$

**Medlin & Associates** Medlin & Associates is a regional certified public accounting (CPA) firm located near Minneapolis. Recently, a team conducted an audit for a discount chain. One part of the audit involved developing an estimate for the mean dollar error in total charges that occurs during the checkout process. The firm wishes to develop a 90% confidence interval estimate for the population mean. To do so, it can use the following steps:

**Step 1**   **Define the population and select a simple random sample of size $n$ from the population.**

In this case, the population consists of errors made in all customers' bills at the discount chain store in a given week. A simple random sample of $n = 20$ is selected, with the following data. (*Note*: Positive values indicate that the customer was overcharged.)

| $0.00 | $1.20 | $0.43 | $1.00 | $1.47 | $0.83 | $0.50 | $3.34 | $1.58 | $1.46 |
| −$0.36 | −$1.10 | $2.60 | $0.00 | $0.00 | −$1.70 | $0.83 | $1.99 | $0.00 | $1.34 |

**Step 2**   **Specify the confidence level.**

A 90% confidence interval estimate is desired.

**Step 3**   **Compute the sample mean and sample standard deviation.**

After the sample has been selected and the billing errors have been determined for each of the 20 customers sampled, the sample mean is computed using

$$\bar{x} = \frac{\sum x}{n} = \frac{\$15.41}{20} = \$0.77$$

The sample standard deviation is computed using

$$s = \sqrt{\frac{\sum(x - \bar{x})^2}{n-1}} = \sqrt{\frac{(0.00 - 0.77)^2 + (1.20 - 0.77)^2 + \cdots + (1.34 - 0.77)^2}{20 - 1}} = \$1.19$$

**Step 4**   **Determine the standard error of the sampling distribution.**

Because the population standard deviation is unknown, the standard error of the sampling distribution is estimated using

$$\sigma_{\bar{x}} = \frac{s}{\sqrt{n}} = \frac{\$1.19}{\sqrt{20}} = \$0.27$$

**Step 5**   **Determine the critical value for the desired level of confidence.**

Because we do not know the population standard deviation and the sample size is reasonably small, the critical value will come from the $t$-distribution, providing we can assume that the population is normally distributed. A box and whisker plot can give some insight about how the population might look.

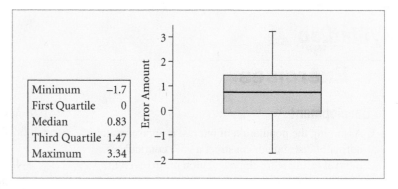

| | |
|---|---|
| Minimum | −1.7 |
| First Quartile | 0 |
| Median | 0.83 |
| Third Quartile | 1.47 |
| Maximum | 3.34 |

This diagram does not indicate that there is any serious skewness or other abnormality in the data, so we will continue with the normal distribution assumption.

The critical value for 90% confidence and $20 - 1 = 19$ degrees of freedom is found in the $t$-distribution table as $t = 1.7291$.

**Step 6  Compute the confidence interval estimate.**
The 90% confidence interval estimate for the population mean is

$$\bar{x} \pm t\frac{s}{\sqrt{n}}$$

$$0.77 \pm 1.7291\frac{1.19}{\sqrt{20}}$$

$$0.77 \pm 0.46$$

$$\$0.31 \text{ ———— } \$1.23$$

Thus, based on the sample data, with 90% confidence, the auditors can conclude that the population mean dollar error at checkout is between $0.31 and $1.23. Since both limits are positive, the auditors should conclude that the clerks overcharge customers on average.

>>**END EXAMPLE**

**TRY PROBLEM** 8-7 (pg. 321)

**Estimation with Larger Sample Sizes**  We saw earlier that a change in sample size can affect the margin of error in a statistical estimation situation when the population standard deviation is known. This is also true in applications in which the standard deviation is not known. In fact, the effect of a change is compounded because the change in sample size affects both the calculation of the standard error and the critical value from the $t$-distribution.

The $t$-distribution table in Appendix F shows degrees of freedom up to 30 and then incrementally to 500. Observe that for any confidence level, as the degrees of freedom increase, the $t$-value gets smaller as it approaches a limit equal to the $z$-value from the standard normal table in Appendix D for the same confidence level. If you need to estimate the population mean with a sample size that is not listed in the $t$-table, you can use the Excel **TINV** function or Minitab's **Calc > Probability Distribution > $t$** command to get the critical $t$-value for any specified degrees of freedom and then use Equation 8.5.

You should have noticed that the format for confidence interval estimates for $\mu$ is essentially the same, regardless of whether the population standard deviation is known. The basic format is

$$\text{Point estimate} \pm (\text{Critical value})(\text{Standard error})$$

Later in this chapter, we introduce estimation examples in which the population value of interest is $\pi$, the population proportion. The same confidence interval format is used. In addition, the trade-offs between margin of error, confidence level, and sample size that were discussed in this section also apply to every other estimation situation.

*MyStatLab*

# 8-1: **Exercises**

## Skill **Development**

**8-1.** Assuming the population of interest is approximately normally distributed, construct a 95% confidence interval estimate for the population mean given the following values:
$$\bar{x} = 18.4 \quad s = 4.2 \quad n = 13$$

**8-2.** Construct a 90% confidence interval estimate for the population mean given the following values:
$$\bar{x} = 70 \quad \sigma = 15 \quad n = 65$$

**8-3.** Construct a 95% confidence interval estimate for the population mean given the following values:
$$\bar{x} = 300 \quad \sigma = 55 \quad n = 250$$

**8-4.** Construct a 98% confidence interval estimate for the population mean given the following values:
$$\bar{x} = 120 \quad \sigma = 20 \quad n = 50$$

**8-5.** Determine the 90% confidence interval estimate for the population mean of a normal distribution given $n = 100$, $\sigma = 121$, and $\bar{x} = 1,200$.

**8-6.** Determine the margin of error for a confidence interval estimate for the population mean of a normal distribution given the following information:
 a. confidence level = 0.98, $n$ = 13, $s$ = 15.68
 b. confidence level = 0.99, $n$ = 25, $\sigma$ = 3.47
 c. confidence level = 0.98, standard error = 2.356

**8-7.** The following sample data have been collected based on a simple random sample from a normally distributed population:

| 2 | 8 | 0 | 2 | 3 |
|---|---|---|---|---|
| 5 | 3 | 1 | 4 | 2 |

 a. Compute a 90% confidence interval estimate for the population mean.
 b. Show what the impact would be if the confidence level is increased to 95%. Discuss why this occurs.

**8-8.** A random sample of size 20 yields $\bar{x}$ = 3.13 and $s^2$ = 1.45. Calculate a confidence interval for the population mean whose confidence level is as follows:
 a. 0.99
 b. 0.98
 c. 0.95
 d. 0.90
 e. 0.80
 f. What assumptions were necessary to establish the validity of the confidence intervals calculated in parts a through e?

**8-9.** A random sample of $n$ = 12 values taken from a normally distributed population resulted in the following sample values:

| 107 | 109 | 99 | 91 | 103 | 105 |
|---|---|---|---|---|---|
| 105 | 94 | 107 | 94 | 97 | 113 |

Use the sample information to construct a 95% confidence interval estimate for the population mean.

**8-10.** A random sample of $n$ = 9 values taken from a normally distributed population with a population variance of 25 resulted in the following sample values:

| 53 | 46 | 55 | 45 | 44 | 52 | 46 | 60 | 49 |
|---|---|---|---|---|---|---|---|---|

Use the sample values to construct a 90% confidence interval estimate for the population mean.

**8-11.** A random sample was selected from a population having a normal distribution. Calculate a 90% confidence interval estimate for $\mu$ for each of the following situations:
 a. $\Sigma x$ = 134, $n$ = 10, $s$ = 3.1
 b. $\Sigma x$ = 3,744, $n$ = 120, $s$ = 8.2
 c. $\Sigma x$ = 40.5, $n$ = 9, $\sigma$ = 2.9
 d. $\Sigma x$ = 585.9, $\Sigma x^2$ = 15,472.37, $n$ = 27 (*Hint*: Refer to Equation 3.13)

## Business Applications

**8-12.** Allante Pizza delivers pizzas throughout its local market area at no charge to the customer. However, customers often tip the driver. The owner is interested in estimating the mean tip income per delivery. To do this, she has selected a simple random sample of 12 deliveries and has recorded the tips that were received by the drivers. These data are

| $2.25 | $2.50 | $2.25 | $2.00 | $2.00 | $1.50 |
|---|---|---|---|---|---|
| $0.00 | $2.00 | $1.50 | $2.00 | $3.00 | $1.50 |

 a. Based on these sample data, what is the best point estimate to use as an estimate of the true mean tip per delivery?
 b. Suppose the owner is interested in developing a 90% confidence interval estimate. Given the fact that the population standard deviation is unknown, what distribution will be used to obtain the critical value?
 c. Referring to part b, what assumption is required to use the specified distribution to obtain the critical value? Develop a box and whisker plot to illustrate whether this assumption seems to be reasonably satisfied.
 d. Referring to parts b and c, construct and interpret the 90% confidence interval estimate for the population mean.

**8-13.** The BelSante Company operates retail pharmacies in 10 Eastern states. Recently, the company's internal audit department selected a random sample of 300 prescriptions issued throughout the system. The objective of the sampling was to estimate the average dollar value of all prescriptions issued by the company. The following data were collected:

$$\bar{x} = \$14.23$$
$$s = 3.00$$

 a. Determine the 90% confidence interval estimate for the true average sales value for prescriptions issued by the company. Interpret the interval estimate.
 b. One of its retail outlets recently reported that it had monthly revenue of $7,392 from 528 prescriptions. Are such results to be expected? Do you believe that the retail outlet should be audited? Support your answer with calculations and logic.

**8-14.** Even before the record gas prices during the summer of 2008, an article written by Will Lester of the Associated Press reported on a poll in which 80% of those surveyed say that Americans who currently own a SUV (sport utility vehicle) should switch to a more fuel-efficient vehicle to ease America's dependency on foreign oil. This study was conducted by the Pew Research Center for the People & the Press. As a follow-up to this report, a consumer group conducted a study of SUV owners to estimate the mean mileage for their vehicles. A simple random sample of 91 SUV owners was selected, and the owners were asked to report their highway mileage. The following results were summarized from the sample data:

$$\bar{x} = 18.2 \text{ mpg}$$
$$s = 6.3 \text{ mpg}$$

Based on these sample data, compute and interpret a 90% confidence interval estimate for the mean highway mileage for SUVs.

**8-15.** According to *USA Today*, customers are not settling for automobiles straight off the production lines. As an example, those who purchase a $355,000 Rolls-Royce typically add $25,000 in accessories. One of the affordable automobiles to receive additions is BMW's Mini Cooper. A sample of 179 recent Mini purchasers yielded a sample mean of $5,000 above the $20,200 base sticker price. Suppose the cost of accessories purchased for all Mini Coopers has a standard deviation of $1,500.

  a. Calculate a 95% confidence interval for the average cost of accessories on Mini Coopers.

  b. Determine the margin of error in estimating the average cost of accessories on Mini Coopers.

  c. What sample size would be required to reduce the margin of error by 50%?

**8-16.** XtraNet, an Internet service provider (ISP), has experienced rapid growth in the past five years. As a part of its marketing strategy, XtraNet promises fast connections and dependable service. To achieve its objectives, XtraNet constantly evaluates the capacity of its servers. One component of its evaluation is an analysis of the average amount of time a customer is connected and using the Internet daily. A random sample of 12 customer records shows the following daily usage times, in minutes:

| 268 | 336 | 296 | 311 | 306 | 335 |
|-----|-----|-----|-----|-----|-----|
| 301 | 278 | 290 | 393 | 373 | 329 |

  a. Using the sample data, compute the best point estimate of the population mean for daily usage times for XtraNet's customers.

  b. The managers of Xtranet's marketing department would like to develop a 99% confidence interval estimate for the population mean daily customer usage time. Because the population standard deviation of daily customer usage time is unknown and the sample size is small, what assumption must the marketing managers make concerning the population of daily customer usage times?

  c. Construct and interpret a 99% confidence interval for the mean daily usage time for XtraNet's customers.

  d. Assume that before the sample was taken, Xtranet's marketing staff believed that mean daily usage for its customers was 267 minutes. Does their assumption concerning mean daily usage seem reasonable based on the confidence interval developed in part c?

**8-17.** In a study conducted by American Express, corporate clients were surveyed to determine the extent to which hotel room rates quoted by central reservation systems differ from the rates negotiated by the companies. The study found that the mean overcharge by hotels was $11.35 per night. Suppose a follow-up study was done in which a random sample of 30 corporate hotel bookings was analyzed. Only those cases where

an error occurred were included in the study. The following data show the amounts by which the quoted rate differs from the negotiated rate. Positive values indicate an overcharge and negative values indicate an undercharge.

| $15.45 | $24.81 | $6.02 | $14.00 | $25.60 | $8.29 |
|--------|--------|-------|--------|--------|-------|
| −$17.34 | −$5.72 | $11.61 | $3.48 | $18.91 | $7.14 |
| $6.64 | $12.48 | $6.31 | −$4.85 | $5.72 | $12.72 |
| $5.23 | $4.57 | $15.84 | $2.09 | −$4.56 | $3.00 |
| $23.60 | $30.86 | $9.25 | $0.93 | $20.73 | $12.45 |

  a. Compute a 95% confidence interval estimate for the mean error in hotel charges. Interpret the confidence interval estimate.

  b. Based on the interval computed in part a, do these sample data tend to support the results of the American Express study? Explain.

**8-18.** A regional U.S. commercial bank issues both Visa credit cards and MasterCard credit cards. As a part of its annual review of the profitability of each type of credit card, the bank randomly samples 36 customers to measure the average annual charges per card. It has completed its analysis of the Visa card accounts and is now focused on its MasterCard customers. A random sample of 36 MasterCard accounts shows the following annual spending per account (rounded to the nearest dollar):

| $2,869 | $3,770 | $2,854 | $2,750 | $2,574 | $2,972 |
|--------|--------|--------|--------|--------|--------|
| $2,549 | $3,267 | $3,013 | $2,707 | $2,794 | $1,189 |
| $2,230 | $2,178 | $3,032 | $3,485 | $2,679 | $2,010 |
| $1,994 | $2,768 | $3,853 | $2,064 | $3,244 | $2,738 |
| $2,807 | $2,395 | $3,405 | $3,006 | $3,368 | $2,691 |
| $1,996 | $3,008 | $2,730 | $2,518 | $2,710 | $3,719 |

  a. Based on these randomly sampled accounts, what is the best point estimate of the true mean annual spending for MasterCard account holders?

  b. If the bank is interested in developing a 95% confidence interval estimate of mean annual spending, what distribution will be used to determine the critical value?

  c. Determine the standard error of the sampling distribution.

  d. Construct the 95% confidence interval estimate for the population mean of annual MasterCard spending for the bank's customers.

  e. If the bank desires to have a higher level of confidence in its interval estimate, what will happen to the margin of error?

**8-19.** Nielsen Media Research reported that the average American home watched more television in 2007 than in any previous season. From September 2006 to September 2007 (the official start and end of television season in the United States), the average time spent by U.S. households tuned into television was 8 hours and

14 minutes per day. This is 13.85% higher than 10 years ago, and the highest levels ever reported since television viewing was first measured by Nielsen Media Research in the 1950s. To determine if television viewing has changed in 2008, a sample (in minutes) similar to the following would be used:

| | | | | | | | | | |
|---|---|---|---|---|---|---|---|---|---|
| 494 | 533 | 597 | 530 | 577 | 514 | 466 | 416 | 403 | 625 |
| 562 | 448 | 592 | 567 | 564 | 537 | 370 | 627 | 416 | 511 |
| 750 | 661 | 570 | 579 | 494 | 533 | 549 | 583 | 610 | 423 |

a. Calculate the sample standard deviation and mean number of minutes spent viewing television.
b. Calculate a 95% confidence interval for the average number of minutes spent viewing television in 2008.
c. Would the results obtained in part b indicate that households viewed more television in 2008 than in 2007?

**8-20.** The concession managers for the Arkansas Travelers (a minor league baseball team located in Little Rock) are interested in estimating the average amount spent on food by fans attending the team's Friday night home games. Suppose a random sample of 36 receipts for food orders was taken from last year's receipts for Friday night home games with the following food expenditures recorded:

| | | | | | |
|---|---|---|---|---|---|
| $30.50 | $10.63 | $3.77 | $21.90 | $21.95 | $9.65 |
| $14.31 | $11.39 | $25.36 | $15.79 | $30.88 | $12.20 |
| $8.48 | $20.70 | $28.54 | $9.13 | $15.54 | $14.95 |
| $11.96 | $11.91 | $8.28 | $12.87 | $24.26 | $21.04 |
| $20.08 | $10.08 | $25.37 | $12.02 | $11.61 | $11.22 |
| $25.36 | $28.07 | $17.71 | $23.00 | $31.79 | $17.70 |

a. Based on the sampled receipts, what is the best point estimate for the mean food expenditures for Friday night home games?
b. Use the sample information to construct a 95% confidence interval estimate for the true mean expenditures for Friday night home games.
c. Before the sample was taken, the food concessions manager stated that mean food expenditures were about $19.00 per order. Does his statement seem consistent with the results obtained in part b?

## Computer Database **Exercises**

**8-21.** Suppose a study of 196 randomly sampled privately insured adults with incomes over 200% of the current poverty level is to be used to measure out-of-pocket medical expenses for prescription drugs for this income class. The sample data are in the file **Drug Expenses**.
a. Based on the sample data, construct a 95% confidence interval estimate for the mean annual out-of-pocket expenditures on prescription drugs for this income class. Interpret this interval.
b. The study's authors hope to use the information to make recommendations concerning insurance reimbursement guidelines and patient copayment recommendations. If the margin of error calculated in part a is considered to be too large for this purpose, what options are available to the study's authors?

**8-22.** One of the reasons for multiple car accidents on highways is thought to be poor visibility. Recently, the National Transportation Agency (NTA) of the federal government sponsored a study of one rural section of highway in Idaho that had been the scene of several multiple car accidents. Two visibility sensors were located near the site for the purposes of recording the number of miles of visibility each time the visibility reading is performed. The two visibility sensors are made by different companies, Scorpion and Vanguard. The NTA would like to develop 95% confidence interval estimates of the mean visibility at this location as recorded by both visibility sensors. The random sample data are in a file called **Visibility**. Also, comment on whether there appears to be a difference between the two sensors in terms of average visibility readings.

**8-23.** The file **German Coffee** contains a random sample of 144 German coffee drinkers and measures the annual coffee consumption in kilograms for each sampled coffee drinker. A marketing research firm wants to use this information to develop an advertising campaign to increase German coffee consumption.
a. Based on the sample's results, what is the best point estimate of average annual coffee consumption for German coffee drinkers?
b. Develop and interpret a 90% confidence interval estimate for the mean annual coffee consumption of German coffee drinkers.

**8-24.** The manager at a new tire and repair shop in Hartford, Connecticut, wants to establish guidelines for the time it should take to put new brakes on vehicles. In particular, he is interested in estimating the mean installation time for brakes for passenger cars and SUVs made by three different manufacturers. To help with this process, he set up an experiment in his shop in which five brake jobs were performed for each manufacturer and each class of vehicle. He recorded the number of minutes that it took to complete the jobs. These data are in a file called **Brake-test** and are also shown as follows:

| | Manufacturer | | |
|---|---|---|---|
| | Company A | Company B | Company C |
| **Passenger Car** | 55 | 68 | 80 |
| | 58 | 49 | 67 |
| | 66 | 78 | 70 |
| | 44 | 60 | 77 |
| | 78 | 72 | 90 |
| **SUV** | 102 | 89 | 119 |
| | 89 | 90 | 102 |
| | 127 | 88 | 98 |
| | 78 | 95 | 80 |
| | 90 | 101 | 106 |

a. Use software such as Excel or Minitab to compute the point estimate for the population mean installation time for each category.

b. Use software such as Excel or Minitab to compute the necessary sample statistics needed to construct 95% confidence interval estimates for the population mean installation times. What assumption is required?

c. Based on the results from part b, what conclusions might you reach about the three companies in terms of the time it takes to install their brakes for passenger cars and for SUVs? Discuss.

8-25. The Transportation Security Administration (TSA) has examined the possibility of a Registered Traveler program. This program is intended to be a way to shorten security lines for "trusted travelers." In a study run at Orlando International Airport, 13,000 people paid an annual $80 fee to participate in the program. They spent an average of four seconds in security lines at Orlando according to Verified Identity Pass, the company that ran the program. For comparison purposes, a sample was obtained of the time it took the other passengers to pass through security at Orlando. The file entitled **PASSTIME** contains these data. Assume the distribution of time required to pass through security at Orlando International Airport

for those flyers in the Registered Traveler program is normally distributed.

a. Calculate the sample mean and the sample standard deviation for this sample of passenger times.

b. Assume that the distribution of time required to pass through security at Orlando International Airport is normally distributed. Use the sample data to construct a 95% confidence interval for the average time required to pass through security.

c. What is the margin of error for the confidence interval constructed in b?

8-26. The per capita consumption of chicken has risen from 28 pounds in 1960 to 90.6 pounds in 2007, according to the U.S. Department of Agriculture. That constitutes an average increase of approximately 1.33 pounds per capita per year. To determine if this trend has continued, in 2008 a random sample of 200 individuals was selected to determine the amount of chicken they consumed in 2008. A file entitled **Chickwt** contains the data.

a. Calculate the mean and standard deviation of the amount of chicken consumed by the individuals in the sample.

b. Calculate a 99% confidence interval for the 2008 per capita consumption of chicken in the United States.

c. Based on your calculation in part b, determine if the specified trend has continued.

**END EXERCISES 8-1**

Chapter Outcome 3. → **8.2** **Determining the Required Sample Size for Estimating a Population Mean**

We have discussed the basic trade-offs that are present in all statistical estimations: The desire is to have a high confidence level, a low margin of error, and a small sample size. The problem is that these three objectives conflict. For a given sample size, a high confidence level will tend to generate a large margin of error. For a given confidence level, a small sample size will result in an increased margin of error. Reducing the margin of error requires either reducing the confidence level or increasing the sample size, or both.

A common question from business decision makers who are planning an estimation application is "How large a sample size do I really need?" To answer this question, we usually begin by asking a couple of questions of our own:

1. How much money do you have budgeted to do the sampling?
2. How much will it cost to select each item in the sample?

The answers to these questions provide the upper limit on the sample size that can be selected. For instance, if the decision maker indicates that she has a $2,000 budget for selecting the sample and the cost will be about $10 per unit to collect the sample, the sample size's upper limit is $2,000 ÷ $10 = 200 units.

Keeping in mind the estimation trade-offs discussed earlier, the issue should be fully discussed with the decision maker. For instance, is a sample of 200 sufficient to give the desired margin of error at a specified confidence level? Is 200 more than is needed to achieve the desired margin of error?

Therefore, before we can give a definite answer about what sample size is needed, the decision maker must specify her confidence level and a desired margin of error. Then the required sample size can be computed.

# Determining the Required Sample Size for Estimating $\mu$, $\sigma$ Known

CALCULATING THE REQUIRED SAMPLE SIZE

**MISSION VALLEY POWER COMPANY** Consider the Mission Valley Power Company (MVP) in northwest Michigan, which has more than 6,000 residential customers. In response to a request by the Michigan Public Utility Commission, MVP needs to estimate the average kilowatts of electricity used by customers on February 1. The only way to get this number is to select a random sample of customers and take a meter reading after 5:00 P.M. on January 31 and again after 5:00 P.M. on February 1. The commission has specified that any estimate presented in the utility's report must be based on a 95% confidence level. Further, the margin of error must not exceed $\pm 30$ kilowatts. Given these requirements, what size sample is needed?

To answer this question, if the population standard deviation is known, we start with Equation 8.3, the equation for calculating the margin of error.

$$e = z\frac{\sigma}{\sqrt{n}}$$

We next substitute into this equation the values we know. For example, the margin of error was specified to be

$$e = 30 \text{ kilowatts}$$

The confidence level was specified to be 95%. The $z$-value for 95% is 1.96. (Refer to the standard normal table in Appendix D.) This gives us

$$30 = 1.96\frac{\sigma}{\sqrt{n}}$$

We need to know the population standard deviation. MVP might know this value from other studies that it has conducted in the past or from similar studies done by other utility companies. Assume for this example that $\sigma$, the population standard deviation, is 200 kilowatts. We can now substitute

$$\sigma = 200$$

into the equation for $e$, as follows:

$$30 = 1.96\frac{200}{\sqrt{n}}$$

We now have a single equation with one unknown, $n$, the sample size. Doing the algebra to solve for $n$, we get

$$n = \left(\frac{1.96(200)}{30}\right)^2 = 170.73 \approx 171 \text{ customers}$$

Thus, to meet the requirements of the utility commission, a sample of $n = 171$ customers should be selected. Equation 8.6 is used to determine the required sample size for estimating a single population mean when $\sigma$ is known.

---

### Sample Size Requirement for Estimating $\mu$, $\sigma$ Known

$$n = \left(\frac{z\sigma}{e}\right)^2 = \frac{z^2\sigma^2}{e^2} \tag{8.6}$$

where:

$z$ = Critical value for the specified confidence level
$e$ = Desired margin of error
$\sigma$ = Population standard deviation

If MVP feels that the cost of sampling 171 customers will be too high, it might appeal to the commission to allow for a higher margin of error or a lower confidence level. For example, if the confidence level is lowered to 90%, the $z$-value is lowered to 1.645, as found in the standard normal table.[3]

We can now use Equation 8.6 to determine the revised sample-size requirement.

$$n = \frac{1.645^2 (200)^2}{30^2} = 120.27 = 121$$

MVP will need to sample only 121 (120.27 rounded up) customers for a confidence level of 90% rather than 95%.

---

| EXAMPLE 8-4 | **DETERMINING THE REQUIRED SAMPLE SIZE, $\sigma$ KNOWN** |

**Dairy Gold Creamery** The general manager for the Dairy Gold Creamery is interested in estimating the mean number of gallons of milk that are purchased by families in the Toledo, Ohio, area. He would like his estimate to be within plus or minus 0.50 gallons per month, and he would like the estimate to be at the 99% confidence level. Past studies have shown that the standard deviation for purchase amount is 4.0 gallons. To determine the required sample size, he can use the following steps:

Step 1    **Specify the desired margin of error.**
The manager wishes to have his estimate be within $\pm 0.50$ gallons, so the margin of error is

$$e = 0.50 \text{ gallons}$$

Step 2    **Determine the population standard deviation.**
Based on other studies, the manager is willing to conclude that the population standard deviation is known. Thus,

$$\sigma = 4.0$$

Step 3    **Determine the critical value for the desired level of confidence.**
The critical value will be a $z$-value from the standard normal table for 99% confidence. This is

$$z = 2.575$$

Step 4    **Compute the required sample size using Equation 8.6.**
The required sample size is

$$n = \frac{z^2 \sigma^2}{e^2} = \frac{2.575^2 4.0^2}{0.50^2} = 424.36 \approx 425 \text{ customers}$$

*Note*: The sample size is always rounded up to the next integer value.

>>**END EXAMPLE**

**TRY PROBLEM** 8-27 (pg. 328)

---

# Determining the Required Sample Size for Estimating $\mu$, $\sigma$ Unknown

Equation 8.6 assumes you know the population standard deviation. Although this may be the case in some situations, most likely we won't know the population standard deviation. To get around this problem, we can use three approaches. One is to use a value for $\sigma$ that is considered to be at least as large as the true $\sigma$. This will provide a conservatively large sample size.

**Pilot Sample**

A sample taken from the population of interest of a size smaller than the anticipated sample size that is used to provide an estimate for the population standard deviation.

The second option is to select a **pilot sample**, a sample from the population that is used explicitly to estimate $\sigma$.

The third option is to use the range of the population to estimate the population's standard deviation. Recall the Empirical Rule in Chapter 3 and the examination in Chapter 6 of

---

[3]You can also use the Excel function, NORMSINV, to determine the $z$-value or Minitab's Calc > Probability Distributions > Normal command.

the normal distribution. Both sources suggest that $\mu \pm 3\sigma$ contains virtually all of the data values of a normal distribution. If this were the case, then $\mu - 3\sigma$ would be approximately the smallest number and $\mu + 3\sigma$ would be approximately the largest number. Remember that the Range = $R$ = Maximum value − Minimum value. So, $R \approx (\mu + 3\sigma) - (\mu - 3\sigma) = 6\sigma$. We can, therefore, obtain an estimate of the standard deviation as

$$\sigma \approx \frac{R}{6}$$

We can also use a procedure that produces a larger estimate of the standard deviation, which will lead to a larger, more conservative sample size. This involves dividing the range by 4 instead of 6.

We seldom know the standard deviation of the population. However, very often we have a very good idea about the largest and smallest value of the population. Therefore, this third method can be used in many instances in which you do not wish to, or cannot, obtain a pilot sample or you are unable to offer a conjecture concerning a conservatively large value of the standard deviation.

---

**EXAMPLE 8-5**    **DETERMINING THE REQUIRED SAMPLE SIZE, $\sigma$ UNKNOWN**

**Jackson's Convenience Stores** Consider a situation in which the regional manager for Jackson's Convenience Stores in Oregon wishes to know the average gallons of gasoline purchased by customers each time they fill up their car. Not only does she not know $\mu$, she also does not know the population standard deviation. She wants a 90% confidence level and is willing to have a margin of error of 0.50 gallons in estimating the true mean gallons purchased. The required sample size can be determined using the following steps.

**Step 1**   **Specify the desired margin of error.**
The manager wants the estimate to be within ±0.50 gallons of the true mean. Thus,
$$e = 0.50$$

**Step 2**   **Determine an estimate for the population standard deviation.**
The manager will select a pilot sample of $n = 20$ fill-ups and record the number of gallons for each. These values are

| 18.9 | 22.4 | 24.6 | 25.7 | 26.3 | 28.4 | 21.7 | 31.0 | 19.0 | 31.7 |
|------|------|------|------|------|------|------|------|------|------|
| 17.4 | 25.5 | 20.1 | 34.3 | 25.9 | 20.3 | 21.6 | 25.8 | 31.6 | 28.8 |

The estimate for the population standard deviation is the sample standard deviation for the pilot sample. This is computed using

$$s = \sqrt{\frac{\sum(x-\overline{x})^2}{n-1}} = \sqrt{\frac{(18.9-25.05)^2 + (22.4-25.05)^2 + \cdots + (28.8-25.05)^2}{20-1}} = 4.85$$

We will use
$$\sigma \approx 4.85$$

**Step 3**   **Determine the critical value for the desired level of confidence.**
The critical value will be a $z$-value from the standard normal table. The 90% confidence level gives
$$z = 1.645$$

**Step 4**   **Calculate the required sample size using Equation 8.6.**
Using the pilot sample's standard deviation the required sample size is
$$n = \frac{z^2\sigma^2}{e^2} = \frac{(1.645^2)(4.85^2)}{0.50^2} = 254.61 = 255$$

The required sample size is 255 fill-ups, but we can use the pilot sample as part of this total. Thus, the net required sample size in this case is $255 - 20 = 235$.

>>**END EXAMPLE**

**TRY PROBLEM** 8-34 (pg. 328)

*MyStatLab*

# 8-2: Exercises

## Skill Development

**8-27.** What sample size is needed to estimate a population mean within ±50 of the true mean value using a confidence level of 95%, if the true population variance is known to be 122,500?

**8-28.** An advertising company wishes to estimate the mean household income for all single working professionals who own a foreign automobile. If the advertising company wants a 90% confidence interval estimate with a margin of error of ±$2,500, what sample size is needed if the population standard deviation is known to be $27,500?

**8-29.** A manager wishes to estimate a population mean using a 95% confidence interval estimate that has a margin of error of ±44.0. If the population standard deviation is thought to be 680, what is the required sample size?

**8-30.** A sample size must be determined for estimating a population mean given that the confidence level is 90% and the desired margin of error is 0.30. The largest value in the population is thought to be 15 and the smallest value is thought to be 5.
   a. Calculate the sample size required to estimate the population using a generously large sample size. (*Hint*: Use the range/4 option.)
   b. If a conservatively small sample size is desired, calculate the required sample size. (*Hint*: Use the range/6 option.) Discuss why the answers in parts a and b are different.

**8-31.** Suppose a study estimated the population mean for a variable of interest using a 99% confidence interval. If the width of the estimated confidence interval (the difference between the upper limit and the lower limit) is 600 and the sample size used in estimating the mean is 1,000, what is the population standard deviation?

**8-32.** Determine the smallest sample size required to estimate the population mean under the following specifications:
   a. $e = 2.4$, confidence level = 80%, data between 50 and 150
   b. $e = 2.4$, confidence level = 90%, data between 50 and 150
   c. $e = 1.2$, confidence level = 90%, data between 50 and 150
   d. $e = 1.2$ confidence level = 90%, data between 25 and 175

**8-33.** Calculate the smallest sample size required to estimate the population mean under the following specifications:
   a. confidence level 95%, $\sigma = 16$, and $e = 4$
   b. confidence level 90%, $\sigma = 23$, and $e = 0.5$
   c. confidence level 99%, $\sigma = 0.5$, and $e = 1$
   d. confidence level 98%, $\sigma = 1.5$, and $e = 0.2$
   e. confidence level 95%, $\sigma = 6$, and $e = 2$

**8-34.** A decision maker is interested in estimating the mean of a population based on a random sample. She wants the confidence level to be 90% and the margin of error to be ±0.30. She does not know what the population standard deviation is, so she has selected the following pilot sample:

| | | | | |
|---|---|---|---|---|
| 8.80 | 4.89 | 10.98 | 15.11 | 14.79 |
| 16.93 | 1.27 | 9.06 | 14.38 | 5.65 |
| 7.24 | 3.24 | 2.61 | 6.09 | 6.91 |

Based on this pilot sample, how many more items must be sampled so that the decision maker can make the desired confidence interval estimate?

## Business Applications

**8-35.** A production process that fills 12-ounce cereal boxes is known to have a population standard deviation of 0.009 ounces. If a consumer protection agency would like to estimate the mean fill, in ounces, for 12-ounce cereal boxes with a confidence level of 92% and a margin of error of 0.001, what size sample must be used?

**8-36.** A public policy research group is conducting a study of health care plans and would like to estimate the average dollars contributed annually to health savings accounts by participating employees. A pilot study conducted a few months earlier indicated that the standard deviation of annual contributions to such plans was $1,225. The research group wants the study's findings to be within $100 of the true mean with a confidence level of 90%. What sample size is required?

**8-37.** With the high cost of fuel and intense competition, the major airline companies have had a very difficult time financially in recent years. Many carriers are now charging for checked bags. One carrier is considering charging a two-tiered rate based on the weight of checked bags. Before deciding at what rate to increase the charge, the airline wishes to estimate the mean weight per bag checked by passengers. It wants the estimate to be within ±0.25 pounds of the true population mean. A pilot sample of bags checked gives the following results:

| | | | | | | | | | |
|---|---|---|---|---|---|---|---|---|---|
| 35 | 33 | 37 | 33 | 36 | 40 | 34 | 40 | 39 | 40 |
| 39 | 41 | 35 | 42 | 43 | 46 | 34 | 41 | 38 | 44 |

   a. What size sample should the airline use if it wants to have 95% confidence?
   b. Suppose the airline managers do not want to take as large a sample as the one you determined in part a. What general options do they have to lower the required sample size?

**8-38.** The Northwest Pacific Phone Company wishes to estimate the average number of minutes its customers spend on long-distance calls per month. The company wants the estimate made with 99% confidence and a margin of error of no more than 5 minutes.

a. A previous study indicated that the standard deviation for long-distance calls is 21 minutes per month. What should the sample size be?

b. Determine the required sample size if the confidence level were changed from 99% to 90%.

c. What would the required sample size be if the confidence level was 95% and the margin of error was 8 minutes?

8-39. An Associated Press article by Eileen Alt Powell discussed the changes that banks are making to the way they calculate the minimum payment due on credit card balances. The changes are being pushed by federal regulators. In the past, minimum payments were set at about 2% of the outstanding balance. Each credit card issuer is making its own changes. For example, Bank of America Corporation in Charlotte, North Carolina, went from a minimum of 2.2% of the balance to a flat amount of $10 plus all fees and interest due.

Suppose that a large California-based bank is in the process of considering what changes to make. It wishes to survey its customers to estimate the mean percent payment on their outstanding balance that customers would like to see. The bank wants to construct a 99% confidence interval estimate with a margin of error of ±0.2 percent. A pilot sample of $n = 50$ customers showed a sample standard deviation of 1.4%.

How many more customers does the bank need to survey in order to construct the interval estimate?

8-40. The Longmont Computer Leasing Company leases computers and peripherals like laser printers. The printers have a counter that keeps track of the number of pages printed. The company wishes to estimate the mean number of pages that will be printed in a month on its leased printers. The plan is to select a random sample of printers and record the number on each printer's counter at the beginning of May. Then, at the end of May, the number on the counter will be recorded again and the difference will be the number of copies on that printer for the month. The company wants the estimate to be within ±100 pages of the true mean with a 95% confidence level.

a. The standard deviation in pages printed is thought to be about 1,400 pages. How many printers should be sampled?

b. Suppose that the conjecture concerning the size of the standard deviation is off (plus or minus) by as much as 10%. What percentage change in the required sample size would this produce?

8-41. The Federal Communications Commission released a report (Leslie Cauley, *USA Today*, "Study: A la Carte Cable Would Be Cheaper," February 10, 2006) refuting an earlier report released in 2004 by the Federal Communications Commission (FCC) under the prior chairman, Michael Powell. The 2006 report indicates that cable subscribers would save as much as 13% on their cable television bills. The average monthly cable prices were estimated to be $41.04. Typically, such reports announce a margin of error of, say, $1.25 and a confidence level of 95%. Suppose the standard deviation of the monthly cost of cable television bills was $10.00.

a. Determine the sample size of the study released by the FCC in 2006.

b. Calculate the sample size required to decrease the margin of error by a dollar.

c. A typical sample size used in national surveys is 1,500 to 2,000. Determine a range for the margin of error corresponding to this range of sample sizes.

8-42. *Business Week* reports that film production companies are gravitating toward Eastern Europe. Studios there have a reputation of skilled technical work at a relatively low cost. But Bulgaria is even cheaper, with costs below those of Hollywood. As an example, weekly soundstage rental prices are quoted as $3.77 per square meter in Bulgaria and $16.50 for its U.S. counterparts. To verify these figures, a sample of 50 rentals was taken, producing the average quoted for Bulgaria.

a. Determine the standard deviation of the weekly rental prices if the margin of error associated with the estimate was $2 using a 95% confidence level.

b. How much would the sample size have to be increased to decrease the margin of error by $1?

c. Calculate the change in the standard deviation that would have to be realized to produce the same decrease in the margin of error as realized in part b.

8-43. A regional chain of fast-food restaurants would like to estimate the mean time required to serve its drive-thru customers. Because speed of service is a critical factor in the success of its restaurants, the chain wants to have as accurate an estimate of the mean service time as possible.

a. If the population standard deviation of service times is known to be 30 seconds, how large a sample must be used to estimate the mean service time for drive-thru customers if a margin of error of no more than ±10 seconds of the true mean with a 99% level of confidence is required?

b. Suppose the manager believes that a margin of error of ±10 seconds is too high and has decided it should be cut in half to a margin of error of ±5 seconds. He is of the opinion that by cutting the margin of error in half, the required sample size will double over what was required for a margin of error of ±10. Is the manager correct concerning the sample-size requirement for the reduced margin of error? (Provide supporting calculations.)

## Computer Database Exercises

8-44. Bruce Leichtman is president of Leichtman Research Group, Inc. (LRG), which specializes in research and consulting on broadband, media, and entertainment industries. In a recent survey, the company determined the cost of extra high-definition (HD) gear needed to watch television in HD. The costs ranged from $5 a month for a set-top box to $200 for a new satellite receiver. The file entitled **HDcosts** contains a sample of the costs of the extras whose purchase is required to watch television in HD.

a. Produce a 95% confidence interval for the population mean cost of the extras whose purchase would be required to watch television in HD.

b. Calculate the margin of error for this experiment.

c. If you were to view the sample used in part a to be a pilot sample, how many additional data values would be required to produce a margin of error of 5? Assume the population standard deviation is 50.353.

**8-45.** Suppose a random sample of 137 households in Detroit was selected to determine the average annual household spending on food at home for Detroit residents. The sample results are contained in the file **Detroit Eats**.

a. Using the sample standard deviation as an estimate for the population standard deviation, calculate the sample size required to estimate the true population mean to within ±$25 with 95% confidence. How many additional samples must be taken?

b. Using the sample standard deviation as an estimate for the population standard deviation, calculate the sample size required to estimate the true population mean to within ±$25 with 90% confidence. How many additional samples must be taken?

**8-46.** The Bureau of Labor Statistics, U.S. Office of Personnel Management, indicated that the average hourly compensation (salary plus benefits) for federal workers (not including military or postal service employees) was $44.82. The rates for private industry and state and local government workers are believed to be considerably less than that. The file entitled **Paychecks** contains a random sample of the hourly amounts paid to state and local government workers.

a. Generate the margin of error for estimating the average hourly amounts paid to state and local government workers with a 98% confidence level.

b. Determine the sample size required to produce a margin of error equal to 1.40 with a confidence level of 98%. Assume the population standard deviation equals 6.22.

c. Does it appear that state and local government workers have a smaller average hourly compensation than federal workers? Support your opinion.

**8-47.** Phone Solutions, Inc., specializes in providing call center services for companies that wish to outsource their call center activities. There are two main ways that Phone Solutions has historically billed its clients: by the call or by the minute. Phone Solutions is currently negotiating with a new client who wants to be billed for the number of minutes that Phone Solutions is on the phone with customers. Before a contract is written, Phone Solutions plans to receive a random sample of calls and keep track of the minutes spent on the phone with the customer. From this it plans to estimate the mean call time. It wishes to develop a 95% confidence interval estimate for the population mean call time and wants this estimate to be within ±0.15 minutes. The question is how many calls should Phone Solutions use in its sample?

Since the population standard deviation is unknown, a pilot sample was taken by having three call centers operated by Phone Solutions each take 50 calls for a total pilot sample of 150 calls. The minutes for each of these calls are listed in the file called **PhoneSolutions**.

a. How many additional calls will be needed to compute the desired confidence interval estimate for the population mean?

b. In the event that the managers at Phone Solutions want a smaller sample size, what options do they have? Discuss in general terms.

**END EXERCISES 8-2**

## 8.3 Estimating a Population Proportion

The previous sections have illustrated the methods for developing confidence interval estimates when the population value of interest is the mean. However, you will encounter many situations in which the value of interest is the proportion of items in the population that possess a particular attribute. For example, you may wish to estimate the proportion of customers who are satisfied with the service provided by your company. The notation for the *population proportion* is $\pi$. The point estimate for $\pi$ is the *sample proportion*, $p$, which is computed using Equation 8.7.

**Sample Proportion**

$$p = \frac{x}{n} \tag{8.7}$$

where:

$p$ = Sample proportion
$x$ = Number of items in the sample with the attribute of interest
$n$ = Sample size

In Chapter 7, we introduced the sampling distribution for proportions. We indicated then that when the sample size is sufficiently large [$n\pi \geq 5$ and $n(1 - \pi) \geq 5$], the sampling distribution can be approximated by a normal distribution centered at $\pi$, with a standard error for $p$ computed using Equation 8.8.

---

**Standard Error for p**

$$\sigma_p = \sqrt{\frac{\pi(1-\pi)}{n}}$$    (8.8)

where:

$\pi$ = Population proportion
$n$ = Sample size

---

Notice that in Equation 8.8, the population proportion, $\pi$, is required. But if we already knew the value for $\pi$, we would not need to determine its estimate. If $\pi$ is unknown, we can estimate the value for the standard error by substituting $p$ for $\pi$, as shown in Equation 8.9, providing that $np \geq 5$ and $n(1 - p) \geq 5$.

---

**Estimate for the Standard Error of p**

$$\sigma_p \approx \sqrt{\frac{p(1-p)}{n}}$$    (8.9)

where:

$p$ = Sample proportion
$n$ = Sample size

---

Figure 8.8 illustrates the sampling distribution for $p$.

**Chapter Outcome 4.** →

# Confidence Interval Estimate for a Population Proportion

The confidence interval estimate for a population proportion is formed using the same general format that we used to estimate a population mean. This was shown originally as Equation 8.1:

Point Estimate $\pm$ (Critical Value)(Standard Error)

Equation 8.10 shows the specific format for *confidence intervals involving population proportions*.

**FIGURE 8.8**

Sample Distribution for *p*

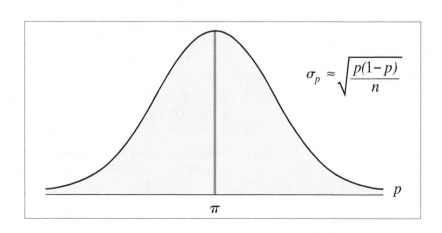

$$\sigma_p \approx \sqrt{\frac{p(1-p)}{n}}$$

---

### Confidence Interval Estimate for $\pi$

$$p \pm z\sqrt{\frac{p(1-p)}{n}} \qquad\qquad (8.10)$$

where:

$p$ = Sample proportion
$n$ = Sample size
$z$ = Critical value from the standard normal distribution for the desired confidence level

---

The critical value for a confidence interval estimate of a population proportion will always be a $z$-value from the standard normal distribution. Recall from Table 8.1 the most commonly used critical values are

| Critical Value | Confidence Level |
|---|---|
| $z = 1.28$ | 80% |
| $z = 1.645$ | 90% |
| $z = 1.96$ | 95% |
| $z = 2.575$ | 99% |

For other confidence levels, you can find the critical $z$-value in the standard normal distribution table in Appendix D.

## How to do it (Example 8-6)

### Developing a Confidence Interval Estimate for a Population Proportion

Here are the steps necessary to develop a confidence interval estimate for a population proportion.

1. Define the population and variable of interest for which to estimate the population proportion.

2. Determine the sample size and select a random sample. Note, the sample must be large enough so that $n\pi \geq 5$ and $n(1 - \pi) \geq 5$.

3. Specify the level of confidence and obtain the critical value from the standard normal distribution table.

4. Calculate $p$, the sample proportion.

5. Construct the interval estimate using Equation 8.10.

$$p \pm z\sqrt{\frac{p(1-p)}{n}}$$

**EXAMPLE 8-6**   **CONFIDENCE INTERVAL FOR A POPULATION PROPORTION**

**Quick Lube** The Quick Lube Company operates a chain of oil-change outlets in several states. When a customer comes in for service, the date of service and the mileage on the car are recorded. A computer program tracks the customers, and when three months have almost passed, a reminder card is sent to the customer.

The marketing manager is interested in estimating the *proportion* of customers who return after getting a card. Of a simple random sample of 100 customers, 62 returned within one month after the card was mailed. A confidence interval estimate for the true population proportion is found using the following steps.

**Step 1** **Define the population and the variable of interest.**
The population is all customers who have their oil changed at Quick Lube, and the variable of interest is the number who respond to a reminder card that is mailed to them.

**Step 2** **Determine the sample size.**
A simple random sample of $n = 100$ customers who receive cards. (Note, as long as $\pi \geq 0.05$ and $\pi \leq 0.95$, a sample size of 100 will meet the requirements that $n\pi \geq 5$ and $n(1 - \pi) \geq 5$.

**Step 3** **Specify the desired level of confidence and determine the critical value.**
Assuming that a 95% confidence level is desired, the critical value from the standard normal distribution table (Appendix D) will be $z = 1.96$.

**Step 4** **Compute the point estimate based on the sample data.**
Equation 8.7 is used to compute the sample proportion.

$$p = \frac{x}{n} = \frac{62}{100} = 0.62$$

**Step 5**  **Compute the confidence interval using Equation 8.10.**
The 95% confidence interval estimate is

$$p \pm z\sqrt{\frac{p(1-p)}{n}}$$

$$0.62 \pm 1.96\sqrt{\frac{0.62(1-0.62)}{100}}$$

$$0.62 \pm 0.095$$

$$0.525 \text{ ——— } 0.715$$

Using the sample of 100 customers and a 95% confidence interval, the manager estimates that the true percentage of customers who will respond to the reminder card will be between 52.5% and 71.5%.

>>**END EXAMPLE**

**TRY PROBLEM** 8-50 (pg. 335)

Chapter Outcome 5. ➞ # Determining the Required Sample Size for Estimating a Population Proportion

Changing the confidence level affects the interval width. Likewise, changing the sample size will affect the interval width. An increase in sample size will reduce the standard error and reduce the interval width. A decrease in the sample size will have the opposite effect. For many applications, decision makers would like to determine a required sample size before doing the sampling. As was the case for estimating the population mean, the required sample size in a proportion application is based on the desired margin of error, the desired confidence level, and the variation in the population. The **margin of error**, $e$, is computed using Equation 8.11.

---

**Margin of Error for Estimating $\pi$**

$$e = z\sqrt{\frac{\pi(1-\pi)}{n}} \tag{8.11}$$

where:

$\pi$ = Population proportion
$z$ = Critical value from standard normal distribution for the desired confidence level
$n$ = Sample size

---

Equation 8.12 is used to determine the required sample size for a given confidence level and margin of error.

---

**Sample Size for Estimating $\pi$**

$$n = \frac{z^2\pi(1-\pi)}{e^2} \tag{8.12}$$

where:

$\pi$ = Value used to represent the population proportion
$e$ = Desired margin of error
$z$ = Critical value from standard normal distribution for the desired confidence level

---

**QUICK LUBE (*CONTINUED*)** Referring to Example 8-6, recall that the marketing manager developed a confidence interval estimate for the proportion of customers who would respond to a reminder card. This interval was

$$0.62 \pm 1.96 \sqrt{\frac{0.62(1-0.62)}{100}}$$

$$0.62 \pm 0.095$$

$$0.525 \text{ ———— } 0.715$$

The calculated margin of error in this situation is 0.095. Suppose the marketing manager wants the margin of error reduced to $e = \pm 0.04$ at a 95% confidence level. This will require an increase in sample size. To apply Equation 8.12, the margin of error and the confidence level are specified by the decision maker. However, the population proportion, $\pi$, is not something you can control. In fact, if you already knew the value for $\pi$, you wouldn't need to estimate it and the sample-size issue wouldn't come up.

Two methods overcome this problem. First, you can select a *pilot sample* and compute the sample proportion, $p$, and substitute $p$ for $\pi$. Then, once the sample size is computed, the pilot sample can be used as part of the overall required sample.

Second, you can select a conservative value for $\pi$. The closer $\pi$ is to 0.50, the greater the variation because $\pi(1 - \pi)$ is greatest when $\pi = 0.50$. If the manager has reason to believe that the population proportion, $\pi$, will be about 0.60, he could use a value for $\pi$ a little closer to 0.50—say, 0.55. If he doesn't have a good idea of what $\pi$ is, he could conservatively use $\pi = 0.50$, which will give a sample size at least large enough to meet requirements.

Suppose the Quick Lube manager selects a pilot sample of $n = 100$ customers and sends these people cards. Further, suppose $x = 62$ of these customers respond to the mailing. Then,

$$p = \frac{62}{100} = 0.62$$

is substituted for $\pi$ in Equation 8.12. For a 95% confidence level, the $z$-value is

$$z = 1.96$$

and the margin of error is equal to

$$e = 0.04$$

Substitute these values into Equation 8.12 and solve for the required sample size.

$$n = \frac{1.96^2 (0.62)(1-0.62)}{0.04^2} = 565.676 = 566$$

Because the pilot sample of 100 can be included, the Quick Lube manager needs to send out an additional 466 cards to randomly selected customers. If this is more than the company can afford or wishes to include in the sample, the margin of error can be increased or the confidence level can be reduced.

**EXAMPLE 8-7**   **SAMPLE SIZE DETERMINATION FOR ESTIMATING $\pi$**

**Naumann Research** The customer account manager for Naumann Research, a marketing research company located in Cincinnati, Ohio, is interested in estimating the proportion of a client's customers who like a new television commercial. She wishes to develop a 90% confidence interval estimate and would like to have the estimate be within $\pm 0.05$ of the true population proportion. To determine the required sample size, she can use the following steps:

**Step 1   Define the population and variable of interest.**
The population is all potential customers in the market area. The variable of interest is the number of customers who like the new television commercial.

**Step 2** **Determine the level of confidence and find the critical z-value using the standard normal distribution table.**

The desired confidence level is 90%. The z-value for 90% confidence is 1.645.

**Step 3** **Determine the desired margin of error.**

The account manager wishes the margin of error to be 0.05.

**Step 4** **Arrive at a value to use for $\pi$.**

Two options can be used to obtain a value for $\pi$:

1. Use a pilot sample and compute $p$, the sample proportion. Use $p$ to approximate $\pi$.
2. Select a value for $\pi$ that is closer to 0.50 than you actually believe the value to be. If you have no idea what $\pi$ might be, use $\pi = 0.50$, which will give the largest possible sample size for the stated confidence level and margin of error.

In this case, suppose the account manager has no idea what $\pi$ is but wants to make sure that her sample is sufficiently large to meet her estimation requirements. Then she will use $\pi = 0.50$.

**Step 5** **Use Equation 8.12 to determine the sample size.**

$$n = \frac{z^2\pi(1-\pi)}{e^2} = \frac{1.645^2(0.50)(1-0.50)}{0.05^2} = 270.0625 = 271$$

The account manager should randomly survey 271 customers. (Always round up.)

>>**END EXAMPLE**

**TRY PROBLEM** 8-49 (pg. 335)

# 8-3: Exercises

## Skill Development

**8-48.** Compute the 90% confidence interval estimate for the population proportion, $\pi$, based on a sample size of 100 when the sample proportion, $p$, is equal to 0.40.

**8-49.** A pilot sample of 75 items was taken, and the number of items with the attribute of interest was found to be 15. How many more items must be sampled to construct a 99% confidence interval estimate for $\pi$ with a 0.025 margin of error?

**8-50.** A decision maker is interested in estimating a population proportion. A sample of size $n = 150$ yields 115 successes. Based on these sample data, construct a 90% confidence interval estimate for the true population proportion.

**8-51.** At issue is the proportion of people in a particular county who do not have health care insurance coverage. A simple random sample of 240 people was asked if they have insurance coverage, and 66 replied that they did not have coverage. Based on these sample data, determine the 95% confidence interval estimate for the population proportion.

**8-52.** A magazine company is planning to survey customers to determine the proportion who will renew their subscription for the coming year. The magazine wants to estimate the population proportion with 95% confidence and a margin of error equal to ±0.02. What sample size is required?

**8-53.** A random sample of size 150 taken from a population yields a proportion equal to 0.35.

a. Determine if the sample size is large enough so that the sampling distribution can be approximated by a normal distribution.

b. Construct a 90% confidence interval for the population proportion.

c. Interpret the confidence interval calculated in part b.

d. Produce the margin of error associated with this confidence interval.

**8-54.** A random sample of 200 items reveals that 144 of the items have the attribute of interest.

a. What is the point estimate for the population proportion for all items having this attribute?

b. Use the information from the random sample to develop a 95% confidence interval estimate for the population proportion, $\pi$, of all items having this attribute of interest.

**8-55.** A random sample of 40 television viewers was asked if they had watched the current week's *Lost* episode. The following data represent their responses:

| | | | | | | | | | |
|---|---|---|---|---|---|---|---|---|---|
| no | no | no | yes | no | no | no | yes | no | yes |
| no | no | no | yes | no | no | no | no | yes | no |
| yes | no | no | no | no | yes | no | no | no | no |
| no | no | no | no | no | no | no | no | no | no |

a. Calculate the proportion of viewers in the sample who indicated they watched the current week's episode of *Lost*.

b. Compute a 95% confidence interval for the proportion of viewers in the sample who indicated they watched the current week's episode of *Lost*.

c. Calculate the smallest sample size that would produce a margin of error of 0.025 if the population proportion is well represented by the sample proportion in part a.

## Business Applications

**8-56.** As the automobile accident rate increases, insurers are forced to increase their premium rates. Companies such as Allstate have recently been running a campaign they hope will result in fewer accidents by their policyholders. For each six-month period that a customer goes without an accident, Allstate will reduce the customer's premium rate by a certain percentage. Companies like Allstate have reason to be concerned about driving habits, based on a survey conducted by Drive for Life, a safety group sponsored by Volvo of North America, in which 1,100 drivers were surveyed. Among those surveyed, 74% said that careless or aggressive driving was the biggest threat on the road. One-third of the respondents said that cell phone usage by other drivers was the driving behavior that annoyed them the most.

Based on these data, assuming that the sample was a simple random sample, construct and interpret a 95% confidence interval estimate for the true proportion in the population of all drivers who are annoyed by cell phone users.

**8-57.** A survey of 499 women for the American Orthopedic Foot and Ankle Society revealed that 38% wear flats to work.

a. Use this sample information to develop a 99% confidence interval for the population proportion of women who wear flats to work.

b. Suppose the society also wishes to estimate the proportion of women who wear athletic shoes to work with a margin of error of 0.01 with 95% confidence. Determine the sample size required.

**8-58.** The television landscape has certainly been changing in recent years as satellite and cable television providers compete for old-line television networks' viewers. In fact, prior to 2005, the networks had lost viewers in the 18–49 age group for over 10 consecutive years, according to a May 2005 article in the *Wall Street Journal* by Brooks Barnes. However, according to the article, in 2005 the networks would post their first gain in viewers. Suppose that CBS plans to conduct interviews with television viewers in an attempt to estimate the proportion of viewers in the 18–49 age group who watch "most" of their television on network television as opposed to cable or satellite. CBS wishes to have 95% confidence and a margin of error in its estimate of ±0.03. A pilot sample of size 50 was selected, and the sample proportion was 0.61. To achieve these results with a simple random sample, how many additional viewers should be sampled?

**8-59.** Most major airlines allow passengers to carry two pieces of luggage (of a certain maximum size) onto the plane. However, their studies show that the more carry-on baggage passengers have, the longer it takes to unload and load passengers. One regional airline is considering changing its policy to allow only one carry-on per passenger. Before doing so, it decided to collect some data. Specifically, a random sample of 1,000 passengers was selected. The passengers were observed, and the number of bags carried on the plane was noted. Out of the 1,000 passengers, 345 had more than one bag.

a. Based on this sample, develop and interpret a 95% confidence interval estimate for the proportion of the traveling population that would have been impacted had the one-bag limit been in effect. Discuss your result.

b. The domestic version of Boeing's 747 has a capacity for 568 passengers. Determine an interval estimate of the number of passengers that you would expect to carry more than one piece of luggage on the plane. Assume the plane is at its passenger capacity.

c. Suppose the airline also noted whether the passenger was male or female. Out of the 1,000 passengers observed, 690 were males. Of this group, 280 had more than one bag. Using this data, obtain and interpret a 95% confidence interval estimate for the proportion of male passengers in the population who would have been affected by the one-bag limit. Discuss.

d. Suppose the airline decides to conduct a survey of its customers to determine their opinion of the proposed one-bag limit. The plan calls for a random sample of customers on different flights to be given a short written survey to complete during the flight. One key question on the survey will be: "Do you approve of limiting the number of carry-on bags to a maximum of one bag?" Airline managers expect that only about 15% will say "yes." Based on this assumption, what size sample should the airline take if it wants to develop a 95% confidence interval estimate for the population proportion who will say "yes" with a margin of error of ±0.02?

**8-60.** Suppose the Akron Chamber of Commerce has decided to conduct a survey to estimate the proportion of adults between the ages of 25 and 35 living in the metropolitan area who have a college degree in a high-technology field. The chamber hopes to use the survey's results to attract more high-technology firms to the region. The chamber wants the survey to estimate the population proportion within a margin of error of 0.03 percentage points with a level of confidence of 95%.

    a. If the chamber has no information concerning the proportion of adults between the ages of 25 and 35 who have a college degree in a high-technology field before the survey is taken, how large a sample size must be used?

    b. Suppose the chamber conducted a pilot study of 200 adults between the ages of 25 and 35 that indicated 28 with the desired attribute. How large a sample would be needed for the survey to estimate the population proportion within a margin of error of $\pm 0.03$ with a 95% level of confidence?

**8-61.** An Associated Press article written by Rukmini Callimachi pointed out that Nike, the world's largest maker of athletic shoes, has started to feature female models who are not the traditional rail-thin women who have graced billboards and magazine covers for the last 20–25 years. These new models, called "real people," may be larger than the former models, but they are still very athletic and represent what Nike spokeswoman Caren Ball calls "what is real" as opposed to "what is ideal." The article also reports on a survey of 1,000 women conducted by *Allure* magazine in which 91% of the respondents said they were satisfied with what they see in the mirror. Nike managers would like to use these data to develop a 90% confidence interval estimate for the true proportion of all women who are satisfied with their bodies. Develop and interpret the 90% confidence interval estimate.

**8-62.** A multinational corporation employing several thousand workers at its campus in a large city in the southwestern United States would like to estimate the proportion of its employees who commute to work by any means other than an automobile. The company hopes to use the information to develop a proposal to encourage more employees to forgo their automobiles as a part of their commute. A pilot study of 100 randomly sampled employees found that 14 commute to work by means other than an automobile.

    a. How many more employees must the company randomly sample to be able to estimate the true population of employees who commute to work by means other than an automobile with a margin of error of $\pm 0.03$ and a level of confidence of 90%?

    b. Suppose that after the full sample is taken it was found that 50 employees commute to work by means other than an automobile. Construct a 90% confidence interval estimate for the true population of employees who commute to work using means other than an automobile. (*Hint*: Your sample size will be the total sample size required for part a.)

**8-63.** A survey of 777 teenagers between the ages of 13 and 18 conducted by JA Worldwide/Deloitte & Touche USA LLP found that 69% agree that people who practice good business ethics are more successful than those who do not.

    a. Calculate the 90% confidence interval estimate for the true population proportion, $\pi$, given the survey information.

    b. What is the largest possible sample size needed to estimate the true population proportion, $\pi$, within a margin of error of $\pm 0.02$ with a confidence level of 95% if there was no prior knowledge concerning the proportion of respondents who would agree with the survey's question?

    c. If the survey in part a had a margin of error of $\pm 0.04$ percentage points, determine the level of confidence that was used in estimating the population proportion if there was no prior knowledge concerning the percentage of teenagers who would respond as they did.

**8-64.** The MainStay Investments of New York Life Investment Management survey of respondents between the ages of 26 to 82 indicated that 66% of seniors, 61% of baby boomers, and 58% of Generation X expect IRAs to be their primary source of income in retirement. The margin of error was given as $\pm 5$ percentage points.

    a. Calculate a 95% confidence interval for the proportion of seniors who expect IRAs to be their primary source of income in retirement.

    b. Although the sample size for the entire survey was listed, the sample size for each of the three generations was not given. Assuming the confidence level was 95%, determine the sample size for each of the three generations.

**8-65.** A report released by the College Board asserted the percentage of students who took and passed Advanced Placement (AP) courses in all subjects has increased in every state and the District of Columbia since 2000. Among public school students, 14.1% earned a passing grade on at least one AP exam, the report indicated. In an attempt to determine if the proportion of those passing the math and science AP exams is equal to the 14.1% success rate, a random sample of 300 students enrolled in AP math and science classes has been selected.

    a. If 35 of the students in the sample passed at least one AP math or science exam, calculate the proportion of those students who passed at least one AP math or science exam. Does this statistic indicate that the proportion of students who pass at least one AP math or science exam is less than that of those taking AP exams as a whole? Support your assertions.

    b. Calculate the probability that a sample proportion equal to or less than that calculated in part a would

occur if the population proportion was actually
0.141. Answer the question posed in part a using
this probability.

c. Calculate a 98% confidence interval for the
proportion of those students who passed at least one
AP math or science exam. Answer the question
posed in part a using this confidence interval. Does
this answer correspond to that of part b? Support
your assertions.

## Computer Database **Exercises**

**8-66.** According to the Employee Benefit Research Institute
(www.ebri.org) 34% of workers between the ages of
35 and 44 owned a 401(k)-type retirement plan. Suppose
a recent survey was conducted by the Atlanta Chamber
of Commerce to determine the participation rate of 35-
to 44-year-old working adults in the Atlanta metropolitan
area in 401(k)-type retirement plans. The Atlanta
survey randomly sampled 144 working adults in
Atlanta between the ages of 35 and 44. The results of
the survey can be found in the file **Atlanta Retirement**.

a. Use the information in the file **Atlanta Retirement**
to compute a 95% confidence interval estimate
for the true population proportion of working
adults in Atlanta between the ages of 35 and 44 in
401(k)-type retirement plans.

b. Based on the confidence interval calculated in part a,
can the Atlanta Chamber of Commerce advertise
that a greater percentage of working adults in
Atlanta between the ages of 35 and 44 have 401(k)
plans than in the nation as a whole for the same age
group? Support your answer with the confidence
level you calculated above.

**8-67.** A study by the Investment Company Institute (ICI),
which randomly surveyed 3,500 households and drew
on information from the Internal Revenue Service,
found that 72% of households have conducted at least
one IRA rollover from an employer-sponsored
retirement plan (www.financial-planning.com).
Suppose a recent random sample of 90 households in
the greater Miami area was taken and respondents were
asked whether they had ever funded an IRA account
with a rollover from an employer-sponsored retirement
plan. The results are in the file **Miami Rollover**.

a. Based on the random sample of Miami households,
what is the best point estimate for the proportion of
all Miami households that have ever funded an IRA
account with a rollover from an employer-sponsored
retirement plan?

b. Construct a 99% confidence interval estimate for
the true population proportion of Miami households
that had ever funded an IRA account with a rollover
from an employer-sponsored retirement plan.

c. If the sponsors of the Miami study found that the
margin of error was too high, what could they do to
reduce it if they were not willing to change the level
of confidence?

**8-68.** Neverslip, Inc., produces belts for industrial use. As
part of its continuous process improvement program,
Neverslip has decided to monitor on-time shipments
of its products. Suppose a random sample of 140
shipments was taken from shipping records for the last
quarter and the shipment was recorded as being either
"on-time" or "late." The results of the sample are
contained in the file **Neverslip**.

a. Using the randomly sampled data, calculate a 90%
confidence interval estimate for the true population
proportion, $\pi$, for on-time shipments for Neverslip.

b. What is the margin of error for the confidence
interval calculated in part a?

c. One of Neverslip's commitments to its customers is
that 95% of all shipments will arrive on time. Based
on the confidence interval calculated in part a, is
Neverslip meeting its on-time commitment?

**8-69.** A survey by Frank N. Magid Associates Inc. concluded
that men, of any age, are twice as likely as women to
play console video games. The survey was based on a
sample of men and women ages 12 and older. A file
entitled **Gameboys** contains responses that would
result in the findings obtained by Magid Associates
for the 18- to 34-year-old age group.

a. Calculate a 99% confidence interval for both the
male and female responses.

b. Using the confidence intervals in part a, provide the
minimum and maximum ratio of the population
proportions.

c. Does your analysis in parts a and b substantiate the
statement that men in this age group are twice as
likely to play console video games? Support your
assertions.

**8-70.** The Emerging Workforce Study conducted by Harris
Interactive on behalf of Spherion, a leader in providing value-added staffing, recruiting, and workforce
solutions, utilized a random sample of 502 senior
human resources executives. The survey asked which
methods the executives felt led them to find their best
candidates. The file entitled **Referrals** contains the
responses indicating those that chose "referrals" as
their best method.

a. Determine the margin of error that would accrue
with a confidence level of 95%.

b. Calculate a 95% confidence interval for the
proportion of executives who chose "referrals"
as their best method.

c. Determine the sample size required to decrease the
margin of error by 25%.

# Visual Summary

**Chapter 8:** In many business situations decision makers need to know a population parameter. Unfortunately, if not impossible, gaining access to an entire population may be too time consuming and expensive to be feasible. In such situations decision makers will select a sample and use the sample data to compute a statistic that estimates the population parameter of interest. The decision maker needs to use procedures that ensure the sample will be large enough to provide valid estimates of the population parameter and needs to be confident that the estimate matches the population parameter of interest.

## 8.1 Point and Confidence Interval Estimates for a Population Mean (pg. 306–324)

### Summary

Whenever it is impossible to know the true population parameter, decision makers will rely on a point estimate. A point estimate is a single statistic, determined from a sample that is used to estimate the corresponding population parameter. Point estimates are subject to sampling error, which is the difference between a statistic and the corresponding population parameter. Sampling error cannot be eliminated, but it can be managed in the decision-making process by calculating a confidence interval. A confidence interval is an interval developed from sample values such that if all possible intervals of a given width are constructed, a percentage of these intervals, known as the confidence level, would include the true population parameter. A confidence interval can be calculated using the general format below:

> Point estimate ± (Critical value) (Standard error)

The size of the sample and the confidence level chosen will have an impact on the interval estimate. The point estimate depends on the parameter being estimated. The critical value depends on the parameter being estimated and, for example, in the case where the population mean is being estimated, whether the population standard deviation is known or not. The standard error measures the spread of the sampling distribution. The amount that is added to and subtracted from the point estimate to determine the endpoints of the confidence interval is referred to as the margin of error. Lowering the confidence level is one way to reduce the margin of error. The margin of error can also be reduced by increasing the sample size.

When estimating a population mean it is necessary to distinguish between those cases where the population standard deviation is known and those cases where it is not known. When the population standard deviation is known the population mean is estimated using a critical value from the standard normal table for a specified confidence interval. When the population standard deviation is not known, the critical value is a $t$-value taken from a family of distributions called the Student's $t$-distributions. The specific $t$-distribution chosen depends on the number of independent data values available to estimate the population's standard deviation; a value known as the degrees of freedom.

> **Outcome 1.** Distinguish between a point estimate and a confidence interval estimate.
> **Outcome 2.** Construct and interpret a confidence interval estimate for a single population mean using both the standard normal and $t$ distributions.

## 8.2 Determining the Required Sample Size for Estimating a Population Mean (pg. 324–330)

### Summary

A common question asked by decision makers who are conducting an estimation of a population parameter is "How large a sample size do I need?" The answer to this question depends on the resources available for sampling and the cost to select and measure each item sampled. The answers to these two questions will provide an upper limit on the sample size that can be selected. Before a definitive answer regarding the sample size can be given the decision maker must also specify the confidence level and the desired margin of error. If the population standard deviation is unknown one option may be to select a **pilot sample**—a sample taken from the population of interest of a size smaller than the anticipated sample size used to provide an estimate of the population standard deviation.

> **Outcome 3.** Determine the required sample size for estimating a single population mean

## 8.3 Estimating a Population Proportion (pg. 330–338)

### Summary

In many situations the objective of sampling will be to estimate a population proportion. The confidence interval estimate for a **population proportion** is formed using the same general format to estimate a population mean:

Point Estimate ± (Critical Value) (Standard Error)

The critical value for a confidence interval estimate of a population proportion will always be a z-value from the standard normal distribution. Changing the confidence level affects the interval width. Likewise, changing the sample size will affect the interval width. An increase in the sample size will reduce the standard error and reduce the interval width. As was the case for estimating the population mean the required sample size for estimating a population proportion is based on the desired **margin of error**.

> **Outcome 4.** Establish and interpret a confidence interval estimate for a single population proportion
> **Outcome 5.** Determine the required sample size for estimating a single population proportion

### Conclusion

Many decision-making applications require that a decision be based on a sample which is used to estimate a population parameter. There are two types of estimates: point estimates and interval estimates. Point estimates are subject to potential sampling error. Point estimates are almost always different from the population value. A confidence interval estimate takes into account the potential for sampling error and provides a range within which we believe the true population value falls. The general format for all confidence interval estimates is:

Point Estimate ± (Critical Value) (Standard Error)

The point estimate falls in the center of the interval. The amount that is added and subtracted from the point estimate is called the margin of error. While the format stays the same, there are differences in the formulas used depending on what population value is being estimated and certain other conditions. **Figure 8-9** provides a useful flow diagram for the alternative confidence interval estimations discussed in the chapter.

**FIGURE 8.9** |

Flow Diagram for Confidence
Interval Estimation
Alternatives

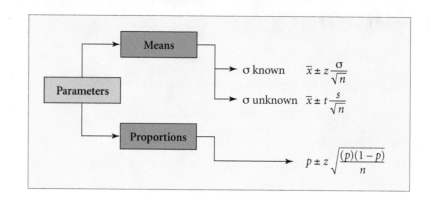

# Equations

**(8.1) Confidence Interval General Format** pg. 309

Point estimate $\pm$ (Critical value)(Standard error)

**(8.2) Confidence Interval Estimate for $\mu$, $\sigma$ Known** pg. 310

$$\bar{x} \pm z \frac{\sigma}{\sqrt{n}}$$

**(8.3) Margin of Error for Estimating $\mu$, $\sigma$ Known** pg. 312

$$e = z \frac{\sigma}{\sqrt{n}}$$

**(8.4) $t$-Value for $\bar{x}$** pg. 315

$$t = \frac{\bar{x} - \mu}{\frac{s}{\sqrt{n}}}$$

**(8.5) Confidence Interval Estimate for $\mu$, $\sigma$ Unknown** pg. 317

$$\bar{x} \pm t \frac{s}{\sqrt{n}}$$

**(8.6) Sample Size Requirement for Estimating $\mu$, $\sigma$ Known** pg. 325

$$n = \left(\frac{z\sigma}{e}\right)^2 = \frac{z^2\sigma^2}{e^2}$$

**(8.7) Sample Proportion** pg. 330

$$p = \frac{x}{n}$$

**(8.8) Standard Error for $p$** pg. 331

$$\sigma_p = \sqrt{\frac{\pi(1-\pi)}{n}}$$

**(8.9) Estimate for the Standard Error of $p$** pg. 331

$$\sigma_p \approx \sqrt{\frac{p(1-p)}{n}}$$

**(8.10) Confidence Interval Estimate for $\pi$** pg. 332

$$p \pm z \sqrt{\frac{p(1-p)}{n}}$$

**(8.11) Margin of Error for Estimating $\pi$** pg. 333

$$e = z\sqrt{\frac{\pi(1-\pi)}{n}}$$

**(8.12) Sample Size for Estimating $\pi$** pg. 333

$$n = \frac{z^2\pi(1-\pi)}{e^2}$$

# Key Terms

Confidence interval pg. 306
Confidence level pg. 309
Degrees of freedom pg. 315

Margin of error pg. 311
Pilot sample pg. 326
Point estimate pg. 306

Sampling error pg. 306
Standard error pg. 308
Student's $t$-distributions pg. 314

# Chapter Exercises

## Conceptual Questions

**8-71.** Explain why the critical value for a given confidence
level when the population variance is not known
is always greater than the critical value for the
same confidence level when the population variance
is known.

**8-72.** When we need to estimate the population mean, and
the population standard deviation is unknown, we are

hit with a "double whammy" when it comes to the margin of error. Explain what the "double whammy" is and why it occurs. (*Hint*: Consider the sources of variation in the margin of error.)

8-73. An insurance company in Iowa recently conducted a survey of its automobile policy customers to estimate the mean miles these customers commute to work each day. The result based on a random sample of 300 policyholders indicated the population mean was between 3.5 and 6.7 miles. This interval estimate was constructed using 95% confidence.

After receiving this result, one of the managers was overheard telling a colleague that 95% of all customers commute between 3.5 and 6.7 miles to work each day. How would you respond to this statement? Is it correct? Why or why not? Discuss.

8-74. Examine the equation for the margin of error when estimating a population mean

$$e = z\frac{\sigma}{\sqrt{n}}$$

Indicate the effect on the margin of error resulting from an increase in each of the following items:
a. confidence level
b. *z*-value
c. standard deviation
d. sample size
e. standard error

## Business Applications

8-75. A random sample of 441 shoppers revealed that 76% made at least one purchase at a discount store last month.
a. Based on this sample information, what is the 90% confidence interval for the population proportion of shoppers who made at least one discount store purchase last month?
b. The city of San Luis Obispo, California, has a population of 35,000 people. Referring to part a, determine a 90% confidence interval for the number of shoppers who made at least one discount store purchase last month.

8-76. According to an investigative reporter (Jim Drinkard, "Legislators Want to Ground 'Fact-Finding' Trips," *USA Today*, January 19, 2006), members of Congress are coming under scrutiny for "fact-finding" trips. Since 2000, members of Congress have made 6,666 trips paid for by private interests. The trips were worth about $19.6 million.
a. Calculate the average cost of these fact-finding trips.
b. If the cost of the trips could be considered to have a normal distribution, determine the standard deviation of the cost of the trips. (*Hint*: Recall the Empirical Rule.)
c. Choose a reasonable confidence level and calculate a confidence interval for the average cost of

congressional fact-finding trips from the year 2000 until January 19, 2006.

8-77. Arco Manufacturing makes electronic pagers. As part of its quality efforts, the company wishes to estimate the mean number of days the pager is used before repair is needed. A pilot sample of 40 pagers indicates a sample standard deviation of 200 days. The company wishes its estimate to have a margin of error of no more than 50 days, and the confidence level must be 95%.
a. Given this information, how many additional pagers should be sampled?
b. The pilot study was initiated because of the costs involved in sampling. Each sampled observation costs approximately $10 to obtain. Originally, it was thought that the population's standard deviation might be as large as 300. Determine the amount of money saved by obtaining the pilot sample. (*Hint*: Determine the total cost of obtaining the required samples for both methods.)

8-78. A random sample of 25 sport utility vehicles (SUVs) of the same year and model revealed the following miles per gallon (mpg) values:

| | | | | |
|------|-------|-------|------|------|
| 12.4 | 13.0  | 12.6  | 12.1 | 13.1 |
| 13.0 | 12.0  | 13.1  | 11.4 | 12.6 |
| 9.5  | 13.25 | 12.4  | 10.7 | 11.7 |
| 10.0 | 14.0  | 10.9  | 9.9  | 10.2 |
| 11.0 | 11.9  | 9.9   | 12.0 | 11.3 |

Assume that the population for mpg for this model year is normally distributed.
a. Use the sample results to develop a 95% confidence interval estimate for the population mean miles per gallon.
b. Determine the average number of gallons of gasoline the SUVs described here would use to travel between Los Angeles and San Francisco— a distance of approximately 400 miles.
c. Another sample of the same size is to be obtained. If you know that the average miles per gallon in the second sample will be larger than the one obtained in part a, determine the probability that the sample mean will be larger than the upper confidence limit of the confidence interval you calculated.

8-79. In an article entitled "Airport Screeners' Strains, Sprains Highest among Workers," Thomas Frank reported that the injury rate for airport screeners was 29%, far exceeding the 4.5% injury rate for the rest of the federal workforce. The 48,000 full- and part-time screeners were reported to have missed nearly a quarter-million days because of injuries in the recent fiscal year.
a. Calculate the average number of days missed by airport screeners.
b. If one were to estimate the average number of days missed to within 1 hour in 2006 with a confidence level of 90%, determine the smallest sample size

that would be required. Assume the standard deviation of the number of days missed is 1.5 days and that a work day consists of 8 hours.

c. How close could the estimate get if a sample of size 100 was used?

## Computer Database **Exercises**

**8-80.** On its first day on the stock market, the Chinese Internet search engine, Baidu, increased its share price from $27.00 to $122.54, an increase of 354%. This was larger than any other Chinese initial public offering (IPO) and the second biggest for a foreign IPO. However, of the nine other biggest foreign IPOs with the largest first-day gains, all are trading below their IPO prices by an average of 88%. To determine the relationship between the IPOs with the largest first-day gains and the other IPOs, a sample might be taken to determine the average percentage decrease in the share prices of those IPOs not in the group of the nine IPOs with the largest first-day gains. A file entitled **BigIPO$** contains such a sample. Note that an increase in share prices is represented as a negative decrease.

a. Calculate a 95% confidence interval for the average percentage decrease after the first-day offering in the share of those IPOs not in the 9 IPOs with the largest first-day gains.

b. Does it appear that there is a difference in the average percentage decrease in the share prices of the two groups? Support your assertions.

**8-81.** The Future-Vision Company is considering applying for a franchise to market satellite television dish systems in a Florida market area. As part of the company's research into this opportunity, staff in the new acquisitions department conducted a survey of 548 homes selected at random in the market area. They asked a number of questions on the survey. The data for some of the variables are in a file called **Future-Vision**. One key question asked whether the household was currently connected to cable TV.

a. Using the sample information, what is the 95% confidence interval estimate for the true proportion of households in the market area that subscribe to cable television?

b. Based on the sample data, develop a 95% confidence interval estimate for the mean income and interpret this estimate.

**8-82.** The quality manager for a major automobile manufacturer is interested in estimating the mean number of paint defects in cars produced by the company. She wishes to have her estimate be within $\pm 0.10$ of the true mean and wants 98% confidence in the estimate. The file called **CarPaint** contains data from a pilot sample that was conducted for the purpose of determining a value to use for the population standard deviation. How many additional cars need to be sampled to provide the estimate required by the quality manager?

**8-83.** The NPD Group recently released its annual U.S. Video Game Industry Retail Sales Report. The report contained the NPD Group's selection of the top 10 video games based on units sold. The top-selling video game was *Madden NFL*, published by Electronic Arts. The average retail price for this video game last year was $46. The file entitled **Madden** contains a sample of the current retail prices paid for *Madden NFL*.

a. Calculate a 95% confidence interval for the current average retail price paid for *Madden NFL*.

b. On the basis of the confidence interval constructed in part a, does it seem likely that the average retail price for *Madden NFL* has decreased? Explain.

c. What sample size would be required to generate a margin of error of $1?

**8-84.** The Jordeen Bottling Company recently did an extensive sampling of its soft-drink inventory in which 5,000 cans were sampled. Employees weighed each can and used these weights to determine the fluid ounces in the cans. The data are in a file called **Jordeen**. Based on this sample data, should the company conclude that the mean volume is 12 ounces? Base your conclusion on a 95% confidence interval estimate and discuss.

**8-85.** Paper-R-Us is a national distributor of printer and copier paper for commercial use. The data file called **Sales** contains the annual, year-to-date sales values for each of the company's customers. Suppose the internal audit department has decided to audit a sample of these accounts. Specifically, they have decided to sample 36 accounts. However, before they actually conduct the in-depth audit (a process that involves tracking all transactions for each sampled account), they want to be sure that the sample they have selected is representative of the population.

a. Compute the population mean.

b. Use all the data in the population to develop a frequency distribution and histogram.

c. Calculate the proportion of accounts for customers in each region of the country.

d. Select a random sample of accounts. Develop a frequency distribution for these sample data. Compare this distribution to that of the population. (*Hint*: You might want to consider using relative frequencies for comparison purposes.)

e. Construct a 95% confidence interval estimate for the population mean sales per customer. Discuss how you would use this interval estimate to help determine whether the sample is a good representation of the population. (*Hint*: You may want to use the finite population correction factor since the sample is large relative to the size of the population.)

f. Use the information developed in parts a–e to draw a conclusion about whether the sample is a representative sample of the population. What other information would be desirable? Discuss.

# Video Case 4

## New Product Introductions @ McDonald's

New product ideas are a staple of our culture. Just take a look around you—how many billboards or television commercials can you count with new products or services? So, where do those ideas come from? If you're a company like McDonald's, the ideas don't come out of thin air. Instead, they're the result of careful monitoring of consumer preferences, trends, and tastes.

McDonald's menu is a good example of how consumer preferences have affected change in food offerings. What used to be a fairly limited lunch and dinner menu consisting of burgers, shakes, and fries has now become incredibly diverse. The Big Mac came along in 1968, and Happy Meals were introduced in 1979. Breakfast now accounts for nearly 30% of business in the United States, and chicken offerings comprise 30% of menu choices. Healthy offerings such as apple dippers, milk jugs, and fruit and yogurt parfaits are huge sellers. The company now rolls out at least three new products a year. Wade Thomas, VP U.S. Menu Management, leads the team behind most of today's menu options. He meets regularly with Chef Dan, the company's executive chef, to give the chef's team some idea anchor points with which to play.

When the chef's team is through playing with the concept, Wade's Menu Management team holds what they call a "rally." At a rally, numerous food concepts developed by Chef Dan's team are presented, tasted, discussed, and voted on. The winners move on to focus group testing. The focus groups are a huge source of the external data that helps the Menu Management team with its decision on whether to introduce a product. If a product scores 8 out of 10 on a variety of rankings, the idea moves forward.

The real test begins in the field. Wade and his team need to determine if the new product idea can actually be executed consistently in the restaurants. Data collected from the company's partnership with its owner/operators and suppliers is key. If a product takes five seconds too long to make or if the equipment doesn't fit into existing kitchen configurations, its chances of implementation are low, even though consumer focus groups indicated a high probability of success.

Throughout the idea development process, various statistical methods are used to analyze the data collected. The data are handed over to the company's U.S. Consumer and Business Insights team

for conversion into meaningful information the menu management team can use. At each step along the way, the statistical analyses are used to decide whether to move to the next step. The recent introduction of the new Asian chicken salad is a good example of a recent new product offering that made it all the way to market. Analysis was performed on data collected in focus groups and eventually revealed the Asian salad met all the statistical hurdles for the salad to move forward.

Data collection and statistical analysis don't stop when the new products hit the market. Wade Thomas's team and the McDonald's U.S. Consumer and Business Insights group continue to forecast and monitor sales, the ingredient supply chain, customer preferences, competitive reactions, and more. As for the new Asian salad, time will tell just how successful it will become. But you can be sure techniques such as statistical estimation will be used to analyze it!

### Discussion Questions:

1. During the past year, McDonald's introduced a new dessert product into its European market area. This product had already passed all the internal hurdles described in this case, including the focus group analysis and the operations analysis. The next step was to see how well the product would be received in the marketplace. In particular, McDonald's managers are interested in estimating the mean number of orders for this dessert per 1,000 customer transactions. A random sample of 142 stores throughout Europe was selected. Store managers tracked the number of dessert orders per 1,000 transactions during a two-week trial period. These sample data are in the data file called **McDonald's New Product Introduction**. Based on these sample data, construct and interpret a 95% confidence interval estimate for mean number of dessert orders per 1,000 orders.

2. Referring to question 1, suppose that Wade Thomas and his group are not happy with the margin of error associated with the confidence interval estimate and want the margin of error to be no greater than $\pm 3$ dessert orders per 1,000 customer orders. To meet this objective, how many more stores should be included in the sample? Alternatively, if the managers don't wish to increase the sample size, what other option is available to reduce the margin of error? Discuss the pros and cons of both approaches.

# Case 8.1

## Management Solutions, Inc.

The round trip to the "site" was just under 360 miles, which gave Fred Kitchener and Mike Kyte plenty of time to discuss the next steps in the project. The site is a rural stretch of highway in Idaho where two visibility sensors are located. The project is part of a contract Fred's company, Management Solutions, Inc., has with the state of Idaho and the Federal Highway Administration. Under the contract, among other things, Management Solutions is charged

with evaluating the performance of a new technology for measuring visibility. The larger study involves determining whether visibility sensors can be effectively tied to electronic message signs that would warn motorists of upcoming visibility problems in rural areas.

Mike Kyte, a transportation engineer and professor at the University of Idaho, has been involved with the project as a consultant to Fred's company since the initial proposal. Mike is very knowledgeable about visibility sensors and traffic systems. Fred's expertise is in managing projects like this one, in which it is important to get people from multiple organizations to work together effectively.

As the pair headed back toward Boise from the site, Mike was more excited than Fred had seen him in a long time. Fred reasoned that the source of excitement was that they had finally been successful in getting solid data to compare the two visibility sensors in a period of low visibility. The previous day at the site had been very foggy. The Scorpion Sensor is a tested technology that Mike has worked with for some time in urban applications. However, it has never before been installed in such a remote location as this stretch of Highway I-84, which connects Idaho and Utah. The other sensor produced by the Vanguard Company measures visibility in a totally new way using laser technology.

The data that had excited Mike so much were collected by the two sensors and fed back to a computer system at the port of entry near the test site. The measurements were collected every five minutes for the 24-hour day. As Fred took advantage of the 75-mph speed limit through southern Idaho, Mike kept glancing at the data on the printout he had made of the first few five-minute time periods. The Scorpion system had not only provided visibility readings, but it also had provided other weather-related data, such as temperature, wind speed, wind direction, and humidity.

Mike's eyes went directly to the two visibility columns. Ideally, the visibility readings for the two sensors would be the same at any five-minute period, but they weren't. After a few exclamations of surprise from Mike, Fred suggested that they come up with an outline for the report they would have to make from these data for the project team meeting next week. Both agreed that a full descriptive analysis of all the data, including graphs and numerical measures, was necessary. In addition, Fred wanted to use these early data to provide an estimate for the mean visibility provided by the two sensors. They agreed that estimates were needed for the day as a whole and also for only those periods when the Scorpion system showed visibility under 1.0 mile. They also felt that the analysis should look at the other weather factors, too, but they weren't sure just what was needed.

As the lights in the Boise Valley became visible, Mike agreed to work up a draft of the report, including a narrative based on the data in the file called **Visibility**. Fred said that he would set up the project team meeting agenda, and Mike could make the presentation. Both men agreed that the data were strictly a sample and that more low-visibility data would be collected when conditions occurred.

# Case 8.2

## Federal Aviation Administration

In January 2003, the FAA ordered that passengers be weighed before boarding 10- to 19-seat passenger planes. The order was instituted in response to a crash that occurred on January 8, 2003, in Charlotte, North Carolina, in which all 21 passengers, including the pilot and co-pilot, of a 19-seat Beech 1900 turboprop died. One possible cause of the crash was that the plane may have been carrying too much weight.

The airlines were asked to weigh adult passengers and carry-on bags randomly over a one-month period to estimate the mean weight per passenger (including luggage). A total of 426 people and their luggage were weighed, and the sample data are contained in a data file called **FAA**.

### Required Tasks:

1. Prepare a descriptive analysis of the data using charts, graphs, and numerical measures.
2. Construct and interpret a 95% confidence interval estimate for the mean weight for male passengers.
3. Construct and interpret a 95% confidence interval estimate for the mean weight for female passengers.
4. Construct and interpret a 95% confidence interval estimate for the mean weight for all passengers.
5. Indicate what sample size would be required if the margin of error in the estimate for the mean of all passengers is to be reduced by half.

# Case 8.3

## Cell Phone Use

Helen Hutchins and Greg Haglund took the elevator together to the fourth-floor meeting room, where they were scheduled to meet the rest of the market research team at the Franklin Company. On the way up, Helen mentioned that she had terminated her contract for the land-line telephone in her apartment and was going to be using her cell phone exclusively to save money. "I rarely use my house phone anymore and about the only calls I get are from organizations wanting donations or doing surveys," she said. Greg said that he and his wife were thinking about doing the same thing.

As Helen and Greg walked toward the meeting room, Helen suddenly stopped. "If everyone did what I am doing, wouldn't that affect our marketing research telephone surveys?" she asked. "I mean, when we make calls the numbers are all to land-line phones. Won't we be missing out on some people we should be talking to when we do our surveys?" Helen continued. Greg indicated that it could be a problem if very many people were using cell phones exclusively like Helen. "Maybe we need to discuss this at the meeting today," Greg said.

When Helen and Greg brought up the subject to the market research team, several others indicated that they had been having similar concerns. It was decided that a special study was needed among the Franklin customer base to estimate the proportion of customers who were now using only a cell phone for telephone service. It was decided to randomly sample customers using personal interviews at their business outlets, but no one had any idea of how many customers they needed to interview. One team member mentioned that he had read an Associated Press article recently that said about 8% of all households have only a cell phone. Greg mentioned that any estimate they came up with should have a margin of error of ±0.03, and the others at the meeting agreed.

**Required Tasks:**

1. Assuming that the group wishes to develop a 95% confidence interval estimate, determine the required sample size if the population proportion of cell phone–only users is 8%.
2. Supposing the group is unwilling to use the 8% baseline proportion and wants to have the sample size be conservatively large enough to provide a margin of error of no greater than ±0.03 with 95% confidence, determine the sample size that will be needed.

# References

Berenson, Mark L., and David M. Levine, *Basic Business Statistics Concepts and Applications*, 11th ed. (Upper Saddle River, NJ: Prentice Hall, 2009).

Hogg, Robert V., and Elliot A. Tanis, *Probability and Statistical Inference*, 8th ed. (Upper Saddle River, NJ: Prentice Hall, 2009).

Larsen, Richard J., and Moriss L. Marx, *An Introduction to Mathematical Statistics and Its Applications*, 4th ed. (Upper Saddle River, NJ: Prentice Hall, 2005).

*Microsoft Excel 2007* (Redmond, WA: Microsoft Corp., 2007).

*Minitab for Windows Version 15* (State College, PA: Minitab, 2007).

Siegel, Andrew F., *Practical Business Statistics*, 5th ed. (Burr Ridge, IL: Irwin, 2002).

# Introduction to Hypothesis Testing

**Outcome 1.** Formulate null and alternative hypotheses for applications involving a single population mean or proportion.

**Outcome 2.** Know what Type I and Type II errors are.

**Outcome 3.** Correctly formulate a decision rule for testing a hypothesis.

**Outcome 4.** Know how to use the test statistic, critical value, and *p*-value approaches to test a hypothesis.

**Outcome 5.** Compute the probability of a Type II error.

## Why you need to know

As a business decision maker, you will encounter many applications that will require you to *estimate* a population parameter. Chapter 8 introduced statistical estimation and included many examples. Estimating a population parameter based on a sample statistic is a component of business statistics called *statistical inference*. An important component of statistical inference is *hypothesis testing*. In hypothesis testing, a hypothesis (or statement) concerning a population parameter is identified that we will certify to be true only if the sample evidence is sufficient. We then use sample data to either deny or confirm the validity of the proposed hypothesis.

For example, suppose an orange juice plant in Orlando, Florida, produces approximately 120,000 bottles of orange juice daily. Each bottle is supposed to contain 32 fluid ounces. However, like all processes, the automated filling machine is subject to variation, and each bottle will contain either slightly more or less than the 32-ounce target. The important thing is that the mean fill is 32 fluid ounces. Every two hours, the plant quality manager selects a random sample of bottles and computes the sample mean. Because the loss of production time and sales is costly, the manager does not wish to assert the *hypothesis* that the average fill is not 32 fluid ounces unless the sample evidence is strong enough to support that assertion. If the sample mean is a "significant" distance from the desired 32 ounces, then the sample data will have provided ample evidence that the average fill is not 32 ounces. The machine would then not be allowed to continue filling bottles until repairs or adjustments had been made. However, if the sample mean is "significantly" close to 32 ounces, the data would not support the hypothesis and the machine would be allowed to continue filling bottles.

Hypothesis testing is performed regularly in many industries. Companies in the pharmaceutical industry must perform many hypothesis tests on new drug products before they are deemed to be safe and effective by the federal Food and Drug Administration (FDA). In these instances, the drug is hypothesized to be both unsafe and ineffective. Here the FDA does not wish to certify that the drug is safe and effective unless sufficient evidence is obtained that this is the case. Then, if the sample results from the studies performed provide "significant" evidence that the drug is safe and effective, the FDA will allow the company to market the drug.

Hypothesis testing is the basis of the legal system in which judges and juries hear evidence in court cases. In a criminal case, the hypothesis in the American legal system is that the defendant is innocent. Based on the totality of the evidence presented in the trial, if the jury concludes that "beyond a reasonable doubt" the defendant committed the crime, the hypothesis of innocence will be rejected and the defendant will be found guilty. If the evidence is not strong enough, the defendant will be judged not guilty.

Hypothesis testing is a major part of business statistics. Chapter 9 introduces the fundamentals involved in conducting hypothesis tests. Many of the remaining chapters in this text will introduce additional hypothesis-testing techniques, so you need to gain a solid understanding of concepts presented in this chapter.

# 9.1 Hypothesis Tests for Means

By now you know that information contained in a sample is subject to sampling error. The sample mean will almost certainly not equal the population mean. Therefore, in situations in which you need to test a claim about a population mean by using the sample mean, you can't simply compare the sample mean to the claim and reject the claim if $\bar{x}$ and the claim are different. Instead, you need a testing procedure that incorporates the potential for sampling error.

*Statistical hypothesis testing* provides managers with a structured analytical method for making decisions of this type. It lets them make decisions in such a way that the probability of decision errors can be controlled, or at least measured. Even though statistical hypothesis testing does not eliminate the uncertainty in the managerial environment, the techniques involved often allow managers to identify and control the level of uncertainty.

The techniques presented in this chapter assume the data are selected using an appropriate statistical sampling process and that the data are interval or ratio level. In short, we assume we are working with good data.

## Formulating the Hypotheses

**Null and Alternative Hypotheses** In hypothesis testing, two hypotheses are formulated. One is the **null hypothesis**. The null hypothesis is represented by $H_0$ and contains an equality sign, such as "$=$," "$\leq$," or "$\geq$." The second hypothesis is the **alternative hypothesis** (represented by $H_A$). Based on the sample data, we either reject $H_0$ or we do not reject $H_0$.

Correctly specifying the null and alternative hypotheses is important. If done incorrectly, the results obtained from the hypothesis test may be misleading. Unfortunately, how you should formulate the null and alternative hypotheses is not always obvious. As you gain experience with hypothesis-testing applications, the process becomes easier. To help you get started, we have developed some general guidelines you should find helpful.

**Testing the Status Quo** In many cases, you will be interested in whether a situation has changed. We refer to this as testing the status quo, and this is a common application of hypothesis testing. For example, the Kellogg Company makes many food products, including a variety of breakfast cereals. At the company's Battle Creek, Michigan, plant, Frosted Mini-Wheats are produced and packaged for distribution around the world. If the packaging process is working properly, the mean fill per box is 16 ounces. Every hour quality analysts at the plant select a random sample of filled boxes and measure their contents. They do not wish to unnecessarily stop the packaging process since doing so can be quite costly. Thus, the packaging process will not be stopped unless there is sufficient evidence that the average fill is different from 16 ounces, i.e., $H_A$: $\mu \neq 16$. The analysts use the sample data to test the following null and alternative hypotheses:

$$H_0: \mu = 16 \text{ ounces (status quo)}$$

$$H_A: \mu \neq 16 \text{ ounces}$$

The null hypothesis is reasonable because the line supervisor would assume the process is operating correctly before starting production. As long as the sample mean is "reasonably" close to 16 ounces, the analysts will assume the filling process is working properly. Only when the sample mean is seen to be too large or too small will the analysts reject the null hypothesis (the status quo) and take action to identify and fix the problem.

**Null Hypothesis**

The statement about the population parameter that will be assumed to be true during the conduct of the hypothesis test. The null hypothesis will be rejected only if the sample data provide substantial contradictory evidence.

**Alternative Hypothesis**

The hypothesis that includes all population values not included in the null hypothesis. The alternative hypothesis will be selected only if there is strong enough sample evidence to support it. The alternative hypothesis is deemed to be true if the null hypothesis is rejected.

As another example, the Transportation Security Administration (TSA), which is responsible for screening passengers at U.S. airports, publishes on its Web site the average waiting times for customers to pass through security. For example, on Mondays between 9:00 A.M. and 10:00 A.M., the average waiting time at Atlanta's Hartsfield International Airport is supposed to be 15 minutes or less. Periodically, TSA staff will select a random sample of passengers during this time slot and will measure their actual wait times to determine if the average waiting time is longer than the guidelines require. The alternative hypothesis is, therefore, stated as: $H_A: \mu > 15$ minutes. The sample data will be used to test the following null and alternative hypotheses:

$$H_0: \mu \leq 15 \text{ minutes (status quo)}$$
$$H_A: \mu > 15 \text{ minutes}$$

Only if the sample mean wait time is "substantially" greater than 15 minutes will TSA employees reject the null hypothesis and conclude there is a problem with staffing levels. Otherwise, they will assume that the 15-minute standard (the status quo) is being met, and no action will be taken.

**Testing a Research Hypothesis**   Many business and scientific applications involve research applications. For example, companies such as Intel, Procter & Gamble, Dell Computers, Pfizer, and 3M continually introduce new and hopefully improved products. However, before introducing a new product, the companies want to determine whether the new product is superior to the original. In the case of drug companies like Pfizer, the government requires them to show their products are both safe and effective. Because statistical evidence is needed to indicate that the new product is effective, the default position (or null hypothesis) is that it is no better than the original (or in the case of a drug, that it is unsafe and ineffective.) The burden of proof is placed on the new product, and the alternative hypothesis is formulated as the **research hypothesis**.

**Research Hypothesis**

The hypothesis the decision maker attempts to demonstrate to be true. Because this is the hypothesis deemed to be the most important to the decision maker, it will be declared true only if the sample data strongly indicates that it is true.

For example, suppose the Goodyear Tire and Rubber Company has a new tread design that its engineers claim will outlast its competitor's leading tire. New technology is able to produce tires whose longevity is better than the competitors' tires but are less expensive. Thus, if Goodyear can be sure that the new tread design will last longer than the competition's, it will realize a profit that will justify the introduction of the tire with the new tread design. The competitor's tire has been demonstrated to provide an average of 60,000 miles of use. Therefore, the research hypothesis for Goodyear is that its tire will last longer than its competitor's, meaning that the tire will last an average of *more than* 60,000 miles. The research hypothesis becomes the alternative hypothesis:

$$H_0: \mu \leq 60,000$$
$$H_A: \mu > 60,000 \text{ (research hypothesis)}$$

The burden of proof is on Goodyear. Only if the sample data show a sample mean that is "substantially" larger than 60,000 miles will the null hypothesis be rejected and Goodyear's position be affirmed.

In another example, suppose the Nunhem Brothers Seed Company has developed a new variety of bean seed. Nunhem will introduce this seed variety on the market only if the seed provides yields superior to the current seed variety. Experience shows the current seed provides a mean yield of 60 bushels per acre. To test the new variety of beans, Nunhem Brothers researchers will set up the following null and alternative hypotheses:

$$H_0: \mu \leq 60 \text{ bushels}$$
$$H_A: \mu > 60 \text{ bushels (research hypothesis)}$$

The alternative hypothesis is the research hypothesis. If the null hypothesis is rejected, then Nunhem Brothers will have statistical evidence to show that the new variety of beans is superior to the existing product.

**Testing a Claim about the Population**   Analyzing claims using hypothesis tests can be complicated. Sometimes you will want to give the benefit of the doubt to the claim, but in other instances you will be skeptical about the claim and will want to place the burden of proof on the claim. For consistency purposes, the rule adopted in this text is that if the claim contains the equality, the claim becomes the null hypothesis. If the claim does not contain the equality, the claim is the alternative hypothesis.

A recent radio commercial stated the average waiting time at a medical clinic is less than 15 minutes. A claim like this can be tested using hypothesis testing. The null and alternative hypotheses should be formulated such that one contains the claim and the other reflects the opposite position. Since the claim does not contain the equality ($\mu < 15$), the claim should be the alternative hypothesis. The appropriate null and alternative hypotheses are, then, as follows:

$$H_0: \mu \geq 15$$
$$H_A: \mu < 15 \text{ (claim)}$$

In cases like this where the claim corresponds to the alternative hypothesis, the *burden of proof* is on the medical clinic. If the sample mean is "substantially" less than 15 minutes, the null hypothesis would be rejected and the alternative hypothesis (and the claim) would be accepted. Otherwise, the null hypothesis would not be rejected and the claim could not be accepted.

---

**Chapter Outcome 1. →**

**How to do it (Example 9-1)**

**Formulating the Null and Alternative Hypotheses**

1. The population parameter of interest (e.g., $\mu$, $\pi$, or $\sigma$) must be identified.

2. The hypothesis of interest to the researcher or the analyst must be identified. This could encompass testing a status quo, a research hypothesis, or a claim.

3. If an equal sign exists in the hypothesis of interest, it will become the null hypothesis, otherwise it will be the alternative hypothesis.

4. The range of possible values for the parameter must be divided between the null and alternative hypothesis. Therefore, if $H_0: \mu \leq 15$, the alternative hypothesis must become $H_A: \mu > 15$.

**EXAMPLE 9-1    FORMULATING THE NULL AND ALTERNATIVE HYPOTHESES**

**Student Work Hours** In today's economy, university students often work many hours to help pay for the high costs of a college education. Suppose a university in the Midwest is considering changing its class schedule to accommodate students working long hours. The registrar has stated a change is needed because the mean number of hours worked by under-graduate students at the university is more than 20 per week. The following steps can be taken to establish the appropriate null and alternative hypotheses:

**Step 1  Determine the population parameter of interest.**
In this case, the population parameter of interest is the mean hours worked, $\mu$. The null and alternative hypotheses must be stated in terms of the population parameter.

**Step 2  Identify the hypothesis of interest.**
In this case, the registrar has made a claim stating that the mean hours worked "is more than 20" per week. Because changing the class scheduling system would be expensive and time-consuming, the hypothesis will not be declared true unless the sample data strongly indicate that it is true. Thus, the burden of proof is placed on the registrar to justify her claim that the mean is greater than 20 hours.

**Step 3  Formulate the null and alternative hypotheses.**
Keep in mind that the equality goes in the null hypothesis.

$$H_0: \mu \leq 20 \text{ hours}$$
$$H_A: \mu > 20 \text{ hours (claim)}$$

**>> END EXAMPLE**

**TRY PROBLEM** 9-13a (pg. 366)

Example 9-2 illustrates another example of how the null and alternative hypotheses are formulated.

---

**EXAMPLE 9-2    FORMULATING THE NULL AND ALTERNATIVE HYPOTHESES**

**The Frito-Lay Company** The Frito-Lay Company produces several snack and food products that are sold throughout the United States and around the world. The company uses an automatic filling machine to fill the sacks with the desired weight. For instance, when the company is running potato chips on the fill line, the machine is set to fill the sacks with 20 ounces. Thus, if the machine is working properly, the mean fill will be 20 ounces. Each hour, a sample of sacks is collected and weighed, and the technicians determine whether the machine is still operating correctly or whether it needs adjustment. The following steps can be used to establish the null and alternative hypotheses to be tested:

Step 1 **Determine the population parameter of interest.**
In this case, the population parameter of interest is the mean weight per sack, $\mu$.

Step 2 **Identify the hypothesis of interest.**
The status quo is that the machine is filling the sacks with the proper amount, which is $\mu = 20$ ounces. We will believe this to be true unless we find evidence to suggest otherwise. If such evidence exists, then the filling process needs to be adjusted.

Step 3 **Formulate the null and alternative hypotheses.**
The null and alternative hypotheses are

$$H_0: \mu = 20 \text{ ounces (status quo)}$$
$$H_A: \mu \neq 20 \text{ ounces}$$

**>> END EXAMPLE**

**TRY PROBLEM** 9-14a (pg. 367)

**Chapter Outcome 2.** ➤ **Types of Statistical Errors** Because of the potential for extreme sampling error, two possible errors can occur when a hypothesis is tested: **Type I** and **Type II errors**. These errors show the relationship between what actually exists (a state of nature) and the decision made based on the sample information.

**Type I Error**

*Rejecting* the null hypothesis when it is, in fact, true.

**Type II Error**

*Failing to reject* the null hypothesis when it is, in fact, false.

Figure 9.1 shows the possible actions and states of nature associated with any hypothesis-testing application. As you can see, there are three possible outcomes: no error (correct decision), Type I error, and Type II error. *Only one of these will be the outcome for a hypothesis test.* From Figure 9.1, if the null hypothesis is true and an error is made, it must be a Type I error. On the other hand, if the null hypothesis is false and an error is made, it must be a Type II error.

Many statisticians argue that you should never use the phrase "accept the null hypothesis." Instead you should use "*do not reject* the null hypothesis." Thus, the only two hypothesis-testing decisions would be *reject $H_0$* or *do not reject $H_0$*. This is why in a jury verdict to acquit a defendant, the verdict is "not guilty" rather than innocent. Just because the evidence is insufficient to convict does not necessarily mean that the defendant is innocent. The same is true with hypothesis testing. Just because the sample data do not lead to rejecting the null hypothesis, we cannot be sure that the null hypothesis is true.

This thinking is appropriate when hypothesis testing is employed in situations in which some future action is not dependent on the results of the hypothesis test. However, in most business applications, the purpose of the hypothesis test is to direct the decision maker to take one action or another, based on the test results. So, in this text, when hypothesis testing is applied to decision-making situations, *not rejecting* the null hypothesis is essentially the same

**FIGURE 9.1**

The Relationship between Decisions and States of Nature

|  |  | State of Nature | |
|---|---|---|---|
|  |  | Null Hypothesis True | Null Hypothesis False |
| Decision | Conclude Null True (Don't Reject $H_0$) | Correct Decision | Type II Error |
|  | Conclude Null False (Reject $H_0$) | Type I Error | Correct Decision |

as *accepting it*. The same action will be taken whether we state the null hypothesis is not rejected or that it is accepted.[1]

---

**BUSINESS APPLICATION**   TYPE I AND TYPE II STATISTICAL ERRORS

**MORGAN LANE REAL ESTATE COMPANY** The Morgan Lane Real Estate Company has offices in and around the Napa Valley in the northern California wine country. Before the financial crisis hit the real estate market in late 2008, the market for homes in the Napa Valley area had been "hot" for a number of years, and homes commonly sold above the asking price very quickly. The standard time for closings in the Napa area was not more than 25 days. The managing partner at Morgan Lane wishes to test whether the mean closing times have changed following the 2008 financial crisis. Treating the average closing time of 25 days or less as the status quo, the null and alternative hypotheses to be tested are

$$H_0: \mu \leq 25 \text{ days (status quo)}$$
$$H_A: \mu > 25 \text{ days}$$

She will select a random sample of home sales in the Napa Valley during 2009. In this application, a Type I error would occur if the sample data lead the manager to conclude that the mean closing time exceeds 25 days ($H_0$ is rejected) when in fact $\mu \leq 25$ days. If a Type I error occurred, the manager would needlessly spend time and resources trying to speed up a process that already meets the original time frame.

Alternatively, a Type II error would occur if the sample evidence leads the manager to incorrectly conclude that $\mu \leq 25$ days ($H_0$ is not rejected) when the mean closing time exceeds 25 days. Now the manager would take no action to improve closing times at Morgan Lane when changes are needed to improve customer service.

**Chapter Outcome 3.**

# Significance Level and Critical Value

The objective of a hypothesis test is to use sample information to decide whether to reject the null hypothesis about a population parameter. How do decision makers determine whether the sample information supports or refutes the null hypothesis? The answer to this question is the key to understanding statistical hypothesis testing.

In hypothesis tests for a single population mean, the sample mean, $\bar{x}$, is used to test the hypotheses under consideration. Depending on how the null and alternative hypotheses are formulated, certain values of $\bar{x}$ will tend to support the null hypothesis, whereas other values will appear to support the alternative hypothesis. In the Morgan Lane example, the null and alternative hypotheses were formulated as

$$H_0: \mu \leq 25 \text{ days}$$
$$H_A: \mu > 25 \text{ days}$$

Values of $\bar{x}$ less than or equal to 25 days would tend to support the null hypothesis. By contrast, values of $\bar{x}$ greater than 25 days would tend to refute the null hypothesis. The larger the value of $\bar{x}$ the greater the evidence that the null hypothesis should be rejected. However, because we expect some sampling error, do we want to reject $H_0$ for any value of $\bar{x}$ that is greater than 25 days? Probably not. But should we reject $H_0$ if $\bar{x} = 26$ days, or $\bar{x} = 30$ days, or $\bar{x} = 35$ days? At what point do we stop attributing the result to sampling error?

To perform the hypothesis test, we need to select a *cutoff* point that is the demarcation between rejecting and not rejecting the null hypothesis. Our *decision rule* for the Morgan Lane application is then

If $\bar{x} > $ Cutoff, reject $H_0$.
If $\bar{x} \leq $ Cutoff, do not reject $H_0$.

---

[1]Whichever language you use, you should make an effort to understand both arguments and make an informed choice. If your instructor requests that you reference the action in a particular way, it would behoove you to follow the instructions. Having gone through this process ourselves, we prefer to state the choice as "don't reject the null hypothesis." This terminology will be used throughout this text.

**FIGURE 9.2**

Sampling Distribution of $\bar{x}$ for Morgan Lane

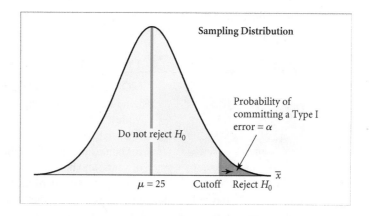

If $\bar{x}$ is greater than the cutoff, we will reject $H_0$ and conclude that the average closing time *does* exceed 25 days. If $\bar{x}$ is less than or equal to the cutoff, we will not reject $H_0$; in this case our test does not give sufficient evidence that the closing time exceeds 25 days.

Recall from the Central Limit Theorem (see Chapter 7) that, for large samples, the distribution of the possible sample means is approximately normal, with a center at the population mean, $\mu$. The null hypothesis in our example is $\mu \leq 25$ days. Figure 9.2 shows the sampling distribution for $\bar{x}$ assuming that $\mu = 25$. The shaded region on the right is called the *rejection region*. The area of the rejection region gives the probability of getting an $\bar{x}$ larger than the cutoff when $\mu$ is really 25, so it is the probability of making a Type I statistical error. This probability is called the **significance level** of the test and is given the symbol $\alpha$ (alpha).

**Significance Level**

The maximum allowable probability of committing a Type I statistical error. The probability is denoted by the symbol $\alpha$.

The decision maker carrying out the test specifies the significance level, $\alpha$. The value of $\alpha$ is determined based on the costs involved in committing a Type I error. If making a Type I error is costly, we will want the probability of a Type I error to be small. If a Type I error is less costly, then we can allow a higher probability of a Type I error.

However, in determining $\alpha$, we must also take into account the probability of making a Type II error, which is given the symbol $\beta$ (beta). The two error probabilities, $\alpha$ and $\beta$, are inversely related. That is, if we reduce $\alpha$, then $\beta$ will increase.[2] Thus, in setting $\alpha$, you must consider both sides of the issue.[3]

Calculating the specific dollar costs associated with making Type I and Type II errors is often difficult and may require a subjective management decision. Therefore, any two managers might well arrive at different alpha levels. However, in the end, the choice for alpha must reflect the decision maker's best estimate of the costs of these two errors.

**Critical Value**

The value corresponding to a significance level that determines those test statistics that lead to rejecting the null hypothesis and those that lead to a decision not to reject the null hypothesis.

Having chosen a significance level, $\alpha$, the decision maker then must calculate the corresponding cutoff point, which is called a **critical value**.

**Chapter Outcome 4.** ➡

# Hypothesis Test for $\mu$, $\sigma$ Known

**Calculating Critical Values** To calculate critical values corresponding to a chosen $\alpha$, we need to know the sampling distribution of the sample mean $\bar{x}$. If our sampling conditions satisfy the Central Limit Theorem requirements or if the population is normally distributed and we know the population standard deviation $\sigma$, then the sampling distribution of $\bar{x}$ is a normal distribution with an average equal to the population mean $\mu$ and standard deviation $\sigma/\sqrt{n}$.[4] With this information we can calculate a critical z-value, called $z_\alpha$, or a critical $\bar{x}$-value, called $\bar{x}_\alpha$. We illustrate both calculations in the Morgan Lane Real Estate example.

---

[2]The sum of alpha and beta may coincidentally equal 1. However, in general, the sum of these two error probabilities does not equal 1.

[3]We will discuss Type II errors more fully later in this chapter. Contrary to the Type I error situation in which we specify the desired alpha level, beta is computed based on certain assumptions. Methods for computing beta are shown in Section 9.3.

[4]For many population distributions, the Central Limit Theorem applies for sample sizes as small as 4 or 5. Sample sizes $n \geq 30$ assure us that the sampling distribution will be approximately normal regardless of population distribution.

**CONDUCTING THE HYPOTHESIS TEST**

**MORGAN LANE REAL ESTATE (*CONTINUED*)** Suppose the managing partners decide they are willing to incur a 0.10 probability of committing a Type I error. Assume also that the population standard deviation, $\sigma$, for closing is 3 days and the sample size is 64 homes. Given that the sample size is large ($n \geq 30$) and that the population standard deviation is known ($\sigma = 3$ days), we can state the critical value in two ways. First, we can establish the critical value as a $z$-value.

Figure 9.3 shows that if the rejection region on the upper end of the sampling distribution has an area of 0.10, the critical $z$-value, $z_\alpha$, from the standard normal table (or by using Excel's NORMSINV function or Minitab's Calc > Probability Distributions command) corresponding to the critical value is 1.28. Thus, $z_{0.10} = 1.28$. If the sample mean lies more than 1.28 standard deviations above $\mu = 25$ days, $H_0$ should be rejected; otherwise we will not reject $H_0$.

We can also express the critical value in the same units as the sample mean. In the Morgan Lane example, we can calculate a critical $\bar{x}$ value, $\bar{x}_\alpha$, so that if $\bar{x}$ is greater than the critical value, we should reject $H_0$. If $\bar{x}$ is less than or equal to $\bar{x}_\alpha$, we should not reject $H_0$. Equation 9.1 shows how $\bar{x}_\alpha$ is computed. Figure 9.4 illustrates the use of Equation 9.1 for computing the critical value, $\bar{x}_\alpha$.

---

**$\bar{x}_\alpha$ for Hypothesis Tests, $\sigma$ Known**

$$\bar{x}_\alpha = \mu + z_\alpha \frac{\sigma}{\sqrt{n}} \tag{9.1}$$

where:

$\mu =$ Hypothesized value for the population mean
$z_\alpha =$ Critical value from the standard normal distribution
$\sigma =$ Population standard deviation
$n =$ Sample size

---

Applying Equation 9.1, we determine the value for $\bar{x}_\alpha$ as follows:

$$\bar{x}_\alpha = \mu + z_\alpha \frac{\sigma}{\sqrt{n}}$$

$$\bar{x}_{0.10} = 25 + 1.28 \frac{3}{\sqrt{64}}$$

$$\bar{x}_{0.10} = 25.48 \text{ days}$$

Also refer to Figure 9.4 for a graphical illustration showing how $\bar{x}_\alpha$ is determined.

If $\bar{x} > 25.48$ days, $H_0$ should be rejected and changes should be made in the process; otherwise, $H_0$ should not be rejected and the process should not be changed. Any sample mean between 25.48 and 25 days would be attributed to sampling error, and the null hypothesis would not be rejected. A sample mean of 25.48 or fewer days will support the null hypothesis.

**FIGURE 9.3**

Determining the Critical Value as a $z$-Value

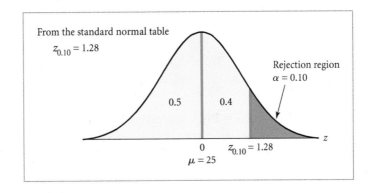

**FIGURE 9.4**

Determining the Critical Value as an $\bar{x}$-Value for the Morgan Lane Example

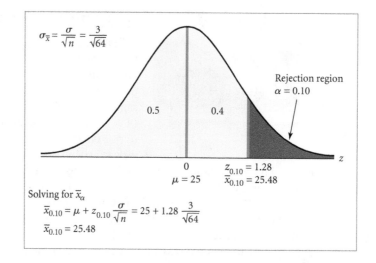

**Decision Rules and Test Statistics** To conduct a hypothesis test, you can use three equivalent approaches. You can calculate a $z$-value and compare it to the critical value, $z_\alpha$. Alternatively, you can calculate the sample mean, $\bar{x}$, and compare it to the critical value, $\bar{x}_\alpha$. Finally, you can use a method called the $p$-value approach, to be discussed later in this section. It makes no difference which approach you use, each method yields the same conclusion.

Suppose $\bar{x} = 26$ days. How we test the null hypothesis depends on the procedure we used to establish the critical value. First, using the $z$-value method, we establish the following decision rule:

**Hypotheses**

$$H_0: \mu \le 25 \text{ days}$$
$$H_A: \mu > 25 \text{ days}$$
$$\alpha = 0.10$$

**Decision Rule**

If $z > z_{0.10}$, reject $H_0$.

If $z \le z_{0.10}$, do not reject $H_0$.

where:

$$z_{0.10} = 1.28$$

Recall that the number of homes sampled is 64 and the population standard deviation is assumed known at 3 days. The calculated $z$-value is called the **test statistic**.

The $z$-test statistic is computed using Equation 9.2.

**Test Statistic**

A function of the sampled observations that provides a basis for testing a statistical hypothesis.

---

**z-Test Statistic for Hypothesis Tests for $\mu$, $\sigma$ Known**

$$z = \frac{\bar{x} - \mu}{\dfrac{\sigma}{\sqrt{n}}} \tag{9.2}$$

where:

$\bar{x} = $ Sample mean
$\mu = $ Hypothesized value for the population mean
$\sigma = $ Population standard deviation
$n = $ Sample size

---

Given that $\bar{x} = 26$ days, applying Equation 9.2 we get

$$z = \frac{\bar{x} - \mu}{\dfrac{\sigma}{\sqrt{n}}} = \frac{26 - 25}{\dfrac{3}{\sqrt{64}}} = 2.67$$

Thus, $\bar{x} = 26$ is 2.67 standard deviations above the hypothesized mean. Because $z$ is greater than the critical value,

$$z = 2.67 > z_{0.10} = 1.28, \text{ reject } H_0.$$

Now we use the second approach, which established (see Figure 9.4) a decision rule, as follows:

**Decision Rule**

$$\text{If } \bar{x} > \bar{x}_{0.10}, \text{ reject } H_0.$$
$$\text{Otherwise, do not reject } H_0.$$

Then,

$$\text{If } \bar{x} > 25.48 \text{ days, reject } H_0.$$
$$\text{Otherwise, do not reject } H_0.$$

Then, because

$$\bar{x} = 26 > \bar{x}_{0.10} = 25.48, \text{ reject } H_0.$$

Note that the two approaches yield the same conclusion, as they always will if you perform the calculations correctly. We have found that academic applications of hypothesis testing tend to use the $z$-value method, whereas business applications of hypothesis testing often use the $\bar{x}$ approach.

You will often come across a different language used to express the outcome of a hypothesis test. For instance, a statement for the hypothesis test just presented would be "The hypothesis test was significant at an $\alpha$ (or significance level) of 0.10." This simply means that the null hypothesis was rejected using a significance level of 0.10.

---

**EXAMPLE 9-3**   **ONE-TAILED HYPOTHESIS TEST FOR $\mu$, $\sigma$ KNOWN**

**Mountain States Surgery Center** The Mountain States Surgery Center in Denver, Colorado, performs many knee replacement surgery procedures each year. Recently, research physicians at Mountain States have developed a surgery process they believe will reduce the average patient recovery time. The hospital board will not recommend the new procedure unless there is substantial evidence to suggest that it is better than the existing procedure. Records indicate that the current mean recovery rate for the standard procedure is 142 days, with a standard deviation of 15 days. To test whether the new procedure actually results in a lower mean recovery time, the procedure was performed on a random sample of 36 patients.

**Step 1** **Specify the population parameter of interest.**
We are interested in the mean recovery time, $\mu$.

**Step 2** **Formulate the null and alternative hypotheses.**

$$H_0: \mu \geq 142 \text{ (status quo)}$$
$$H_A: \mu < 142$$

**Step 3** **Specify the desired significance level ($\alpha$).**
The researchers wish to test the hypothesis using a 0.05 level of significance.

**Step 4** **Construct the rejection region.**
This will be a one-tailed test, with the rejection region in the lower (left-hand) tail of the sampling distribution. The critical value is $-z_{0.05} = -1.645$. Therefore, the decision rule becomes

$$\text{If } z < -1.645, \text{ reject } H_0; \text{ otherwise, do not reject } H_0.$$

**Step 5** **Compute the test statistic.**
For this example we will use $z$. Assume the sample mean, computed using $\bar{x} = \dfrac{\sum x}{n}$, is 140.2 days. Then,

$$z = \frac{\bar{x} - \mu}{\dfrac{\sigma}{\sqrt{n}}} = \frac{140.2 - 142}{\dfrac{15}{\sqrt{36}}} = -0.72$$

---

**How to do it** (Example 9-3)

**One-Tailed Test for a Hypothesis about a Population Mean, $\sigma$ Known**

To test the hypothesis, perform the following steps:

1. Specify the population parameter of interest.

2. Formulate the null hypothesis and the alternative hypothesis in terms of the population mean, $\mu$.

3. Specify the desired significance level ($\alpha$).

4. Construct the rejection region. (We strongly suggest you draw a picture showing where in the distribution the rejection region is located.)

5. Compute the test statistic.

$$\bar{x} = \frac{\sum x}{n} \quad \text{or} \quad z = \frac{\bar{x} - \mu}{\dfrac{\sigma}{\sqrt{n}}}$$

6. Reach a decision. Compare the test statistic with $\bar{x}_\alpha$ or $z_\alpha$.

7. Draw a conclusion regarding the null hypothesis.

**FIGURE 9.5**

Mountain States Surgery
Hypothesis Test

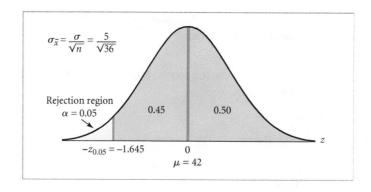

$$\sigma_{\bar{x}} = \frac{\sigma}{\sqrt{n}} = \frac{5}{\sqrt{36}}$$

Rejection region
$\alpha = 0.05$

0.45    0.50

$-z_{0.05} = -1.645$    0

$\mu = 42$

z

**Step 6   Reach a decision. (See Figure 9.5.)**
The decision rule is

If $z < -1.645$, reject $H_0$.
Otherwise, do not reject.

Because $-0.72 > -1.645$, do not reject $H_0$.

**Step 7   Draw a conclusion.**
There is not sufficient evidence to conclude that the new knee replacement
procedure results in a shorter average recovery period. Thus, Mountain States
will not be able to recommend the new procedure on the grounds that it
reduces recovery time.

**>> END EXAMPLE**

**TRY PROBLEM** 9-5 (pg. 366)

---

**EXAMPLE 9-4**    **HYPOTHESIS TEST FOR $\mu$, $\sigma$ KNOWN**

**Business Statistics Exams** The Testing Center in Southern
California creates standardized exams for a variety of quantitative
disciplines, including business statistics. Recently the Testing Center
received complaints from faculty who have used its latest business
statistics test saying the mean time required to complete the exam
exceeds the advertised mean of 40 minutes. Before responding,
employees at the Testing Center plan to test this claim using an alpha
level equal to 0.05 and a random sample size of $n = 100$ business
statistics students. Based on previous studies, suppose that the population standard deviation is
known to be $\sigma = 8$ minutes. The hypothesis test can be conducted using the following steps:

**Step 1   Specify the population parameter of interest.**
The population parameter of interest is the mean test time, $\mu$.

**Step 2   Formulate the null and alternative hypotheses.**
The new claim is that $\mu > 40$. Because this claim does not contain the equality,
it will become the alternative hypothesis. Thus, the null and alternative
hypotheses are

$H_0: \mu \le 40$ minutes
$H_A: \mu > 40$ minutes (claim)

**Step 3   Specify the significance level.**
The alpha level is specified to be 0.05.

**Step 4   Construct the rejection region.**
Alpha is the area under the standard normal distribution to the right of the
critical value. Because the population standard deviation is known, the test
statistic has a standard normal distribution. Therefore the critical $z$-value, $z_{0.05}$,
is found by locating the $z$-value that corresponds to an area equal to $0.50 -
0.05 = 0.45$. The critical $z$-value from the standard normal table is 1.645.

We can calculate $\bar{x}_\alpha = \bar{x}_{0.05}$ using Equation 9.1 as follows:

$$\bar{x}_\alpha = \mu + z_\alpha \frac{\sigma}{\sqrt{n}}$$

$$\bar{x}_{0.05} = 40 + 1.645\left(\frac{8}{\sqrt{100}}\right)$$

$$\bar{x}_{0.05} = 41.32$$

Step 5    **Compute the test statistic.**
Suppose that the sample of 100 students produced a sample mean of 43.5 minutes.

Step 6    **Reach a decision.**
The decision rule is

If $\bar{x} > 41.32$, reject $H_0$.
Otherwise, do not reject.

Because $\bar{x} = 43.5 > 41.32$, we reject $H_0$.

Step 7    **Draw a conclusion.**
There is sufficient evidence to conclude that the mean time required to complete the exam exceeds the advertised time of 40 minutes. The Testing Center will likely want to modify the exam to shorten the average completion time.

>>**END EXAMPLE**

**TRY PROBLEM** 9-7 (pg. 366)

***p*-Value Approach** In addition to the two hypothesis-testing approaches discussed previously, a third approach for conducting hypothesis tests also exists. This third approach uses a ***p*-value** instead of a critical value.

*p*-Value

The probability (assuming the null hypothesis is true) of obtaining a test statistic at least as extreme as the test statistic we calculated from the sample. The *p*-value is also known as the *observed significance level.*

If the calculated *p*-value is smaller than the probability in the rejection region ($\alpha$), then the null hypothesis is rejected. If the calculated *p*-value is greater than or equal to $\alpha$, then the hypothesis will not be rejected. The *p*-value approach is popular today because *p*-values are usually computed by statistical software packages, including Excel and Minitab. The advantage to reporting test results using a *p*-value is that it provides more information than simply stating whether the null hypothesis is rejected. The decision maker is presented with a measure of the degree of significance of the result (i.e., the *p*-value). This allows the reader the opportunity to evaluate the *extent* to which the data disagree with the null hypothesis, not just whether they disagree.

**EXAMPLE 9-5**    **HYPOTHESIS TEST USING *p*-VALUES, $\sigma$ KNOWN**

**Dodger Stadium Parking** The parking manager for the Los Angeles Dodgers baseball team has studied the exit times for cars leaving the ballpark after a game and believes that recent changes to the traffic flow leaving the stadium have increased, rather than decreased, average exit times. Prior to the changes the previous mean exit time per vehicle was 36 minutes, with a population standard deviation equal to 11 minutes. To test the parking manager's belief, a simple random sample of $n = 200$ vehicles is selected, and a sample mean of 36.8 minutes is calculated. Using an alpha = 0.05 level, the following steps can be used to conduct the hypothesis test:

Step 1    **Specify the population parameter of interest.**
The Dodger Stadium parking manager is interested in the mean exit time per vehicle, $\mu$.

Step 2    **Formulate the null and alternative hypotheses.**
Based on the manager's claim that the current mean stay is longer than before the remodeling, the null and alternative hypotheses are

$H_0$: $\mu \leq 36$ minutes
$H_A$: $\mu > 36$ minutes (claim)

Step 3    **Specify the significance level.**
The alpha level specified for this test is $\alpha = 0.05$.

Step 4    **Construct the rejection region.**
The decision rule is

If $p$-value $< \alpha = 0.05$, reject $H_0$.
Otherwise, do not reject $H_0$.

Step 5    **Compute the test statistic (find the $p$-value.)**
Because the sample size is large and the population standard deviation is assumed known, the test statistic will be a $z$-value, which is computed as follows:

$$z = \frac{\bar{x} - \mu}{\frac{\sigma}{\sqrt{n}}} = \frac{36.8 - 36}{\frac{11}{\sqrt{200}}} = 1.0285 = 1.03$$

In this example, the $p$-value is the probability of a $z$-value from the standard normal distribution being at least as large as 1.03. This is stated as

$$p\text{-value} = P(z \geq 1.03)$$

From the standard normal distribution table in Appendix D,

$$P(z \geq 1.03) = 0.5000 - 0.3485 = 0.1515$$

Step 6    **Reach a decision.**
Because the $p$-value $= 0.1515 > \alpha = 0.05$, do not reject the null hypothesis.

Step 7    **Draw a conclusion.**
The difference between the sample mean and the hypothesized population mean is not large enough to attribute the difference to anything but sampling error.

>>**END EXAMPLE**

**TRY PROBLEM** 9-6 (pg. 366)

Why do we need three methods to test the same hypothesis when they all give the same result? The answer is that we don't. However, you need to be aware of all three methods because you will encounter each in business situations. The $p$-value approach is especially important because many statistical software packages provide a $p$-value that you can use to test a hypothesis quite easily, and a $p$-value provides a measure of the degree of significance associated with the hypothesis test. This text will use both test-statistic approaches, as well as the $p$-value approach to hypothesis testing.

## Types of Hypothesis Tests

Hypothesis tests are formulated as either **one-tailed tests** or **two-tailed tests** depending on how the null and alternative hypotheses are presented.

For instance, in the Morgan Lane application, the null and alternative hypotheses are

Null hypothesis        $H_0: \mu \leq 25$ days

Alternative hypothesis        $H_A: \mu > 25$ days

This hypothesis test is one-tailed because the entire rejection region is located in the upper tail and the null hypothesis will be rejected only when the sample mean falls in the extreme upper tail of the sampling distribution (see Figure 9.4). In this application, it will take a sample mean substantially larger than 25 days to reject the null hypothesis.

In Example 9.2 involving the Frito-Lay Company, the null and alternative hypotheses involving the mean fill of potato chip sacks is

$$H_0: \mu = 20 \text{ ounces (status quo)}$$

$$H_A: \mu \neq 20 \text{ ounces}$$

**One-Tailed Test**

A hypothesis test in which the entire rejection region is located in one tail of the sampling distribution. In a one-tailed test, the entire alpha level is located in one tail of the distribution.

**Two-Tailed Test**

A hypothesis test in which the entire rejection region is split into the two tails of the sampling distribution. In a two-tailed test, the alpha level is split evenly between the two tails.

In this two-tailed hypothesis test, the null hypothesis will be rejected if the sample mean is extremely large (upper tail) or extremely small (lower tail). The alpha level would be split evenly between the two tails.

## *p*-Value for Two-Tailed Tests

In the previous *p*-value example, the rejection region was located in one tail of the sampling distribution. In those cases, the null hypothesis was of the $\geq$ or $\leq$ format. However, sometimes the null hypothesis will be stated as a direct equality. The following application involving the Golden Peanut Company shows how to use the *p*-value approach for a two-tailed test.

---

**BUSINESS APPLICATION**   **USING *p*-VALUES TO TEST A NULL HYPOTHESIS**

**GOLDEN PEANUT COMPANY** Consider the Golden Peanut Company in Alpharetta, Georgia, which packages salted and unsalted unshelled peanuts in 16-ounce sacks. The company's filling process strives for an average fill amount equal to 16 ounces. Therefore, Golden would test the following null and alternative hypotheses:

$$H_0: \mu = 16 \text{ ounces (status quo)}$$

$$H_A: \mu \neq 16 \text{ ounces}$$

The null hypothesis will be rejected if the test statistic falls in either tail of the sampling distribution. The size of the rejection region is determined by $\alpha$. Each tail has an area equal to $\alpha/2$.

The *p*-value for the two-tailed test is computed in a manner similar to that for a one-tailed test. First, determine the *z*-test statistic as follows:

$$z = (\overline{x} - \mu)/(\sigma/\sqrt{n})$$

Suppose for this situation, Golden managers calculated a $z = 3.32$. In a one-tailed test, the area that will be calculated to form the *p*-value is determined by the direction in which the inequality is pointing in the alternative hypotheses. However, in a two-tailed test, the tail area in which the test statistic is located is initially calculated. In this case we find $P(z > 3.32)$ using either the standard normal table in Appendix D, Excel's **NORMSDIST** function, or Minitab's **Calc > Probability Distributions** command. In this case, because $z = 3.32$ exceeds the table values, we will use Excel or Minitab to obtain

$$P(z \leq 3.32) = 0.9995$$

Then

$$P(z > 3.32) = 1 - 0.9995 = 0.0005$$

However, because this is a two-tailed hypothesis test, the *p*-value is found by multiplying the 0.0005 value by 2 (to account for the chance that our sample result could have been on either side of the distribution). Thus

$$p\text{-value} = 2(0.0005) = 0.0010$$

Assuming an alpha $= 0.10$ level, then because the

$$p\text{-value} = 0.0010 < \alpha = 0.10, \text{ we reject } H_0.$$

Figure 9.6 illustrates the two-tailed test for the Golden Peanut Company example.

---

### How to do it (Example 9-6)

**Two-Tailed Test for a Hypothesis about a Population Mean, $\sigma$ Known**

To conduct a two-tailed hypothesis test when the population standard deviation is known, you can perform the following steps:

1. Specify the population parameter of interest.

2. Formulate the null and alternative hypotheses in terms of the population mean, $\mu$.

3. Specify the desired significance level, $\alpha$.

4. Construct the rejection region.

   Determine the critical values for each tail, $z_{\alpha/2}$ and $-z_{\alpha/2}$ from the standard normal table. If needed, calculate $\overline{x}_{(\alpha/2)L}$ and $\overline{x}_{(\alpha/2)U}$

   Define the two-tailed decision rule using one of the following:

   - If $z > z_{\alpha/2}$, or if $z < -z_{\alpha/2}$ reject $H_0$; otherwise, do not reject $H_0$.

   - If $\overline{x} < \overline{x}_{(\alpha/2)L}$ or $\overline{x} > \overline{x}_{(\alpha/2)U}$ reject $H_0$; otherwise, do not reject $H_0$.

   - If *p*-value $< \alpha$, reject $H_0$; otherwise, do not reject $H_0$.

5. Compute the test statistic, $z = (\overline{x} - \mu)/(\sigma/\sqrt{n})$, or $\overline{x}$, or find the *p*-value.

6. Reach a decision.

7. Draw a conclusion.

---

**EXAMPLE 9-6**   **TWO-TAILED HYPOTHESIS TEST FOR $\mu$, $\sigma$ KNOWN**

**The Potlatch Corporation** The Potlatch Corporation is a wood products company with lumber, plywood, and paper plants in several areas of the United States. At its St. Maries, Idaho, plywood plant, the company makes plywood used in residential and commercial building. One product made at the St. Maries plant is 3/8-inch plywood which must have a mean thickness of 0.375 inches. The standard deviation, $\sigma$, is known to be 0.05 inch. Before

**FIGURE 9.6**

Two-Tailed Test for the
Golden Peanut Example

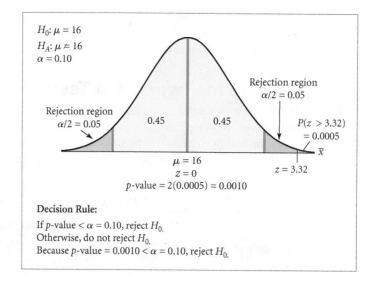

$H_0: \mu = 16$
$H_A: \mu \neq 16$
$\alpha = 0.10$

Rejection region
$\alpha/2 = 0.05$

Rejection region
$\alpha/2 = 0.05$

0.45   0.45

$P(z > 3.32)$
$= 0.0005$

$\bar{x}$

$\mu = 16$
$z = 0$

$z = 3.32$

$p\text{-value} = 2(0.0005) = 0.0010$

**Decision Rule:**
If $p\text{-value} < \alpha = 0.10$, reject $H_0$.
Otherwise, do not reject $H_0$.
Because $p\text{-value} = 0.0010 < \alpha = 0.10$, reject $H_0$.

sending a shipment to customers, Potlatch managers test whether they are meeting the 0.375 inch requirements by selecting a random sample of $n = 100$ sheets of plywood and collecting thickness measurements.

**Step 1   Specify the population parameter of interest.**
The mean thickness of plywood is of interest.

**Step 2   Formulate the null and the alternative hypotheses.**
The null and alternative hypotheses are

$$H_0: \mu = 0.375 \text{ inch (status quo)}$$

$$H_A: \mu \neq 0.375 \text{ inch}$$

Note, the test is two-tailed because the company is concerned that the plywood could be too thick or too thin.

**Step 3   Specify the desired significance level ($\alpha$).**
The managers wish to test the hypothesis using an $\alpha = 0.05$.

**Step 4   Construct the rejection region.**
This is a two-tailed test. The critical $z$ values for the upper and lower tails are found in the standard normal table. These are

$$-z_{\alpha/2} = -z_{0.05/2} = -z_{0.025} = -1.96$$

and

$$z_{\alpha/2} = z_{0.05/2} = z_{0.025} = 1.96$$

Define the two-tailed decision rule:

If $z > 1.96$, or if $z < -1.96$, reject $H_0$; otherwise, do not reject $H_0$.

**Step 5   Compute the test statistic.**
Select the random sample and calculate the sample mean.
Suppose that the sample mean for the random sample of 100 measurements is

$$\bar{x} = \frac{\Sigma x}{n} = 0.378 \text{ inch}$$

The $z$-test statistic is

$$z = \frac{\bar{x} - \mu}{\dfrac{\sigma}{\sqrt{n}}} = \frac{0.378 - 0.375}{\dfrac{0.05}{\sqrt{100}}} = 0.60$$

Step 6  **Reach a decision.**
Because $-1.96 < z = 0.60 < 1.96$, do not reject the null hypothesis.

Step 7  **Draw a conclusion.**
The Potlatch Corporation does not have sufficient evidence to reject the null hypothesis. Thus, it will ship the plywood.

>>END EXAMPLE

TRY PROBLEM 9-5 (pg. 366)

# Hypothesis Test for $\mu$, $\sigma$ Unknown

In Chapter 8, we introduced situations where the objective was to estimate a population mean when the population standard deviation was not known. In those cases, the critical value is a $t$-value from the $t$-distribution rather than a $z$-value from the standard normal distribution. The same logic is used in hypothesis testing when $\sigma$ is unknown (which will usually be the case). Equation 9.3 is used to compute the test statistic for testing hypotheses about a population mean when the population standard deviation is unknown.

**$t$-Test Statistic for Hypothesis Tests for $\mu$, $\sigma$ Unknown**

$$t = \frac{\bar{x} - \mu}{\frac{s}{\sqrt{n}}}$$

(9.3)

where:

$\bar{x}$ = Sample mean
$\mu$ = Hypothesized value for the population mean
$s$ = Sample standard deviation, $s = \sqrt{\dfrac{\sum(x-\bar{x})^2}{n-1}}$
$n$ = Sample size

To employ the $t$-distribution, we must make the following assumption:

**Assumption**

The population is normally distributed.

If the population from which the simple random sample is selected is approximately normal, the $t$-test statistic computed using Equation 9.3 will be distributed according to a $t$-distribution with $n-1$ degrees of freedom.

**EXAMPLE 9-7    HYPOTHESIS TEST FOR $\mu$, $\sigma$ UNKNOWN**

**Dairy Fresh Ice Cream** The Dairy Fresh Ice Cream plant in Greensboro, Alabama, uses a filling machine for its 64-ounce cartons. There is some variation in the actual amount of ice cream that goes into the carton. The machine can go out of adjustment and put a mean amount either less or more than 64 ounces in the cartons. To monitor the filling process, the production manager selects a simple random sample of 16 filled ice cream cartons each day. He can test whether the machine is still in adjustment using the following steps:

Step 1  **Specify the population parameter of interest.**
The manager is interested in the mean amount of ice cream.

Step 2  **Formulate the appropriate null and alternative hypotheses.**
The status quo is that the machine continues to fill ice cream cartons with a mean equal to 64 ounces. Thus, the null and alternative hypotheses are

$H_0$: $\mu = 64$ ounces (Machine is in adjustment.)
$H_A$: $\mu \neq 64$ ounces (Machine is out of adjustment.)

Step 3  **Specify the desired level of significance.**
The test will be conducted using an alpha level equal to 0.05.

**How to do it** (Example 9-7)

**One- or Two-Tailed Tests for $\mu$, $\sigma$ Unknown**

1. Specify the population parameter of interest, $\mu$.

2. Formulate the null hypothesis and the alternative hypothesis.

3. Specify the desired significance level ($\alpha$).

4. Construct the rejection region.

   If it is a two-tailed test, determine the critical values for each tail, $t_{\alpha/2}$ and $-t_{\alpha/2}$, from the $t$-distribution table. If the test is a one-tailed test, find either $t_{\alpha}$ or $-t_{\alpha}$, depending on the tail of the rejection region. Degrees of freedom are $n-1$. If desired, the critical $t$-values can be used to find the appropriate $\overline{x}_{\alpha}$ or the $\overline{x}_{(\alpha/2)L}$ and $\overline{x}_{(\alpha/2)U}$ values. Define the decision rule.

   a. If the test statistic is in the rejection region, reject $H_0$; otherwise, do not reject $H_0$.

   b. If the $p$-value is less than $\alpha$, reject $H_0$; otherwise, do not reject $H_0$.

5. Compute the test statistic or find the $p$-value.

   Select the random sample and calculate the sample mean, $\overline{x} = \sum x/n$, and the sample standard deviation,

   $$s = \sqrt{\frac{\sum(x-\overline{x})^2}{n-1}}.$$

   Then calculate

   $$t = \frac{\overline{x}-\mu}{\dfrac{s}{\sqrt{n}}}$$

   or the $p$-value.

6. Reach a decision.

7. Draw a conclusion.

**Step 4** **Construct the rejection region.**
We first produce a box and whisker plot for a rough check on the normality assumption.

The sample data are

| 62.7 | 64.7 | 64.0 | 64.5 | 64.6 | 65.0 | 64.4 | 64.2 |
|------|------|------|------|------|------|------|------|
| 64.6 | 65.5 | 63.6 | 64.7 | 64.0 | 64.2 | 63.0 | 63.6 |

The box and whisker plot is

| Minimum | 62.7 |
|---------|------|
| First Quartile | 63.6 |
| Median | 64.3 |
| Third Quartile | 64.7 |
| Maximum | 65.5 |

**Box and Whisker Plot**

The box and whisker diagram does not indicate that the population distribution is unduly skewed. The median line is close to the middle of the box, the whiskers extend approximately equal distances above and below the box, and there are no outliers. Thus, the normal distribution assumption is reasonable based on these sample data.

Now we determine the critical values from the $t$-distribution.

Based on the null and alternative hypotheses, this test is two-tailed. Thus, we will split the alpha into two tails and determine the critical values from the $t$-distribution with $n-1$ degrees of freedom. Using Appendix F, the critical $t$'s for $\alpha/2 = 0.025$, and $16-1 = 15$ degrees of freedom are $t = \pm 2.1315$.

The decision rule for this two-tailed test is

If $t < -2.1315$ or $t > 2.1315$, reject $H_0$.

Otherwise, do not reject $H_0$.

**Step 5** **Compute the $t$-test statistic.**
The sample mean is

$$\overline{x} = \frac{\sum x}{n} = \frac{1,027.3}{16} = 64.2$$

The sample standard deviation is

$$s = \sqrt{\frac{\sum(x-\overline{x})^2}{n-1}} = 0.72$$

The $t$-test statistic, using Equation 9.3, is

$$t = \frac{\overline{x}-\mu}{\dfrac{s}{\sqrt{n}}} = \frac{64.2-64}{\dfrac{0.72}{\sqrt{16}}} = 1.11$$

**Step 6** **Reach a decision.**
Because $t = 1.11$ is not less than $-2.1315$ and not greater than 2.1315, we do not reject the null hypothesis.

**Step 7** **Draw a conclusion.**
Based on these sample data, the company does not have sufficient evidence to conclude that the filling machine is out of adjustment.

>> **END EXAMPLE**

**TRY PROBLEM** 9-12 (pg. 366)

**EXAMPLE 9-8**    **TESTING THE HYPOTHESIS FOR $\mu$, $\sigma$ UNKNOWN**

**Hewlett-Packard Call Centers** The Hewlett-Packard (HP) Company operates service centers in various locations in the United States and abroad where customers can call to get answers to questions about HP products. Previous studies indicate that the distribution of time required for each call is normally distributed, with a mean equal to 540 seconds. Company officials have selected a random sample of 16 calls and wish to determine whether the mean call time is now fewer than 540 seconds after a training program was given to call center employees.

**Step 1**    **Specify the population parameter of interest.**
The mean call time is the population parameter of interest.

**Step 2**    **Formulate the null and alternative hypotheses.**
The null and alternative hypotheses are

$$H_0: \mu \geq 540 \text{ seconds (status quo)}$$

$$H_A: \mu < 540 \text{ seconds}$$

**Step 3**    **Specify the significance level.**
The test will be conducted at the 0.01 level of significance. Thus, $\alpha = 0.01$.

**Step 4**    **Construct the rejection region.**
Because this is a one-tailed test and the rejection region is in the lower tail, as indicated in $H_A$, the critical value from the $t$-distribution with $16 - 1 = 15$ degrees of freedom is $-t_\alpha = -t_{0.01} = -2.6025$.

The decision rule for this one-tailed test is

If $t < -2.6025$, reject $H_0$.
Otherwise, do not reject $H_0$.

**Step 5**    **Compute the test statistic.**
The sample mean for the random sample of 16 calls is $\bar{x} = \sum x/n = 510$

seconds, and the sample standard deviation is $\sqrt{\dfrac{\sum(x - x)^2}{n - 1}} = 45$ seconds.

Assuming that the population distribution is approximately normal, the test statistic is

$$t = \frac{\bar{x} - \mu}{\dfrac{s}{\sqrt{n}}} = \frac{510 - 540}{\dfrac{45}{\sqrt{16}}} = -2.67$$

**Step 6**    **Reach a decision.**
Because $t = -2.67 < -2.6025$, the null hypothesis is rejected.

**Step 7**    **Draw a conclusion.**
There is sufficient evidence to conclude that the mean call time for service calls has been reduced below 540 seconds.

>>**END EXAMPLE**

**TRY PROBLEM** 9-15 (pg. 367)

**BUSINESS APPLICATION**    **HYPOTHESIS TESTS USING SOFTWARE**

**Excel and Minitab Tutorial**

**FRANKLIN TIRE AND RUBBER COMPANY** The Franklin Tire and Rubber Company recently conducted a test on a new tire design to determine whether the company could make the claim that the mean tire mileage would exceed 60,000 miles. The test was conducted in Alaska. A simple random sample of 100 tires was tested, and the number of miles each tire lasted until it no longer met the federal government minimum tread thickness was recorded. The data (shown in thousands of miles) are in the file called **Franklin**.

The null and alternative hypotheses to be tested are

$$H_0: \mu \leq 60$$

$$H_A: \mu > 60 \text{ (research hypothesis)}$$

$$\alpha = 0.05$$

Excel does not have a special procedure for testing hypotheses for single population means. However, the Excel add-ins software called PHStat has the necessary hypothesis-testing tools.[5] Figure 9.7a and Figure 9.7b show the Excel PHStat and the Minitab outputs.

We denote the critical value of an upper- or lower-tail test with a significance level of $\alpha$ as $t_\alpha$ or $-t_\alpha$. The critical value for $\alpha = 0.05$ and 99 degrees of freedom is $t_{0.05} = 1.6604$. Using the critical value approach, the decision rule is:

If the $t$ test statistic $> 1.6604 = t_{0.05}$, reject $H_0$; otherwise, do not reject $H_0$.

The sample mean, based on a sample of 100 tires, is $\bar{x} = 60.17$ (60,170 miles), and the sample standard deviation is $s = 4.701$ (4,701 miles). The $t$ test statistics shown in Figure 9.7a and 9.7b are computed as follows:

$$t = \frac{\bar{x} - \mu}{\dfrac{s}{\sqrt{n}}} = \frac{60.17 - 60}{\dfrac{4.701}{\sqrt{100}}} = 0.3616$$

Because

$$t = 0.3616 < t_{0.05} = 1.6604, \text{ do not reject the null hypothesis.}$$

Thus, based on the sample data, the evidence is insufficient to conclude that the new tires have an average life exceeding 60,000 miles. Based on this test, the company would not be justified in making the claim.

**FIGURE 9.7A**

Excel 2007 (PHStat) Output for Franklin Tire Hypothesis Test Results

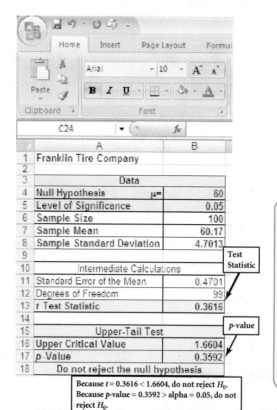

Excel 2007 (PHStat) Instructions:

1. Open file Franklin.xls.
2. Click on **PHStat** tab.
3. Select **One Sample Test**, *t*-test for **Mean, Sigma Unknown**.
4. Enter Hypothesized Mean.
5. Check "**Sample Statistics Unknown**".
6. Check **Test Option > Upper Tail** Test.

---

[5]This test can be done in Excel without the benefit of the PHStat add-ins by using Excel equations. Please refer to the Excel tutorial for the specifics.

**FIGURE 9.7B**

Minitab Output for Franklin
Tire Hypothesis Test Results

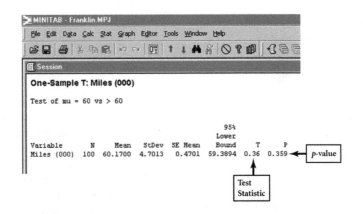

**Minitab Instructions:**
1. Open file: Franklin.MTW.
2. Choose **Stat > Basic Statistics > 1-sample t**.
3. In **Samples in columns**, enter data column.
4. Select **Perform hypothesis test** and enter hypothesized mean.
5. Select **Options**, in **Confidence level** insert confidence level.
6. In **Alternative**, select hypothesis direction.
7. Click **OK**.

Franklin managers could also use the $p$-value approach to test the null hypothesis because the output shown in Figures 9.7a and 9.7b provides the $p$-value. In this case, the $p$-value = 0.3592. The decision rule for a test is

If $p$-value $< \alpha$ reject $H_0$; otherwise, do not reject $H_0$.

Because

$$p\text{-value} = 0.3592 > \alpha = 0.05$$

we do not reject the null hypothesis. This is the same conclusion we reached using the $t$ test statistic approach.

This section has introduced the basic concepts of hypothesis testing. There are several ways to test a null hypothesis. Each method will yield the same result; however, computer software such as Minitab and Excel show the $p$-values automatically. Therefore, decision makers increasingly use the $p$-value approach.

# 9-1: **Exercises**

## Skill **Development**

**9-1.** Determine the appropriate critical value(s) for each of the following tests concerning the population mean:
   a. upper-tailed test: $\alpha = 0.025$; $n = 25$; $\sigma = 3.0$
   b. lower-tailed test: $\alpha = 0.05$; $n = 30$; $s = 9.0$
   c. two-tailed test: $\alpha = 0.02$; $n = 51$; $s = 6.5$
   d. two-tailed test: $\alpha = 0.10$; $n = 36$; $\sigma = 3.8$

**9-2.** For each of the following pairs of hypotheses, determine whether each pair represents valid hypotheses for a hypothesis test. Explain reasons for any pair that is indicated to be invalid.
   a. $H_0: \mu = 15, H_A: \mu > 15$
   b. $H_0: \mu = 20, H_A: \mu \neq 20$

   c. $H_0: \mu < 30, H_A: \mu > 30$
   d. $H_0: \mu \leq 40, H_A: \mu \geq 40$
   e. $H_0: \bar{x} \leq 45, H_A: \bar{x} > 45$
   f. $H_0: \mu \leq 50, H_A: \mu > 55$

**9-3.** Provide the relevant critical value(s) for each of the following circumstances:
   a. $H_A: \mu > 13, n = 15, \sigma = 10.3, \alpha = 0.05$
   b. $H_A: \mu \neq 21, n = 23, s = 35.40, \alpha = 0.02$
   c. $H_A: \mu \neq 35, n = 41, \sigma = 35.407, \alpha = 0.01$
   d. $H_A: \mu < 49$; data: 12.5, 15.8, 44.3, 22.6, 18.4; $\alpha = 0.10$
   e. $H_A: \bar{x} > 15, n = 27, \sigma = 12.4$

**9-4.** For each of the following z-test statistics, compute the p-value assuming that the hypothesis test is a one-tailed test:
   a. $z = 1.34$
   b. $z = 2.09$
   c. $z = -1.55$

**9-5.** For the following hypothesis test:

$$H_0: \mu = 200$$
$$H_A: \mu \neq 200$$
$$\alpha = 0.01$$

with $n = 64$, $\sigma = 9$, and $\bar{x} = 196.5$, state
   a. the decision rule in terms of the critical value of the test statistic
   b. the calculated value of the test statistic
   c. the conclusion

**9-6.** For the following hypothesis test:

$$H_0: \mu \leq 45$$
$$H_A: \mu > 45$$
$$\alpha = 0.02$$

with $n = 80$, $\sigma = 9$, and $\bar{x} = 47.1$, state
   a. the decision rule in terms of the critical value of the test statistic
   b. the calculated value of the test statistic
   c. the appropriate p-value
   d. the conclusion

**9-7.** For the following hypothesis test:

$$H_0: \mu \geq 23$$
$$H_A: \mu < 23$$
$$\alpha = 0.025$$

with $n = 25$, $s = 8$, and $\bar{x} = 20$, state
   a. the decision rule in terms of the critical value of the test statistic
   b. the calculated value of the test statistic
   c. the conclusion

**9-8.** For the following hypothesis test:

$$H_0: \mu = 60.5$$
$$H_A: \mu \neq 60.5$$
$$\alpha = 0.05$$

with $n = 15$, $s = 7.5$, and $\bar{x} = 62.2$, state
   a. the decision rule in terms of the critical value of the test statistic
   b. the calculated value of the test statistic
   c. the conclusion

**9-9.** For the following hypothesis:

$$H_0: \mu \leq 70$$
$$H_A: \mu > 70$$

with $n = 20$, $\bar{x} = 71.2$, $s = 6.9$, and $\alpha = 0.1$, state
   a. the decision rule in terms of the critical value of the test statistic
   b. the calculated value of the test statistic
   c. the conclusion

**9-10.** A sample taken from a population yields a sample mean of 58.4. Calculate the p-value for each of the following circumstances:
   a. $H_A: \mu > 58$, $n = 16$, $\sigma = 0.8$

   b. $H_A: \mu \neq 45$, $n = 41$, $s = 35.407$
   c. $H_A: \mu \neq 45$, $n = 41$, $\sigma = 35.407$
   d. $H_A: \mu < 69$; data: 60.1, 54.3, 57.1, 53.1, 67.4

**9-11.** For each of the following scenarios, indicate which type of statistical error could have been committed or, alternatively, that no statistical error was made. When warranted, provide a definition for the indicated statistical error.
   a. Unknown to the statistical analyst, the null hypothesis is actually true.
   b. The statistical analyst fails to reject the null hypothesis.
   c. The statistical analyst rejects the null hypothesis.
   d. Unknown to the statistical analyst, the null hypothesis is actually true and the analyst fails to reject the null hypothesis.
   e. Unknown to the statistical analyst, the null hypothesis is actually false.
   f. Unknown to the statistical analyst, the null hypothesis is actually false and the analyst rejects the null hypothesis.

## Business Applications

**9-12.** The National Club Association does periodic studies on issues important to its membership. The 2008 Executive Summary of the Club Managers Association of America reported that the average country club initiation fee was $31,912. Suppose a random sample taken in 2009 of 12 country clubs produced the following initiation fees:

| | | | | | |
|---|---|---|---|---|---|
| $29,121 | $31,472 | $28,054 | $31,005 | $36,295 | $32,771 |
| $26,205 | $33,299 | $25,602 | $33,726 | $39,731 | $27,816 |

Based on the sample information, can you conclude at the $\alpha = 0.05$ level of significance that the average 2009 country club initiation fees are lower than the 2008 average? Conduct your test at the $\alpha = 0.05$ level of significance.

**9-13.** The director of a state agency believes that the average starting salary for clerical employees in the state is less than $30,000 per year. To test her hypothesis, she has collected a simple random sample of 100 starting clerical salaries from across the state and found that the sample mean is $29,750.
   a. State the appropriate null and alternative hypotheses.
   b. Assuming the population standard deviation is known to be $2,500 and the significance level for the test is to be 0.05, what is the critical value (stated in dollars)?
   c. Referring to your answer in part b, what conclusion should be reached with respect to the null hypothesis?
   d. Referring to your answer in part c, which of the two statistical errors might have been made in this case? Explain.

**9-14.** A mail-order business prides itself in its ability to fill customers' orders in six calendar days or less on the average. Periodically, the operations manager selects a random sample of customer orders and determines the number of days required to fill the orders. Based on this sample information, he decides if the desired standard is not being met. He will assume that the average number of days to fill customers' orders is six or less unless the data suggest strongly otherwise.

a. Establish the appropriate null and alternative hypotheses.

b. On one occasion where a sample of 40 customers was selected, the average number of days was 6.65, with a sample standard deviation of 1.5 days. Can the operations manager conclude that his mail-order business is achieving its goal? Use a significance level of 0.025 to answer this question.

c. Calculate the $p$-value for this test. Conduct the test using this $p$-value.

d. The operations manager wishes to monitor the efficiency of his mail-order service often. Therefore, he does not wish to repeatedly calculate $t$-values to conduct the hypothesis tests. Obtain the critical value, $\bar{x}_\alpha$, so that the manager can simply compare the sample mean to this value to conduct the test. Use $\bar{x}$ as the test statistic to conduct the test.

**9-15.** A recent internal report issued by the marketing manager for a national oil-change franchise indicated that the mean number of miles between oil changes for franchise customers is at least 3,600 miles. One Texas franchise owner conducted a study to determine whether the marketing manager's statement was accurate for his franchise's customers. He selected a simple random sample of 10 customers and determined the number of miles each had driven the car between oil changes. The following sample data were obtained:

| | | | | |
|---|---|---|---|---|
| 3,655 | 4,204 | 1,946 | 2,789 | 3,555 |
| 3,734 | 3,208 | 3,311 | 3,920 | 3,902 |

a. State the appropriate null and alternative hypotheses.

b. Use the test statistic approach with $\alpha = 0.05$ to test the null hypothesis.

**9-16.** The makers of Mini-Oats Cereal have an automated packaging machine that can be set at any targeted fill level between 12 and 32 ounces. Every box of cereal is not expected to contain exactly the targeted weight, but the average of all boxes filled should. At the end of every shift (eight hours), 16 boxes are selected at random and the mean and standard deviation of the sample are computed. Based on these sample results, the production control manager determines whether the filling machine needs to be readjusted or whether it remains all right to operate. Use $\alpha = 0.05$.

a. Establish the appropriate null and alternative hypotheses to be tested for boxes that are supposed to have an average of 24 ounces.

b. At the end of a particular shift during which the machine was filling 24-ounce boxes of Mini-Oats, the sample mean of 16 boxes was 24.32 ounces, with a standard deviation of 0.70 ounce. Assist the production control manager in determining if the machine is achieving its targeted average.

c. Why do you suppose the production control manager would prefer to make this hypothesis test a two-tailed test? Discuss.

d. Conduct the test using a $p$-value. (*Hint*: Use Excel's TDIST function.)

e. Considering the result of the test, which of the two types of errors in hypothesis testing could you have made?

**9-17.** Starting in 2008 an increasing number of people found themselves facing mortgages that were worth more than the value of their homes. A fund manager who had invested in debt obligations involving grouped mortgages was interested in determining the group most likely to default on their mortgage. He speculates that older people are less likely to default on their mortgage and thinks the average age of those who do is 55 years. To test this, a random sample of 30 who had defaulted was selected; the following sample data reflect the ages of the sampled individuals:

| | | | | | |
|---|---|---|---|---|---|
| 40 | 55 | 78 | 27 | 55 | 33 |
| 51 | 76 | 54 | 67 | 40 | 31 |
| 60 | 61 | 50 | 42 | 78 | 80 |
| 25 | 38 | 74 | 46 | 48 | 57 |
| 30 | 65 | 80 | 26 | 46 | 49 |

a. State the appropriate null and alternative hypotheses.

b. Use the test statistic approach to test the null hypothesis with $\alpha = 0.01$.

## Computer Database **Exercises**

**9-18.** At a recent meeting, the manager of a national call center for a major Internet bank made the statement that the average past-due amount for customers who have been called previously about their bills is now no larger than $20.00. Other bank managers at the meeting suggested that this statement may be in error and that it might be worthwhile to conduct a test to see if there is statistical support for the call center manager's statement. The file called **Bank Call Center** contains data for a random sample of 67 customers from the call center population. Assuming that the population standard deviation for past due amounts is known to be $60.00, what should be concluded based on the sample data? Test using $\alpha = 0.10$.

**9-19.** The U.S. Bureau of Labor Statistics (www.bls.gov) released its *Consumer Expenditures in 2006* report in October 2008. Among its findings is that average annual household spending on food at home for 2006 was $3,417. Suppose a random sample of 137 households in Detroit was taken to determine whether the average annual expenditure on food at home was less for consumer units in Detroit than in the nation as a whole. The sample results are in the file **Detroit Eats**. Based on the sample results, can it be concluded at the $\alpha = 0.02$ level of significance that average consumer-unit spending for food at home in Detroit is less than the national average?

**9-20.** The Center on Budget and Policy Priorities (www. cbpp.org) reported that average out-of-pocket medical expenses for prescription drugs for privately insured adults with incomes over 200% of the poverty level was $173 in 2002. Suppose an investigation was conducted in 2009 to determine whether the increased availability of generic drugs, Internet prescription drug purchases, and cost controls have reduced out-of-pocket drug expenses. The investigation randomly sampled 196 privately insured adults with incomes over 200% of the poverty level, and the respondents' 2009 out-of-pocket medical expenses for prescription drugs were recorded. These data are in the file **Drug Expenses**. Based on the sample data, can it be concluded that 2009 out-of-pocket prescription drug expenses are lower than the 2002 average reported by the Center on Budget and Policy Priorities? Use a level of significance of 0.01 to conduct the hypothesis test.

**9-21.** A key factor in the world's economic condition is the population growth of the countries in the world. The file called **Countries** contains data for 74 countries in alphabetical order. Consider these 74 countries to be the population of all countries in the world.

   a. From this population, suppose a systematic random sample of every fifth country is selected starting with the fifth country on the list. From this sample, test the null hypothesis that the mean population growth percentage between the years 1990 and 2000 is equal to 1.5%. Test using $\alpha = 0.05$.

   b. Now compute the average population growth rate for all 74 countries. After examining the result of the hypothesis test in part a, what type of statistical error, if any, was committed? Explain your answer.

**9-22.** Hono Golf is a manufacturer of golf products in Taiwan and China. One of the golf accessories it produces at its plant in Tainan Hsing, Taiwan, is plastic golf tees. The injector molder produces golf tees that are designed to have an average height of 66 mm. To determine if this specification is met, random samples are taken from the production floor. One sample is contained in the file labeled **THeight**.

   a. Determine if the process is not producing the tees to specification. Use a significance level of 0.01.

   b. If the hypothesis test determines the specification is not being met, the production process will be shut down while causes and remedies are determined. At times this occurs even though the process is functioning to specification. What type of statistical error would this be?

**END EXERCISES 9-1**

# 9.2 Hypothesis Tests for a Proportion

So far, this chapter has focused on hypothesis tests about a single population mean. Although many decision problems involve a test of a population mean, there are also cases in which the parameter of interest is the population proportion. For example, a production manager might consider the proportion of defective items produced on an assembly line to determine whether the line should be restructured. Likewise, a life insurance salesperson's performance assessment might include the proportion of existing clients who renew their policies.

**Chapter Outcome 1.** → ## Testing a Hypothesis about a Single Population Proportion

The basic concepts of hypothesis testing for proportions are the same as for means.

1. The null and alternative hypotheses are stated in terms of a population parameter, now $\pi$ instead of $\mu$, and the sample statistic becomes $p$ instead of $\bar{x}$.
2. The null hypothesis should be a statement concerning the parameter that includes the equality.
3. The significance level of the hypothesis determines the size of the rejection region.
4. The test can be one- or two-tailed, depending on how the alternative hypothesis is formulated.

**BUSINESS APPLICATION**    **TESTING A HYPOTHESIS FOR A POPULATION PROPORTION**

**FIRST AMERICAN BANK AND TITLE** The internal auditors at First American Bank and Title Company routinely test the bank's system of internal controls. Recently, the audit manager examined the documentation on the bank's 22,500 outstanding automobile loans. The bank's procedures require that the file on each auto loan account contain certain specific documentation, such as a list of applicant assets, statement of monthly income, list of liabilities, and certificate of automobile insurance. If an account contains all the required documentation, then it complies with bank procedures.

The audit manager has established a 1% noncompliance rate as the bank's standard. If more than 1% of the 22,500 loans do not have appropriate documentation, then the internal controls are not effective and the bank needs to improve the situation. The audit staff does not have enough time to examine all 22,500 files to determine the true population noncompliance rate. As a result, the audit staff selects a random sample of 600 files, examines them, and determines the number of files not in compliance with bank documentation requirements. The sample findings will tell the manager if the bank is exceeding the 1% noncompliance rate for the population of all 22,500 loan files. The manager will not act unless the noncompliance rate exceeds 1%. The default position is that the internal controls are effective. Thus, the null and alternative hypotheses are

$$H_0: \pi \le 0.01 \text{ (Internal controls are effective.)}$$

$$H_A: \pi > 0.01 \text{ (Internal controls are not effective.)}$$

Suppose the sample of 600 accounts uncovered 9 files with inadequate loan documentation. The question is whether 9 out of 600 is sufficient to conclude that the bank has a problem. To answer this question statistically, we need to recall a lesson from Chapter 7.

**Requirement**

The sample size, $n$, is large such that $n\pi \ge 5$ and $n(1 - \pi) \ge 5$.[6]

If this requirement is satisfied, the sampling distribution is approximately normal with mean = $\pi$ and standard deviation = $\sqrt{\pi(1-\pi)/n}$.

The bank's auditors have a general policy of performing these tests with a significance level of

$$\alpha = 0.02$$

They are willing to reject a true null hypothesis 2% of the time. In this case, if a Type I statistical error is committed, the internal controls will be considered ineffective when, in fact, they are working as intended.

Once the null and alternative hypotheses and the significance level have been specified, we can formulate the decision rule for this test. Figure 9.8 shows how the decision rule is developed. Notice the critical value, $p_{0.02}$, is 2.05 standard deviations above $\pi = 0.01$. Thus, the decision rule is:

$$\text{If } p > p_{0.02} = 0.0182, \text{ reject } H_0.$$

Because there were 9 deficient files in the sample of 600 files, this means that

$$p = 9/600 = 0.015$$

Because

$$p = 0.015 < p_{0.02} = 0.0182, \text{ do not reject } H_0.$$

The null hypothesis, $H_0$, should not be rejected, based on these sample data. Therefore, the auditors will conclude the system of internal controls is working effectively.

---

[6]A paper published in *Statistical Science* by L. Brown et al. entitled "Interval Estimation for a Binomial Proportion" in 2001, pp. 101–133, suggests that the requirement should be $n\pi \ge 15$ and $n(1 - \pi) \ge 15$. However, most sources still use the $\ge 5$ limit.

**FIGURE 9.8**

Decision Rule for First
American Bank and Title
Example

$H_0: \pi \leq 0.01$
$H_A: \pi > 0.01$
$\alpha = 0.02$

$\sigma_p = \sqrt{\dfrac{\pi(1-\pi)}{n}}$

$\sigma_p = \sqrt{\dfrac{0.01(1-0.01)}{600}} = 0.004$

$\pi = 0.01$

$\alpha = 0.02$

$p_{0.02} = ?$

Solving for $p_\alpha$:    $p_\alpha = \pi + z_\alpha \sigma_p$
From the normal table $z_{0.02} = 2.05$; then:

$p_{0.02} = 0.01 + (2.05)(0.004)$
$p_{0.02} = 0.0182$

Sample results:
$x = 9$ bad files
$p = x/n = 9/600$
$= 0.015$

**Decision Rule:**
If $p > 0.0182$, reject $H_0$; otherwise, do not reject.
Because $p = 0.015 < 0.0182$, do not reject $H_0$.

Alternatively, we could have based the test on a test statistic ($z$) with a standard normal distribution. This test statistic is calculated using Equation 9.4.

## z-Test Statistic for Proportions

$$z = \frac{p - \pi}{\sqrt{\dfrac{\pi(1-\pi)}{n}}} \qquad (9.4)$$

where:

$p$ = Sample proportion
$\pi$ = Hypothesized population proportion
$n$ = Sample size

The $z$-value for this test statistic is

$$z = \frac{0.015 - 0.01}{0.004} = 1.25$$

As was established in Figure 9.8, the critical value is

$$z_{0.02} = 2.05$$

We reject the null hypothesis only if $z > z_{0.02}$. Because

$$z = 1.25 < 2.05$$

we don't reject the null hypothesis. This, of course, was the same conclusion we reached when we used $p$ as the test statistic. Both test statistics must yield the same decision.

### How to do it (Example 9-9)

**Testing Hypotheses about a Single Population Proportion**

1. Specify the population parameter of interest.

2. Formulate the null and alternative hypotheses.

3. Specify the significance level for testing the null hypothesis.

4. Construct the rejection region.

   For a one-tail test, determine the critical value, $z_\alpha$, from the standard normal distribution table or

   $$p_\alpha = \pi + z_\alpha \sqrt{\dfrac{\pi(1-\pi)}{n}}$$

   For a two-tail test, determine the critical values:

   $z_{(\alpha/2)L}$ and $z_{(\alpha/2)U}$ from the standard normal table or $p_{(\alpha/2)L}$ and $P_{(\alpha/2)U}$

5. Compute the test statistic,

   $$p = \frac{x}{n} \text{ or } z = \frac{p - \pi}{\sqrt{\pi(1-\pi)/n}}$$

   or determine the $p$-value.

6. Reach a decision by comparing $z$ to $z_\alpha$ or $p$ to $p_\alpha$ or by comparing the $p$-value to $\alpha$.

7. Draw a conclusion.

**EXAMPLE 9-9**    **TESTING HYPOTHESES FOR A SINGLE POPULATION PROPORTION**

**The Developmental Basketball League** Several years ago when the Continental Basketball League folded, the NBA started a new professional basketball league called the Developmental League, or D-League for short, where players who were not on NBA rosters could fine-tune their skills in hopes of getting called up to the NBA. The teams in this league are privately owned but connected to NBA teams. One of the D-League's teams is considering increasing the season ticket prices for basketball games. The marketing manager is concerned that some people will terminate their ticket orders if this change occurs. If more than 10% of the season ticket orders would be terminated, the marketing manager does not want to implement the price increase. To test this, a random sample of ticket holders is surveyed and asked what they would do if the prices were increased.

**Step 1** **Specify the population parameter of interest.**
The parameter of interest is the population proportion of season ticket holders who would terminate their orders.

**Step 2** **Formulate the null and alternative hypotheses.**
The null and alternative hypotheses are

$$H_0: \pi \leq 0.10$$

$$H_A: \pi > 0.10 \text{ (research hypothesis)}$$

**Step 3** **Specify the significance level.**
The alpha level for this test is $\alpha = 0.05$.

**Step 4** **Construct the rejection region.**

1. Using the $z$ critical value:

   The critical value from the standard normal table for this upper-tailed test is $z_\alpha = z_{0.05} = 1.645$.
   The decision rule is

   If $z > 1.645$, reject $H_0$; otherwise, do not reject.

2. Using the $p$ critical value:

   As you learned in Section 9.1, there are alternative approaches to testing a hypothesis. In addition to the $z$-test statistic approach, you could compute the critical value, $p_\alpha$, and compare $p$ to $p_\alpha$. The critical value is computed as follows:

   $$p_\alpha = \pi + z_\alpha \sqrt{\frac{\pi(1-\pi)}{n}}$$

   $$p_{0.05} = 0.10 + 1.645 \sqrt{\frac{0.10(1-0.10)}{100}} = 0.149$$

   The decision rule is

   If $p > p_{0.05} = 0.149$, reject $H_0$. Otherwise, do not reject.

3. Using the $p$-value:

   The decision rule is

   If $p$-value $< \alpha = 0.05$, reject $H_0$. Otherwise, do not reject.

**Step 5** **Compute the test statistic or the $p$-value.**
The random sample of $n = 100$ season ticket holders showed that 14 would cancel their ticket orders if the price change were implemented.

1. The sample proportion and $z$-test statistic are

$$p = \frac{x}{n} = \frac{14}{100} = 0.14$$

$$z = \frac{p - \pi}{\sqrt{\dfrac{\pi(1-\pi)}{n}}} = \frac{0.14 - 0.10}{\sqrt{\dfrac{0.10(1-0.10)}{100}}} = 1.33$$

2. Using the *p*-critical value:

The *p*-critical value was previously calculated to be $p = 0.149$.

3. Using the *p*-value:

To find the *p*-value for a one-tailed test, we use the calculated *z*-value shown previously in step 5 to be $z = 1.33$. Then,

$$p\text{-value} = P(z > 1.33)$$

From the standard normal table, the probability associated with $z = 1.33$, i.e., $P(0 \le z \le 1.33)$, is 0.4082. Then,

$$p\text{-value} = 0.5 - 0.4082 = 0.0918$$

**Step 6  Reach a decision.**

1. Using the *z*-test statistic:

The decision rule is

$$\text{If } z > z_{0.05}, \text{ reject } H_0.$$

Because $z = 1.33 < 1.645$, do not reject $H_0$.

2. Using the *p*-critical value

The decision rule is

$$\text{If } p > p_{0.05}, \text{ reject } H_0.$$

Because $0.14 < 0.149$, do not reject $H_0$. This is the same decision we reached using the *z*-test statistic approach.

3. Using the *p*-value:

The decision rule is

$$\text{If } p\text{-value} < \alpha = 0.05, \text{ reject } H_0.$$

Because $p\text{-value} = 0.0918 > 0.05$, do not reject $H_0$.

All three hypothesis-testing approaches provide the same decision.

**Step 7  Draw a conclusion.**

Based on the sample data, the marketing manager does not have sufficient evidence to conclude that more than 10% of the season ticket holders will cancel their ticket orders.

>>**END EXAMPLE**

**TRY PROBLEM** 9-28 (pg. 373)

# 9-2: **Exercises**

## Skill **Development**

**9-23.** Determine the appropriate critical value(s) for each of the following tests concerning the population proportion:

a. upper-tailed test: $\alpha = 0.025, n = 48$
b. lower-tailed test: $\alpha = 0.05, n = 30$
c. two-tailed test: $\alpha = 0.02, n = 129$
d. two-tailed test: $\alpha = 0.10, n = 36$

**9-24.** Calculate the *z*-test statistic for a hypothesis test in which the null hypothesis states that the population proportion, $\pi$, equals 0.40 if the following sample information is present:

$$n = 150, x = 30$$

**9-25.** Given the following null and alternative hypotheses

$$H_0: \pi \ge 0.60$$
$$H_A: \pi < 0.60$$

test the hypothesis using $\alpha = 0.01$ assuming that a sample of $n = 200$ yielded $x = 105$ items with the desired attribute.

**9-26.** For the following hypothesis test:

$$H_0: \pi = 0.40$$
$$H_A: \pi \neq 0.40$$
$$\alpha = 0.01$$

with $n = 64$ and $p = 0.42$, state
a. the decision rule in terms of the critical value of the test statistic
b. the calculated value of the test statistic
c. the conclusion

**9-27.** For the following hypothesis test

$$H_0: \pi \geq 0.75$$
$$H_A: \pi < 0.75$$
$$\alpha = 0.025$$

with $n = 100$ and $p = 0.66$, state
a. the decision rule in terms of the critical value of the test statistic
b. the calculated value of the test statistic
c. the conclusion

**9-28.** A test of hypothesis has the following hypotheses:

$$H_0: \pi \leq 0.45$$
$$H_A: \pi > 0.45$$

For a sample size of 30, and a sample proportion of 0.55,
a. For an $\alpha = 0.025$, determine the critical value.
b. Calculate the numerical value of the test statistic.
c. State the test's conclusion.
d. Determine the $p$-value.

**9-29.** A sample of size 25 was obtained to test the hypotheses

$$H_0: \pi = 0.30$$
$$H_A: \pi \neq 0.30$$

Calculate the $p$-value for each of the following sample results:
a. $p = 0.12$
b. $p = 0.35$
c. $p = 0.42$
d. $p = 0.5$

## Business Applications

**9-30.** Suppose a recent random sample of employees nationwide that have a 401(k) retirement plan found that 18% of them had borrowed against it in the last year. A random sample of 100 employees from a local company who have a 401(k) retirement plan found that 14 had borrowed from their plan. Based on the sample results, is it possible to conclude, at the $\alpha = 0.025$ level of significance, that the local company had a lower proportion of borrowers from its 401(k) retirement plan than the 18% reported nationwide?

**9-31.** An issue that faces individuals investing for retirement is allocating assets among different investment choices. Suppose a study conducted 10 years ago showed that

65% of investors preferred stocks to real estate as an investment. In a recent random sample of 900 investors, 360 preferred real estate to stocks. Is this new data sufficient to allow you to conclude that the proportion of investors preferring stocks to real estate has declined from 10 years ago? Conduct your analysis at the $\alpha = 0.02$ level of significance.

**9-32.** A major issue facing many states is whether to legalize casino gambling. Suppose the governor of one state believes that more than 55% of the state's registered voters would favor some form of legal casino gambling. However, before backing a proposal to allow such gambling, the governor has instructed his aides to conduct a statistical test on the issue. To do this, the aides have hired a consulting firm to survey a simple random sample of 300 voters in the state. Of these 300 voters, 175 actually favored legalized gambling.
a. State the appropriate null and alternative hypotheses.
b. Assuming that a significance level of 0.05 is used, what conclusion should the governor reach based on these sample data? Discuss.

**9-33.** A recent article in *The Wall Street Journal* entitled "As Identity Theft Moves Online, Crime Rings Mimic Big Business" states that 39% of the consumer scam complaints by American consumers are about identity theft. Suppose a random sample of 90 complaints is obtained. Of these complaints, 40 were regarding identity theft. Based on these sample data, what conclusion should be reached about the statement made in *The Wall Street Journal*? (Test using $\alpha = 0.10$.)

**9-34.** Because of the complex nature of the U.S. income tax system, many people have questions for the Internal Revenue Service (IRS). Yet, an article published by the *Detroit Free Press* entitled "Assistance: IRS Help Centers Give the Wrong Information" discusses the propensity of IRS staff employees to give incorrect tax information to taxpayers who call with questions. Then IRS Inspector General Pamela Gardiner told a Senate subcommittee that "the IRS employees at 400 taxpayer assistance centers nationwide encountered 8.5 million taxpayers face-to-face last year. The problem: When inspector general auditors posing as taxpayers asked them to answer tax questions, the answers were right 69% of the time."

Suppose an independent commission was formed to test whether the 0.69 accuracy rate is correct or whether it is actually higher or lower. The commission has randomly selected $n = 180$ tax returns that were completed by IRS assistance employees and found that 105 of the returns were accurately completed.
a. State the appropriate null and alternative hypotheses.
b. Using an $\alpha = 0.05$ level, based on the sample data, what conclusion should be reached about the IRS rate of correct tax returns? Discuss your results.

**9-35.** A *Washington Post*–ABC News poll found that 72% of people are concerned about the possibility that their personal records could be stolen over the Internet. If a random sample of 300 college students at a Midwestern university were taken and 228 of them were concerned about the possibility that their personal records could be stolen over the Internet, could you conclude at the 0.025 level of significance that a higher proportion of the university's college students are concerned about Internet theft than the public at large? Report the $p$-value for this test.

**9-36.** Assume that the sports page of your local newspaper reported that 65% of males over the age of 17 in the United States would skip an important event such as a birthday party or an anniversary dinner to watch their favorite professional sports team play. A random sample of 676 adult males over the age of 17 in the Dallas-Fort Worth market reveals that 507 would be willing to skip an important event to watch their favorite team play. Given the results of the survey, can you conclude that the proportion of adult males who would skip an important event to watch their favorite team play is greater in the Dallas-Fort Worth area than in the nation as a whole? Conduct your test at the $\alpha = 0.01$ level of significance.

**9-37.** An Associated Press article written by Eileen Powell entitled "Credit Card Payments Going Up" described a recent change in credit card policies. Under pressure from federal regulators, credit card issuers have started to raise the minimum payment that consumers are required to pay on outstanding credit card balances. Suppose a claim is made that more than 40% of all credit card holders pay the minimum payment. To test this claim, a random sample of payments made by credit card customers was collected. The sample contained data for 400 customers, of which 174 paid the minimum payment.
   a. State the appropriate null and alternative hypotheses.
   b. Based on the sample data, test the null hypothesis using an alpha level equal to 0.05. Discuss the results of the test.

**9-38.** CEO Chris Foreman of Pacific Theaters Exhibition Corp. is taking steps to reverse the decline in movie attendance. Moviegoers' comfort is one of the issues facing theaters. Pacific Theaters has begun offering assigned seating, no in-theater advertising, and a live announcer who introduces films and warns patrons to turn off cell phones. Despite such efforts, an Associated Press/America Online News poll of 1,000 adults discovered that 730 of those surveyed preferred seeing movies in their homes.
   a. Using a significance level of 0.025, conduct a statistical procedure to determine if the Associated Press/America Online News poll indicates that more than 70% of adults prefer seeing movies in their homes. Use a $p$-value approach.

   b. Express a Type II error in the context of this exercise's scenario.

**9-39.** The practice of "phishing," or using the Internet to pilfer personal information, has become an increasing concern, not only for individual computer users but also for online retailers and financial institutions. *The Wall Street Journal* reported 28% of people who bank online have cut back on their Internet use. The North Central Educators Credit Union instituted an extensive online security and educational program six months ago in an effort to combat phishing before the problem became extreme. The credit union's managers are certain that while Internet use may be down, the rate for their customers is much less than 28%. However, they believe that if more than 10% of their customers have cut back on their Internet banking transactions, they will be required to take more stringent action to lower this percentage.

   The credit union's Information Technology department analyzed 200 randomly selected accounts and determined that 24 indicated they had cut back on their Internet banking transactions.
   a. State the appropriate null and alternative hypotheses for this situation.
   b. Using $\alpha = 0.05$ and the $p$-value approach, indicate whether the sample data support the managers' contention.

**9-40.** A large number of complaints have been received in the past six months regarding airlines losing fliers' baggage. The airlines claim the problem is nowhere near as great as the newspaper articles have indicated. In fact, one airline spokesman claimed that less than 1% of all bags fail to arrive at the destination with the passenger. To test this claim, 800 bags were randomly selected at various airports in the United States when they were checked with this airline. Of these, 6 failed to reach the destination when the passenger (owner) arrived.
   a. Is this sufficient evidence to support the airline spokesman's claim? Test using a significance level of 0.05. Discuss.
   b. Estimate the proportion of bags that fail to arrive at the proper destination using a technique for which 95% confidence applies.

**9-41.** Harris Interactive Inc., the 15th largest market research firm in the world, is a Rochester, New York–based company. One of its surveys indicated that 26% of women have had experience with a Global Positioning System (GPS) device. The survey indicated that 36% of the men surveyed have used a GPS device.
   a. If the survey was based on a sample size of 290 men, do these data indicate that the proportion of men is the same as the proportion of women who have had experience with a GPS device? Use a significance level of 0.05.
   b. Obtain the $p$-value for the test indicated in part a.

## Computer Database **Exercises**

**9-42.** A survey by the Pew Internet & American Life Project found that 21% of workers with an e-mail account at work say they are getting more spam than a year ago. Suppose a large multinational company, after implementing a policy to combat spam, asked 198 randomly selected employees with e-mail accounts at work whether they are receiving more spam today than they did a year ago. The results of the survey are in the file **Spam**. At the 0.025 level of significance, can the company conclude that the percentage of its employees receiving more spam than a year ago is smaller than that found by the Pew study?

**9-43.** A study by the Investment Company Institute (ICI) in 2004, which randomly surveyed 3,500 households and drew on information from the IRS, found that 72% of households have conducted at least one IRA rollover from an employer-sponsored retirement plan (www.financial-planning.com). Suppose a recent random sample of 90 households in the greater Miami area was taken and respondents were asked whether they had ever funded an IRA account with a rollover from an employer-sponsored retirement plan. The results are in the file **Miami Rollover**. Based on the sample data, can you conclude at the 0.10 level of significance that the proportion of households in the greater Miami area that have funded an IRA with a rollover is different from the proportion for all households reported in the ICI study?

**9-44.** According to the Employee Benefit Research Institute (www.ebri.org), 34% of workers between the ages of 35 and 44 owned a 401(k)-type retirement plan in 2002. Suppose a recent survey was conducted by the Atlanta Chamber of Commerce to determine the rate of 35- to 44-year-old working adults in the Atlanta metropolitan area who owned 401(k)-type retirement plans. The results of the survey can be found in the file **Atlanta Retirement**. Based on the survey results, can the Atlanta Chamber of Commerce conclude that the participation rate for 35- to 44-year-old working adults in Atlanta is higher than the 2002 national rate? Conduct your analysis at the 0.025 level of significance.

**9-45.** The Electronic Controls Company (ECCO) is one of the largest makers of backup alarms in the world. Backup alarms are the safety devices that emit a high-pitched beeping sound when a truck, forklift, or other equipment is operated in reverse. ECCO is well known in the industry for its high quality and excellent customer service, but some products are returned under warranty due to quality problems. ECCO's operations manager recently stated that less than half of the warranty returns are wiring-related problems. To verify if she is correct, a company intern was asked to select a random sample of warranty returns and determine the proportion that were returned due to wiring problems. The data the intern collected are shown in the data file called **ECCO**.

a. State the appropriate null and alternative hypotheses.

b. Conduct the hypothesis test using $\alpha = 0.02$ and provide an interpretation of the result of the hypothesis test in terms of the operation manager's claim.

**9-46.** Cell phones are becoming an integral part of our daily lives. Commissioned by Motorola, a new behavioral study took researchers to nine cities worldwide from New York to London. Using a combination of personal interviews, field studies, and observation, the study identified a variety of behaviors that demonstrate the dramatic impact cell phones are having on the way people interact. The study found cell phones give people a newfound personal power, enabling unprecedented mobility and allowing them to conduct their business on the go. Interesting enough, gender differences can be found in phone use. Women see their cell phone as a means of expression and social communication, whereas males tend to use it as an interactive toy. A cell phone industry spokesman stated that half of all cell phones in use are registered to females.

a. State the appropriate null and alternative hypotheses for testing the industry claim.

b. Based on a random sample of cell phone owners shown in the data file called **Cell Phone Survey**, test the null hypothesis. (Use $\alpha = 0.05$.)

**9-47.** Joseph-Armand Bombardier in the 1930s founded the company that is now known as Seadoo in Canada. His initial invention of the snowmobile in 1937 led the way to what is now a 7,600-employee, worldwide company specializing in both snow and water sports vehicles. The company stresses high quality in both manufacturing and dealer service. Suppose that the company standard for customer satisfaction is 95% "highly satisfied." Company managers recently completed a customer survey of 700 customers from around the world. The responses to the question "What is your overall level of satisfaction with Seadoo?" are provided in the file called **Seadoo**.

a. State the appropriate null and alternative hypotheses to be tested.

b. Using an alpha level of 0.05, conduct the hypothesis test and discuss the conclusions.

# 9.3 Type II Errors

Sections 9.1 and 9.2 provided several examples that illustrated how hypotheses and decision rules for tests of the population mean or population proportion are formulated. In these examples, we determined the critical values by first specifying the significance level, alpha: the maximum allowable probability of committing a Type I error. As we indicated, if the cost of committing a Type I error is high, the decision maker will want to specify a small significance level.

This logic provides a basis for establishing the critical value for the hypothesis test. However, it ignores the possibility of committing a Type II error. Recall that a Type II error occurs if a false null hypothesis is "accepted." The probability of a Type II error is given by the symbol $\beta$, the Greek letter *beta*. We discussed in Section 9.1 that $\alpha$ and $\beta$ are inversely related. That is, if we make $\alpha$ smaller, $\beta$ will increase. However, the two are not proportional. A case in point: Cutting $\alpha$ in half will not necessarily double $\beta$.

**Chapter Outcome 5.** ➡ ## Calculating Beta

Once $\alpha$ has been specified for a hypothesis test involving a particular sample size, $\beta$ cannot also be specified. Rather, the $\beta$ value is fixed for any specified value in that alternative hypothesis, and all the decision maker can do is calculate it. Therefore, $\beta$ is not a single value, it depends on the selected value taken from the range of values in the alternative hypothesis. Because a Type II error occurs when a false null hypothesis is "accepted" (refer to Figure 9.1, do not reject $H_0$ block), there is a $\beta$ value for each possible population value for which the alternative hypothesis is true. To calculate beta, we must first specify a "what-if" value for a true population parameter taken from the alternative hypothesis. Then, $\beta$ is computed conditional on that parameter being true. Keep in mind that $\beta$ is computed before the sample is taken, so its value is not dependent on the sample outcome.

For instance, if the null hypothesis is that the mean income for a population is equal to or greater than \$30,000, then $\beta$ could be calculated for any value of $\mu$ less than \$30,000. We would get a different $\beta$ for each value of $\mu$ in that range. An application will help clarify this concept.

**BUSINESS APPLICATION** **CALCULATING THE PROBABILITY OF A TYPE II ERROR**

**AMERICAN LIGHTING COMPANY** The American Lighting Company has developed a new light bulb to last more than 700 hours on average. If a hypothesis test could confirm this, the company would use the "greater than 700 hours" statement in its advertising. The null and alternative hypotheses are

$$H_0: \mu \leq 700 \text{ hours}$$

$$H_A: \mu > 700 \text{ hours (research hypothesis)}$$

The null hypothesis is false for all possible values of $\mu > 700$ hours. Thus, for each of the infinite number of possibilities, a value of $\beta$ can be determined for each of the parametric values in the range $\mu > 700$ hours. (*Note:* $\sigma$ is assumed to be a known value of 15 hours.)

Figure 9.9 shows how $\beta$ is calculated if the true value of $\mu$ is 701 hours. By specifying the significance level to be 0.05 and a sample size of 100 bulbs, the chance of committing a Type II error is approximately 0.8365. This means that if the true population mean is 701 hours, there is nearly an 84% chance that the sampling plan American Lighting is using will not reject the assumption that the mean is 700 hours or less.

Figure 9.10 shows that if the "what-if" mean value ($\mu = 704$) is farther from the hypothesized mean ($\mu = 700$), beta becomes smaller. The greater the difference between the mean specified in $H_0$ and the mean selected from $H_A$, the easier it is to tell the two apart, and the less likely we are to not reject the null hypothesis when it is actually false. Of course the opposite is also true. As the mean selected from $H_A$ moves increasingly closer to the mean specified in $H_0$, the harder it is for the hypothesis test to distinguish between the two.

**FIGURE 9.9**

Beta Calculation for True
$\mu = 701$

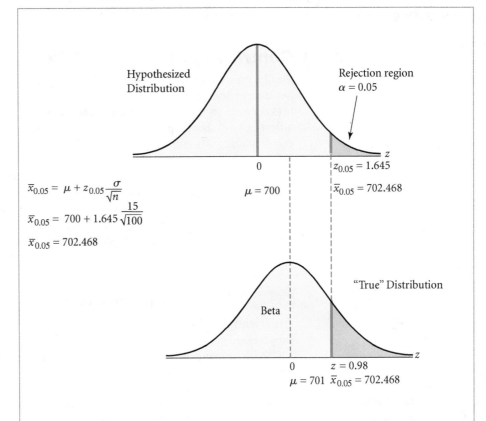

$$\bar{x}_{0.05} = \mu + z_{0.05}\frac{\sigma}{\sqrt{n}}$$

$$\bar{x}_{0.05} = 700 + 1.645\frac{15}{\sqrt{100}}$$

$$\bar{x}_{0.05} = 702.468$$

$$z = \frac{\bar{x}_{0.05} - \mu}{\frac{\sigma}{\sqrt{n}}} = \frac{702.468 - 701}{\frac{15}{\sqrt{100}}} = 0.98$$

From the standard normal table, $P(0 \le z \le 0.98) = 0.3365$
Beta $= 0.5000 + 0.3365 = 0.8365$

**FIGURE 9.10**

Beta Calculation for True
$\mu = 704$

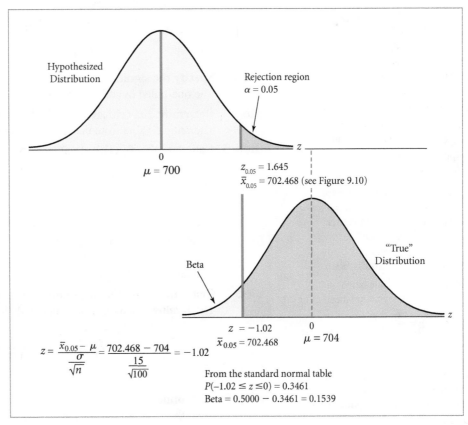

$$z = \frac{\bar{x}_{0.05} - \mu}{\frac{\sigma}{\sqrt{n}}} = \frac{702.468 - 704}{\frac{15}{\sqrt{100}}} = -1.02$$

From the standard normal table
$P(-1.02 \le z \le 0) = 0.3461$
Beta $= 0.5000 - 0.3461 = 0.1539$

## Controlling Alpha and Beta

Ideally, we want both alpha and beta to be as small as possible. Although we can set alpha at any desired level, for a specified sample size and standard deviation, the calculated value of beta depends on the population mean chosen from the alternative hypothesis and on the significance level. For a specified sample size, reducing alpha will increase beta. However, we can simultaneously control the size of both alpha and beta if we are willing to change the sample size.

The American Lighting Company planned to take a sample of 100 light bulbs. In Figure 9.9, we showed that beta = 0.8365 when the "true" population mean was 701 hours. This is a very large probability and would be unacceptable to the company. However, if the company is willing to incur the cost associated with a sample size of 500 bulbs, the probability of a Type II error could be reduced to 0.5596, as shown in Figure 9.11. This is a big improvement and is due to the fact that the standard error $(\sigma/\sqrt{n})$ is reduced because of the increased sample size.

---

**EXAMPLE 9-10    CALCULATING BETA**

**American Tax Services** American Tax Services, a regional income tax preparation company located primarily in southern states, has claimed its clients save an average of more than $200 each by using the company's services. A consumer's group plans to randomly sample 64 customers to test this claim. The standard deviation of the amount saved is assumed to be $100. Before testing, the consumer's group is interested in knowing the probability that it will mistakenly conclude that the mean savings is less than or equal to $200 when, in fact, it does exceed $200, as the company claims. To find beta if the true population mean is $210, the company can use the following steps.

**Step 1    Specify the population parameter of interest.**
The consumer group is interested in the mean savings of American Tax Services' clients, $\mu$.

**Step 2    Specify the null and alternative hypotheses.**
The null and alternative hypotheses are

$$H_0: \mu \leq \$200$$
$$H_A: \mu > \$200 \text{ (claim)}$$

**Step 3    Specify the significance level.**
The one-tailed hypothesis test will be conducted using $\alpha = 0.05$.

**Step 4    Determine the critical value, $z_\alpha$, from the standard normal distribution.**
The critical value from the standard normal is $z_\alpha = z_{0.05} = 1.645$.

**Step 5    Calculate the $\bar{x}_\alpha$ critical value.**

$$\bar{x}_{0.05} = \mu + z_{0.05}\frac{\sigma}{\sqrt{n}} = 200 + 1.645\frac{100}{\sqrt{64}} = 220.56$$

Thus, the null hypothesis will be rejected if $\bar{x} > 220.56$.

**Step 6    Specify the stipulated value for $\mu$.**
The null hypothesis is false for all values greater than $200. What is beta if the stipulated mean is $210?

**Step 7    Compute the $z$-value based on the stipulated population mean.**
The $z$-value based on stipulated population mean is

$$z = \frac{\bar{x}_{0.05} - \mu}{\frac{\sigma}{\sqrt{n}}} = \frac{220.56 - 210}{\frac{100}{\sqrt{64}}} = 0.84$$

**Step 8    Determine beta.**
From the standard normal table, the probability associated with $z = 0.84$ is 0.2995. Then $\beta = 0.5000 + 0.2995 = 0.7995$. There is a 0.7995 probability

---

**How to do it** (Example 9-10)

**Calculating Beta**
**The probability of committing a Type II error can be calculated using the following steps.**

1. Specify the population parameter of interest.

2. Formulate the null and alternative hypotheses.

3. Specify the significance level. (*Hint*: Draw a picture of the hypothesized sampling distribution showing the rejection region(s) and the acceptance region found by specifying the significance level.)

4. Determine the critical value, $z_\alpha$, from the standard normal distribution.

5. Determine the critical value, $\bar{x}_\alpha = \mu + z_\alpha\,\sigma/\sqrt{n}$ for an upper-tail test, or $\bar{x}_\alpha = \mu - z_\alpha\,\sigma/\sqrt{n}$ for a lower-tail test.

6. Specify the stipulated value for $\mu$, the "true" population mean for which you wish to compute $\beta$. (*Hint*: Draw the "true" distribution immediately below the hypothesized distribution.)

7. Compute the $z$-value based on the stipulated population mean as
$$z = \frac{\bar{x}_\alpha - \mu}{\frac{\sigma}{\sqrt{n}}}$$

8. Use the standard normal table to find $\beta$, the probability associated with "accepting" (not rejecting) the null hypothesis when it is false.

**FIGURE 9.11**

American Lighting Company, Beta Calculation for "True" $\mu = 701$ and $n = 500$

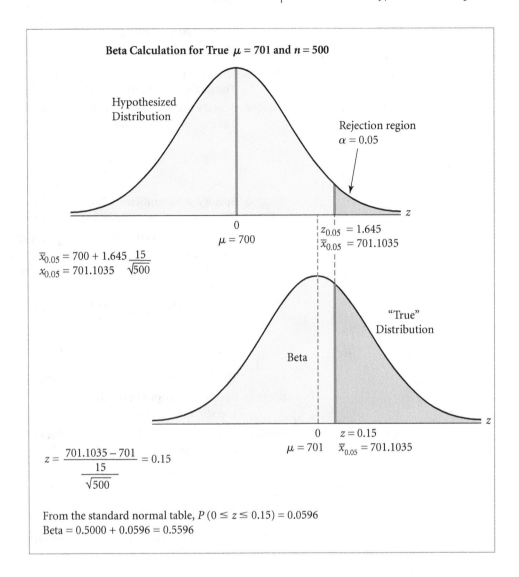

Beta Calculation for True $\mu = 701$ and $n = 500$

Hypothesized Distribution

Rejection region $\alpha = 0.05$

0
$\mu = 700$

$z_{0.05} = 1.645$
$\bar{x}_{0.05} = 701.1035$

$z$

$\bar{x}_{0.05} = 700 + 1.645 \dfrac{15}{\sqrt{500}}$
$x_{0.05} = 701.1035$

"True" Distribution

Beta

0                 $z = 0.15$
$\mu = 701$   $\bar{x}_{0.05} = 701.1035$

$z$

$z = \dfrac{701.1035 - 701}{\dfrac{15}{\sqrt{500}}} = 0.15$

From the standard normal table, $P(0 \leq z \leq 0.15) = 0.0596$
Beta $= 0.5000 + 0.0596 = 0.5596$

that the hypothesis test will lead the consumer agency to mistakenly believe that the mean tax savings is less than or equal to $200 when, in fact, the mean savings is $210.

>>**END EXAMPLE**

**TRY PROBLEM** 9-49 (pg. 383)

---

**EXAMPLE 9-11**   **CALCULATING BETA FOR A TWO-TAILED TEST**

**Billiard Ball Production** Saluc, a Belgium-based manufacturer of billiard balls, produces and distributes billiard balls under the registered trademark Aramith in more than 85 countries and has a market share of 80% worldwide. High-technology machinery and computerized equipment allow the company to produce balls that require tight dimensional tolerances. Perhaps the most important dimension is the diameter of the balls. They must have a diameter that is 2.25 inches for the American market. If the diameter is too large or small, it affects the playing characteristics of the balls. Therefore, each hour the quality control engineers select a random sample of 20 balls from the production line and measure the diameter of each ball. The standard deviation is tightly controlled as well. Assume $\sigma = 0.005$ inches. Experience might show that as the production machinery ages, the diameter of the balls tends to increase. Suppose that the quality engineers are interested in how likely the test procedure they use will conclude that the mean diameter is equal to 2.25 inches when, in fact, the mean equals

2.255 inches. They want to know the probability of a Type II error. To find beta for this test procedure under these conditions, the engineers can use the following steps:

**Step 1** **Specify the population parameter of interest.**
The quality engineers are interested in the mean diameter of the billiard balls, $\mu$.

**Step 2** **Specify the null and alternative hypotheses.**
The null and alternative hypotheses are

$$H_0: \mu = 2.25 \text{ (status quo)}$$

$$H_A: \mu \neq 2.25$$

**Step 3** **Specify the significance level.**
The two-tailed hypothesis test will be conducted using $\alpha = 0.05$.

**Step 4** **Determine the critical values, $z_{(\alpha/2)L}$ and $z_{(\alpha/2)U}$, from the standard normal distribution.**
The critical value from the standard normal is $z_{(\alpha/2)L}$ and $z_{(\alpha/2)U} = \pm z_{0.025} = \pm 1.96$.

**Step 5** **Calculate the $\bar{x}_{(\alpha/2)L}$ and $\bar{x}_{(\alpha/2)U}$ critical values.**

$$\bar{x}_{L,U} = \mu \pm z_{0.025} \frac{\sigma}{\sqrt{n}} = 2.25 \pm 1.96 \frac{0.005}{\sqrt{20}} \rightarrow \bar{x}_L = 2.2478; \bar{x}_U = 2.2522$$

Thus, the null hypothesis will be rejected if $\bar{x} < 2.2478$ or $\bar{x} > 2.2522$

**Step 6** **Specify the stipulated value of $\mu$.**
The stipulated value of $\mu$ is 2.255.

**Step 7** **Compute the $z$-values based on the stipulated population mean.**
The $z$-values based on the stipulated population mean is

$$z = \frac{\bar{x}_L - \mu}{\frac{\sigma}{\sqrt{n}}} = \frac{2.2478 - 2.255}{\frac{0.005}{\sqrt{20}}} = -6.44 \quad \text{and} \quad z = \frac{\bar{x}_U - \mu}{\frac{\sigma}{\sqrt{n}}} = \frac{2.2522 - 2.255}{\frac{0.005}{\sqrt{20}}} = -2.50$$

**Step 8** **Determine beta and reach a conclusion.**
Beta is the probability from the standard normal distribution between $z = -6.44$ and $z = -2.50$. From the standard normal table, we get

$$(0.5000 - 0.5000) + (0.5000 - 0.4938) = 0.0062$$

Thus, beta = 0.0062. There is a very small chance (only 0.0062) that this hypothesis test will fail to detect that the mean diameter has shifted to 2.255 inches from the desired mean of 2.25 inches. This low beta will give the engineers confidence that their test can detect problems when they occur.

>>**END EXAMPLE**

**TRY PROBLEM** 9-59 (pg. 384)

As shown in Section 9.2, many business applications will involve hypotheses tests about population proportions rather than population means. Example 9-12 illustrates the steps needed to compute the beta for a hypothesis test involving proportions.

**EXAMPLE 9-12**   **CALCULATING BETA FOR A TEST OF A POPULATION PROPORTION**

**The National Federation of Independent Business** The National Federation of Independent Business (NFIB) has offices in Washington, D.C., and all 50 state capitals. NFIB is the nation's largest small-business lobbying group. Its research foundation provides policymakers, small-business owners, and other interested parties with empirically based information on small businesses. NFIB often initiates surveys to provide this information. A speech by a senior administration official claimed that at least 30% of all small businesses were owned, or operated, by women. NFIB internal analyses had the number at closer to 25%. As a result, the NFIB analysts planned to conduct a test to determine if the percentage of small businesses owned by women was less than 30%. Additionally, they were quite interested in determining the probability (beta) of "accepting" the claim ($\geq$30%) of the senior administration official if in fact the true percentage was 25%. A simple random sample of 500 small businesses will be selected.

**Step 1** **Specify the population parameter of interest.**
NFIB is interested in the proportion of female-owned small businesses, $\pi$.

**Step 2** **Specify the null and alternative hypotheses.**

$$H_0: \pi \geq 0.30 \text{ (claim)}$$

$$H_A: \pi < 0.30$$

**Step 3** **Specify the significance level.**
The one-tailed hypothesis test will be conducted using $\alpha = 0.025$.

**Step 4** **Determine the critical value, $z_\alpha$, from the standard normal distribution.**
The critical value from the standard normal is $z_\alpha = z_{0.025} = -1.96$.

**Step 5** **Calculate the $p_\alpha$ critical value.**

$$p_{0.025} = \pi - z_{0.025}\sqrt{\frac{\pi(1-\pi)}{n}} = 0.30 - 1.96\sqrt{\frac{0.30(1-0.30)}{500}} = 0.2598$$

Therefore, the null hypothesis will be rejected if $p < 0.2598$.

**Step 6** **Specify the stipulated value for the "true" $\pi$.**
The stipulated value is 0.25.

**Step 7** **Compute the $z$-value based on the stipulated population proportion.**
The $z$-value is

$$z = \frac{p_\alpha - \pi}{\sqrt{\frac{\pi(1-\pi)}{n}}} = \frac{0.2598 - 0.25}{\sqrt{\frac{0.25(1-0.25)}{500}}} = 0.51$$

**Step 8** **Determine beta.**
From the standard normal table, the probability associated with $z = 0.51$ is 0.1950. Then $\beta = 0.5000 - 0.1950 = 0.3050$. Thus, there is a 0.3050 chance that the hypothesis test will "accept" the null hypothesis that the percentage of women-owned or operated small businesses is $\geq$30% if in fact the true percentage is only 25%. The NFIB may wish to increase the sample size to improve beta.

>>**END EXAMPLE**

**TRY PROBLEM** 9-57 (pg. 384)

As you now know, hypothesis tests are subject to error. The two potential statistical errors are

Type I (rejecting a true null hypothesis)

Type II (failing to reject or "accepting" a false null hypothesis)

In most business applications, there are adverse consequences associated with each type of error. In some cases, the errors can mean dollar costs to a company. For instance, suppose a health insurance company is planning to set its premium rates based on a hypothesized mean annual claims amount per participant as follows:

$$H_0: \mu \leq \$1,700$$

$$H_A: \mu > \$1,700$$

If the company tests the hypothesis and "accepts" the null, it will institute the planned premium rate structure. However, if a Type II error is committed, the actual average claim will exceed $1,700, and the company will incur unexpected payouts and suffer reduced profits. On the other hand, if the company rejects the null hypothesis, it will probably increase its premium rates. But if a Type I error is committed, there would be no justification for the rate increase, and the company may not be competitive in the marketplace and could lose customers.

In other cases, the costs associated with either a Type I or a Type II error may be even more serious. If a drug company's hypothesis tests for a new drug incorrectly conclude that the drug is safe when in fact it is not (Type I error), the company's customers may become ill or even die as a result. You might refer to recent reports dealing with pain medications such as Vicodin. On the other hand, a Type II error would mean that a potentially useful and safe drug would most likely not be made available to people who need it if the hypothesis tests incorrectly determined that the drug was not safe.

In the U.S. legal system where a defendant is hypothesized to be innocent, a Type I error by a jury would result in a conviction of an innocent person. DNA evidence has recently resulted in a number of convicted people being set free. A case in point is Hubert Geralds, who was convicted of killing Rhonda King in 1994 in the state of Illinois. On the other hand, Type II errors in our court system result in guilty people being set free to potentially commit other crimes.

The bottom line is that as a decision maker using hypothesis testing, you need to be aware of the potential costs associated with both Type I and Type II statistical errors and conduct your tests accordingly.

## Power of the Test

In the previous examples, we have been concerned about the chance of making a Type II error. We would like beta to be as small as possible. If the null hypothesis is false, we want to reject it. Another way to look at this is that we would like the hypothesis test to have a high probability of rejecting a false null hypothesis. This concept is expressed by what is called the **power** of the test. When the alternative hypothesis is true, the power of the test is computed using Equation 9.5.

**Power**

The probability that the hypothesis test will correctly reject the null hypothesis when the null hypothesis is false.

---

**Power**

$$\text{Power} = 1 - \beta \qquad\qquad (9.5)$$

---

Refer again to the business application involving the American Lighting Company. Beta calculations were presented in Figures 9.9, 9.10, and 9.11. For example, in Figure 9.9, the company was interested in the probability of a Type II error if the "true" population mean was 701 hours instead of the hypothesized mean of 700 hours. This probability, called beta, was shown to be 0.8365. Then for this same test,

$$\text{Power} = 1 - \beta$$
$$\text{Power} = 1 - 0.8365 = 0.1635$$

Thus, in this situation, there is only a 0.1635 chance that the hypothesis test will correctly reject the null hypothesis that the mean is 700 or fewer hours when in fact it really is 701 hours.

In Figure 9.10, when a "true" mean of 704 hours was considered, the value of beta dropped to 0.1539. Likewise, power is increased:

$$\text{Power} = 1 - 0.1539 = 0.8461$$

So the probability of correctly rejecting the null hypothesis increases to 0.8461 when the "true" mean is 704 hours.

We also saw in Figure 9.11 that an increase in sample size resulted in a decreased beta value. For a "true" mean of 701 but with a sample size increase from 100 to 500, the value of beta dropped from 0.8365 to 0.5596. That means that power is increased from 0.1635 to 0.4404 due to the increased size of the sample.

A graph called a **power curve** can be created to show the power of a hypothesis test for various levels of the "true" population parameter. Figure 9.12 shows the power curve for the American Lighting Company application for a sample size of $n = 100$.

**Power Curve**

A graph showing the probability that the hypothesis test will correctly reject a false null hypothesis for a range of possible "true" values for the population parameter.

**FIGURE 9.12**

American Lighting
Company—Power Curve

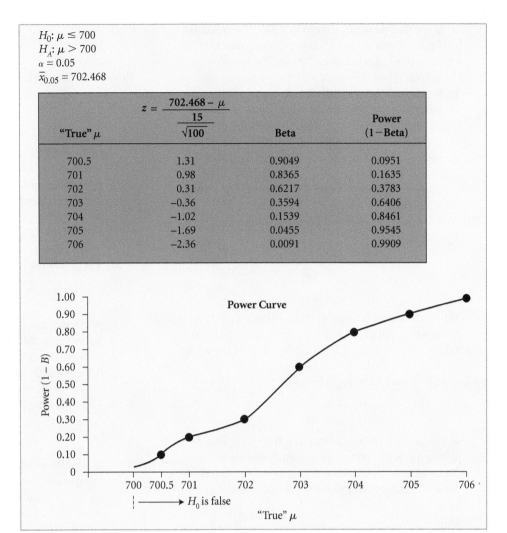

$H_0: \mu \leq 700$
$H_A: \mu > 700$
$\alpha = 0.05$
$\bar{x}_{0.05} = 702.468$

| "True" $\mu$ | $z = \dfrac{702.468 - \mu}{\frac{15}{\sqrt{100}}}$ | Beta | Power $(1 - \text{Beta})$ |
|---|---|---|---|
| 700.5 | 1.31 | 0.9049 | 0.0951 |
| 701 | 0.98 | 0.8365 | 0.1635 |
| 702 | 0.31 | 0.6217 | 0.3783 |
| 703 | −0.36 | 0.3594 | 0.6406 |
| 704 | −1.02 | 0.1539 | 0.8461 |
| 705 | −1.69 | 0.0455 | 0.9545 |
| 706 | −2.36 | 0.0091 | 0.9909 |

## MyStatLab

# 9-3: Exercises

## Skill Development

**9-48.** You are given the following null and alternative hypotheses:

$$H_0: \mu = 200$$
$$H_A: \mu \neq 200$$
$$\alpha = 0.10$$

Calculate the probability of committing a Type II error when the population mean is 197, the sample size is 36, and the population standard deviation is known to be 24.

**9-49.** You are given the following null and alternative hypotheses:

$$H_0: \mu = 1.20$$
$$H_A: \mu \neq 1.20$$
$$\alpha = 0.10$$

a. If the true population mean is 1.25, determine the value of beta. Assume the population standard deviation is known to be 0.50 and the sample size is 60.
b. Referring to part a, calculate the power of the test.
c. Referring to parts a and b, what could be done to increase power and reduce beta when the true population mean is 1.25? Discuss.
d. Indicate clearly the decision rule that would be used to test the null hypothesis, and determine what decision should be made if the sample mean were 1.23.

**9-50.** You are given the following null and alternative hypotheses:

$$H_0: \mu \geq 4,350$$
$$H_A: \mu < 4,350$$
$$\alpha = 0.05$$

a. If the true population mean is 4,345, determine the value of beta. Assume the population standard deviation is known to be 200 and the sample size is 100.

b. Referring to part a, calculate the power of the test.

c. Referring to parts a and b, what could be done to increase power and reduce beta when the true population mean is 4,345? Discuss.

d. Indicate clearly the decision rule that would be used to test the null hypothesis, and determine what decision should be made if the sample mean were 4,337.50.

**9-51.** You are given the following null and alternative hypotheses:

$$H_0: \mu \leq 500$$
$$H_A: \mu > 500$$
$$\alpha = 0.01$$

Calculate the probability of committing a Type II error when the population mean is 505, the sample size is 64, and the population standard deviation is known to be 36.

**9-52.** Consider the following hypotheses:

$$H_0: \mu \geq 103$$
$$H_A: \mu < 103$$

A sample of size 20 is to be taken from a population with a mean of 100 and a standard deviation of 4. Determine the probability of committing a Type II error for each of the following significance levels:

a. $\alpha = 0.01$

b. $\alpha = 0.025$

c. $\alpha = 0.05$

**9-53.** Solve for beta when the "true" population mean is 103 and the following information is given:

$$H_0: \mu \leq 100$$
$$H_A: \mu > 100$$
$$\alpha = 0.05$$
$$\sigma = 10$$
$$n = 49$$

**9-54.** For each of the following situations, indicate what the general impact on the Type II error probability will be:

a. The alpha level is increased.

b. The "true" population mean is moved farther from the hypothesized population mean.

c. The alpha level is decreased.

d. The sample size is increased.

**9-55.** Consider the following hypotheses:

$$H_0: \mu = 30$$
$$H_A: \mu \neq 30$$

A sample of size 50 is to be taken from a population with a standard deviation of 13. The hypothesis test is to be conducted using a significance level of 0.05. Determine the probability of committing a Type II error when

a. $\mu = 22$

b. $\mu = 25$

c. $\mu = 29$

**9-56.** Consider the following hypotheses:

$$H_0: \mu \leq 201$$
$$H_A: \mu > 201$$

A sample is to be taken from a population with a mean of 203 and a standard deviation of 3. The hypothesis test is to be conducted using a significance level of 0.05. Determine the probability of committing a Type II error when

a. $n = 10$

b. $n = 20$

c. $n = 50$

**9-57.** The following hypotheses are to be tested:

$$H_0: \pi \leq 0.65$$
$$H_A: \pi > 0.65$$

A random sample of 500 is taken. Using each set of information following, compute the power of the test.

a. $\alpha = 0.01$, true $\pi = 0.68$

b. $\alpha = 0.025$, true $\pi = 0.67$

c. $\alpha = 0.05$, true $\pi = 0.66$

**9-58.** The following hypotheses are to be tested:

$$H_0: \pi \geq 0.35$$
$$H_A: \pi < 0.35$$

A random sample of 400 is taken. Using each set of information following, compute the power of the test.

a. $\alpha = 0.01$, true $\pi = 0.32$

b. $\alpha = 0.025$, true $\pi = 0.33$

c. $\alpha = 0.05$, true $\pi = 0.34$

## Business Applications

**9-59.** According to data from the Environmental Protection Agency, the average daily water consumption for a household of four people in the United States is approximately at least 243 gallons. (*Source*: http://www.catskillcenter.org/programs/csp/H20/Lesson3/house3.htm) Suppose a state agency plans to test this claim using an alpha level equal to 0.05 and a random sample of 100 households with four people.

a. State the appropriate null and alternative hypotheses.

b. Calculate the probability of committing a Type II error if the true population mean is 230 gallons. Assume that the population standard deviation is known to be 40 gallons.

**9-60.** Swift is the holding company for Swift Transportation Co., Inc., a truckload carrier headquartered in Phoenix, Arizona. Swift operates the largest truckload fleet in the United States. Before Swift switched to its current computer-based billing system, the average payment time from customers was approximately 40 days. Suppose before purchasing the present billing system, it performed a test by examining a random sample of 24 invoices to see if the system would reduce the average billing time. The sample indicates that the average payment time is 38.7 days.

a. The company that created the billing system indicates that the system would reduce the average billing time to less than 40 days. Conduct a hypothesis test to determine if the new computer-based billing system would reduce the average billing time to less than 40 days. Assume the standard deviation is known to be 6 days. Use a significance level of 0.025.

b. If the billing system actually reduced the average billing time to 36 days, determine the probability that a wrong decision was made in part a.

9-61. Waiters at Finegold's Restaurant and Lounge earn most of their income from tips. Each waiter is required to "tip-out" a portion of tips to the table bussers and hostesses. The manager has based the "tip-out" rate on the assumption that the mean tip is at least 15% of the customer bill. To make sure that this is the correct assumption, he has decided to conduct a test by randomly sampling 60 bills and recording the actual tips.

a. State the appropriate null and alternative hypotheses.

b. Calculate the probability of a Type II error if the true mean is 14%. Assume that the population standard deviation is known to be 2% and that a significance level equal to 0.01 will be used to conduct the hypothesis test.

9-62. Nationwide Mutual Insurance, based in Columbus, Ohio, is one of the largest diversified insurance and financial services organizations in the world, with more than $157 billion in assets. Nationwide ranked 108th on the Fortune 100 list in 2008. The company provides a full range of insurance and financial services. In a recent news release Nationwide reported the results of a new survey of 1,097 identity theft victims. The survey shows victims spend an average of 81 hours trying to resolve their cases. If the true average time spent was 81 hours, determine the probability that a test of hypothesis designed to test that the average was less than 85 hours would select the research hypothesis. Use $\alpha = 0.05$ and a standard deviation of 50.

9-63. According to CNN business partner Careerbuilder.com, the average starting salary for accounting graduates in 2008 was at least $47,413. Suppose that the American Society for Certified Public Accountants planned to test this claim by randomly sampling 200 accountants who graduated in 2008.

a. State the appropriate null and alternative hypotheses.

b. Compute the power of the hypothesis test to reject the null hypothesis if the true average starting salary is only $47,000. Assume that the population standard deviation is known to be $4,600 and the test is to be conducted using an alpha level equal to 0.01.

9-64. According to the Internet source Smartbrief.com, per capita U. S. beer consumption increased in 2008 after several years of decline. Current per capita is 22 gallons per year. A survey is designed to determine if the per capita consumption has changed in the current year. A hypothesis test is to be conducted using a sample size of 1,500, a significance level of 0.01, and a standard deviation of 40. Determine the probability that the test will be able to correctly detect that the per capita consumption has changed if it has declined by 10%.

9-65. Runzheimer International, a management consulting firm specializing in transportation reimbursement, released the results of a survey on July 28, 2005. It indicated that it costs more to own a car in Detroit, an amazing $11,844 a year for a mid-sized sedan, than in any other city in the country. The survey revealed that insurance, at $5,162 annually for liability, collision, and comprehensive coverage, is the biggest single reason that maintaining a car in the Motor City is so expensive. A sample size of 100 car owners in Los Angeles was used to determine if the cost of owning a car was more than 10% less than in Detroit. A hypothesis test with a significance level of 0.01 and a standard deviation of $750 is used. Determine the probability that the test will conclude the cost of owning a car in Los Angeles is not more than 10% less than in Detroit when in fact the average cost is $10,361.

9-66. The union negotiations between labor and management at the Stone Container paper mill in Minnesota hit a snag when management asked labor to take a cut in health insurance coverage. As part of its justification, management claimed that the average amount of insurance claims filed by union employees did not exceed $250 per employee. The union's chief negotiator requested that a sample of 100 employees' records be selected and that this claim be tested statistically. The claim would be accepted if the sample data did not strongly suggest otherwise. The significance level for the test was set at 0.10.

a. State the null and alternative hypotheses.

b. Before the sample was selected, the negotiator was interested in knowing the power of the test if the mean amount of insurance claims was $260. (Assume the standard deviation in claims is $70.00, as determined in a similar study at another plant location.) Calculate this probability for the negotiator.

c. Referring to part b, how would the power of the test change if $\alpha = 0.05$ is used?

d. Suppose alpha is left at 0.10, but the standard deviation of the population is $50.00 rather than $70.00. What will be the power of the test? State the generalization that explains the relationship between the answers to part b and d.

e. Referring to part d, based on the probability computed, if you were the negotiator, would you be satisfied with the sampling plan in this situation? Explain why or why not. What steps could be taken to improve the sampling plan?

## Computer Database **Exercises**

**9-67.** *USA Today* reports (Gary Stoller, "Hotel Bill Mistakes Mean Many Pay Too Much") that George Hansen, CEO of Wichita-based Corporate Lodging Consultants, conducted a recent review of hotel bills over a 12-month period. The review indicated that, on average, errors in hotel bills resulted in overpayment of $11.35 per night. To determine if such mistakes are being made at a major hotel chain, the CEO might direct a survey yielding the following data:

| | | | | | | | | | |
|---|---|---|---|---|---|---|---|---|---|
| ·9.99 | 9.87 | 11.53 | 12.40 | 12.36 | 11.68 | 12.52 | 9.34 | 13.13 | 10.78 |
| 9.76 | 10.88 | 10.61 | 10.29 | 10.23 | 9.29 | 8.82 | 8.70 | 8.22 | 11.01 |
| 12.40 | 9.55 | 11.30 | 10.21 | 8.19 | 10.56 | 8.49 | 7.99 | 8.03 | 10.53 |

The file **OverPay** contains these data.

a. Conduct a hypothesis test with $\alpha = 0.05$ to determine if the average overpayment is smaller than that indicated by Corporate Lodging Consultants.

b. If the actual average overpayment at the hotel chain was $11 with an actual standard deviation of $1.50, determine the probability that the hypothesis test would correctly indicate that the actual average is less than $11.35.

**9-68.** In an article in *Business Week* ("Living on the Edge at American Apparel"), Dov Chaney, the CEO of American Apparel, indicated that the apparel store industry's average sales were $1,800/7 (= $257.14) a square foot. A hypothesis test was requested to determine if the data supported the statement made by the American Apparel CEO using an $\alpha = 0.05$ and a sample size of 41. Produce the probability that the data will indicate that American Apparel stores produce an average of seven times the apparel industry average when in fact they only produce an average six times the apparel industry average with a standard deviation of 100. The file called **Apparel** contains data for a random sample of several competitors' sales per square foot. Use $\alpha = 0.05$.

**END EXERCISES** 9-3

# Visual Summary

**Chapter 9:** Hypothesis testing is a major part of business statistics. Statistical hypothesis testing provides managers with a structured analytical method for making decisions where a claim about a population parameter is tested using a sample statistic in a way that incorporates the potential for sampling error. By providing a structured approach, statistical hypothesis testing allows decision makers to identify and control the level of uncertainty associated with making decisions about a population based on a sample.

 **9.1** Hypothesis Tests for Means (pg. 347–368)

## Summary

In hypothesis testing, two hypotheses are formulated: the **null hypothesis** and the **alternative hypothesis**. The **null hypothesis** is a statement about the population parameter which will be rejected only if the sample data provide substantial contradictory evidence. The null hypothesis always contains an equality sign. The **alternative hypothesis** is a statement that contains all population values not included in the null hypothesis. If the null hypothesis is rejected, then the alternative hypothesis is deemed to be true. It is important to specify the null and alternative hypotheses correctly so that the results obtained from the test are not misleading.

Because of sampling error, two possible errors can occur when a hypothesis is tested: **Type I** and **Type II errors**. A **Type I Error** occurs when the null hypothesis is rejected, when, in fact, it is true. The maximum allowable probability of committing a Type I statistical error is called the **significance level**. The significance level is specified by the decision maker conducting the test. **A Type II Error** occurs when the decision maker fails to reject the null hypothesis when it is, in fact, false. Controlling for this type of error is more difficult than controlling for the probability of committing a Type I error. Once the null and alternative hypotheses have been stated and the significance level specified, the decision maker must then determine the **critical value**. The **critical value** is the value corresponding to a significance level that determines those test statistics that lead to rejecting the null hypothesis and those that lead to not rejecting the null hypothesis. A **test statistic** is then calculated from the sample data and compared to the critical value. A decision regarding whether to reject or to not reject the null hypothesis is then made.

In many case, especially where hypothesis testing is conducted using a computer, a **p-value** is often used to test hypotheses. The **p-value** is the probability (assuming that the null hypothesis is true) of obtaining a test statistic at least as extreme as the test statistic calculated from the sample. If the *p*-value is smaller than the significance level, then the null hypothesis is rejected.

Hypothesis tests may be either **one-tailed** or **two-tailed**. A **one-tailed test** is a hypothesis test in which the entire rejection region is located in one tail of the sampling distribution. A **two-tailed test** is a hypothesis test in which the entire rejection region is divided evenly into the two tails of the sampling distribution.

> **Outcome 1.** Formulate the null and alternative hypotheses for applications involving a single population mean or proportion.
> **Outcome 2.** Know what Type I and Type II errors are.
> **Outcome 3.** Correctly formulate a decision rule for testing a null hypothesis.
> **Outcome 4.** Know how to use the test statistic, critical value, and *p*-value approaches to test the null hypothesis

 **9.2** Hypothesis Tests for Proportions (pg. 368–375)

## Summary

Hypotheses tests for a single population proportion follow the same steps as hypotheses tests for a single population mean. Those steps are:

1. State the null and alternative hypotheses in terms of the population parameter, now $\pi$ instead of $\mu$.
2. The null hypothesis is a statement concerning the parameter that includes the equality sign.
3. The significance level specified by the decision maker determines the size of the rejection region.
4. The test can be a one- or two-tailed test, depending on how the alternative hypothesis is formulated.

 **9.3** Type II Errors (pg. 376–386)

## Summary

A Type II error occurs when a false null hypothesis is "accepted." The probability of committing a Type II error is denoted by $\beta$. Unfortunately, once the significance level for a hypothesis test has been specified, $\beta$ cannot also be specified. Rather, $\beta$ is a fixed value and all the decision maker can do is calculate it. However, $\beta$ is not a single value. Because a Type II error occurs when a false null hypothesis is "accepted," there is a $\beta$ value for each possible population value for which the null hypothesis is false. To calculate $\beta$, the decision maker must first specify a "what-if" value for the true population parameter. Then, $\beta$ is computed before the sample is taken, so its value is not dependent on the sample outcome. The size of both $\alpha$ and $\beta$ can be simultaneously controlled if the decision maker is willing to increase the sample size.

The probability that the hypothesis test will correctly reject the null hypothesis when the null hypothesis is false is referred to as the **power** of the test. The power of the test is computed as $1 - \beta$. A **power curve** is a graph showing the probability that the hypothesis test will correctly reject a false null hypothesis for a range of possible "true" values for the population parameter.

> **Outcome 5.** Compute the probability of a Type II error.

 ## Conclusion

Many decision-making applications require that a hypothesis test of a single population parameter be conducted. This chapter discusses how to conduct hypothesis tests of a single population mean and a single population proportion. The chapter has emphasized the importance of recognizing that when a hypothesis is tested, an error might occur. Statistical hypothesis testing provides managers with a structured analytical method for making decisions where a claim about a population parameter is tested using a sample statistic in a way that incorporates the potential for sampling error. **Figure 9.13** provides a flowchart for deciding which hypothesis testing procedure to use.

**FIGURE 9.13** |

Deciding Which Hypothesis
Testing Procedure to Use

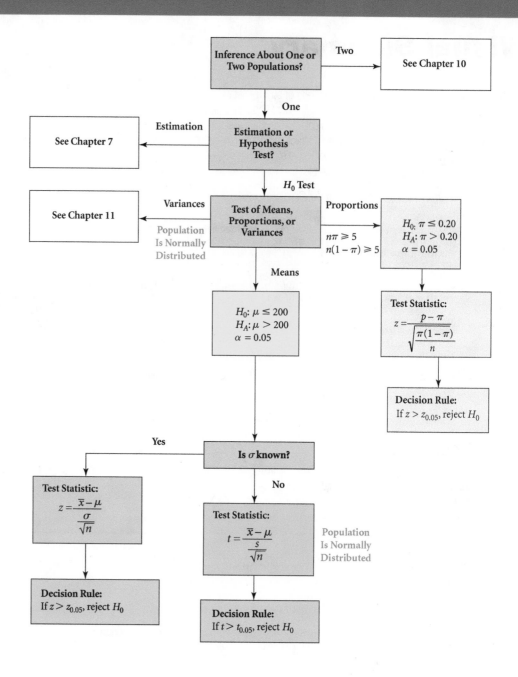

# Equations

**(9.1)** $\bar{x}_\alpha$ for Hypothesis Tests, $\sigma$ Known pg. 353

$$\bar{x}_\alpha = \mu + z_\alpha \frac{\sigma}{\sqrt{n}}$$

**(9.2)** z-Test Statistic for Hypothesis Tests for $\mu$, $\sigma$ Known pg. 354

$$z = \frac{\bar{x} - \mu}{\frac{\sigma}{\sqrt{n}}}$$

**(9.3)** t-Test Statistic for Hypothesis Tests for $\mu$, $\sigma$ Unknown pg. 361

$$t = \frac{\bar{x} - \mu}{\frac{s}{\sqrt{n}}}$$

**(9.4)** z-Test Statistic for Proportions pg. 370

$$z = \frac{p - \pi}{\sqrt{\frac{\pi(1 - \pi)}{n}}}$$

**(9.5)** Power pg. 382

$$\text{Power} = 1 - \beta$$

# Key Terms

Alternative hypothesis pg. 347
Critical value pg. 352
Null hypothesis pg. 347
One-tailed test pg. 358
p-value pg. 357

Power pg. 382
Power curve pg. 382
Research hypothesis pg. 348
Significance level pg. 352
Two-tailed test pg. 358

Test statistic pg. 354
Type I error pg. 350
Type II error pg. 350

# Chapter Exercises

MyStatLab

## Conceptual Questions

**9-69.** What is meant by the term *critical value* in a hypothesis-testing situation? Illustrate what you mean with a business example.

**9-70.** Discuss the issues a decision maker should consider when determining the significance level to use in a hypothesis test.

**9-71.** Discuss the two types of statistical errors that can occur when a hypothesis is tested. Illustrate what you mean by using a business example for each.

**9-72.** Discuss why it is necessary to use an estimate of the standard error for a confidence interval and not for a hypothesis test concerning a population proportion.

**9-73.** Examine the test statistic used in testing a population proportion. Why is it impossible to test the hypothesis that the population proportion equals zero using such a test statistic? Try to determine a way that such a test could be conducted.

**9-74.** Recall that the power of the test is the probability the null hypothesis is rejected when $H_0$ is false. Explain whether power is definable if the given parameter is the value specified in the null hypothesis.

**9-75.** What is the maximum probability of committing a Type I error called? How is this probability determined? Discuss.

**9-76.** In a hypothesis test, indicate the type of statistical error that can be made if
   a. The null hypothesis is rejected.
   b. The null hypothesis is not rejected.
   c. The null hypothesis is true.
   d. The null hypothesis is not true.

**9-77.** While conducting a hypothesis test, indicate the effect on
   a. $\beta$ when $\alpha$ is decreased while the sample size remains constant
   b. $\beta$ when $\alpha$ is held constant and the sample size is increased
   c. the power when $\alpha$ is held constant and the sample size is increased
   d. the power when $\alpha$ is decreased and the sample size is held constant

**9-78.** The Oasis Chemical Company develops and manufactures pharmaceutical drugs for distribution and sale in the United States. The pharmaceutical business can be very lucrative when useful and safe drugs are introduced into the market. Whenever the Oasis research lab considers putting a drug into production, the company must actually establish the following sets of null and alternative hypotheses:

| Set 1 | Set 2 |
|---|---|
| $H_0$: The drug is safe. | $H_0$: The drug is effective. |
| $H_A$: The drug is not safe. | $H_A$: The drug is not effective. |

Take each set of hypotheses separately.
   a. Discuss the considerations that should be made in establishing alpha and beta.
   b. For each set of hypotheses, describe what circumstances would suggest that a Type I error would be of more concern.
   c. For each set of hypotheses, describe what circumstances would suggest that a Type II error would be of more concern.

**9-79.** For each of the following scenarios, indicate which test statistic would be used or which test could not be conducted using the materials from this chapter:
   a. testing a mean when $\sigma$ is known and the population sampled from has a normal distribution
   b. testing a mean when $\sigma$ is unknown and the population sampled from has a normal distribution
   c. testing a proportion in which $n\pi = 12$ and $n(1 - \pi) = 4$
   d. Testing a mean when $s$ is obtained from a small sample and the population sampled from has a skewed distribution

## Business Applications

**9-80.** Fairfield Automotive is the local dealership selling Honda automobiles. It recently stated in an advertisement that Honda owners average more than 85,000 miles before trading in or selling their Hondas. To test this, an independent agency selected a simple random sample of 80 Honda owners who have either traded or sold their Hondas and determined the number of miles on the car when the owner parted with the car. It plans to test Fairfield's claim at the alpha = 0.05 level.

a. State the appropriate null and alternative hypotheses.
b. If the sample mean is 86,200 miles and the sample standard deviation is 12,000 miles, what conclusion should be reached about the claim?

**9-81.** Sanchez Electronics sells electronic components for car stereos. It claims that the average life of a component exceeds 4,000 hours. To test this claim, it has selected a random sample of $n = 12$ of the components and traced the life between installation and failure. The following data were obtained:

| | | | | | |
|---|---|---|---|---|---|
| 1,973 | 4,838 | 3,805 | 4,494 | 4,738 | 5,249 |
| 4,459 | 4,098 | 4,722 | 5,894 | 3,322 | 4,800 |

a. State the appropriate null and alternative hypotheses.
b. Assuming that the test is to be conducted using a 0.05 level of significance, what conclusion should be reached based on these sample data? Be sure to examine the required normality assumption.

**9-82.** The Utah State Tax Commission attempts to set up payroll tax–withholding tables such that by the end of the year, an employee's income tax withholding is about $100 below his actual income tax owed to the state. The commission director claims that when all the Utah tax returns are in, the average additional payment will be less than $100.

A random sample of 50 accounts revealed an average additional payment of $114 with a sample standard deviation of $50.

a. Testing at a significance level of 0.10, do the sample data refute the director's claim?
b. Determine the largest sample mean (with the same sample size and standard deviation) that would fail to refute the director's claim.

**9-83.** Technological changes in golf equipment have meant people, in particular professional golfers, are able to hit golf balls much farther. *Golf Digest* reported on a survey conducted involving 300 golfers in which the respondents were asked their views about the impact of new technologies on the game of golf. Before the study, a group of United States Golf Association (USGA) officials believed that less than 50% of golfers thought professional golfers should have different equipment rules than amateurs. The survey conducted by *Golf Digest* found 67% did not favor different equipment rules.

a. If the claim made by the USGA is to be tested, what should the null and alternative hypotheses be?
b. Based on the sample data, and an alpha level equal to 0.05, use the *p*-value approach to conduct the hypothesis test.

**9-84.** *USA Today* reports (Darryl Haralson, "It's All about Overstock.com") on an ad for Overstock.com, which sells discounted merchandise on its Web site. To evaluate the effectiveness of the ads, Harris Interactive conducted a nationwide poll of 883 adults. Of the 883 adults, 168 thought the ads were very effective. This was compared to the Harris Ad Track average of 21%.

a. Determine if the sample size is large enough for the test to warrant approximating the sample proportion's distribution with a normal distribution.
b. Does the Harris poll provide evidence to contend that the proportion of adults who find Overstock. com's ads to be very effective is smaller than the Harris Ad Track average? Use a significance level of 0.05.

**9-85.** The college of business at a state university has a computer literacy requirement for all graduates. Students must show proficiency with a computer spreadsheet software package and with a word-processing software package. To assess whether students are computer literate, a test is given at the end of each semester. The test is designed so that at least 70% of all students who have taken a special micro-computer course will pass. The college does not wish to declare that fewer than 70% of the students pass the test unless there is strong sample evidence to indicate this. Suppose that, in a random sample of 100 students who have recently finished the microcomputer course, 63 pass the proficiency test.

a. Using a significance level of 0.05, what conclusions should the administrators make regarding the difficulty of the test?
b. Describe a Type II error in the context of this problem.

**9-86.** The makers of Mini-Oats Cereal have an automated packaging machine that can be set at any targeted fill level between 12 and 32 ounces. At the end of every shift (eight hours), 16 boxes are selected at random and the mean and standard deviation of the sample are computed. Based on these sample results, the production control manager determines whether the filling machine needs to be readjusted or whether it remains all right to operate. Previous data suggest the fill level has a normal distribution with a standard deviation of 0.65 ounces. Use $\alpha = 0.05$. The test is a two-sided test to determine if the mean fill level was equal to 24 ounces.

a. Calculate the probability that the test procedure will detect that the average fill level is not equal to 24 ounces when in fact it equals 24.5 ounces.
b. On the basis of your calculation in part a, would you suggest a change in the test procedure? Explain what change you would make and the reasons you would make this change.

**9-87.** ACNielsen is a New York–based leading global provider of marketing research information services, analytical systems and tools, and professional client service. A recent issue of its magazine (Todd Hale, "Winning Retail Strategies Start with High Value Consumers," *Consumer Insight*, Spring 2005) addressed, in part, consumers' attitudes to self-checkout lines. Of the 17,346 EDLP (every day low price) shoppers, only 3,470 indicated an interest in this service. If Wal-Mart's CEO, Lee Scott, had decided not to install self-checkout lines unless consumer interest was more than 17.5%, would he order the installation?

a. Determine if the sample size for the test indicated is large enough to warrant approximating the sample proportion's distribution with a normal distribution.

b. Use a significance level of 0.05 and the $p$-value approach to answer the question put forward above.

9-88. The Sledge Tire and Rubber Company plans to warranty its new mountain bike tire for 12 months. However, before it does this, the company wants to be sure that the mean lifetime of the tires is at least 18 months under normal operations. It will put the warranty in place unless the sample data strongly suggest that the mean lifetime of the tires is less than 18 months. The company plans to test this statistically using a random sample of tires. The test will be conducted using an alpha level of 0.03.

a. If the population mean is actually 16.5 months, determine the probability the hypothesis test will lead to incorrectly failing to reject the null hypothesis. Assume that the population standard deviation is known to be 2.4 months and the sample size is 60.

b. If the population mean is actually 17.3, calculate the chance of committing a Type II error. This is a specific example of a generalization relating the probability of committing a Type II error and the parameter being tested. State this generalization.

c. Without calculating the probability, state whether the probability of a Type II error would be larger or smaller than that calculated in part b if you were to calculate it for a hypothesized mean of 15 months. Justify your answer.

d. Suppose the company decides to increase the sample size from 60 to 100 tires. What can you expect to happen to the probabilities calculated in part a?

9-89. About 74% of Freddie Mac–owned loans were refinanced in the second quarter of 2005 (*USA Today*, Lifeline, August 3, 2005), resulting in new mortgages carrying loan amounts at least 5% above the original mortgage balance. The median loan refinanced in the second quarter was 2.6 years old. If a sample size of 2,500 was used to obtain this information,

a. Determine if the sample size for the test is large enough to warrant approximating the sample proportion's distribution with a normal distribution.

b. Use this information to determine if less than 75% of new mortgages had a loan amount at least 5% above the original mortgage balance. Use a test statistic approach with $\alpha = 0.025$.

9-90. The personnel manager for a large airline has claimed that, on average, workers are asked to work no more than 3 hours overtime per week. Past studies show the standard deviation in overtime hours per worker to be 1.2 hours.

Suppose the union negotiators wish to test this claim by sampling payroll records for 250 employees. They believe that the personnel manager's claim is untrue but want to base their conclusion on the sample results.

a. State the research, null, and alternative hypotheses and discuss the meaning of Type I and Type II errors in the context of this case.

b. Establish the appropriate decision rule if the union wishes to have no more than a 0.01 chance of a Type I error.

c. The payroll records produced a sample mean of 3.15 hours. Do the union negotiators have a basis for a grievance against the airline? Support your answer with a relevant statistical procedure.

9-91. The Lazer Company has a contract to produce a part for Boeing Corporation that must have an average diameter of 6 inches and a standard deviation of 0.10 inch. The Lazer Company has developed the process that will meet the specifications with respect to the standard deviation, but it is still trying to meet the mean specifications. A test run (considered a random sample) of parts was produced, and the company wishes to determine whether this latest process that produced the sample will produce parts meeting the requirement of an average diameter equal to 6 inches.

a. Specify the appropriate research, null, and alternative hypotheses.

b. Develop the decision rule assuming that the sample size is 200 parts and the significance level is 0.01.

c. What should the Lazer Company conclude if the sample mean diameter for the 200 parts is 6.03 inches? Discuss.

9-92. Cisco Systems, Inc., is the leading maker of networking gear that connects computers to the Internet. Company managers are concerned with the productivity of their workers as well as their job satisfaction. Kate D'Camp is the senior vice president for human resources. She often initiates surveys concerning Cisco's personnel. A typical survey asked, "Do you feel it's OK for your company to monitor your Internet use?" Of the 405 respondents, 223 chose "Only after informing me." Cisco would consider monitoring if more than 50% of its workers wouldn't mind if informed beforehand that the company was going to monitor their Internet usage.

a. D'Camp may have read the *USA Today* issue that indicated 55% of American workers wouldn't object after being informed. So she might desire that the test indicate with a high probability that more than 50% of Cisco workers wouldn't object when in fact her workers reflect the opinion of all American workers. Calculate the probability that this would be the case. (*Hint*: Review the procedure concerning the sample mean and perform the analogous procedure for a proportion.)

b. Conduct the procedure to determine if the proportion of workers who wouldn't object to the company monitoring their Internet use after they were informed is more than 50%. Use a significance level of 0.05.

**9-93.** Many companies have moved employee retirement plans to ones based on 401(k) savings. In fact, most large mutual fund companies, like Vanguard, offer 401(k) options. However, according to Nancy Trejos of the *Washington Post*, the average amount in a 401(k) plan decreased from $69,200 in 2007 to $50,000 in 2008. A local investment advisor, seeing this figure, thinks those using her managed fund have more than the reported amount. She selects a random sample of 55 and finds a sample average of $51,035.

   a. If the standard deviation for the amount in the investors' accounts is $1,734.23, determine if the investment advisor is correct in her assumption that those she is advising have more than the reported average amount. Use a significance level of 0.025 and discuss any assumptions you made to answer this question.

   b. Determine the largest plausible average balance the accounts of those using her managed fund in which you could have 90% confidence.

## Computer Database Exercises

**9-94.** The Cell Tone Company sells cellular phones and airtime in several northwestern states. At a recent meeting, the marketing manager stated that the average age of its customers is under 40. This came up in conjunction with a proposed advertising plan that is to be directed toward a young audience. Before actually completing the advertising plan, Cell Tone decided to randomly sample customers. Among the questions asked in the survey of 50 customers in the Jacksonville, Florida, area was the customer's age. The data are available in a data file called **Cell Phone Survey**.

   a. Based on the statement made by the marketing manager, formulate the appropriate null and alternative hypotheses.

   b. The marketing manager must support his statement concerning average customer age in an upcoming board meeting. Using a significance level of 0.10, provide this support for the marketing manager.

   c. Consider the result of the hypothesis test you conducted in part b. Which of the two types of hypothesis-test errors could you have committed? How could you discover if you had, indeed, made this error?

   d. Calculate the critical value, $\bar{x}_\alpha$.

   e. Determine the $p$-value and conduct the test using the $p$-value approach.

   f. Note that the sample data list the customer's age to the nearest year. (1) If we denote a randomly selected customer's age (to the nearest year) as $x_i$, is $x_i$ a continuous or discrete random variable? (2) Is it possible that $x_i$ has a normal distribution? Consider

your answers to (1) and (2) and the fact that $\bar{x}$ must have a normal distribution to facilitate the calculation in part b. Does this mean that the calculation you have performed in part b is inappropriate? Explain your answer.

**9-95.** The AJ Fitness Center has surveyed 1,214 of its customers. Of particular interest is whether over 60% of the customers who express overall service satisfaction with the club (represented by codes 4 or 5) are female. If this is not the case, the promotions director feels she must initiate new exercise programs that are designed specifically for women. Should the promotions director initiate the new exercise programs? Support your answer with the relevant hypothesis test utilizing a $p$-value to perform the test. The data are found in a data file called **AJ Fitness** ($\alpha = 0.05$).

**9-96.** The Wilson Company uses a great deal of water in the process of making industrial milling equipment. To comply with the federal clean water laws, it has a water purification system that all wastewater goes through before being discharged into a settling pond on the company's property. To determine whether the company is complying with the federal requirements, sample measures are taken every so often. One requirement is that the average pH levels not exceed 7.4. A sample of 95 pH measures has been taken. The data for these measures are shown in a file called **Wilson Water**.

   a. Considering the requirement for pH level, state the appropriate null and alternative hypotheses. Discuss why it is appropriate to form the hypotheses with the federal standard as the alternative hypothesis.

   b. Based on the sample data of pH level, what should the company conclude about its current status on meeting the federal requirement? Test the hypothesis at the 0.05 level. Discuss your results in a memo to the company's environmental relations manager.

**9-97.** The Haines Lumber Company makes plywood for the furniture industry. One product it makes is 3/4-inch oak veneer panels. It is very important that the panels conform to specifications. One specification calls for the panels to be made to an average thickness of 0.75 inches. Each hour, 5 panels are selected at random and measured. After 20 hours a total of 100 panels have been measured. The thickness measures are in a file called **Haines**.

   a. Formulate the appropriate null and alternative hypotheses relative to the thickness specification.

   b. Based on the sample data, what should the company conclude about the status of its product meeting the thickness specification? Test at a significance level of 0.01. Discuss your results in a report to the production manager.

**9-98.** The Inland Empire Food Store Company has stated in its advertising that the average shopper will save more than $5.00 per week by shopping at Inland stores.

A consumer group has decided to test this assertion by sampling 50 shoppers who currently shop at other stores. It selects the customers and then notes each item purchased at their regular stores. These same items are then priced at the Inland store, and the total bill is compared. The data in the file **Inland Foods** reflect savings at Inland for the 50 shoppers. Note that those cases where the bill was higher at Inland are marked with a minus sign.

a. Set up the appropriate null and alternative hypotheses to test Inland's claim.

b. Using a significance level of 0.05, develop the decision rule and test the hypothesis. Can Inland Empire support its advertising claim?

c. Which type of hypothesis error would the consumer group be most interested in controlling? Which type of hypothesis test error would the company be most interested in controlling? Explain your reasoning.

**9-99.** MBNA offers personal and business credit cards, loans, and savings products. It was bought by Bank of America in June 2005. One of the selling points for MBNA was its position relative to the rest of the credit card industry. MBNA's customers' average annual spending per active account before the purchase was $6,920. To demonstrate its relative position in the industry, MBNA's CFO, H. Vernon Wright, might authorize a survey producing the following data on the annual spending, to the nearest dollar, of accounts in the industry:

| | | | | | | | | | |
|---|---|---|---|---|---|---|---|---|---|
| 3,680 | 6,255 | 6,777 | 7,412 | 4,902 | 5,522 | 5,190 | 7,976 | 4,116 | 3,949 |
| 6,814 | 2,264 | 4,991 | 5,353 | 5,914 | 5,828 | 6,059 | 6,354 | 6,193 | 5,648 |
| 6,117 | 7,315 | 6,458 | 4,973 | 6,554 | 1,926 | 4,395 | 5,341 | 4,921 | 6,268 |
| 4,061 | 4,777 | 5,876 | 5,984 | 3,381 | 5,441 | 4,268 | 7,657 | 6,449 | 4,821 |

This sample is contained in the file labeled **ASpending**.

a. Conduct a hypothesis test to determine if MBNA has larger average annual spending per active account than the rest of the credit card industry. Use a p-value approach and a significance level of 0.025.

b. If the industry's annual spending per active account was normally distributed with a mean of $5,560 and a standard deviation of $1,140, determine the probability that a randomly chosen account would have an annual spending larger than MBNA's.

**9-100.** At the annual meeting of the Golf Equipment Manufacturer's Association, a speaker made the claim that over 30% of all golf clubs being used by nonprofessional United States Golf Association (USGA) members are "knock-offs." These knock-offs are clubs that look very much like the more expensive originals, such as Big Bertha drivers, but are actually nonauthorized copies that are sold at a very reduced

rate. This claim prompted the association to conduct a study to see if the problem was as big as the speaker said. A random sample of 400 golfers was selected from the USGA membership ranks. The players were called and asked to indicate the brand of clubs that they used and several other questions. Out of the 400 golfers, data were collected from 294 of them. Based on the response to club brand, a determination was made whether the club was "original" or a "copy." The data are in a file called **Golf Survey**.

a. Based on the sample data, what conclusion should be reached if the hypothesis is tested at a significance level of 0.05? Show the decision rule.

b. Determine whether a Type I or Type II error for this hypothesis test would be more severe. Given your determination, would you advocate raising or lowering the significance level for this test? Explain your reasoning.

c. Confirm that the sample proportion's distribution can be approximated by a normal distribution.

d. Based on the sample data, what should the USGA conclude about the use of knock-off clubs by the high-handicap golfers? Is the official's statement justified?

**9-101.** TOMRA Systems ASA is a Norwegian company that manufactures reverse vending machines (RVMs). In most cases, RVMs are used in markets that have deposits on beverage containers, offering an efficient and convenient method of identifying the deposit amount of each container returned and providing a refund to the customer. Prices for such machines range from about $9,000 for single-container machines to about $35,000 for higher volume, multi-container (can, plastic, glass) machines. For a single-container machine to pay for itself in one year, it would need to generate an average monthly income of more than $750. The following sample of single-machine monthly incomes was obtained to determine if that goal could be reached:

| | | | | | | | |
|---|---|---|---|---|---|---|---|
| 765.37 | 748.21 | 813.77 | 633.21 | 714.74 | 802.96 | 696.06 | 880.65 |
| 701.80 | 696.16 | 905.01 | 688.51 | 922.43 | 753.97 | 728.60 | 690.06 |
| 839.48 | 1010.56 | 789.13 | 754.35 | 749.97 | 802.31 | 809.15 | 775.27 |

This sample is contained in the file labeled **RVMIncome**.

a. Conduct a hypothesis test to determine if the goal can be reached. Use a significance level of 0.05 and the p-value approach.

b. There are 10 sites in which an RVM could be placed. Unknown to the vendor, only 4 of the sites will allow the vendor to meet the goal of paying for the machine in one year. If he installs 4 of the RVMs, determine the probability that at least 2 of them will be paid off in a year.

# Video Case 4

## New Product Introductions @ McDonald's

New product ideas are a staple of our culture. Just take a look around you—how many billboards or television commercials can you count advertising new products or services? So, where do those ideas come from? If you're a company like McDonald's, the ideas don't come out of thin air. Instead, they're the result of careful monitoring of consumer preferences, trends, and tastes.

McDonald's menu is a good example of how consumer preferences have affected change in food offerings. What used to be a fairly limited lunch and dinner menu consisting of burgers, shakes, and fries has now become incredibly diverse. The Big Mac came along in 1968, and Happy Meals were introduced in 1979. Breakfast now accounts for nearly 30% of business in the United States, and chicken offerings comprise 30% of menu choices. Healthy offerings such as apple dippers, milk jugs, and fruit and yogurt parfaits are huge sellers. The company now rolls out at least three new products a year. Wade Thomas, VP U.S. Menu Management, leads the team behind most of today's menu options. He meets regularly with Chef Dan, the company's executive chef, to give the chef's team some idea anchor points to play with.

When the chef's team is through playing with the concept, Wade's Menu Management team holds what they call a "rally." At a rally, numerous food concepts developed by Chef Dan's team are presented, tasted, discussed, and voted on. The winners move on to focus group testing. The focus groups are a huge source of external data, which help the Menu Management team with its decision on whether to introduce a product. If a product scores 8 out of 10 on a variety of rankings, the idea moves forward.

The real test begins in the field. Wade and his team need to determine if the new product idea can be executed consistently in the restaurants. Data collected from the company's partnership with its owner/operators and suppliers are key. If a product takes five seconds too long to make or if the equipment doesn't fit into existing kitchen configurations, its chances of implementation are low, even though consumer focus groups indicated a high probability of success.

Throughout the idea development process, various statistical methods are used to analyze the data collected. The data are handed over to the company's U.S. Consumer and Business Insights team for conversion into meaningful information the menu management team can use. At each step along the way, the statistical analyses are used to decide whether to move to the next step. The recent introduction of the new Asian chicken salad is a good example of a recent new product offering that made it all the way to market. Analysis was performed on data collected in focus groups and eventually revealed that the Asian salad met all the statistical hurdles for the salad to move forward.

Data collection and statistical analysis don't stop when the new products hit the market. Wade Thomas's team and the McDonald's U.S. Consumer and Business Insights group continue to forecast and monitor sales, the ingredient supply chain, customer preferences, competitive reactions, and more. As for the new Asian salad, time will tell just how successful it will become. But you can be sure statistical techniques such as multiple regression will be used to analyze it!

### Discussion Questions:

1. During the past year, McDonald's introduced a new dessert product into its European market area. This product had already passed all the internal hurdles described in this case including the focus group analysis and the operations analysis. The next step was to see how well the product would be received in the marketplace. The hurdle rate that has been set for this product is a mean equal to 160 orders per 1,000 transactions. If the mean exceeds 160, the product will be introduced on a permanent basis. A random sample of 142 stores throughout Europe was selected. Store managers tracked the number of dessert orders per 1,000 transactions during a two-week trial period. These sample data are in the data file called **McDonald's New Product Introduction**. Using a significance level equal to 0.05, conduct the appropriate hypothesis test. Be sure to state the null and alternative hypotheses and show the results of the test. Write a short report that summarizes the hypothesis test and indicate what conclusion Wade Thomas and his group should reach about this new dessert product.

2. Referring to question 1, suppose a second hurdle is to be used in this case in determining whether the new dessert product should be introduced. This hurdle involves the proportion of every 1,000 transactions that the number of dessert orders exceeds 200. Wade Thomas has indicated that this proportion must exceed 0.15. Based on the sample data, using a significance level equal to 0.05, what conclusion should be reached? Write a short report that specifies the null and alternative hypotheses and shows the test results. Indicate what conclusion should be reached based on this hypothesis test.

# Case 9.1

## Campbell Brewery, Inc.—Part 1

Don Campbell and his younger brother, Edward, purchased Campbell Brewery from their father in 1983. The brewery makes and bottles beer under two labels and distributes it throughout the Southwest. Since purchasing the brewery, Don has been instrumental in modernizing operations.

One of the latest acquisitions is a filling machine that can be adjusted to fill at any average fill level desired. Because the bottles and cans filled by the brewery are exclusively the 12-ounce size, when they received the machine Don set the fill level to 12 ounces and left it that way. According to the manufacturer's specifications, the machine will fill bottles or cans around the average, with a standard deviation of 0.15 ounce.

Don just returned from a brewery convention in which he attended a panel discussion related to problems with filling machines. One brewery representative discussed a problem her company had. It failed to learn that its machine's average fill went out of adjustment until several months later, when its cost accounting department reported some problems with beer production in bulk not matching output in bottles and cans. It turns out that the machine's average fill had increased from 12 ounces to 12.07 ounces. With large volumes of production, this deviation meant a substantial loss in profits.

Another brewery reported the same type of problem, but in the opposite direction. Its machine began filling bottles with slightly less than 12 ounces on the average. Although the consumers could not detect the shortage in a given bottle, the state and federal agencies responsible for checking the accuracy of packaged products discovered the problem in their testing and substantially fined the brewery for the underfill.

These problems were a surprise to Don Campbell. He had not considered the possibility that the machine might go out of adjustment and pose these types of problems. In fact, he became very concerned because the problems of losing profits and potentially being fined by the government were ones that he wished to avoid, if possible. After the convention, Don and Ed decided to hire a consulting firm with expertise in these matters to assist them in setting up a procedure for monitoring the performance of the filling machine.

The consultant suggested that they set up a sampling plan in which once a month they would sample some number of bottles and measure their volumes precisely. If the average of the sample deviated too much from 12 ounces, they would shut the machine down and make the necessary adjustments. Otherwise, they would let the filling process continue. The consultant identified two types of problems that could occur from this sort of sampling plan:

1. They might incorrectly decide to adjust the machine when it was not really necessary to do so.
2. They might incorrectly decide to allow the filling process to continue when, in fact, the true average had deviated from 12 ounces.

After carefully considering what the consultant told them, Don indicated that he wanted no more than a 0.02 chance of the first problem occurring because of the costs involved. He also decided that if the true average fill had slipped to 11.99 ounces, he wanted no more than a 0.05 chance of not detecting this with his sampling plan. He wanted to avoid problems with state and federal agencies. Finally, if the true average fill had actually risen to 12.007 ounces, he wanted to be able to detect this 98% of the time with his sampling plan. Thus, he wanted to avoid the lost profits that would result from such a problem.

In addition, Don needs to determine how large a sample size is necessary to meet his requirements.

# Case 9.2

## Wings of Fire

Following his graduation from college, Tony Smith wanted to continue to live and work in Oxford. However, the community was small and there were not a lot of readily available opportunities for a new college graduate. Fortunately, Tony had some experience working in the food service industry gained in the summers and throughout high school at his uncle's restaurant in Buffalo. When Tony decided to leverage his experience into a small delivery and take-out restaurant located close to the university, he thought he had hit on a great idea. Tony would offer a limited fare consisting of the buffalo wings his uncle had perfected at his restaurant. Tony called his restaurant Wings of Fire. Although success came slowly, the uniqueness of Tony's offering coupled with the growth of the university community made Wings of Fire a success.

Tony's business was pretty simple. Tony purchased wings locally. The wings were then seasoned and prepared in Tony's restaurant. Once an order was received, Tony cooked the wings, which were then delivered or picked up by the customer. Tony's establishment was small and there was no place for customers to dine in the restaurant. However, his wings proved so popular that over time Tony hired several employees, including three delivery drivers. Business was steady and predictable during the week, with the biggest days being home-football Saturdays.

A little over a year ago, Oxford really began to grow and expand. Tony noticed that his business was beginning to suffer when other fast-food delivery restaurants opened around campus. Some of these restaurants were offering guarantees such as "30 minutes or it's free." Tony's Wings of Fire now had to compete with fish tacos, specialty pizzas, and gourmet burgers. Most of these new restaurants, however, were dine-in establishments that provided carry-out and delivery as a customer convenience. However, Tony was certain that he would need to offer a delivery guarantee to remain competitive with the newer establishments.

Tony was certain that a delivery guarantee of "30 minutes or it's free" could easily be accomplished every day except on football Saturdays. Tony thought that if he could offer a 30-minute guarantee on his busiest day, he would be able to hold onto and perhaps even recover market share from the competition. However, before he was willing to commit to such a guarantee, Tony wanted to ensure that it was possible to meet the 30-minute promise.

Tony knew it would be no problem for customers to pick up orders within 30 minutes of phoning them in. However, he was less confident about delivering orders to customers in 30 minutes or less. Not only would the wings need to be cooked and packaged, but the delivery time might be affected by the availability of drivers. Tony decided that he needed to analyze the opportunity further.

As a part of his analysis, Tony decided to take a random sample of deliveries over five different football weekends. Cooking time and packaging time were not considered in his analysis because wings were not cooked for individual orders. Rather, large numbers of wings were cooked at a single time and then packaged in boxes of 12. Tony therefore decided to focus his analysis on the time required to deliver cooked and packaged wings. He collected information on the amount of time an order had to wait for a driver (the pick-up time) as well as the amount of time required to transport the wings to the customer (the drive time). The sampled information is in the file **Wings of Fire**. Tony is not willing to offer the guarantee on football Saturdays unless he can be reasonably sure that the total time to deliver a customer's order is less than 30 minutes, on average. Tony would also like to have an estimate of the actual time required to deliver a customer's order on football Saturdays. Finally, Tony would like to know how likely it is that the total time to make a delivery would take more than 30 minutes. Based on the sampled data, should Tony offer the guarantee? What percent of the Saturday deliveries would result in a customer receiving a free order? What recommendations might help Tony improve his Saturday delivery times?

## Required Tasks:

1. Use the sample information to compute a measure of performance that Tony can use to analyze his delivery performance.
2. State a hypothesis test that would help Tony decide to offer the delivery guarantee or not.
3. Calculate sample statistics and formally test the hypothesis stated in (2).
4. Estimate the probability of an order taking longer than 30 minutes.
5. Summarize your findings and make a recommendation in a short report.

# References

Berenson, Mark L., Timothy C. Krehbiel, and David M. Levine, *Basic Business Statistics*: *Concepts and Applications and CD Package*, 11th ed. (Upper Saddle River, NJ: Prentice Hall, 2009).

Brown, L., et al., "Interval Estimation for a Binomial Proportion," *Statistical Science*, 2001, pp. 101–133.

Hogg, Robert V., and Elliot A. Tanis, *Probability and Statistical Inference*, 8th ed. (Upper Saddle River, NJ: Prentice Hall, 2009).

Larsen, Richard J., and Morris L. Marx, *An Introduction to Mathematical Statistics and Its Applications*, 4th ed. (Upper Saddle River, NJ, Prentice Hall, 2005).

*Microsoft Excel 2007* (Redmond, WA: Microsoft Corp., 2007).

*Minitab Release 15 Statistical Software for Windows* (State College, PA: Minitab, 2007).

Siegel, Andrew F., *Practical Business Statistics with Student CD ROM*, 5th ed. (Burr Ridge, IL: Irwin, 2002).

# Analysis of Variance

**Outcome 1.** Understand the basic logic of analysis of variance.

**Outcome 2.** Perform a hypothesis test for a single-factor design using analysis of variance manually and with the aid of Excel or Minitab software.

**Outcome 3.** Conduct and interpret post-analysis of variance pairwise comparisons procedures.

**Outcome 4.** Recognize when randomized block analysis of variance is useful and be able to perform analysis of variance on a randomized block design.

**Outcome 5.** Perform analysis of variance on a two-factor design of experiments with replications using Excel or Minitab and interpret the output.

# Why you need to know

Chapters 9 through 11 introduced hypothesis testing. By now you should understand that regardless of the population parameter in question, hypothesis-testing steps are basically the same:

1. Specify the population parameter of interest.
2. Formulate the null and alternative hypotheses.
3. Specify the level of significance.
4. Determine a decision rule defining the rejection and "acceptance" regions.
5. Select a random sample of data from the population(s). Compute the appropriate sample statistic(s). Finally, calculate the test statistic.
6. Reach a decision. Reject the null hypothesis, $H_0$, if the sample statistic falls in the rejection region; otherwise, do not reject the null hypothesis. If the test is conducted using the $p$-value approach, $H_0$ is rejected whenever the $p$-value is smaller than the significance level; otherwise, $H_0$ is not rejected.
7. Draw a conclusion. State the result of your hypothesis test in the context of the exercise or analysis of interest.

Chapter 9 focused on hypothesis tests involving a single population. Chapters 10 and 11 expanded the hypothesis-testing process to include applications in which differences between two populations are involved. However, you will encounter many instances involving more than two populations. For example, the vice president of operations at Farber Rubber, Inc., oversees production at Farber's six different U.S. manufacturing plants. Because each plant uses slightly different manufacturing processes, the vice president needs to know if there are any differences in average strength of the products produced at the different plants.

Similarly, *Golf Digest*, a major publisher of articles about golf, might wish to determine which of five major brands of golf balls has the highest mean distance off the tee. The Environmental Protection Agency (EPA) might conduct a test to determine if there is a difference in the average miles-per-gallon performance of cars manufactured by the Big Three U.S. automobile producers. In each of these cases, testing a hypothesis involving more than two population means could be required.

This chapter introduces a tool called analysis of variance (ANOVA), which can be used to test whether there are differences among three or more population means. There are several ANOVA procedures, depending on the type of test being conducted. Our aim in this chapter is to introduce you to ANOVA and to illustrate how to use Microsoft Excel and Minitab to help conduct hypothesis tests involving three or more population parameters. You will almost certainly need either to apply ANOVA in future decision-making situations or to interpret the results of an ANOVA study performed by someone else. Thus, you need to be familiar with this powerful statistical technique.

**Chapter Outcome 1.** → **12.1 One-Way Analysis of Variance**

In Chapter 10 we introduced the *t*-test for testing whether two populations have equal means when the samples from the two populations are independent. However, you will often encounter situations in which you are interested in determining whether three or more populations have equal means. To conduct this test, you will need a new tool called *analysis of variance* (*ANOVA*). There are many different analysis of variance designs to fit different situations; the simplest is a **completely randomized design**. Analyzing a completely randomized design results in a **one-way analysis of variance**.

**Completely Randomized Design**

An experiment is completely randomized if it consists of the independent random selection of observations representing each level of one factor.

**One-Way Analysis of Variance**

An analysis of variance design in which independent samples are obtained from two or more levels of a single factor for the purpose of testing whether the levels have equal means.

## Introduction to One-Way ANOVA

**BUSINESS APPLICATION** **APPLYING ONE-WAY ANALYSIS OF VARIANCE**

**BAYHILL MARKETING COMPANY** The Bayhill Marketing Company is a full-service marketing and advertising firm in San Francisco. Although Bayhill provides many different marketing services, one of its most lucrative in recent years has been Web site sales designs. Companies that wish to increase Internet sales have contracted with Bayhill to design effective Web sites. Bayhill executives have learned that certain Web site features are more effective than others.

For example, a major greeting card company wants to work with Bayhill on developing a Web-based sales campaign for its "Special Events" card set. The company plans to work with Bayhill designers to come up with a Web site that will maximize sales effectiveness. Sales effectiveness can be determined by the dollar value of the greeting card sets purchased.

Through a series of meetings with the client and focus-group sessions with potential customers, Bayhill has developed four Web site design options. Bayhill plans to test the effectiveness of the designs by sending e-mails to a random sample of regular greeting card customers. The sample of potential customers will be divided into four groups of eight customers each. Group 1 will be directed to a Web site with design 1, group 2 to a Web site with design 2, and so forth. The dollar value of the cards ordered are recorded and shown in Table 12.1.

In this example, we are interested in whether the different Web site designs result in different mean order sizes. In other words, we are trying to determine if "Web site designs" are one of the possible causes of the variation in the dollar value of the card sets ordered (the response variable). In this case, Web site design is called a **factor**.

The *single factor* of interest is Web site design. This factor has four categories, measurements, or strata, called **levels**. These four levels are the four designs: 1, 2, 3, and 4. Because we are using only one factor, each dollar value of card sets ordered is associated with only one level (that is, with Web site design—type 1, 2, 3, or 4), as you can see in Table 12.1. Each level is a population of interest, and the values seen in Table 12.1 are sample values taken from those populations.

The null and alternative hypotheses to be tested are

$H_0$: $\mu_1 = \mu_2 = \mu_3 = \mu_4$ (mean order sizes are equal)
$H_A$: At least two of the population means are different

**Factor**

A quantity under examination in an experiment as a possible cause of variation in the response variable.

**Levels**

The categories, measurements, or strata of a factor of interest in the current experiment.

**Balanced Design**

An experiment has a balanced design if the factor levels have equal sample sizes.

The appropriate statistical tool for conducting the hypothesis test related to this experimental design is analysis of variance. Because this ANOVA addresses an experiment with only one factor, it is a one-way ANOVA, or a one-factor ANOVA. Because the sample size for each Web site design (level) is the same, the experiment has a **balanced design**.

**TABLE 12.1** | **Bayhill Marketing Company Web Site Order Data**

| Customer | Web Site Design 1 | Web Site Design 2 | Web Site Design 3 | Web Site Design 4 | |
|---|---|---|---|---|---|
| 1 | $4.10 | $6.90 | $4.60 | $12.50 | |
| 2 | 5.90 | 9.10 | 11.40 | 7.50 | |
| 3 | 10.45 | 13.00 | 6.15 | 6.25 | |
| 4 | 11.55 | 7.90 | 7.85 | 8.75 | |
| 5 | 5.25 | 9.10 | 4.30 | 11.15 | |
| 6 | 7.75 | 13.40 | 8.70 | 10.25 | |
| 7 | 4.78 | 7.60 | 10.20 | 6.40 | |
| 8 | 6.22 | 5.00 | 10.80 | 9.20 | |
| | | | | | Grand Mean |
| Mean | $\bar{x}_1 = \$7.00$ | $\bar{x}_2 = \$9.00$ | $\bar{x}_3 = \$8.00$ | $\bar{x}_4 = \$9.00$ | $\bar{\bar{x}} = \$8.25$ |
| Variance | $s_1^2 = 7.341$ | $s_2^2 = 8.423$ | $s_3^2 = 7.632$ | $s_4^2 = 5.016$ | |

*Note:* Data are the dollar value of card sets ordered with each Web site design.

ANOVA tests the null hypothesis that three or more populations have the same mean. The test is based on four assumptions:

1. All populations are normally distributed.
2. The population variances are equal.
3. The observations are independent—that is, the occurrence of any one individual value does not affect the probability that any other observation will occur.
4. The data are interval or ratio level.

If the null hypothesis is true, the populations have identical distributions. If so, the sample means for random samples from each population should be close in value. The basic logic of ANOVA is the same as the two-sample *t*-test introduced in Chapter 10. The null hypothesis should be rejected only if the sample means are substantially different.

## Partitioning the Sum of Squares

To understand the logic of ANOVA, you should note several things about the data in Table 12.1. First, the dollar values of the orders are different throughout the data table. Some values are higher; others are lower. Thus, variation exists across all customer orders. This variation is called the **total variation** in the data.

Next, within any particular Web site design (i.e., factor level), not all customers ordered the same dollar value of greeting card sets. For instance, within level 1, order size ranged from $4.10 to $11.55. Similar differences occur within the other levels. The variation within the factor levels is called the **within-sample variation**.

Finally, the sample means for the four Web site designs are not all equal. Thus, variation exists between the four designs' averages. This variation between the factor levels is referred to as the **between-sample variation**.

Recall that the sample variance is computed as

$$s^2 = \frac{\sum (x - \bar{x})^2}{n - 1}$$

**Total Variation**

The aggregate dispersion of the individual data values across the various factor levels is called the *total variation* in the data.

**Within-Sample Variation**

The dispersion that exists among the data values within a particular factor level is called the *within-sample variation*.

**Between-Sample Variation**

Dispersion among the factor sample means is called the *between-sample variation*.

The sample variance is the sum of squared deviations from the sample mean divided by its degrees of freedom. When all the data from all the samples are included, $s^2$ is the estimator of the *total variation*. The numerator of this estimator is called the *total sum of squares* (*SST*) and can be partitioned into the sum of squares associated with the estimators of the between-sample variation and the within-sample variation, as shown in Equation 12.1.

**Partitioned Sum of Squares**

$$SST = SSB + SSW \tag{12.1}$$

where:

$SST$ = Total sum of squares
$SSB$ = Sum of squares between
$SSW$ = Sum of squares within

After separating the sum of squares, $SSB$ and $SSW$ are divided by their respective degrees of freedom to produce two estimates for the overall population variance. If the between-sample variance estimate is large relative to the within-sample estimate, the ANOVA procedure will lead us to reject the null hypothesis and conclude the population means are different. The question is, how can we determine at what point any difference is statistically significant?

## The ANOVA Assumptions

Chapter Outcome 2.→ BUSINESS APPLICATION    UNDERSTANDING THE ANOVA ASSUMPTIONS

**BAYHILL MARKETING COMPANY (CONTINUED)** Recall that Bayhill is testing whether the four Web site designs generate orders of equal average dollar value. The null and alternative hypotheses are

$$H_0: \mu_1 = \mu_2 = \mu_3 = \mu_4$$
$$H_A: \text{At least two population means are different}$$

Before we jump into the ANOVA calculations, recall the four basic assumptions of ANOVA:

1. All populations are normally distributed.
2. The population variances are equal.
3. The sampled observations are independent.
4. The data's measurement level is interval or ratio.

Figure 12.1 illustrates the first two assumptions. The populations are normally distributed and the spread (variance) is the same for each population. However, this figure shows the

**FIGURE 12.1**

Normal Populations with Equal Variances and Unequal Means

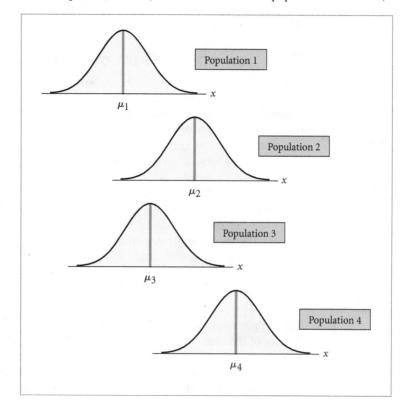

**FIGURE 12.2**

Normal Populations with Equal Variances and Equal Means

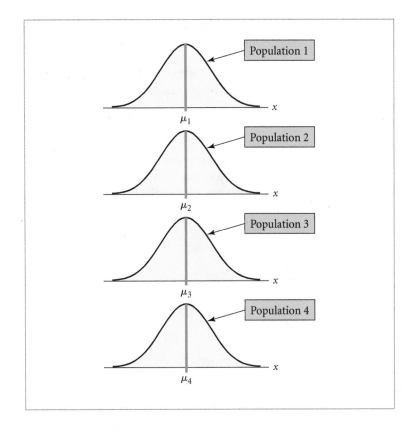

populations have different means—and therefore the null hypothesis is false. Figure 12.2 illustrates the same assumptions but in a case in which the population means are equal; therefore, the null hypothesis is true.

You can do a rough check to determine whether the normality assumption is satisfied by developing graphs of the sample data from each population. Histograms are probably the best graphical tool for checking the normality assumption, but they require a fairly large sample size. The stem and leaf diagram and box and whisker plot are alternatives when sample sizes are smaller. If the graphical tools show plots consistent with a normal distribution, then that evidence suggests the normality assumption is satisfied.[1] Figure 12.3 illustrates the box and

**FIGURE 12.3**

Box and Whisker Plot for Bayhill Marketing Company

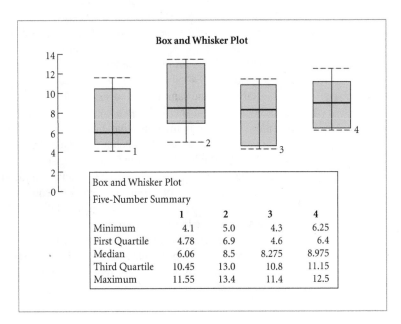

**Box and Whisker Plot**

Box and Whisker Plot

Five-Number Summary

|  | 1 | 2 | 3 | 4 |
|---|---|---|---|---|
| Minimum | 4.1 | 5.0 | 4.3 | 6.25 |
| First Quartile | 4.78 | 6.9 | 4.6 | 6.4 |
| Median | 6.06 | 8.5 | 8.275 | 8.975 |
| Third Quartile | 10.45 | 13.0 | 10.8 | 11.15 |
| Maximum | 11.55 | 13.4 | 11.4 | 12.5 |

---

[1]Chapter 13 introduces a goodness-of-fit approach to testing whether sample data come from a normally distributed population.

whisker plot for the Bayhill data. Note, when the sample sizes are very small, as they are here, the graphical techniques may not be very effective.

In Chapter 11, you learned how to test whether two populations have equal variances using the $F$-test. To determine whether the second assumption is satisfied, we can hypothesize that all the population variances are equal:

$$H_0: \sigma_1^2 = \sigma_2^2 = \cdots = \sigma_k^2$$
$$H_A: \text{Not all variances are equal}$$

Because you are now testing a null hypothesis involving more than two population variances, you need an alternative to the $F$-test introduced in Chapter 11. This alternative method is called *Hartley's $F_{max}$*. The Hartley's $F$-test statistic is computed as shown in Equation 12.2.

---

**Hartley's *F*-Test Statistic**

$$F_{max} = \frac{s_{max}^2}{s_{min}^2} \tag{12.2}$$

where:

$$s_{max}^2 = \text{Largest sample variance}$$
$$s_{min}^2 = \text{Smallest sample variance}$$

---

We can use the $F$-value computed using Equation 12.2 to test whether the variances are equal by comparing the calculated $F$ to a critical value from the *Hartley's $F_{max}$ distribution*, which appears in Appendix I.[2] For the Bayhill example, the computed variance for each of the four samples is

$$s_1^2 = 7.341 \qquad s_2^2 = 8.423 \qquad s_3^3 = 7.632 \qquad s_4^2 = 5.016$$

Using Equation 12.2, we compute the $F_{max}$ value as

$$F_{max} = \frac{8.423}{5.016} = 1.679$$

This value is now compared to the critical value $F_\alpha$ from the table in Appendix I for $\alpha = 0.05$, with $k = 4$ and $\bar{n} - 1 = 7$ degrees of freedom. The value $k$ is the number of populations ($k = 4$). The value $\bar{n}$ is the average sample size, which equals 8 in this example. If $\bar{n}$ is not an integer value, then set $\bar{n}$ equal to the integer portion of the computed $\bar{n}$. If $F_{max} > F_\alpha$, reject the null hypothesis of equal variances. If $F_{max} \leq F_\alpha$, do not reject the null hypothesis and conclude the population variances are equal. From the Hartley's $F_{max}$ distribution table, the critical $F_{0.05} = 8.44$. Because $F_{max} = 1.679 \leq 8.44$, the null hypothesis of equal variances is not rejected.[3]

Examining the sample data to see whether the basic assumptions are satisfied is always a good idea, but you should be aware that the analysis of variance procedures discussed in this chapter are *robust*, in the sense that the analysis of variance test is relatively unperturbed when the equal-variance assumption is not met. This is especially so when all samples are the same size, as in the Bayhill Marketing Company example. Hence, for one-way analysis of variance, or any other ANOVA design, try to have equal sample sizes when possible. Recall, we earlier referred to an analysis of variance design with equal sample sizes as a *balanced design*. If for some reason you are unable to use a balanced design, the rule of thumb is that the ratio of the largest sample size to the smallest sample size should not exceed 1.5.

When the samples are the same size (or meet the 1.5 ratio rule), the analysis of variance is also robust with respect to the assumption that the populations are normally distributed. So, in brief, the one-way ANOVA for independent samples can be applied to virtually any set of interval- or ratio-level data.

---

[2]Other tests for equal variances exist. For example, Minitab has a procedure that uses Bartlett's and Levine's test.
[3]Hartley's $F_{max}$ test is very dependent on the populations being normally distributed and should not be used if the populations' distributions are skewed. Note also in Hartley's $F_{max}$ table, $c = k$ and $v = \bar{n} - 1$.

Finally, if the data are not interval or ratio level, or if they do not satisfy the normal distribution assumption, Chapter 17 introduces an ANOVA procedure called the Kruskal-Wallis One-Way ANOVA, which does not require these assumptions.

## Applying One-Way ANOVA

Although the previous discussion covers the essence of ANOVA, to determine whether the null hypothesis should be rejected requires that we actually determine values of the estimators for the total variation, between-sample variation, and within-sample variation. Most ANOVA tests are done using a computer, but we will illustrate the manual computational approach one time to show you how it is done. Because software such as Excel and Minitab can be used to perform all calculations, future examples will be done using the computer. The software packages will do all the computations while we focus on interpreting the results.

---

**BUSINESS APPLICATION**    **DEVELOPING THE ANOVA TABLE**

**BAYHILL MARKETING COMPANY (*CONTINUED*)** Now we are ready to perform the necessary one-way ANOVA computations for the Bayhill example. Recall from Equation 12.1 that we can partition the total sum of squares into two components:

$$SST = SSB + SSW$$

The *total sum of squares* is computed as shown in Equation 12.3.

---

**Total Sum of Squares**

$$SST = \sum_{i=1}^{k} \sum_{j=1}^{n_i} (x_{ij} - \overline{\overline{x}})^2 \tag{12.3}$$

where:

$SST$ = Total sum of squares

$k$ = Number of populations (treatments)

$n_i$ = Sample size from population $i$

$x_{ij}$ = $j$th measurement from population $i$

$\overline{\overline{x}}$ = Grand mean (mean of all the data values)

---

Equation 12.3 is not as complicated as it appears. Manually applying Equation 12.3 to the Bayhill data shown in Table 12.1 on page 477 (Grand mean = $\overline{\overline{x}} = 8.25$), we can compute the *SST* as follows:

$$SST = (4.10 - 8.25)^2 + (5.90 - 8.25)^2 + (10.45 - 8.25)^2 + \cdots + (9.20 - 8.25)^2$$

$$SST = 220.88$$

Thus, the sum of the squared deviations of all values from the grand mean is 220.88. Equation 12.3 can also be restated as

$$SST = \sum_{i=1}^{k} \sum_{j=1}^{n_i} (x_{ij} - \overline{\overline{x}})^2 = (n_T - 1)s^2$$

where $s^2$ is the sample variance for all data combined, and $n_T$ is the sum of the combined sample sizes.

We now need to determine how much of this total sum of squares is due to between-sample sum of squares and how much is due to within-sample sum of squares. The between-sample portion is called the *sum of squares between* and is found using Equation 12.4.

---

### Sum of Squares Between

$$SSB = \sum_{i=1}^{k} n_i (\bar{x}_i - \bar{\bar{x}})^2$$  (12.4)

where:

$SSB$ = Sum of squares between samples
$k$ = Number of populations
$n_i$ = Sample size from population $i$
$\bar{x}_i$ = Sample mean from population $i$
$\bar{\bar{x}}$ = Grand mean

---

We can use Equation 12.4 to manually compute the sum of squares between for the Bayhill data, as follows:

$$SSB = 8(7 - 8.25)^2 + 8(9 - 8.25)^2 + 8(8 - 8.25)^2 + 8(9 - 8.25)^2$$

$$SSB = 22$$

Once both the *SST* and *SSB* have been computed, the *sum of squares within* (also called the sum of squares error, *SSE*) is easily computed using Equation 12.5. The sum of squares within can also be computed directly, using Equation 12.6.

---

### Sum of Squares Within

$$SSW = SST - SSB$$  (12.5)

or

### Sum of Squares Within

$$SSW = \sum_{i=1}^{k} \sum_{j=1}^{n_i} (x_{ij} - \bar{x}_i)^2$$  (12.6)

where:

$SSW$ = Sum of squares within samples
$k$ = Number of populations
$n_i$ = Sample size from population $i$
$\bar{x}_i$ = Sample mean from population $i$
$x_{ij}$ = $j$th measurement from population $i$

---

For the Bayhill example, the *SSW* is

$$SSW = 220.88 - 22.00$$

$$= 198.88$$

These computations are the essential first steps in performing the ANOVA test to determine whether the population means are equal. Table 12.2 illustrates the ANOVA table format used to conduct the test. The format shown in Table 12.2 is the standard ANOVA table layout. For the Bayhill example, we substitute the numerical values for *SSB*, *SSW*, and *SST* and complete the ANOVA table, as shown in Table 12.3. The mean square column contains the *MSB* (mean square between samples) and the *MSW* (mean square within samples).[4] These values are computed by dividing the sum of squares by their respective degrees of freedom, as shown in Table 12.3.

---

[4]*MSW* is also known as the *mean square for error (MSE)*.

**TABLE 12.2** | **One-Way ANOVA Table: The Basic Format**

| Source of Variation | SS | df | MS | F-Ratio |
|---|---|---|---|---|
| Between samples | SSB | $k - 1$ | MSB | $\dfrac{MSB}{MSW}$ |
| Within samples | SSW | $n_T - k$ | MSW | |
| Total | SST | $n_T - 1$ | | |

where:

$$k = \text{Number of populations}$$
$$n_T = \text{Sum of the sample sizes from all populations}$$
$$df = \text{Degrees of freedom}$$
$$MSB = \text{Mean square between} = \frac{SSB}{k-1}$$
$$MSW = \text{Mean square within} = \frac{SSW}{n_T - k}$$

Restating the null and alternative hypotheses for the Bayhill example:

$$H_0: \mu_1 = \mu_2 = \mu_3 = \mu_4$$

$$H_A: \text{At least two population means are different}$$

Glance back at Figures 12.1 and 12.2. If the null hypothesis is true (that is, all the means are equal—Figure 12.2), the MSW and MSB will be equal, except for the presence of sampling error. However, the more the sample means differ (Figure 12.1), the larger the MSB becomes. As the MSB increases, it will tend to get larger than the MSW. When this difference gets too large, we will conclude that the population means must not be equal, and the null hypothesis will be rejected. But how do we determine what "too large" is? How do we know when the difference is due to more than just sampling error?

To answer these questions, recall from Chapter 11 the $F$-distribution is used to test whether two populations have the same variance. In the ANOVA test, if the null hypothesis is true, the ratio of MSB over MSW forms an $F$-distribution with $D_1 = k - 1$ and $D_2 = n_T - k$ degrees of freedom. If the calculated $F$-ratio in Table 12.3 gets too large, the null hypothesis is rejected.

Figure 12.4 illustrates the hypothesis test for a significance level of 0.05. Because the calculated $F$-ratio = 1.03 is less than the critical $F_{0.05} = 2.95$ (found using Excel's FINV function) with 3 and 28 degrees of freedom, the null hypothesis cannot be rejected. The $F$-ratio indicates that the between-levels estimate and the within-levels estimate are not different enough to conclude that the population means are different. This means there is insufficient statistical evidence to conclude that any one of the four Web site designs will generate higher average dollar values of orders than any of the other designs. Therefore, the choice of which Web site design to use can be based on other factors, such as company preference.

**TABLE 12.3** | **One-Way ANOVA Table for the Bayhill Marketing Company**

| Source of Variation | SS | df | MS | F-Ratio |
|---|---|---|---|---|
| Between samples | 22.00 | 3 | 7.33 | $\dfrac{7.33}{7.10} = 1.03$ |
| Within samples | 198.88 | 28 | 7.10 | |
| Total | 220.88 | 31 | | |

where:

$$MSB = \text{Mean square between} = \frac{SSB}{k-1} = \frac{22}{3} = 7.33$$

$$MSW = \text{Mean square within} = \frac{SSW}{n_T - k} = \frac{198.88}{28} = 7.10$$

**FIGURE 12.4**

Bayhill Company
Hypothesis Test

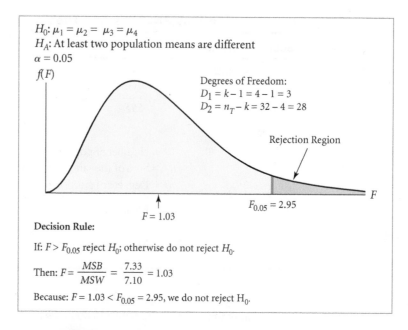

$H_0: \mu_1 = \mu_2 = \mu_3 = \mu_4$
$H_A:$ At least two population means are different
$\alpha = 0.05$

Degrees of Freedom:
$D_1 = k - 1 = 4 - 1 = 3$
$D_2 = n_T - k = 32 - 4 = 28$

Rejection Region

$F_{0.05} = 2.95$

$F = 1.03$

**Decision Rule:**

If: $F > F_{0.05}$ reject $H_0$; otherwise do not reject $H_0$.

Then: $F = \dfrac{MSB}{MSW} = \dfrac{7.33}{7.10} = 1.03$

Because: $F = 1.03 < F_{0.05} = 2.95$, we do not reject $H_0$.

**Chapter Outcome 2.** →  **EXAMPLE 12-1**   **ONE-WAY ANALYSIS OF VARIANCE**

**Roderick, Wilterding & Associates** Roderick, Wilterding & Associates (RWA) operates automobile dealerships in three regions: the West, Southwest, and Northwest. Recently, RWA's general manager questioned whether the company's mean profit margin per vehicle sold differed by region. To determine this, the following steps can be performed:

**Step 1** **Specify the parameter(s) of interest.**

The parameter of interest is the mean dollars of profit margin in each region.

**Step 2** **Formulate the null and alternative hypotheses.**

The appropriate null and alternative hypotheses are

$H_0: \mu_W = \mu_{SW} = \mu_{NW}$

$H_A:$ At least two populations have different means

**Step 3** **Specify the significance level ($\alpha$) for testing the hypothesis.**

The test will be conducted using an $\alpha = 0.05$.

**Step 4** **Select independent simple random samples from each population, and compute the sample means and the grand mean.**

There are three regions. Simple random samples of vehicles sold in these regions have been selected: 10 in the West, 8 in the Southwest, and 12 in the Northwest. Note, even though the sample sizes are not equal, the largest sample is not more than 1.5 times as large as the smallest sample size. The following sample data were collected (in dollars):

| West | Southwest | Northwest | West | Southwest | Northwest |
|------|-----------|-----------|------|-----------|-----------|
| 3,700 | 3,300 | 2,900 | 5,300 | 2,700 | 3,300 |
| 2,900 | 2,100 | 4,300 | 2,200 | 4,500 | 3,700 |
| 4,100 | 2,600 | 5,200 | 3,700 | 2,400 | 2,400 |
| 4,900 | 2,100 | 3,300 | 4,800 | | 4,400 |
| 4,900 | 3,600 | 3,600 | 3,000 | | 3,300 |
| | | | | | 4,400 |
| | | | | | 3,200 |

The sample means are

$$\bar{x}_W = \frac{\Sigma x}{n} = \frac{\$39,500}{10} = \$3,950$$

$$\bar{x}_{SW} = \frac{\$23,300}{8} = \$2,912.50$$

$$\bar{x}_{NW} = \frac{\$44,000}{12} = \$3,666.67$$

and the grand mean, the mean of the data from all samples, is

$$\bar{\bar{x}} = \frac{\Sigma\Sigma x}{n_T} = \frac{\$3,700 + \$2,900 + \cdots + \$3,200}{30}$$

$$= \frac{\$106,800}{30}$$

$$= \$3,560$$

**Step 5**  **Determine the decision rule.**
The $F$-critical value from the $F$-distribution table in Appendix H for $D_1 = 2$ and $D_2 = 27$ degrees of freedom is a value between 3.316 and 3.403. The exact value $F_{0.05} = 3.354$ can be found using Excel's FINV function or Minitab's Calc > Probability Distributions command.

The decision rule is

If $F > 3.354$, reject the null hypothesis;
otherwise, do not reject the null hypothesis.

**Step 6**  **Check to see that the equal variance assumption has been satisfied.**
As long as we assume that the populations are normally distributed, Hartley's $F_{max}$ test can be used to test whether the three populations have equal variances. The test statistic is

$$F_{max} = \frac{s^2_{max}}{s^2_{min}}$$

The three variances are computed using

$$s^2_W = \frac{\Sigma(x - \bar{x}_w)^2}{n-1} = 1,062,777.8 \qquad s^2_{SW} = 695,535.7$$

$$s^2_{NW} = 604,242.4$$

$$\text{Hartley's } F_{max} = \frac{1,062,777.8}{604,242.4} = 1.76$$

From the $F_{max}$ table in Appendix I, the critical value for $\alpha = 0.05$, $c = 3$ ($c = k$), and $v = 9$ ($v = \bar{n} - 1 = 10 - 1 = 9$) is 5.34. Because $1.76 \leq 5.34$, we do not reject the null hypothesis of equal variances.

**Step 7**  **Create the ANOVA table.**
Compute the total sum of squares, sum of squares between, and sum of squares within, and complete the ANOVA table.

**Total Sum of Squares**

$$SST = \sum_{i=1}^{k} \sum_{j=1}^{n_i} (x_{ij} - \bar{\bar{x}})^2$$

$$= (3,700 - 3,560)^2 + (2,900 - 3,560)^2 + \cdots + (3,200 - 3,560)^2$$

$$= 26,092,000$$

**Sum of Squares Between**

$$SSB = \sum_{i=1}^{k} n_i (\bar{x}_i - \bar{\bar{x}})^2$$

$$= 10(3,950 - 3,560)^2 + 8(2,912.50 - 3,560)^2 + 12(3,666.67 - 3,560)^2$$

$$= 5,011,583$$

**Sum of Squares Within**

$$SSW = SST - SSB = 26,092,000 - 5,011,583 = 21,080,417$$

The ANOVA table is

| Source of Variation | SS | df | MS | F-Ratio |
|---|---|---|---|---|
| Between samples | 5,011,583 | 2 | 2,505,792 | $\dfrac{2,505,792}{780,756} = 3.209$ |
| Within samples | 21,080,417 | 27 | 780,756 | |
| Total | 26,092,000 | 29 | | |

**Step 8  Reach a decision.**

Because the $F$-test statistic $= 3.209 < F_{0.05} = 3.354$, we do not reject the null hypothesis based on these sample data.

**Step 9  Draw a conclusion.**

We are not able to detect a difference in the mean profit margin per vehicle sold by region.

>>**END EXAMPLE**

**TRY PROBLEM** 12-2 (pg. 493)

---

**BUSINESS APPLICATION**  USING SOFTWARE TO PERFORM ONE-WAY ANOVA

**Excel and Minitab Tutorial**

**HYDRONICS CORPORATION** The Hydronics Corporation makes and distributes health products. Currently, the company's research department is experimenting with two new herb-based weight loss–enhancing products. To gauge their effectiveness, researchers at the company conducted a test using 300 human subjects over a six-week period. All the people in the study were between 30 and 40 pounds overweight.

One third of the subjects were randomly selected to receive a placebo—in this case, a pill containing only vitamin C. One third of the subjects were randomly selected and given product 1. The remaining 100 people received product 2. The subjects did not know which pill they had been assigned. Each person was asked to take the pill regularly for six weeks and otherwise observe his or her normal routine. At the end of six weeks, the subjects' weight loss was recorded. The company was hoping to find statistical evidence that at least one of the products is an effective weight-loss aid.

The file **Hydronics** shows the study data. Positive values indicate that the subject lost weight, whereas negative values indicate that the subject gained weight during the six-week study period. As often happens in studies involving human subjects, people drop out. Thus, at the end of six weeks, only 89 placebo subjects, 91 product 1 subjects, and 83 product 2 subjects with valid data remained. Consequently, this experiment resulted in an unbalanced design. Although the sample sizes are not equal, they are close to being the same size and do not violate the 1.5-ratio rule of thumb mentioned earlier.

**FIGURE 12.5A**

Excel 2007 Output:
Hydronics Weight Loss
ANOVA Results

**Excel 2007 Instructions:**
1. Open file: Hydronics.xls.
2. On the **Data** tab, click **Data Analysis**.
3. Select **ANOVA: Single Factor**.
4. Define data range (columns B, C, and D).
5. Specify alpha level = 0.05.
6. Indicate output location.
7. Click **OK**.

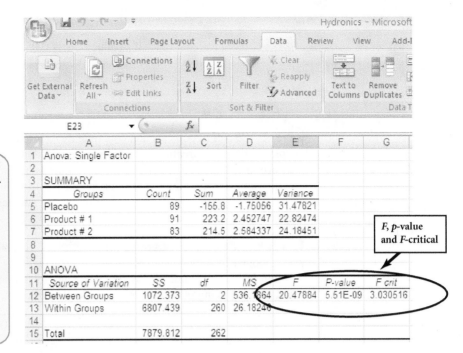

The null and alternative hypotheses to be tested using a significance level of 0.05 are

$$H_0: \mu_1 = \mu_2 = \mu_3$$
$$H_A: \text{At least two population means are different}$$

The experimental design is completely randomized. The factor is diet supplement, which has three levels: placebo, product 1, and product 2. We will use a significance level of $\alpha = 0.05$.

Figure 12.5a and Figure 12.5b show the Excel and Minitab analysis of variance results. The top section of the Excel ANOVA and the bottom section of the Minitab ANOVA output provide descriptive information for the three levels. The ANOVA table is shown in the other section of the output. These tables look like the one we generated manually in the Bayhill example. However, Excel and Minitab also compute the $p$-value. In addition, Excel displays the critical value, $F$-critical, from the $F$-distribution table. Thus, you can test the null hypothesis by comparing the calculated $F$ to the $F$-critical or by comparing the $p$-value to the significance level.

The decision rule is

$$\text{If } F > F_{0.05} = 3.03, \text{ reject } H_0;$$
$$\text{otherwise, do not reject } H_0.$$

**FIGURE 12.5B**

Minitab Output:
Hydronics Weight Loss
ANOVA Results

**Minitab Instructions:**
1. Open file: Hydronics. MTW.
2. Choose **Stat > ANOVA > One way**.
3. In **Response**, enter data column, *Loss*.
4. In **Factor**, enter factor level column, *Program*.
5. Click **OK**.

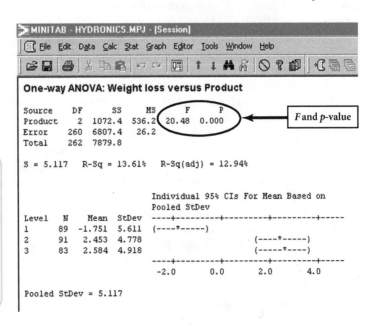

or

If $p$-value $< \alpha = 0.05$, reject $H_0$;
otherwise, do not reject $H_0$.

Because

$$F = 20.48 > F_{0.05} = 3.03 \text{ (or } p\text{-value} = 0.0000 < \alpha = 0.05)$$

we reject the null hypothesis and conclude there is a difference in the mean weight loss for people on the three treatments. At least two of the populations have different means. The top portion of Figure 12.5a shows the descriptive measures for the sample data. For example, the subjects who took the placebo actually gained an average of 1.75 pounds. Subjects on product 1 lost an average of 2.45 pounds, and subjects on product 2 lost an average of 2.58 pounds.

**Chapter Outcome 3.** → **The Tukey-Kramer Procedure for Multiple Comparisons** What does this conclusion imply about which treatment results in greater weight loss? One approach to answering this question is to use confidence interval estimates for all possible pairs of population means, based on the pooling of the two relevant sample variances, as introduced in Chapter 10.

$$s_p = \sqrt{\frac{(n_1 - 1)s_1^2 + (n_2 - 1)s_2^2}{n_1 + n_2 - 2}}$$

These confidence intervals are constructed using the formula also given in Chapter 10:

$$(\bar{x}_1 - \bar{x}_2) \pm t s_p \sqrt{\frac{1}{n_1} + \frac{1}{n_2}}$$

It uses a weighted average of only the two sample variances corresponding to the two sample means in the confidence interval. However, in the Hydronics example, we have three samples, and thus three variances, involved. If we were to use the pooled standard deviation, $s_p$ shown here, we would be disregarding one third of the information available to estimate the common population variance. Instead, we use confidence intervals based on the pooled standard deviation obtained from the square root of *MSW*. This is the square root of the weighted average of all (three in this example) sample variances. This is preferred to the interval estimate shown here because we are assuming that each of the three sample variances is an estimate of the common population variance.

A better method for testing which populations have different means after the one-way ANOVA has led us to reject the null hypothesis is called the *Tukey-Kramer procedure for multiple comparisons*.[5] To understand why the Tukey-Kramer procedure is superior, we introduce the concept of an **experiment-wide error rate**.

**Experiment-Wide Error Rate**
The proportion of experiments in which at least one of the set of confidence intervals constructed does not contain the true value of the population parameter being estimated.

The Tukey-Kramer procedure is based on the simultaneous construction of confidence intervals for all differences of pairs of treatment means. In this example, there are three different pairs of means ($\mu_1 - \mu_2, \mu_1 - \mu_3, \mu_2 - \mu_3$). The Tukey-Kramer procedure simultaneously constructs three different confidence intervals for a specified confidence level, say 95%. Intervals that do not contain zero imply that a difference exists between the associated population means.

Suppose we repeat the study a large number of times. Each time, we construct the Tukey-Kramer 95% confidence intervals. The Tukey-Kramer method assures us that in 95% of these experiments, the three confidence intervals constructed will include the true difference between the population means, $\mu_i - \mu_j$. In 5% of the experiments, at least one of the confidence intervals will not contain the true difference between the population means. Thus in 5% of the situations, we would make at least one mistake in our conclusions about which populations have different means. This proportion of errors (0.05) is known as the experiment-wide error rate.

For a 95% confidence interval, the Tukey-Kramer procedure controls the experiment-wide error to a 0.05 level. However, because we are concerned with only this one experiment (with one set of sample data), the error rate associated with any one of the three confidence intervals is actually less than 0.05.

---

[5]There are other methods for making these comparisons. Statisticians disagree over which method to use. Later, we introduce alternative methods.

The Tukey-Kramer procedure allows us to simultaneously examine all pairs of populations *after* the ANOVA test has been completed without increasing the true alpha level. Because these comparisons are made after the ANOVA *F*-test, the procedure is called a post-test (or post-hoc) procedure.

The first step in using the Tukey-Kramer procedure is to compute the absolute differences between each pair of sample means. Using the results shown in Figure 12.5a, we get the following absolute differences:

$$|\bar{x}_1 - \bar{x}_2| = |-1.75 - 2.45| = 4.20$$
$$|\bar{x}_1 - \bar{x}_3| = |-1.75 - 2.58| = 4.33$$
$$|\bar{x}_2 - \bar{x}_3| = |2.45 - 2.58| = 0.13$$

The Tukey-Kramer procedure requires us to compare these absolute differences to the *critical range* that is computed using Equation 12.7.

---

### Tukey-Kramer Critical Range

$$\text{Critical range} = q_{1-\alpha}\sqrt{\frac{MSW}{2}\left(\frac{1}{n_i}+\frac{1}{n_j}\right)} \tag{12.7}$$

where:

$q_{1-\alpha}$ = Value from studentized range table (Appendix J), with $D_1 = k$ and $D_2 = n_T - k$ degrees of freedom for the desired level of $1 - \alpha$ [$k$ = Number of groups or factor levels, and $n_T$ = Total number of data values from all populations (levels) combined]

$MSW$ = Mean square within

$n_i$ and $n_j$ = Sample sizes from populations (levels) $i$ and $j$, respectively

---

A critical range is computed for each pairwise comparison, but if the sample sizes are equal, only one critical-range calculation is necessary because the quantity under the radical in Equation 12.7 will be the same for all comparisons. If the calculated pairwise comparison value is greater than the critical range, we conclude the difference is significant.

To determine the $q$-value from the studentized range table in Appendix J for a significance level equal to

$$\alpha = 0.05$$

and

$$k = 3 \text{ and } n_T - k = 260 \text{ degrees of freedom}$$

For $D_2 = n_T - k = 260$ degrees of freedom, we use the row labeled $\infty$. The studentized range value for $1 - 0.05 = 0.95$ is approximately

$$q_{0.95} = 3.31$$

Then, for the placebo versus product 1 comparison,

$$n_1 = 89 \quad \text{and} \quad n_2 = 91$$

we use Equation 12.7 to compute the critical range, as follows:

$$\text{Critical range} = q_{1-\alpha}\sqrt{\frac{MSW}{2}\left(\frac{1}{n_i}+\frac{1}{n_j}\right)}$$

$$\text{Critical range} = 3.31\sqrt{\frac{26.18}{2}\left(\frac{1}{89}+\frac{1}{91}\right)} = 1.785$$

**TABLE 12.4** | **Hydronics Pairwise Comparisons—Tukey-Kramer Test**

|  | $|\bar{x}_i - \bar{x}_j|$ | Critical Range | Significant? |
|---|---|---|---|
| Placebo vs. product 1 | 4.20 | 1.785 | Yes |
| Placebo vs. product 2 | 4.33 | 1.827 | Yes |
| Product 1 vs. product 2 | 0.13 | 1.818 | No |

Because

$$|\bar{x}_1 - \bar{x}_2| = 4.20 > 1.785$$

we conclude that

$$\mu_1 \neq \mu_2$$

The mean weight loss for the placebo group is not equal to the mean weight loss for the product 1 group. Table 12.4 summarizes the results for the three pairwise comparisons. From the table we see that product 1 and product 2 both offer significantly higher average weight loss than the placebo. However, the sample data do not indicate a difference in the average weight loss between product 1 and product 2. Thus, the company can conclude that both product 1 and product 2 are superior to taking a placebo.

**Chapter Outcome 3.**  **EXAMPLE 12-2**    **THE TUKEY-KRAMER PROCEDURE FOR MULTIPLE COMPARISON**

**Excel and Minitab Tutorial**

**Digitron, Inc.** Digitron, Inc., makes disc brakes for automobiles. Digitron's research and development (R&D) department recently tested four brake systems to determine if there is a difference in the average stopping distance among them. Forty identical mid-sized cars were driven on a test track. Ten cars were fitted with brake A, 10 with brake B, and so forth. An electronic, remote switch was used to apply the brakes at exactly the same point on the road. The number of feet required to bring the car to a full stop was recorded. The data are in the file **Digitron**. Because we care to determine only whether the four brake systems have the same or different mean stopping distances, the test is a one-way (single-factor) test with four levels and can be completed using the following steps:

Step 1  **Specify the parameter(s) of interest.**
The parameter of interest is the mean stopping distance for each brake type. The company is interested in knowing whether a difference exists in mean stopping distance for the four brake types.

Step 2  **Formulate the appropriate null and alternative hypotheses.**
The appropriate null and alternative hypotheses are

$$H_0: \mu_1 = \mu_2 = \mu_3 = \mu_4$$

$H_A$: At least two population means are different

Step 3  **Specify the significance level for the test.**
The test will be conducted using $\alpha = 0.05$.

Step 4  **Select independent simple random samples from each population.**

Step 5  **Check to see that the normality and equal-variance assumptions have been satisfied.**

Because of the small sample size, the box and whisker plot is used.

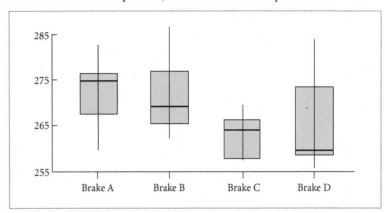

The box plots indicate some skewness in the samples and question the assumption of equality of variances. However, if we assume that the populations are approximately normally distributed, Hartley's $F_{max}$ test can be used to test whether the four populations have equal variances. The test statistic is

$$F_{max} = \frac{s^2_{max}}{s^2_{min}}$$

The four variances are computed using $s^2 = \dfrac{\Sigma(x - \overline{x})^2}{n-1}$:

$$s_1^2 = 49.9001 \quad s_2^2 = 61.8557 \quad s_3^2 = 21.7356 \quad s_4^2 = 106.4385$$

Hartley's $F_{max} = \dfrac{106.4385}{21.7356} = 4.8970$

From the $F_{max}$ table in Appendix I, the critical value for $\alpha = 0.05$, $k = 4$, and $\overline{n} - 1 = 9$ is $F_{0.05} = 6.31$. Because $4.8970 < 6.31$, we conclude that the population variances could be equal. Recall our earlier discussion stating that when the sample sizes are equal, as they are in this example, the ANOVA test is robust in regards to both the equal variance and normality assumptions.

**Step 6  Determine the decision rule.**
Because $k - 1 = 3$ and $n_T - k = 36$, from Excel or Minitab $F_{0.05} = 2.8663$. The decision rule is

If the calculated $F > F_{0.05} = 2.8663$, reject $H_0$, or
if the $p$-value $< \alpha = 0.05$, reject $H_0$; otherwise, do not reject $H_0$.

**Step 7  Use Excel or Minitab to construct the ANOVA table.**
Figure 12.6 shows the Excel output for the ANOVA.

**Step 8  Reach a decision.**
From Figure 12.6, we see that

$$F = 3.89 > F_{0.05} = 2.8663, \text{ and } p\text{-value} = 0.0167 < 0.05$$

We reject the null hypothesis.

**Step 9  Draw a conclusion.**
We conclude that not all population means are equal. But which systems are different? Is one system superior to all the others?

**Step 10  Use the Tukey-Kramer test to determine which populations have different means.**
Because we have rejected the null hypothesis of equal means, we need to perform a post–ANOVA multiple comparisons test. Using Equation 12.7 to

**FIGURE 12.6**

Excel 2007 One-Way ANOVA Output for the Digitron Example

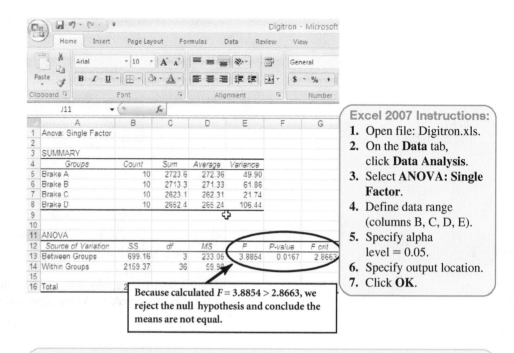

**Excel 2007 Instructions:**
1. Open file: Digitron.xls.
2. On the **Data** tab, click **Data Analysis**.
3. Select **ANOVA: Single Factor**.
4. Define data range (columns B, C, D, E).
5. Specify alpha level = 0.05.
6. Specify output location.
7. Click **OK**.

Because calculated $F = 3.8854 > 2.8663$, we reject the null hypothesis and conclude the means are not equal.

**Minitab Instructions (for similar results):**
1. Open file: Digitron.MTW.
2. Choose **Stat > ANOVA > One-way**.
3. In **Response**, enter data column, *Distance*.
4. In **Factor**, enter factor level column, *Brake*.
5. Click **OK**.

construct the critical range to compare to the absolute differences in all possible pairs of sample means, the critical range is[6]

$$\text{Critical range} = q_{1-\alpha}\sqrt{\frac{MSW}{2}\left(\frac{1}{n_i} + \frac{1}{n_j}\right)} = 3.85\sqrt{\frac{59.98}{2}\left(\frac{1}{10} + \frac{1}{10}\right)}$$

$$\text{Critical range} = 9.43$$

Only one critical range is necessary because the sample sizes are equal. If any pair of sample means has an absolute difference, $|\bar{x}_i - \bar{x}_j|$, greater than the critical range, we can infer that a difference exists in those population means. The possible pairwise comparisons (part of a family of comparisons called *contrasts*) are

| Contrast | Significant Difference |
|---|---|
| $|\bar{x}_1 - \bar{x}_2| = |272.3590 - 271.3299| = 1.0291 < 9.43$ | No |
| $|\bar{x}_1 - \bar{x}_3| = |272.3590 - 262.3140| = 10.0450 > 9.43$ | Yes |
| $|\bar{x}_1 - \bar{x}_4| = |272.3590 - 265.2357| = 7.1233 < 9.43$ | No |
| $|\bar{x}_2 - \bar{x}_3| = |271.3299 - 262.3140| = 9.0159 < 9.43$ | No |
| $|\bar{x}_2 - \bar{x}_4| = |271.3299 - 265.2357| = 6.0942 < 9.43$ | No |
| $|\bar{x}_3 - \bar{x}_4| = |262.3140 - 265.2357| = 2.9217 < 9.43$ | No |

---

[6]The $q$-value from the studentized range table with $\alpha = 0.05$ and degrees of freedom equal to $k = 4$ and $n_T - k = 36$ must be approximated using degrees of freedom 4 and 30 because the table does not show degrees of freedom of 4 and 36. This value is 3.85. Rounding down to 30 will give a larger $q$ value and a conservatively large critical range.

Therefore, based on the Tukey-Kramer procedure, we can infer that population 1 (brake system A) and population 3 (brake system C) have different mean stopping distances. Because short stopping distances are preferred, system C would be preferred over system A, but no other differences are supported by these sample data. For the other contrasts, the difference between the two sample means is insufficient to conclude that a difference in population means exists.

>>**END EXAMPLE**

**TRY PROBLEM** 12-6 (pg. 494)

## Fixed Effects Versus Random Effects in Analysis of Variance

In the Digitron brake example, the company was testing four brake systems. These were the only brake systems under consideration. The ANOVA was intended to determine whether there was a difference in these four brake systems only. In the Hydronics weight-loss example, the company was interested in determining whether there was a difference in mean weight loss for two supplements and the placebo. In the Bayhill example involving Web site designs, the company narrowed its choices to four different designs, and the ANOVA test was used to determine whether there was a difference in means for these four designs only. Thus, in each of these examples, the inferences extend only to the factor levels being analyzed, and the levels are assumed to be the only levels of interest. This type of test is called a *fixed effects analysis of variance test.*

Suppose in the Bayhill Web site example that instead of reducing the list of possible Web site designs to a final four, the company had simply selected a random sample of four Web site designs from all possible designs being considered. In that case, the factor levels included in the test would be a random sample of the possible levels. Then, if the ANOVA leads to rejecting the null hypothesis, the conclusion applies to all possible Web site designs. The assumption is the possible levels have a normal distribution and the tested levels are a random sample from this distribution. When the factor levels are selected through random sampling, the analysis of variance test is called a *random effects test.*

## 12-1: **Exercises**

### Skill Development

**12-1.** A start-up cell phone applications company is interested in determining whether household incomes are different for subscribers to three different service providers. A random sample of 25 subscribers to each of the three service providers was taken, and the annual household income for each subscriber was recorded. The partially completed ANOVA table for the analysis is shown here:

**ANOVA**

| Source of Variation | SS | df | MS | F |
|---|---|---|---|---|
| Between Groups | 2,949,085,157 | | | |
| Within Groups | | | | |
| Total | 9,271,678,090 | | | |

a. Complete the ANOVA table by filling in the missing sums of squares, the degrees of freedom for each source, the mean square, and the calculated F-test statistic.

b. Based on the sample results, can the start-up firm conclude that there is a difference in household incomes for subscribers to the three service providers? You may assume normal distributions and equal variances. Conduct your test at the $\alpha = 0.10$ level of significance. Be sure to state a critical F-statistic, a decision rule, and a conclusion.

**12-2.** An analyst is interested in testing whether four populations have equal means. The following sample data have been collected from populations that are assumed to be normally distributed with equal variances:

| Sample 1 | Sample 2 | Sample 3 | Sample 4 |
|---|---|---|---|
| 9 | 12 | 8 | 17 |
| 6 | 16 | 8 | 15 |
| 11 | 16 | 12 | 17 |
| 14 | 12 | 7 | 16 |
| 14 | 9 | 10 | 13 |

Conduct the appropriate hypothesis test using a significance level equal to 0.05.

**12-3.** A manager is interested in testing whether three populations of interest have equal population means. Simple random samples of size 10 were selected from each population. The following ANOVA table and related statistics were computed:

### ANOVA: Single Factor

#### Summary

| Groups | Count | Sum | Average | Variance |
|---|---|---|---|---|
| Sample 1 | 10 | 507.18 | 50.72 | 35.06 |
| Sample 2 | 10 | 405.79 | 40.58 | 30.08 |
| Sample 3 | 10 | 487.64 | 48.76 | 23.13 |

#### ANOVA

| Source | SS | df | MS | F | p-value | F-crit |
|---|---|---|---|---|---|---|
| Between Groups | 578.78 | 2 | 289.39 | 9.84 | 0.0006 | 3.354 |
| Within Groups | 794.36 | 27 | 29.42 | | | |
| Total | 1,373.14 | 29 | | | | |

a. State the appropriate null and alternative hypotheses.

b. Conduct the appropriate test of the null hypothesis assuming that the populations have equal variances and the populations are normally distributed. Use a 0.05 level of significance.

c. If warranted, use the Tukey-Kramer procedure for multiple comparisons to determine which populations have different means. (Assume $\alpha = 0.05$.)

**12-4.** Respond to each of the following questions using this partially completed one-way ANOVA table:

| Source of Variation | SS | df | MS | F-ratio |
|---|---|---|---|---|
| Between Samples | 1,745 | | | |
| Within Samples | ___ | 240 | | |
| Total | 6,504 | 246 | | |

a. How many different populations are being considered in this analysis?

b. Fill in the ANOVA table with the missing values.

c. State the appropriate null and alternative hypotheses.

d. Based on the analysis of variance F-test, what conclusion should be reached regarding the null hypothesis? Test using a significance level of 0.01.

**12-5.** Respond to each of the following questions using this partially completed one-way ANOVA table:

| Source of Variation | SS | df | MS | F-ratio |
|---|---|---|---|---|
| Between Samples | | 3 | | |
| Within Samples | | 405 | ___ | |
| Total | 888 | 31 | | |

a. How many different populations are being considered in this analysis?

b. Fill in the ANOVA table with the missing values.

c. State the appropriate null and alternative hypotheses.

d. Based on the analysis of variance F-test, what conclusion should be reached regarding the null hypothesis? Test using $\alpha = 0.05$.

**12-6.** Given the following sample data

| Item | Group 1 | Group 2 | Group 3 | Group 4 |
|---|---|---|---|---|
| 1 | 20.9 | 28.2 | 17.8 | 21.2 |
| 2 | 27.2 | 26.2 | 15.9 | 23.9 |
| 3 | 26.6 | 21.6 | 18.4 | 19.5 |
| 4 | 22.1 | 29.7 | 20.2 | 17.4 |
| 5 | 25.3 | 30.3 | 14.1 | |
| 6 | 30.1 | 25.9 | | |
| 7 | 23.8 | | | |

a. Based on the computations for the within- and between-sample variation, develop the ANOVA table and test the appropriate null hypothesis using $\alpha = 0.05$. Use the p-value approach.

b. If warranted, use the Tukey-Kramer procedure to determine which populations have different means. Use $\alpha = 0.05$.

**12-7.** Examine the three samples obtained independently from three populations:

| Item | Group 1 | Group 2 | Group 3 |
|---|---|---|---|
| 1 | 14 | 17 | 17 |
| 2 | 13 | 16 | 14 |
| 3 | 12 | 16 | 15 |
| 4 | 15 | 18 | 16 |
| 5 | 16 | | 14 |
| 6 | | | 16 |

a. Conduct a one-way analysis of variance on the data. Use alpha = 0.05.

b. If warranted, use the Tukey-Kramer procedure to determine which populations have different means. Use an experiment-wide error rate of 0.05.

## Business Applications

**12-8.** In conjunction with the housing foreclosure crisis of 2009, many economists expressed increasing concern about the level of credit card debt and efforts of banks to raise interest rates on these cards. The banks claimed the increases were justified. A Senate sub-committee decided to determine if the average credit card balance depends on the type of credit card used. Under consideration are Visa, MasterCard, Discover, and American Express. The sample sizes to be used for each level are 25, 25, 26, and 23, respectively.

a. Describe the parameter of interest for this analysis.

b. Determine the factor associated with this experiment.

c. Describe the levels of the factor associated with this analysis.

d. State the number of degrees of freedom available for determining the between-samples variation.

e. State the number of degrees of freedom available for determining the within-samples variation.

f. State the number of degrees of freedom available for determining the total variation.

**12-9.** EverRun Incorporated produces treadmills for use in exercise clubs and recreation centers. EverRun assembles, sells, and services its treadmills, but it does not manufacture the treadmill motors. Rather, treadmill motors are purchased from an outside vendor. Currently, EverRun is considering which motor to include in its new ER1500 series. Three potential suppliers have been identified: Venetti, Madison, and Edison; however, only one supplier will be used. The motors produced by these three suppliers are identical in terms of noise and cost. Consequently, EverRun has decided to make its decision based on how long a motor operates at a high level of speed and incline before it fails. A random sample of 10 motors of each type is selected, and each motor is tested to determine how many minutes (rounded to the nearest minute) it operates before it needs to be repaired. The sample information for each motor is as follows:

| Venetti | Madison | Edison |
|---|---|---|
| 14,722 | 13,649 | 13,296 |
| 14,699 | 13,592 | 13,262 |
| 12,627 | 11,788 | 11,552 |
| 13,010 | 12,623 | 11,036 |
| 13,570 | 14,552 | 12,978 |
| 14,217 | 13,441 | 12,170 |
| 13,687 | 13,404 | 12,674 |
| 13,465 | 13,427 | 11,851 |
| 14,786 | 12,049 | 12,342 |
| 12,494 | 11,672 | 11,557 |

a. At the $\alpha = 0.01$ level of significance, is there a difference in the average time before failure for the three different supplier motors?

b. Is it possible for EverRun to decide on a single motor supplier based on the analysis of the sample results? Support your answer by conducting the appropriate post-test analysis.

**12-10.** ESSROC Cement Corporation is a leading North American cement producer, with over 6.5 million metric tons of annual capacity. With headquarters in Nazareth, Pennsylvania, ESSROC operates production facilities strategically located throughout the United States, Canada, and Puerto Rico. One of its products is Portland cement. Portland cement's properties and performance standards are defined by its type designation. Each type is designated by a Roman numeral. Ninety-two percent of the Portland cement produced in North America is Type I, II, or I/II.

One characteristic of the type of cement is its compressive strength. Sample data for the compressive strength (psi) are shown as follows:

| Type | Compressive Strength | | | |
|---|---|---|---|---|
| I | 4,972 | 4,983 | 4,889 | 5,063 |
| II | 3,216 | 3,399 | 3,267 | 3,357 |
| I/II | 4,073 | 3,949 | 3,936 | 3,925 |

a. Develop the appropriate ANOVA table to determine if there is a difference in the average compressive strength among the three types of Portland cement. Use a significance level of 0.01.

b. If warranted, use the Tukey-Kramer procedure to determine which populations have different mean compressive strengths. Use an experiment-wide error rate of 0.01.

**12-11.** The Weidmann Group Companies, with headquarters in Rapperswil, Switzerland, are worldwide leaders in insulation systems technology for power and distribution transformers. One facet of its expertise is the development of dielectric fluids in electrical equipment. Mineral oil–based dielectric fluids have been used more extensively than other dielectric fluids. Their only shortcomings are their relatively low flash and fire point. One study examined the fire point of mineral oil, high-molecular-weight hydrocarbon (HMWH), and silicone. The fire points for each of these fluids were as follows:

| Fluid | Fire Points (°C) | | | | |
|---|---|---|---|---|---|
| Mineral Oil | 162 | 151 | 168 | 165 | 169 |
| HMWH | 312 | 310 | 300 | 311 | 308 |
| Silicone | 343 | 337 | 345 | 345 | 337 |

a. Develop the appropriate ANOVA table to determine if there is a difference in the average fire points among the types of dielectric fluids. Use a significance level of 0.05.

b. If warranted, use the Tukey-Kramer procedure to determine which populations have different mean fire points. Use an experiment-wide error rate of 0.05.

**12-12.** The manager at the Hillsberg Savings and Loan is interested in determining whether there is a difference in the mean time that customers spend completing their transactions depending on which of four tellers they use. To conduct the test, the manager has selected simple random samples of 15 customers for each of the tellers and has timed them (in seconds) from the moment they start their transaction to the time the transaction is completed and they leave the teller station. The manager then asked one of her assistants to perform the appropriate statistical test. The assistant returned with the following partially completed ANOVA table.

| Summary | | | | |
|---|---|---|---|---|
| Groups | Count | Sum | Average | Variance |
| Teller 1 | 15 | 3,043.9 | | 827.4 |
| Teller 2 | 15 | 3,615.5 | | 472.2 |
| Teller 3 | 15 | 3,427.7 | | 445.6 |
| Teller 4 | 15 | 4,072.4 | | 619.4 |

| ANOVA | | | | | | |
|---|---|---|---|---|---|---|
| Source of Variation | SS | df | MS | F-ratio | p-value | F-crit |
| Between Groups | 36,530.6 | | | | 4.03E–09 | 2.7694 |
| Within Groups | | | | | | |
| Total | 69,633.7 | 59 | | | | |

a. State the appropriate null and alternative hypotheses.

b. Test to determine whether the population variances are equal. Use a significance level equal to 0.05.

c. Fill in the missing parts of the ANOVA table and perform the statistical hypothesis test using $\alpha = 0.05$.

d. Based on the result of the test in part c, if warranted, use the Tukey-Kramer method with $\alpha = 0.05$ to determine which teller require the most time on average to complete a customer's transaction.

**12-13.** Suppose as part of your job you are responsible for installing emergency lighting in a series of state office buildings. Bids have been received from four manufacturers of battery-operated emergency lights. The costs are about equal, so the decision will be based on the length of time the lights last before failing. A sample of four lights from each manufacturer has been tested with the following values (time in hours) recorded for each manufacturer:

| Type A | Type B | Type C | Type D |
|---|---|---|---|
| 1,024 | 1,270 | 1,121 | 923 |
| 1,121 | 1,325 | 1,201 | 983 |
| 1,250 | 1,426 | 1,190 | 1,087 |
| 1,022 | 1,322 | 1,122 | 1,121 |

a. Using a significance level equal to 0.01, what conclusion should you reach about the four manufacturers' battery-operated emergency lights? Explain.

b. If the test conducted in part a reveals that the null hypothesis should be rejected, what manufacturer should be used to supply the lights? Can you eliminate one or more manufacturers based on these data? Use the appropriate test and $\alpha = 0.01$ for multiple comparisons. Discuss.

## Computer Database Exercises

**12-14.** Damage to homes caused by burst piping can be expensive to repair. By the time the leak is discovered, hundreds of gallons of water may have already flooded the home. Automatic shutoff valves can prevent extensive water damage from plumbing failures. The valves contain sensors that cut off water flow in the event of a leak, thereby preventing flooding. One important characteristic is the time (in milliseconds) required for the sensor to detect the water leak. Sample data obtained for four different shutoff valves are contained in the file entitled **Waterflow**.

a. Produce the relevant ANOVA table and conduct a hypothesis test to determine if the mean detection time differs among the four shutoff valve models. Use a significance level of 0.05.

b. Use the Tukey-Kramer multiple comparison technique to discover any differences in the average detection time. Use a significance level of 0.05.

c. Which of the four shutoff valves would you recommend? State your criterion for your selection.

**12-15.** A regional package delivery company is considering changing from full-size vans to minivans. The company sampled minivans from each of three manufacturers. The number sampled represents the number the manufacturer was able to provide for the test. Each minivan was driven for 5,000 miles, and the operating cost per mile was computed. The operating costs, in cents per mile, for the 12 are provided in the data file called **Delivery**:

| Mini 1 | Mini 2 | Mini 3 |
|---|---|---|
| 13.3 | 12.4 | 13.9 |
| 14.3 | 13.4 | 15.5 |
| 13.6 | 13.1 | 15.2 |
| 12.8 | | 14.5 |
| 14.0 | | |

a. Perform an analysis of variance on these data. Assume a significance level of 0.05. Do the experimental data provide evidence that the average operating costs per mile for the three types of minivans are different? Use a p-value approach.

b. Referring to part a, based on the sample data and the appropriate test for multiple comparisons, what conclusions should be reached concerning which type of car the delivery company should adopt? Discuss and prepare a report to the company CEO. Use $\alpha = 0.05$.

c. Provide an estimate of the maximum and minimum difference in average savings per year if the CEO chooses the "best" versus the "worst" minivan using operating costs as a criterion. Assume that minivans are driven 30,000 miles a year. Use a 90% confidence interval.

**12-16.** The Lottaburger restaurant chain in central New Mexico is conducting an analysis of its restaurants, which take pride in serving burgers and fries to go faster than the competition. As a part of its analysis, Lottaburger wants to determine if its speed of service is different across its four outlets. Orders at Lottaburger restaurants are tracked electronically, and the chain is able to determine the speed with which every order is filled. The chain decided to randomly sample 20 orders from each of the four restaurants it operates. The speed of service for each randomly sampled order was noted and is contained in the file **Lottaburger**.

a. At the $\alpha = 0.05$ level of service, can Lottaburger conclude that the speed of service is different across the four restaurants in the chain?

b. If the chain concludes that there is a difference in speed of service, is there a particular restaurant the chain should focus its attention on? Use the appropriate test for multiple comparisons to support your decision. Use $\alpha = 0.05$.

**12-17.** Most auto batteries are made by just three manufacturers—Delphi, Exide, and Johnson Controls Industries. Each makes batteries sold under several different brand names. Delphi makes ACDelco and some EverStart (Wal-Mart) models. Exide makes Champion, Exide, Napa, and some EverStart batteries. Johnson Controls makes Diehard (Sears), Duralast (AutoZone), Interstate, Kirkland (Costco), Motorcraft (Ford), and some EverStarts. To determine if who makes the auto batteries affects the average length of life of the battery, the samples in the file entitled **Start** were obtained. The data represent the length of life (months) for batteries of the same specifications for each of the three manufacturers.

a. Determine if the average length of battery life is different among the batteries produced by the three manufacturers. Use a significance level of 0.05.

b. Which manufacturer produces the battery with the longest average length of life? If warranted, conduct the Tukey-Kramer procedure to determine this. Use a significance level of 0.05. (*Note:* You will need to manipulate the data columns to obtain the appropriate factor levels).

**END EXERCISES 12-1**

---

Chapter Outcome 4. ➤ ## 12.2 Randomized Complete Block Analysis of Variance

Section 12.1 introduced one-way ANOVA for testing hypotheses involving three or more population means. This ANOVA method is appropriate as long as we are interested in analyzing one factor at a time and we select independent random samples from the populations. For instance, Example 12-2 involving brake assembly systems at the Digitron Corporation (Figure 12.6) illustrated a situation in which we were interested in only one factor: type of brake assembly system. The measurement of interest was the stopping distance with each brake system. To test the hypothesis that the four brake systems were equal with respect to average stopping distance, four groups of the same make and model cars were assigned to each brake system independently. Thus, the one-way ANOVA design was appropriate.

There are, however, situations in which another factor may affect the observed response in a one-way design. Often, this additional factor is unknown. This is the reason for randomization within the experiment. However, there are also situations in which we know the factor that is impinging on the response variable of interest. Chapter 10 introduced the concept of paired samples and indicated that there are instances when you will want to test for differences in two population means by controlling for sources of variation that might adversely affect the analysis. For instance, in the Digitron example, we might be concerned that, even though we used the same make and model of car in the study, the cars themselves may interject a source of variability that could affect the result. To control for this, we could use the concept of *paired samples* by using the same 10 cars for each of the four brake systems. When an additional factor with two or more levels is involved, a design technique called *blocking* can be used to eliminate the additional factor's effect on the statistical analysis of the main factor of interest.

### Randomized Complete Block ANOVA

**BUSINESS APPLICATION**    A RANDOMIZED BLOCK DESIGN

**Excel and Minitab Tutorial**

**CITIZEN'S STATE BANK** At Citizen's State Bank, homeowners can borrow money against the equity they have in their homes. To determine equity, the bank determines the home's value and subtracts the mortgage balance. The maximum loan is 90% of the equity.

The bank outsources the home appraisals to three companies: Allen & Associates, Heist Appraisal, and Appraisal International. The bank managers know that appraisals are not exact. Some appraisal companies may overvalue homes on average, whereas others might undervalue homes.

Bank managers wish to test the hypothesis that there is no difference in the average house appraisal among the three different companies. The managers could select a random sample of homes for Allen & Associates to appraise, a second sample of homes for Heist Appraisal to work on, and a third sample of homes for Appraisal International. One-way ANOVA would be used to compare the sample means. Obviously a problem could occur if, by chance, one company received larger, higher-quality homes located in better neighborhoods than the other companies. This company's appraisals would naturally be higher on average, not because it tended to appraise higher, but because the homes were simply more expensive.

Citizen's State Bank officers need to control for the variation in size, quality, and location of homes to fairly test that the three companies' appraisals are equal on the average. To do this, they select a random sample of properties and have each company appraise the same properties. In this case, the properties are called *blocks*, and the test design is called a *randomized complete block design*.

The data in Table 12.5 were obtained when each appraisal company was asked to appraise the same five properties. The bank managers wish to test the following hypothesis:

$$H_0: \mu_1 = \mu_2 = \mu_3$$

$H_A$: At least two populations have different means

The randomized block design requires the following assumptions:

**Assumptions**

1. The populations are normally distributed.
2. The populations have equal variances.
3. The observations within samples are independent.
4. The data measurement must be interval or ratio level.

Because the managers have chosen to have the same properties appraised by each company (block on property), the samples are not independent, and a method known as *randomized complete block ANOVA* must be employed to test the hypothesis. This method is similar to the one-way ANOVA in Section 12.1. However, there is one more source of variation to be accounted for, the block variation. As was the case in Section 12.1, we must find estimators for each source of variation. Identifying the appropriate sums of squares and then dividing each by its degrees of freedom does this. As was the case in the one-way ANOVA, the sums of squares are obtained by partitioning the total sum of squares (*SST*). However, in this case the *SST* is divided into three components instead of two, as shown in Equation 12.8.

**TABLE 12.5** | **Citizen's State Bank Property Appraisals (in thousands of dollars)**

| Property (Block) | Appraisal Company | | | |
| | Allen & Associates | Heist Appraisal | Appraisal International | Block Mean |
|---|---|---|---|---|
| 1 | 78 | 82 | 79 | 79.67 |
| 2 | 102 | 102 | 99 | 101.00 |
| 3 | 68 | 74 | 70 | 70.67 |
| 4 | 83 | 88 | 86 | 85.67 |
| 5 | 95 | 99 | 92 | 95.33 |
| Factor-Level Mean | $\bar{x}_1 = 85.2$ | $\bar{x}_2 = 89$ | $\bar{x}_3 = 85.2$ | $\bar{\bar{x}} = 86.47 =$ Grand mean |

---

**Sum of Squares Partitioning for Randomized Complete Block Design**

$$SST = SSB + SSBL + SSW \tag{12.8}$$

where:

$SST$ = Total sum of squares
$SSB$ = Sum of squares between factor levels
$SSBL$ = Sum of squares between blocks
$SSW$ = Sum of squares within levels

---

Both *SST* and *SSB* are computed just as we did with one-way ANOVA, using Equations 12.3 and 12.4. The *sum of squares for blocking (SSBL)* is computed using Equation 12.9.

---

**Sum of Squares for Blocking**

$$SSBL = \sum_{j=1}^{b} k(\bar{x}_j - \bar{\bar{x}})^2 \tag{12.9}$$

where:

$k$ = Number of levels for the factor
$b$ = Number of blocks
$\bar{x}_j$ = The mean of the $j$th block
$\bar{\bar{x}}$ = Grand mean

---

Finally, the *sum of squares within (SSW)* is computed using Equation 12.10. This sum of squares is what remains (the residual) after the variation for all known factors has been removed. This residual sum of squares may be due to the inherent variability of the data, measurement error, or other unidentified sources of variation. Therefore, the sum of squares within is also known as the sum of squares of error, *SSE*.

---

**Sum of Squares Within**

$$SSW = SST - (SSB + SSBL) \tag{12.10}$$

---

The effect of computing *SSBL* and subtracting it from *SST* in Equation 12.10 is that *SSW* is reduced. Also, if the corresponding variation in the blocks is significant, the variation within the factor levels will be significantly reduced. This can make it easier to detect a difference in the population means if such a difference actually exists. If it does, the estimator for the within variability will in all likelihood be reduced, and thus, the denominator for the *F*-test statistic will be smaller. This will produce a larger *F*-test statistic, which will more likely lead to rejecting the null hypothesis. This will depend, of course, on the relative size of *SSBL* and the respective changes in the degrees of freedom.

Table 12.6 shows the completely randomized block ANOVA table format and equations for degrees of freedom, mean squares, and *F*-ratios. As you can see, we now have two *F*-ratios. The reason for this is that we test not only to determine whether the population means are equal but also to obtain an indication of whether the blocking was necessary by examining the ratio of the mean square for blocks to the mean square within.

Although you could manually compute the necessary values for the randomized block design, both Excel and Minitab contain a procedure that will do all the computations and build the ANOVA table. The Citizen's State Bank appraisal data are included in the file **Citizens**. (Note that the first column contains labels for each block.)

Figures 12.9a and 12.9b show the ANOVA output. Using Excel or Minitab to perform the computations frees the decision maker to focus on interpreting the results. Note that Excel

**TABLE 12.6**  |  **Basic Format for the Randomized Block ANOVA Table**

| Source of Variation | SS | df | MS | F-ratio |
|---|---|---|---|---|
| Between blocks | SSBL | $b-1$ | MSBL | $\dfrac{MSBL}{MSW}$ |
| Between samples | SSB | $k-1$ | MSB | $\dfrac{MSB}{MSW}$ |
| Within samples | $\dfrac{SSW}{SST}$ | $\dfrac{(k-1)(b-1)}{n_T - 1}$ | MSW | |
| Total | | | | |

where:

$$k = \text{Number of levels}$$
$$b = \text{Number of blocks}$$
$$df = \text{Degrees of freedom}$$
$$n_T = \text{Combined sample size}$$
$$MSBL = \text{Mean square blocking} = \frac{SSBL}{b-1}$$
$$MSB = \text{Mean square between} = \frac{SSB}{k-1}$$
$$MSW = \text{Mean square within} = \frac{SSW}{(k-1)(b-1)}$$

*Note:* Some randomized block ANOVA tables put *SSB* first, followed by *SSBL*.

refers to the randomized block ANOVA as Two-Factor ANOVA without replication. Minitab refers to the randomized block ANOVA as Two-Way ANOVA.

The main issue is to determine whether the three appraisal companies differ in average appraisal values. The primary test is

$$H_0: \mu_1 = \mu_2 = \mu_3$$
$H_A$: At least two populations have different means
$\alpha = 0.05$

Using the output presented in Figures 12.7a and 12.7b, you can test this hypothesis two ways. First, we can use the *F*-distribution approach. Figure 12.8 shows the results of this test. Based on the sample data, we reject the null hypothesis and conclude that the three appraisal companies do not provide equal average values for properties.

The second approach to testing the null hypothesis is the *p*-value approach. The decision rule in an ANOVA application for *p*-values is

If *p*-value $< \alpha$ reject $H_0$; otherwise, do not reject $H_0$.

In this case, $\alpha = 0.05$ and the *p*-value in Figure 12.9a is 0.0103. Because *p*-value $= 0.0103 < \alpha = 0.05$ we reject the null hypothesis.

Both the *F*-distribution approach and the *p*-value approach give the same result, as they must.

**Was Blocking Necessary?**  Before we take up the issue of determining which company provides the highest mean property values, we need to discuss one other issue. Recall that the bank managers chose to control for variation between properties by having each appraisal company evaluate the same five properties. This restriction is called blocking, and the properties are the blocks. The ANOVA output in Figure 12.7a contains information that allows us to test whether blocking was necessary.

If blocking was necessary, it would mean that appraisal values are in fact influenced by the particular property being appraised. The blocks then form a second factor of interest, and we formulate a secondary hypothesis test for this factor, as follows:

$$H_0: \mu_{b1} = \mu_{b2} = \mu_{b3} = \mu_{b4} = \mu_{b5}$$
$H_A$: Not all block means are equal

**FIGURE 12.7A**

Excel 2007 Output: Citizen's State Bank Analysis of Variance

**Excel 2007 Instructions:**
1. Open file: Citizens.xls.
2. On the **Data** tab, click **Data Analysis**.
3. Select **ANOVA: Two-Factor Without Replication**.
4. Define data range (include column A).
5. Specify alpha level = 0.05.
6. Indicate output location.
7. Click **OK**.

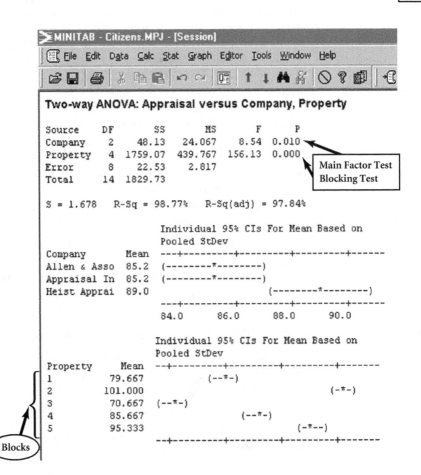

**FIGURE 12.7B**

Minitab Output: Citizen's State Bank Analysis of Variance

**Minitab Instructions:**
1. Open file: Citizens.MTW.
2. Choose **Stat > ANOVA > Two-way**.
3. In **Response**, enter the data column (*Appraisal*).
4. In **Row Factor**, enter main factor indicator column (*Company*) and select **Display Means**.
5. In **Column Factor**, enter the block indicator column (*Property*) and select **Display Means**.
6. Choose **Fit additive model**.
7. Click **OK**.

Note that we are using $\mu_{bj}$ to represent the mean of the *j*th block.

It seems only natural to use a test statistic that consists of the ratio of the mean square for blocks to the mean square within. However, certain (randomization) restrictions placed on the complete block design make this proposed test statistic invalid from a theoretical statistics

**FIGURE 12.8**

Appraisal Company
Hypothesis Test for Citizen's
State Bank

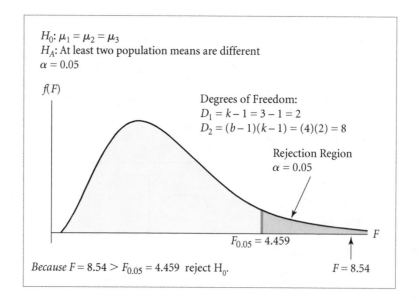

$H_0: \mu_1 = \mu_2 = \mu_3$
$H_A$: At least two population means are different
$\alpha = 0.05$

$f(F)$

Degrees of Freedom:
$D_1 = k - 1 = 3 - 1 = 2$
$D_2 = (b - 1)(k - 1) = (4)(2) = 8$

Rejection Region
$\alpha = 0.05$

$F_{0.05} = 4.459$

$F$

$F = 8.54$

*Because $F = 8.54 > F_{0.05} = 4.459$ reject $H_0$.*

point of view. As an approximate procedure, however, the examination of the ratio *MSBL/MSW* is certainly reasonable. If it is large, it implies that the blocks had a large effect on the response variable and that they were probably helpful in improving the precision of the *F*-test for the primary factor's means.[7] In performing the analysis of variance, we may also conduct a pseudotest to see whether the average appraisals for each property are equal. If the null hypothesis is rejected, we have an indication that the blocking is necessary and that the randomized block design is justified. However, we should be careful to present this only as an indication and not as a precise test of hypothesis for the blocks. The output in Figure 12.9a provides the *F*-value and *p*-value for this pseudotest to determine if the blocking was a necessity. Because $F = 156.13 > F_{0.05} = 3.838$, we definitely have an indication that the blocking design was necessary.

If a hypothesis test indicates blocking is not necessary, the chance of a Type II error for the primary hypothesis has been unnecessarily increased by the use of blocking. The reason is that by blocking we not only partition the sum of squares, we also partition the degrees of freedom. Therefore, the denominator of *MSW* is decreased, and *MSW* will most likely increase. If blocking isn't needed, the *MSW* will tend to be relatively larger than if we had run a one-way design with independent samples. This can lead to failing to reject the null hypothesis for the primary test when it actually should have been rejected.

Therefore, if blocking is indicated to be unnecessary, follow these rules:

1. If the primary $H_0$ is rejected, proceed with your analysis and decision making. There is no concern.
2. If the primary $H_0$ is not rejected, redo the study without using blocking. Run a one-way ANOVA with independent samples.

**Chapter Outcome 4.** → | **EXAMPLE 12-3** | **PERFORMING A RANDOMIZED BLOCK ANALYSIS OF VARIANCE**

**Frankle Training & Education** Frankle Training & Education conducts project management training courses throughout the eastern United States and Canada. The company has developed three 1,000-point practice examinations meant to simulate the certification exams given by the Project Management Institute (PMI). The Frankle leadership wants to know if the three exams will yield the same or different mean scores. To test this, a random sample of fourteen people who have been through the project management

[7]Many authors argue that the randomization restriction imposed by using blocks means that the *F*-ratio really is a test for the equality of the block means plus the randomization restriction. For a summary of this argument and references, see D. C. Montgomery, *Design and Analysis of Experiments*, 4th ed. (New York City: John Wiley & Sons, 1997) pp. 175–176.

training are asked to take the three tests. The order the tests are taken is randomized and the scores are recorded. A randomized block analysis of variance test can be performed using the following steps:

**Step 1 Specify the parameter of interest and formulate the appropriate null and alternative hypotheses.**

The parameter of interest is the mean test score for the three different exams, and the question is whether there is a difference among the mean scores for the three. The appropriate null and alternative hypotheses are

$$H_0: \mu_1 = \mu_2 = \mu_3$$

$H_A$: At least two populations have different means

In this case, the Frankle leadership wants to control for variation in student ability by having the same students take all three tests. The test scores will be independent because the scores achieved by one student do not influence the scores achieved by other students. Here, the students are the blocks.

**Step 2 Specify the level of significance for conducting the tests.**

The tests will be conducted using $\alpha = 0.05$.

**Step 3 Select simple random samples from each population, and compute treatment means, block means, and the grand mean.**

The following sample data were observed:

| Student | Exam 1 | Exam 2 | Exam 3 | Block Means |
|---|---|---|---|---|
| 1 | 830 | 647 | 630 | 702.33 |
| 2 | 743 | 840 | 786 | 789.67 |
| 3 | 652 | 747 | 730 | 709.67 |
| 4 | 885 | 639 | 617 | 713.67 |
| 5 | 814 | 943 | 632 | 796.33 |
| 6 | 733 | 916 | 410 | 686.33 |
| 7 | 770 | 923 | 727 | 806.67 |
| 8 | 829 | 903 | 726 | 819.33 |
| 9 | 847 | 760 | 648 | 751.67 |
| 10 | 878 | 856 | 668 | 800.67 |
| 11 | 728 | 878 | 670 | 758.67 |
| 12 | 693 | 990 | 825 | 836.00 |
| 13 | 807 | 871 | 564 | 747.33 |
| 14 | 901 | 980 | 719 | 866.67 |
| Treatment means | 793.57 | 849.50 | 668.00 | 770.36 = Grand mean |

**Step 4 Compute the sums of squares and complete the ANOVA table.**

Four sums of squares are required:

**Total Sum of Squares** (Equation 12.3)

$$SST = \sum_{i=1}^{k} \sum_{j=1}^{n_i} (x_{ij} - \bar{\bar{x}})^2 = 614{,}641.6$$

**Sum of Squares Between** (Equation 12.4)

$$SSB = \sum_{i=1}^{k} n_i (\bar{x}_i - \bar{\bar{x}})^2 = 241{,}912.7$$

**Sum of Squares Blocking** (Equation 12.9)

$$SSBL = \sum_{j=1}^{b} k(\bar{x}_j - \bar{\bar{x}})^2 = 116,605.0$$

**Sum of Squares Within** (Equation 12.10)

$$SSW = SST - (SSB + SSBL) = 256,123.9$$

The ANOVA table is (see Table 12.6 format)

| Source | SS | df | MS | F-Ratio |
|--------|-----|-----|-----|---------|
| Between blocks | 116,605.0 | 13 | 8,969.6 | 0.9105 |
| Between samples | 241,912.7 | 2 | 120,956.4 | 12.2787 |
| Within samples | 256,123.9 | 26 | 9,850.9 | |
| Total | 614,641.6 | 41 | | |

**Step 5** **Test to determine whether blocking is effective.**

Fourteen people were used to evaluate the three tests. These people constitute the blocks, so if blocking is effective, the mean test scores across the three tests will not be the same for all 14 students. The null and alternative hypotheses are

$H_0: \mu_{b1} = \mu_{b2} = \mu_{b3} = \ldots = \mu_{b14}$

$H_A$: Not all means are equal (blocking is effective)

As shown in step 3, the $F$-test statistic to test this null hypothesis is formed by

$$F = \frac{MSBL}{MSW} = \frac{8,969.6}{9,850.9} = 0.9105$$

The $F$-critical from the $F$-distribution, with $\alpha = 0.05$ and $D_1 = 13$ and $D_2 = 26$ degrees of freedom, can be approximated using the $F$-distribution table in Appendix H as

$$F_{\alpha=0.05} \approx 2.15$$

The exact $F$-critical can be found using the FINV function in Excel or the Calc > Probability Distributions command in Minitab as $F_{0.05} = 2.119$. Then, because

$F = 0.9105 < F_{\alpha=0.05} = 2.119$, do not reject the null hypothesis.

This means that based on these sample data we cannot conclude that blocking was effective.

**Step 6** **Conduct the main hypothesis test to determine whether the populations have equal means.**

We have three different project management exams being considered. At issue is whether the mean score is equal for the three exams. The appropriate null and alternative hypotheses are

$H_0: \mu_1 = \mu_2 = \mu_3$

$H_A$: At least two populations have different means

As shown in the ANOVA table in Step 3, the $F$-test statistic for this null hypothesis is formed by

$$F = \frac{MSB}{MSW} = \frac{120,956.4}{9,850.9} = 12.2787$$

The $F$-critical from the $F$-distribution, with $\alpha = 0.05$ and $D_1 = 2$ and $D_2 = 26$ degrees of freedom, can be approximated using the $F$-distribution table in Appendix H as

$$F_{\alpha=0.05} \approx 3.40$$

The exact $F$-critical can be found using the FINV function in Excel or the Calc > Probability Distributions command in Minitab as $F = 3.369$. Then, because

$$F = 12.2787 > F_{\alpha=0.05} = 3.369, \text{ reject the null hypothesis.}$$

Even though in step 5 we concluded that blocking was not effective, the sample data still lead us to reject the primary null hypothesis and conclude that the three tests do not all have the same mean score. The Frankle leaders will now be interested in looking into the issue in more detail to determine which tests yield higher or lower average scores. (See Example 12-4.)

>>**END EXAMPLE**

**TRY PROBLEM** 12-21 (pg. 507)

**Chapter Outcome 3.** ➤ # Fisher's Least Significant Difference Test

An analysis of variance test can be used to test whether the populations of interest have different means. However, even if the null hypothesis of equal population means is rejected, the ANOVA does not specify which population means are different. In Section 12.1, we showed how the Tukey-Kramer multiple comparisons procedure is used to determine where the population differences occur for a one-way ANOVA design. Likewise, *Fisher's least significant difference test* is one test for multiple comparisons that we can use for a randomized block ANOVA design.

If the primary null hypothesis has been rejected, then we can compare the absolute differences in sample means from any two populations to the *least significant difference (LSD)*, as computed using Equation 12.11.

---

**Fisher's Least Significant Difference**

$$LSD = t_{\alpha/2} \sqrt{MSW} \sqrt{\frac{2}{b}}$$  (12.11)

where:

$t_{\alpha/2} =$ One-tailed value from Student's $t$-distribution for $\alpha/2$ and $(k-1)(b-1)$ degrees of freedom
$MSW =$ Mean square within from ANOVA table
$b =$ Number of blocks
$k =$ Number of levels of the main factor

---

**EXAMPLE 12-4**     **APPLYING FISHER'S LEAST SIGNIFICANT DIFFERENCE TEST**

**Frankle Training & Education** (*Continued*) Recall that in Example 12-3 the Frankle leadership used a randomized block ANOVA design to conclude that the three project management tests do not all have the same mean test score. To determine which populations (tests) have different means, you can use the following steps:

**Step 1** Compute the *LSD* statistic using Equation 12.11.

$$LSD = t_{\alpha/2} \sqrt{MSW} \sqrt{\frac{2}{b}}$$

Using a significance level equal to 0.05, the $t$-critical value for $(3-1)(14-1) = 26$ degrees of freedom is

$$t_{0.05/2} = 2.0555$$

The mean square within from the ANOVA table (see Example 12-3, Step 3) is

$$MSW = 9,850.9$$

The *LSD* is

$$LSD = t_{\alpha/2}\sqrt{MSW}\sqrt{\frac{2}{b}} = 2.0555\sqrt{9,850.9}\sqrt{\frac{2}{14}} = 77.11$$

**Step 2**  **Compute the sample means from each population.**

$$\bar{x}_1 = \frac{\sum x}{n} = 793.57 \qquad \bar{x}_2 = \frac{\sum x}{n} = 849.50 \qquad \bar{x}_3 = \frac{\sum x}{n} = 668$$

**Step 3**  **Form all possible contrasts by finding the absolute differences between all pairs of sample means. Compare these to the *LSD* value.**

| Absolute Difference | Comparison | Significant Difference |
|---|---|---|
| $\lvert \bar{x}_1 - \bar{x}_2 \rvert = \lvert 793.57 - 849.50 \rvert = 55.93$ | $55.93 < 77.11$ | No |
| $\lvert \bar{x}_1 - \bar{x}_3 \rvert = \lvert 793.57 - 668 \rvert = 125.57$ | $125.57 > 77.11$ | Yes |
| $\lvert \bar{x}_2 - \bar{x}_3 \rvert = \lvert 849.50 - 668 \rvert = 181.50$ | $181.50 > 77.11$ | Yes |

We infer, based on the sample data, that the mean score for test 1 exceeds the mean for test 3, and the mean for test 2 exceeds the mean for test 3. Now the manager may wish to evaluate test 3 to see why the scores are lower than for the other two tests. No difference is detected between tests 1 and 2.

>>**END EXAMPLE**

**TRY PROBLEM** 12-22 (pg. 507)

# 12-2: Exercises

## Skill Development

**12-18.** A study was conducted to determine if differences in new textbook prices exist between on-campus bookstores, off-campus bookstores, and Internet bookstores. To control for differences in textbook prices that might exist across disciplines, the study randomly selected 12 textbooks and recorded the price of each of the 12 books at each of the three retailers. You may assume normality and equal-variance assumptions have been met. The partially completed ANOVA table based on the study's findings is shown here:

**ANOVA**

| Source of Variation | SS | df | MS | F |
|---|---|---|---|---|
| Textbooks | 16,624 | | | |
| Retailer | 2.4 | | | |
| Error | | | | |
| Total | 17,477.6 | | | |

a. Complete the ANOVA table by filling in the missing sums of squares, the degrees of freedom for each source, the mean square, and the calculated *F*-test statistic for each possible hypothesis test.

b. Based on the study's findings, was it correct to block for differences in textbooks? Conduct the appropriate test at the $\alpha = 0.10$ level of significance.

c. Based on the study's findings, can it be concluded that there is a difference in the average price of textbooks across the three retail outlets? Conduct the appropriate hypothesis test at the $\alpha = 0.10$ level of significance.

**12-19.** The following data were collected for a randomized block analysis of variance design with four populations and eight blocks:

| | Group 1 | Group 2 | Group 3 | Group 4 |
|---|---|---|---|---|
| **Block 1** | 56 | 44 | 57 | 84 |
| **Block 2** | 34 | 30 | 38 | 50 |
| **Block 3** | 50 | 41 | 48 | 52 |
| **Block 4** | 19 | 17 | 21 | 30 |
| **Block 5** | 33 | 30 | 35 | 38 |
| **Block 6** | 74 | 72 | 78 | 79 |
| **Block 7** | 33 | 24 | 27 | 33 |
| **Block 8** | 56 | 44 | 56 | 71 |

a. State the appropriate null and alternative hypotheses for the treatments and determine whether blocking is necessary.
b. Construct the appropriate ANOVA table.
c. Using a significance level equal to 0.05, can you conclude that blocking was necessary in this case? Use a test-statistic approach.
d. Based on the data and a significance level equal to 0.05, is there a difference in population means for the four groups? Use a $p$-value approach.
e. If you found that a difference exists in part d, use the *LSD* approach to determine which populations have different means.

**12-20.** The following ANOVA table and accompanying information are the result of a randomized block ANOVA test.

| Summary | Count | Sum | Average | Variance |
|---|---|---|---|---|
| 1 | 4 | 443 | 110.8 | 468.9 |
| 2 | 4 | 275 | 68.8 | 72.9 |
| 3 | 4 | 1,030 | 257.5 | 1891.7 |
| 4 | 4 | 300 | 75.0 | 433.3 |
| 5 | 4 | 603 | 150.8 | 468.9 |
| 6 | 4 | 435 | 108.8 | 72.9 |
| 7 | 4 | 1,190 | 297.5 | 1891.7 |
| 8 | 4 | 460 | 115.0 | 433.3 |
| Sample 1 | 8 | 1,120 | 140.0 | 7142.9 |
| Sample 2 | 8 | 1,236 | 154.5 | 8866.6 |
| Sample 3 | 8 | 1,400 | 175.0 | 9000.0 |
| Sample 4 | 8 | 980 | 122.5 | 4307.1 |

**ANOVA**

| Source of Variation | SS | df | MS | F | p-value | F-crit |
|---|---|---|---|---|---|---|
| Rows | 199,899 | 7 | 28557.0 | 112.8 | 0.0000 | 2.488 |
| Columns | 11,884 | 3 | 3961.3 | 15.7 | 0.0000 | 3.073 |
| Error | 5,317 | 21 | 253.2 | | | |
| Total | 217,100 | 31 | | | | |

a. How many blocks were used in this study?
b. How many populations are involved in this test?
c. Test to determine whether blocking is effective using an alpha level equal to 0.05.
d. Test the main hypothesis of interest using $\alpha = 0.05$.
e. If warranted, conduct an *LSD* test with $\alpha = 0.05$ to determine which population means are different.

**12-21.** The following sample data were recently collected in the course of conducting a randomized block analysis of variance. Based on these sample data, what conclusions should be reached about blocking effectiveness and about the means of the three populations involved? Test using a significance level equal to 0.05.

| Block | Sample 1 | Sample 2 | Sample 3 |
|---|---|---|---|
| 1 | 30 | 40 | 40 |
| 2 | 50 | 70 | 50 |
| 3 | 60 | 40 | 70 |
| 4 | 40 | 40 | 30 |
| 5 | 80 | 70 | 90 |
| 6 | 20 | 10 | 10 |

**12-22.** A randomized complete block design is carried out, resulting in the following statistics:

| Source | $\bar{x}_1$ | $\bar{x}_2$ | $\bar{x}_3$ | $\bar{x}_4$ |
|---|---|---|---|---|
| Primary Factor | 237.15 | 315.15 | 414.01 | 612.52 |
| Block | 363.57 | 382.22 | 438.33 | |
| $SST = 364,428$ | | | | |

a. Determine if blocking was effective for this design.
b. Using a significance level of 0.05, produce the relevant ANOVA and determine if the average responses of the factor levels are equal to each other.
c. If you discovered that there were differences among the average responses of the factor levels, use the *LSD* approach to determine which populations have different means.

## Business Applications

**12-23.** Frasier and Company manufactures four different products that it ships to customers throughout the United States. Delivery times are not a driving factor in the decision as to which type of carrier to use (rail, plane, or truck) to deliver the product. However, breakage cost is very expensive, and Frasier would like to select a mode of delivery that reduces the amount of product breakage. To help it reach a decision, the managers have decided to examine the dollar amount of breakage incurred by the three alternative modes of transportation under consideration. Because each product's fragility is different, the executives conducting the study wish to control for differences due to type of product. The company randomly assigns each product to each carrier and monitors the dollar breakage that occurs over the course of 100 shipments. The dollar breakage per shipment (to the nearest dollar) is as follows:

| | Rail | Plane | Truck |
|---|---|---|---|
| Product 1 | $7,960 | $8,053 | $8,818 |
| Product 2 | $8,399 | $7,764 | $9,432 |
| Product 3 | $9,429 | $9,196 | $9,260 |
| Product 4 | $6,022 | $5,821 | $5,676 |

a. Was Frasier and Company correct in its decision to block for type of product? Conduct the appropriate hypothesis test using a level of significance of 0.01.
b. Is there a difference due to carrier type? Conduct the appropriate hypothesis test using a level of significance of 0.01.

**12-24.** The California Lettuce Research Board was originally formed as the Iceberg Lettuce Advisory Board in 1973. The primary function of the board is to fund research on iceberg and leaf lettuce. The California Lettuce Research Board published research (M. Cahn and H. Ajwa, "Salinity Effects on Quality and Yield of Drip Irrigated Lettuce") concerning the effect of varying levels of sodium absorption ratios (SAR) on the yield of head lettuce. The trials followed a randomized complete block design where variety of lettuce (Salinas and Sniper) was the main factor and salinity levels were the blocks. The measurements (the number of lettuce heads from each plot) of the kind observed were

| SAR | Salinas | Sniper |
|-----|---------|--------|
| 3 | 104 | 109 |
| 5 | 160 | 163 |
| 7 | 142 | 146 |
| 10 | 133 | 156 |

a. Determine if blocking was effective for this design.
b. Using a significance level of 0.05, produce the relevant ANOVA and determine if the average number of lettuce heads among the SARs are equal to each other.
c. If you discovered that there were differences among the average number of lettuce heads among the SARs, use the *LSD* approach to determine which populations have different means.

**12-25.** CB Industries operates three shifts every day of the week. Each shift includes full-time hourly workers, nonsupervisory salaried employees, and supervisors/managers. CB Industries would like to know if there is a difference among the shifts in terms of the number of hours of work missed due to employee illness. To control for differences that might exist across employee groups, CB Industries randomly selects one employee from each employee group and shift and records the number of hours missed for one year. The results of the study are shown here:

| | Shift 1 | Shift 2 | Shift 3 |
|-----|---------|---------|---------|
| **Hourly** | 48 | 54 | 60 |
| **Nonsupervisory** | 31 | 36 | 55 |
| **Supervisors/Managers** | 25 | 33 | 40 |

a. Develop the appropriate test to determine whether blocking is effective or not. Conduct the test at the $\alpha = 0.05$ level of significance.
b. Develop the appropriate test to determine whether there are differences in the average number of hours missed due to illness across the three shifts. Conduct the test at the $\alpha = 0.05$ level of significance.
c. If it is determined that a difference in the average hours of work missed due to illness is not the same for the three shifts, use the *LSD* approach to determine which shifts have different means.

**12-26.** Grant Thornton LLP is the U.S. member firm of Grant Thornton International, one of the six global accounting, tax, and business advisory organizations. It provides firmwide auditing training for its employees in three different auditing methods. Auditors were grouped into four blocks according to the education they had received: (1) high school, (2) bachelor's, (3) master's, (4) doctorate. Three auditors at each education level were used—one assigned to each method. They were given a posttraining examination consisting of complicated auditing scenarios. The scores for the 12 auditors were as follows:

| | Method 1 | Method 2 | Method 3 |
|-----|----------|----------|----------|
| **Doctorate** | 83 | 81 | 82 |
| **Master's** | 77 | 75 | 79 |
| **Bachelor's** | 74 | 73 | 75 |
| **High School** | 72 | 70 | 69 |

a. Indicate why blocking was employed in this design.
b. Determine if blocking was effective for this design by producing the relevant ANOVA.
c. Using a significance level of 0.05, determine if the average posttraining examination scores among the auditing methods are equal to each other.
d. If you discovered that there were differences among the average posttraining examination scores among the auditing methods, use the *LSD* approach to determine which populations have different means.

## Computer Database **Exercises**

**12-27.** Applebee's International, Inc., is a U.S. company that develops, franchises, and operates the Applebee's Neighborhood Grill and Bar restaurant chain. It is the largest chain of casual dining restaurants in the country, with over 1,500 restaurants across the United States. The headquarters is located in Overland Park, Kansas. The company is interested in determining if mean weekly revenue differs among three restaurants in a particular city. The file entitled **Applebees** contains revenue data for a sample of weeks for each of the three locations.
a. Test to determine if blocking the week on which the testing was done was necessary. Use a significance level of 0.05.
b. Based on the data gathered by Applebee's, can it be concluded that there is a difference in the average revenue among the three restaurants?
c. If you did conclude that there was a difference in the average revenue, use Fisher's *LSD* approach to determine which restaurant has the lowest mean sales.

**12-28.** In a local community there are three grocery chain stores. The three have been carrying out a spirited advertising campaign in which each claims to have the lowest prices. A local news station recently sent a reporter to the three stores to check prices on several items. She found that for certain items each store had the lowest price. This survey didn't really answer the question for consumers. Thus, the station set up a test in which 20 shoppers were given different lists of grocery items and were sent to each of the three chain stores. The sales receipts from each of the three stores are recorded in the data file **Groceries**.

a. Why should this price test be conducted using the design that the television station used? What was it attempting to achieve by having the same shopping lists used at each of the three grocery stores?

b. Based on a significance level of 0.05 and these sample data, test to determine whether blocking was necessary in this example. State the null and alternative hypotheses. Use a test-statistic approach.

c. Based on these sample data, can you conclude the three grocery stores have different sample means? Test using a significance level of 0.05. State the appropriate null and alternative hypotheses. Use a *p*-value approach.

d. Based on the sample data, which store has the highest average prices? Use Fisher's *LSD* test if appropriate.

**12-29.** The Cordage Institute, based in Wayne, Pennsylvania, is an international association of manufacturers, producers, and resellers of cordage, rope, and twine. It is a not-for-profit corporation that reports on research concerning these products. Although natural fibers like manila, sisal, and cotton were once the predominant rope materials, industrial synthetic fibers dominate the marketplace today, with most ropes made of nylon, polyester, or polypropylene. One of the principal traits of rope material is its breaking strength. A research project generated data given in the file entitled **Knots**. The data listed were gathered on 10 different days from ½"-diameter ropes.

a. Test to determine if inserting the day on which the testing was done was necessary. Use a significance level of 0.05.

b. Based on the data gathered by the Cordage Institute, can it be concluded that there is a difference in the average breaking strength of nylon, polyester, and polypropylene?

c. If you concluded that there was a difference in the average breaking strength of the rope material, use Fisher's *LSD* approach to determine which material has the highest breaking strength.

**12-30.** When the world's largest retailer, Wal-Mart, decided to enter the grocery marketplace in a big way with its "Super Stores," it changed the retail grocery landscape in a major way. The other major chains such as Albertsons have struggled to stay competitive. In addition, regional discounters such as WINCO in the western United States have made it difficult for the traditional grocery chains. Recently, a study was conducted in which a "market basket" of products was selected at random from those items offered in three stores in Boise, Idaho: Wal-Mart, Winco, and Albertsons. At issue was whether the mean prices at the three stores are equal or whether there is a difference in prices. The sample data are in the data file called **Food Price Comparisons**. Using an alpha level equal to 0.05, test to determine whether the three stores have equal population mean prices. If you conclude that there are differences in the mean prices, perform the appropriate posttest to determine which stores have different means.

**END EXERCISES 12-2**

**Chapter Outcome 5.** → **12.3 Two-Factor Analysis of Variance with Replication**

Section 12.2 introduced an ANOVA procedure called the randomized complete block ANOVA. This method is used when we are interested in testing whether the means for the populations (levels) for a factor of interest are equal and we want to control for potential variation due to a second factor. The second factor is called the blocking factor. Consider again the Citizen's State Bank property appraisal application, in which the bank was interested in determining whether the mean property valuation was the same for three different appraisal companies. The company used the same five properties to test each appraisal company in an attempt to reduce any variability that might exist due to the properties involved in the test. The properties were the blocks in that example, but we were not really interested in knowing whether the mean appraisal was the same for all properties. The single factor of interest was the appraisal companies.

However, you will encounter many situations in which there are actually two or more factors of interest in the same study. In this section, we limit our discussion to situations involving only two factors. The technique that is used when we wish to analyze two factors is called *two-factor ANOVA with replications*.

# Two-Factor ANOVA with Replications

**Excel and Minitab Tutorial**

**FLY HIGH AIRLINES** Like other major U.S. airlines, Fly High Airlines is concerned because many of its frequent flier program members have accumulated large quantities of free miles.[8] The airline worries that at some point in the future there will be a big influx of customers wanting to use their miles and the airline will have difficulty satisfying all the requests at once. Thus, Fly High recently conducted an experiment in which each of three methods for redeeming frequent flier miles was offered to a sample of 16 customers. Each customer had accumulated more than 100,000 frequent flier miles. The customers were equally divided into four age groups. The variable of interest was the number of miles redeemed by the customers during the six-week trial. Table 12.7 shows the number of miles redeemed for each person in the study. These data are also contained in the **Fly High** file.

Method 1 offered cash inducements to use miles. Method 2 offered discount vacation options, and method 3 offered access to a discount-shopping program through the Internet. The airline wants to know if the mean number of miles redeemed under the three redemption methods is equal and whether the mean miles redeemed is the same across the four age groups.

A *two-factor ANOVA* design is the appropriate method in this case because the airline has two factors of interest. Factor A is the redemption offer type with three levels. Factor B is the age group of each customer with four levels. As shown in Table 12.7, there are $3 \times 4 = 12$ cells in the study and four customers in each cell. The measurements are called *replications* because we get four measurements (miles redeemed) at each combination of redemption offer level (factor A) and age level (factor B).

Two-factor ANOVA follows the same logic as all other ANOVA designs. Each factor of interest introduces variability into the experiment. As was the case in Sections 12.1 and 12.2, we must find estimators for each source of variation. Identifying the appropriate sums of squares and then dividing each by its degrees of freedom does this. As in the one-way ANOVA, the total sum of squares (*SST*) in two-factor ANOVA can be partitioned. The SST is partitioned into four parts as follows:

1. One part is due to differences in the levels of factor A ($SS_A$).
2. Another part is due to the levels of factor B ($SS_B$).
3. Another part is due to the *interaction* between factor A and factor B ($SS_{AB}$). (We will discuss the concept of interaction between factors later.)
4. The final component making up the total sum of squares is the sum of squares due to the inherent random variation in the data (*SSE*).

**TABLE 12.7** | **Fly High Airlines Frequent Flier Miles Data**

|  | Cash Option | Vacation | Shopping |
|---|---|---|---|
| **Under 25 years** | 30,000 | 40,000 | 25,000 |
|  | 0 | 25,000 | 25,000 |
|  | 25,000 | 0 | 75,000 |
|  | 0 | 0 | 5,000 |
| **25 to 40 years** | 60,000 | 40,000 | 30,000 |
|  | 0 | 25,000 | 25,000 |
|  | 0 | 5,000 | 50,000 |
|  | 25,000 | 25,000 | 0 |
| **41 to 60 years** | 40,000 | 25,000 | 25,000 |
|  | 25,000 | 50,000 | 50,000 |
|  | 25,000 | 0 | 0 |
|  | 0 | 25,000 | 0 |
| **Over 60 years** | 0 | 45,000 | 30,000 |
|  | 5,000 | 25,000 | 25,000 |
|  | 25,000 | 0 | 25,000 |
|  | 50,000 | 50,000 | 50,000 |

---

[8]Name changed at request of the airline.

**FIGURE 12.9** |

Two-Factor ANOVA—
Partitioning of Total Sums
of Squares

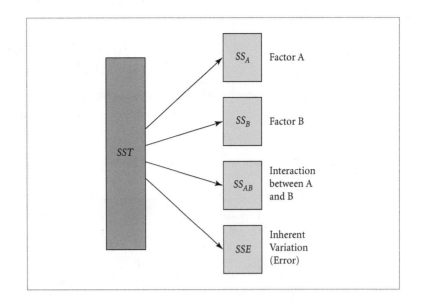

Figure 12.9 illustrates this partitioning concept. The variations due to each of these components will be estimated using the respective *mean squares* obtained by dividing the sums of squares by their degrees of freedom. If the variation accounted for by factor A and factor B is large relative to the error variation, we will tend to conclude that the factor levels have different means.

Table 12.8 illustrates the format of the two-factor ANOVA. Three different hypotheses can be tested from the information in this ANOVA table. First, for factor A (redemption options), we have

$$H_0: \mu_{A1} = \mu_{A2} = \mu_{A3}$$
$$H_A: \text{Not all factor A means are equal}$$

**TABLE 12.8** | **Basic Format of the Two-Factor ANOVA Table**

| Source of Variation | SS | df | MS | F-Ratio |
|---|---|---|---|---|
| Factor A | $SS_A$ | $a - 1$ | $MS_A$ | $\dfrac{MS_A}{MSE}$ |
| Factor B | $SS_B$ | $b - 1$ | $MS_B$ | $\dfrac{MS_B}{MSE}$ |
| AB interaction | $SS_{AB}$ | $(a - 1)(b - 1)$ | $MS_{AB}$ | $\dfrac{MS_{AB}}{MSE}$ |
| Error | $SSE$ | $n_T - ab$ | $MSE$ | |
| Total | $SST$ | $n_T - 1$ | | |

where:

$a = $ Number of levels of factor A

$b = $ Number of levels of factor B

$n_T = $ Total number of observation in all cells

$MS_A = $ Mean square factor A $= \dfrac{SS_A}{a - 1}$

$MS_B = $ Mean square factor B $= \dfrac{SS_B}{b - 1}$

$MS_{AB} = $ Mean square interaction $= \dfrac{SS_{AB}}{(a - 1)(b - 1)}$

$MSE = $ Mean square error $= \dfrac{SSE}{n_T - ab}$

For factor B (age levels):

$$H_0: \mu_{B1} = \mu_{B2} = \mu_{B3} = \mu_{B4}$$

$H_A$: Not all factor B means are equal

Test to determine whether interaction exists between the two factors:

$H_0$: Factors A and B do not interact to affect the mean response

$H_A$: Factors A and B do interact

Here is what we must assume to be true to use two-factor ANOVA:

**Assumptions**

---

1. The population values for each combination of pairwise factor levels are normally distributed.
2. The variances for each population are equal.
3. The samples are independent.
4. The data measurement is interval or ratio level.

---

Although all the necessary values to complete Table 12.8 could be computed manually using the equations shown in Table 12.9, this would be a time-consuming task for even a small example because the equations for the various sum-of-squares values are quite complicated. Instead, you will want to use software such as Excel or Minitab to perform the two-factor ANOVA.

**Interaction Explained** Before we share the ANOVA results for the Fly High Airlines example, a few comments regarding the concept of *factor interaction* are needed. Consider our example involving the two factors: miles-redemption-offer type and age category of customer. The response variable is the number of miles redeemed in the six weeks after the offer. Suppose one redemption-offer type is really better and results in a higher average miles being redeemed. If there is no interaction between age and offer type, then customers of all ages will have uniformly higher average miles redeemed for this offer type compared with the other offer types. If another offer type yields lower average miles, and if there is no interaction, all age groups receiving this offer type will redeem uniformly lower miles on average than the other offer types. Figure 12.10 illustrates a situation with no interaction between the two factors.

However, if interaction exists between the factors, we would see a graph similar to the one shown in Figure 12.11. Interaction would be indicated if one age group redeemed higher average miles than the other age groups with one program but lower average miles than the other age groups on the other mileage-redemption programs. In general, interaction occurs if the differences in the averages of the response variable for the various levels of one factor—say, factor A—are not the same for each level of the other factor—say, factor B. The general idea is that interaction between two factors means that the effect due to one of them is not uniform across all levels of the other factor.

Another example in which potential interaction might exist occurs in plywood manufacturing, where thin layers of wood called veneer are glued together to form plywood. One of the important quality attributes of plywood is its strength. However, plywood is made from different species of wood (pine, fir, hemlock, etc.), and different types of glue are available. If some species of wood work better (stronger plywood) with certain glues, whereas other species work better with different glues, we say that the wood species and the glue type interact.

If interaction is suspected, it should be accounted for by subtracting the interaction term ($SS_{AB}$) from the total sum-of-squares term in the ANOVA. From a strictly arithmetic point of view, the effect of computing $SS_{AB}$ and subtracting it from $SST$ is that $SSE$ is reduced. Also, if the corresponding variation due to interaction is significant, the variation within the factor levels (error) will be significantly reduced. This can make it easier to detect a difference in the population means if such a difference actually exists. If so, MSE will most likely be reduced.

**TABLE 12.9** | **Two-Factor ANOVA Equations**

*Total Sum of Squares*

$$SST = \sum_{i=1}^{a} \sum_{j=1}^{b} \sum_{k=1}^{n} \left( x_{ijk} - \overline{\overline{x}} \right)^2 \qquad \text{(12.12)}$$

*Sum of Squares Factor A*

$$SS_A = bn \sum_{i=1}^{a} \left( \overline{x}_{i..} - \overline{\overline{x}} \right)^2 \qquad \text{(12.13)}$$

*Sum of Squares Factor B*

$$SS_B = an \sum_{j=1}^{b} \left( \overline{x}_{.j.} - \overline{\overline{x}} \right)^2 \qquad \text{(12.14)}$$

*Sum of Squares Interaction between Factors A and B*

$$SS_{AB} = n \sum_{i=1}^{a} \sum_{j=1}^{b} \left( \overline{x}_{ij.} - \overline{x}_{i..} - \overline{x}_{.j.} + \overline{\overline{x}} \right)^2 \qquad \text{(12.15)}$$

*Sum of Squares Error*

$$SSE = \sum_{i=1}^{a} \sum_{j=1}^{b} \sum_{k=1}^{n} \left( x_{ijk} - \overline{x}_{ij.} \right)^2 \qquad \text{(12.16)}$$

where:

$$\overline{\overline{x}} = \frac{\displaystyle\sum_{i=1}^{a} \sum_{j=1}^{b} \sum_{k=1}^{n}}{abn} = \text{Grand mean}$$

$$\overline{x}_{i..} = \frac{\displaystyle\sum_{j=1}^{b} \sum_{k=1}^{n} x_{ijk}}{bn} = \text{Mean of each level of factor A}$$

$$\overline{x}_{.j.} = \frac{\displaystyle\sum_{i=1}^{a} \sum_{k=1}^{n} x_{ijk}}{an} = \text{Mean of each level of factor B}$$

$$\overline{x}_{ij.} = \sum_{k=1}^{n} \frac{x_{ijk}}{n} = \text{Mean of each cell}$$

$a$ = Number of levels of factor A
$b$ = Number of levels of factor B
$n$ = Number of replications in each cell

**FIGURE 12.10**

Differences between Factor-Level Mean Values: No Interaction

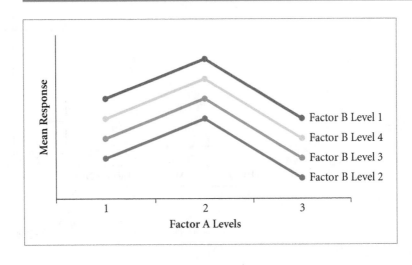

Differences between Factor-Level Mean Values when Interaction is Present

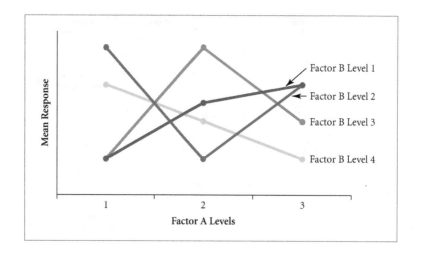

This will produce a larger $F$-test statistic, which will more likely lead to correctly rejecting the null hypothesis. Thus by considering potential interaction, your chances of finding a difference in the factor A and factor B mean values, if such a difference exists, is improved. This will depend, of course, on the relative size of $SS_{AB}$ and the respective changes in the degrees of freedom. We will comment later on the appropriateness of testing the factor hypotheses if interaction is present. *Note that to measure the interaction effect, the sample size for each combination of factor A and factor B must be 2 or greater.*

Excel and Minitab contain a data analysis tool for performing two-factor ANOVA with replications. They can be used to compute the different sums of squares and complete the ANOVA table. However, Excel requires that the data be organized in a special way, as shown in Figure 12.12.[9] (Note, the first row must contain the names for each level of factor A. Also, column 1 contains the factor B level names. These must be in the row corresponding to the first sample item for each factor B level.)

The Excel two-factor ANOVA output for this example is actually too big to fit on one screen. The top portion of the printout shows summary information for each cell, including

**FIGURE 12.12**

Excel 2007 Data Format for Two-Factor ANOVA for Fly High Airlines

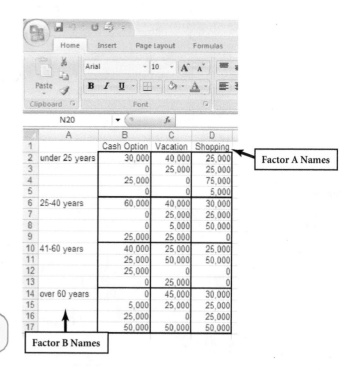

Excel 2007 Instruction:
1. Open file: Fly High.xls.

---

[9]Minitab uses the same data input format for two-factor ANOVA as for randomized block ANOVA (see Section 12.2).

**FIGURE 12.13**

Excel 2007 Output (Part 1) for Two-Factor ANOVA for Fly High Airlines

**Excel 2007 Instructions:**
1. Open file: Fly High.xls.
2. On the **Data** tab, click **Data Analysis**.
3. Select **ANOVA: Two Factor with Replication**.
4. Define data range (include factor A and B labels).
5. Specify the number of **rows per sample**.
6. Specify alpha level.

means and variances (see Figure 12.13). At the bottom of the output (scroll down) is the ANOVA table shown in Figure 12.14a. Figure 12.14b shows the Minitab output. Excel changes a few labels. For example, factor A (the miles redemption options) is now referred to as *Columns*. Factor B (age groups) is referred to as *Sample*. In Figures 12.14a and 12.14b, we see all the information necessary to test whether the three redemption offers (factor A) result in different mean miles redeemed.

$$H_0: \mu_{A1} = \mu_{A2} = \mu_{A3}$$

$H_A$: Not all factor A means are equal

$$\alpha = 0.05$$

Both the *p*-value and *F*-distribution approaches can be used. Because

$$p\text{-value (columns)} = 0.5614 > \alpha = 0.05$$

the null hypothesis $H_0$ is not rejected. (Also, $F = 0.59 < F_{0.05} = 3.259$; the null hypothesis is not rejected.) This means the test data do not indicate that a difference exists between the average amounts of mileage redeemed for the three types of offers. None seems superior to the others.

We can also test to determine if age level makes a difference in frequent flier miles redeemed.

$$H_0: \mu_{B1} = \mu_{B2} = \mu_{B3} = \mu_{B4}$$

$H_A$: Not all factor B means are equal

$$\alpha = 0.05$$

**FIGURE 12.14A**

Excel 2007 Output (Part 2) for Two-Factor ANOVA for Fly High Airlines

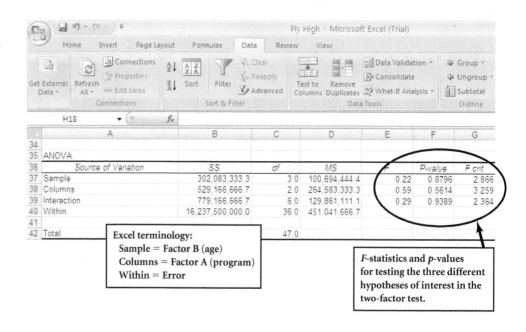

In Figure 12.14a, we see that the

$$p\text{-value} = 0.8796 > \alpha = 0.05$$

$$(\text{Also, } F = 0.22 < F_{0.05} = 2.866)$$

Thus, the null hypothesis is not rejected. The test data do not indicate that customer age significantly influences the average number of frequent flier miles that will be redeemed.

Finally, we can also test for interaction. The null hypothesis is that no interaction exists. The alternative is that interaction does exist between the two factors. The ANOVA table in Figure 12.14b shows a $p$-value of 0.939, which is greater than $\alpha = 0.05$. Based on these data,

**FIGURE 12.14B**

Minitab Output for Two-Factor ANOVA for Fly High Airlines

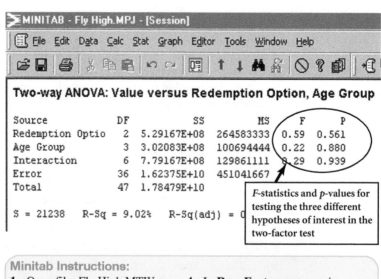

interaction between the two factors does not appear to exist. This would indicate that the differences in the average mileage redeemed between the various age categories are the same for each redemption-offer type.

## A Caution about Interaction

In this example, the sample data indicate that no interaction between factors A and B is present. Based on the sample data, we were unable to conclude that the three redemption offers resulted in different average frequent flier miles redeemed. Finally, we were unable to conclude that a difference in average miles redeemed occurred over the four different age groups.

The appropriate approach is to begin by testing for interaction. If the interaction null hypothesis is not rejected, proceed to test the factor A and factor B hypotheses. However, if we conclude that interaction is present between the two factors, hypothesis tests for factors A and B generally *should not* be performed. The reason is that findings of significance for either factor might be due only to interactive effects when the two factors are combined and not to the fact that the levels of the factor differ significantly. It is also possible that interactive effects might mask differences between means of one of the factors for at least some of the levels of the other factor. If significant interaction is present, the experimenter may conduct a one-way ANOVA to test the levels of one of the factors, for example, factor A, using only one level of the other factor, factor B.

Thus, when conducting hypothesis tests for a two-factor ANOVA:

1. Test for interaction.
2. If interaction is present, conduct a one-way ANOVA to test the levels of one of the factors using only one level of the other factor.[10]
3. If no interaction is found, test factor A and factor B.

---

[10]There are, however, some instances in which the effects of the factors provide important and meaningful information even though interaction is present. See D. R. Cox, *Planning of Experiments* (New York City: John Wiley and Sons, 1992), pp. 107–108.

## 12-3: Exercises

### Skill Development

**12-31.** Consider the following data from a two-factor experiment:

|  | Factor A | | |
| --- | --- | --- | --- |
| **Factor B** | **Level 1** | **Level 2** | **Level 3** |
| **Level 1** | 43 | 25 | 37 |
|  | 49 | 26 | 45 |
| **Level 2** | 50 | 27 | 46 |
|  | 53 | 31 | 48 |

a. Determine if there is interaction between factor A and factor B. Use the *p*-value approach and a significance level of 0.05.
b. Does the average response vary among the levels of factor A? Use the test-statistic approach and a significance level of 0.05.

c. Determine if there are differences in the average response between the levels of factor B. Use the *p*-value approach and a significance level of 0.05.

**12-32.** Examine the following two-factor analysis of variance table:

| Source | SS | df | MS | F-Ratio |
| --- | --- | --- | --- | --- |
| Factor A | 162.79 | 4 |  |  |
| Factor B |  |  | 28.12 |  |
| AB Interaction | 262.31 | 12 |  |  |
| Error | ——— | — |  |  |
| Total | 1,298.74 | 84 |  |  |

a. Complete the analysis of variance table.
b. Determine if interaction exists between factor A and factor B. Use $\alpha = 0.05$.

c. Determine if the levels of factor A have equal means. Use a significance level of 0.05.

d. Does the ANOVA table indicate that the levels of factor B have equal means? Use a significance level of 0.05.

**12-33.** Consider the following data for a two-factor experiment:

|  |  | | Factor A | |
|  |  | Level 1 | Level 2 | Level 3 |
|---|---|---|---|---|
| | Level 1 | 33 | 30 | 21 |
| | | 31 | 42 | 30 |
| | | 35 | 36 | 30 |
| Factor B | | | | |
| | Level 2 | 23 | 30 | 21 |
| | | 32 | 27 | 33 |
| | | 27 | 25 | 18 |

a. Based on the sample data, do factors A and B have significant interaction? State the appropriate null and alternative hypotheses and test using a significance level of 0.05.

b. Based on these sample data, can you conclude that the levels of factor A have equal means? Test using a significance level of 0.05.

c. Do the data indicate that the levels of factor B have different means? Test using a significance level equal to 0.05.

**12-34.** Consider the following partially completed two-factor analysis of variance table, which is an outgrowth of a study in which factor A has four levels and factor B has three levels. The number of replications was 11 in each cell.

| Source of Variation | SS | df | MS | F-Ratio |
|---|---|---|---|---|
| Factor A | 345.1 | 4 | | |
| Factor B | | | 28.12 | |
| AB Interaction | 1,123.2 | 12 | | |
| Error | 256.7 | | | |
| Total | 1,987.3 | 84 | | |

a. Complete the analysis of variance table.

b. Based on the sample data, can you conclude that the two factors have significant interaction? Test using a significance level equal to 0.05.

c. Based on the sample data, should you conclude that the means for factor A differ across the four levels or the means for factor B differ across the three levels? Discuss.

d. Considering the outcome of part b, determine what can be said concerning the differences of the levels of factors A and B. Use a significance level of 0.10 for any hypothesis tests required. Provide a rationale for your response to this question.

**12-35.** A two-factor experiment yielded the following data:

| Factor B | | Factor A | |
|  | Level 1 | Level 2 | Level 3 |
|---|---|---|---|
| Level 1 | 375 | 402 | 395 |
| | 390 | 396 | 390 |
| Level 2 | 335 | 336 | 320 |
| | 342 | 338 | 331 |
| Level 3 | 302 | 485 | 351 |
| | 324 | 455 | 346 |

a. Determine if there is interaction between factor A and factor B. Use the $p$-value approach and a significance level of 0.05.

b. Given your findings in part a, determine any significant differences among the response means of the levels of factor A for level 1 of factor B.

c. Repeat part b at levels 2 and 3 of factor B, respectively.

## Business Applications

**12-36.** A PEW Research Center survey concentrated on the issue of weight loss. It investigated how many pounds heavier the respondents were than their perceived ideal weight. It investigated whether these perceptions differed among different regions of the country and gender of the respondents. The following data (pounds) reflect the survey results:

| Gender | Region | | | |
|  | West | Midwest | South | Northeast |
|---|---|---|---|---|
| Men | 14 | 18 | 15 | 16 |
| | 13 | 16 | 15 | 14 |
| Women | 16 | 20 | 17 | 17 |
| | 13 | 18 | 17 | 13 |

a. Determine if there is interaction between Region and Gender. Use the $p$-value approach and a significance level of 0.05.

b. Given your findings in part a, determine any significant differences among the discrepancy between the average existing and desired weights in the regions.

c. Repeat part b for the Gender factor.

**12-37.** A manufacturing firm produces a single product on three production lines. Because the lines were developed at different points in the firm's history, they use different equipment. The firm is considering changing the layouts of the lines and would like to know what effects different layouts would have on production output. A study was conducted to determine the average output for each line over four randomly selected weeks using each of the three layouts under consideration. The output (in hundreds of units produced) was measured for each line for each of the four weeks for each layout being evaluated. The results of the study are as follows:

|          | Line 1 | Line 2 | Line 3 |
|----------|--------|--------|--------|
| **Layout 1** | 12 | 12 | 11 |
|          | 10 | 14 | 10 |
|          | 12 | 10 | 14 |
|          | 12 | 11 | 12 |
| **Layout 2** | 17 | 16 | 18 |
|          | 18 | 15 | 18 |
|          | 15 | 16 | 17 |
|          | 17 | 17 | 18 |
| **Layout 3** | 12 | 10 | 11 |
|          | 12 | 11 | 11 |
|          | 11 | 11 | 10 |
|          | 11 | 11 | 12 |

a. Based on the sample data, can the firm conclude that there is an interaction effect between the type of layout and the production line? Conduct the appropriate test at the 0.05 level of significance.
b. At the 0.05 level of significance, can the firm conclude that there is a difference in mean output across the three production lines?
c. At the 0.05 level of significance, can the firm conclude that there is a difference in mean output due to the type of layout used?

**12-38.** A popular consumer staple was displayed in different locations in the same aisle of a grocery store to determine what, if any, effect different placement might have on its sales. The product was placed at one of three heights on the aisle—low, medium, and high—and at one of three locations in the store—at the front of the store, at the middle of the store, or at the rear of the store. The number of units sold of the product at the various height and distance combinations was recorded each week for five weeks. The following results were obtained:

|          | Front | Middle | Rear |
|----------|-------|--------|------|
| **Low**    | 125 | 195 | 126 |
|          | 143 | 150 | 136 |
|          | 150 | 160 | 129 |
|          | 138 | 195 | 136 |
|          | 149 | 162 | 147 |
| **Medium** | 141 | 186 | 128 |
|          | 137 | 161 | 133 |
|          | 145 | 157 | 148 |
|          | 150 | 165 | 145 |
|          | 130 | 194 | 141 |
| **High**   | 129 | 157 | 149 |
|          | 141 | 152 | 137 |
|          | 148 | 186 | 138 |
|          | 130 | 164 | 126 |
|          | 137 | 176 | 138 |

a. At the 0.10 level of significance, is there an interaction effect?
b. At the 0.10 level of significance, does the height of the product's placement have an effect on the product's mean sales?
c. At the 0.10 level of significance, does the location in the store have an effect on the product's mean sales?

## Computer Database **Exercises**

**12-39.** Mt. Jumbo Plywood Company makes plywood for use in furniture production. The first major step in the plywood process is the peeling of the logs into thin layers of veneer. A lathe that rotates the logs through a knife that peels the log into layers 3/8-inch thick conducts the peeling process. Ideally, when a log is reduced to a 4-inch core diameter, the lathe releases the core and a new log is loaded onto the lathe. However, a problem called "spinouts" occurs if the lathe kicks out a core that has more than 4 inches left. This wastes wood and costs the company money.

Before going to the lathe, the logs are conditioned in a heated water-filled vat to warm the logs. The company is concerned that improper log conditioning may lead to excessive spinouts. Two factors are believed to affect the core diameter: the vat temperature and the time the logs spend in the vat prior to peeling. The lathe supervisor has recently conducted a test during which logs were peeled at each combination of temperature and time. The sample data for this experiment are in the data file called **Mt Jumbo**. The data are the core diameters in inches.

a. Based on the sample data, is there an interaction between water temperature and vat hours? Test using a significance level of 0.01. Discuss what interaction would mean in this situation. Use a *p*-value approach.
b. Based on the sample data, is there a difference in mean core diameter at the three water temperatures? Test using a significance level of 0.01.
c. Do the sample data indicate a difference in mean core diameter across the three vat times analyzed in this study? Use a significance level of 0.10 and a *p*-value approach.

**12-40.** A psychologist is conducting a study to determine whether there are differences between the ability of history majors and mathematics majors to solve various types of puzzles. Five mathematics majors and five history majors were randomly selected from the students at a liberal arts college in Maine. Each student was given five different puzzles to complete: a crossword puzzle, a cryptogram, a logic problem, a maze, and a cross sums. The time in minutes (rounded to the nearest minute) was recorded for each student in the study. If a student could not complete a puzzle in the maximum time allowed, or completed a puzzle incorrectly, then a penalty of 10 minutes was added to his or her time. The results are shown in the file **Puzzle**.

a. Plot the mean time to complete a puzzle for each puzzle type by major. What conclusion would you reach about the interaction between major and puzzle type?

b. At the 0.05 level of significance, is there an interaction effect?

c. If interaction is present, conduct a one-way ANOVA to test whether the mean time to complete a puzzle for history majors depends on the type of puzzle. Does the mean time to complete a puzzle for mathematics majors depend on the type of puzzle? Conduct the one-way ANOVA tests at a level of significance of 0.05.

**12-41.** The Iams Company sells Eukanuba and Iams premium dog and cat foods (dry and canned) in 70 countries. Iams makes dry dog and cat food at plants in Lewisburg, Ohio; Aurora, Nebraska; Henderson, North Carolina; Leipsic, Ohio; and Coevorden, The Netherlands. Its Eukanuba brand dry dog foods come in five formulas. One of the ingredients is of particular importance: crude fat. To discover if there is a difference in the average percent of crude fat among the five formulas and among the production sites, the sample data found in the file entitled **Eukanuba** were obtained.

a. Determine if there is interaction between the Eukanuba formulas and the plant sites where they are produced. Use the $p$-value approach and a significance level of 0.025.

b. Given your findings in part a, determine if there is a difference in the average percentage of crude fat in the Eukanuba formulas. Use a test-statistic approach with a significance level of 0.025.

c. Repeat part b for the plant sites in which the formulas are produced.

d. One important finding will be whether the average percent of crude fat for the "Reduced Fat" formula is equal to the advertised 9%. Conduct a relevant hypothesis test to determine this using a significance level of 0.05.

**12-42.** The amount of sodium in food has been of increasing concern due to its health implications. Beers from various producers have been analyzed for their sodium content. The file entitled **Sodium** contains the amount of sodium (mg) discovered in 12 fluid ounces of beer produced by the four major producers: Anheuser-Busch Inc., Miller Brewing Co., Coors Brewing Co., and Pabst Brewing Co. The types of beer (ales, lager, and specialty beers) were also scrutinized in the analysis.

a. Determine if there is interaction between the producer and the type of beer. Use a significance level of 0.05.

b. Given your findings in part a, determine if there is a difference in the average amount of sodium in 12 ounces of beer among the producers of the beer. Use a significance level of 0.05.

c. Repeat part b for the types of beer. Use a significance level of 0.05.

**END EXERCISES 12-3**

# Visual Summary

**Chapter 12:** A group of procedures known as analysis of variance, ANOVA, was introduced in this chapter. The procedures presented here represent a wide range of techniques used to determine whether three or more populations have equal means. Depending upon the experimental design employed, there are different hypothesis tests that must be performed. The one-way design is used to test whether three or more populations have equal mean values when the samples from the populations are considered to be independent. If an outside source of variation is present, the randomized complete block design is used. If there are two factors of interest and we wish to test to see whether the levels of each separate factor have equal means, then a two-factor design with replications is used. Regardless of which method is used, if the null hypothesis of equal means is rejected, methods presented in this chapter enable you to determine which pairs of populations have different means.

Analysis of variance is actually an array of statistical techniques used to test hypotheses related to these (and many other) experimental designs. By completing this chapter, you have been introduced to some of the most popular ANOVA techniques.

## 12.1 One-Way Analysis of Variance (pg. 476–497)

### Summary

There are often circumstances in which independent samples are obtained from two or more levels of a single **factor** to determine if the **levels** have equal means. The experimental design which produces the data for this experiment is referred to as a **completely randomized design**. The appropriate statistical tool for conducting the hypothesis test related to this experimental design is analysis of variance. Because this procedure addresses an experiment with only one factor, it is called a **one-way analysis of variance**. The concept acknowledges that the data produced by the completely randomized design will not all be the same value. This indicates that there is variation in the data. This is referred to as the **total variation**. Each level's data exhibits dispersion as well and is called the **within-sample variation**. The dispersion between the factor levels is designated as the **between-sample variation**. The ratio between estimators of these two variances forms the test statistic used to detect differences in the levels' means. If the null hypothesis of equal means is rejected, the Tukey-Kramer procedure was presented to determine which pairs of populations have different means.

> **Outcome 1.** Understand the basic logic of analysis of variance.
>
> **Outcome 2.** Perform a hypothesis test for a single-factor design using analysis of variance manually and with the aid of Excel or Minitab software.
>
> **Outcome 3.** Conduct and interpret post-analysis of variance pairwise comparisons procedures.

## 12.2 Randomized Complete Block Analysis of Variance (pg. 497–509)

### Summary

Section 12.1 addressed procedures for determining the equality of three or more population means of the levels of a single factor. In this case all other unknown sources of variation are addressed by the use of randomization. However, there are situations in which an additional known factor with at least two levels is impinging on the response variable of interest. A technique called blocking is used in such cases to eliminate the effects of the levels of the additional known factor on the analysis of variance.

As was the case in Section 12.1, a multiple comparisons procedure known as *Fisher's least significant difference* can be used to determine any difference among the population means of a randomized block ANOVA design.

> **Outcome 3.** Conduct and interpret post-analysis of variance pairwise comparisons procedures.
>
> **Outcome 4.** Recognize when randomized block analysis of variance is useful and be able to perform analysis of variance on a randomized block design.

## 12.3 Two-Factor Analysis of Variance with Replication (pg. 509–520)

### Summary

Two-factor ANOVA follows the same logic as was the case in the one-way and complete block ANOVA designs. In the latter two procedures, there is only one factor of interest. In the two-factor ANOVA, there are two factors of interest. Each factor of interest introduces variability into the experiment. There are circumstances in which the presence of a level of one factor affects the relationship between the response variable and the levels of the other factor. This effect is called interaction and, if present, is another source of variation. As was the case in Sections 12.1 and 12.2, we must find estimators for each source of variation. Identifying the appropriate sums of squares and then dividing each by its degrees of freedom does this. If the variation accounted for by factor A, factor B, and interaction is large relative to the error variation, we will tend to conclude that the factor levels have different means. The technique that is used when we wish to analyze two factors as described above is called *two-factor ANOVA with replications*.

> **Outcome 5.** Perform analysis of variance on a two-factor design of experiments with replications using Excel or Minitab and interpret the output.

## Conclusion

Chapter 12 has illustrated there are many instances in business in which we are interested in testing to determine whether three or more populations have equal means. The technique for performing such tests is called analysis of variance. If the sample means tend to be substantially different, then the hypothesis of equal means is rejected. The most elementary ANOVA experimental design is the one-way design, which is used to test whether three or more populations have equal mean values when the samples from the populations are considered to be independent. If we need to control for an outside source of variation (analogous to forming paired samples in Chapter 10), we can use the randomized complete block design. If there are two factors of interest and we wish to test to see whether the levels of each separate factor have equal means, then a two-factor design with replications is used.

# Equations

**(12.1) Partitioned Sum of Squares** pg. 478

$$SST = SSB + SSW$$

**(12.2) Hartley's _F_-Test Statistic** pg. 480

$$F_{max} = \frac{s_{max}^2}{s_{min}^2}$$

**(12.3) Total Sum of Squares** pg. 481

$$SST = \sum_{i=1}^{k} \sum_{j=1}^{n_i} (x_{ij} - \overline{\overline{x}})^2$$

**(12.4) Sum of Squares Between** pg. 482

$$SSB = \sum_{i=1}^{k} n_i (\overline{x}_i - \overline{\overline{x}})^2$$

**(12.5) Sum of Squares Within** pg. 482

$$SSW = SST - SSB$$

**(12.6)**
$$SSW = \sum_{i=1}^{k} \sum_{j=1}^{n_i} (x_{ij} - \overline{x}_i)^2$$

**(12.7) Tukey-Kramer Critical Range** pg. 489

$$\text{Critical range} = q_{1-\alpha} \sqrt{\frac{MSW}{2} \left( \frac{1}{n_i} + \frac{1}{n_j} \right)}$$

**(12.8) Sum of Squares Partitioning for Randomized Complete Block Design** pg. 499

$$SST = SSB + SSBL + SSW$$

**(12.9) Sum of Squares for Blocking** pg. 499

$$SSBL = \sum_{j=1}^{b} k(\overline{x}_j - \overline{\overline{x}})^2$$

**(12.10) Sum of Squares Within** pg. 499

$$SSW = SST - (SSB + SSBL)$$

**(12.11) Fisher's Least Significant Difference** pg. 505

$$LSD = t_{\alpha/2} \sqrt{MSW} \sqrt{\frac{2}{b}}$$

**(12.12) Total Sum of Squares** pg. 513

$$SST = \sum_{i=1}^{a} \sum_{j=1}^{b} \sum_{k=1}^{n} (x_{ijk} - \overline{\overline{x}})^2$$

**(12.13) Sum of Squares Factor A** pg. 513

$$SS_A = bn \sum_{i=1}^{a} (\overline{x}_{i..} - \overline{\overline{x}})^2$$

**(12.14) Sum of Squares Factor B** pg. 513

$$SS_B = an \sum_{j=1}^{b} (\overline{x}_{.j.} - \overline{\overline{x}})^2$$

**(12.15) Sum of Squares Interaction between Factors A and B** pg. 513

$$SS_{AB} = n \sum_{i=1}^{a} \sum_{j=1}^{b} (\overline{x}_{ij.} - \overline{x}_{i..} - \overline{x}_{.j.} + \overline{\overline{x}})^2$$

**(12.16) Sum of Squares Error** pg. 513

$$SSE = \sum_{i=1}^{a} \sum_{j=1}^{b} \sum_{k=1}^{n} (x_{ijk} - \overline{x}_{ij.})^2$$

# Key Terms

Balanced design pg. 476
Between-sample variation pg. 477
Completely randomized design pg. 476

Experiment-wide error rate pg. 488
Factor pg. 476
Levels pg. 476

One-way analysis of variance pg. 476
Total variation pg. 477
Within-sample variation pg. 477

# Chapter Exercises

_MyStatLab_

## Conceptual Questions

**12-43.** A one-way analysis of variance has just been performed. The conclusion reached is that the null hypothesis stating the population means are equal has not been rejected. What would you expect the

Tukey-Kramer procedure for multiple comparisons to show if it were performed for all pairwise comparisons? Discuss.

**12-44.** In journals related to your major locate two articles where tests of three or more population means were important. Discuss the issue being addressed, how the data were collected, the results of the statistical test, and any conclusions drawn based on the analysis.

**12-45.** Discuss why in some circumstances it is appropriate to use the randomized complete block design. Give an example other than those discussed in the text where this design could be used.

**12-46.** A two-way analysis of variance experiment is to be conducted to examine CEO salaries ($K) as a function of the number of years the CEO has been with the company and the size of the company's sales. The years spent with the company are categorized into 0–3, 4–6, 7–9, and >9 years. The size of the company is categorized using sales ($million) per year into three categories: 0–50, 51–100, and >100.
   a. Describe the factors associated with this experiment.
   b. List the levels of each of the factors identified in part a.
   c. List the treatment combinations of the experiment.
   d. Indicate the components of the ANOVA table that will be used to explain the variation in the CEOs' salaries.
   e. Determine the degrees of freedom for each of the components in the ANOVA if two replications are used.

**12-47.** In any of the multiple comparison techniques (Tukey-Kramer, *LSD*), the estimate of the within-sample variance uses data from the entire experiment. However, if one were to do a two-sample *t*-test to determine if there were a difference between any two means, the estimate of the population variances would only include data from the two specific samples under consideration. Explain this seeming discrepancy.

## Business Applications

**12-48.** The development of the Internet has made many things possible, in addition to downloading music. In particular, it allows an increasing number of people to telecommute, or work from home. Although this has many advantages, it has required some companies to provide employees with the necessary equipment, which has made your job as office manager more difficult. Your company provides computers, printers, and Internet service to a number of engineers and programmers, and although the cost of hardware has decreased, the cost of supplies, in this case printer cartridges, has not. Because of the cost of name-brand printer replacement cartridges, several companies have entered the secondary market. You are currently considering offers from four companies. The prices are equivalent, so you will make your decision based on length of service, specifically number of pages printed. You have given samples of four cartridges to

16 programmers and engineers and have received the following values:

| Supplier A | Supplier B | Supplier C | Supplier D |
|---|---|---|---|
| 424 | 650 | 521 | 323 |
| 521 | 725 | 601 | 383 |
| 650 | 826 | 590 | 487 |
| 422 | 722 | 522 | 521 |

   a. Using a significance level equal to 0.01, what conclusion should you reach about the four manufacturers' printer cartridges? Explain.
   b. If the test conducted in part a reveals that the null hypothesis should be rejected, which supplier should be used? Is there one or more you can eliminate based on these data? Use the appropriate test for multiple comparisons. Discuss.

**12-49.** The W. Atlee Burpee Co. was founded in Philadelphia in 1876 by an 18-year-old with a passion for plants and animals and a mother willing to lend him $1,000 of "seed money" to get started in business. Today, it is owned by George Ball Jr. One of Burpee's most demanded seeds is corn. Burpee continues to increase production to meet the growing demand. To this end, an experiment such as presented here is used to determine the combination of fertilizer and seed type that produces the largest number of kernels per ear.

|  | Fert. 1 | Fert. 2 | Fert. 3 | Fert. 4 |
|---|---|---|---|---|
| **Seed A** | 807 | 995 | 894 | 903 |
|  | 800 | 909 | 907 | 904 |
| **Seed B** | 1,010 | 1,098 | 1,000 | 1,008 |
|  | 912 | 987 | 801 | 912 |
| **Seed C** | 1,294 | 1,286 | 1,298 | 1,199 |
|  | 1,097 | 1,099 | 1,099 | 1,201 |

   a. Determine if there is interaction between the type of seed and the type of fertilizer. Use a significance level of 0.05.
   b. Given your findings in part a, determine if there is a difference in the average number of kernels per ear among the seeds.
   c. Repeat part b for the types of fertilizer. Use a significance level of 0.05.

**12-50.** Recent news stories have highlighted errors national companies such as H & R Block have made in preparing taxes. However, many people rely on local accountants to handle their tax work. A local television station, which prides itself on doing investigative reporting, decided to determine whether similar preparation problems occur in its market area.

   The station selected eight people to have their taxes figured at each of three accounting offices in its market area. The following data shows the tax bills (in dollars) as figured by each of the three accounting offices:

| Return | Office 1 | Office 2 | Office 3 |
|---|---|---|---|
| 1 | 4,376.20 | 5,100.10 | 4,988.03 |
| 2 | 5,678.45 | 6,234.23 | 5,489.23 |
| 3 | 2,341.78 | 2,242.60 | 2,121.90 |
| 4 | 9,875.33 | 10,300.30 | 9,845.60 |
| 5 | 7,650.20 | 8,002.90 | 7,590.88 |
| 6 | 1,324.80 | 1,450.90 | 1,356.89 |
| 7 | 2,345.90 | 2,356.90 | 2,345.90 |
| 8 | 15,468.75 | 16,080.70 | 15,376.70 |

a. Discuss why this test was conducted as a randomized block design. Why did the station think it important to have all three offices do the returns for each of the eight people?

b. Test to determine whether blocking was necessary in this situation. Use a significance level of 0.01. State the null and alternative hypotheses.

c. Based on the sample data, can the station report statistical evidence that there is a difference in the mean taxes due on tax returns? Test using a significance level of 0.01. State the appropriate null and alternative hypotheses.

d. Referring to part c, if you did conclude that a difference exists, use the appropriate test to determine which office has the highest mean tax due.

**12-51.** A senior analyst working for Ameritrade has reviewed purchases his customers have made over the last six months. He has categorized the mutual funds purchased into eight categories: (1) Aggressive Growth (AG), (2) Growth (G), (3) Growth-Income (G-I), (4) Income Funds (IF), (5) International (I), (6) Asset Allocation (AA), (7) Precious Metal (PM), and (8) Bond (B). The percentage gains accrued by 3 randomly selected customers in each group are as follows:

| Mutual Fund | AG | G | G-I | IF | I | AA | PM | B |
|---|---|---|---|---|---|---|---|---|
| | 6 | 7 | 5 | 1 | 14 | −3 | 5 | −1 |
| | 7 | −2 | 6 | 0 | 13 | 7 | 7 | 3 |
| | 12 | 0 | 2 | 6 | 10 | 7 | 5 | 2 |

a. Develop the appropriate ANOVA table to determine if there is a difference in the average percentage gains accrued by his customers among the mutual fund types. Use a significance level of 0.05.

b. Use the Tukey-Kramer procedure to determine which mutual fund type has the highest average percentage gain. Use an experiment-wide error rate of 0.05.

**12-52.** Anyone who has gone into a supermarket or discount store has walked by displays at the end of aisles. These are referred to as endcaps and are often prized because they increase the visibility of products. A manufacturer of tortilla chips has recently developed a new product, a blue corn tortilla chip. The manufacturer has arranged with a regional supermarket chain to display the chips on endcaps at four different locations in stores that have had similar weekly sales in snack foods. The dollar volumes of sales for the last six weeks in the four stores are as follows:

| | | Store | | |
|---|---|---|---|---|
| Week | 1 | 2 | 3 | 4 |
| 1 | $1,430 | $ 980 | $1,780 | $2,300 |
| 2 | $2,200 | $1,400 | $2,890 | $2,680 |
| 3 | $1,140 | $1,200 | $1,500 | $2,000 |
| 4 | $ 880 | $1,300 | $1,470 | $1,900 |
| 5 | $1,670 | $1,300 | $2,400 | $2,540 |
| 6 | $ 990 | $ 550 | $1,600 | $1,900 |

a. If the assumptions of a one-way ANOVA design are satisfied in this case, what should be concluded about the average sales at the four stores? Use a significance level of 0.05.

b. Discuss whether you think the assumptions of a one-way ANOVA are satisfied in this case and indicate why or why not. If they are not, what design is appropriate? Discuss.

c. Perform a randomized block analysis of variance test using a significance level of 0.05 to determine whether the mean sales for the four stores are different.

d. Comment on any differences between the means in parts b and c.

e. Suppose blocking was necessary and the researcher chooses not to use blocks. Discuss what impact this could have on the results of the analysis of variance.

f. Use Fisher's least significant difference procedure to determine which, if any, stores have different true average weekly sales.

## Computer Database **Exercises**

**12-53.** A *USA Today* editorial addressed the growth of compensation for corporate CEOs. As an example, quoting a study made by *BusinessWeek*, *USA Today* indicated that the pay packages for CEOs have increased almost sevenfold on average from 1994 to 2004. The file entitled **CEODough** contains the salaries of CEOs in 1994 and in 2004, adjusted for inflation.

a. Use analysis of variance to determine if there is a difference in the CEOs' average salaries between 1994 and 2004, adjusted for inflation.

b. Determine if there is a difference in the CEOs' average salaries between 1994 and 2004 using the two-sample *t*-test procedure.

c. What is the relationship between the two test statistics and the critical values, respectively, that were used in parts a and b?

**12-54.** The use of high-technology materials and design has dramatically impacted the game of golf. Not only are the professionals hitting the balls farther but so too are the average players. This has led to a rush to design new and better equipment.

Gordon Manufacturing produces golf balls. Recently, Gordon developed a golf ball made from a space-age material. This new golf ball promises greater distance off the tee. To test Gordon Manufacturing's claim, a test was set up to measure the average distance of four different golf balls (the New Gordon, Competitor 1, Competitor 2, Competitor 3) hit by a driving machine using three different types of drivers (Driver 1, Driver 2, Driver 3). The results (rounded to the nearest yard) are listed in the data file called **Gordon**. Conduct a test to determine if there are significant differences due to type of golf ball.

a. Does there appear to be interaction between type of golf ball and type of driver?

b. Conduct a test to determine if there is a significant effect due to the type of driver used.

c. How could the results of the tests be used by Gordon Manufacturing?

**12-55.** Maynards, a regional home improvement store chain located in the Intermountain West, is considering upgrading to a new series of scanning systems for its automatic checkout lanes. Although scanners can save customers a great deal of time, scanners will sometimes misread an item's price code. Before investing in one of three new systems, Maynards would like to determine if there is a difference in scanner accuracy. To investigate possible differences in scanner accuracy, 30 shopping carts were randomly selected from customers at the Golden, Colorado, store. The 30 carts differed from each other in both the number and types of items each contained. The items in each cart were then scanned by the three new scanning systems under consideration as well as by the current scanner used in all stores at a specially designed test facility for the purposes of the analysis. Each item was also checked manually, and a count was kept of the number of scanning errors made by each scanner for each basket. Each of the scannings was repeated 30 times, and the average number of scanning errors was determined. The sample data are in the data file called **Maynards**.

a. What type of experimental design did Maynards use to test for differences among scanning systems? Why was this type of design selected?

b. State the primary hypotheses of interest for this test.

c. At the 0.01 level of significance, is there a difference in the average number of errors among the four different scanners?

d. (1) Is there a difference in the average number of errors by cart? (2) Was Maynards correct in blocking by cart?

e. If you determined that there is a difference in the average number of errors among the four different scanners, identify where those differences exist.

f. Do you think that Maynards should upgrade from its existing scanner to Scanner A, Scanner B, or Scanner C? What other factors may it want to consider before making a decision?

**12-56.** PhoneEx provides call center services for many different companies. A large increase in its business has made it necessary to establish a new call center. Four cities are being considered—Little Rock, Wichita, Tulsa, and Memphis. The new center will employ approximately 1,500 workers, and PhoneEx will transfer 75 people from its Omaha center to the new location. One concern in the choice of where to locate the new center is the cost of housing for the employees who will be moving there. To help determine whether significant housing cost differences exist across the competing sites, PhoneEx has asked a real estate broker in each city to randomly select a list of 33 homes between 5 and 15 years old and ranging in size between 1,975 and 2,235 square feet. The prices (in dollars) that were recorded for each city are contained in the file called **PhoneEx**.

a. At the 0.05 level of significance, is there evidence to conclude that the average price of houses between 5 and 15 years old and ranging in size between 1,975 and 2,235 square feet is not the same in the four cities? Use the $p$-value approach.

b. At the 0.05 level of significance, is there a difference in average housing price between Wichita and Little Rock? Between Little Rock and Tulsa? Between Tulsa and Memphis?

c. Determine the sample size required to estimate the average housing price in Wichita to within $500 with a 95% confidence level. Assume the required parameters' estimates are sufficient for this calculation.

**12-57.** An investigation into the effects of various levels of nitrogren (M. L. Vitosh, *Tri-State Fertilizer Recommendations for Corn, Soybeans, Wheat and Alfalfa*, Bulletin E-2567) at Ohio State University addressed the pounds per acre of nitrogen required to produce certain yield levels of corn on fields that had previously been planted with other crops. The file entitled **Nitrogen** indicates the amount of nitrogen required to produce given quantities of corn planted.

a. Determine if there is interaction between the yield levels of corn and the crop that had been previously planted in the field. Use a significance level of 0.05.

b. Given your findings in part a, determine any significant differences among the average pounds per acre of nitrogen required to produce yield levels of corn on fields that had been planted with corn as the previous crop.

c. Repeat part b for soybeans and grass sod, respectively.

# Video Case 3

## Drive-Thru Service Times @ McDonald's

When you're on the go and looking for a quick meal, where do you go? If you're like millions of people every day, you make a stop at McDonald's. Known as "quick service restaurants" in the industry (not "fast food"), companies such as McDonald's invest heavily to determine the most efficient and effective ways to provide fast, high-quality service in all phases of their business.

Drive-thru operations play a vital role. It's not surprising that attention is focused on the drive-thru process. After all, over 60% of individual restaurant revenues in the United States come from the drive-thru experience. Yet, understanding the process is more complex than just counting cars. Marla King, professor at the company's international training center, Hamburger University, got her start 25 years ago working at a McDonald's drive-thru. She now coaches new restaurant owners and managers. "Our stated drive-thru service time is 90 seconds or less. We train every manager and team member to understand that a quality customer experience at the drive-thru depends on them," says Marla. Some of the factors that affect a customer's ability to complete their purchases within 90 seconds include restaurant staffing, equipment layout in the restaurant, training, efficiency of the grill team, and frequency of customer arrivals, to name a few. Customer-order patterns also play a role. Some customers will just order drinks, whereas others seem to need enough food to feed an entire soccer team. And then there are the special orders. Obviously, there is plenty of room for variability here.

Yet, that doesn't stop the company from using statistical techniques to better understand the drive-thru action. In particular, McDonald's utilizes statistical techniques to display data and to help transform the data into useful information. For restaurant managers to achieve the goal in their own restaurants, they need training in proper restaurant and drive-thru operations. Hamburger University, McDonald's training center located near Chicago, satisfies that need. In the mock-up restaurant service lab, managers go thru a "before and after" training scenario. In the "before" scenario, they run the restaurant for 30 minutes as if they were back in their home restaurants. Managers in the training class are assigned to be crew, customers, drive-thru cars, special needs guests (such as hearing impaired, indecisive, or clumsy), or observers. Statistical data about the operations, revenues, and service times are collected and analyzed. Without the right training, the restaurant's operations usually start breaking down after 10–15 minutes. After debriefing and analyzing the data collected, the managers make suggestions for adjustments and head back to the service lab to try again. This time, the results usually come in well within standards. "When presented with the quantitative results, managers are pretty quick to make the connections between better operations, higher revenues, and happier customers," Marla states.

When managers return to their respective restaurants, the training results and techniques are shared with staff charged with implementing the ideas locally. The results of the training eventually are measured when McDonald's conducts a restaurant operations improvement process study, or ROIP. The goal is simple: improved operations. When the ROIP review is completed, statistical analyses are performed and managers are given their results. Depending on the results, decisions might be made that require additional financial resources, building construction, staff training, or reconfiguring layouts. Yet one thing is clear: Statistics drive the decisions behind McDonald's drive-thru service operations.

### Discussion Questions:

1. After returning from the training session at Hamburger University, a McDonald's store owner selected a random sample of 362 drive-thru customers and carefully measured the time it took from when a customer entered the McDonald's property until the customer had received the order at the drive-thru window. These data are in the file called **McDonald's Drive-Thru Waiting Times**. Note, the owner selected some customers during the breakfast period, others during lunch, and others during dinner. Test, using an alpha level equal to 0.05, to determine whether the mean drive-thru time is equal during the three dining periods (breakfast, lunch, and dinner.)

2. Referring to question 1, write a short report discussing the results of the test conducted. Make sure to include a discussion of any ramifications the results of this test might have regarding the efforts the manager will need to take to reduce drive-thru times.

# Case 12.1

## Agency for New Americans

Denise Walker collapsed at home after her first outing as a volunteer for the Agency for New Americans in Raleigh, North Carolina. Denise had a fairly good career going with various federal agencies after graduating with a degree in accounting. She decided to stay at home after she and her husband started a family. Now that their youngest is in high school, Denise decided she needed something more to do than manage the household. She decided on volunteer work and joined the Agency for New Americans.

The purpose of the Agency for New Americans is to help new arrivals become comfortable with the basic activities necessary to function in American society. One of the major activities, of course, is shopping for food and other necessities. Denise had just returned from her first outing to a supermarket with a recently arrived Somali Bantu family. It was their first time also, and they were astonished by both the variety and selection. Since the family was on a very limited budget, Denise spent much time talking about comparison shopping, and for someone working with a new currency this was hard. She didn't even want to tell them the store they were in was only one of four possible chains within a mile of their apartment. Denise realized the store she started with would be the one they would automatically return to when on their own.

Next week Denise and the family were scheduled to go to a discount store. Denise typically goes to a national chain close to her house but hasn't felt the need to be primarily a value shopper for some time. Since she feels the Somali family will automatically return to the store she picks, and she has her choice of two national chains and one regional chain, she decides to not automatically take them to "her" store. Because each store advertises low prices and meeting all competitors' prices, she also doesn't want to base her decision on what she hears on commercials. Instead, she picks

a random selection of items and finds the prices in each store. The items and prices are shown in the file **New Americans**. In looking at the data, Denise sees there are differences in some prices but wonders if there is any way to determine which store to take the family to.

### Required Tasks:

1. Identify the major issue in the case.
2. Identify the appropriate statistical test that could be conducted to address the case's major issue.
3. Explain why you selected the test you choose in (2).
4. State the appropriate null and alternative hypotheses for the statistical test you identified.
5. Perform the statistical test(s). Be sure to state your conclusion(s).
6. If possible, identify the stores that Diane should recommend to the family.
7. Summarize your analysis and findings in a short report.

# Case 12.2

## McLaughlin Salmon Works

John McLaughlin's father correctly predicted that a combination of declining wild populations of salmon and an increase in demand for fish in general would create a growing market for salmon grown in "fish farms." Over recent years, an increasing percentage of salmon, trout, and catfish, for example, come from commercial operations. At first, operating a fish farm consisted of finding an appropriate location, installing the pens, putting in smelt, and feeding the fish until they grew to the appropriate size. However, as the number of competitors increased, successful operation required taking a more scientific approach to raising fish.

Over the past year, John has been looking at the relationship between food intake and weight gain. Since food is a major cost of the operation, the higher the weight gain for a given amount of food, the more cost-effective the food. John's most recent effort involved trying to determine the relationship between four component mixes and three size progressions for the food pellets. Since smaller fish require smaller food pellets but larger pellets contain more food, one question John was addressing is at what rate to move from smaller to larger pellets. Also, since fish are harder to individually identify than livestock, the study involved constructing small individual pens and giving fish in each pen a different

combination of pellet mix and size progression. This involved a reasonable cost but a major commitment of time, and John's father wasn't sure the cost and time were justified. John had just gathered his first set of data and has started to analyze it. The data are shown in the file called **McLaughlin Salmon Works**. John is not only interested in whether one component mix, or one pellet size progression, seemed to lead to maximum weight gain but would really like to find one combination of mix and size progression that proved to be superior.

### Required Tasks:

1. Identify the major issues in the case.
2. Identify an appropriate statistical analysis to perform.
3. Explain why you selected the test you choose in (2)
4. State the appropriate null and alternative hypotheses for the statistical test you identified.
5. Perform the statistical test(s). Be sure to state your conclusion(s).
6. Is there one combination of mix and size progression that is superior to the others?
7. Summarize your analysis and findings in a short report.

# Case 12.3

## NW Pulp and Paper

Cassie Coughlin had less than a week to finish her presentation to the CEO of NW Pulp and Paper. Cassie had inherited a project started by her predecessor as head of the new-product development section of the company, and by the nature of the business, dealing with wood products, projects tended to have long lifetimes. Her

predecessor had successfully predicted the consequences of a series of events that, in fact, had occurred:

1. The western United States, where NW Pulp and Paper had its operations, was running out of water, caused by a combination of population growth and increased irrigation. The situation

had currently been made worse by several years of drought. This meant many farming operations were becoming unprofitable.

2. The amount of timber harvesting from national forests continued to be limited.

3. At least some of the land that had been irrigated would become less productive due to alkaline deposits caused by taking water from rivers.

Based on these three factors, Cassie's predecessor had convinced the company to purchase a 2,000-acre farm that had four types of soil commonly found in the West and also had senior water rights. Water rights in the West are given by the state, and senior rights are those that will continue to be able to get irrigation water after those with junior rights are cut off. His idea had been to plant three types of genetically modified poplar trees (these are generally fast-growing trees) on the four types of soil and assess growth rates. His contention was it might be economically feasible for the company to purchase more farms that were becoming less productive and to become self-sufficient in its supply of raw material for making paper.

The project had been started 15 years ago, and since her predecessor had since retired, Cassie was now in charge of the project. The primary focus of the 15-year review was tree growth. Growth in this case did not refer to height but wood volume. Volume is assessed by measuring the girth of the tree three feet above the ground. She had just received data from the foresters who had been managing the experiment. They had taken a random sample of measurements from each of the tree types. The data are shown in the file **NW Pulp and Paper**. Cassie knew the CEO would at least be interested in whether one type of tree was generally superior and whether there was some unique combination of soil type and tree type that stood out.

# Case 12.4

## Quinn Restoration

Last week John Quinn sat back in a chair with his feet on his deck and nodded at his wife, Kate. They had just finished a conversation that would likely influence the direction of their lives for the next several years or longer.

John retired a little less than a year ago after 25 years in the Lake Oswego police department. He had steadily moved up the ranks and retired as a captain. Although his career had, in his mind, gone excellently, he had been working much more than he had been home. Initially upon retiring he had reveled in the ability to spend time doing things he was never able to do while working: complete repairs around the house, travel with his wife, spend time with the children still at home, and visit those who had moved out. He was even able to knock five strokes off his golf handicap. However, he had become increasingly restless, and both he and Kate agreed he needed something to do, but that something did not involve a full-time job.

John had, over the years, bought, restored, and sold a series of older Corvettes. Although this had been entirely a hobby, it also had been a profitable one. The discussion John and Kate just concluded involved expanding this hobby, not into a full-time job, but into a part-time business. John would handle the actual restoration, which he enjoyed, and Kate would cover the paperwork, ordering parts, keeping track of expenses, and billing clients, which John did not like. The last part of their conversation involved ordering parts.

In the past John had ordered parts for old Corvettes from one of three possible sources: Weckler's, American Auto Parts, or Corvette Central. Kate, however, didn't want to call all three any time John needed a part but instead wanted to set up an account with one of the three and be able to order parts over the Internet. The question was which company, if any, would be the appropriate choice. John agreed to develop a list of common parts. Kate would then call each of the companies asking for their prices, and, based on this information, determine with which company to establish the account. Kate spent time over the last week on the phone developing the data located in the data file called **Quinn Restoration**. The question John now faced is whether the prices he found could lead him to conclude one company will be less expensive, on average, than the other two.

# Business Statistics Capstone Project

## Theme: Analysis of Variance

### Project Objective:

The objective of this business statistics capstone project is to provide you with an opportunity to integrate the statistical tools and concepts you have learned in your business statistics course. As in all real-world applications, it is not expected through the completion of this project that you will have utilized every statistical technique you have been taught in this course. Rather, an objective of the assignment will be for you to determine which of the statistical tools and techniques are appropriate to employ for the situation you have selected.

### Project Description:

You are to identify a business or organizational issue that is appropriately addressed using analysis of variance or experimental design. You will need to specify one or more sets of null and alternative hypotheses to be tested in order to reach conclusions pertaining to the business or organizational issue you have selected. You are responsible for designing and carrying out an "experiment" or otherwise collecting appropriate data required to test the hypotheses using one or more of the analysis of variance designs introduced in your text and statistics course.

There is no minimum sample size. The sample size should depend on the design you choose and the cost and difficulty in obtaining the data. You are responsible for making sure that the data are accurate. All methods (or sources) for data collection should be fully documented.

## Project Deliverables:

To successfully complete this capstone project, you are required to deliver, at a minimum, the following items in the context of a management report:

- A complete description of the central issue of your project and of the background of the company or organization you have selected as the basis for the project

- A clear and concise explanation of the data collection method used. Included should be a discussion of your rationale for selecting the analysis of variance technique(s) used in your analysis.
- A complete descriptive analysis of all variables in the data set, including both numerical and graphical analysis. You should demonstrate the extent to which the basic assumptions of the analysis of variance designs have been satisfied.
- Provide a clear and concise review of the hypotheses tests that formed the objective of your project. Show any post–ANOVA multiple comparison tests where appropriate.
- Offer a summary and conclusion section that relates back to the central issue(s) of your project and discusses the results of the hypothesis tests.
- All pertinent appendix materials

The final report should be presented in a professional format using the style or format suggested by your instructor.

# References

Berenson, Mark L., and David M. Levine, *Basic Business Statistics: Concepts and Applications*, 11th ed. (Upper Saddle River, NJ: Prentice Hall, 2009).

Bowerman, Bruce L., and Richard T. O'Connell, *Linear Statistical Models: An Applied Approach*, 2nd ed. (Belmont, CA: Duxbury Press, 1990).

Cox, D. R., *Planning of Experiments* (New York City: John Wiley & Sons, 1992).

Cryer, Jonathan D., and Robert B. Miller, *Statistics for Business: Data Analysis and Modeling*, 2nd ed. (Belmont, CA: Duxbury Press, 1994).

Kutner, Michael H., Christopher J. Nachtsheim, John Neter, William Li, *Applied Linear Statistical Models*, 5th ed. (New York City, McGraw-Hill Irwin, 2005).

*Microsoft Excel 2007* (Redmond, WA: Microsoft Corp., 2007).

*Minitab for Windows Version 15* (State College, PA: Minitab, 2007).

Montgomery, D. C., *Design and Analysis of Experiments*, 6th ed. (New York City: John Wiley & Sons, 2004).

Searle, S. R., and R. F. Fawcett, "Expected mean squares in variance component models having finite populations." *Biometrics* 26 (1970), pp. 243–254.

# Special Review Section

This review section, which is presented using block diagrams and flowcharts, is intended to help you tie together the material from several key chapters. This section is not a substitute for reading and studying the chapters covered by the review. However, you can use this review material to add to your understanding of the individual topics in the chapters.

## Chapters 8–12

Statistical inference is the process of reaching conclusions about a population based on a random sample selected from the population. Chapters 8 to 12 introduced the fundamental concepts of statistical inference involving two major categories of inference, *estimation and hypothesis testing*. These chapters have covered a fairly wide range of different situations that for beginning students can sometimes seem overwhelming. The following diagrams will, we hope, help you better identify which specific estimation or hypothesis-testing technique to use in a given situation. These diagrams form something resembling a decision support system that you should be able to use as a guide through the estimation and hypothesis-testing processes.

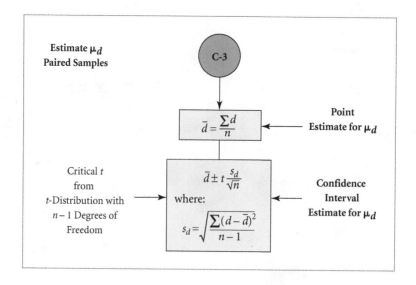

Estimate $\mu_d$
Paired Samples

C-3

Point
Estimate for $\mu_d$

$$\bar{d} = \frac{\sum d}{n}$$

Critical $t$
from
$t$-Distribution with
$n - 1$ Degrees of
Freedom

$$\bar{d} \pm t \frac{s_d}{\sqrt{n}}$$
where:
$$s_d = \sqrt{\frac{\sum (d - \bar{d})^2}{n - 1}}$$

Confidence
Interval
Estimate for $\mu_d$

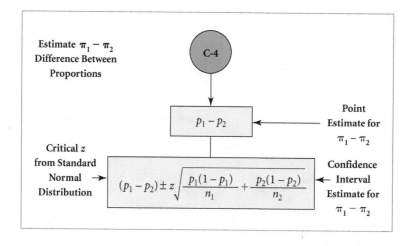

Estimate $\pi_1 - \pi_2$
Difference Between
Proportions

C-4

Point
Estimate for
$\pi_1 - \pi_2$

$$p_1 - p_2$$

Critical $z$
from Standard
Normal
Distribution

$$(p_1 - p_2) \pm z \sqrt{\frac{p_1(1 - p_1)}{n_1} + \frac{p_2(1 - p_2)}{n_2}}$$

Confidence
Interval
Estimate for
$\pi_1 - \pi_2$

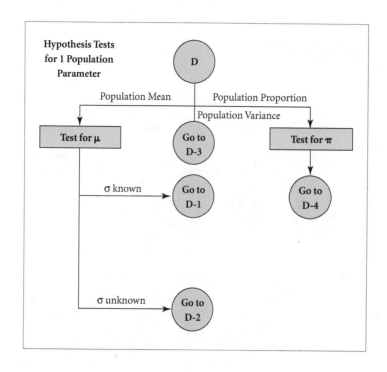

Hypothesis Tests
for 1 Population
Parameter

D

Population Mean

Population Proportion

Population Variance

Test for $\mu$

Go to
D-3

Test for $\pi$

$\sigma$ known

Go to
D-1

Go to
D-4

$\sigma$ unknown

Go to
D-2

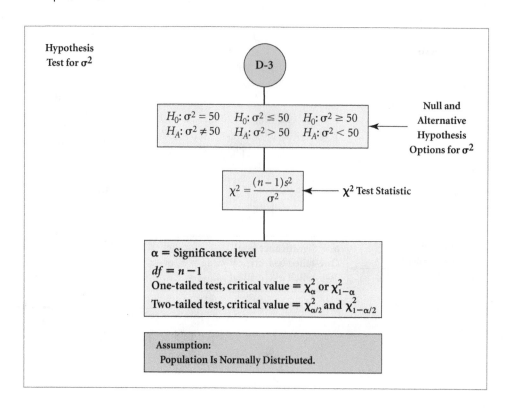

Hypothesis Test for $\sigma^2$

D-3

$H_0: \sigma^2 = 50$   $H_0: \sigma^2 \leq 50$   $H_0: \sigma^2 \geq 50$
$H_A: \sigma^2 \neq 50$   $H_A: \sigma^2 > 50$   $H_A: \sigma^2 < 50$

Null and Alternative Hypothesis Options for $\sigma^2$

$$\chi^2 = \frac{(n-1)s^2}{\sigma^2}$$

$\chi^2$ Test Statistic

$\alpha$ = Significance level
$df = n - 1$
One-tailed test, critical value = $\chi^2_\alpha$ or $\chi^2_{1-\alpha}$
Two-tailed test, critical value = $\chi^2_{\alpha/2}$ and $\chi^2_{1-\alpha/2}$

Assumption:
Population Is Normally Distributed.

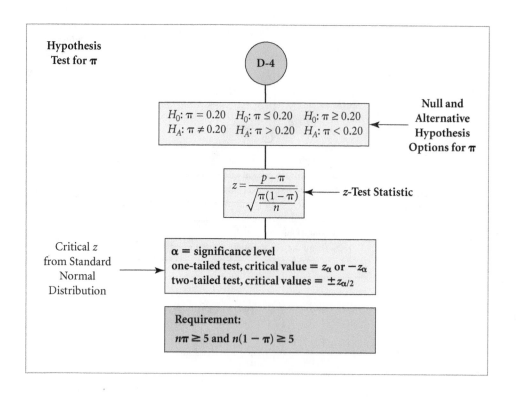

Hypothesis Test for $\pi$

D-4

$H_0: \pi = 0.20$   $H_0: \pi \leq 0.20$   $H_0: \pi \geq 0.20$
$H_A: \pi \neq 0.20$   $H_A: \pi > 0.20$   $H_A: \pi < 0.20$

Null and Alternative Hypothesis Options for $\pi$

$$z = \frac{p - \pi}{\sqrt{\dfrac{\pi(1 - \pi)}{n}}}$$

$z$-Test Statistic

Critical $z$ from Standard Normal Distribution

$\alpha$ = significance level
one-tailed test, critical value = $z_\alpha$ or $-z_\alpha$
two-tailed test, critical values = $\pm z_{\alpha/2}$

Requirement:
$n\pi \geq 5$ and $n(1 - \pi) \geq 5$

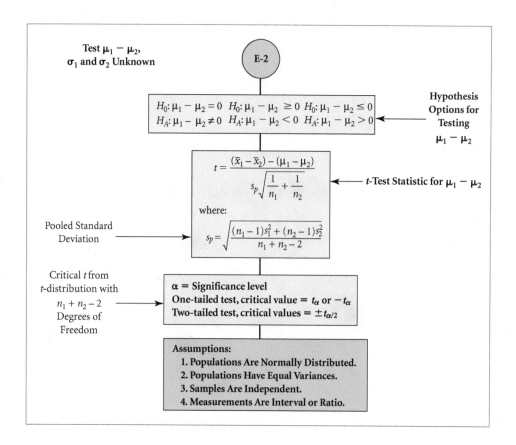

Test $\mu_1 - \mu_2$, $\sigma_1$ and $\sigma_2$ Unknown

E-2

$H_0: \mu_1 - \mu_2 = 0$  $H_0: \mu_1 - \mu_2 \geq 0$  $H_0: \mu_1 - \mu_2 \leq 0$
$H_A: \mu_1 - \mu_2 \neq 0$  $H_A: \mu_1 - \mu_2 < 0$  $H_A: \mu_1 - \mu_2 > 0$

Hypothesis Options for Testing $\mu_1 - \mu_2$

$$t = \frac{(\bar{x}_1 - \bar{x}_2) - (\mu_1 - \mu_2)}{s_p \sqrt{\frac{1}{n_1} + \frac{1}{n_2}}}$$

where:

$$s_p = \sqrt{\frac{(n_1 - 1)s_1^2 + (n_2 - 1)s_2^2}{n_1 + n_2 - 2}}$$

$t$-Test Statistic for $\mu_1 - \mu_2$

Pooled Standard Deviation

Critical $t$ from $t$-distribution with $n_1 + n_2 - 2$ Degrees of Freedom

$\alpha$ = Significance level
One-tailed test, critical value = $t_\alpha$ or $-t_\alpha$
Two-tailed test, critical values = $\pm t_{\alpha/2}$

Assumptions:
1. Populations Are Normally Distributed.
2. Populations Have Equal Variances.
3. Samples Are Independent.
4. Measurements Are Interval or Ratio.

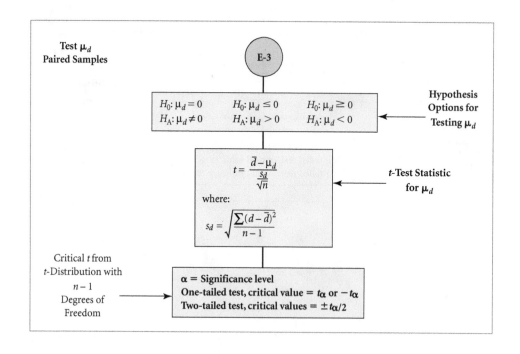

Test $\mu_d$ Paired Samples

E-3

$H_0: \mu_d = 0$    $H_0: \mu_d \leq 0$    $H_0: \mu_d \geq 0$
$H_A: \mu_d \neq 0$    $H_A: \mu_d > 0$    $H_A: \mu_d < 0$

Hypothesis Options for Testing $\mu_d$

$$t = \frac{\bar{d} - \mu_d}{\frac{s_d}{\sqrt{n}}}$$

where:

$$s_d = \sqrt{\frac{\sum(d - \bar{d})^2}{n - 1}}$$

$t$-Test Statistic for $\mu_d$

Critical $t$ from $t$-Distribution with $n - 1$ Degrees of Freedom

$\alpha$ = Significance level
One-tailed test, critical value = $t_\alpha$ or $-t_\alpha$
Two-tailed test, critical values = $\pm t_{\alpha/2}$

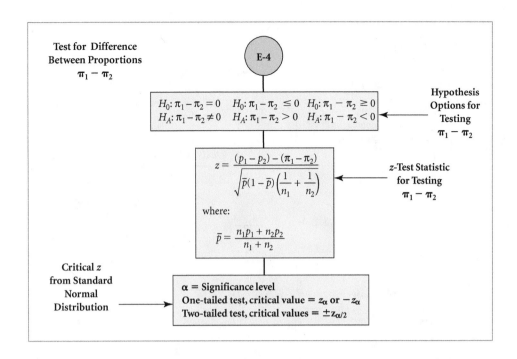

**Test for Difference Between Proportions**
$\pi_1 - \pi_2$

E-4

$H_0: \pi_1 - \pi_2 = 0 \quad H_0: \pi_1 - \pi_2 \leq 0 \quad H_0: \pi_1 - \pi_2 \geq 0$
$H_A: \pi_1 - \pi_2 \neq 0 \quad H_A: \pi_1 - \pi_2 > 0 \quad H_A: \pi_1 - \pi_2 < 0$

Hypothesis Options for Testing $\pi_1 - \pi_2$

$$z = \frac{(p_1 - p_2) - (\pi_1 - \pi_2)}{\sqrt{\bar{p}(1 - \bar{p})\left(\dfrac{1}{n_1} + \dfrac{1}{n_2}\right)}}$$

where:

$$\bar{p} = \frac{n_1 p_1 + n_2 p_2}{n_1 + n_2}$$

z-Test Statistic for Testing $\pi_1 - \pi_2$

Critical z from Standard Normal Distribution

$\alpha$ = Significance level
One-tailed test, critical value = $z_\alpha$ or $-z_\alpha$
Two-tailed test, critical values = $\pm z_{\alpha/2}$

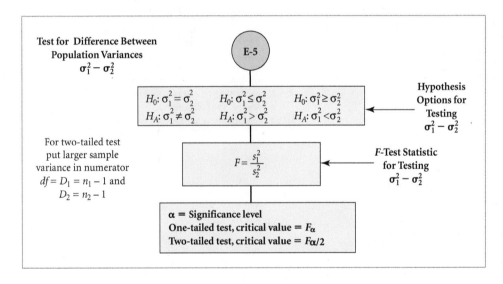

**Test for Difference Between Population Variances**
$\sigma_1^2 - \sigma_2^2$

E-5

$H_0: \sigma_1^2 = \sigma_2^2 \qquad H_0: \sigma_1^2 \leq \sigma_2^2 \qquad H_0: \sigma_1^2 \geq \sigma_2^2$
$H_A: \sigma_1^2 \neq \sigma_2^2 \qquad H_A: \sigma_1^2 > \sigma_2^2 \qquad H_A: \sigma_1^2 < \sigma_2^2$

Hypothesis Options for Testing $\sigma_1^2 - \sigma_2^2$

For two-tailed test put larger sample variance in numerator
$df = D_1 = n_1 - 1$ and $D_2 = n_2 - 1$

$$F = \frac{s_1^2}{s_2^2}$$

F-Test Statistic for Testing $\sigma_1^2 - \sigma_2^2$

$\alpha$ = Significance level
One-tailed test, critical value = $F_\alpha$
Two-tailed test, critical value = $F_{\alpha/2}$

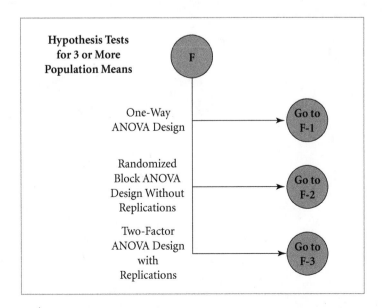

**Hypothesis Tests for 3 or More Population Means**

F

One-Way ANOVA Design → Go to F-1

Randomized Block ANOVA Design Without Replications → Go to F-2

Two-Factor ANOVA Design with Replications → Go to F-3

One-Way
ANOVA Design
for 3 or More
Population Means

F-1

$H_0: \mu_1 = \mu_2 = \mu_3 = \cdots = \mu_k$
$H_A$: At least two populations have
different means.

Null and Alternative
Hypotheses

ANOVA Table

| Source of Variation | SS | df | MS | F-Ratio |
|---|---|---|---|---|
| Between samples | SSB | $k-1$ | MSB | $\dfrac{MSB}{MSW}$ |
| Within samples | SSW | $n_T - k$ | MSW | |
| Total | SST | $n_T - 1$ | | |

Critical $F$
from $F$-Distribution with
$D_1 = k - 1$ and $D_2 = n_T - k$
Degrees of Freedom

$\alpha$ = **Significance level**
**Critical value = $F_\alpha$**

If null hypothesis is
rejected, compare all
possible pairs,
$|\bar{x}_i - \bar{x}_j|$ to Tukey-
Kramer Critical Range

*Tukey-Kramer Critical Range*

critical range $= q_{1-\alpha} \sqrt{\dfrac{MSW}{2}\left(\dfrac{1}{n_i} + \dfrac{1}{n_j}\right)}$

**Assumptions:**
  1. **Populations Are Normally Distributed.**
  2. **Populations Have Equal Variances.**
  3. **Samples Are Independent.**
  4. **Measurements Are Interval or Ratio.**

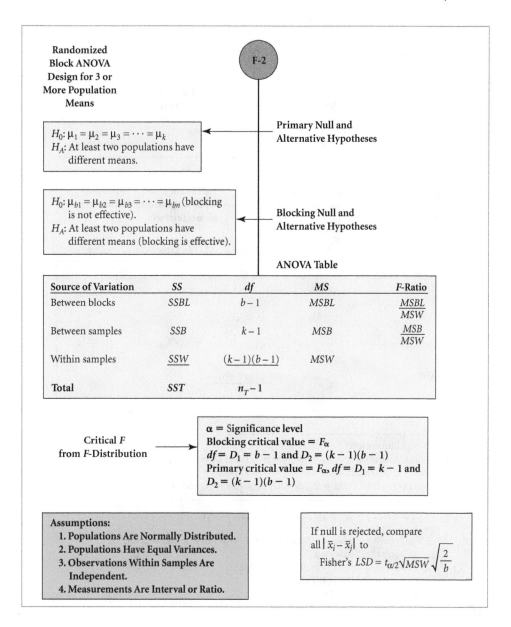

Randomized Block ANOVA Design for 3 or More Population Means

**F-2**

$H_0: \mu_1 = \mu_2 = \mu_3 = \cdots = \mu_k$
$H_A:$ At least two populations have different means.

→ Primary Null and Alternative Hypotheses

$H_0: \mu_{b1} = \mu_{b2} = \mu_{b3} = \cdots = \mu_{bn}$ (blocking is not effective).
$H_A:$ At least two populations have different means (blocking is effective).

→ Blocking Null and Alternative Hypotheses

ANOVA Table

| Source of Variation | SS | df | MS | F-Ratio |
|---|---|---|---|---|
| Between blocks | SSBL | $b-1$ | MSBL | $\dfrac{MSBL}{MSW}$ |
| Between samples | SSB | $k-1$ | MSB | $\dfrac{MSB}{MSW}$ |
| Within samples | SSW | $(k-1)(b-1)$ | MSW | |
| Total | SST | $n_T - 1$ | | |

Critical F from F-Distribution →

$\alpha$ = Significance level
Blocking critical value = $F_\alpha$
$df = D_1 = b - 1$ and $D_2 = (k-1)(b-1)$
Primary critical value = $F_\alpha$, $df = D_1 = k - 1$ and $D_2 = (k-1)(b-1)$

Assumptions:
1. Populations Are Normally Distributed.
2. Populations Have Equal Variances.
3. Observations Within Samples Are Independent.
4. Measurements Are Interval or Ratio.

If null is rejected, compare all $|\bar{x}_i - \bar{x}_j|$ to
Fisher's $LSD = t_{\alpha/2}\sqrt{MSW}\sqrt{\dfrac{2}{b}}$

Two-Factor
ANOVA Design
with Replications

Factor A Null and
Alternative Hypotheses

$H_0: \mu_{A1} = \mu_{A1} = \mu_{A3} = \cdots = \mu_{Ak}$
$H_A$: Not all Factor A means are equal.

Factor B Null and
Alternative Hypotheses

$H_0: \mu_{B1} = \mu_{B2} = \mu_{B3} = \cdots = \mu_{Bn}$
$H_A$: Not all Factor B means are equal.

$H_0$: Factors A and B do not interact
   to affect the mean response.
$H_A$: Factors A and B do interact.

Null and alternative hypotheses
for testing whether the two
factors interact

ANOVA Table

| Source of Variation | SS | df | MS | F-Ratio |
|---|---|---|---|---|
| Factor A | $SS_A$ | $a - 1$ | $MS_A$ | $\dfrac{MS_A}{MSE}$ |
| Factor B | $SS_B$ | $b - 1$ | $MS_B$ | $\dfrac{MS_B}{MSE}$ |
| AB Interaction | $SS_{AB}$ | $(a-1)(b-1)$ | $MS_{AB}$ | $\dfrac{MS_{AB}}{MSE}$ |
| Error | $\underline{SSE}$ | $\underline{n_T - ab}$ | $MSE$ | |
| Total | $SST$ | $n_T - 1$ | | |

$\alpha$ = Significance level
Factor A critical value = $F_\alpha$, $df = D_1 = a - 1$ and $D_2 = n_T - ab$
Factor B critical value = $F_\alpha$, $df = D_1 = b - 1$ and $D_2 = n_T - ab$
Interaction critical value = $F_\alpha$, $df = D_1 = (a-1)(b-1)$ and $D_2 = n_T - ab$

Assumptions:
1. The Population Values for Each Combination of Pairwise Factor Levels
   Are Normally Distributed.
2. The Variances for Each Population Are Equal.
3. The Samples Are Independent.
4. Measurements Are Interval or Ratio.

# Using the Flow Diagrams

**Example Problem:** A travel agent in Florida is interested in determining whether there is a difference in the mean out-of-pocket costs incurred by customers on two major cruise lines. To test this, she has selected a simple random sample of 20 customers who have taken cruise line I and has asked these people to track their costs over and above the fixed price of the cruise. She did the same for a second simple random sample of 15 people who took cruise line II.

You can use the flow diagrams to direct you to the appropriate statistical tool.

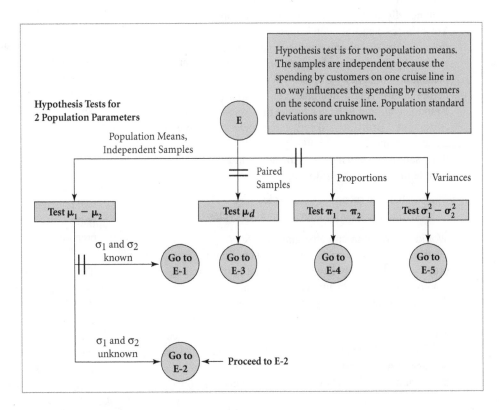

At E-2, we determine the null hypothesis to be

$$H_0: \mu_1 - \mu_2 = 0$$
$$H_A: \mu_1 - \mu_2 \neq 0$$

Next, we establish the test statistic as

$$t = \frac{(\bar{x}_1 - \bar{x}_2) - (\mu_1 - \mu_2)}{s_p\sqrt{\dfrac{1}{n_1} + \dfrac{1}{n_2}}}$$

where:

$$s_p = \sqrt{\frac{(n_1 - 1)s_1^2 + (n_2 - 1)s_2^2}{n_1 + n_2 - 2}}$$

Finally, the critical value is a $t$-value from the $t$-distribution with $20 + 15 - 2 = 33$ degrees of freedom. Note, if the degrees of freedom are not shown in the $t$ table, use Excel's **TINV** or use Minitab to determine the $t$-value.

Thus, by using the flow diagrams and answering a series of basic questions, you should be successful in identifying the statistical tools required to address any problem or application covered in Chapters 8 to 12. You are encouraged to apply this process to the application problems and projects listed here.

*MyStatLab*

# Exercises

## Integrative **Application Problems**

**SR.1.** Brandon Outdoor Advertising supplies neon signs to retail stores. A major complaint from its clients is that letters in the signs can burn out and leave the signs looking silly, depending on which letters stop working. The primary cause of neon letters not working is the failure of the starter unit attached to each letter. Starter units fail primarily based on turn-on/turn-off cycles. The present unit bought by Brandon averages 1,000 cycles before failure. A new manufacturer has approached Brandon claiming to have a model that is superior to the current unit. Brandon is skeptical but agrees to sample 50 starter units. It says it will buy from the new supplier if the sample results indicated the new unit is better. The sample of 50 gives the following values:

Sample mean = 1,010 cycles
Sample standard deviation = 48 cycles

Would you recommend changing suppliers?

**SR.2.** PestFree Chemicals has developed a new fungus preventative that may have a significant market among potato growers. Unfortunately, the actual extent of the fungus problem in any year depends on rainfall, temperature, and many other factors. To test the new chemical, PestFree has used it on 500 acres of potatoes and has used the leading competitor on an additional 500 acres. At the end of the season, 120 acres treated by the new chemical show significant levels of fungus infestation, whereas 160 of the acres treated by the leading chemical show significant infestation.

Do these data provide statistical proof that the new product is superior to the leading competitor?

**SR.3.** Last year Tucker Electronics decided to try to do something about turnover among assembly-line workers at its plants. It implemented two trial personnel policies, one based on an improved hiring policy and the other based on increasing worker responsibility. These policies were put into effect at two different plants, with the following results:

|  | Plant 1 | Plant 2 |
| --- | --- | --- |
|  | **Improved Hiring** | **Increased Responsibility** |
| Workers in trial group | 800 | 900 |
| Turnover proportion | 0.05 | 0.09 |

Do these data provide evidence that there is a difference between the turnover rates for the two trial policies?

**SR.4.** A Big 10 University has been approached by Wilson Sporting Goods. Wilson has developed a football designed specifically for practice sessions. Wilson would like to claim the ball will last for 500 practice hours before it needs to be replaced. Wilson has supplied six balls for use during spring and fall practice. The following data have been gathered on the time used before the ball must be replaced.

| Hours | |
|-------|-----|
| 551 | 511 |
| 479 | 435 |
| 440 | 466 |

Do you see anything wrong with Wilson claiming the ball will last 500 hours?

**SR.5.** The management of a chain of movie theaters believes the average weekend attendance at its downtown theater is greater than at its suburban theater. The following sample results were found from their accounting data.

| | Downtown | Suburban |
|---|---|---|
| Number of weekends | 11 | 10 |
| Average attendance | 855 | 750 |
| Sample variance | 1,684 | 1,439 |

Do these data provide sufficient evidence to indicate there is a difference in average attendance? The company is also interested in whether there is a significant difference in the variability of attendance.

**SR.6.** A large mail-order company has placed an order for 5,000 thermal-powered fans to sit on wood-burning stoves from a supplier in Canada, with the stipulation that no more than 2% of the units will be defective. To check the shipment, the company tests a random sample of 400 fans and finds 11 defective. Should this sample evidence lead the company to conclude the supplier has violated the terms of the contract?

**SR.7.** A manufacturer of automobile shock absorbers is interested in comparing the durability of its shocks with that of its two biggest competitors. To make the comparison, a set of one each of the manufacturer's and of the competitor's shocks were randomly selected and installed on the rear wheels of each of six randomly selected cars of the same type. After the cars had been driven 20,000 miles, the strength of each test shock was measured, coded, and recorded.

| Car number | Manufacturer's | Competitor 1 | Competitor 2 |
|---|---|---|---|
| 1 | 8.8 | 9.3 | 8.6 |
| 2 | 10.5 | 9.0 | 13.7 |
| 3 | 12.5 | 8.4 | 11.2 |
| 4 | 9.7 | 13.0 | 9.7 |
| 5 | 9.6 | 12.0 | 12.2 |
| 6 | 13.2 | 10.1 | 8.9 |

Do these data present sufficient evidence to conclude there is a difference in the mean strength of the three types of shocks after 20,000 miles?

**SR.8.** AstraZeneca is the maker of the stomach medicine Prilosec, which is the second-best-selling drug in the world. Recently, the company has come under close scrutiny concerning the cost of its medicines. The company's internal audit department selected a random sample of 300 purchases for Prilosec. They wished to characterize how much is being spent on this medicine. In the sample, the mean price per 20-milligram tablet of Prilosec was $2.70. The sample had a standard deviation of $0.30. Determine an estimate that will characterize the average range of values charged for a tablet of Prilosec.

**SR.9.** A manufacturer of PC monitors is interested in the effects that the type of glass and the type of phosphor used in the manufacturing process have on the brightness of the monitors. The director of research and development has received anecdotal evidence that the type of glass does not affect the brightness of the monitor as long as phosphor type 2 is used. However, the evidence seems to indicate that the type of glass does make a difference if two other phosphor types are used. Here are data to validate this anecdotal evidence.

| | Phosphor Type | | |
|---|---|---|---|
| Glass Type | 1 | 2 | 3 |
| 1 | 279 | 307 | 287 |
| | 254 | 313 | 290 |
| | 297 | 294 | 285 |
| 2 | 243 | 253 | 252 |
| | 245 | 232 | 236 |
| | 267 | 223 | 278 |

Conduct a procedure to verify or repudiate the anecdotal evidence.

**SR.10.** The Vilmore Corporation is considering two word processing programs for its PCs. One factor that will influence its decision is the ease of use in preparing a business report. Consequently, Jody Vilmore selected a random sample of nine typists from the clerical pool and asked them to type a typical report using both word processors. The typists then were timed (in seconds) to determine how quickly they could type one of the frequently used forms. The results were as follows.

| Typist | Processor 1 | Processor 2 |
|---|---|---|
| 1 | 82 | 75 |
| 2 | 76 | 80 |
| 3 | 90 | 70 |
| 4 | 55 | 58 |
| 5 | 49 | 53 |
| 6 | 82 | 75 |
| 7 | 90 | 80 |
| 8 | 45 | 45 |
| 9 | 70 | 80 |

Jody wishes to have an estimate of the smallest and biggest differences that might exist in the average time required for typing the business form using the two programs. Provide this information.

**SR.11.** The research department of an appliance manufacturing firm has developed a solid-state switch for its blender that the department claims will reduce the percentage of appliances being returned under the one-year full warranty by a range of 3% to 6%. To determine if the claim can be supported, the testing department selects a group of the blenders manufactured with the new switch and the old switch and subjects them to a normal year's worth of wear. Out of 250 blenders tested with the new switch, 9 would have been returned. Sixteen would have been returned out of the 250 blenders with the old switch. Use a statistical procedure to verify or refute the department's claim.

**SR.12.** The Ecco Company makes electronics products for distribution throughout the world. As a member of the quality department, you are interested in the warranty claims that are made by customers who have experienced problems with Ecco products. The file called **Ecco** contains data for a random sample of warranty claims. Large warranty claims not only cost the company money but also provide adverse publicity. The quality manager has asked you to provide her with a range of values that would represent the percentage of warranty claims filed for more than $300. Provide this information for your quality manager.

**END EXERCISES**

# Term Project Assignments

Investigate whether there are differences in grocery prices for three or more stores in your city.

a. Specify the type of testing procedure you will use.

b. What type of experimental design will be used? Why?

c. Develop a "typical" market basket of at least 10 items that you will price-check. Collect price data on these items at three or more different stores that sell groceries.

d. Analyze your price data using the testing procedure and experimental design you specified in parts a and b.

e. Present your findings in a report. Did you find differences in average prices of the "market basket" across the different grocery stores?

# Business Statistics Capstone Project

## Theme: Financial Data Analysis

### Project Objective:

The objective of this business statistics capstone project is to provide you with an opportunity to integrate the statistical tools and concepts that you have learned in your business statistics course. Like all real-world applications, it is not expected that through the completion of this project you will have utilized every statistical technique you have been taught in this course. Rather, an objective of the assignment will be for you to determine which of the statistical tools and techniques are appropriate to apply for the situation you have selected.

### Project Description:

Assume that you are working as an intern for a financial management company. Your employer has a large number of clients who trust the company managers to invest their funds. In your position, you have the responsibility for producing reports for clients when they request information. Your company has two large data files with financial information for a large number of U.S. companies. The first is called **US Companies 2003**, which contains financial information for the companies' 2001 or 2002 fiscal-year end. The second file is called **US Companies 2005**, which has data for the fiscal 2003 or 2004 year-end. The 2003 file has data for 7,441 companies. The 2005 file has data for 6,992 companies. Thus, many companies are listed in both files but some are just in one or the other.

The two files have many of the same variables, but the 2003 file has a larger range of financial variables than the 2005 file. For some companies, the data for certain variables are not available and a code of NA is used to so indicate. The 2003 file has a special worksheet containing the description of each variable. These descriptions apply to the 2005 data file as well.

You have been given access to these two data files for use in preparing your reports. Your role will be to perform certain statistical analyses that can be used to help convert these data into useful information in order to respond to the clients' questions.

This morning, one of the partners of your company received a call from a client who asked for a report that would compare companies in the financial services industry (SIC codes in the 6000's) to companies in production-oriented industries (SIC codes in the 2000's and 3000's) There are no firm guidelines on what the report should entail, but the partner has suggested the following:

- Start with the 2005 data file. Pull the data for all companies with the desired SIC codes into a new worksheet.

- Prepare a complete descriptive analysis of key financial variables using appropriate charts and graphs to help compare the two types of businesses.

- Determine whether there are statistical differences between the two classes of companies in terms of key financial measures.

- Using data from the 2003 file for companies that have these SIC codes and which are also in the 2005 file, develop a comparison that shows the changes over the time span both within SIC code grouping and between SIC code grouping.

### Project Deliverables:

To successfully complete this capstone project, you are required to deliver a management report that addresses the partner's requests (listed above) and also contains at least one other substantial type of analysis not mentioned by the partner. This latter work should be set off in a special section of the report.

The final report should be presented in a professional format using the style or format suggested by your instructor.

**Chapter 13 Quick Prep Links**

- **Review** the logic involved in testing a hypothesis discussed in Chapter 9.

- **Review** the characteristics of probability distributions such as the binomial, Poisson, uniform, and normal distributions in Chapters 5 and 6.

- **Review** the definitions of Type I and Type II errors in Chapter 9.

chapter **13**

# Goodness-of-Fit Tests and Contingency Analysis

## Why you need to know

The previous 12 chapters introduced a wide variety of statistical techniques that are frequently used in business decision making. We have discussed numerous descriptive tools and techniques, as well as estimation and hypothesis tests for one and two populations, hypothesis tests using the $t$-distribution, and analysis of variance. However, as we have often mentioned, these statistical tools are limited to use under those conditions for which they were originally developed. For example, the tests based on the standard normal distribution assume that the data can be measured at least at the interval level. The tests that employ the $t$-distribution assume that the sampled populations are normally distributed.

In those situations in which the conditions just mentioned are not satisfied, we suggest using nonparametric statistics. Several of the more widely used nonparametric techniques will be discussed in Chapter 17. These procedures will be shown to be generally the nonparametric equivalent of the classical procedures discussed in Chapters 8–12. The obvious questions when faced with a realistic decision-making situation are "Which test do I use? Should I consider a nonparametric test?" These questions are generally followed by a second question: "Do the data come from a normal distribution?" But recall that we also described situations involving data from Poisson or binomial distributions. How do we know which distribution applies to our situation? Fortunately, a statistical technique called *goodness-of-fit* exists that can help us answer this question. Using goodness-of-fit tests, we can decide whether a set of data comes from a specific hypothesized distribution.

You will also encounter many business situations in which the level of data measurement for the variable of interest is either nominal or ordinal, not interval or ratio. For example, a bank may use a code to indicate whether a customer is a good or poor credit risk. The bank may also have data for these customers that indicate, by a code, whether each person is buying or renting a home. The loan officer may be interested in determining whether credit-risk status is independent of home ownership. Because both credit risk and home ownership are qualitative, or categorical, variables, their measurement level is nominal and the statistical techniques introduced in Chapters 8–12 cannot be used to analyze this problem. We therefore need a new statistical tool to assist the manager in reaching an inference about the customer population. That statistical tool is contingency analysis. Contingency analysis is a widely used tool for analyzing the relationship between qualitative variables, one that decision makers in all business areas find helpful for data analysis.

**Chapter Outcome 1.** → # 13.1 Introduction to Goodness-of-Fit Tests

Many of the statistical procedures introduced in earlier chapters require that the sample data come from populations that are normally distributed. For example, when we use the *t*-distribution in confidence interval estimation or hypothesis testing about one or two population means, the population(s) of interest is (are) assumed to be normally distributed. The *F*-test introduced in Chapters 11 and 12 is based on the assumption that the populations are normally distributed. But how can you determine whether these assumptions are satisfied? In other instances, you may wish to employ a particular probability distribution to help solve a problem related to an actual business process. To solve the problem, you may find it necessary to know whether the actual data from the process fit the probability distribution being considered. In such instances, a statistical technique known as a *goodness-of-fit test* can be used.

The term *goodness-of-fit* aptly describes the technique. Suppose Macy's, a major retail department store, believes the proportions of customers who use each of the four entrances to its Portland, Oregon, store are the same. This would mean that customer arrivals are *uniformly* distributed across the four entrances. Suppose a sample of 1,000 customers is observed entering the store, and the entrance (East, West, North, South) selected by each customer is recorded. Table 13.1 shows the results of the sample. If the manager's assumption about the entrances being used uniformly holds and if there was no sampling error involved, we would expect one fourth of the customers, or 250, to enter through each door. When we allow for the potential of sampling error, we would still expect close to 250 customers to enter through each entrance. The question is, how "good is the fit" between the sample data in Table 13.1 and the expected number of 250 people at each entrance? At what point do we no longer believe that the differences between what is actually observed at each entrance and what we expected can be attributed to sampling error? If these differences get too big, we will reject the uniformity assumption and conclude that customers prefer some entrances to others.

**TABLE 13.1** │ **Customer Door Entrance Data**

| Entrance | Number of Customers |
|----------|---------------------|
| East | 260 |
| West | 290 |
| North | 230 |
| South | 220 |

## Chi-Square Goodness-of-Fit Test

The *chi-square goodness-of-fit test* is one of the statistical tests that can be used to determine whether the sample data come from any hypothesized distribution. Consider the following application.

**BUSINESS APPLICATION**   **CONDUCTING A GOODNESS-OF-FIT TEST**

**VISTA HEALTH GUARD** Vista Health Guard, a Pennsylvania health clinic with 25 offices, is open seven days a week. The operations manager was recently hired from a similar position at a smaller chain of clinics in Florida. She is naturally concerned that the level of staffing—physicians, nurses, and other support personnel—be balanced with patient demand.

Currently, the staffing level is balanced Monday through Friday, with reduced staffing on Saturday and Sunday. Her predecessor explained that patient demand is fairly level throughout the week and about 25% less on weekends, but the new manager suspects that the staff members want to have weekends free. Although she was willing to operate with this schedule for a while, she has decided to study patient demand to see whether the assumed demand pattern still applies.

The operations manager requested a random sample of 20 days for each day of the week that showed the number of patients on each of the sample days. A portion of those data follows:

| Day | Patient Count | Day | Patient Count |
|-----|---------------|-----|---------------|
| Monday, May 6 | 325 | Monday, July 15 | 323 |
| Monday, October 7 | 379 | Wednesday, April 3 | 467 |
| Tuesday, July 2 | 456 | etc. | etc. |

Graph of Actual Frequencies
for Vista Health Guard

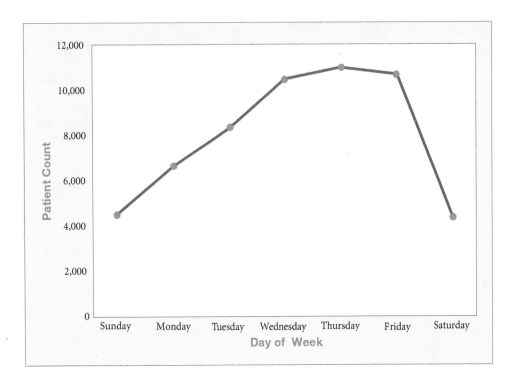

**TABLE 13.2** | **Patient Count Data for the Vista Health Guard Example**

| Day | Total Patient Count |
|---|---|
| Sunday | 4,502 |
| Monday | 6,623 |
| Tuesday | 8,308 |
| Wednesday | 10,420 |
| Thursday | 11,032 |
| Friday | 10,754 |
| Saturday | 4,361 |
| Total | 56,000 |

For the 140 days observed, the total count was 56,000 patients. The total patient counts for each day of the week are shown in Table 13.2 and are graphed in Figure 13.1.

Recall that the previous operations manager at Vista Health Guard based his staffing on the premise that from Monday to Friday the patient count remained essentially the same and on Saturdays and Sundays it went down 25%. If this is so, how many of the 56,000 patients would we expect on Monday? How many on Tuesday, and so forth? To figure out this demand, we determine weighting factors by allocating four units each to days Monday through Friday and three units each (representing the 25% reduction) to Saturday and Sunday. The total number of units is then $(5 \times 4) + (2 \times 3) = 26$. The proportion of total patients expected on each weekday is 4/26 and the proportion expected on each weekend day is 3/26. The expected number of patients on a weekday is $(4/26) \times 56,000 = 8,615.38$, and the expected number on each weekend day is $(3/26) \times 56,000 = 6,461.54$.

Figure 13.2 shows a graph with the actual sample data and the expected values. With the exception of what might be attributed to sampling error, if the distribution claimed by the previous operations manager is correct, the actual frequencies for each day of the week should fit quite closely with the expected frequencies. As you can see in Figure 13.2, the actual data and the expected data do not match perfectly. However, is the difference enough to warrant a change in staffing patterns? The situation facing Vista Health Guard is one for which a number of statistical tests have been developed. One of the most frequently used is the *chi-square goodness-of-fit test*. What we need to examine is how well the sample data fit the hypothesized distribution. The following null and alternative hypotheses can represent this:

$H_0$: The patient demand distribution is evenly spread through the weekdays and is 25% lower on the weekend.

$H_A$: The patient demand follows some other distribution.

Equation 13.1 is the equation for the chi-square goodness-of-fit test statistic. The logic behind this test is based on determining how far the actual *observed frequency* is from the *expected frequency*. Because we are interested in whether a difference exists, positive or negative, we remove the effect of negative values by squaring the differences. In addition, how important this difference is really depends on the magnitude of the expected frequency (e.g., a difference of 5 is more important if the expected frequency is 10 than if the expected

**FIGURE 13.2**

Actual and Expected
Frequencies for Vista Health
Guard

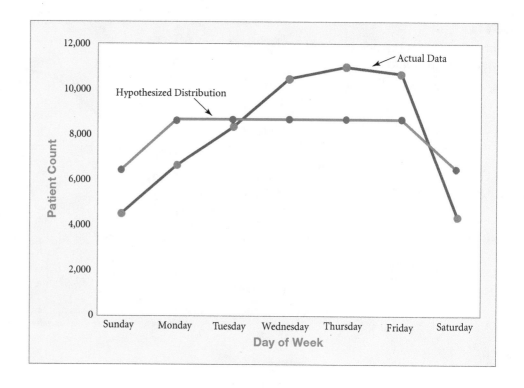

frequency is 1,000), so we divide the squared difference by the expected frequency. Finally, we sum these difference ratios for all days. This sum is a statistic that has an approximate chi-square distribution.

---

**Chi-Square Goodness-of-Fit Test Statistic**

$$\chi^2 = \sum_{i=1}^{k} \frac{(o_i - e_i)^2}{e_i}$$

**(13.1)**

where:

$o_i$ = Observed frequency for category $i$
$e_i$ = Expected frequency for category $i$
$k$ = Number of categories

---

The $\chi^2$ statistic is distributed approximately as a chi-square only if the sample size is large.

**Special Note**

A sample size of at least 30 is sufficient in most cases provided that none of the expected frequencies is too small.

This issue of expected cell frequencies will be discussed later. If the calculated chi-square statistic gets large, this is evidence to suggest that the fit of the actual data to the hypothesized distribution is not good and that the null hypothesis should be rejected.

Figure 13.3 shows the hypothesis-test process and results for this chi-square goodness-of-fit test. Note that the degrees of freedom for the chi-square test are equal to $k - 1$, where $k$ is the number of categories or observed cell frequencies. In this example, we have 7 categories corresponding to the days of the week, so the degrees of freedom are $7 - 1 = 6$. The critical value of 12.5916 is found in Appendix G for an upper-tail test with 6 degrees of freedom and a significance level of 0.05.

**FIGURE 13.3** |

Chi-Square Goodness-of-Fit
Test for Vista Health Guard

**Hypotheses:**

$H_0$: Patient demand is evenly spread through the weekdays and is 25% lower on weekends.
$H_A$: Patient demand follows some other distribution.

$\alpha = 0.05$

| | Total Patient Count | |
|---|---|---|
| | Observed | Expected |
| Day | $o_i$ | $e_i$ |
| Sunday | 4,502 | 6,461.54 |
| Monday | 6,623 | 8,615.38 |
| Tuesday | 8,308 | 8,615.38 |
| Wednesday | 10,420 | 8,615.38 |
| Thursday | 11,032 | 8,615.38 |
| Friday | 10,754 | 8,615.38 |
| Saturday | 4,361 | 6,461.54 |
| Total | 56,000 | 56,000 |

**Test Statistic:**

$$\chi^2 = \sum_{i=1}^{k} \frac{(o_i - e_i)^2}{e_i} = \frac{(4{,}502 - 6{,}461.54)^2}{6{,}461.54} + \frac{(6{,}623 - 8{,}615.38)^2}{8{,}615.38} + \cdots + \frac{(4{,}361 - 6{,}461.54)^2}{6{,}461.54}$$

$$\chi^2 = 594.2 + 460.8 + \cdots + 682.9$$

$$\chi^2 = 3{,}335.6$$

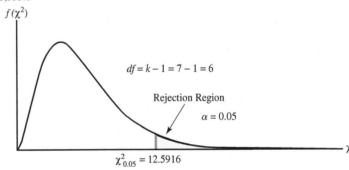

$df = k - 1 = 7 - 1 = 6$

Rejection Region

$\alpha = 0.05$

$\chi^2_{0.05} = 12.5916$

**Decision Rule:**

If $\chi^2 > 12.5916$, reject $H_0$.
Otherwise, do not reject $H_0$.

Because $3{,}335.6 > 12.5916$, reject $H_0$.
Based on the sample data, we can conclude that the patient distribution is not the same as previously indicated.

As Figure 13.3 indicates, $\chi^2 = 3{,}335.6 > 12.5916$, so the null hypothesis is rejected and we should conclude that the demand pattern does not match the previously defined distribution. The data in Figure 13.3 indicate that demand is heavier than expected Wednesday through Friday and less than expected on the other days. The operations manager may now wish to increase staffing on Wednesday, Thursday, and Friday to more closely approximate current demand patterns.

---

**EXAMPLE 13-1**　　**CHI-SQUARE GOODNESS-OF-FIT TEST**

**Standardized Exams** Now that you are in college you have already taken a number of standardized exams such as the SAT and ACT exams. A Southern California company that creates standardized exams a variety of organizations use for applications such as employee aptitude assessment, tries to develop multiple choice questions that are not so difficult that those taking the exams are forced to guess at the answers to most questions. Recently, the company received a complaint about one of the math problems on an exam. The problem listed five possible answers. If the test takers were forced to guess, the company might expect an even percentage of choices across the five possible answers. That is, each answer is as likely to be a guess as any other answer. To determine if people were actually forced to guess, the company plans to conduct a study to see if the choices on this question are in fact *uniformly distributed* across the five answers. A chi-square goodness-of-fit test can be conducted to determine whether test takers are forced to guess at the answer using the following steps:

**Step 1   Formulate the appropriate null and alternative hypotheses.**
Because the number of selected choices is supposed to be the same across the five possible answers, the following null and alternative hypotheses are formed:

$H_0$: Distribution of choices is uniform across the five answers.

$H_A$: Distribution of choices is not uniform.

**Step 2   Specify the significance level.**
The test will be conducted using $\alpha = 0.05$.

**Step 3   Determine the critical value.**
The critical value for the goodness-of-fit test is a chi-square value from the chi-square distribution, with $k - 1 = 5 - 1 = 4$ degrees of freedom, and $\alpha = 0.05$ is 9.4877.

**Step 4   Collect the sample data and compute the chi-square test statistic.**
A random sample of the responses to the exam question for 2,120 people is selected. The following data represent the number of times each of the possible answers was chosen:

| Answer | 1 | 2 | 3 | 4 | 5 |
|---|---|---|---|---|---|
| Times Selected | 358 | 402 | 577 | 403 | 380 |

Under the hypothesis of a uniform distribution, 20% of this total (424) should be selected for each answer. This is the expected cell frequency.

Equation 13.1 is used to form the test statistic based on these sample data.

$$\chi^2 = \sum_{i=1}^{k} \frac{(o_i - e_i)^2}{e_i} = \frac{(358 - 424)^2}{424} + \frac{(402 - 424)^2}{424}$$
$$+ \frac{(577 - 424)^2}{424} + \frac{(403 - 424)^2}{424} + \frac{(380 - 424)^2}{424}$$
$$= 72.231$$

**Step 5   Reach a decision.**
The decision rule is

If $\chi^2 > 9.4877$, reject $H_0$.

Otherwise, do not reject $H_0$.

Because $\chi^2 = 72.231 > 9.4877$, reject the null hypothesis.

**Step 6   Draw a conclusion.**
We conclude that the answer choices are not occurring equally across the five possible answers. This is evidence to suggest that this particular question is not being answered by random guessing.

>> **END EXAMPLE**

**TRY PROBLEM** 13-2 (pg. 559)

**Excel and Minitab Tutorial**

**BUSINESS APPLICATION**   **USING SOFTWARE TO CONDUCT A GOODNESS-OF-FIT TEST**

**WOODTRIM PRODUCTS, INC.** Woodtrim Products, Inc., makes wood moldings, doorframes, and window frames. It purchases lumber from mills throughout New England and eastern Canada. The first step in the production process is to rip the lumber into narrower strips. Different widths are used for different products. For example, wider pieces with no imperfections are used to make door and window frames. Once an operator decides on the appropriate width, that information is locked into a computer and a ripsaw automatically cuts the board to the desired size. The manufacturer of the saw claims that the ripsaw cuts an average deviation of zero from target and that the differences from target will be normally distributed, with a standard deviation of 0.01 inch.

Woodtrim has recently become concerned that the ripsaw may not be cutting to the manufacturer's specifications because operators at other machines downstream in the production process are finding excessive numbers of ripped pieces that are too wide or too narrow.

A quality improvement team (QIT) has started to investigate the problem. Team members selected a random sample of 300 boards just as they came off the ripsaw. To provide a measure of control, the only pieces sampled in the initial study had stated widths of 2⅞ (2.875) inches. Each piece's width was measured halfway from its end. A portion of the data and the differences between the target 2.875 inches and the actual measured width are shown in Figure 13.4. The full data set is contained in the file **Woodtrim**. The team can use these data and the chi-square goodness-of-fit testing procedure to test the following null and alternative hypotheses:

$H_0$: The differences are normally distributed, with $\mu = 0$ and $\sigma = 0.01$.
$H_A$: The differences are not normally distributed, with $\mu = 0$ and $\sigma = 0.01$.

This example differs slightly from the previous examples because the hypothesized distribution is continuous rather than discrete. Thus, we must organize the data into a grouped-data frequency distribution (see Chapter 2), as shown in Figure 13.5. Our choice of classes requires careful consideration. The chi-square goodness-of-fit test compares the actual cell frequencies with the expected cell frequencies. The test statistic from Equation 13.1,

$$\chi^2 = \sum_{i=1}^{k} \frac{(o_i - e_i)^2}{e_i}$$

is approximately chi-square distributed if the expected cell frequencies are large. Because the expected cell frequencies are used in computing the test statistic, the general recommendation is that the goodness-of-fit test be performed only when all expected cell frequencies are at least 5. If any of the cells have expected frequencies less than 5, the cells should be combined in a meaningful way such that the expected frequencies are at least 5. We have chosen to use $k = 6$ classes. The number of classes is your choice. You can perform the chi-square goodness-of-fit

**FIGURE 13.4**

Woodtrim Products Test Data

Excel 2007 Instruction:
1. Open file: Woodtrim.xls.

| | A | B | C | D |
|---|---|---|---|---|
| 1 | Sample | Actual Width | Target Width | Difference |
| 2 | 1 | 2.870 | 2.875 | -0.005 |
| 3 | 2 | 2.863 | 2.875 | -0.012 |
| 4 | 3 | 2.885 | 2.875 | 0.010 |
| 5 | 4 | 2.872 | 2.875 | -0.003 |
| 6 | 5 | 2.891 | 2.875 | 0.016 |
| 7 | 6 | 2.893 | 2.875 | 0.018 |
| 8 | 7 | 2.868 | 2.875 | -0.007 |
| 9 | 8 | 2.861 | 2.875 | -0.014 |

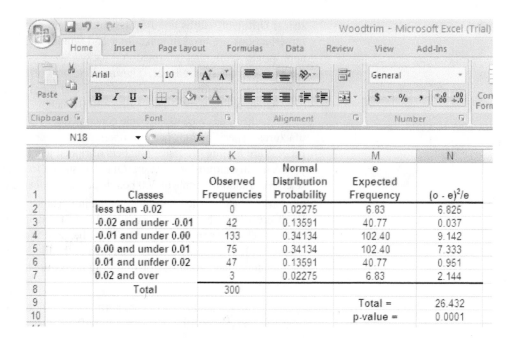

| Classes | o Observed Frequencies | Normal Distribution Probability | e Expected Frequency | $(o - e)^2/e$ |
|---|---|---|---|---|
| less than -0.02 | 0 | 0.02275 | 6.83 | 6.825 |
| -0.02 and under -0.01 | 42 | 0.13591 | 40.77 | 0.037 |
| -0.01 and under 0.00 | 133 | 0.34134 | 102.40 | 9.142 |
| 0.00 and umder 0.01 | 75 | 0.34134 | 102.40 | 7.333 |
| 0.01 and unfder 0.02 | 47 | 0.13591 | 40.77 | 0.951 |
| 0.02 and over | 3 | 0.02275 | 6.83 | 2.144 |
| Total | 300 | | | |
| | | | Total = | 26.432 |
| | | | p-value = | 0.0001 |

**Excel 2007 Instructions:**

1. Open file: Woodtrim.xls (see Figure 13.4).
2. Define Classes (column J).
3. Determine observed frequencies [(i.e., cell K4 formula is =COUNTIF($D$2: $D$301,"<0.0")-SUM($K$2:K3)].
4. Determine normal distribution probabilities, assuming the mean = 0.0 and st.dev = 0.01 [ i.e., cell L4 formula is =NORMDIST(0,0,0.01,TRUE)-SUM ($L$2:L3)].

5. Determine expected frequencies by multiplying normal probability by the sample size $(n = 300)$.
6. Compute values for chi-square in column N (cell N5 formula is =[K5-M5)^2/M5].
7. Sum column N to get chi-square statistic.
8. Find p-value using **CHITEST** function [cell N10 formula is =**CHITEST(K2:K7, M2:M7)**].

test using Excel functions and formulas and Minitab commands. (The Excel and Minitab tutorials that accompany this text take you through the specific steps required to complete this example.) Figure 13.5 shows the normal distribution probabilities, expected cell frequencies, and the chi-square calculation. The calculated chi-square statistic is $x^2 = 26.432$. The p-value associated with $x^2 = 26.432$ and $6 - 1 = 5$ degrees of freedom is 0.0001. Therefore, because p-value = 0.0001 is less than any reasonable level of alpha, we reject the null hypothesis and conclude the ripsaw is not currently meeting the manufacturer's specification. The saw errors are not normally distributed with mean equal to 0 and a standard deviation equal to 0.01.

**Special Note**

Note that in this case, because the null hypothesis specified both the mean and the standard deviation, the normal distribution probabilities were computed using these values. However, if the mean and/or the standard deviation had not been specified, the sample mean and standard deviation would be used in the probability computation. You would lose 1 additional degree of freedom for each parameter that was estimated from the sample data. This is true any time sample statistics are specified in place of population parameters in the hypothesis.

Minitab has a procedure for performing a goodness-of-fit test for a normal distribution. In fact, it offers three different approaches, none of which are exactly the chi-square approach

**FIGURE 13.6**

Minitab Output—Test of Normal-Distributed Ripsaw Cuts for the Woodtrim Example

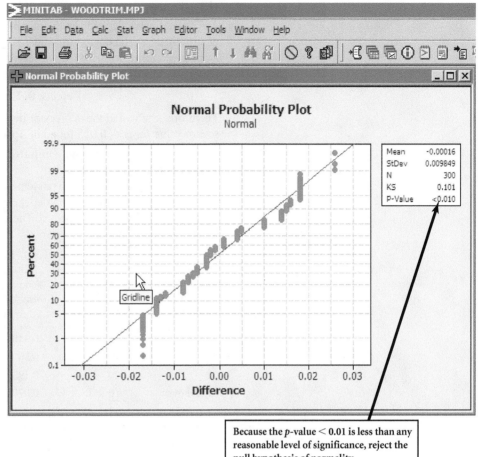

**Minitab Instructions:**

1. Open file: Woodtrim.MTW.
2. Choose **Stat > Basic Statistics > Normality Test**.
3. In **Variable**, enter data column *(Difference)*.
4. Under Normality test, select **Kolmogorov-Smirnov**.
5. Click **OK**.

Because the *p*-value < 0.01 is less than any reasonable level of significance, reject the null hypothesis of normality.

just outlined. Figure 13.6 shows the Minitab results for the Woodtrim example. Consistent with our other Minitab and Excel results, this output illustrates that the null hypothesis should be rejected because the *p*-value < 0.01.

**EXAMPLE 13-2    GOODNESS-OF-FIT TEST**

**Early Dawn Egg Company** The Early Dawn Egg Company operates an egg-producing operation in Maine. One of the key steps in the egg-production business is packaging eggs into cartons so that eggs arrive at stores unbroken. That means the eggs have to leave the Early Dawn plant unbroken. Because of the high volumes of egg cartons shipped each day, the employees at Early Dawn can't inspect every carton of eggs. Instead, every hour, 10 cartons are inspected. If two or more contain broken or cracked eggs, a full inspection is done for all eggs produced since the previous inspection an hour earlier. If the inspectors find one or fewer cartons containing cracked or broken eggs, they ship that hour's production without further analysis. The company's contract with retailers calls for at most 10% of the egg cartons to have broken or cracked eggs. At issue is whether Early Dawn Egg Company managers can evaluate this sampling plan using a binomial distribution with $n = 10$ and $\pi = 0.10$. To test this, a goodness-of-fit test can be performed using the following steps:

**Step 1  State the appropriate null and alternative hypotheses.**
In this case, the null and alternative hypotheses are

$H_0$: Distribution of defects is binomial, with $n = 10$ and $\pi = 0.10$.
$H_A$: Distribution is not binomial, with $n = 10$ and $\pi = 0.10$.

**Step 2  Specify the level of significance.**
The test will be conducted using $\alpha = 0.025$.

Step 3   **Determine the critical value.**
The critical value depends on the number of degrees of freedom and the level of significance. The degrees of freedom will be equal to $k - 1$, where $k$ is the number of categories for which observed and expected frequencies will be recorded. In this case, the managers have set up the following groups:

Defects: 0  1  2  3 and over

Therefore, $k = 4$, and the degrees of freedom are $4 - 1 = 3$. The critical chi-square value for $\alpha = 0.025$ found in Appendix G is 9.3484.

Step 4   **Collect the sample data and compute the chi-square test statistic using Equation 13.1.**
The company selected a simple random sample of 100 hourly test results from past production records and recorded the number of defective cartons when the sample of 10 cartons was inspected. The following table shows the computations for the chi-square statistic.

| Defective Cartons | $o$ Observed Defects | Binomial Probability $n = 10$, $\pi = 0.10$ | $e$ Expected Frequency | $\dfrac{(o_i - e_i)^2}{e_i}$ |
|---|---|---|---|---|
| 0 | 30 | 0.3487 | 34.87 | 0.6802 |
| 1 | 40 | 0.3874 | 38.74 | 0.0410 |
| 2 | 20 | 0.1937 | 19.37 | 0.0205 |
| 3 and over | 10 | 0.0702 | 7.02 | 1.2650 |
| Total | 100 | | | 2.0067 |

The calculated chi-square test statistic is $\chi^2 = 2.0067$.

Step 5   **Reach a decision.**
Because $\chi^2 = 2.0067$ is less than the critical value of 9.3484, we do not reject the null hypothesis.

Step 6   **Draw a conclusion.**
The binomial distribution may be the appropriate distribution to describe the company's sampling plan.

**>>END EXAMPLE**

**TRY PROBLEM** 13-1 (pg. 559)

---

**EXAMPLE 13-3**   **GOODNESS-OF-FIT TEST**

University Internet Service Students in a computer information systems class at a major university have established an Internet service provider (ISP) company for the university's students, faculty, and staff. Customers of this ISP connect via a wireless signal available throughout the campus and surrounding business area. Capacity is always an issue for an ISP, and the students had to estimate the capacity demands for their service. Before opening for business, the students conducted a survey of likely customers. Based on this survey, they estimated that demand during the late afternoon and evening hours is Poisson distributed (refer to Chapter 5) with a mean equal to 10 users per hour. Based on this assumption, the students developed the ISP with the capacity to handle 20 users simultaneously. However, they have lately been receiving complaints from customers saying they have been denied access to the system because 20 users are already online. The students are now interested in determining whether the demand distribution is still Poisson distributed with a mean equal to 10 per hour. To test this, they have collected data on the number of user requests for ISP access for 225 randomly selected time periods during the heavy-use hours. The following steps can be used to conduct the statistical test:

**Step 1** **State the appropriate null and alternative hypotheses.**

The null and alternative hypotheses are

$H_0$: Demand distribution is Poisson distributed with mean equal to 10 users per time period.

$H_A$: The demand distribution is not distributed as a Poisson distribution with mean equal to 10 per period.

**Step 2** **Specify the level of significance.**

The hypothesis test will be conducted using $\alpha = 0.05$.

**Step 3** **Determine the critical value.**

The critical value depends on the level of significance and the number of degrees of freedom. The degrees of freedom is equal to $k - 1$, where $k$ is the number of categories. In this case, after collapsing the categories to get the expected frequencies to be at least 5, we have 13 categories. Thus, the degrees of freedom for the chi-square critical value is $13 - 1 = 12$. For 12 degrees of freedom and a level of significance equal to 0.05, from Appendix G we find a critical value of $X^2 = 21.0261$. Thus the decision rule is

If $X^2 > 21.0261$, reject the null hypothesis.

Otherwise, do not reject.

**Step 4** **Collect the sample data and compute the chi-square test statistic using Equation 13.1.**

A random sample of 225 time periods was selected, and the number of users requesting access to the ISP at each time period was recorded. The observed frequencies based on the sample data are as follows:

| Number of Requests | Observed Frequency | Number of Requests | Observed Frequency |
|---|---|---|---|
| 0 | 0 | 10 | 18 |
| 1 | 2 | 11 | 14 |
| 2 | 1 | 12 | 17 |
| 3 | 3 | 13 | 18 |
| 4 | 4 | 14 | 25 |
| 5 | 3 | 15 | 28 |
| 6 | 8 | 16 | 23 |
| 7 | 6 | 17 | 17 |
| 8 | 11 | 18 | 9 |
| 9 | 7 | 19 and over | 11 |
| | | Total | 225 |

To compute the chi-square test statistic you must determine the expected frequencies. Start by determining the probability for each number of user requests based on the hypothesized distribution. (Poisson with $\lambda t = 10$.)

The expected frequencies are calculated by multiplying the probability by the total observed frequency of 225. These results are as follows:

| Number of Requests | Observed Frequency | Poisson Probability $\lambda t = 10$ | Expected Frequency |
|---|---|---|---|
| 0 | 0 | 0.0000 | 0.00 |
| 1 | 2 | 0.0005 | 0.11 |
| 2 | 1 | 0.0023 | 0.52 |
| 3 | 3 | 0.0076 | 1.71 |
| 4 | 4 | 0.0189 | 4.25 |
| 5 | 3 | 0.0378 | 8.51 |
| 6 | 8 | 0.0631 | 14.20 |
| 7 | 6 | 0.0901 | 20.27 |
| 8 | 11 | 0.1126 | 25.34 |
| 9 | 7 | 0.1251 | 28.15 |
| 10 | 18 | 0.1251 | 28.15 |
| 11 | 14 | 0.1137 | 25.58 |
| 12 | 17 | 0.0948 | 21.33 |
| 13 | 18 | 0.0729 | 16.40 |
| 14 | 25 | 0.0521 | 11.72 |
| 15 | 28 | 0.0347 | 7.81 |
| 16 | 23 | 0.0217 | 4.88 |
| 17 | 17 | 0.0128 | 2.88 |
| 18 | 9 | 0.0071 | 1.60 |
| 19 and over | 11 | 0.0072 | 1.62 |
| Total | 225 | 1 | 225 |

Now you need to check if any of the expected cell frequencies are less than 5. In this case, we see there are several instances where this is so. To deal with this, collapse categories so that all expected frequencies are at least 5. Doing this gives the following:

| Number of Requests | Observed Frequency | Poisson Probability $\lambda t = 10$ | Expected Frequency |
|---|---|---|---|
| 4 or fewer | 10 | 0.0293 | 6.59 |
| 5 | 3 | 0.0378 | 8.51 |
| 6 | 8 | 0.0631 | 14.20 |
| 7 | 6 | 0.0901 | 20.27 |
| 8 | 11 | 0.1126 | 25.34 |
| 9 | 7 | 0.1251 | 28.15 |
| 10 | 18 | 0.1251 | 28.15 |
| 11 | 14 | 0.1137 | 25.58 |
| 12 | 17 | 0.0948 | 21.33 |
| 13 | 18 | 0.0729 | 16.40 |
| 14 | 25 | 0.0521 | 11.72 |
| 15 | 28 | 0.0347 | 7.81 |
| 16 or more | 60 | 0.0488 | 10.98 |
| Total | 225 | 1 | 225 |

Now we can compute the chi-square test statistic using Equation 13.1 as follows:

$$\chi^2 = \sum_{i=1}^{k} \frac{(o_i - e_i)^2}{e_i}$$

$$= \frac{(10 - 6.59)^2}{6.59} + \frac{(3 - 8.51)^2}{8.51} + \cdots + \frac{(60 - 10.98)^2}{10.98}$$

$$= 338.1$$

**Step 5  Reach a decision.**
Because $\chi^2 = 338.1 > 21.0261$, reject the null hypothesis.

**Step 6  Draw a conclusion.**
The demand distribution is not Poisson distributed with a mean of 10. The students should conclude that either the mean demand per period has increased from 10 or the distribution is not Poisson or both. They may need to add more capacity to the ISP business.

>>END EXAMPLE

TRY PROBLEM 13-3 (pg. 559)

# 13-1: Exercises

## Skill Development

**13-1.** A large retailer receives shipments of batteries for consumer electronic products in packages of 50 batteries. The packages are held at a distribution center and are shipped to retail stores as requested. Because some packages may contain defective batteries, the retailer randomly samples 400 packages from its distribution center and tests to determine whether the batteries are defective or not. The most recent sample of 400 packages revealed the following observed frequencies for defective batteries per package:

| # of Defective Batteries per Package | Frequency of Occurrence |
|:---:|:---:|
| 0 | 165 |
| 1 | 133 |
| 2 | 65 |
| 3 | 28 |
| 4 or more | 9 |

The retailer's managers would like to know if they can evaluate this sampling plan using a binomial distribution with $n = 50$ and $\pi = 0.02$. Test at the $\alpha = 0.01$ level of significance.

**13-2.** The following frequency distribution shows the number of times an outcome was observed from the toss of a die. Based on the frequencies that were observed from 2,400 tosses of the die, can it be concluded at the 0.05 level of significance that the die is fair?

| Outcome | Frequency |
|:---:|:---:|
| 1 | 352 |
| 2 | 418 |
| 3 | 434 |
| 4 | 480 |
| 5 | 341 |
| 6 | 375 |

**13-3.** Based on the sample data in the following frequency distribution, conduct a test to determine whether the population from which the sample data were selected is Poisson distributed with mean equal to 6. Test using $\alpha = 0.05$.

| x | Frequency | x | Frequency |
|:---:|:---:|:---:|:---:|
| 2 or less | 7 | 9 | 53 |
| 3 | 29 | 10 | 35 |
| 4 | 26 | 11 | 28 |
| 5 | 52 | 12 | 18 |
| 6 | 77 | 13 | 13 |
| 7 | 77 | 14 or more | 13 |
| 8 | 72 | Total | 500 |

**13-4.** A chi-square goodness-of-fit test is to be conducted to test whether a population is normally distributed. No statement has been made regarding the value of the population mean and standard deviation. A frequency distribution has been formed based on a random sample of 1,000 values. The frequency distribution has $k = 8$ classes. Assuming that the test is to be conducted at the $\alpha = 0.10$ level, determine the correct decision rule to be used.

**13-5.** An experiment is run that is claimed to have a binomial distribution with $\pi = 0.15$ and $n = 18$ and the number of successes is recorded. The experiment is conducted 200 times with the following results:

| Number of Successes | 0 | 1 | 2 | 3 | 4 | 5 |
|---|---|---|---|---|---|---|
| Observed Frequency | 80 | 75 | 39 | 6 | 0 | 0 |

Using a significance level of 0.01, is there sufficient evidence to conclude that the distribution is binomially distributed with $\pi = 0.15$ and $n = 18$?

**13-6.** Data collected from a hospital emergency room reflect the number of patients per day that visited the emergency room due to cardiac-related symptoms. It is believed that the distribution of the number of cardiac patients entering the emergency room per day over a two-month period has a Poisson distribution with a mean of 8 patients per day.

| | | | | | | | | | |
|---|---|---|---|---|---|---|---|---|---|
| 6 | 7 | 9 | 7 | 5 | 6 | 7 | 7 | 5 | 10 |
| 9 | 9 | 7 | 2 | 8 | 5 | 7 | 10 | 6 | 7 |
| 12 | 12 | 10 | 8 | 8 | 14 | 7 | 9 | 10 | 7 |
| 4 | 9 | 6 | 4 | 11 | 9 | 10 | 7 | 5 | 10 |
| 8 | 8 | 10 | 7 | 9 | 2 | 10 | 12 | 10 | 9 |
| 8 | 11 | 7 | 9 | 11 | 7 | 16 | 7 | 9 | 10 |

Use a chi-square goodness-of-fit test to determine if the data come from a Poisson distribution with mean of 8. Test using a significance level of 0.01.

## Business **Applications**

**13-7.** HSBC Bank is a large, London-based international banking company. One of its most important sources of income is home loans. A component of its effort to maintain and increase its customer base is excellent service. The loan manager at one of its branches in New York keeps track of the number of loan applicants who visit his branch's loan department per week. Having enough loan officers available is one of the ways of providing excellent service. Over the last year, the loan manager accumulated the following data:

| Number of Customers | 0 | 1 | 2 | 3 | 4 | 5 | $\geq 6$ |
|---|---|---|---|---|---|---|---|
| Frequencies | | 1 | 2 | 9 | 11 | 14 | 6 | 9 |

From previous years, the manager believes that the distribution of the number of customer arrivals has a Poisson distribution with an average of 3.5 loan applicants per week. Determine if the loan officer's belief is correct using a significance level of 0.025.

**13-8.** Managers of a major book publisher believe that the occurrence of typographical errors in the books the company publishes is Poisson distributed with a mean of 0.2 per page. Because of some customer quality complaints, the managers have arranged for a test to be conducted to determine if the error distribution still holds. A total of 400 pages were randomly selected and the number of errors per page was counted. These data are summarized in the following frequency distribution:

| Errors | Frequency |
|---|---|
| 0 | 335 |
| 1 | 56 |
| 2 | 7 |
| 3 | 2 |
| Total | 400 |

Conduct the appropriate hypothesis test using a significance level equal to 0.01. Discuss the results.

**13-9.** The Baltimore Steel and Pipe Company recently developed a new pipe product for a customer. According to specifications, the pipe is supposed to have an average outside diameter of 2.00 inches with a standard deviation equal to 0.10 inch, and the distribution of outside diameters is to be normally distributed. Before going into full-scale production, the company selected a random sample of 30 sections of pipe from the initial test run. The following data were recorded:

| Pipe Section | Diameter (inches) | Pipe Section | Diameter (inches) |
|---|---|---|---|
| 1 | 2.04 | 16 | 1.96 |
| 2 | 2.13 | 17 | 1.89 |
| 3 | 2.07 | 18 | 1.99 |
| 4 | 1.99 | 19 | 2.13 |
| 5 | 1.90 | 20 | 1.90 |
| 6 | 2.06 | 21 | 1.91 |
| 7 | 2.19 | 22 | 1.95 |
| 8 | 2.01 | 23 | 2.18 |
| 9 | 2.05 | 24 | 1.94 |
| 10 | 1.98 | 25 | 1.93 |
| 11 | 1.95 | 26 | 2.08 |
| 12 | 1.90 | 27 | 1.82 |
| 13 | 2.10 | 28 | 1.94 |
| 14 | 2.02 | 29 | 1.96 |
| 15 | 2.11 | 30 | 1.81 |

a. Using a significance level of 0.01, perform the appropriate test.
b. Based on these data, should the company conclude that it is meeting the product specifications? Explain your reasoning.

**13-10.** Quality control managers work in every type of production environment possible, from producing dictionaries to dowel cutting for boat plugs. The Cincinnati Dowel & Wood Products Co., located in

Mount Orab, Ohio, manufactures wood dowels and wood turnings. Four-inch-diameter boat plugs are one of its products. The quality control procedures aimed at maintaining the 4-inch diameter are only valid if the diameters have a normal distribution. The quality control manager recently obtained the following summary diameters taken from randomly selected boat plugs on the production line:

| Interval | Frequency | Interval | Frequency |
|----------|-----------|----------|-----------|
| < 3.872 | 4 | 4.001–4.025 | 8 |
| 3.872–3.916 | 6 | 4.026–4.052 | 2 |
| 3.917–3.948 | 11 | 4.053–4.084 | 4 |
| 3.949–3.975 | 9 | 4.085–4.128 | 0 |
| 3.976–4.000 | 5 | > 4.128 | 1 |

The boat plug diameters are specified to have a normal distribution with a mean of 4 inches and a standard deviation of 0.10. Determine if the distribution of the 4-inch boat plugs is currently adhering to specification. Use a chi-square goodness-of-fit test and a significance level of 0.05.

## Computer Database Exercises

**13-11.** The owners of Big Boy Burgers are considering remodeling their facility to include a drive-thru window. There will be room for three cars in the drive-thru line if they build it. However, they are concerned that the capacity may be too low during their busy lunch time hours between 11:00 A.M. and 1:30 P.M. One of the factors they need to know is the distribution of the length of time it takes to fill an order for cars coming to the drive-thru. To collect information on this, the owners have received permission from a similar operation owned by a relative in a nearby town to collect some data at that drive-thru. The data in the file called **Clair's Deli** reflect the service time per car.

Based on these sample data, is there sufficient evidence to conclude that the distribution of service time is not normally distributed? Test using the chi-square distribution and $\alpha = 0.05$.

**13-12.** Executives at The Walt Disney Company are interested in estimating the mean spending per capita for people who visit Disney World in Orlando, Florida. Since they do not know the population standard deviation, they plan to use the $t$-distribution (see Chapter 9) to conduct the test. However, they realize that the $t$-distribution requires that the population be normally distributed. Six hundred customers were randomly surveyed, and the amount spent during their stay at Disney World was recorded. These data are in the file called **Disney**. Before using these sample data to estimate the population mean, the managers wish to test to determine whether the population is normally distributed.
a. State the appropriate null and alternative hypotheses.

b. Organize the data into six classes and form the grouped data frequency distribution (refer to Chapter 2).
c. Using the sample mean and sample standard deviation, calculate the expected frequencies, assuming that the null hypothesis is true.
d. Conduct the test statistic and compare it to the appropriate critical value for a significance level equal to 0.05. What conclusion should be reached? Discuss.

**13-13.** Again, working with the data in Problem 13-11, the number of cars that arrive in each 10-minute period is another factor that will determine whether there will be the capacity to handle the drive-thru business. In addition to studying the service times, the owners also counted the number of cars that arrived at the deli in the nearby town in a sample of 10-minute time periods. These data are as follows:

| | | |
|---|---|---|
| 3 | 2 | 0 |
| 2 | 3 | 3 |
| 3 | 3 | 3 |
| 0 | 2 | 3 |
| 0 | 3 | 3 |
| 1 | 1 | 0 |
| 2 | 4 | 9 |
| 1 | 2 | 4 |
| 2 | 1 | 1 |
| 4 | 1 | 3 |

Based on these data, is there evidence to conclude that the arrivals are not Poisson distributed? State the appropriate null and alternative hypotheses and test using a significance level of 0.025.

**13-14.** Damage to homes caused by burst piping can be expensive to repair. By the time the leak is discovered, hundreds of gallons of water may have already flooded the home. Automatic shutoff valves can prevent extensive water damage from plumbing failures. The valves contain sensors that cut off water flow in the event of a leak, thereby preventing flooding. One important characteristic is the time (in milliseconds) required for the sensor to detect the water flow. The data obtained for four different shutoff valves are contained in the file entitled **Waterflow**. The differences between the observed time for the sensor to detect the water flow and the predicted time (termed *residuals*) are listed and are assumed to be normally distributed. Using the four sets of residuals given in the data file, determine if the residuals have a normal distribution. Use a chi-square goodness-of-fit test and a significance level of 0.05. Use five groups of equal width to conduct the test.

**13-15.** An article in the *San Francisco Chronicle* indicated that just 38% of drivers crossing the San Francisco Bay Area's seven state-owned bridges pay their tolls electronically, compared with rates nearing 80% at systems elsewhere in the nation. Albert Yee, director of highway and arterial operations for the regional Metropolitan Transportation Commission, indicated that the commission is eager to drive up the percentage of tolls paid electronically. In an attempt to see if its efforts are producing the required results, 15 vehicles each day are tracked through the toll lanes of the Bay Area bridges. The number of drivers using electronic payment to pay their toll for a period of three months appears in the file entitled **Fastrak**.

a. Determine if the distribution of the number of FasTrak users could be described as a binomial distribution with a population proportion equal to 0.50. Use a chi-square goodness-of-fit test and a significance level of 0.05.

b. Conduct a test of hypothesis to determine if the percent of tolls paid electronically has increased to more than 70% since Yee's efforts.

**END EXERCISES 13-1**

**Chapter Outcome 2.** → # 13.2 Introduction to Contingency Analysis

In Chapters 9 and 10 you were introduced to hypothesis tests involving one and two population proportions. Although these techniques are useful in many cases, you will also encounter many situations involving multiple population proportions. For example, a mutual fund company offers six different mutual funds. The president of the company may wish to determine if the proportion of customers selecting each mutual fund is related to the four sales regions in which the customers reside. A hospital administrator who collects service-satisfaction data from patients might be interested in determining whether there is a significant difference in patient rating by hospital department. A personnel manager for a large corporation might be interested in determining whether there is a relationship between level of employee job satisfaction and job classification. In each of these cases, the proportions relate to characteristic categories of the variable of interest. The six mutual funds, four sales regions, hospital departments, and job classifications are all specific categories.

These situations involving categorical data call for a new statistical tool known as *contingency analysis* to help make decisions when multiple proportions are involved. Contingency analysis can be used when a level of data measurement is either nominal or ordinal and the values are determined by counting the number of occurrences in each category.

## 2 × 2 Contingency Tables

**BUSINESS APPLICATION** APPLYING CONTINGENCY ANALYSIS

**DALGARNO PHOTO, INC.** Dalgarno Photo, Inc., gets much of its business from taking photographs for college yearbooks. Dalgarno hired a first-year masters of business administration (MBA) student to develop the survey it mailed to 850 yearbook representatives at the colleges and universities in its market area. The representatives were unaware that Dalgarno Photo had developed the survey.

The survey asked about the photography and publishing activities associated with yearbook development. For instance, what photographer and publisher services did the schools use, and what factors were most important in selecting services? The survey instrument contained 30 questions, which were coded into 137 separate variables.

Among his many interests in this study, Dalgarno's marketing manager questioned whether college funding source and gender of the yearbook editor were related in some manner. To analyze this issue, we examine these two variables more closely. Source of university funding is a categorical variable, coded as follows:

1 = Private funding

2 = State funding

Of the 221 respondents who provided data for this variable, 155 came from privately funded colleges or universities and 66 were from state funded institutions.

The second variable, gender of the yearbook editor, is also a categorical variable, with two response categories, coded as follows:

$$1 = \text{Male}$$
$$2 = \text{Female}$$

Of the 221 responses to the survey, 164 were from females and 57 were from males.

In cases in which the variables of interest are both categorical and the decision maker is interested in determining whether a relationship exists between the two, a statistical technique known as contingency analysis is useful. We first set up a two-dimensional table called a **contingency table**. The contingency table for these two variables is shown in Table 13.3.

Table 13.3 shows that 14 of the respondents were males from schools that are privately funded. The numbers at the extreme right and along the bottom are called the *marginal frequencies*. For example, 57 respondents were males, and 155 respondents were from privately funded institutions.

The issue of whether there is a relationship between responses to these two variables is formally addressed through a hypothesis test, in which the null and alternative hypotheses are stated as follows:

$H_0$: Gender of yearbook editor is independent of the college's funding source.

$H_A$: Gender of yearbook editor *is not* independent of the college's funding source.

If the null hypothesis is true, the population proportion of yearbook editors from private institutions who are males should be equal to the proportion of male editors from state-funded institutions. These two proportions should also equal the population proportion of male editors without regard to a school's funding source. To illustrate, we can use the sample data to determine the sample proportion of male editors as follows:

$$P_M = \frac{\text{Number of male editors}}{\text{Number of respondents}} = \frac{57}{221} = 0.2579$$

Then, if the null hypothesis is true, we would expect 25.79% of the 155 privately funded schools, or 39.98 schools, to have a male yearbook editor. We would also expect 25.79% of the 66 state-funded schools, or 17.02, to have male yearbook editors. (Note that the expected numbers need not be integer values. Note also that the sum of expected frequencies in any column or row add up to the marginal frequency.) We can use this reasoning to determine the expected number of respondents in each cell of the contingency table, as shown in Table 13.4.

You can simplify the calculations needed to produce the expected values for each cell. Note that the first cell's expected value, 39.98, was obtained by the following calculation:

$$e_{11} = 0.2579(155) = 39.98$$

However, because the probability, 0.2579, is calculated by dividing the row total, 57, by the grand total, 221, the calculation can also be represented as

$$e_{11} = \frac{(\text{Row total})(\text{Column total})}{\text{Grand total}} = \frac{(57)(155)}{221} = 39.98$$

**Contingency Table**

A table used to classify sample observations according to two or more identifiable characteristics. It is also called a *crosstabulation table*.

**TABLE 13.3** | **Contingency Table for Dalgarno Photo**

| | Source of Funding | | |
|---|---|---|---|
| Gender | Private | State | |
| Male | 14 | 43 | 57 |
| Female | 141 | 23 | 164 |
| | 155 | 66 | 221 |

**TABLE 13.4** | **Contingency Table for Dalgarno Photo**

| | Source of Funding | | |
|---|---|---|---|
| Gender | Private | State | |
| Male | $o_{11} = 14$ | $o_{12} = 43$ | 57 |
| | $e_{11} = 39.98$ | $e_{12} = 17.02$ | |
| Female | $o_{21} = 141$ | $o_{22} = 23$ | 164 |
| | $e_{21} = 115.02$ | $e_{22} = 48.98$ | |
| | 155 | 66 | 221 |

As a further example, we can calculate the expected value for the next cell in the same row. The expected number of male yearbook editors in state-funded schools is

$$e_{12} = \frac{\text{(Row total)(Column total)}}{\text{Grand total}} = \frac{(57)(66)}{221} = 17.02$$

Keep in mind that the row and column totals (the marginal frequencies) must be the same for the expected values as for the observed values. Therefore, when there is only one cell left in a row or a column for which you must calculate an expected value, you can obtain it by subtraction. So, as an example, the expected value $e_{12}$ could have been calculated as

$$e_{12} = 57 - 39.98 = 17.02$$

Allowing for sampling error, we would expect the actual frequencies in each cell to approximately match the corresponding expected cell frequencies when the null hypothesis is true. The greater the difference between the actual and the expected frequencies, the more likely the null hypothesis of independence is false and should be rejected. The statistical test to determine whether the sample data support or refute the null hypothesis is given by Equation 13.2. Do not be confused by the double summation in Equation 13.2; it merely indicates that all rows and columns must be used in calculating $x^2$. As was the case in the goodness-of-fit tests, the degrees of freedom are the number of independent data values obtained from the experiment. In any given row, once you know $c - 1$ of the data values, the remaining data value is determined. For instance, once you know that 14 of the 57 male editors were from privately funded institutions, you know that 43 were from state-funded institutions.

---

**Chi-Square Contingency Test Statistic**

$$\chi^2 = \sum_{i=1}^{r}\sum_{j=1}^{c} \frac{(o_{ij} - e_{ij})^2}{e_{ij}} \qquad \text{with } df = (r-1)(c-1) \tag{13.2}$$

where:

$$o_{ij} = \text{Observed frequency in cell } (i, j)$$
$$e_{ij} = \text{Expected frequency in cell } (i, j)$$
$$r = \text{Number of rows}$$
$$c = \text{Number of columns}$$

---

Similarly, once $r - 1$ data values in a column are known, the remaining data value is determined. Therefore, the degrees of freedom are obtained by the expression $(r - 1)(c - 1)$.

Figure 13.7 presents the hypotheses and test results for this example. As was the case in the goodness-of-fit tests, the test statistic has a distribution that can be approximated by the chi-square distribution if the expected values are larger than 5. Note that the calculated chi-square statistic is compared to the tabled value of chi-square for an $\alpha = 0.05$ and degrees of freedom $= (2 - 1)(2 - 1) = 1$. Because $x^2 = 76.19 > 3.8415$, the null hypothesis of independence should be rejected. Dalgarno Photo representatives should conclude that the gender of the yearbook editor and each school's source of funding are not independent. By examining the data in Figure 13.7, you can see that private schools are more likely to have female editors, whereas state schools are more likely to have male yearbook editors.

---

**EXAMPLE 13-4** **2 × 2 CONTINGENCY ANALYSIS**

**Wireridge Marketing** Before releasing a major advertising campaign to the media, Wireridge Marketing managers run a test on the media material. Recently, they randomly called 100 people and asked them to listen to a commercial that was slated to run nationwide on the radio. At the end of the commercial, the respondents were asked to name the company that was in the advertisement. The company is interested in determining

**FIGURE 13.7**

Chi-Square Contingency
Analysis Test for Dalgarno
Photo

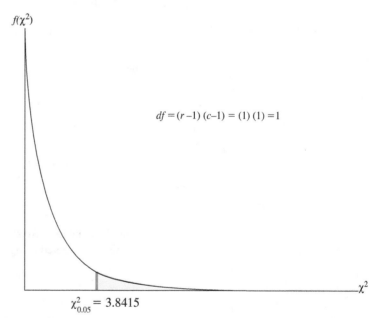

**Hypotheses:**

$H_0$: Gender of yearbook editor is independent of college's funding source.
$H_A$: Gender of yearbook editor is not independent of college's funding source.
$\alpha = 0.05$

|        | Private | State |
|--------|---------|-------|
| Male   | $o_{11} = 14$<br>$e_{11} = 39.98$ | $o_{12} = 43$<br>$e_{12} = 17.02$ |
| Female | $o_{21} = 141$<br>$e_{21} = 115.02$ | $o_{22} = 23$<br>$e_{22} = 48.98$ |

**Test Statistic:**

$$\chi^2 = \sum_{i=1}^{r} \sum_{j=1}^{c} \frac{(o_{ij} - e_{ij})^2}{e_{ij}} = \frac{(14 - 39.98)^2}{39.98} + \frac{(43 - 17.02)^2}{17.02}$$
$$+ \frac{(141 - 115.02)^2}{115.02} + \frac{(23 - 48.98)^2}{48.98} = 76.19$$

$df = (r-1)(c-1) = (1)(1) = 1$

$\chi^2_{0.05} = 3.8415$

**Decision Rule:**

If $\chi^2 > 3.8415$, reject $H_0$;
Otherwise, do not reject $H_0$.
Because $76.19 > 3.8415$, reject $H_0$. Thus, the gender of the yearbook editor and the school's source
of funding are not independent.

whether there is a relationship between gender and a person's ability to recall the company
name. To test this, the following steps can be used:

**Step 1** **Specify the null and alternative hypotheses.**
The company is interested in testing whether a relationship exists between gender and recall ability. Here are the appropriate null and alternative hypotheses.

$H_0$: Ability to correctly recall the company name is independent of gender.

$H_A$: Recall ability and gender are not independent.

**Step 2** **Determine the significance level.**
The test will be conducted using a 0.01 level of significance.

**Step 3** **Determine the critical value.**
The critical value for this test will be the chi-square value, with $(r - 1)(c - 1) = (2 - 1)(2 - 1) = 1$ degree of freedom with an $\alpha = 0.01$. From Appendix G, the critical value is 6.6349.

**Step 4**  **Collect the sample data and compute the chi-square test statistic using Equation 13.2.**

The following contingency table shows the results of the sampling:

|  | Female | Male | Total |
|---|---|---|---|
| Correct Recall | 33 | 25 | 58 |
| Incorrect Recall | 22 | 20 | 42 |
| Total | 55 | 45 | 100 |

Note that 58 percent of the entire data values result in a correct recall. If the ability to correctly recall the company name is independent of gender you would expect the same percentage (58%) would occur for each gender. Thus, 58% of the males [.58(45) = 26.10] would be expected to have a correct recall. In general, the expected cell frequencies are determined by multiplying the row total by the column total and dividing by the overall sample size. For example, for the cell corresponding to female and correct recall, we get

$$\text{Expected} = \frac{58 \times 55}{100} = 31.90$$

The expected cell values for all cells are

|  | Female | Male | Total |
|---|---|---|---|
| Correct Recall | $o = 33$ | $o = 25$ | 58 |
|  | $e = 31.90$ | $e = 26.10$ |  |
| Incorrect Recall | $o = 22$ | $o = 20$ | 42 |
|  | $e = 23.10$ | $e = 18.90$ | — |
| Total | 55 | 45 | 100 |

After checking to make sure all the expected cell frequencies $\geq 5$, the test statistic is computed using Equation 13.2.

$$\chi^2 = \sum_{i=1}^{r} \sum_{j=1}^{c} \frac{(o_{ij} - e_{ij})^2}{e_{ij}}$$

$$= \frac{(33 - 31.90)^2}{31.90} + \frac{(25 - 26.10)^2}{26.10} + \frac{(22 - 23.10)^2}{23.10} + \frac{(20 - 18.90)^2}{18.90} = 0.20$$

**Step 5**  **Reach a decision.**

Because $\chi^2 = 0.20 < 6.6349$, do not reject the null hypothesis.

**Step 6**  **Draw a conclusion.**

Based on the sample data, there is no reason to believe that being able to recall the name of the company in the ad is related to gender.

>>**END EXAMPLE**

**TRY PROBLEM** 13-17 (pg. 569)

# *r* × *c* Contingency Tables

**BUSINESS APPLICATION**  **LARGER CONTINGENCY TABLES**

**BENTON STONE & TILE**  Benton Stone & Tile makes a wide variety of products for the building industry. It pays market wages, provides competitive benefits, and offers attractive options for employees in an effort to create a satisfied workforce and reduce turnover. Recently, however, several supervisors have complained that employee absenteeism is becoming a problem. In response to these complaints, the human resources manager studied a random

**Excel and Minitab Tutorial**

sample of 500 employees. One aim of this study was to determine whether there is a relationship between absenteeism and marital status. Absenteeism during the past year was broken down into three levels:

1. 0 absences
2. 1 to 5 absences
3. Over 5 absences

Marital status was divided into four categories:

1. Single        2. Married
3. Divorced      4. Widowed

Table 13.5 shows the contingency table for the sample of 500 employees. The table is also shown in the file **Benton**. The null and alternative hypotheses to be tested are

$H_0$: Absentee behavior is independent of marital status.

$H_A$: Absentee behavior is not independent of marital status.

As with $2 \times 2$ contingency analysis, the test for independence can be made using the chi-square test, where the expected cell frequencies are compared to the actual cell frequencies and the test statistic shown as Equation 13.2 is used. The logic of the test says that if the actual and expected frequencies closely match, then the null hypothesis of independence is not rejected. However, if the actual and expected cell frequencies are substantially different overall, the null hypothesis of independence is rejected. The calculated chi-square statistic is compared to an Appendix G critical value for the desired significance and degrees of freedom equal to $(r - 1)(c - 1)$.

The expected cell frequencies are determined assuming that the row and column variables are independent. This means, for example, that the probability of a married person being absent more than 5 days during the year is the same as the probability of any employee being absent more than 5 days. An easy way to compute the expected cell frequencies, $e_{ij}$, is given by Equation 13.3.

**Expected Cell Frequencies**

$$e_{ij} = \frac{(i\text{th row total})(j\text{th column total})}{\text{total sample size}}$$

(13.3)

For example, the expected cell frequency for row 1, column 1 is

$$e_{11} = \frac{(200)(200)}{500} = 80$$

and the expected cell frequency for row 2, column 3 is

$$e_{23} = \frac{(150)(100)}{500} = 30$$

**TABLE 13.5** | **Contingency Table for Benton Stone & Tile**

| Marital Status | Absentee Rate | | | |
| --- | --- | --- | --- | --- |
| | 0 | 1–5 | Over 5 | Row Totals |
| Single | 84 | 82 | 34 | 200 |
| Married | 50 | 64 | 36 | 150 |
| Divorced | 50 | 34 | 16 | 100 |
| Widowed | 16 | 20 | 14 | 50 |
| Column Total | 200 | 200 | 100 | 500 |

**FIGURE 13.8A**

Excel 2007 Output—Benton
Stone & Tile Contingency
Analysis Test

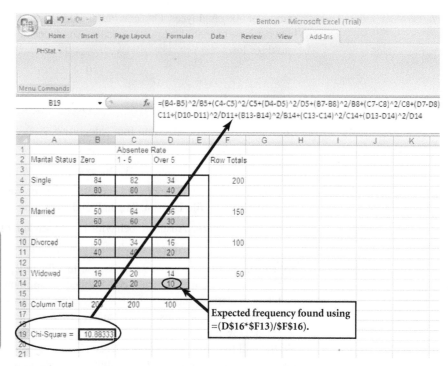

**Excel 2007 Instructions:**
1. Open file: Benton.xls.
2. Compute expected cell frequencies using Excel formula.
3. Compute chi-square statistics using Excel formula.

Figures 13.8a and 13.8b show the completed contingency table with the actual and expected cell frequencies that were developed using Excel and Minitab. The calculated chi-square test value is computed as follows:

$$\chi^2 = \sum_{i=1}^{r}\sum_{j=1}^{c} \frac{(o_{ij} - e_{ij})^2}{e_{ij}}$$

$$= \frac{(84-80)^2}{80} + \frac{(82-80)^2}{80} + \cdots + \frac{(20-20)^2}{20} + \frac{(14-10)^2}{10}$$

$$= 10.88$$

**FIGURE 13.8B**

Minitab Output—Benton
Stone & Tile Contingency
Analysis Test

**Minitab Instructions:**
1. Open file: Benton.MTW.
2. Choose **Stat > Tables > Chi-Square Test**.
3. In Columns containing the table, enter data columns.
4. Click **OK**.

The degrees of freedom are $(r - 1)(c - 1) = (4 - 1)(3 - 1) = 6$. You can use the chi-square table in Appendix G to get the chi-square critical value for $\alpha = 0.05$ and 6 degrees of freedom, or you can use Minitab's Probability Distributions command or Excel's CHIINV function (CHIINV(0.05,6) = 12.5916). Because the calculated chi-square value (10.883) shown in Figures 13.8a and 13.8b is less than 12.5916, we cannot reject the null hypothesis. Based on these sample data, there is *insufficient evidence* to conclude that absenteeism and marital status are not independent.

## Chi-Square Test Limitations

The chi-square distribution is only an approximation for the true distribution for contingency analysis. We use the chi-square approximation because the true distribution is impractical to compute in most instances. However, the approximation (and, therefore, the conclusion reached) is quite good when all expected cell frequencies are at least 5.0. When expected cell frequencies drop below 5.0, the calculated chi-square value tends to be inflated and may inflate the true probability of a Type I error beyond the stated significance level. As a rule, if the null hypothesis is not rejected, you do not need to worry when the expected cell frequencies drop below 5.0.

There are two alternatives that can be used to overcome the small expected-cell-frequency problem. The first is to increase the sample size. This may increase the marginal frequencies in each row and column enough to increase the expected cell frequencies. The second option is to combine the categories of the row and/or column variables. If you do decide to group categories together, there should be some logic behind the resulting categories. You don't want to lose the meaning of the results through poor groupings. You will need to examine each situation individually to determine whether the option of grouping classes to increase expected cell frequencies makes sense.

# 13-2: Exercises

## Skill Development

**13-16.** The billing department of a national cable service company is conducting a study of how customers pay their monthly cable bills. The cable company accepts payment in one of four ways: in person at a local office, by mail, by credit card, or by electronic funds transfer from a bank account. The cable company randomly sampled 400 customers to determine if there is a relationship between the customer's age and the payment method used. The following sample results were obtained:

| | Age of Customer | | | |
|---|---|---|---|---|
| **Payment Method** | **20–30** | **31–40** | **41–50** | **Over 50** |
| In Person | 8 | 12 | 11 | 13 |
| By Mail | 29 | 67 | 72 | 50 |
| By Credit Card | 26 | 19 | 5 | 7 |
| By Funds Transfer | 23 | 35 | 17 | 6 |

Based on the sample data, can the cable company conclude that there is a relationship between the age of the customer and the payment method used? Conduct the appropriate test at the $\alpha = 0.01$ level of significance.

**13-17.** A contingency analysis table has been constructed from data obtained in a phone survey of customers in a market area in which respondents were asked to indicate whether they owned a domestic or foreign car and whether they were a member of a union or not. The following contingency table is provided.

| | Union | |
|---|---|---|
| **Car** | **Yes** | **No** |
| Domestic | 155 | 470 |
| Foreign | 40 | 325 |

a. Use the chi-square approach to test whether type of car owned (domestic or foreign) is independent of union membership. Test using an $\alpha = 0.05$ level.

b. Calculate the *p*-value for this hypothesis test.

**13-18.** Utilize the following contingency table to answer the questions listed below.

| | $C_1$ | $C_2$ |
|---|---|---|
| $R_1$ | 51 | 207 |
| $R_2$ | 146 | 185 |
| $R_3$ | 240 | 157 |

a. State the relevant null and alternative hypotheses.

b. Calculate the expected values for each of the cells.

c. Compute the chi-square test statistic for the hypothesis test.

d. Determine the appropriate critical value and reach a decision for the hypothesis test. Use a significance level of 0.05.

e. Obtain the *p*-value for this hypothesis test.

**13-19.** A manufacturer of sports drinks has randomly sampled 198 men and 202 women. Each sampled participant was asked to taste an unflavored version and a flavored version of a new sports drink currently in development. The participants' preferences are shown below:

|       | Flavored | Unflavored |
|-------|----------|------------|
| Men   | 101      | 97         |
| Women | 68       | 134        |

a. State the relevant null and alternative hypotheses.

b. Conduct the appropriate test and state a conclusion. Use a level of significance of 0.05.

**13-20.** A marketing research firm is conducting a study to determine if there is a relationship between an individual's age and the individual's preferred source of news. The research firm asked 1,000 individuals to list their preferred source for news: newspaper, radio and television, or the Internet. The following results were obtained:

| Preferred News Source | Age of Respondent | | | |
|-----------------------|-------|-------|-------|---------|
|                       | 20–30 | 31–40 | 41–50 | Over 50 |
| Newspaper             | 19    | 62    | 95    | 147     |
| Radio/TV              | 27    | 125   | 168   | 88      |
| Internet              | 104   | 113   | 37    | 15      |

At the 0.01 level of significance, can the marketing research firm conclude that there is a relationship between the age of the individual and the individual's preferred source for news?

**13-21.** A loan officer wished to determine if the marital status of loan applicants was independent of the approval of loans. The following table presents the result of her survey:

|          | Approved | Rejected |
|----------|----------|----------|
| Single   | 213      | 189      |
| Married  | 374      | 231      |
| Divorced | 358      | 252      |

a. Conduct the appropriate hypothesis test that will provide an answer to the loan officer. Use a significance level of 0.01.

b. Calculate the *p*-value for the hypothesis test in part a.

**13-22.** An instructor in a large accounting class is interested in determining whether the grades that students get are related to how close to the front of the room the students sit. He has categorized the room seating as "Front," "Middle," and "Back." The following data were collected over two sections with 400 total students. Based on the sample data, can you conclude that there is a dependency relationship between seating location and grade using a significance level equal to 0.05?

|        | A  | B   | C   | D  | F | Total |
|--------|----|-----|-----|----|---|-------|
| Front  | 18 | 55  | 30  | 3  | 0 | 106   |
| Middle | 7  | 42  | 95  | 11 | 1 | 156   |
| Back   | 3  | 15  | 104 | 14 | 2 | 138   |
| Total  | 28 | 112 | 229 | 28 | 3 | 400   |

## Business Applications

**13-23.** A study was conducted to determine if there is a difference between the investing preferences of mid-level managers working in the public and private sectors in New York City. A random sample of 320 public sector employees and 380 private sector employees was taken. The sampled participants were then asked about their retirement investment decisions and classified as being either "aggressive," if they invested only in stocks or stock mutual funds, or "balanced," if they invested in some combination of stocks, bonds, cash, and other. The following results were found:

|         | Aggressive | Balanced |
|---------|------------|----------|
| Public  | 164        | 156      |
| Private | 236        | 144      |

a. State the hypothesis of interest and conduct the appropriate hypothesis test to determine whether there is a relationship between employment sector and investing preference. Use a level of significance of 0.01.

b. State the conclusion of the test conducted in part a.

c. Calculate the *p*-value for the hypothesis test conducted in part a.

**13-24.** The following table classifies a stock's price change as up, down, or no change for both today's and yesterday's prices. Price changes were examined for 100 days. A financial theory states that stock prices follow what is called a "random walk." This means, in part, that the price change today for a stock must be independent of yesterday's price change. Test the hypothesis that daily stock price changes for this stock are independent. Let $\alpha = 0.05$.

| Price Change Today | Price Change Previous Day | | |
|--------------------|-----|-----------|------|
|                    | Up  | No Change | Down |
| Up                 | 14  | 16        | 12   |
| No Change          | 6   | 8         | 6    |
| Down               | 16  | 14        | 8    |

**13-25.** A local appliance retailer handles four washing machine models for a major manufacturer: standard, deluxe, superior, and XLT. The marketing manager has recently conducted a study on the purchasers of the washing machines. The study recorded the model of appliance purchased and the credit account balance of the customer at the time of purchase. The sample data are in the following table. Based on these data, is there evidence of a relationship between the account balance and the model of washer purchased? Use a significance level of 0.025. Conduct the test using a *p*-value approach.

| Credit Balance | Washer Model Purchased | | | |
|---|---|---|---|---|
| | **Standard** | **Deluxe** | **Superior** | **XLT** |
| **Under $200** | 10 | 16 | 40 | 5 |
| **$200–$800** | 8 | 12 | 24 | 15 |
| **Over $800** | 16 | 12 | 16 | 30 |

**13-26.** A random sample of 980 heads of households was taken from the customer list for State Bank and Trust. Those sampled were asked to classify their own attitudes and their parents' attitudes toward borrowing money as follows:

A: Borrow only for real estate and car purchases

B: Borrow for short-term purchases such as appliances and furniture

C: Never borrow money

The following table indicates the responses from those in the study.

| Parent | Respondent | | |
|---|---|---|---|
| | **A** | **B** | **C** |
| A | 240 | 80 | 20 |
| B | 180 | 120 | 40 |
| C | 180 | 80 | 40 |

Test the hypothesis that the respondents' borrowing habits are independent from what they believe their parents' attitudes to be. Let $\alpha = 0.01$.

**13-27.** The California Lettuce Research board was originally formed as the Iceberg Lettuce Advisory Board in 1973. The primary function of the board is to fund research on iceberg and leaf lettuce. A recent project involved studying the effect of varying levels of sodium absorption ratios (SAR) on the yield of head lettuce. The measurements (the number of lettuce heads from each plot) of the kind observed were as follows:

| SAR | Lettuce Type | |
|---|---|---|
| | **Salinas** | **Sniper** |
| 3 | 104 | 109 |
| 5 | 160 | 163 |
| 7 | 142 | 146 |
| 10 | 133 | 156 |

a. Determine if the number of lettuce heads harvested for the two lettuce types is independent of the levels of sodium absorption ratios (SAR). Use a significance level of 0.025 and a *p*-value approach.

b. Which type of lettuce would you recommend?

**13-28.** In its ninth year, the Barclaycard Business Travel Survey has become an information source for business travelers not only in the United Kingdom but internationally as well. Each year, as a result of the research, Barclaycard Business has been able to predict and comment on trends within the business travel industry. One question asked in the 2003/2004 and 2004/2005 surveys was, "Have you considered reducing hours spent away from home to increase quality of life?" The following table represents the responses:

| | 2003/2004 | 2004/2005 | Total |
|---|---|---|---|
| Yes—have reduced | 400 | 384 | 784 |
| Yes—not been able to | 400 | 300 | 700 |
| No—not certain | 400 | 516 | 916 |
| Total | 1200 | 1200 | 2400 |

a. Determine if the response to the survey question was independent of the year in which the question was asked. Use a significance level of 0.05.

b. Determine if there is a significant difference between the proportion of travelers who say they have reduced hours spent away from home between the 2003/2004 and the 2004/2005 years.

## Computer Database Exercises

**13-29.** Daniel Vinson of the University of Missouri–Columbia led a team of researchers investigating the increased risk when people are angry of serious injuries in the workplace requiring emergency medical care. The file entitled **Angry** contains the data collected by the team of researchers. It displays the emotions reported by patients just before they were injured.

a. Use the data in the file entitled **Angry** to construct a contingency table.

b. Determine if the type of emotion felt by patients just before they were injured is independent of the severity of that emotion. Use a contingency analysis and a significance level of 0.05.

**13-30.** *Gift of the Gauche*, a left-handedness information Web site (www.left-handedness.info), provides information concerning left-handed activities, products, and demography. It indicates that about 10%–11% of the population of Europe and North America are left-handed. It also reports on demographic surveys. It cites an American study in which over one million magazine respondents found that 12.6% of the male respondents were left-handed as were 9.9% of the female respondents, although this was not a random sample. The data obtained by a British survey of over 8,000 randomly selected men and women, published in Issue 37 of *The Graphologist* in 1992, is furnished in a file entitled **Lefties**. Based on this data, determine if the "handedness" of an individual is independent of gender. Use a significance level of 0.01 and a *p*-value approach.

**13-31.** The Marriott Company owns and operates a number of different hotel chains, including the Courtyard chain. Recently, a survey was mailed to a random sample of

400 Courtyard customers. A total of 62 customers responded to the survey. The customers were asked a number of questions related to their satisfaction with the chain as well as several demographic questions. Among the issues of interest was whether there is a relationship between the likelihood that customers will stay at the chain again and whether or not this was the customer's first stay at the Courtyard. The following contingency table has been developed from the data set contained in the file called **CourtyardSurvey**:

| | First Stay | | |
|---|---|---|---|
| **Stay Again?** | **Yes** | **No** | **Total** |
| **Definitely Will** | 9 | 12 | 21 |
| **Probably Will** | 18 | 2 | 20 |
| **Maybe** | 15 | 3 | 18 |
| **Probably Not** | 2 | 1 | 3 |
| **Total** | 44 | 18 | 62 |

Using a significance level equal to 0.05, test to see whether these sample data imply a relationship between the two variables. Discuss the results.

**13-32.** ECCO (Electronic Controls Company) makes backup alarms that are used on such equipment as forklifts and delivery trucks. The quality manager recently performed a study involving a random sample of 110 warranty claims. One of the questions the manager wanted to answer was whether there is a relationship between the type of warranty complaint and the plant at which the alarm was made. The data are in the file called **ECCO**.
   a. Calculate the expected values for the cells in this analysis. Suggest a way in which cells can be combined to assure that the expected value of each cell is at least 5 so that as many level combinations of the two variables as possible are retained.
   b. Using a significance level of 0.01, conduct a relevant hypothesis test and provide an answer to the manager's question.

**13-33.** Referring to Problem 13-32, can the quality control manager conclude that the type of warranty problem is independent of the shift on which the alarm was manufactured? Test using a significance level of 0.05. Discuss your results.

# Visual Summary

**Chapter 13:** Many of the statistical procedures introduced in earlier chapters require that the sample data come from populations that are normally distributed and that the data be measured at least at the interval level. However, you will encounter many situations in which these specifications are not met. This chapter introduces two sets of procedures that are used to address each of these issues in turn. Goodness-of–fit procedures are used to determine if sample data has been drawn from a specific hypothesized distribution. Contingency analysis is an often used technique to determine the relationship between qualitative variables. Though these procedures are not used as much as those requiring normal population, you will discover that far too few of the procedures presented in this chapter are used when they should be. It is, therefore, important that you learn when and how to use the procedures presented in this chapter.

## 13.1 Introduction to Goodness-of-Fit Tests (pg. 548–562)

### Summary

The chi-square goodness-of-fit test can be used to determine if a set of data comes from a specific hypothesized distribution. Recall that several of the procedures presented in Chapters 8-12 require that the sampled populations are normally distributed. For example, tests involving the $t$-distribution are based on such a requirement. In order to verify this requirement, the goodness-of-fit test determines if the observed set of values agree with a set of data obtained from a specified probability distribution. Perhaps the goodness-of-fit test is most often used to verify a normal distribution. However, it can be used to detect many other probability distributions.

**Outcome 1.** Utilize the chi-square goodness-of-fit test to determine whether data from a process fit a specified distribution

## 13.2 Introduction to Contingency Analysis (pg. 562–572)

### Summary

You will encounter many business situations in which the level of data measurement for the variable of interest is either nominal or ordinal, not interval or ratio. In Chapters 9 and 10 you were introduced to hypothesis tests involving one and two population proportions. However, you will also encounter many situations involving multiple population proportions for which two population procedures are not applicable. In each of these cases, the proportions relate to characteristic categories of the variable of interest. These situations involving categorical data call for a new statistical tool known as *contingency analysis* to help make decisions when multiple proportions are involved. Contingency analysis can be used when a level of data measurement is either nominal or ordinal and the values are determined by counting the number of occurrences in each category.

**Outcome 2.** Set up a contingency table analysis and perform a chi-square test of independence

## Conclusion

This chapter has introduced two very useful statistical tools: goodness-of-fit tests and contingency analysis. Goodness-of-fit testing is used when a decision maker wishes to determine whether sample data come from a population having specific characteristics. The chi-square goodness-of-fit procedure that was introduced in this chapter addresses this issue. This test relies on the idea that if the distribution of the sample data is substantially different from the hypothesized population distribution, then the population distribution from which these sample data came must not be what was hypothesized.

Contingency analysis is a frequently used statistical tool that allows the decision maker to test whether responses to two variables are independent. Market researchers, for example, use contingency analysis to determine whether attitude about the quality of their company's product is independent of the gender of a customer. By using contingency analysis and the chi-square contingency test, they can make this determination based on a sample of customers.

# Equations

**(13.1)** Chi-Square Goodness-of-Fit Test Statistic  pg. 550

$$\chi^2 = \sum_{i=1}^{k} \frac{(o_i - e_i)^2}{e_i}$$

**(13.2)** Chi-Square Contingency Test Statistic  pg. 564

$$\chi^2 = \sum_{i=1}^{r}\sum_{j=1}^{c} \frac{(o_{ij} - e_{ij})^2}{e_{ij}} \quad \text{with } df = (r-1)(c-1)$$

**(13.3)** Expected Cell Frequencies  pg. 567

$$e_{ij} = \frac{(i\text{th row total})\,(j\text{th column total})}{\text{total sample size}}$$

# Key Term

Contingency table pg. 563

# Chapter Exercises

## Conceptual Questions

**13-34.** Locate a journal article that uses either contingency analysis or a goodness-of-fit test. Discuss the article, paying particular attention to the reasoning behind using the particular statistical test.

**13-35.** Find a marketing research book (or borrow one from a friend). Does it discuss either of the tests considered in this chapter? If yes, outline the discussion. If no, determine where in the text such a discussion would be appropriate.

**13-36.** One of the topics in Chapter 10 was hypothesis testing for the difference between two population proportions. For the test to have validity, there were conditions set on the sample sizes with respect to the sample proportions. A 2 × 2 contingency table may also be utilized to test the difference between proportions of two independent populations. This procedure has conditions placed on the expected value of each cell. Discuss the relationship between these two conditions.

**13-37.** A 2 × 2 contingency table and a hypothesis test of the difference between two population proportions can be used to analyze the same data set. However, besides all the similarities of the two methods, the hypothesis test of the difference between two proportions has two advantages. Identify these advantages.

## Business Applications

**13-38.** The College Bookstore has just hired a new manager, one with a business background. Claudia Markman has been charged with increasing the profitability of the bookstore, with the profits going to the general

scholarship fund. Claudia started her job just before the beginning of the semester and was analyzing the sales during the days when students are buying their textbooks. The store has four checkout stands, and Claudia noticed registers three and four served more students than registers one and two. She is not sure whether the layout of the store channels customers into these registers, whether the checkout clerks in these lines are simply slower than the other two, or whether she was just seeing random differences.

Claudia kept a record of which stands the next 1,000 students chose for checkout. The students checked out of the four stands according to the following pattern:

| Stand 1 | Stand 2 | Stand 3 | Stand 4 |
|---------|---------|---------|---------|
| 338 | 275 | 201 | 186 |

a. Based on these data, can Claudia conclude the proportion of students using the four checkout stands is equal? (Use an $\alpha = 0.05$.)

b. A friend suggested that you could just as well conduct four hypothesis tests that the proportion of customers visiting each stand is equal to $\pi = 0.25$. Discuss the merits of this suggestion.

**13-39.** A regional cancer treatment center has had success treating localized cancers with a linear accelerator. Whereas admissions for further treatment nationally average 2.1 per patient per year, the center's director thinks that re-admissions with the new treatment are Poisson distributed, with a mean of 1.2 patients per year. He has collected the following data on a random sample of 300 patients:

| Re-admissions Last Year | Patients |
|---|---|
| 0 | 139 |
| 1 | 87 |
| 2 | 48 |
| 3 | 14 |
| 4 | 8 |
| 5 | 1 |
| 6 | 1 |
| 7 | 0 |
| 8 | 2 |
| | 300 |

a. Adjust the data so that you can test the director's claim using a test statistic whose sampling distribution can be approximated by a chi-square distribution.
b. Assume the Type I error rate is to be controlled at 0.05. Do you agree with the director's claim? Why? Conduct a statistical procedure to support your opinion.

**13-40.** Cooper Manufacturing, Inc., of Dallas, Texas, has a contract with the U.S. Air Force to produce a part for a new fighter plane being manufactured. The part is a bolt that has specifications requiring that the length be normally distributed with a mean of 3.05 inches and a standard deviation of 0.015 inch. As part of the company's quality control efforts, each day Cooper's engineers select a random sample of 100 bolts produced that day and carefully measure the bolts to determine whether the production is within specifications. The following data were collected yesterday:

| Length (inches) | Frequency |
|---|---|
| Under 3.030 | 5 |
| 3.030 and under 3.035 | 16 |
| 3.035 and under 3.040 | 7 |
| 3.040 and under 3.050 | 20 |
| 3.050 and under 3.060 | 36 |
| 3.060 and under 3.065 | 8 |
| 3.065 and over | 8 |

Based on these sample data, what should Cooper's engineers conclude about the production output if they test using an $\alpha = 0.01$? Discuss.

**13-41.** The Cooper Company discussed in Problem 13-40 has a second contract with a private firm for which it makes fuses for an electronic instrument. The quality control department at Cooper periodically selects a random sample of five fuses and tests each fuse to

determine whether it is defective. Based on these findings, the production process is either shut down (if too many defectives are observed) or allowed to run. The quality control department believes that the sampling process follows a binomial distribution, and it has been using the binomial distribution to compute the probabilities associated with the sampling outcomes.

The contract allows for at most 5% defectives. The head of quality control recently compiled a list of the sampling results for the past 300 days in which five randomly selected fuses were tested, with the following frequency distribution for the number of defectives observed. She is concerned that the binomial distribution with a sample size of 5 and a probability of defectives of 0.05 may not be appropriate.

| Number of Defectives | Frequency |
|---|---|
| 0 | 209 |
| 1 | 33 |
| 2 | 43 |
| 3 | 10 |
| 4 | 5 |
| 5 | 0 |

a. Calculate the expected values for the cells in this analysis. Suggest a way in which cells can be combined to assure that the expected value of each cell is at least 5.
b. Using a significance level of 0.10, what should the quality control manager conclude based on these sample data? Discuss.

**13-42.** A survey performed by Simmons Market Research investigated the percentage of individuals in various age groups who indicated they were willing to pay more for environmentally friendly products. The results were presented in *USA Today* "Snapshots" (July 21, 2005). The survey had approximately 3,240 respondents in each age group. Results of the survey follow:

| Age Group | 18–24 | 25–34 | 35–44 | 45–54 | 55–64 | 65 and over |
|---|---|---|---|---|---|---|
| Percentage | 11 | 17 | 19 | 20 | 14 | 19 |

Conduct a goodness-of-fit test analysis to determine if the proportions of individuals willing to pay more for environmentally friendly products in the various age groups are equal. Use a significance level of 0.01.

**13-43.** An article published in *USA Today* asserts that many children are abandoning outdoor for indoor activities. The National Sporting Goods Association annual survey for 2004 (the latest data available) compared activity levels in 1995 versus 2004. A random selection of children (7- to 11-year-olds) indicating their favorite outdoor activity is given in the following table:

|  | Bicycling | Swimming | Baseball | Fishing | Touch Football |
|---|---|---|---|---|---|
| 1995 | 68 | 60 | 29 | 25 | 16 |
| 2004 | 47 | 42 | 22 | 18 | 10 |

Construct a contingency analysis to determine if the type of preferred outdoor activity is dependent on the year in this survey. Use a significance level of 0.05 and the *p*-value approach.

## Computer Database Exercises

**13-44.** With the economic downturn that started in late 2007, many people started worrying about retirement and whether they even would be able to retire. A study recently done by the Employee Benefit Research Institute (EBRI) found about 69% of workers said they and/or their spouses have saved for retirement. The file entitled **Retirement** contains the total savings and investments indicated. Use a contingency analysis to determine if the amount of total savings and investments is dependent on the age of the worker.

**13-45.** The airport manager at the Sacramento, California, airport recently conducted a study of passengers departing from the airport. A random sample of 100 passengers was selected. The data are in the file called **Airline Passengers**. An earlier study showed the following usage by airline:

| | |
|---|---|
| Delta | 20% |
| Horizon | 10% |
| Northwest | 10% |
| Skywest | 3% |
| Southwest | 25% |
| United | 32% |

a. If the manager wishes to determine whether the airline usage pattern has changed from that reported in the earlier study, state the appropriate null and alternative hypotheses.

b. Based on the sample data, what should be concluded? Test using a significance level of 0.01.

**13-46.** A pharmaceutical company is planning to market a drug that is supposed to help reduce blood pressure. The company claims that if the drug is taken properly,

the amount of blood pressure decrease will be normally distributed with a mean equal to 10 points on the diastolic reading and a standard deviation equal to 4.0. One hundred patients were administered the drug, and data were collected showing the reduction in blood pressure at the end of the test period. The data are located in the file labeled **Blood Pressure**.

a. Using a goodness-of-fit test and a significance level equal to 0.05, what conclusion should be reached with respect to the distribution of diastolic blood pressure reduction? Discuss.

b. Conduct a hypothesis test to determine if the standard deviation for this population could be considered to be 4.0. Use a significance level of 0.10.

c. Given the results of the two tests in parts a and b, is it appropriate to construct a confidence interval based on a normal distribution with a population standard deviation of 4.0? Explain your answer.

d. If appropriate, construct a 99% confidence interval for the mean reduction in blood pressure. Based on this confidence interval, does an average diastolic loss of 10 seem reasonable for this procedure? Explain your reasoning.

**13-47.** An Ariel Capital Management and Charles Schwab survey addressed the proportion of African-Americans and White Americans who have money invested in the stock market. Suppose the file entitled **Stockrace** contains data obtained in the surveys. The survey asked 500 African-American and 500 White respondents if they personally had money invested in the stock market.

a. Create a contingency table using the data in the file **Stockrace**.

b. Conduct a contingency analysis to determine if the proportion of African-Americans differs from the proportion of White Americans who invest in stocks. Use a significance level of 0.05.

**13-48.** The state transportation department recently conducted a study of motorists in Idaho. Two main factors of interest were whether the vehicle was insured with liability insurance and whether the driver was wearing a seat belt. A random sample of 100 cars was stopped at various locations throughout the state. The data are in the file called **Liabins**. The investigators were interested in determining whether seat belt status is independent of insurance status.

Conduct the appropriate hypothesis test using a 0.05 level of significance and discuss your results.

# Case 13.1

## American Oil Company

Chad Williams sat back in his airline seat to enjoy the hour-long flight between Los Angeles and Oakland, California. The hour would give him time to reflect on his upcoming trip to Australia and the work he had been doing the past week in Los Angeles.

Chad is one man on a six-man crew employed by the American Oil Company to literally walk the earth searching for oil. His college degrees in geology and petroleum engineering landed him the job with American, but he never dreamed he would be doing the exciting work he now does. Chad and his crew spend several months in special locations around the world using highly sensitive electronic equipment for oil exploration.

The upcoming trip to Australia is one that Chad has been looking forward to since it was announced that his crew would be going there to search the Outback for oil. In preparation for the trip, the crew has been in Los Angeles at American's engineering research facility working on some new equipment that will be used in Australia.

Chad's thoughts centered on the problem he was having with a particular component part on the new equipment. The specifications called for 200 of the components, with each having a diameter of between 0.15 and 0.18 inch. The only available supplier of the component manufactures the components in New Jersey to specifications calling for normally distributed output, with a mean of 0.16 inches and a standard deviation of 0.02 inches.

Chad faces two problems. First, he is unsure that the supplier actually does produce parts with means of 0.16 inches and standard deviations of 0.02 inches according to a normal distribution. Second, if the parts are made to specifications, he needs to determine how many components to purchase if enough acceptable components are to be received to make two oil exploration devices.

The supplier has sent Chad the following data for 330 randomly selected components. Chad believes that the supplier is honest and that he can rely on the data.

| Diameter (Inch) | Frequency |
|---|---|
| Under 0.14 | 5 |
| 0.14 and under 0.15 | 70 |
| 0.15 and under 0.16 | 90 |
| 0.16 and under 0.17 | 105 |
| 0.17 and under 0.18 | 50 |
| Over 0.18 | 10 |
| Total | 330 |

Chad needs to have a report ready for Monday indicating whether he believes the supplier delivers at its stated specifications and, if so, how many of the components American should order to have enough acceptable components to outfit two oil exploration devices.

### Required Tasks:

1. State the problems faced by Chad Williams.
2. Identify the statistical test Chad Williams can use to determine whether the supplier's claim is true or not.
3. State the null and alternative hypotheses for the test to determine whether the supplier's claim is true or not.
4. Assuming that the supplier produces output whose diameter is normally distributed with a mean of 0.16 inches and a standard deviation of 0.02 inches, determine the expected frequencies that Chad would expect to see in a sample of 330 components.
5. Based on the observed and expected frequencies, calculate the appropriate test statistic.
6. Calculate the critical value of the test statistic. Select an alpha value.
7. State a conclusion. Is the supplier's claim with respect to specifications of the component parts supported by the sample data?
8. Provide a short report that summarizes your analysis and conclusion.

# Case 13.2

## Bentford Electronics—Part 1

On Saturday morning, Jennifer Bentford received a call at her home from the production supervisor at Bentford Electronics Plant 1. The supervisor indicated that she and the supervisors from Plants 2, 3, and 4 had agreed that something must be done to improve company morale and thereby increase the production output of their plants. Jennifer Bentford, president of Bentford Electronics, agreed to set up a Monday morning meeting with the supervisors to see if they could arrive at a plan for accomplishing these objectives.

By Monday each supervisor had compiled a list of several ideas, including a four-day work week and interplant competitions of various kinds. A second meeting was set for Wednesday to discuss the issue further.

Following the Wednesday afternoon meeting, Jennifer Bentford and her plant supervisors agreed to implement a weekly contest called the NBE Game of the Week. The plant producing the most each week would be considered the NBE Game of the Week winner and would receive 10 points. The second-place plant would receive 7 points, and the third- and fourth-place plants would receive 3 points and 1 point, respectively. The contest would last 26 weeks. At the end of that period, a $200,000 bonus would be divided among the employees in the four plants proportional to the total points accumulated by each plant.

The announcement of the contest created a lot of excitement and enthusiasm at the four plants. No one complained about the rules because the four plants were designed and staffed to produce equally.

At the close of the contest, Jennifer Bentford called the supervisors into a meeting, at which time she asked for data to determine whether the contest had significantly improved productivity. She indicated that she had to know this before she could authorize a second contest. The supervisors, expecting this request, had put together the following data:

| Units Produced (4 Plants Combined) | Before-Contest Frequency | During-Contest Frequency |
|---|---|---|
| 0–2,500 | 11 | 0 |
| 2,501–8,000 | 23 | 20 |
| 8,001–15,000 | 56 | 83 |
| 15,001–20,000 | 15 | 52 |
| | 105 days | 155 days |

Jennifer examined the data and indicated that the contest looked to be a success, but she wanted to base her decision to continue the contest on more than just an observation of the data. "Surely there must be some way to statistically test the worthiness of this contest," Jennifer stated. "I have to see the results before I will authorize the second contest."

# References

Berenson, Mark L., and David M. Levine, *Basic Business Statistics: Concepts and Applications*, 11th ed. (Upper Saddle River, NJ: Prentice Hall, 2009).

Conover, W. J., *Practical Nonparametric Statistics*, 3rd ed. (New York City: Wiley, 1999).

Higgins, James J., *Introduction to Modern Nonparametric Statistics*, 1st ed. (Pacific Grove, CA: Duxbury, 2004).

Marascuilo, Leonard, and M. McSweeney, *Nonparametric and Distribution Free Methods for the Social Sciences* (Monterey, CA: Brooks/Cole, 1977).

*Microsoft Excel 2007* (Redmond, WA: Microsoft Corp., 2007).

*Minitab for Windows Version 15* (State College, PA: Minitab, Inc., 2007).

**Chapter 14 Quick Prep Links**

- **Review** the methods for testing a null hypothesis using the *t*-distribution in Chapter 9.
- **Review** confidence intervals discussed in Chapter 8.

- **Make sure** you review the discussion about scatter plots in Chapter 2.
- **Review** the concepts associated with selecting a simple random sample in Chapter 1.

- **Review** the *F*-distribution and the approach for finding critical values from the *F*-table as discussed in Chapters 11 and 12.

# Introduction to Linear Regression and Correlation Analysis

## Why you need to know

Although some business situations involve only one variable, others require decision makers to consider the relationship between two or more variables. For example, a financial manager might be interested in the relationship between stock prices and the dividends issued by a publicly traded company. A marketing manager would be interested in examining the relationship between product sales and the amount of money spent on advertising. Finally, consider a loan manager at a bank who is interested in determining the fair market value of a home or business. She would begin by collecting data on a sample of comparable properties that have sold recently. In addition to the selling price, she would collect data on other factors, such as the size and age of the property. She might then analyze the relationship between the price and the other variables and use this relationship to determine an appraised price for the property in question.

Simple linear regression and correlation analysis, which are introduced in this chapter, are statistical techniques the broker, marketing director, and appraiser will need in their analyses. These techniques are two of the most often applied statistical procedures used by business decision makers for analyzing the relationship between two variables. In Chapter 15, we will extend the discussion to include three or more variables.

# 14.1 Scatter Plots and Correlation

**Scatter Plot**

A two-dimensional plot showing the values for the joint occurrence of two quantitative variables. The scatter plot may be used to graphically represent the relationship between two variables. It is also known as a scatter diagram.

Decision-making situations that call for understanding the relationship between two quantitative variables are aided by the use of **scatter plots**, or *scatter diagrams*. Figure 14.1 shows scatter plots that depict several potential relationships between values of a dependent variable, *y*, and an independent variable, *x*. A *dependent* (or *response*) *variable* is the variable whose variation we wish to explain. An *independent* (or *explanatory*) *variable* is a variable used to explain variation in the dependent variable. In Figure 14.1, (a) and (b) are examples of strong *linear* (or straight line) relationships between *x* and *y*. Note that the linear relationship can be either positive (as the *x* variable increases, the *y* variable also increases) or negative (as the *x* variable increases, the *y* variable decreases).

Figures 14.1 (c) and (d) illustrate situations in which the relationship between the *x* and *y* variable is nonlinear. There are many possible nonlinear relationships that can occur. The scatter plot is very useful for visually identifying the nature of the relationship.

Figures 14.1 (e) and (f) show examples in which there is no identifiable relationship between the two variables. This means that as *x* increases, *y* sometimes increases and sometimes decreases but with no particular pattern.

## The Correlation Coefficient

**Correlation Coefficient**

A quantitative measure of the strength of the linear relationship between two variables. The correlation ranges from $-1.0$ to $+1.0$. A correlation of $\pm 1.0$ indicates a perfect linear relationship, whereas a correlation of 0 indicates no linear relationship.

In addition to analyzing the relationship between two variables graphically, we can also measure the strength of the linear relationship between two variables using a measure called the **correlation coefficient**.

The correlation coefficient of two variables can be estimated from sample data using Equation 14.1 or the algebraic equivalent, Equation 14.2.

**Chapter Outcome 1.** →

**Sample Correlation Coefficient**

$$r = \frac{\sum(x - \bar{x})(y - \bar{y})}{\sqrt{[\sum(x - \bar{x})^2][\sum(y - \bar{y})^2]}}$$    **(14.1)**

**FIGURE 14.1**  |  Two-Variable Relationships

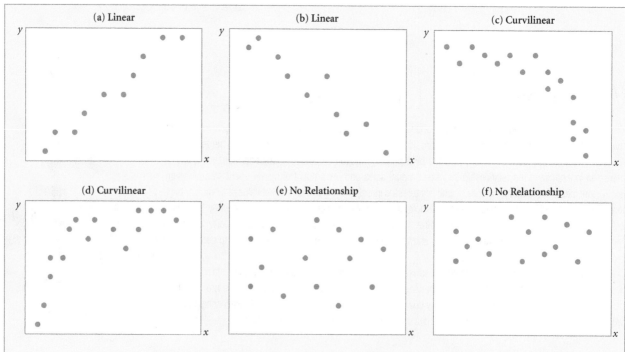

or the algebraic equivalent:

$$r = \frac{n\sum xy - \sum x \sum y}{\sqrt{[n(\sum x^2) - (\sum x)^2][n(\sum y^2) - (\sum y)^2]}}$$

(14.2)

where:

$r$ = Sample correlation coefficient
$n$ = Sample size
$x$ = Value of the independent variable
$y$ = Value of the dependent variable

The sample correlation coefficient computed using Equations 14.1 and 14.2 is called the *Pearson Product Moment Correlation*. The sample correlation coefficient, $r$, can range from a perfect positive correlation, $+1.0$, to a perfect negative correlation, $-1.0$. A perfect correlation is one in which all points on the scatter plot fall on a straight line. If two variables have no linear relationship, the correlation between them is 0 and there is no linear relationship between the change in $x$ and $y$. Consequently, the more the correlation differs from 0.0, the stronger the linear relationship between the two variables. The sign of the correlation coefficient indicates the direction of the relationship.

Figure 14.2 illustrates some examples of correlation between two variables. Once again, for the correlation coefficient to equal plus or minus 1.0, all the ($x$, $y$) points form a perfectly straight line. The more the points depart from a straight line, the weaker (closer to 0.0) the correlation is between the two variables.

**BUSINESS APPLICATION** | **TESTING FOR SIGNIFICANT CORRELATIONS**

**MIDWEST DISTRIBUTION COMPANY** Consider the application involving Midwest Distribution, which supplies soft drinks and snack foods to convenience stores in Michigan, Illinois, and Iowa. Although Midwest Distribution has been profitable, the director of marketing has been concerned about the rapid turnover in her salesforce. In the course of exit interviews, she discovered a major concern with the compensation structure.

Midwest Distribution has a two-part wage structure: a base salary and a commission computed on monthly sales. Typically, about half of the total wages paid comes from the base

**Excel and Minitab Tutorial**

**FIGURE 14.2** | Correlation between Two Variables

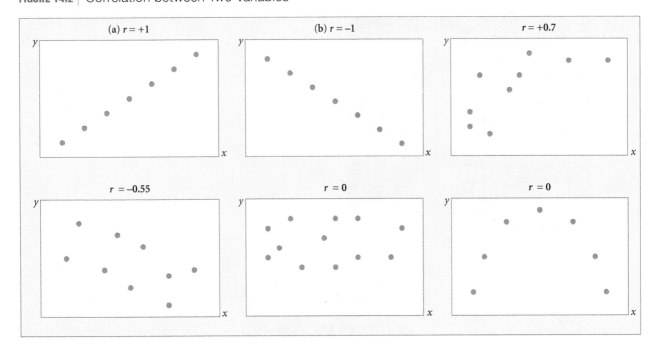

salary, which increases with longevity with the company. This portion of the wage structure is not an issue. The concern expressed by departing employees is that new employees tend to be given parts of the sales territory previously covered by existing employees and are assigned prime customers as a recruiting inducement.

At issue, then, is the relationship between sales (on which commissions are paid) and number of years with the company. The data for a random sample of 12 sales representatives are in the file called **Midwest**. The first step is to develop a scatter plot of the data. Both Excel and Minitab have procedures for constructing a scatter plot and computing the correlation coefficient.

The scatter plot for the Midwest data is shown in Figure 14.3. Based on this plot, total sales and years with the company appear to be linearly related. However, the strength of this relationship is uncertain. That is, how close do the points come to being on a straight line? To answer this question, we need a quantitative measure of the strength of the linear relationship between the two variables. That measure is the correlation coefficient.

Equation 14.1 is used to determine the correlation between sales and years with the company. Table 14.1 shows the manual calculations that were used to determine this correlation coefficient of 0.8325. However, because the calculations are rather tedious and long, we almost always use computer software to perform the computation, as shown in Figure 14.4. The $r = 0.8325$ indicates that there is a fairly strong, positive correlation between these two variables for the sample data.

**Significance Test for the Correlation**   Although a correlation coefficient of 0.8325 seems quite large (relative to 0), you should remember that this value is based on a sample of 12 data points and is subject to sampling error. Therefore, a formal hypothesis-testing

**FIGURE 14.3** | Excel 2007 Scatter Plot of Sales vs. Years with Midwest Distribution

**Excel 2007 Instructions:**
1. Open file: Midwest.xls.
2. Move the *Sales* column to the *right* of *Years with midwest* column.
3. Select data for chart.
4. On **Insert tab**, click **XY (Scatter)**, and then click the **Scatter with only Markers** Option.
5. Use the **Layout** tab of the **Chart Tools** to add titles and remove grid lines.
6. Use the **Design** tab of the **Chart Tools** to move the chart to a new worksheet.

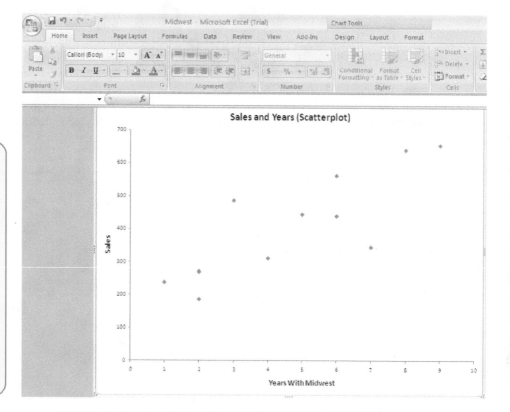

**Minitab Instructions (for similar results):**
1. Open file: Midwest.MTW.
2. Choose **Graph > Scatterplot**.
3. Under **Scatterplot**, choose **Simple OK**.
4. Under **Y variable**, enter *y* column.
5. In **X variable**, enter *x* column.
6. Click **OK**.

**TABLE 14.1** | **Correlation Coefficient Calculations for the Midwest Distribution Example**

| Sales | Years | | | | | |
|---|---|---|---|---|---|---|
| $y$ | $x$ | $x - \bar{x}$ | $y - \bar{y}$ | $(x - \bar{x})(y - \bar{y})$ | $(x - \bar{x})^2$ | $(y - \bar{y})^2$ |
| 487 | 3 | −1.58 | 82.42 | −130.22 | 2.50 | 6,793.06 |
| 445 | 5 | 0.42 | 40.42 | 16.98 | 0.18 | 1,633.78 |
| 272 | 2 | −2.58 | −132.58 | 342.06 | 6.66 | 17,577.46 |
| 641 | 8 | 3.42 | 236.42 | 808.56 | 11.70 | 55,894.42 |
| 187 | 2 | −2.58 | −217.58 | 561.36 | 6.66 | 47,341.06 |
| 440 | 6 | 1.42 | 35.42 | 50.30 | 2.02 | 1,254.58 |
| 346 | 7 | 2.42 | −58.58 | −141.76 | 5.86 | 3,431.62 |
| 238 | 1 | −3.58 | −166.58 | 596.36 | 12.82 | 27,748.90 |
| 312 | 4 | −0.58 | −92.58 | 53.70 | 0.34 | 8,571.06 |
| 269 | 2 | −2.58 | −135.58 | 349.80 | 6.66 | 18,381.94 |
| 655 | 9 | 4.42 | 250.42 | 1,106.86 | 19.54 | 62,710.18 |
| 563 | 6 | 1.42 | 158.42 | 224.96 | 2.02 | 25,096.90 |
| $\Sigma = 4,855$ | $\Sigma = 55$ | | | $\Sigma = 3,838.92$ | $\Sigma = 76.92$ | $\Sigma = 276,434.92$ |

$$\bar{y} = \frac{\Sigma y}{n} = \frac{4,855}{12} = 404.58 \qquad \bar{x} = \frac{\Sigma x}{n} = \frac{55}{12} = 4.58$$

**Using Equation 14.1,**

$$r = \frac{\Sigma(x - \bar{x})(y - \bar{y})}{\sqrt{\Sigma(x - \bar{x})^2 \, \Sigma(y - \bar{y})^2}} = \frac{3,838.92}{\sqrt{(76.92)(276,434.92)}} = 0.8325$$

**FIGURE 14.4** | Excel 2007 Correlation Output for Midwest Distribution

Excel 2007 Instructions:
1. Open file: Midwest.xls.
2. On the **Data** tab, click **Data Analysis**.
3. Select **Correlation**.
4. Define Data Range.
5. Click on **Labels in First Row**.
6. Specify output location.
7. Click **OK**.

Minitab Instructions (for similar results):
1. Open file: Midwest.MTW.
2. Choose **Stat > Basic Statistics > Correlation**.
3. In **Variables**, enter $Y$ and $X$ columns.
4. Click **OK**.

procedure is needed to determine whether the linear relationship between sales and years with the company is significant.

The null and alternative hypotheses to be tested are

$$H_0: \rho = 0 \quad \text{(no correlation)}$$
$$H_A: \rho \neq 0 \quad \text{(correlation exists)}$$

where the Greek symbol $\rho$ (rho) represents the population correlation coefficient.

We must test whether the sample data support or refute the null hypothesis. The test procedure utilizes the $t$-test statistic in Equation 14.3.

**Chapter Outcome 2.→**

**Test Statistic for Correlation**

$$t = \frac{r}{\sqrt{\dfrac{1 - r^2}{n - 2}}} \qquad df = n - 2 \qquad \textbf{(14.3)}$$

where:

$t$ = Number of standard errors $r$ is from 0
$r$ = Sample correlation coefficient
$n$ = Sample size

The degrees of freedom for this test are $n - 2$, because we lose 1 degree of freedom for each of the two sample means ($\bar{x}$ and $\bar{y}$) that are used to estimate the population means for the two variables.

Figure 14.5 shows the hypothesis test for the Midwest Distribution example using an alpha level of 0.05. Recall that the sample correlation coefficient was $r = 0.8325$. Based on these sample data, we should conclude there is a significant, positive linear relationship in the population between years of experience and total sales for Midwest Distribution sales representatives.

**FIGURE 14.5**

Correlation Significance Test for the Midwest Distribution Example

Hypothesis:

$H_0: \rho = 0$ (no correlation)
$H_A: \rho \neq 0$
$\alpha = 0.05$

$df = n - 2 = 10$

Rejection Region
$\alpha/2 = 0.025$

Rejection Region
$\alpha/2 = 0.025$

$-t_{0.025} = -2.228$

$t_{0.025} = 2.228$

The calculated $t$-value is

$$t = \frac{r}{\sqrt{\dfrac{1 - r^2}{n - 2}}} = \frac{0.8325}{\sqrt{\dfrac{1 - 0.6931}{10}}}$$
$$= 4.752$$

**Decision Rule:**

If $t > t_{0.025} = 2.228$, reject $H_0$.
If $t < -t_{0.025} = -2.228$, reject $H_0$.
Otherwise, do not reject $H_0$.
Because $4.752 > 2.228$, reject $H_0$.

Based on the sample evidence, we conclude there is a significant positive linear relationship between years with the company and sales volume.

The implication is that the more years an employee has been with the company, the more sales that employee generates. This runs counter to the claims made by some of the departing employees. The manager will probably want to look further into the situation to see whether a problem might exist in certain regions.

The *t*-test for determining whether the population correlation is significantly different from 0 requires the following assumptions:

**Assumptions**

---

1. The data are interval or ratio-level.
2. The two variables (*y* and *x*) are distributed as a *bivariate normal* distribution.

---

Although the formal mathematical representation is beyond the scope of this text, *two variables are bivariate normal if their joint distribution is normally distributed*. Although the *t*-test assumes a bivariate normal distribution, it is robust—that is, correct inferences can be reached even with slight departures from the normal-distribution assumption. (See Kutner et al., *Applied Linear Statistical Models*, for further discussion of bivariate normal distributions.)

---

**EXAMPLE 14-1**    **CORRELATION ANALYSIS**

---

**Stock Portfolio Analysis** A student intern at the investment firm of McMillan & Associates was given the assignment of determining whether there is a positive correlation between the number of individual stocks in a client's portfolio (*x*) and the annual rate of return (*y*) for the portfolio. The intern selected a simple random sample of 12 client portfolios and determined the number of individual company stocks and the annual rate of return earned by the client on his or her portfolio. To determine whether there is a statistically significant positive correlation between the two variables, the following steps can be employed:

**Step 1**  **Specify the population parameter of interest.**
The intern wishes to determine whether the number of stocks is positively correlated with the rate of return earned by the client. The parameter of interest is, therefore, the population correlation, $\rho$.

**Step 2**  **Formulate the appropriate null and alternative hypotheses.**
Because the intern was asked to determine whether a positive correlation exists between the variables of interest, the hypothesis test will be one-tailed, as follows:

$$H_0: \rho \leq 0$$
$$H_A: \rho > 0$$

**Step 3**  **Specify the level of significance.**
A significance level of 0.05 is chosen.

**Step 4**  **Compute the correlation coefficient and the test statistic.**
Compute the sample correlation coefficient using Equation 14.1 or 14.2, or by using software such as Excel or Minitab.
The following sample data were obtained:

| Number of Stocks | Rate of Return |
|:---:|:---:|
| 9 | 0.13 |
| 16 | 0.16 |
| 25 | 0.21 |
| 16 | 0.18 |
| 20 | 0.18 |
| 16 | 0.19 |
| 20 | 0.15 |
| 20 | 0.17 |
| 16 | 0.13 |
| 9 | 0.11 |

Using Equation 14.1, we get

$$r = \frac{\sum(x - \bar{x})(y - \bar{y})}{\sqrt{[\sum(x - \bar{x})^2][\sum(y - \bar{y})^2]}} = 0.7796$$

Compute the $t$-test statistic using Equation 14.3:

$$t = \frac{r}{\sqrt{\dfrac{1 - r^2}{n - 2}}} = \frac{0.7796}{\sqrt{\dfrac{1 - 0.7796^2}{10 - 2}}} = 3.52$$

**Step 5  Construct the rejection region and decision rule.**
For an alpha level equal to 0.05, the one-tailed, upper-tail, critical value for $n - 2 = 10 - 2 = 8$ degrees of freedom is $t_{0.05} = 1.8595$. The decision rule is

If $t > 1.8595$, reject the null hypothesis.

Otherwise, do not reject the null hypothesis.

**Step 6  Reach a decision.**
Because

$t = 3.52 > 1.8595$, reject the null hypothesis.

**Step 7  Draw a conclusion.**
Because the null hypothesis is rejected, the sample data do support the contention that there is a positive linear relationship between the number of individual stocks in a client's portfolio and the portfolio's rate of return.

>>END EXAMPLE

TRY PROBLEM 14-3 (pg. 587)

**Cause-and-Effect Interpretations**  Care must be used when interpreting the correlation results. For example, even though we found a significant linear relationship between years of experience and sales for the Midwest Distribution sales force, the correlation does not imply cause and effect. Although an increase in experience may, in fact, cause sales to change, simply because the two variables are correlated does not guarantee a cause-and-effect situation. Two seemingly unconnected variables may be highly correlated. For example, over a period of time, teachers' salaries in North Dakota might be highly correlated with the price of grapes in Spain. Yet, we doubt that a change in grape prices will *cause* a corresponding change in salaries for teachers in North Dakota, or vice versa. When a correlation exists between two seemingly unrelated variables, the correlation is said to be a *spurious correlation*. You should take great care to avoid basing conclusions on spurious correlations.

The Midwest Distribution marketing director has a logical reason to believe that years of experience with the company and total sales are related. That is, sales theory and customer feedback hold that product knowledge is a major component in successfully marketing a product. However, a statistically significant correlation alone does not prove that this cause-and-effect relationship exists. When two seemingly unrelated variables are correlated, they may both be responding to changes in some third variable. For example, the observed correlation could be the effect of a company policy of giving better sales territories to more senior salespeople.

# 14-1: Exercises

## Skill Development

**14-1.** An industry study was recently conducted in which the sample correlation between units sold and marketing expenses was 0.57. The sample size for the study included 15 companies. Based on the sample results, test to determine whether there is a significant positive correlation between these two variables. Use an $\alpha = 0.05$.

**14-2.** The following data for the dependent variable, $y$, and the independent variable, $x$, have been collected using simple random sampling:

| $x$ | $y$ |
|-----|-----|
| 10 | 120 |
| 14 | 130 |
| 16 | 170 |
| 12 | 150 |
| 20 | 200 |
| 18 | 180 |
| 16 | 190 |
| 14 | 150 |
| 16 | 160 |
| 18 | 200 |

a. Construct a scatter plot for these data. Based on the scatter plot, how would you describe the relationship between the two variables?
b. Compute the correlation coefficient.

**14-3.** A random sample of the following two variables was obtained:

| $x$ | 29 | 48 | 28 | 22 | 28 | 42 | 33 | 26 | 48 | 44 |
|-----|----|----|----|----|----|----|----|----|----|----|
| $y$ | 16 | 46 | 34 | 26 | 49 | 11 | 41 | 13 | 47 | 16 |

a. Calculate the correlation between these two variables.
b. Conduct a test of hypothesis to determine if there exists a correlation between the two variables in the population. Use a significance level of 0.10.

**14-4.** A random sample of two variables, $x$ and $y$, produced the following observations:

| $x$ | $y$ |
|-----|-----|
| 19 | 7 |
| 13 | 9 |
| 17 | 8 |
| 9 | 11 |
| 12 | 9 |
| 25 | 6 |
| 20 | 7 |
| 17 | 8 |

a. Develop a scatter plot for the two variables and describe what relationship, if any, exists.
b. Compute the correlation coefficient for these sample data.
c. Test to determine whether the population correlation coefficient is negative. Use a significance level of 0.05 for the hypothesis test.

**14-5.** You are given the following data for variables $x$ and $y$:

| $x$ | $y$ |
|-----|-----|
| 3.0 | 1.5 |
| 2.0 | 0.5 |
| 2.5 | 1.0 |
| 3.0 | 1.8 |
| 2.5 | 1.2 |
| 4.0 | 2.2 |
| 1.5 | 0.4 |
| 1.0 | 0.3 |
| 2.0 | 1.3 |
| 2.5 | 1.0 |

a. Plot these variables in scatter plot format. Based on this plot, what type of relationship appears to exist between the two variables?
b. Compute the correlation coefficient for these sample data. Indicate what the correlation coefficient measures.
c. Test to determine whether the population correlation coefficient is positive. Use the $\alpha = 0.01$ level to conduct the test. Be sure to state the null and alternative hypotheses and show the test and decision rule clearly.

**14-6.** For each of the following circumstances, perform the indicated hypothesis tests:
a. $H_A: \rho > 0$, $r = 0.53$, and $n = 30$ with $\alpha = 0.01$, using a test-statistic approach.
b. $H_A: \rho \neq 0$, $r = -0.48$, and $n = 20$ with $\alpha = 0.05$, using a $p$-value approach.
c. $H_A: \rho \neq 0$, $r = 0.39$, and $n = 45$ with $\alpha = 0.02$, using a test-statistic approach.
d. $H_A: \rho < 0$, $r = 0.34$, and $n = 25$ with $\alpha = 0.05$, using a test-statistic approach.

## Business Applications

**14-7.** The Federal No Child Left Behind Act requires periodic testing in standard subjects. A random sample of 50 junior high school students from Atlanta was selected, and each student's scores on a standardized mathematics examination and a standardized English examination were recorded. School administrators were interested in the relation between the two scores. Suppose the correlation coefficient for the two examination scores is 0.75.

a. Provide an explanation of the sample correlation coefficient in this context.

b. Using a level of significance of $\alpha = 0.01$, test to determine whether there is a positive linear relationship between mathematics scores and English scores for junior high school students in Atlanta.

**14-8.** Because of the current concern over credit card balances, a bank's Chief Financial Officer is interested in whether there is a relationship between account balances and the number of times a card is used each month. A random sample of 50 accounts was selected. The account balance and the number of charges during the past month were the two variables recorded. The correlation coefficient for the two variables was $-0.23$.

a. Discuss what the $r = -0.23$ measures. Make sure to frame your discussion in terms of the two variables mentioned here.

b. Using an $\alpha = 0.10$ level, test to determine whether there is a significant linear relationship between account balance and the number of card uses during the past month. State the null and alternative hypotheses and show the decision rule.

c. Consider the decision you reached in part b. Describe the type of error you could have made in the context of this problem.

**14-9.** Farmers National Bank issues MasterCard credit cards to its customers. A main factor in determining whether a credit card will be profitable to the bank is the average monthly balance that the customer will maintain on the card that will be subject to finance charges. Bank analysts wish to determine whether there is a relationship between the average monthly credit card balance and the income stated on the original credit card application form. The following sample data have been collected from existing credit card customers:

| Income | Credit Balance |
|--------|----------------|
| $43,000 | $345 |
| $35,000 | $1,370 |
| $47,000 | $1,140 |
| $55,000 | $201 |
| $55,000 | $56 |
| $59,000 | $908 |
| $28,000 | $2,345 |
| $43,000 | $104 |
| $54,000 | $0 |
| $36,000 | $1,290 |
| $39,000 | $130 |
| $31,000 | $459 |
| $30,000 | $0 |
| $37,000 | $1,950 |
| $39,000 | $240 |

a. Indicate which variable is to be the independent variable and which is to be the dependent variable in the bank's analysis and indicate why.

b. Construct a scatter plot for these data and describe what, if any, relationship appears to exist between these two variables.

c. Calculate the correlation coefficient for these two variables and test to determine whether there is a significant correlation at the $\alpha = 0.05$ level.

**14-10.** Amazon.com has become one of the most successful online merchants. Two measures of its success are sales and net income/loss figures (all figures in $million). These values for the years 1995–2007 are shown as follows.

| Year | Net Income/Loss | Sales |
|------|-----------------|-------|
| 1995 | −0.3 | 0.5 |
| 1996 | −5.7 | 15.7 |
| 1997 | −27.5 | 147.7 |
| 1998 | −124.5 | 609.8 |
| 1999 | −719.9 | 1,639.8 |
| 2000 | −1,411.2 | 2,761.9 |
| 2001 | −567.3 | 3,122.9 |
| 2002 | −149.1 | 3,933 |
| 2003 | 35.3 | 5,263.7 |
| 2004 | 588.5 | 6,921 |
| 2005 | 359 | 8,490 |
| 2006 | 190 | 10,711 |
| 2007 | 476 | 14,835 |

a. Produce a scatter plot for Amazon's net income/loss and sales figures for the period 1995 to 2007. Does there appear to be a linear relationship between these two variables? Explain your response.

b. Calculate the correlation coefficient between Amazon's net income/loss and sales figures for the period 1995 to 2007.

c. Conduct a hypothesis test to determine if a positive correlation exists between Amazon's net income/loss and sales figures. Use a significance level of 0.05 and assume that these figures form a random sample.

**14-11.** Complaints concerning excessive commercials seem to grow as the amount of "clutter," including commercials and advertisements for other television shows, steadily increases on network and cable television. A recent analysis by Nielsen Monitor-Plus compares the average nonprogram minutes in an hour of prime time for both network and cable television. Data for selected years are shown as follows.

| Year | 1996 | 1999 | 2001 | 2004 |
|------|------|------|------|------|
| **Network** | 9.88 | 14.00 | 14.65 | 15.80 |
| **Cable** | 12.77 | 13.88 | 14.50 | 14.92 |

a. Calculate the correlation coefficient for the average nonprogram minutes in an hour of prime time between network and cable television.

b. Conduct a hypothesis test to determine if a positive correlation exists between the average nonprogram minutes in an hour of prime time between network and cable television. Use a significance level of 0.05 and assume that these figures form a random sample.

## Computer Database Exercises

**14-12.** Platinum Billiards, Inc., is a retailer of billiard supplies based in Jacksonville, Florida. It stands out among billiard suppliers because of the research it does to assure its products are top-notch. One experiment was conducted to measure the speed attained by a cue ball struck by various weighted pool cues. The conjecture is that a light cue generates faster speeds while breaking the balls at the beginning of a game of pool. Anecdotal experience has indicated that a billiard cue weighing less than 19 ounces generates faster speeds. Platinum used a robotic arm to investigate this claim. Its research generated the data given in the file entitled **Breakcue**.

a. To determine if there is a negative relationship between the weight of the pool cue and the speed attained by the cue ball, calculate a correlation coefficient.

b. Conduct a test of hypothesis to determine if there is a negative relationship between the weight of the pool cue and the speed attained by the cue ball. Use a significance level of 0.025 and a *p*-value approach.

**14-13.** Customers who made online purchases last quarter from an Internet retailer were randomly sampled from the retailer's database. The dollar value of each customer's quarterly purchases along with the time the customer spent shopping the company's online catalog that quarter were recorded. The sample results are contained in the file **Online**.

a. Create a scatter plot of the variables Time (*x*) and Purchases (*y*). What relationship, if any, appears to exist between the two variables?

b. Compute the correlation coefficient for these sample data. What does the correlation coefficient measure?

c. Conduct a hypothesis test to determine if there is a positive relationship between time viewing the retailer's catalog and dollar amount purchased. Use a level of significance equal to 0.025. Provide a managerial explanation of your results.

**14-14.** A regional accreditation board for colleges and universities is interested in determining whether a relationship exists between student applicant verbal SAT scores and the in-state tuition costs at the university. Data have been collected on a sample of colleges and universities and are in the data file called **Colleges and Universities**.

a. Develop a scatter plot for these two variables and discuss what, if any, relationship you see between the two variables based on the scatter plot.

b. Compute the sample correlation coefficient.

c. Based on the correlation coefficient computed in part b, test to determine whether the population correlation coefficient is positive for these two variables. That is, can we expect schools that charge higher in-state tuition will attract students with higher average verbal SAT scores? Test using a 0.05 significance level.

**14-15.** As the number of air travelers with time on their hands increases, logic would indicate spending on retail purchases in airports would increase as well. A study by *Airport Revenue News* addressed the per person spending at select airports for merchandise, excluding food, gifts, and news items. A file entitled **Revenues** contains sample data selected from airport retailers in 2001 and again in 2004.

a. Produce a scatter plot for the per person spending at selected airports for merchandise, excluding food, gifts, and news items, for the years 2001 and 2004. Does there appear to be a linear relationship between spending in 2001 and spending in 2004? Explain your response.

b. Calculate the correlation coefficient between the per person spending in 2001 and the per person spending in 2004. Does it appear that an increase in per person spending in 2001 would be associated with an increase in spending in 2004? Support your assertion.

c. Conduct a hypothesis test to determine if a positive correlation exists between the per person spending in 2001 and that in 2004. Use a significance level of 0.05 and assume that these figures form a random sample.

**END EXERCISES 14-1**

## 14.2 Simple Linear Regression Analysis

In the Midwest Distribution application, we determined that the relationship between years of experience and total sales is linear and statistically significant, based on the correlation analysis performed in the previous section. Because hiring and training costs have been increasing, we would like to use this relationship to help formulate a more acceptable wage package for the sales force.

The statistical method we will use to analyze the relationship between years of experience and total sales is *regression analysis*. When we have only two variables—a dependent variable, such as sales, and an independent variable, such as years with the company—the technique is referred to as *simple regression analysis*. When the relationship between the dependent variable and the independent variable is linear, the technique is **simple linear regression**.

**Simple Linear Regression**

The method of regression analysis in which a single independent variable is used to predict the dependent variable.

## The Regression Model and Assumptions

The objective of simple linear regression (which we shall call *regression analysis*) is to represent the relationship between values of $x$ and $y$ with a model of the form shown in Equation 14.4.

---

### Simple Linear Regression Model (Population Model)

$$y = \beta_0 + \beta_1 x + \varepsilon \qquad \text{(14.4)}$$

where:

$y$ = Value of the dependent variable
$x$ = Value of the independent variable
$\beta_0$ = Population's $y$ intercept
$\beta_1$ = Slope of the population regression line
$\varepsilon$ = Random error term

---

The simple linear regression population model described in Equation 14.4 has four assumptions:

**Assumptions**

1. Individual values of the error terms, $\varepsilon$, are statistically independent of one another, and these values represent a random sample from the population of possible $\varepsilon$-values at each level of $x$.
2. For a given value of $x$, there can exist many values of $y$ and therefore many values of $\varepsilon$. Further, the distribution of possible $\varepsilon$-values for any $x$-value is normal.
3. The distributions of possible $\varepsilon$-values have equal variances for all values of $x$.
4. The means of the dependent variable, $y$, for all specified values of the independent variable, $(\mu_{y|x})$, can be connected by a straight line called the population regression model.

Figure 14.6 illustrates assumptions 2, 3, and 4. The regression model (straight line) connects the average of the $y$-values for each level of the independent variable, $x$. The actual $y$-values for each level of $x$ are normally distributed around the mean of $y$. Finally, observe that the spread of possible $y$-values is the same regardless of the level of $x$. The population regression line is determined by two values, $\beta_0$ and $\beta_1$. These values are known as the population *regression coefficients*. Value $\beta_0$ identifies the $y$ intercept and $\beta_1$ the slope of the regression line. Under the regression assumptions, the coefficients define the true population model. For each observation, the actual value of the dependent variable, $y$, for any $x$ is the sum of two components:

$$y = \underbrace{\beta_0 + \beta_1 x}_{\text{Linear component}} + \underbrace{\varepsilon}_{\text{Random error component}}$$

The random error component, $\varepsilon$, may be positive, zero, or negative, depending on whether a single value of $y$ for a given $x$ falls above, on, or below the population regression line. Section 15.5 in Chapter 15 discusses how to check whether assumptions have been violated and the possible courses of action if the violations occur.

**FIGURE 14.6**

Graphical Display of Linear Regression Assumptions

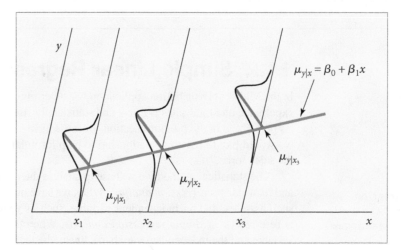

# Meaning of the Regression Coefficients

**Regression Slope Coefficient**

The average change in the dependent variable for a unit change in the independent variable. The slope coefficient may be positive or negative, depending on the relationship between the two variables.

Coefficient $\beta_1$, the **regression slope coefficient** of the population regression line, measures the average change in the value of the dependent variable, $y$, for each unit change in $x$. The regression slope can be either positive, zero, or negative, depending on the relationship between $x$ and $y$. For example, a positive population slope of 12 ($\beta_1 = 12$) means that for a 1-unit increase in $x$, we can expect an average 12-unit increase in $y$. Correspondingly, if the population slope is negative 12 ($\beta_1 = -12$), we can expect an average decrease of 12 units in $y$ for a 1-unit increase in $x$.

The population's $y$ intercept, $\beta_0$, indicates the mean value of $y$ when $x$ is 0. However, this interpretation holds only if the population could have $x$ values equal to 0. When this cannot occur, $\beta_0$ does not have a meaningful interpretation in the regression model.

---

**BUSINESS APPLICATION**  SIMPLE LINEAR REGRESSION ANALYSIS

---

**MIDWEST DISTRIBUTION (*CONTINUED*)** The Midwest Distribution marketing manager has data for a sample of 12 sales representatives. In Section 14.1, she has established that a significant linear relationship exists between years of experience and total sales using correlation analysis. (Recall that the sample correlation between the two variables was $r = 0.8325$.) Now she would like to estimate the regression equation that

defines the *true* linear relationship (that is, the population's linear relationship) between years of experience and sales. Figure 14.3 shows the scatter plot for two variables: years with the company and sales. We need to use the sample data to estimate $\beta_0$ and $\beta_1$, the true intercept and slope of the line representing the relationship between two variables. The *regression line* through the sample data is the best estimate of the population regression line. However, there are an infinite number of possible regression lines for a set of points. For example, Figure 14.7 shows three of the

**FIGURE 14.7** | Possible Regression Lines

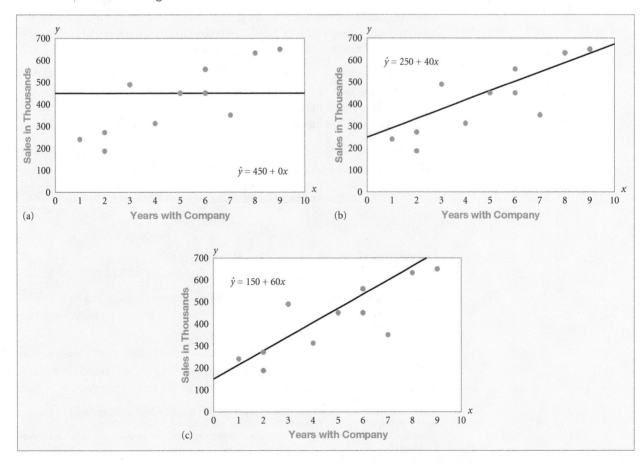

**FIGURE 14.8**

Computation of Regression Error for the Midwest Distribution Example

possible different lines that pass through the Midwest Distribution data. Which line should be used to estimate the true regression model?

We must establish a criterion for selecting the best line. The criterion used is the **least squares criterion**. To understand the least squares criterion, you need to know about prediction error, or **residual**, which is the distance between the actual $y$ coordinate of an $(x, y)$ point and the predicted value of that $y$ coordinate produced by the regression line. Figure 14.8 shows how the prediction error is calculated for the employee who was with Midwest for four years ($x = 4$) using one possible regression line: (where $\hat{y}$ is the predicted sales value). The predicted sales value is

$$\hat{y} = 150 + 60(4) = 390$$

However, the actual sales ($y$) for this employee is 312 (see Table 14.2). Thus, when $x = 4$, the difference between the observed value, $y = 312$, and the predicted value, $\hat{y} = 390$, is $312 - 390 = -78$. The residual (or prediction error) for this case when $x = 4$ is $-78$. Table 14.2 shows the calculated prediction errors and sum of squared errors for each of the three regression lines shown in Figure 14.7.[1] Of these three potential regression models, the line with the equation $\hat{y} = 150 + 60x$ has the smallest sum of squared errors. However, is there a better line than this? That is, would $\sum_{i=1}^{n}(y_i - \hat{y}_i)^2$ be smaller for some other line? One way to determine this is to calculate the sum of squared errors for all other regression lines. However, because there are an infinite number of these lines, this approach is not feasible. Fortunately, through the use of calculus, equations can be derived to directly determine the slope and intercept estimates such that $\sum_{i=1}^{n}(y_i - \hat{y}_i)^2$ is minimized.[2] This is accomplished by letting the estimated regression model be of the form shown in Equation 14.5.

**Least Squares Criterion**

The criterion for determining a regression line that minimizes the sum of squared prediction errors.

**Residual**

The difference between the actual value of the dependent variable and the value predicted by the regression model.

Chapter Outcome 3. →

---

### Estimated Regression Model (Sample Model)

$$\hat{y} = b_0 + b_1 x \tag{14.5}$$

where:

$\hat{y}$ = Estimated, or predicted, $y$-value
$b_0$ = Unbiased estimate of the regression intercept, found using Equation 14.8
$b_1$ = Unbiased estimate of the regression slope, found using Equation 14.6 or 14.7
$x$ = Value of the independent variable

---

Equations 14.6 and 14.8 are referred to as the solutions to the *least squares equations* because they provide the slope and intercept that minimize the sum of squared errors. Equation 14.7 is

[1]The reason we are using the sum of the squared residuals is that the sum of the residuals will be zero for the best regression line (the positive values of the residuals will balance the negative values).
[2]The calculus derivation of the least squares equations is contained in the Kutner et al. reference shown at the end of this chapter.

**TABLE 14.2** | **Sum of Squared Errors for Three Linear Equations for Midwest Distribution**

From Figure 14.7(a):

$\hat{y} = 450 + 0x$

| | | | Residual | |
|---|---|---|---|---|
| *x* | *ŷ* | *y* | *y* − *ŷ* | (*y* − *ŷ*)² |
| 3 | 450 | 487 | 37 | 1,369 |
| 5 | 450 | 445 | −5 | 25 |
| 2 | 450 | 272 | −178 | 31,684 |
| 8 | 450 | 641 | 191 | 36,481 |
| 2 | 450 | 187 | −263 | 69,169 |
| 6 | 450 | 440 | −10 | 100 |
| 7 | 450 | 346 | −104 | 10,816 |
| 1 | 450 | 238 | −212 | 44,944 |
| 4 | 450 | 312 | −138 | 19,044 |
| 2 | 450 | 269 | −181 | 32,761 |
| 9 | 450 | 655 | 205 | 42,025 |
| 6 | 450 | 563 | 113 | 12,769 |
| | | | | $\Sigma = 301{,}187$ |

From Figure 14.7(b):

$\hat{y} = 250 + 40x$

| | | | Residual | |
|---|---|---|---|---|
| *x* | *ŷ* | *y* | *y* − *ŷ* | (*y* − *ŷ*)² |
| 3 | 370 | 487 | 117 | 13,689 |
| 5 | 450 | 445 | −5 | 25 |
| 2 | 330 | 272 | −58 | 3,364 |
| 8 | 570 | 641 | 71 | 5,041 |
| 2 | 330 | 187 | −143 | 20,449 |
| 6 | 490 | 440 | −50 | 2,500 |
| 7 | 530 | 346 | −184 | 33,856 |
| 1 | 290 | 238 | −52 | 2,704 |
| 4 | 410 | 312 | −98 | 9,604 |
| 2 | 330 | 269 | −61 | 3,721 |
| 9 | 610 | 655 | 45 | 2,025 |
| 6 | 490 | 563 | 73 | 5,329 |
| | | | | $\Sigma = 102{,}307$ |

From Figure 14.7(c):

$\hat{y} = 150 + 60x$

| | | | Residual | |
|---|---|---|---|---|
| *x* | *ŷ* | *y* | *y* − *ŷ* | (*y* − *ŷ*)² |
| 3 | 330 | 487 | 157 | 24,649 |
| 5 | 450 | 445 | −5 | 25 |
| 2 | 270 | 272 | 2 | 4 |
| 8 | 630 | 641 | 11 | 121 |
| 2 | 270 | 187 | −83 | 6,889 |
| 6 | 510 | 440 | −70 | 4,900 |
| 7 | 570 | 346 | −224 | 50,176 |
| 1 | 210 | 238 | 28 | 784 |
| 4 | 390 | 312 | −78 | 6,084 |
| 2 | 270 | 269 | −1 | 1 |
| 9 | 690 | 655 | −35 | 1,225 |
| 6 | 510 | 563 | 53 | 2,809 |
| | | | | $\Sigma = 97{,}667$ |

the algebraic equivalent of Equation 14.6 and may be easier to use when the computation is performed using a calculator.

---

### Least Squares Equations

$$b_1 = \frac{\sum(x_i - \bar{x})(y_i - \bar{y})}{\sum(x_i - \bar{x})^2} \tag{14.6}$$

algebraic equivalent:

$$b_1 = \frac{\sum xy - \dfrac{\sum x \sum y}{n}}{\sum x^2 - \dfrac{(\sum x)^2}{n}} \tag{14.7}$$

and

$$b_0 = \bar{y} - b_1 \bar{x} \tag{14.8}$$

---

Table 14.3 shows the manual calculations, which are subject to rounding, for the least squares estimates for the Midwest Distribution example. However, you will almost always

**TABLE 14.3** ｜ **Manual Calculations for Least Squares Regression Coefficients for the Midwest Distribution Example**

| y | x | xy | $x^2$ | $y^2$ |
|---|---|---|---|---|
| 487 | 3 | 1,461 | 9 | 237,169 |
| 445 | 5 | 2,225 | 25 | 198,025 |
| 272 | 2 | 544 | 4 | 73,984 |
| 641 | 8 | 5,128 | 64 | 410,881 |
| 187 | 2 | 374 | 4 | 34,969 |
| 440 | 6 | 2,640 | 36 | 193,600 |
| 346 | 7 | 2,422 | 49 | 119,716 |
| 238 | 1 | 238 | 1 | 56,644 |
| 312 | 4 | 1,248 | 16 | 97,344 |
| 269 | 2 | 538 | 4 | 72,361 |
| 655 | 9 | 5,895 | 81 | 429,025 |
| 563 | 6 | 3,378 | 36 | 316,969 |
| $\sum y = 4{,}855$ | $\sum x = 55$ | $\sum xy = 26{,}091$ | $\sum x^2 = 329$ | $\sum y^2 = 2{,}240{,}687$ |

$$\bar{y} = \frac{\sum y}{n} = \frac{4{,}855}{12} = 404.58 \qquad \bar{x} = \frac{\sum x}{n} = \frac{55}{12} = 4.58$$

$$b_1 = \frac{\sum xy - \dfrac{\sum x \sum y}{n}}{\sum x^2 - \dfrac{(\sum x)^2}{n}} = \frac{26{,}091 - \dfrac{55(4{,}855)}{12}}{329 - \dfrac{(55)^2}{12}}$$

$$= 49.91$$

Then,

$$b_0 = \bar{y} - b_1 \bar{x} = 404.58 - 49.91(4.58) = 175.99$$

The least squares regression line is, therefore,

$$\hat{y} = 175.99 + 49.91x$$

There is a slight difference between the manual calculation and the computer result due to rounding.

**FIGURE 14.9A**

Excel 2007 Midwest Distribution Regression Results

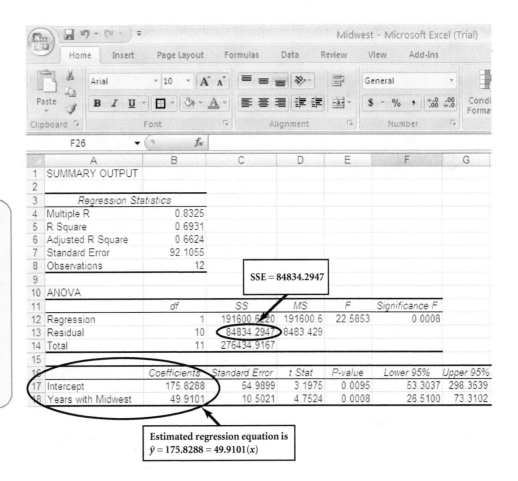

**Excel 2007 Instructions:**
1. Open file: Midwest.xls.
2. On the **Data** tab, click **Data Analysis**.
3. Select **Regression Analysis**.
4. Define $x$ (*Years* with Midwest) and $y$ (*Sales*) variable data range.
5. Select output location.
6. Check **Labels**.
7. Click **Residuals**.
8. Click **OK**.

use a software package such as Excel or Minitab to perform these computations. (Figures 14.9a and 14.9b show the Excel and Minitab output.) In this case, the "best" regression line, given the least squares criterion, is $\hat{y} = 175.8288 + 49.9101(x)$. Figure 14.10 shows the predicted sales values along with the prediction errors and squared errors associated with this best simple linear regression line. Keep in mind that the prediction errors are also referred to as residuals. From Figure 14.10, the sum of the squared errors is 84,834.29. This is the smallest sum of squared residuals possible for this set of sample data. No other simple linear regression line

**FIGURE 14.9B**

Minitab Midwest Distribution Regression Results

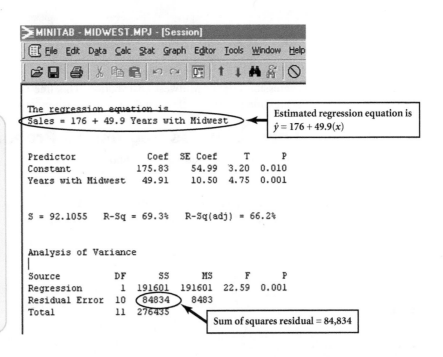

**Minitab Instructions:**
1. Open file: Midwest. MTW.
2. Choose **Stat > Regression > Regression**.
3. In **Response,** enter the $y$ variable column.
4. In **Predictors,** enter the $x$ variable column.
5. Click **Storage**; under **Diagnostic Measures** select **Residuals**.
6. Click **OK. OK.**

**FIGURE 14.10** | Residuals and Squared Residuals for the Midwest Distribution Example

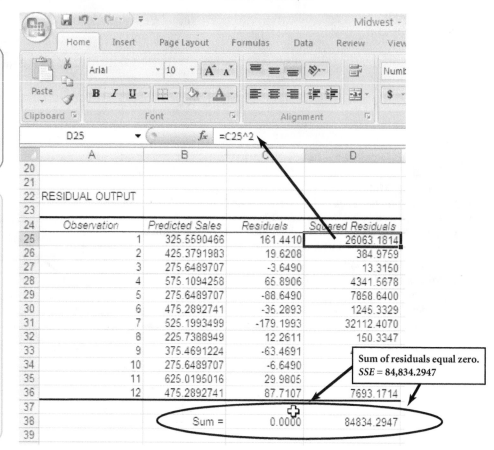

**Excel 2007 Instructions:**
1. Create Squared Residuals using Excel formula (i.e., for cell D25, use = C25^2).
2. Sum the residuals and squared residuals columns.

**Minitab Instructions**
**(for similar results):**
1. Choose **Calc > Column Statistics.**
2. Under **Statistics,** Choose **Sum.**
3. In **Input variable,** enter residual column.
4. Click **OK.**
5. Choose **Calc > Column Statistics.**
6. Under **Statistic,** choose **Sum of Squares.**
7. In **Input variable,** enter residual column.
8. Click **OK.**

through these 12 $(x, y)$ points will produce a smaller sum of squared errors. Equation 14.9 presents a formula that can be used to calculate the sum of squared errors manually.

---

**Sum of Squared Errors**

$$SSE = \Sigma y^2 - b_0 \Sigma y - b_1 \Sigma xy \qquad\qquad \textbf{(14.9)}$$

---

Figure 14.11 shows the scatter plot of sales and years of experience and the least squares regression line for Midwest Distribution. This line is the *best fit* for these sample data. The regression line passes through the point corresponding to $(\bar{x}, \bar{y})$. This will always be the case.

## Least Squares Regression Properties

Figure 14.10 illustrates several important properties of least squares regression. These are as follows:

1. The sum of the residuals from the least squares regression line is 0 (Equation 14.10). The total underprediction by the regression model is exactly offset by the total overprediction.

---

**Sum of Residuals**

$$\sum_{i=1}^{n}(y_i - \hat{y}_i) = 0 \qquad\qquad \textbf{(14.10)}$$

---

**FIGURE 14.11**

Least Squares Regression Line
for Midwest Distribution

**Excel 2007 Instructions:**

1. Open file: Midwest.xls.
2. Move the *Sales* column to the right of *Years with Midwest* column.
3. Select data for chart.
4. On **Insert** tab, click **XY (Scatter)**, and then click **Scatter with only Markers** option.
5. Use the **Layout** tab of the **Chart Tools** to add titles and remove grid lines.
6. Use the **Design** tab of the **Chart Tools** to move the chart to a new worksheet.
7. Click on a chart point.
8. Right click and select **Add Trendline**.
9. Select **Linear**.

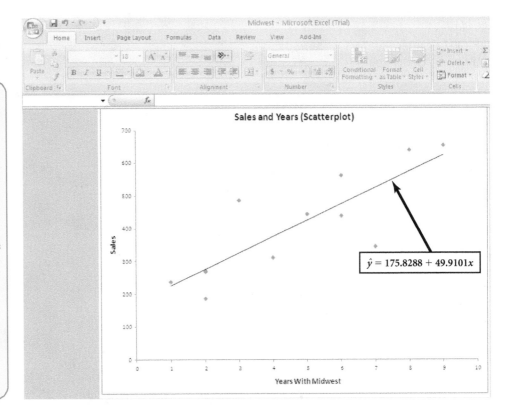

$\hat{y} = 175.8288 + 49.9101x$

2. The sum of the squared residuals is the minimum (Equation 14.11).

**Sum of Squared Residuals (Errors)**

$$SSE = \sum_{i=1}^{n} (y_i - \hat{y}_i)^2 \tag{14.11}$$

This property provided the basis for developing the equations for $b_0$ and $b_1$.

3. The simple regression line always passes through the mean of the $y$ variable, $\bar{y}$, and the mean of the $x$ variable, $\bar{x}$. So, to manually draw any simple linear regression line, all you need to do is to draw a line connecting the least squares $y$ intercept with the $(\bar{x}, \bar{y})$ point.
4. The least squares coefficients are unbiased estimates of $\beta_0$ and $\beta_1$. Thus, the expected values of $b_0$ and $b_1$ equal $\beta_0$ and $\beta_1$, respectively.

**EXAMPLE 14-2    SIMPLE LINEAR REGRESSION AND CORRELATION**

**Fitzpatrick & Associates** The investment firm Fitzpatrick & Associates wants to manage the pension fund of a major Chicago retailer. For their presentation to the retailer, the Fitzpatrick analysts want to use simple linear regression to model the relationship between profits and numbers of employees for 50 Fortune 500 companies in the firm's portfolio. The data for the analysis are contained in the file **Fortune 50**. This analysis can be done using the following steps:

**Step 1  Specify the independent and dependent variables.**
The object in this example is to model the linear relationship between number of employees (the independent variable) and each company's profits (the dependent variable).

**Step 2  Develop a scatter plot to graphically display the relationship between the independent and dependent variables.**
Figure 14.12 shows the scatter plot, where the dependent variable, $y$, is company profits and the independent variable, $x$, is number of employees.

**Excel and Minitab Tutorial**

**FIGURE 14.12**

Excel 2007 Scatter Plot for
Fitzpatrick & Associates

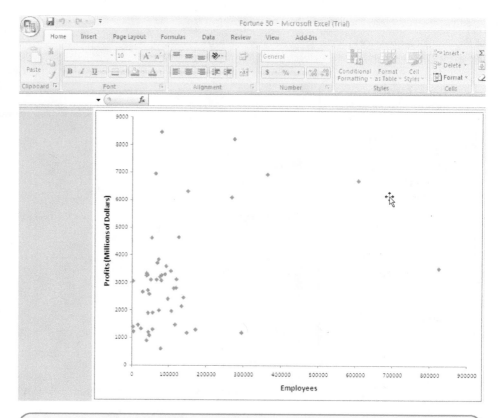

**Excel 2007 Instructions:**
1. Open file: Fortune 50.xls.
2. Copy the *Profits* column to the immediate right of *Employees* column.
3. Select data for chart (*Employees and Profits*).
4. On **Insert** tab, click **XY (Scatter)**, and then click the **Scatter with only Markers** option.
5. Use the **Layout** tab of the **Chart Tools** to add titles and remove grid lines.
6. Use the **Design** tab of the **Chart Tools** to move the chart to a new worksheet.

**Minitab Instructions (for similar result):**
1. Open file: Fortune 50.MTW.
2. Choose **Graph > Character Graphs > Scatterplot.**
3. In **Y variable**, enter *y* column.
4. In **X variable**, enter *x* column.
5. Click **OK.**

There appears to be a slight positive linear relationship between the two variables.

**Step 3**   **Calculate the correlation coefficient and the linear regression equation.**
Do either manually using Equations 14.1, 14.6 (or 14.7), and 14.8, respectively, or by using Excel or Minitab software. Figure 14.13 shows the regression results. The sample correlation coefficient (called "Multiple *R*" in Excel) is

$$r = 0.3638$$

The regression equation is

$$\hat{y} = 2{,}556.88 + 0.0048x$$

The regression slope is estimated to be 0.0048, which means that for each additional employee, the average increase in company profit is 0.0048 million dollars, or \$4,800. The intercept can only be interpreted when a value equal to zero for the *x* variable (employees) is plausible. Clearly, no company has zero employees, so the intercept in this case has no meaning other than it locates the height of the regression line for $x = 0$.

**FIGURE 14.13**

Excel 2007 Regression Results for Fitzpatrick & Associates

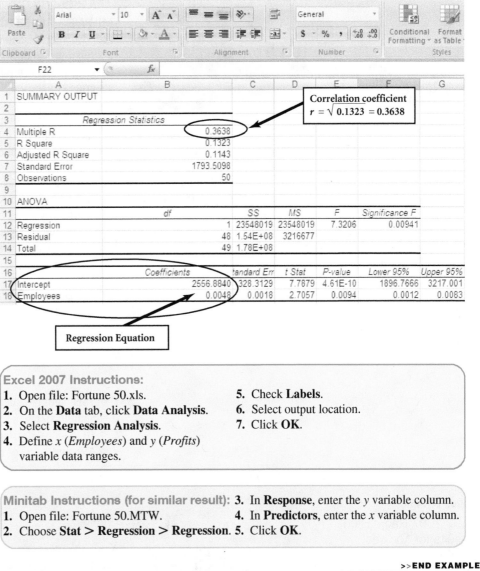

TRY PROBLEM 14-17 a,b,c (pg. 610)

## Significance Tests in Regression Analysis

Chapter Outcome 4.

In Section 14.1, we pointed out that the correlation coefficient computed from sample data is a point estimate of the population correlation coefficient and is subject to sampling error. We also introduced a test of significance for the correlation coefficient. Likewise, the regression coefficients developed from a sample of data are also point estimates of the true regression coefficients for the population. The regression coefficients are subject to sampling error. For example, due to sampling error the estimated slope coefficient may be positive or negative while the population slope is really 0. Therefore, we need a test procedure to determine whether the regression slope coefficient is statistically significant. As you will see in this section, the test for the simple linear regression slope coefficient is equivalent to the test for the correlation coefficient. That is, if the correlation between two variables is found to be significant, then the regression slope coefficient will also be significant.

## The Coefficient of Determination, $R^2$

**MIDWEST DISTRIBUTION (*CONTINUED*)** Recall that the Midwest Distribution marketing manager was analyzing the relationship between the number of years an employee had been with the company (independent variable) and the sales generated by the employee (dependent variable). We note when looking at the sample data for 12 employees (see Table 14.3) that sales vary among employees. Regression analysis aims to determine the extent to which an independent variable can explain this variation. In this case, does number of years with the company help explain the variation in sales from employee to employee?

The *SST* (total sum of squares) can be used in measuring the variation in the dependent variable. *SST* is computed using Equation 14.12. For Midwest Distribution, the total sum of squares for sales is provided in the output generated by Excel or Minitab, as shown in Figure 14.14a and Figure 14.14b. As you can see, the total sum of squares in sales that needs to be explained is 276,434.92. Note that the *SST* value is in squared units and has no particular meaning.

### Total Sum of Squares

$$SST = \sum_{i=1}^{n} (y_i - \overline{y})^2 \tag{14.12}$$

where:

$SST$ = Total sum of squares
$n$ = Sample size
$y_i$ = *i*th value of the dependent variable
$\overline{y}$ = Average value of the dependent variable

**FIGURE 14.14A**

Excel 2007 Regression Results for Midwest Distribution

**Excel 2007 Instructions:**
1. Open file: Midwest.xls.
2. On the **Data** tab, click **Data Analysis**.
3. Select **Regression Analysis**.
4. Define *x* (*Years with Midwest*) and *y* (*Sales*) variable data range.
5. Click on **Labels**.
6. Specify output location.
7. Click **OK**.

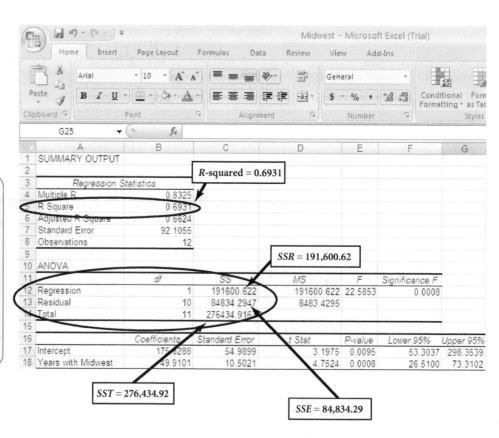

**FIGURE 14.14B**

Minitab Regression Results for Midwest Distribution

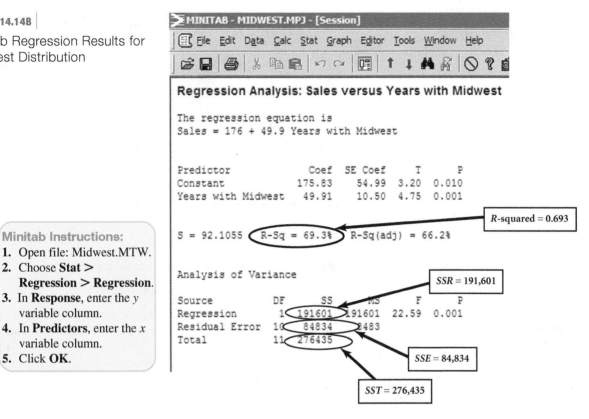

**Minitab Instructions:**
1. Open file: Midwest.MTW.
2. Choose **Stat > Regression > Regression**.
3. In **Response**, enter the *y* variable column.
4. In **Predictors**, enter the *x* variable column.
5. Click **OK**.

The least squares regression line is computed so that the sum of squared residuals is minimized (recall the discussion of the least squares equations). The sum of squared residuals is also called the *sum of squares error (SSE)* and is defined by Equation 14.13.

---

**Sum of Squares Error**

$$SSE = \sum_{i=1}^{n}(y_i - \hat{y}_i)^2 \qquad \textbf{(14.13)}$$

where:

$n$ = Sample size
$y_i$ = $i$th value of the dependent variable
$\hat{y}_i$ = $i$th predicted value of $y$ given the $i$th value of $x$

---

*SSE* represents the amount of the total sum of squares in the dependent variable that *is not explained* by the least squares regression line. Excel refers to *SSE* as *sum of squares residual* and Minitab refers to SSE as *residual error*. This value is contained in the regression output shown in Figure 14.14a and Figure 14.14b.

$$SSE = \Sigma(y - \hat{y})^2 = 84,834.29$$

Thus, of the total sum of squares (*SST* = 276,434.92), the regression model leaves *SSE* = 84,834.29 unexplained. Then, the portion of the total sum of squares that *is explained* by the regression line is called the *sum of squares regression (SSR)* and is calculated by Equation 14.14.

---

### Sum of Squares Regression

$$SSR = \sum_{i=1}^{n} (\hat{y}_i - \bar{y})^2 \qquad \text{(14.14)}$$

where:

$\hat{y}_i$ = Estimated value of $y$ for each value of $x$

$\bar{y}$ = Average value of the $y$ variable

---

The sum of squares regression ($SSR = 191{,}600.62$) is also provided in the regression output shown in Figure 14.14a and Figure 14.14b. You should also note that the following holds:

$$SST = SSR + SSE$$

For the Midwest Distribution example, in the Minitab output we get

$$276{,}435 = 191{,}601 + 84{,}834$$

We can use these calculations to compute an important measure in regression analysis called the **coefficient of determination**. The coefficient of determination is calculated using Equation 14.15.

**Coefficient of Determination**

The portion of the total variation in the dependent variable that is explained by its relationship with the independent variable. The coefficient of determination is also called $R$-squared and is denoted as $R^2$.

---

### Coefficient of Determination, $R^2$

$$R^2 = \frac{SSR}{SST} \qquad \text{(14.15)}$$

---

Then, for the Midwest Distribution example, the proportion of variation in sales that can be explained by its linear relationship with the years of sales force experience is

$$R^2 = \frac{SSR}{SST} = \frac{191{,}600.62}{276{,}434.92} = 0.6931$$

This means that 69.31% of the variation in the sales data for this sample can be explained by the linear relationship between sales and years of experience. Notice that $R^2$ is part of the regression output in Figures 14.14a and 14.14b.

$R^2$ can be a value between 0 and 1.0. If there is a perfect linear relationship between two variables, then the coefficient of determination, $R^2$, will be 1.0. This would correspond to a situation in which the least squares regression line would pass through each of the points in the scatter plot. $R^2$ is the measure used by many decision makers to indicate how well the linear regression line fits the $(x, y)$ data points. The better the fit, the closer $R^2$ will be to 1.0. $R^2$ will be close to 0 when there is a weak linear relationship.

Finally, when you are employing *simple linear regression* (a linear relationship between a single independent variable and the dependent variable), there is an alternative way of computing $R^2$, as shown in Equation 14.16.

---

### Coefficient of Determination for the Single Independent Variable Case

$$R^2 = r^2 \qquad \text{(14.16)}$$

where:

$R^2$ = Coefficient of determination

$r$ = Sample correlation coefficient

---

Therefore, by squaring the correlation coefficient, we can get $R^2$ for the simple regression model. Figure 14.14a shows the correlation, $r = 0.8325$, which is referred to as *Multiple R* in Excel. Then, using Equation 14.16, we get $R^2$.

$$R^2 = r^2$$
$$= 0.8325^2$$
$$= 0.6931$$

Keep in mind that $R^2 = 0.6931$ is based on the random sample of size 12 and is subject to sampling error. Thus, just because $R^2 = 0.6931$ for the sample data does not mean that knowing the number of years an employee has worked for the company will explain 69.31% of the variation in sales for the population of all employees with the company. Likewise, just because $R^2 > 0.0$ for the sample data does not mean that the population coefficient of determination, noted as $\rho^2$ (rho-squared), is greater than zero.

However, a statistical test exists for testing the following null and alternative hypotheses:

$$H_0: \rho^2 = 0$$
$$H_A: \rho^2 > 0$$

The test statistic is an $F$-test with the test statistic defined as shown in Equation 14.17.

---

**Test Statistic for Significance of the Coefficient of Determination**

$$F = \frac{\dfrac{SSR}{1}}{\dfrac{SSE}{(n-2)}} \qquad df = (D_1 = 1, D_2 = n - 2) \qquad \text{(14.17)}$$

where:

$$SSR = \text{Sum of squares regression}$$
$$SSE = \text{Sum of squares error}$$

---

For the Midwest Distribution example, the test statistic is computed using Equation 14.17 as follows:

$$F = \frac{\dfrac{191,600.62}{1}}{\dfrac{84,834.29}{(12-2)}} = 22.58$$

The critical value from the $F$-distribution table in Appendix H for $\alpha = 0.05$ and for 1 and 10 degrees of freedom is 4.965. This gives the following decision rule:

> If $F > 4.965$, reject the null hypothesis.
> Otherwise, do not reject the null hypothesis.

Because $F = 22.58 > 4.965$, we reject the null hypothesis and conclude the population coefficient of determination ($\rho^2$) is greater than zero. This means the independent variable explains a significant proportion of the variation in the dependent variable.

For a simple regression model (a regression model with a single independent variable), the test for $\rho^2$ is equivalent to the test shown earlier for the population correlation coefficient, $\rho$. Refer to Figure 14.5 to see that the $t$-test statistic for the correlation coefficient was $t = 4.752$. If we square this $t$-value we get

$$t^2 = 4.752^2 = F = 22.58$$

Thus, the tests are equivalent. They will provide the same conclusions about the relationship between the $x$ and $y$ variables.

**Significance of the Slope Coefficient** For a simple linear regression model (one independent variable), there are three equivalent statistical tests:

1. Test for significance of the correlation between $x$ and $y$.
2. Test for significance of the coefficient of determination.
3. Test for significance of the regression slope coefficient.

We have already introduced the first two of these tests. The third one deals specifically with the significance of the regression slope coefficient. The null and alternative hypotheses to be tested are

$$H_0: \beta_1 = 0$$
$$H_A: \beta_1 \neq 0$$

To test the significance of the simple linear regression slope coefficient, we are interested in determining whether the population regression slope coefficient is 0. A slope of 0 would imply that there is no linear relationship between $x$ and $y$ variables and that the $x$ variable, in its linear form, is of no use in explaining the variation in $y$. If the linear relationship is useful, then we should reject the hypothesis that the regression slope is 0. However, because the estimated regression slope coefficient, $b_1$, is calculated from sample data, it is subject to sampling error. Therefore, even though $b_1$ is not 0, we must determine whether its difference from 0 is greater than would generally be attributed to sampling error.

If we selected several samples from the same population and for each sample determined the least squares regression line, we would likely get regression lines with different slopes and different $y$ intercepts. This is analogous to getting different sample means from different samples when attempting to estimate a population mean. Just as the distribution of possible sample means has a standard error, the possible regression slopes also have a standard error, which is given in Equation 14.18.

---

**Simple Regression Standard Error of the Slope Coefficient (Population)**

$$\sigma_{b_1} = \frac{\sigma_\varepsilon}{\sqrt{\sum(x - \bar{x})^2}} \qquad (14.18)$$

where:

$\sigma_{b_1} =$ Standard deviation of the regression slope
(called the *standard error of the slope*)

$\sigma_\varepsilon =$ Population standard error of the estimate

---

Equation 14.18 requires that we know the *standard error of the estimate*. It measures the dispersion of the dependent variable about its mean value at each value of the dependent variable in the original units of the dependent variable. However, because we are sampling from the population, we can estimate $\sigma_\varepsilon$ as shown in Equation 14.19.

---

**Simple Regression Estimator for the Standard Error of the Estimate**

$$s_\varepsilon = \sqrt{\frac{SSE}{n-2}} \qquad (14.19)$$

where:

$SSE =$ Sum of squares error
$n =$ Sample size

---

Equation 14.18, the standard error of the regression slope, applies when we are dealing with a population. However, in most cases, such as the Midwest Distribution example, we are dealing with a sample from the population. Thus, we need to estimate the regression slope's standard error using Equation 14.20.

---

**Simple Regression Estimator for the Standard Error of the Slope**

$$s_{b_1} = \frac{s_\varepsilon}{\sqrt{\sum(x - \bar{x})^2}} \qquad (14.20)$$

where:

$s_{b_1}$ = Estimate of the standard error of the least squares slope

$s_\varepsilon = \sqrt{\dfrac{SSE}{n-2}}$ = Sample standard error of the estimate (the measure of deviation of the actual $y$-values around the regression line)

---

**BUSINESS APPLICATION**  REGRESSION ANALYSIS USING COMPUTER SOFTWARE

**MIDWEST DISTRIBUTION (CONTINUED)** For Midwest Distribution, the regression outputs in Figures 14.15a and 14.15b show $b_1 = 49.91$. The question is whether this value is different enough from 0 to have not been caused by sampling error. We find the answer by looking at the value of the estimate of the standard error of the slope, calculated using Equation 14.20, which is also shown in Figure 14.15a. The standard error of the slope coefficient is 10.50.

If the standard error of the slope $\sigma_{b_1}$ is large, then the value of $b_1$ will be quite variable from sample to sample. Conversely, if $\sigma_{b_1}$ is small, the possible slope values will be less variable. However, regardless of the standard error of the slope, the average value of $b_1$ will equal $\beta_1$, the true regression slope, if the assumptions of the regression analysis are satisfied. Figure 14.16 illustrates what this means. Notice that when the standard error of the slope is

**FIGURE 14.15A**

Excel 2007 Regression Results for Midwest Distribution

**Excel 2007 Instructions:**
1. Open file: Midwest.xls.
2. On the **Data** tab, click **Data Analysis**.
3. Select **Regression Analysis**.
4. Define $x$ (*Years with Midwest*) and $y$ (*Sales*) variable data range.
5. Click on **Labels**.
6. Specify output location.
7. Click **OK**.

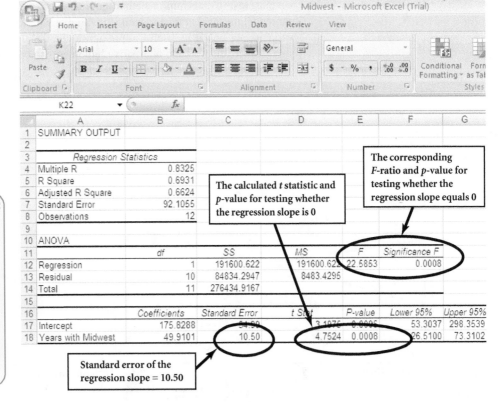

The calculated $t$ statistic and $p$-value for testing whether the regression slope is 0

The corresponding $F$-ratio and $p$-value for testing whether the regression slope equals 0

Standard error of the regression slope = 10.50

**FIGURE 14.15B**

Minitab Regression Results
for Midwest Distribution

**FIGURE 14.15B**

Minitab Regression Results
for Midwest Distribution

**Minitab Instructions:**
1. Open file: Midwest.
   MTW.
2. Choose **Stat >
   Regression >
   Regression**.
3. In **Response**, enter the *y*
   variable column.
4. In **Predictors** enter the *x*
   variable column.
5. Click **OK**.

large, the sample slope can take on values *much* different from the true population slope. As Figure 14.16(a) shows, a sample slope and the true population slope can even have different signs. However, when $\sigma_{b_1}$ is small, the sample regression lines will cluster closely around the true population line [Figure 14.16(b)].

Because the sample regression slope will most likely not equal the true population slope, we must test to determine whether the true slope could possibly be 0. A slope of 0 in the linear model means that the independent variable will not explain any variation in the dependent variable, nor will it be useful in predicting the dependent variable. Assuming a 0.05 level of significance, the null and alternative hypotheses to be tested are

$$H_0: \beta_1 = 0$$
$$H_A: \beta_1 \neq 0$$

**FIGURE 14.16** | Standard Error of the Slope

(a) Large Standard Error

(b) Small Standard Error

To test the significance of a slope coefficient, we use the $t$-test value in Equation 14.21.

---

**Simple Linear Regression Test Statistic for Test of the Significance of the Slope**

$$t = \frac{b_1 - \beta_1}{s_{b_1}} \qquad df = n - 2 \qquad\qquad \textbf{(14.21)}$$

where:

$b_1$ = Sample regression slope coefficient

$\beta_1$ = Hypothesized slope (usually $\beta_1 = 0$)

$s_{b_1}$ = Estimator of the standard error of the slope

---

Figure 14.17 illustrates this test for the Midwest Distribution example. The calculated $t$-value of 4.752 exceeds the critical value, $t = 2.228$, from the $t$-distribution with 10 degrees of freedom and $\alpha/2 = 0.025$. This indicates that we should reject the hypothesis that the true regression slope is 0. Thus, years of experience can be used to help explain the variation in an individual representative's sales. This is not a coincidence. This test is always equivalent to the tests for $\rho$ and $\rho^2$ presented earlier.

The output shown in Figures 14.15a and 14.15b also contains the calculated $t$ statistic. The $p$-value for the calculated $t$ statistic is also provided. As with other situations involving two-tailed hypothesis tests, if the $p$-value is less than $\alpha$, the null hypothesis is rejected. In this case, because $p$-value $= 0.0008 < 0.05$, we reject the null hypothesis.

**FIGURE 14.17**

Significance Test of the Regression Slope for Midwest Distribution

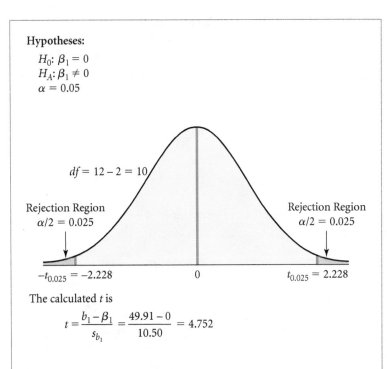

Hypotheses:

$H_0: \beta_1 = 0$
$H_A: \beta_1 \neq 0$
$\alpha = 0.05$

$df = 12 - 2 = 10$

Rejection Region
$\alpha/2 = 0.025$

Rejection Region
$\alpha/2 = 0.025$

$-t_{0.025} = -2.228$     $0$     $t_{0.025} = 2.228$

The calculated $t$ is

$$t = \frac{b_1 - \beta_1}{s_{b_1}} = \frac{49.91 - 0}{10.50} = 4.752$$

**Decision Rule:**

If $t > t_{0.025} = 2.228$, reject $H_0$.
If $t < -t_{0.025} = -2.228$, reject $H_0$.
Otherwise, do not reject $H_0$.

Because $4.752 > 2.228$, we should reject the null hypothesis and conclude that the true slope is not 0. Thus, the simple linear relationship that utilizes the independent variable, years with the company, is useful in explaining the variation in the dependent variable, sales volume.

## How to do it (Example 14-3)

**Simple Linear Regression Analysis**
The following steps outline the process that can be used in developing a simple linear regression model and the various hypotheses tests used to determine the significance of a simple linear regression model.

1. Define the independent ($x$) and dependent ($y$) variables and select a simple random sample of pairs of ($x$, $y$) values.

2. Develop a scatter plot of $y$ and $x$. You are looking for a linear relationship between the two variables.

3. Compute the correlation coefficient for the sample data.

4. Calculate the least squares regression line for the sample data and the coefficient of determination, $R^2$. The coefficient of determination measures the proportion of variation in the dependent variable explained by the independent variable.

5. Conduct any of the following tests for determining whether the regression model is statistically significant.

   a. Test to determine whether the true regression slope is 0. The test statistic with $df = n - 2$ is

   $$t = \frac{b_1 - \beta_1}{s_{b_1}} = \frac{b_1 - 0}{s_{b_1}}$$

   b. Test to see whether $\rho$ is significantly different from 0. The test statistic is

   $$t = \frac{r}{\sqrt{\frac{1 - r^2}{n - 2}}}$$

   c. Test to see whether $\rho^2$ is significantly greater than 0. The test statistic is

   $$F = \frac{\frac{SSR}{1}}{\frac{SSE}{(n - 2)}}$$

6. Reach a decision.
7. Draw a conclusion.

---

**EXAMPLE 14-3** | **SIMPLE LINEAR REGRESSION ANALYSIS**

**Vantage Electronic Systems** Consider the example involving Vantage Electronic Systems in Deerfield, Michigan, which started out supplying electronic equipment for the automobile industry but in recent years has ventured into other areas. One area is visibility sensors used by airports to provide takeoff and landing information and by transportation departments to detect low visibility on roadways during fog and snow. The recognized leader in the visibility sensor business is the SCR Company, which makes a sensor called the Scorpion. The research and development (R&D) department at Vantage has recently performed a test on its new unit by locating a Vantage sensor and a Scorpion sensor side-by-side. Various data, including visibility measurements, were collected at randomly selected points in time over a two-week period. These data are contained in a file called **Vantage**.

**Step 1** **Define the independent ($x$) and dependent ($y$) variables.**
The analysis included a simple linear regression using the Scorpion visibility measurement as the dependent variable, $y$, and the Vantage visibility measurement as the independent variable, $x$.

**Step 2** **Develop a scatter plot of $y$ and $x$.**
The scatter plot is shown in Figure 14.18. There does not appear to be a strong linear relationship.

**Step 3** **Compute the correlation coefficient for the sample data.**
Equation 14.1 or 14.2 can be used for manual computation, or we can use Excel or Minitab. The sample correlation coefficient is

$$r = 0.5778$$

**Step 4** **Calculate the least squares regression line for the sample data and the coefficient of determination, $R^2$.**
Equations 14.7 and 14.8 can be used to manually compute the regression slope coefficient and intercept, respectively, and Equation 14.15 or 14.16 can be used to manually compute $R^2$. Excel and Minitab can also be used to eliminate the computational burden. The coefficient of determination is

$$R^2 = r^2 = 0.5778^2 = 0.3339$$

**FIGURE 14.18** | Scatter Plot—Example 14-3

**Excel and Minitab Tutorial**

Thus, approximately 33% of the variation in the Scorpion visibility measures is explained by knowing the corresponding Vantage system visibility measure. The least squares regression equation is

$$\hat{y} = 0.586 + 3.017x$$

**Step 5**  **Conduct a test to determine whether the regression model is statistically significant (or whether the population correlation is equal to 0).**

The null and alternative hypotheses to test the correlation coefficient are

$$H_0: \rho = 0$$
$$H_A: \rho \neq 0$$

The $t$-test statistic using Equation 14.3 is

$$t = \frac{r}{\sqrt{\dfrac{1-r^2}{n-2}}} = \frac{0.5778}{\sqrt{\dfrac{1-0.5778^2}{280-2}}} = 11.8$$

The $t = 11.8$ exceeds the critical $t$ for any reasonable level of $\alpha$ for 278 degrees of freedom, so the null hypothesis is rejected and we conclude that there is a statistically significant linear relationship between visibility measures for the two visibility sensors.

Alternatively, the null and alternative hypotheses to test the regression slope coefficient are

$$H_0: \beta_1 = 0$$
$$H_A: \beta_1 \neq 0$$

The $t$-test statistic is

$$t = \frac{b_1 - \beta_1}{s_{b_1}} = \frac{3.017 - 0}{0.2557} = 11.8$$

**Step 6**  **Reach a decision.**

The $t$-test statistic of 11.8 exceeds the $t$-critical for any reasonable level of $\alpha$ for 278 degrees of freedom.

**Step 7**  **Draw a conclusion.**

The population regression slope coefficient is not equal to 0. This means that knowing the Vantage visibility reading provides useful help in knowing what the Scorpion visibility reading will be.

**>>END EXAMPLE**

**TRY PROBLEM** 14-16 (pg. 609)

# 14-2: **Exercises**

## Skill **Development**

**14-16.** You are given the following sample data for variables $y$ and $x$:

| $y$ | 140.1 | 120.3 | 80.8 | 100.7 | 130.2 | 90.6 | 110.5 | 120.2 | 130.4 | 130.3 | 100.1 |
|---|---|---|---|---|---|---|---|---|---|---|---|
| $x$ | 5 | 3 | 2 | 4 | 5 | 4 | 4 | 5 | 6 | 5 | 4 |

a. Develop a scatter plot for these data and describe what, if any, relationship exists.

b. (1) Compute the correlation coefficient. (2) Test to determine whether the correlation is significant at the significance level of 0.05. Conduct this hypothesis test using the $p$-value approach. (3) Compute the regression equation based on these sample data and interpret the regression coefficients.

c. Test the significance of the overall regression model using a significance level equal to 0.05.

**14-17.** You are given the following sample data for variables $x$ and $y$:

| x (independent) | y (dependent) |
|---|---|
| 1 | 16 |
| 7 | 50 |
| 3 | 22 |
| 8 | 59 |
| 11 | 63 |
| 5 | 46 |
| 4 | 43 |

a. Construct a scatter plot for these data and describe what, if any, relationship appears to exist.
b. Compute the regression equation based on these sample data and interpret the regression coefficients.
c. Based on the sample data, what percentage of the total variation in the dependent variable can be explained by the independent variable?
d. Test the significance of the overall regression model using a significance level of 0.01.
e. Test to determine whether the true regression slope coefficient is equal to 0. Use a significance level of 0.01.

**14-18.** The following data for the dependent variable, $y$, and the independent variable, $x$, have been collected using simple random sampling:

| x | y |
|---|---|
| 10 | 120 |
| 14 | 130 |
| 16 | 170 |
| 12 | 150 |
| 20 | 200 |
| 18 | 180 |
| 16 | 190 |
| 14 | 150 |
| 16 | 160 |
| 18 | 200 |

a. Develop a simple linear regression equation for these data.
b. Calculate the sum of squared residuals, the total sum of squares, and the coefficient of determination.
c. Calculate the standard error of the estimate.
d. Calculate the standard error for the regression slope.
e. Conduct the hypothesis test to determine whether the regression slope coefficient is equal to 0. Test using $\alpha = 0.02$.

**14-19.** Consider the following sample data for the variables $y$ and $x$:

| x | 30.3 | 4.8 | 15.2 | 24.9 | 8.6 | 20.1 | 9.3 | 11.2 |
|---|---|---|---|---|---|---|---|---|
| y | 14.6 | 27.9 | 17.6 | 15.3 | 19.8 | 13.2 | 25.6 | 19.4 |

a. Calculate the linear regression equation for these data.
b. Determine the predicted $y$-value when $x = 10$.
c. Estimate the change in the $y$ variable resulting from the increase in the $x$ variable of 10 units.
d. Conduct a hypothesis test to determine if an increase of 1 unit in the $x$ variable will result in the decrease of the average value of the $y$ variable. Use a significance of 0.025.

**14-20.** Examine the following sample data for the variables $y$ and $x$:

| x | 1 | 2 | 3 | 4 | 5 |
|---|---|---|---|---|---|
| y | 4 | 2 | 5 | 8 | 9 |

a. Construct a scatter plot of these data. Describe the relationship between $x$ and $y$.
b. Calculate the sum of squares error for the following equations: (1) $\hat{y} = 0.8 + 1.60x$, (2) $\hat{y} = 1 + 1.50x$, and (3) $\hat{y} = 0.7 + 1.60x$.
c. Which of these equations provides the "best" fit of these data? Describe the criterion you used to determine "best" fit.
d. Determine the regression line that minimizes the sum of squares error.

## Business Applications

**14-21.** The Skelton Manufacturing Company recently did a study of its customers. A random sample of 50 customer accounts was pulled from the computer records. Two variables were observed:

$y$ = Total dollar volume of business this year
$x$ = Miles customer is from corporate headquarters

The following statistics were computed:

$$\hat{y} = 2,140.23 - 10.12x$$
$$s_{b_1} = 3.12$$

a. Interpret the regression slope coefficient.
b. Using a significance level of 0.01, test to determine whether it is true that the farther a customer is from the corporate headquarters, the smaller the total dollar volume of business.

**14-22.** A shipping company believes that the variation in the cost of a customer's shipment can be explained by differences in the weight of the package being shipped. To investigate whether this relationship is useful, a random sample of 20 customer shipments was selected, and the weight (in lb) and the cost (in dollars, rounded to the nearest dollar) for each shipment were recorded. The following results were obtained:

| Weight (x) | Cost (y) |
|---|---|
| 8 | 11 |
| 6 | 8 |
| 5 | 11 |
| 7 | 11 |

| Weight (x) | Cost (y) |
|:---:|:---:|
| 12 | 17 |
| 9 | 11 |
| 17 | 27 |
| 13 | 16 |
| 8 | 9 |
| 18 | 25 |
| 17 | 21 |
| 17 | 24 |
| 10 | 16 |
| 20 | 24 |
| 9 | 21 |
| 5 | 10 |
| 13 | 21 |
| 6 | 16 |
| 6 | 11 |
| 12 | 20 |

a. Construct a scatter plot for these data. What, if any, relationship appears to exist between the two variables?

b. Compute the linear regression model based on the sample data. Interpret the slope and intercept coefficients.

c. Test the significance of the overall regression model using a significance level equal to 0.05.

d. What percentage of the total variation in shipping cost can be explained by the regression model you developed in part b?

**14-23.** College tuition has risen at a pace faster than inflation for more than two decades, according to an article in *USA Today*. The following data indicate the average college tuition (in 2003 dollars) for private and public colleges:

| Period | 1983–1984 | 1988–1989 | 1993–1994 | 1998–1999 | 2003–2004 | 2008–2009 |
|---|---|---|---|---|---|---|
| Private | 9,202 | 12,146 | 13,844 | 16,454 | 19,710 | 21,582 |
| Public | 2,074 | 2,395 | 3,188 | 3,632 | 4,694 | 5,652 |

a. Conduct a simple linear regression analysis of these data in which the average tuition for private colleges is predicted by the average public college tuition. Test the significance of the model using an $\alpha = 0.10$.

b. How much does the average private college tuition increase when the average public college tuition increases by $100?

c. When the average public college tuition reaches $7,500, how much would you expect the average private college tuition to be?

## Computer Database Exercises

**14-24.** The file **Online** contains a random sample of 48 customers who made purchases last quarter from an online retailer. The file contains information related to the time each customer spent viewing the online catalog and the dollar amount of purchases made.

The retailer would like to analyze the sample data to determine whether a relationship exists between the time spent viewing the online catalog and the dollar amount of purchases.

a. Compute the regression equation based on these sample data and interpret the regression coefficients.

b. Compute the coefficient of determination and interpret its meaning.

c. Test the significance of the overall regression model using a significance level of 0.01.

d. Test to determine whether the true regression slope coefficient is equal to 0. Use a significance level of 0.01 to conduct the hypothesis test.

**14-25.** The National Football League (NFL) is arguably the most successful professional sports league in the United States. Following the recent season, the commissioner's office staff performed an analysis in which a simple linear regression model was developed with average home attendance used as the dependent variable and the total number of games won during the season as the independent variable. The staff was interested in determining whether games won could be used as a predictor for average attendance. Develop the simple linear regression model. The data are in the file called **NFL**.

a. What percentage of total variation in average home attendance is explained by knowing the number of games the team won?

b. What is the standard error of the estimate for this regression model?

c. Using $\alpha = 0.05$, test to determine whether the regression slope coefficient is significantly different from 0.

d. After examining the regression analysis results, what should the NFL staff conclude about how the average attendance is related to the number of games the team won?

**14-26.** The consumer price index (CPI) is a measure of the average change in prices over time in a fixed market basket of goods and services typically purchased by consumers. The CPI for all urban consumers covers about 80% of the total population. It is prepared and published by the Bureau of Labor Statistics of the Department of Labor, which measures average changes in prices of goods and services. The CPI is one way the government measures the general level of inflation—the annual percentage change in the value of this index is one way of measuring the annual inflation rate. The file entitled **CPI** contains the monthly CPI and inflation rate for the period 2000–2005.

a. Construct a scatter plot of the CPI versus inflation for the period 2000–2005. Describe the relationship that appears to exist between these two variables.

b. Conduct a hypothesis test to confirm your preconception of the relationship between the CPI and the inflation rate. Use $\alpha = 0.05$.

c. Does it appear that the CPI and the inflation rate are measuring the same component of our economy? Support your assertion with statistical reasoning.

**14-27.** The College Board, administrator of the SAT test for college entrants, has made several changes to the test in recent years. One recent change occurred between years 2005 and 2006. In a press release the College Board announced SAT scores for students in the class of 2005, the last class to take the former version of the SAT featuring math and verbal sections. The board indicated that for the class of 2005, the average SAT math scores continued their strong upward trend, increasing from 518 in 2004 to 520 in 2005, 14 points above 10 years previous and an all-time high. The file entitled **MathSAT** contains the math SAT scores for the interval 1967 to 2005.

a. Produce a scatter plot of the average SAT math scores versus the year the test was taken for all students (male and female) during the last 10 years (1996–2005).

b. Construct a regression equation to predict the average math scores with the year as the predictor.

c. Use regression to determine if the College Board's assertion concerning the improvement in SAT average math test scores over the last 10 years is overly optimistic.

**14-28.** One of the editors of a major automobile publication has collected data on 30 of the best-selling cars in the United States. The data are in a file called **Automobiles**. The editor is particularly interested in the relationship

between highway mileage and curb weight of the vehicles.

a. Develop a scatter plot for these data. Discuss what the plot implies about the relationship between the two variables. Assume that you wish to predict highway mileage by using vehicle curb weight.

b. Compute the correlation coefficient for the two variables and test to determine whether there is a linear relationship between the curb weight and the highway mileage of automobiles.

c. (1) Compute the linear regression equation based on the sample data. (2) A CTS Sedan weighs approximately 4,012 pounds. Provide an estimate of the average highway mileage you would expect to obtain from this model.

**14-29.** *The Insider View of Las Vegas* Web site (www.insidervlv .com) furnishes information and facts concerning Las Vegas. A set of data published by them provides the amount of gaming revenue for various portions of Clark County, Nevada. The file entitled "**VEGAS**" provides the gaming revenue for the year 2005.

a. Compute the linear regression equation to predict the gaming revenue for Clark County based on the gaming revenue of the Las Vegas Strip.

b. Conduct a hypothesis test to determine if the gaming revenue from the Las Vegas Strip can be used to predict the gaming revenue for all of Clark County.

c. Estimate the increased gaming revenue that would accrue to all of Clark County if the gaming revenue on the Las Vegas Strip were to increase by a million dollars.

**END EXERCISES 14-2**

---

**Chapter Outcome 5.** ▶ **14.3  Uses for Regression Analysis**

Regression analysis is a statistical tool that is used for two main purposes: description and prediction. This section discusses these two applications.

## Regression Analysis for Description

**BUSINESS APPLICATION**   **USING REGRESSION ANALYSIS FOR DECISION-MAKING**

**CAR MILEAGE** In the summer of 2006, gasoline prices soared to record levels in the United States, heightening motor vehicle customers' concern for fuel economy. Analysts at a major automobile company collected data on a variety of variables for a sample of 30 different cars and small trucks. Included among those data were the Environmental Protection Agency (EPA)'s highway mileage rating and the horsepower of each vehicle. The analysts were interested in the relationship between horsepower ($x$) and highway mileage ($y$). The data are contained in the file **Automobiles**.

A simple linear regression model can be developed using Excel or Minitab. The Excel output is shown in Figure 14.19. For these sample data, the coefficient of determination,

**FIGURE 14.19**

Excel 2007 Regression
Results for the Automobile
Mileage Study

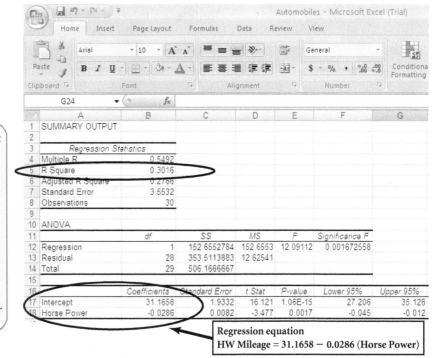

**Excel 2007 Instructions:**
1. Open file:
   Automobiles.xls.
2. Click on **Data** tab.
3. Select **Data Analysis >
   Regression**.
4. Define *y* variable range
   (*Highway Mileage*) and
   *x* variable range (*Horse
   Power*).
5. Check **Labels**.
6. Specify Output Location.
7. Click **OK**.

Regression equation
HW Mileage = 31.1658 − 0.0286 (Horse Power)

**Minitab Instructions (for similar results):**
1. Open file: Automobiles.MTW.
2. Choose **Stat > Regression >
   Regression**.
3. In **Response**, enter the *y* variable column.
4. In **Predictors**, enter the *x* variable column.
5. Click **OK**.

**Excel and Minitab Tutorial**

$R^2 = 0.3016$, indicates that knowing the horsepower of the vehicle explains 30.16% of the variation in the highway mileage. The estimated regression equation is

$$\hat{y} = 31.1658 - 0.0286x$$

Before the analysts attempt to describe the relationship between horsepower and highway mileage, they first need to test whether there is a statistically significant linear relationship between the two variables. To do this, they can apply the *t*-test described in Section 14.2 to test the following null and alternative hypotheses:

$$H_0: \beta_1 = 0$$
$$H_A: \beta_1 \neq 0$$

at the significance level

$$\alpha = 0.05$$

The calculated *t* statistic and the corresponding *p*-value are shown in Figure 14.19. Because the

$$p\text{-value (Significance } F) = 0.0017 < 0.05$$

the null hypothesis, $H_0$, is rejected and the analysts can conclude that the population regression slope is not equal to 0.

The sample slope, $b_1$, equals −0.0286. This means that for each 1-unit increase in horsepower, the highway mileage is estimated to decrease by an average of 0.0286 miles per gallon. However, $b_1$ is subject to sampling error and is considered a *point estimate* for the true regression slope coefficient. From earlier discussions about point estimates in Chapters 8 and 10, we expect that $b_1 \neq \beta_1$. Therefore, to help describe the relationship between the independent variable, horsepower, and the dependent variable, highway miles per gallon, we need to develop a *confidence interval estimate* for $\beta_1$. Equation 14.22 is used to do this.

**Chapter Outcome 6.** →

---

### Confidence Interval Estimate for the Regression Slope, Simple Linear Regression

$$b_1 \pm t s_{b_1} \qquad \text{(14.22)}$$

or equivalently,

$$b_1 \pm t \frac{s_\varepsilon}{\sqrt{\sum(x - \bar{x})^2}} \qquad df = n - 2$$

where:

$s_{b_1}$ = Standard error of the regression slope coefficient
$s_\varepsilon$ = Standard error of the estimate

---

The regression output shown in Figure 14.19 contains the 95% confidence interval estimate for the slope coefficient, which is

$$-0.045 \text{ ——————— } -0.012$$

Thus, at the 95% confidence level, based on the sample data, the analysts for the car company can conclude that a 1-unit increase in horsepower will result in a drop in mileage by an average amount between 0.012 and 0.045 miles per gallon.

There are many other situations in which the prime purpose of regression analysis is description. Economists use regression analysis for descriptive purposes as they search for a way of explaining the economy. Market researchers also use regression analysis, among other techniques, in an effort to describe the factors that influence the demand for products.

---

**EXAMPLE 14-4**  **DEVELOPING A CONFIDENCE INTERVAL ESTIMATE FOR THE REGRESSION SLOPE**

**Home Prices** Home values are determined by a variety of factors. One factor is the size of the house (square feet). Recently, a study was conducted by First City Real Estate aimed at estimating the average value of each additional square foot of space in a house. A simple random sample of 319 homes sold within the past year was collected. Here are the steps required to compute a confidence interval estimate for the regression slope coefficient:

**Step 1** **Define the $y$ (dependent) and $x$ (independent) variables.**
The dependent variable is sales price, and the independent variable is square feet.

**Step 2** **Obtain the sample data.**
The study consists of sales prices and corresponding square feet for a random sample of 319 homes. The data are in a file called **First-City**.

**Step 3** **Compute the regression equation and the standard error of the slope coefficient.**
These computations can be performed manually using Equations 14.7 and 14.8 for the regression model and Equation 14.20 for the standard error of the slope. Alternatively, we can use Excel or Minitab to obtain these values.

|  | Coefficients | Standard Error |
|---|---|---|
| Intercept ($b_0$) | 39,838.48 | 7,304.95 |
| Square Feet ($b_1$) | 75.70 | 3.78 |

The point estimate for the regression slope coefficient is $75.70. Thus, for a 1-square-foot increase in the size of a house, house prices increase by an average of $75.70. This is a point estimate and is subject to sampling error.

**Step 4**   **Construct and interpret the confidence interval estimate for the regression slope using Equation 14.22.**
The confidence interval estimate is

$$b_1 \pm ts_{b_1}$$

where the degrees of freedom for the critical $t$ is $319 - 2 = 317$. The critical $t$ for a 95% confidence interval estimate is approximately 1.97, and the interval estimate is

$$\$75.70 \pm 1.97(\$3.78)$$

$$\$75.70 \pm \$7.45$$

$$\$68.25 \text{———} \$83.15$$

So, for a 1-square-foot increase in house size, at the 95% confidence level, we estimate that homes increase in price by an average of between $68.25 and $83.15.

>>**END EXAMPLE**

**TRY PROBLEM** 14-31 (pg. 620)

**Chapter Outcome 5. → Regression Analysis for Prediction**

| BUSINESS APPLICATION | PREDICTING HOSPITAL COSTS USING REGRESSION ANALYSIS |

**Excel and Minitab Tutorial**

**FREEDOM HOSPITAL** One of the main uses of regression analysis is *prediction*. You may need to predict the value of the dependent variable based on the value of the independent variable. Consider the administrator for Freedom Hospital, who has been asked by the hospital's board of directors to develop a model to predict the total charges for a geriatric patient. The file **Patients** contains the data that the administrator has collected.

Although the Regression tool in Excel works well for generating the simple linear regression equation and other useful information, it does not provide predicted values for the dependent variable. However, both Minitab and the PHStat add-ins do provide predictions. We will illustrate the Minitab output, which is formatted somewhat differently from the Excel output but contains the same basic information.

The administrator is attempting to construct a simple linear regression model, with total charges as the dependent ($y$) variable and length of stay as the independent ($x$) variable. Figure 14.20 shows the Minitab regression output. The least squares regression equation is

$$\hat{y} = 528 + 1{,}353x$$

As shown in the figure, the regression slope coefficient is significantly different from 0 ($t = 14.17$; $p$-value $= 0.000$). The model explains 59.6% of the variation in the total charges ($R^2 = 59.6\%$). Notice in Figure 14.20 that Minitab has rounded the regression coefficient. The more precise values are provided in the column headed "Coef" and are

$$\hat{y} = 527.6 + 1{,}352.80x$$

The administrator could use this equation to predict total charges by substituting the length of stay into the regression equation for $x$. For example, suppose a patient has a five-day stay. The predicted total charges are

$$\hat{y} = 527.6 + 1{,}352.80(5)$$
$$\hat{y} = \$7{,}291.60$$

Note that this predicted value is a *point estimate* of the actual charges for this patient. The true charges will be either higher or lower than this amount. The administrator can develop a prediction interval, which is similar to the confidence interval estimates developed in Chapter 8.

**FIGURE 14.20**

Minitab Regression Output for Freedom Hospital

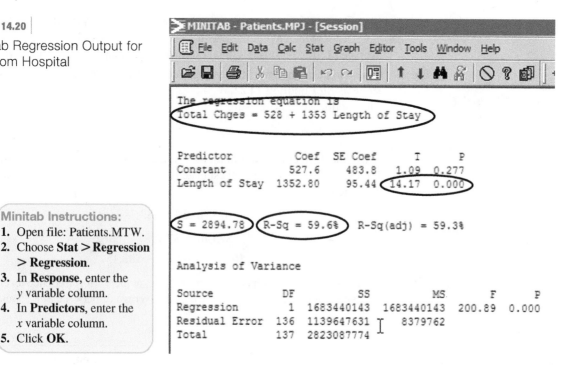

Minitab Instructions:
1. Open file: Patients.MTW.
2. Choose **Stat > Regression > Regression**.
3. In **Response**, enter the y variable column.
4. In **Predictors**, enter the x variable column.
5. Click **OK**.

**Chapter Outcome 6.** ➤ **Confidence Interval for the Average y, Given x** The marketing manager might like a 95% confidence interval for *average*, or expected value, for charges of patients who stay in the hospital five days. The confidence interval for the expected value of a dependent variable, given a specific level of the independent variable, is determined by Equation 14.23. Observe that the specific value of x used to provide the prediction is denoted as $x_p$.

---

**Confidence Interval for $E(y)|x_p$**

$$\hat{y} \pm t s_\varepsilon \sqrt{\frac{1}{n} + \frac{(x_p - \bar{x})^2}{\sum(x - \bar{x})^2}} \qquad (14.23)$$

where:

$\hat{y}$ = Point estimate of the dependent variable
$t$ = Critical value with $n - 2$ degrees of freedom
$n$ = Sample size
$x_p$ = Specific value of the independent variable
$\bar{x}$ = Mean of the independent variable observations in the sample
$s_\varepsilon$ = Estimate of the standard error of the estimate

---

Although the confidence interval estimate can be manually computed using Equation 14.23, using your computer is much easier. Both PHStat and Minitab have built-in options to generate the confidence interval estimate for the dependent variable for a given value of the x variable. Figure 14.21 shows the Minitab results when length of stay, x, equals five days. Given this length of stay, the point estimate for the mean total charges is rounded by Minitab to $7,292, and at the 95% confidence level, the administrators believe the mean total charges will be in the interval $6,790 to $7,794.

**Prediction Interval for a Particular y, Given x** The confidence interval shown in Figure 14.21 is for the average value of y given $x_p$. The administrator might also be interested in predicting the total charges for a *particular* patient with a five-day stay, rather than the average of the charges for all patients staying five days. Developing this 95% prediction interval requires only a slight modification to Equation 14.23. This prediction interval is given by Equation 14.24.

**FIGURE 14.21**

Minitab Output: Freedom Hospital Confidence Interval Estimate

Minitab Instructions:
1. Use Instructions in Figure 14.20 to get regression results.
2. Before clicking **OK**, select **Options**.
3. In **Prediction Interval for New Observations,** enter value(s) of x variable.
4. In **Confidence level**, enter 0.95.
5. Click **OK. OK**.

---

**Prediction Interval for y|x_p**

$$\hat{y} \pm t s_\varepsilon \sqrt{1 + \frac{1}{n} + \frac{(x_p - \bar{x})^2}{\Sigma(x - \bar{x})^2}} \qquad (14.24)$$

As was the case with the confidence interval application discussed previously, the manual computations required to use Equation 14.24 can be onerous. We recommend using your computer and software such as Minitab or PHStat to find the prediction interval. Figure 14.22 shows the PHStat results. Note that the same PHStat process generates both the prediction and confidence interval estimates.

**FIGURE 14.22**

Excel 2007 (PHStat) Prediction Interval for Freedom Hospital

Excel 2007 (PHStat) Instructions:
1. Open file: Patients.xls.
2. Click on **Add-Ins > PHStat**.
3. Select **Regression > Simple Linear Regression**.
4. Define y variable range (*Total Charges*) and x variable range (*Length of Stay*).
5. Select **Confidence and Prediction Interval** – set x = 5 and 95% confidence.

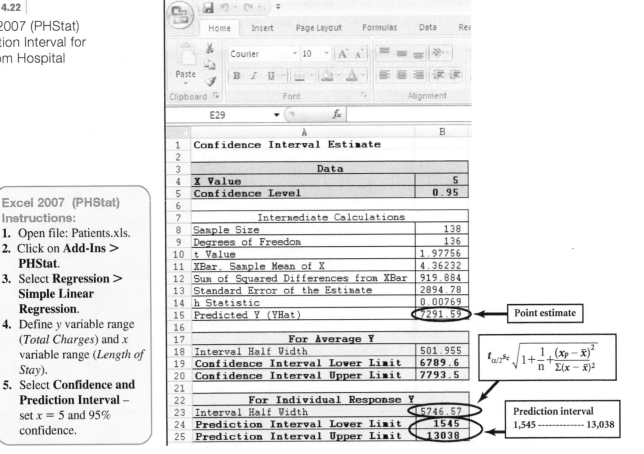

Based on this regression model, at the 95% confidence level, the hospital administrators can predict total charges for any patient with length of stay of five days to be between $1,545 and $13,038. As you can see, this prediction has extremely poor precision. We doubt any hospital administrator will use a prediction interval that is so wide. Although the regression model explains a significant proportion of variation in the dependent variable, it is relatively imprecise for predictive purposes. To improve the precision, we might decrease the confidence level or increase the sample size and redevelop the model.

The prediction interval for a specific value of the dependent variable is wider (less precise) than the confidence interval for predicting the average value of the dependent variable. This will always be the case, as seen in Equations 14.23 and 14.24. From an intuitive viewpoint, we should expect to come closer to predicting an average value than a single value.

Note, the term $(x_p - \bar{x})^2$ has a particular effect on the confidence interval determined by both Equations 14.23 and 14.24. The farther $x_p$ (the value of the independent variable used to predict $y$), is from $\bar{x}$, the greater $(x_p - \bar{x})^2$ becomes. Figure 14.23 shows two regression lines developed from two samples with the same set of $x$-values. We have made both lines pass through the same $(\bar{x}, \bar{y})$ point; however, they have different slopes and intercepts. At $x_p = x_1$, the two regression lines give predictions of $y$ that are close to each other. However, for $x_p = x_2$, the predictions of $y$ are quite different. Thus, when $x_p$ is close to $\bar{x}$, the problems caused by variations in regression slopes are not as great as when $x_p$ is far from $\bar{x}$. Figure 14.24 shows the prediction intervals over the range of possible $x_p$ values. The band around the estimated regression line bends away from the regression line as $x_p$ moves in either direction from $\bar{x}$.

**Chapter Outcome 7.** ➤ **Common Problems Using Regression Analysis**

Regression is perhaps the most widely used statistical tool other than descriptive statistical techniques. Because it is so widely used, you need to be aware of the common problems encountered when the technique is employed.

One potential problem occurs when decision makers apply regression analysis for predictive purposes. The conclusions and inferences made from a regression line are statistically valid only over the range of the data contained in the sample used to develop the regression line. For instance, in the Midwest Distribution example, we analyzed the performance of sales representatives with one to nine years of experience. Therefore, predicting sales levels for employees with one to nine years of experience would be justified. However, if we were to try to predict the sales performance of someone with more than nine years of experience, the relationship between sales and experience might be different. Because no observations were

**FIGURE 14.23** |

Regression Lines Illustrating the Increase in Potential Variation in $y$ as $x_p$ Moves Farther from $\bar{x}$

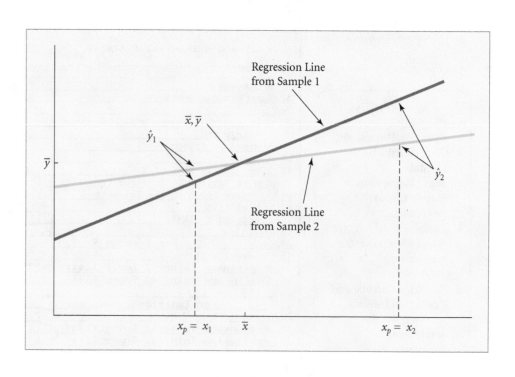

**FIGURE 14.24**

Confidence Intervals for $y|x_p$ and $E(y)|x_p$

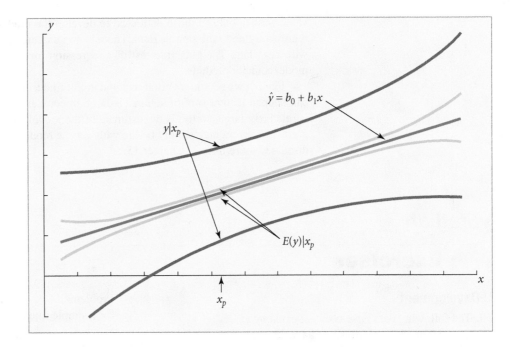

taken for experience levels beyond the 1- to 9-year range, we have no information about what might happen outside that range. Figure 14.25 shows a case in which the true relationship between sales and experience reaches a peak value at about 20 years and then starts to decline. If a linear regression equation were used to predict sales based on experience levels beyond the relevant range of data, large prediction errors could occur.

A second important consideration, one that was discussed previously, involves correlation and causation. The fact that a significant linear relationship exists between two variables does not imply that one variable causes the other. Although there may be a cause-and-effect relationship, you should not infer that such a relationship is present based only on regression and/or correlation analysis. You should also recognize that a cause-and-effect relationship between two variables is not necessary for regression analysis to be an effective tool. What matters is that the regression model accurately reflects the relationship between the two variables and that the relationship remains stable.

Many users of regression analysis mistakenly believe that a high coefficient of determination ($R^2$) guarantees that the regression model will be a good predictor. You should remember that $R^2$ is a measure of the variation in the dependent variable explained by the independent variable. Although the least squares criterion assures us that $R^2$ will be maximized (because the sum of squares error is a minimum) for the given set of sample data, the

**FIGURE 14.25**

Graph for a Sales Peak at 20 Years

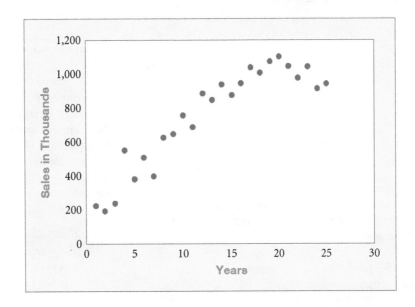

value applies only to those data used to develop the model. Thus, $R^2$ measures the fit of the regression line to the sample data. There is no guarantee that there will be an equally good fit with new data. The only true test of a regression model's predictive ability is how well the model actually predicts.

Finally, we should mention that you might find a large $R^2$ with a large standard error. This can happen if total sum of squares is large in comparison to the $SSE$. Then, even though $R^2$ is relatively large, so too is the estimate of the model's standard error. Thus, confidence and prediction errors may simply be too wide for the model to be used in many situations. This is discussed more fully in Chapter 15.

## MyStatLab

## 14-3: Exercises

### Skill Development

**14-30.** The following data have been collected by an accountant who is performing an audit of paper products at a large office supply company. The dependent variable, $y$, is the time taken (in minutes) by the accountant to count the units. The independent variable, $x$, is the number of units on the computer inventory record.

| $y$ | 23.1 | 100.5 | 242.9 | 56.4 | 178.7 | 10.5 | 94.2 | 200.4 | 44.2 | 128.7 | 180.5 |
| $x$ | 24 | 120 | 228 | 56 | 190 | 13 | 85 | 190 | 32 | 120 | 230 |

  a. Develop a scatter plot for these data.
  b. Determine the regression equation representing the data. Is the model significant? Test using a significance level of 0.10 and the $p$-value approach.
  c. Develop a 90% confidence interval estimate for the true regression slope and interpret this interval estimate. Based on this interval, could you conclude the accountant takes an additional minute to count each additional unit?

**14-31.** You are given the following sample data:

| $x$ | $y$ |
|-----|-----|
| 10 | 3 |
| 6 | 7 |
| 9 | 3 |
| 3 | 8 |
| 2 | 9 |
| 8 | 5 |
| 3 | 7 |

  a. Develop a scatter plot for these data.
  b. Determine the regression equation for the data.
  c. Develop a 95% confidence interval estimate for the true regression slope and interpret this interval estimate.
  d. Provide a 95% prediction interval estimate for a particular $y$, given $x_p = 7$.

Problems 14-32 and 14-33 refer to the following output for a simple linear regression model:

**Summary Output**

| Regression Statistics | |
|---|---|
| Multiple $R$ | 0.1027 |
| $R$-Square | 0.0105 |
| Adjusted $R$-Square | $-0.0030$ |
| Standard Error | 9.8909 |
| Observations | 75 |

**Anova**

| | df | SS | MS | F | Significance F |
|---|---|---|---|---|---|
| Regression | 1 | 76.124 | 76.12 | 0.778 | 0.3806 |
| Residual | 73 | 7141.582 | 97.83 | | |
| Total | 74 | 7217.706 | | | |

| | Coefficents | Standard Error | $t$-Statistic |
|---|---|---|---|
| Intercept | 4.0133 | 3.878 | 1.035 |
| $x$ | 0.0943 | 0.107 | 0.882 |

| | $p$-value | Lower 95% | Upper 95% |
|---|---|---|---|
| Intercept | 0.3041 | $-3.715$ | 11.742 |
| $x$ | 0.3806 | $-0.119$ | 0.307 |

**14-32.** Referring to the displayed regression model, what percent of variation in the $y$ variable is explained by the $x$ variable in the model?

**14-33.** Construct and interpret a 90% confidence interval estimate for the regression slope coefficient.

**14-34.** You are given the following summary statistics from a regression analysis:

$$\hat{y} = 200 + 150x$$
$$SSE = 25.25$$
$$SSX = \text{Sum of squares } X = \Sigma(x - \bar{x})^2 = 99,645$$
$$n = 18$$
$$\bar{x} = 52.0$$

a. Determine the point estimate for $y$ if $x_p = 48$ is used.

b. Provide a 95% confidence interval estimate for the average $y$, given $x_p = 48$. Interpret this interval.

c. Provide a 95% prediction interval estimate for a particular $y$, given $x_p = 48$. Interpret.

d. Discuss the difference between the estimates provided in parts b and c.

**14-35.** The sales manager at Sun City Real Estate Company in Tempe, Arizona, is interested in describing the relationship between condo sales prices and the number of weeks the condo is on the market before it sells. He has collected a random sample of 17 low-end condos that have sold within the past three months in the Tempe area. These data are shown as follows:

| Weeks on the Market | Selling Price |
|---|---|
| 23 | $76,500 |
| 48 | $102,000 |
| 9 | $53,000 |
| 26 | $84,200 |
| 20 | $73,000 |
| 40 | $125,000 |
| 51 | $109,000 |
| 18 | $60,000 |
| 25 | $87,000 |
| 62 | $94,000 |
| 33 | $76,000 |
| 11 | $90,000 |
| 15 | $61,000 |
| 26 | $86,000 |
| 27 | $70,000 |
| 56 | $133,000 |
| 12 | $93,000 |

a. Develop a simple linear regression model to explain the variation in selling price based on the number of weeks the condo is on the market.

b. Test to determine whether the regression slope coefficient is significantly different from 0 using a significance level equal to 0.05.

c. Construct and interpret a 95% confidence interval estimate for the regression slope coefficient.

**14-36.** A sample of 10 yields the following data:

| $x$ | 10 | 8 | 11 | 7 | 10 | 11 | 6 | 7 | 15 | 9 |
|---|---|---|---|---|---|---|---|---|---|---|
| $y$ | 103 | 85 | 115 | 73 | 97 | 102 | 65 | 75 | 155 | 95 |

a. Provide a 95% confidence interval for the average $y$ when $x_p = 9.4$.

b. Provide a 95% confidence interval for the average $y$ when $x_p = 10$.

c. Obtain the margin of errors for both part a and part b. Explain why the margin of error obtained in part b is larger than that in part a.

**14-37.** A regression analysis from a sample of 15 produced the following:

$$\Sigma(x_i - \bar{x})(y_i - \bar{y}) = 156.4$$

$$\Sigma(x_i - \bar{x})^2 = 173.5$$

$$\Sigma(y_i - \bar{y})^2 = 181.6$$

$$\Sigma(y_i - \hat{y})^2 = 40.621$$

$$\bar{x} = 13.4 \text{ and } \bar{y} = 56.4$$

a. Produce the regression line.

b. Determine if there is a linear relationship between the dependent and independent variables. Use a significance level of 0.05 and a $p$-value approach.

c. Calculate a 90% confidence interval for the amount the dependent variable changes when the independent variable increases by 1 unit.

## Business **Applications**

**14-38.** During the recession that began in 2008, not only did some people stop making house payments, they also stopped making payments for local government services such as trash collection and water and sewer services. The following data have been collected by an accountant who is performing an audit of account balances for a major city billing department. The population from which the data were collected represent those accounts for which the customer had indicated the balance was incorrect. The dependent variable, $y$, is the actual account balance as verified by the accountant. The independent variable, $x$, is the computer account balance.

| $y$ | 233 | 10 | 24 | 56 | 78 | 102 | 90 | 200 | 344 | 120 | 18 |
|---|---|---|---|---|---|---|---|---|---|---|---|
| $x$ | 245 | 12 | 22 | 56 | 90 | 103 | 85 | 190 | 320 | 120 | 23 |

a. Compute the least squares regression equation.

b. If the computer account balance was 100, what would you expect to be the actual account balance as verified by the accountant?

c. The computer balance for Timothy Jones is listed as 100 in the computer account record. Provide a 90% interval estimate for Mr. Jones's actual account balance.

d. Provide a 90% interval estimate for the average of all customers' actual account balances in which a computer account balance is the same as that of Mr. Jones (part c). Interpret.

**14-39.** Gym Outfitters sells and services exercise equipment such as treadmills, ellipticals, and stair climbers to gymnasiums and recreational centers. The company's management would like to determine if there is a relationship between the number of minutes required to complete a routine service call and the number of machines serviced. A random sample of 12 records revealed the following information concerning the number of machines serviced and the time (in minutes) to complete the routine service call:

| Number of Machines | Service Time (minutes) |
|---|---|
| 11 | 115 |
| 8 | 60 |
| 9 | 80 |
| 10 | 90 |
| 7 | 55 |
| 6 | 65 |
| 8 | 70 |
| 4 | 33 |
| 10 | 95 |
| 5 | 50 |
| 5 | 40 |
| 12 | 110 |

a. Estimate the least squares regression equation.
b. If a gymnasium had six machines, how many minutes should Gym Outfitters expect a routine service call to require?
c. Provide a 90% confidence interval for the average amount of time required to complete a routine service call when the number of machines being serviced is nine.
d. Provide a 90% prediction interval for the time required to complete a particular routine service call for a gymnasium that has seven machines.

**14-40.** The National Association of Realtors (NAR) Existing-Home Sales Series provides a measurement of the residential real estate market. On or about the 25th of each month, NAR releases statistics on sales and prices of condos and co-ops, in addition to existing single-family homes, for the nation and the four regions. The data presented here indicate the number of (in thousands) existing-home sales as well as condo/co-op sales:

| Year | Month | Single-Family Sales | Condo/Co-op Sales |
|---|---|---|---|
| 2009 | Apr | 6,270 | 895 |
| | May | 6,230 | 912 |
| | Jun | 6,330 | 943 |
| | Jul | 6,220 | 914 |
| | Aug | 6,280 | 928 |
| | Sept | 6,290 | 908 |
| | Oct | 6,180 | 867 |
| | Nov | 6,150 | 876 |
| | Dec | 5,860 | 885 |
| 2010 | Jan | 5,790 | 781 |
| | Feb | 6,050 | 852 |
| | Mar | 6,040 | 862 |
| | Apr | 5,920 | 839 |

a. Construct the regression equation that would predict the number of condo/co-op sales using the number of single-family sales.
b. One might conjecture that these two markets (single-family sales and condo/co-op sales) would be competing for the same audience. Therefore, we would expect that as the number of single-family sales increases, the number of condo/co-op sales would decrease. Conduct a hypothesis test to determine this using a significance level of 0.05.
c. Provide a prediction interval for the number of condo/co-op sales when the number of single-family sales is 6,000 (thousands). Use a confidence level of 95%.

**14-41.** J.D. Power and Associates conducts an initial quality study (IQS) each year to determine the quality of newly manufactured automobiles. IQS measures 135 attributes across nine categories, including ride/handling/braking, engine and transmission, and a broad range of quality problem symptoms reported by vehicle owners. The 2008 IQS was based on responses from more than 62,000 purchasers and lessees of new 2008 model-year cars and trucks, who were surveyed after 90 days of ownership. The data given here portray the industry average of the number of reported problems per 100 vehicles for 1998–2008.

| Year | 1998 | 1999 | 2000 | 2001 | 2002 | 2003 | 2004 | 2005 | 2006 | 2007 | 2008 |
|---|---|---|---|---|---|---|---|---|---|---|---|
| Problems | 176 | 167 | 154 | 147 | 133 | 133 | 125 | 121 | 119 | 118 | 118 |

a. Construct a scatter plot of the number of reported problems per 100 vehicles as a function of the year.
b. Determine if the average number of reported problems per 100 vehicles declines from year to year. Use a significance level of 0.01 and a $p$-value approach.
c. Assume the relationship between the number of reported problems per 100 vehicles and the year continues into the future. Provide a 95% prediction interval for the initial quality industry average of the number of reported problems per 100 vehicles for 2010.

## Computer Database **Exercises**

**14-42.** A manufacturer produces a wash-down motor for the food service industry. The company manufactures the motors to order by modifying a base model to meet the specifications requested by the customer. The motors are produced in a batch environment with the batch size equal to the number ordered. The manufacturer has recently sampled 27 customer orders. The motor manufacturer would like to determine if there is a relationship between the cost of producing the order and the order size so that it could estimate the cost of producing a particular size order. The sampled data are contained in the file **Washdown Motors**.

a. Use the sample data to estimate the least squares regression model.

b. Provide an interpretation of the regression coefficients.

c. Test the significance of the overall regression model using a significance level of 0.01.

d. The company has just received an order for 30 motors. Use the regression model developed in part a to estimate the cost of producing this particular order.

e. Referring to part d, what is the 90% confidence interval for an average cost of an order of 30 motors?

**14-43.** Each month, the Bureau of Labor Statistics (BLS) of the U.S. Department of Labor announces the total number of employed and unemployed persons in the United States for the previous month. At the same time, it also publishes the inflation rate, which is the rate of change in the price of goods and services from one month to the next. It seems quite plausible that there should be some relationship between these two indicators. The file entitled **CPI** provides the monthly unemployment and inflation rates for the period 2000–2005.

a. Construct a scatter plot of the unemployment rate versus inflation rate for the period 2000–2005. Describe the relationship that appears to exist between these two variables.

b. Produce a 95% prediction interval for the unemployment rate for the maximum inflation rate in the period 2000–2005. Interpret the interval.

c. Produce a 95% prediction interval for the unemployment rate when the inflation rate is 0.00.

d. Which of the prediction intervals in parts b and c has the larger margin of error? Explain why this is the case.

**14-44.** The National Highway Transportation Safety Administration's National Center for Statistics and Analysis released its Vehicle Survivability Travel Mileage Schedules in January 2006. One item investigated was the relationship between the annual vehicle miles traveled (VMT) as a function of vehicle age for passenger cars up to 25 years old. The VMT data were collected by asking consumers to estimate the number of miles driven in a given year. The data were collected over a 14-month period, starting in March 2001 and ending in May 2002. The file entitled **Miles** contains this data.

a. Produce a regression equation modeling the relationship between VMT and the age of the vehicle. Estimate how many more annual vehicle miles would be traveled for a vehicle that is 10 years older than another vehicle.

b. Provide a 90% confidence interval estimate for the average annual vehicle miles traveled when the age of the vehicle is 15 years.

c. Determine if it is plausible for a vehicle that is 10 years old to travel 12,000 miles in a year. Support your answer with statistical reasoning.

**END EXERCISES** 14-3

# Visual Summary

**Chapter 14:** Although some business situations involve only one variable, others require decision makers to consider the relationship between two or more variables. In analyzing the relationship between two variables, there are two basic models that we can use. The regression model covered in this chapter is referred to as **simple linear regression**. This relationship between $x$ and $y$ assumes that the $x$ variable takes on known values specifically selected from all the possible values for $x$. The $y$ variable is a random variable observed at the different levels of $x$. Testing that a linear relationship exists between the dependent and independent variables is performed using the standard statistical procedures of hypothesis testing and confidence intervals. A second model is referred to as the correlation model and is used in applications in which both the $x$ and $y$ variables are considered to be random variables. These two models arise in practice by the way in which the data are obtained. Regression analysis and correlation analysis are two of the most often applied statistical tools for business decision making.

## 14.1 Scatter Plots and Correlation (pg. 580–589)

### Summary

Decision-making situations that call for understanding the relationship between two quantitative variables are aided by the use of **scatter plots**, or *scatter diagrams*. A scatter plot is a two-dimensional plot showing the values for the joint occurrence of two quantitative variables. The scatter plot may be used to graphically represent the relationship between two variables. A numerical quantity that measures the strength of the linear relationship between two variables is labeled the **correlation coefficient**. The sample correlation coefficient, r, can range from a perfect positive correlation, +1.0, to a perfect negative correlation, −1.0. A test based upon the *t*-distribution can determine whether the population correlation coefficient is significantly different from 0 and, therefore, whether a linear relationship exists between the dependent and independent variables.

**Outcome 1.** Calculate and interpret the correlation between two variables.
**Outcome 2.** Determine whether the correlation is significant.

## 14.2 Simple Linear Regression Analysis (pg. 589–612)

### Summary

The statistical technique we use to analyze the relationship between the dependent variable and the independent variable is known as regression analysis. When the relationship between the dependent variable and the independent variable is linear, the technique is referred as **simple linear regression**. The population regression model is determined by three values known as the population regression coefficients: (1) the $y$-intercept, (2) the slope of the regression line, and (3) the random error term. The criterion used to determine the best estimate of the population regression line is known as the **least squares criterion**. It chooses values for the $y$-intercept and slope that will produce the smallest possible sum of squared prediction errors. Testing that the population's slope coefficient is equal to zero provides a method to determine if there is no linear relationship between the dependent and independent variables. The test for the simple linear regression is equivalent to the test that the correlation coefficient is significant. A less involved procedure that indicates the goodness of fit of the regression equation to the data is known as the **coefficient of determination**. Simple linear regression, which is introduced in this chapter, is one of the most often applied statistical tools by business decision makers for analyzing the relationship between two variables.

**Outcome 3.** Calculate the simple linear regression equation for a set of data and know the basic assumptions behind regression analysis.
**Outcome 4.** Determine whether a regression model is significant.

## 14.3 Uses for Regression Analysis (pg. 612–623)

### Summary

Regression analysis is a statistical tool that is used for two main purposes: description and prediction. Description is accomplished by describing the plausible values the population slope coefficient may attain. To provide this, a confidence interval estimator of the population slope is employed. There are many other situations in which the prime purpose of regression analysis is description. Market researchers also use regression analysis, among other techniques, in an effort to describe the factors that influence the demand for their products. The analyst may wish to provide a confidence interval for the expected value of a dependent variable, given a specific level of the independent variable. This is obtained by the use of a confidence interval for the average $y$, given $x$. Another confidence interval is available in the case that the analyst wishes to predict a particular $y$ for a given $x$. This interval estimator is called a prediction interval.

Any procedure in statistics is valid only if the assumptions it is built upon is valid. This is particularly true in regression analysis. Therefore, before using a regression model for description or prediction, you should check to see if the assumptions associated with linear regression analysis are valid. Residual analysis is the procedure that is used for that purpose

### Conclusion

Correlation and regression analysis are two of the most frequently used statistical techniques by business decision makers. This chapter has introduced the basics of these two topics. The discussion of regression analysis has been limited to situations in which you have one dependent variable and one independent variable. Chapter 15 will extend the discussion of regression analysis by showing how two or more independent variables are included in the analysis. The focus of that chapter will be on building a model for explaining the variation in the dependent variable. However, the basic concepts presented in this chapter will be carried forward.

**Outcome 5.** Recognize regression analysis applications for purposes of description and prediction.
**Outcome 6.** Calculate and interpret confidence intervals for the regression analysis.
**Outcome 7.** Recognize some potential problems if regression analysis is used incorrectly.

# Equations

**(14.1)** Sample Correlation Coefficient  pg. 580

$$r = \frac{\sum(x - \bar{x})(y - \bar{y})}{\sqrt{[\sum(x - \bar{x})^2][\sum(y - \bar{y})^2]}}$$

**(14.2)** or the algebraic equivalent:  pg. 581

$$r = \frac{n\sum xy - \sum x \sum y}{\sqrt{[n(\sum x^2) - (\sum x)^2][n(\sum y^2) - (\sum y)^2]}}$$

**(14.3)** Test Statistic for Correlation  pg. 584

$$t = \frac{r}{\sqrt{\dfrac{1 - r^2}{n - 2}}} \qquad df = n - 2$$

**(14.4)** Simple Linear Regression Model (Population Model)  pg. 590

$$y = \beta_0 + \beta_1 x + \varepsilon$$

**(14.5)** Estimated Regression Model (Sample Model)  pg. 592

$$\hat{y} = b_0 + b_1 x$$

**(14.6)** Least Squares Equations  pg. 594

$$b_1 = \frac{\sum(x - \bar{x})(y - \bar{y})}{\sum(x - \bar{x})^2}$$

**(14.7)** or the algebraic equivalent:  pg. 594

$$b_1 = \frac{\sum xy - \dfrac{\sum x \sum y}{n}}{\sum x^2 - \dfrac{(\sum x)^2}{n}}$$

**(14.8)** and  pg. 594

$$b_0 = \bar{y} - b_1 \bar{x}$$

**(14.9)** Sum of Squared Errors  pg. 596

$$SSE = \sum y^2 - b_0 \sum y - b_1 \sum xy$$

**(14.10)** Sum of Residuals  pg. 596

$$\sum_{i=1}^{n}(y_i - \hat{y}_i) = 0$$

**(14.11)** Sum of Squared Residuals (Errors)  pg. 597

$$SSE = \sum_{i=1}^{n}(y_i - \hat{y}_i)^2$$

**(14.12)** Total Sum of Squares  pg. 600

$$SST = \sum_{i=1}^{n}(y_i - \bar{y})^2$$

**(14.13)** Sum of Squares Error  pg. 601

$$SSE = \sum_{i=1}^{n}(y_i - \hat{y}_i)^2$$

**(14.14)** Sum of Squares Regression  pg. 602

$$SSR = \sum_{i=1}^{n}(\hat{y}_i - \bar{y})^2$$

**(14.15)** Coefficient of Determination, $R^2$  pg. 602

$$R^2 = \frac{SSR}{SST}$$

**(14.16)** Coefficient of Determination for the Single Independent Variable Case  pg. 602

$$R^2 = r^2$$

**(14.17)** Test Statistic for Significance of the Coefficient of Determination  pg. 603

$$F = \frac{SSR/1}{SSE/(n-2)} \qquad df = (D_1 = 1, D_2 = n - 2)$$

**(14.18)** Simple Regression Standard Error of the Slope Coefficient (Population)  pg. 604

$$\sigma_{b_1} = \frac{\sigma_\varepsilon}{\sqrt{\sum(x - \bar{x})^2}}$$

**(14.19)** Simple Regression Estimator for the Standard Error of the Estimate  pg. 604

$$s_\varepsilon = \sqrt{\frac{SSE}{n-2}}$$

**(14.20)** Simple Regression Estimator for the Standard Error of the Slope  pg. 605

$$s_{b_1} = \frac{s_\varepsilon}{\sqrt{\sum(x - \bar{x})^2}}$$

**(14.21)** Simple Linear Regression Test Statistic for Test of the Significance of the Slope  pg. 607

$$t = \frac{b_1 - \beta_1}{s_{b_1}} \qquad df = n - 2$$

**(14.22)** Confidence Interval Estimate for the Regression Slope, Simple Linear Regression  pg. 614

$$b_1 \pm t s_{b_1}$$

or equivalently,

$$b_1 \pm t \frac{s_\varepsilon}{\sqrt{\sum(x-\bar{x})^2}} \qquad df = n-2$$

**(14.23)** Confidence Interval for $E(y)|x_p$ pg. 616

$$\hat{y} \pm t s_\varepsilon \sqrt{\frac{1}{n} + \frac{(x_p - \bar{x})^2}{\sum(x-\bar{x})^2}}$$

**(14.24)** Prediction Interval for $y|x_p$ pg. 617

$$\hat{y} \pm t s_\varepsilon \sqrt{1 + \frac{1}{n} + \frac{(x_p - \bar{x})^2}{\sum(x-\bar{x})^2}}$$

# Key Terms

Coefficient of determination pg. 602
Correlation coefficient pg. 580
Least squares criterion pg. 592

Regression slope coefficient pg. 591
Residual pg. 592

Scatter plot pg. 580
Simple linear regression pg. 589

# Chapter Exercises

MyStatLab

## Conceptual Questions

**14-45.** A statistics student was recently working on a class project that required him to compute a correlation coefficient for two variables. After careful work he arrived at a correlation coefficient of 0.45. Interpret this correlation coefficient for the student who did the calculations.

**14-46.** Referring to the previous problem, another student in the same class computed a regression equation relating the same two variables. The slope of the equation was found to be −0.735. After trying several times and always coming up with the same result, she felt that she must have been doing something wrong since the value was negative and she knew that this could not be right. Comment on this student's conclusion.

**14-47.** If we select a random sample of data for two variables and, after computing the correlation coefficient, conclude that the two variables may have zero correlation, can we say that there is no relationship between the two variables? Discuss.

**14-48.** Discuss why prediction intervals that attempt to predict a particular $y$-value are less precise than confidence intervals for predicting an average $y$.

**14-49.** Consider the two following scenarios:
a. The number of new workers hired per week in your county has a high positive correlation with the average weekly temperature. Can you conclude that an increase in temperature causes an increase in the number of new hires? Discuss.
b. Suppose the stock price and the common dividends declared for a certain company have a high positive correlation. Are you safe in concluding on the basis of the correlation coefficient that an increase in the common dividends declared causes an increase in

the stock price? Present other reasons than the correlation coefficient that might lead you to conclude that an increase in common dividends declared causes an increase in the stock price.

**14-50.** Consider the following set of data:

| $x$ | 48 | 27 | 34 | 24 | 49 | 29 | 39 | 38 | 46 | 32 |
|-----|----|----|----|----|----|----|----|----|----|----|
| $y$ | 47 | 23 | 31 | 20 | 50 | 48 | 47 | 47 | 42 | 47 |

a. Calculate the correlation coefficient of these two variables.
b. Multiply each value of the variable $x$ by 5 and add 10 to the resulting products. Now multiply each value of the variable $y$ by 3 and subtract 7 from the resulting products. Finally, calculate the correlation coefficient of the new $x$ and $y$ variables.
c. Describe the principle that the example developed in parts a and b demonstrates.

**14-51.** Go to the library and locate an article in a journal related to your major (*Journal of Marketing*, *Journal of Finance*, etc.) that uses linear regression. Discuss the following:
a. How the author chose the dependent and independent variables
b. How the data were gathered
c. What statistical tests the author used
d. What conclusions the analysis allowed the author to draw

## Business Applications

**14-52.** The Smithfield Organic Milk Company recently studied a random sample of 30 of its distributors and found the correlation between sales and advertising dollars to be 0.67.

a. Is there a significant linear relationship between sales and advertising? If so, is it fair to conclude that advertising causes sales to increase?

b. If a regression model were developed using sales as the dependent variable and advertising as the independent variable, determine the proportion of the variation in sales that would be explained by its relationship to advertising. Discuss what this says about the usefulness of using advertising to predict sales.

**14-53.** A previous exercise discussed the relationship between the average college tuition (in 2003 dollars) for private and public colleges. The data indicated in the article follow:

| Period | 1983–1984 | 1988–1989 | 1993–1994 |
|---|---|---|---|
| Private | 9,202 | 12,146 | 13,844 |
| Public | 2,074 | 2,395 | 3,188 |
| Period | 1998–1999 | 2003–2004 | 2008–2009 |
| Private | 16,454 | 19,710 | 21,582 |
| Public | 3,632 | 4,694 | 5,652 |

a. Construct the regression equation that would predict the average college tuition for private colleges using that of the public colleges.

b. Determine if there is a linear tendency for the average college tuition for private colleges to increase when the average college tuition for public colleges increases. Use a significance level of 0.05 and a $p$-value approach.

c. Provide a 95% confidence interval for the average college tuition for private colleges when the average college tuition for public colleges reaches $7,000.

d. Is it plausible that the average college tuition for private colleges would be larger than $35,000 when the average college tuition for public colleges reaches $7,000? Support your assertion with statistical reasoning.

**14-54.** The Farmington City Council recently commissioned a study of park users in their community. Data were collected on the age of the person surveyed and the amount of hours he or she spent in the park in the past month. The data collected were as follows:

| Time in Park | Age | Time in Park | Age |
|---|---|---|---|
| 7.2 | 16 | 4.4 | 48 |
| 3.5 | 15 | 8.8 | 18 |
| 6.6 | 28 | 4.9 | 24 |
| 5.4 | 16 | 5.1 | 33 |
| 1.5 | 29 | 1.0 | 56 |
| 2.3 | 38 | | |

a. Draw a scatter plot for these data and discuss what, if any, relationship appears to be present between the two variables.

b. Compute the correlation coefficient between age and the amount of time spent in the park. Provide an explanation to the Farmington City Council of what the correlation measures.

c. Test to determine whether the amount of time spent in the park decreases with the age of the park user. Use a significance level of 0.10. Use a $p$-value approach to conduct this hypothesis test.

**14-55.** At State University, a study was done to establish whether a relationship exists between students' graduating grade point average (GPA) and the SAT verbal score when the student originally entered the university. The sample data are reported as follows:

| GPA | 2.5 | 3.2 | 3.5 | 2.8 | 3.0 | 2.4 | 3.4 | 2.9 | 2.7 | 3.8 |
|---|---|---|---|---|---|---|---|---|---|---|
| SAT | 640 | 700 | 550 | 540 | 620 | 490 | 710 | 600 | 505 | 710 |

a. Develop a scatter plot for these data and describe what, if any, relationship exists between the two variables, GPA and SAT score.

b. (1) Compute the correlation coefficient. (2) Does it appear that the success of students at State University is related to the SAT verbal scores of those students? Conduct a statistical procedure to answer this question. Use a significance level of 0.01.

c. (1) Compute the regression equation based on these sample data if you wish to predict the university GPA using the student SAT score. (2) Interpret the regression coefficients.

**14-56.** An American airline company recently performed a customer survey in which it asked a random sample of 100 passengers to indicate their income and the total cost of the airfares they purchased for pleasure trips during the past year. A regression model was developed for the purpose of determining whether income could be used as a variable to explain the variation in the total cost of airfare on airlines in a year. The following regression results were obtained:

$$\hat{y} = 0.25 + 0.0150x$$
$$s_\varepsilon = 721.44$$
$$R^2 = 0.65$$
$$s_{b_1} = 0.0000122$$

a. Produce an estimate of the maximum and minimum differences in the amounts allocated to purchase airline tickets by two families that have a difference of $20,000 in family income. Assume that you wish to use a 90% confidence level.

b. Can the intercept of the regression equation be interpreted in this case, assuming that no one who was surveyed had an income of 0 dollars? Explain.

c. Use the information provided to perform an *F*-test for the significance of the regression model. Discuss your results, assuming the test is performed at the significance level of 0.05.

**14-57.** One of the advances that have helped to diminish carpal tunnel syndrome is ergonomic keyboards. The ergonomic keyboards may also increase typing speed. Ten administrative assistants were chosen to type on both standard and ergonomic keyboards. The resulting typing speeds follow:

| Ergonomic: | 69 | 80 | 60 | 71 | 73 | 64 | 63 | 70 | 63 | 74 |
|---|---|---|---|---|---|---|---|---|---|---|
| Standard: | 70 | 68 | 54 | 56 | 58 | 64 | 62 | 51 | 64 | 53 |

a. Produce a scatter plot of the typing speed of administrative assistants using ergonomic and standard keyboards. Does there appear to be a linear relationship between these two variables? Explain your response.

b. Calculate the correlation coefficient of the typing speed of administrative assistants using ergonomic and standard keyboards.

c. Conduct a hypothesis test to determine if a positive correlation exists between administrative assistants using ergonomic and standard keyboards. Use a significance level of 0.05.

**14-58.** A company is considering recruiting new employees from a particular college and plans to place a great deal of emphasis on the student's college GPA. However, the company is aware that not all schools have the same grading standards, so it is possible that a student at this school might have a lower (or higher) GPA than a student from another school, yet really be on par with the other student. To make this comparison between schools, the company has devised a test that it has administered utilizing a sample size of 400 students. With the results of the test, it has developed a regression model that it uses to predict student GPA. The following equation represents the model:

$$\hat{y} = 1.0 + 0.028x$$

The $R^2$ for this model is 0.88 and the standard error of the estimate is 0.20, based on the sample data used to develop the model. Note that the dependent variable is the GPA and the independent variable is test score, where this score can range from 0 to 100. For the sample data used to develop the model, the following values are known:

$$\bar{y} = 2.76$$
$$\bar{x} = 68$$
$$\Sigma(x - \bar{x})^2 = 148,885.73$$

a. Based on the information contained in this problem, can you conclude that as the test score increases,

the GPA will also increase, using a significance level of 0.05?

b. Suppose a student interviews with this company, takes the company test, and scores 80 correct. What is the 90% prediction interval estimate for this student's GPA? Interpret the interval.

c. Suppose the student in part b actually has a 2.90 GPA at this school. Based on this evidence, what might be concluded about this person's actual GPA compared with other students with the same GPA at other schools? Discuss the limitations you might place on this conclusion.

d. Suppose a second student with a 2.45 GPA took the test and scored 65 correct. What is the 90% prediction interval for this student's "real" GPA? Interpret.

## Computer Database **Exercises**

**14-59.** Although the Jordan Banking System, a smaller regional bank, generally avoided the subprime mortgage market and consequently did not take money from the Federal Troubled Asset Relief Program (TARP), its board of directors has decided to look into all aspects of revenues and costs. One service the bank offers is free checking, and the board is interested in whether the costs of this service are offset by revenues from interest earned on the deposits. One aspect in studying checking accounts is to determine whether changes in average checking account balance can be explained by knowing the number of checks written per month. The sample data selected are contained in the data file named **Jordan**.

a. Draw a scatter plot for these data.

b. Develop the least squares regression equation for these data.

c. Develop the 90% confidence interval estimate for the change in the average checking account balance when a person who formerly wrote 25 checks a month doubles the number of checks used.

d. Test to determine if an increase in the number of checks written by an individual can be used to predict the checking account balance of that individual. Use $\alpha = 0.05$. Comment on this result and the result of part c.

**14-60.** An economist for the state government of Mississippi recently collected the data contained in the file called **Mississippi** on the percentage of people unemployed in the state at randomly selected points in time over the past 25 years and the interest rate of Treasury bills offered by the federal government at that point in time.

a. (1) Develop a plot showing the relationship between the two variables. (2) Describe the relationship as being either linear or curvilinear.

b. (1) Develop a simple linear regression model with unemployment rate as the dependent variable. (2) Write a short report describing the model and indicating the important measures.

**14-61.** Terry Downes lost his job as an operations analyst last year in a company downsizing effort. In looking for job opportunities Terry remembered reading an article in *Fortune* stating companies were looking to outsource activities they were currently doing that were not part of their core competence. Terry decided no company's core competence involved cleaning its facilities, and so using his savings, he started a cleaning company. In a surprise to his friends, Terry's company proved to be successful. Recently, Terry decided to survey customers to determine how satisfied they are with the work performed. He devised a rating scale between 0 and 100, with 0 being poor and 100 being excellent service. He selected a random sample of 14 customers and asked them to rate the service. He also recorded the number of worker hours spent in the customer's facility. These data are in the data file named **Downes**.

a. (1) Draw a scatter plot showing these two variables, with the *y* variable on the vertical axis and the *x* variable on the horizontal axis. (2) Describe the relationship between these two variables.

b. (1) Develop a linear regression model to explain the variation in the service rating. (2) Write a short report describing the model and showing the results of pertinent hypothesis tests, using a significance level of 0.10.

**14-62.** A previous problem discussed the College Board changing the SAT test between 2005 and 2006. The class of 2005 was the last to take the former version of the SAT featuring math and verbal sections. The file entitled **MathSAT** contains the math SAT scores for the interval 1967 to 2005. One point of interest concerning the data is the relationship between the average scores of male and female students.

a. Produce a scatter plot depicting the relationship between the average math SAT score of males (the dependent variable) and females (independent variable) over the period 1967 to 2005. Describe the relationship between these two variables.

b. Is there a linear relationship between the average score for males and females over the period 1967 to 2005? Use a significance level of 0.05 and the *p*-value approach to determine this.

**14-63.** The housing market in the United States saw a major decrease in value between 2007 and 2008. The file entitled **House** contains the data on average and median housing prices between November 2007 and November 2008. Assume the data can be viewed as samples of the relevant populations.

a. Determine the linear relationship that could be used to predict the average selling prices for November 2007 using the median selling prices for that period.

b. Conduct a hypothesis test to determine if the median selling prices for November 2007 could be used to determine the average selling prices in that period. Use a significance level of 0.05 and the *p*-value approach to conduct the test.

c. Provide an interval estimate of the average selling price of homes in November 2007 if the median selling price was $195,000. Use a 90% confidence interval.

**14-64.** The Grinfield Service Company's marketing director is interested in analyzing the relationship between her company's sales and the advertising dollars spent. In the course of her analysis, she selected a random sample of 20 weeks and recorded the sales for each week and the amount spent on advertising. These data are contained in the data file called **Grinfield**.

a. Identify the independent and dependent variables.

b. Draw a scatter plot with the dependent variable on the vertical axis and the independent variable on the horizontal axis.

c. The marketing director wishes to know if increasing the amount spent on advertising increases sales. As a first attempt, use a statistical test that will provide the required information. Use a significance level of 0.025. On careful consideration, the marketing manager realizes that it takes a certain amount of time for the effect of advertising to register in terms of increased sales. She therefore asks you to calculate a correlation coefficient for sales of the current week against amount of advertising spent in the previous week and to conduct a hypothesis test to determine if, under this model, increasing the amount spent on advertising increases sales. Again, use a significance level of 0.025.

**14-65.** Refer to the Grinfield Service Company discussed in Problem 14-64.

a. Develop the least squares regression equation for these variables. Plot the regression line on the scatter plot.

b. Develop a 95% confidence interval estimate for the increase in sales resulting from increasing the advertising budget by $50. Interpret the interval.

c. Discuss whether it is appropriate to interpret the intercept value in this model. Under what conditions is it appropriate? Discuss.

d. Develop a 90% confidence interval for the mean sales amount achieved during all weeks in which advertising is $200 for the week.

e. Suppose you are asked to use this regression model to predict the weekly sales when advertising is to be set at $100. What would you reply to the request? Discuss.

# Case 14.1

## A & A Industrial Products

Alex Court, the cost accountant for A & A Industrial Products, was puzzled by the repair cost analysis report he had just reviewed. This was the third consecutive report where unscheduled plant repair costs were out of line with the repair cost budget allocated to each plant. A & A budgets for both scheduled maintenance and unscheduled repair costs for its plants' equipment, mostly large industrial machines. Budgets for scheduled maintenance activities are easy to estimate and are based on the equipment manufacturer's recommendations. The unscheduled repair costs, however, are harder to determine. Historically, A & A Industrial Products has estimated unscheduled maintenance using a formula based on the average number of hours of operation between major equipment failures at a plant. Specifically, plants were given a budget of $65.00 per hour of operation between major failures. Alex had arrived at this amount by dividing aggregate historical repair costs by the total number of hours between failures. Then plant averages would be used to estimate unscheduled repair cost. For example, if a plant averaged 450 hours of run time before a major repair occurred, the plant would be allocated a repair budget of $450 \times \$65 = \$29,250$ per repair. If the plant was expected to be in operation 3,150 hours per year, the company would anticipate seven unscheduled repairs (3,150/450) annually and budget $204,750 for annual unscheduled repair costs.

Alex was becoming more and more convinced that this approach was not working. Not only was upper management upset about the variance between predicted and actual costs of repair, but plant managers believed that the model did not account for potential differences among the company's three plants when allocating dollars for unscheduled repairs. At the weekly management meeting, Alex was informed that he needed to analyze his cost projections further

and produce a report that provided a more reliable method for predicting repair costs. On leaving the meeting, Alex had his assistant randomly pull 64 unscheduled repair reports. The data are in the file **A & A Costs**. The management team is anxiously waiting for Alex's analysis.

### Required Tasks:

1. Identify the major issue(s) of the case.
2. Analyze the overall cost allocation issues by developing a scatterplot of Cost v. Hours of Operation. Which variable, cost or hours of operation, should be the dependent variable? Explain why.
3. Fit a linear regression equation to the data.
4. Explain how the results of the linear regression equation could be used to develop a cost allocation formula. State any adjustments or modification you have made to the regression output to develop a cost allocation formula that can be used to predict repair costs.
5. Sort the data by plant.
6. Fit a linear regression equation to each plant's data.
7. Explain how the results of the individual plant regression equations can help the manager determine whether a different linear regression equation could be used to develop a cost allocation formula for each plant. State any adjustments or modification you have made to the regression output to develop a cost allocation formula.
8. Based on the individual plant regression equations determine whether there is reason to believe there are differences among the repair costs of the company's three plants.
9. Summarize your analysis and findings in a report to the company's manager.

# Case 14.2

## Sapphire Coffee—Part 1

Jennie Garcia could not believe that her career had moved so far so fast. When she left graduate school with a master's degree in anthropology, she intended to work at a local coffee shop until something else came along that was more related to her academic background. But after a few months she came to enjoy the business, and in a little over a year she was promoted to store manager. When the company for whom she worked continued to grow, Jennie was given oversight of a few stores.

Now, eight years after she started as a barista, Jennie was in charge of operations and planning for the company's southern region. As a part of her responsibilities, Jennie tracks store revenues and forecasts coffee demand. Historically, Sapphire Coffee would base its demand forecast on the number of stores, believing that each store sold approximately the same amount of coffee. This approach seemed to work well when the company had shops of similar size and layout, but as the company grew, stores became more varied. Now, some stores had drive-thru windows, a feature that

top management added to some stores believing that it would increase coffee sales for customers who wanted a cup of coffee on their way to work but who were too rushed to park and enter the store to place an order.

Jennie noticed that weekly sales seemed to be more variable across stores in her region and was wondering what, if anything, might explain the differences. The company's financial vice president had also noticed the increased differences in sales across stores and was wondering what might be happening. In an e-mail to Jennie he stated that weekly store sales are expected to average $5.00 per square foot. Thus, a 1,000-square-foot store would have average weekly sales of $5,000. He asked that Jennie analyze the stores in her region to see if this rule of thumb was a reliable measure of a store's performance.

The vice president of finance was expecting the analysis to be completed by the weekend. Jennie decided to randomly select weekly sales records for 53 stores. The data are in the file **Sapphire Coffee-1**. A full analysis needs to be sent to the corporate office by Friday.

## Required Tasks:

1. Identify the major issue(s) of the case.
2. Develop a scatter plot of the variables Store Size and Weekly Sales. Identify the dependent variable. Briefly describe the relationship between the two variables.
3. Fit a linear regression equation to the data. Does the variable Store Size explain a significant amount of the variation in Weekly Sales?
4. Based on the estimated regression equation does it appear the $5.00 per square foot weekly sales expectation the company currently uses is a valid one?
5. Summarize your analysis and findings in a report to the company's vice president of finance.

# Case 14.3

## Alamar Industries

While driving home in northern Kentucky at 8:00 P.M., Juan Alamar wondered whether his father had done him any favor by retiring early and letting him take control of the family machine tool–restoration business. When his father started the business of overhauling machine tools (both for resale and on a contract basis), American companies dominated the tool manufacturing market. During the past 30 years, however, the original equipment industry had been devastated, first by competition from Germany and then from Japan. Although foreign competition had not yet invaded the over-haul segment of the business, Juan had heard about foreign companies establishing operations on the West Coast.

The foreign competitors were apparently stressing the high-quality service and operations that had been responsible for their great inroads into the original equipment market. Last week Juan attended a daylong conference on total quality management that had discussed the advantages of competing for the Baldrige Award, the national quality award established in 1987. Presenters from past Baldrige winners, including Xerox, Federal Express, Cadillac, and Motorola, stressed the positive effects on their companies of winning and said similar effects would be possible for any company. This assertion of only positive effects was what Juan questioned. He was certain that the effect on his remaining free time would not be positive.

The Baldrige Award considers seven corporate dimensions of quality. Although the award is not based on a numerical score, an overall score is calculated. The maximum score is 1,000, with most recent winners scoring about 800. Juan did not doubt the award was good for the winners, but he wondered about the non-winners. In particular, he wondered about any relationship between attempting to improve quality according to the Baldrige dimensions and company profitability. Individual company scores are not released, but Juan was able to talk to one of the conference presenters, who shared some anonymous data, such as companies' scores in the year they applied, their returns on investment (ROIs) in the year applied, and returns on investment in the year after application. Juan decided to commit the company to a total quality management process if the data provided evidence that the process would lead to increased profitability.

| Baldrige Score | ROI Application Year | ROI Next Year |
|---|---|---|
| 470 | 11% | 13% |
| 520 | 10 | 11 |
| 660 | 14 | 15 |
| 540 | 12 | 12 |
| 600 | 15 | 16 |
| 710 | 16 | 16 |
| 580 | 11 | 12 |
| 600 | 12 | 13 |
| 740 | 16 | 16 |
| 610 | 11 | 14 |
| 570 | 12 | 13 |
| 660 | 17 | 19 |

# Case 14.4

## Continental Trucking

Norm Painter is the newly hired cost analyst for Continental Trucking. Continental is a nationwide trucking firm, and until recently, most of its routes were driven under regulated rates. These rates were set to allow small trucking firms to earn an adequate profit, leaving little incentive to work to reduce costs by efficient management techniques. In fact, the greatest effort was made to try to influence regulatory agencies to grant rate increases.

A recent rash of deregulation has made the long-distance trucking industry more competitive. Norm has been hired to ana-lyze Continental's whole expense structure. As part of this study, Norm is looking at truck repair costs. Because the trucks are involved in long hauls, they inevitably break down. In the past, little preventive maintenance was done, and if a truck broke down in the middle of a haul, either a replacement tractor was sent or an independent contractor finished the haul. The truck was then repaired at the nearest local shop. Norm is sure this procedure has led to more expense than if major repairs had been made before the trucks failed.

Norm thinks that some method should be found for determining when preventive maintenance is needed. He believes that fuel consumption is a good indicator of possible breakdowns; as trucks begin to run badly, they will consume more fuel. Unfortunately, the major determinants of fuel consumption are the weight of a truck and headwinds. Norm picks a sample of a single truck model and gathers data relating fuel consumption to truck weight. All trucks in the sample are in good condition. He separates the data by direction of the haul, realizing that winds tend to blow predominantly out of the west.

Although he can rapidly gather future data on fuel consumption and haul weight, now that Norm has these data, he is not quite sure what to do with them.

| East-West Haul | | West-East Haul | |
|---|---|---|---|
| Miles/Gallon | Haul Weight | Miles/Gallon | Haul Weight |
| 4.1 | 41,000 lb | 4.3 | 40,000 lb |
| 4.7 | 36,000 | 4.5 | 37,000 |
| 3.9 | 37,000 | 4.8 | 36,000 |
| 4.3 | 38,000 | 5.2 | 38,000 |
| 4.8 | 32,000 | 5.0 | 35,000 |
| 5.1 | 37,000 | 4.7 | 42,000 |
| 4.3 | 46,000 | 4.9 | 37,000 |
| 4.6 | 35,000 | 4.5 | 36,000 |
| 5.0 | 37,000 | 5.2 | 42,000 |
| | | 4.8 | 41,000 |

# References

Berenson, Mark L., and David M. Levine, *Basic Business Statistics: Concepts and Applications*, 11th ed. (Upper Saddle River, NJ: Prentice Hall, 2009).

Cryer, Jonathan D., and Robert B. Miller, *Statistics for Business: Data Analysis and Modeling*, 2nd ed. (Belmont, CA: Duxbury Press, 1994).

Dielman, Terry E., *Applied Regression Analysis—A Second Course in Business and Economic Statistics*, 4th ed. (Belmont, CA: Duxbury Press, 2005).

Draper, Norman R., and Harry Smith, *Applied Regression Analysis*, 3rd ed. (New York City: John Wiley and Sons, 1998).

Frees, Edward W., *Data Analysis Using Regression Models: The Business Perspective* (Upper Saddle River, NJ: Prentice Hall, 1996).

Kleinbaum, David G., Lawrence L. Kupper, Azhar Nizam, and Keith E. Muller, *Applied Regression Analysis and Multivariable Methods*, 4th ed. (Florence, KY: Cengage Learning, 2008).

Kutner, Michael H., Christopher J. Nachtsheim, John Neter, and William Li, *Applied Linear Statistical Models*, 5th ed. (New York: McGraw-Hill Irwin, 2005).

*Microsoft Excel 2007* (Redmond, WA: Microsoft Corp., 2007).

*Minitab for Windows Version 15* (State College, PA: Minitab, 2007).

**Chapter 15** Quick Prep Links

- **Review** the methods for testing a null hypothesis using the *t*-distribution in Chapter 9.
- **Review** confidence intervals discussed in Chapter 8.

- **Make sure** you review the discussion about scatter plots in Chapters 2 and 14.
- **Review** the concepts associated with simple linear regression and correlation analysis presented in Chapter 14.

- **In Chapter 14**, review the steps involved in using the *t*-distribution for testing the significance of a correlation coefficient and a regression coefficient.

chapter 15

# Multiple Regression Analysis and Model Building

## Why you need to know

Chapter 14 introduced linear regression and correlation analyses for analyzing the relationship between two variables. As you might expect, business problems are not limited to linear relationships involving only two variables. Many practical situations involve analyzing the relationships among three or more variables. For example, a vice president of planning for an automobile manufacturer would be interested in the relationship between her company's automobile sales and the variables that influence those sales. Included in her analysis might be such independent or explanatory variables as automobile price, competitors' sales, and advertising, as well as economic variables such as disposable personal income, the inflation rate, and the unemployment rate.

When multiple independent variables are to be included in an analysis simultaneously, the technique introduced in this chapter—multiple linear regression—is very useful. When a relationship between variables is nonlinear, we may be able to transform the independent variables in ways that allow us to use multiple linear regression analysis to model the nonlinear relationships. This chapter examines the general topic of model building by extending the concepts of simple linear regression analysis provided in Chapter 14.

# 15.1 Introduction to Multiple Regression Analysis

Chapter 14 introduced the concept of simple linear regression analysis. The simple regression model is characterized by two variables: $y$, the *dependent variable*, and $x$, the *independent variable*. The single independent variable explains some variation in the dependent variable, but unless $x$ and $y$ are perfectly correlated, the proportion explained will be less than 100%. In multiple regression analysis, additional independent variables are added to the regression model to clear up some of the as yet unexplained variation in the dependent variable. Multiple regression is merely an extension of simple regression analysis; however, as we expand the model for the population from one independent variable to two or more, there are some new considerations.

The general format of a *multiple regression model for the population* is given by Equation 15.1.

---

**Population Multiple Regression Model**

$$y = \beta_0 + \beta_1 x_1 + \beta_2 x_2 + \cdots + \beta_k x_k + \varepsilon \qquad \text{(15.1)}$$

where:

$\beta_0$ = Population's regression constant
$\beta_j$ = Population's regression coefficient for each variable $x_j = 1, 2, \ldots k$
$k$ = Number of independent variables
$\varepsilon$ = Model error

---

Four assumptions similar to those that apply to the simple linear regression model must also apply to the multiple regression model.

**Assumptions**

---

1. Individual model errors, $\varepsilon$, are statistically independent of one another, and these values represent a random sample from the population of possible errors at each level of $x$.
2. For a given value of $x$ there can exist many values of $y$, and therefore many possible values for $\varepsilon$. Further, the distribution of possible model errors for any level of $x$ is normally distributed.
3. The distributions of possible $\varepsilon$-values have equal variances at each level of $x$.
4. The means of the dependent variable, $y$, for all specified values of $x$ can be connected with a line called the population regression model.

---

Equation 15.1 represents the multiple regression model for the population. However, in most instances, you will be working with a random sample from the population. Given the preceding assumptions, the estimated multiple regression model, based on the sample data, is of the form shown in Equation 15.2.

---

**Estimated Multiple Regression Model**

$$\hat{y} = b_0 + b_1 x_1 + b_2 x_2 + \cdots + b_k x_k \qquad \text{(15.2)}$$

---

This estimated model is an extension of an estimated simple regression model. The principal difference is that whereas the estimated simple regression model is the equation for a straight line in a two-dimensional space, the estimated multiple regression model forms a hyperplane (or response surface) through multidimensional space. Each regression coefficient represents a different slope. Therefore, using Equation 15.2, a value of the dependent variable can be

**TABLE 15.1** | **Sample Data to Illustrate the Difference between Simple and Multiple Regression Models**

| (A) One Independent Variable | | (B) Two Independent Variables | | |
| --- | --- | --- | --- | --- |
| $y$ | $x_1$ | $y$ | $x_1$ | $x_2$ |
| 564.99 | 50 | 564.99 | 50 | 10 |
| 601.06 | 60 | 601.06 | 60 | 13 |
| 560.11 | 40 | 560.11 | 40 | 14 |
| 616.41 | 50 | 616.41 | 50 | 12 |
| 674.96 | 60 | 674.96 | 60 | 15 |
| 630.58 | 45 | 630.58 | 45 | 16 |
| 554.66 | 53 | 554.66 | 53 | 14 |

**Regression Hyperplane**

The multiple regression equivalent of the simple regression line. The plane typically has a different slope for each independent variable.

estimated using values of two or more independent variables. The **regression hyperplane** represents the relationship between the dependent variable and the $k$ independent variables.

For example, Table 15.1A shows sample data for a dependent variable, $y$, and one independent variable, $x_1$. Figure 15.1 shows a scatter plot and the regression line for the simple regression analysis for $y$ and $x_1$. The points are plotted in two-dimensional space, and the regression model is represented by a line through the points such that the sum of squared errors $[SSE = \Sigma(y - \hat{y})^2]$ is minimized.

If we add variable $x_2$ to the model, as shown in Table 15.1B, the resulting multiple regression equation becomes

$$\hat{y} = 307.71 + 2.85x_1 + 10.94x_2$$

For the time being don't worry about how this equation was computed. That will be discussed shortly. Note, however, that the $(y, x_1, x_2)$ points form a three-dimensional space, as shown in Figure 15.2. The regression equation forms a slice (hyperplane) through the data such that $\Sigma(y - \hat{y})^2$ is minimized. This is the same *least squares criterion* that is used with simple linear regression.

The mathematics for developing the least squares regression equation for simple linear regression involves differential calculus. The same is true for the multiple regression equation but the mathematical derivation is beyond the scope of this text.[1]

**FIGURE 15.1** |

Simple Regression Line

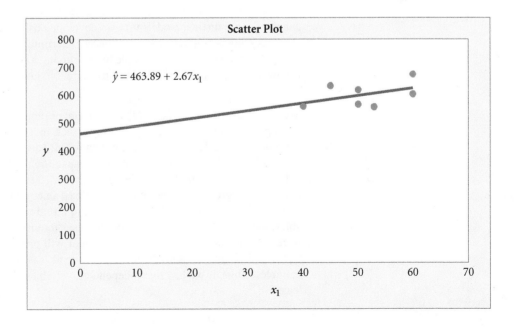

---

[1]For a complete treatment of the matrix algebra approach for estimating multiple regression coefficients, consult *Applied Linear Statistical Models* by Kutner et al.

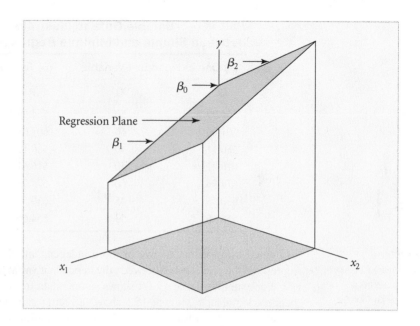

Multiple regression analysis is usually performed with the aid of a computer and appropriate software. Both Minitab and Excel contain procedures for performing multiple regression. Minitab has a far more complete regression procedure. However, the PHStat Excel add-ins expand Excel's capabilities. Each software package presents the output in a slightly different format; however, the same basic information will appear in all regression output.

**Chapter Outcome 1.** ➤ # Basic Model-Building Concepts

**Model**

A representation of an actual system using either a physical or a mathematical portrayal.

An important activity in business decision making is referred to as **model** building. Models are often used to test changes in a system without actually having to change the real system. Models are also used to help describe a system or to predict the output of a system based on certain specified inputs. You are probably quite aware of physical models. Airlines use flight simulators to train pilots. Wind tunnels are used to determine the aerodynamics of automobile designs. Golf ball makers use a physical model of a golfer called "Iron Mike" that can be set to swing golf clubs in a very controlled manner to determine how far a golf ball will fly. Although physical models are very useful in business decision making, our emphasis in this chapter is on statistical models that are developed using multiple regression analysis.

Modeling is both an art and a science. Determining an appropriate model is a challenging task, but it can be made manageable by employing a model-building process consisting of the following three components: model specification, model fitting, and model diagnosis.

**Model Specification** *Model specification*, or model identification, is the process of determining the dependent variable, deciding which independent variables should be included in the model, and obtaining the sample data for all variables. As with any statistical procedure, the larger the sample size the better, because the potential for extreme sampling error is reduced when the sample size is large. However, at a minimum, the sample size required to compute a regression model must be at least one greater than the number of independent variables.[2] If we are thinking of developing a regression model with five independent variables, the absolute minimum number of cases required is six. Otherwise, the computer software will indicate an error has been made or will print out meaningless values. However, as a practical matter, the sample size should be at least four times the number of independent variables. Thus, if we had five independent variables ($k = 5$), we would want a sample of at least 20.

---

[2]There are mathematical reasons for this sample-size requirement that are beyond the scope of this text. In essence, there is no unique solution to the regression coefficient in Equation 15.2 if the sample size is not at least one larger than the number of independent variables.

**Model Building** *Model building* is the process of actually constructing a mathematical equation in which some or all of the independent variables are used in an attempt to explain the variation in the dependent variable.

**Model Diagnosis** *Model diagnosis* is the process of analyzing the quality of the model you have constructed by determining how well a specified model fits the data you just gathered. You will examine output values such as *R*-squared and the standard error of the model. At this stage, you will also assess the extent to which the model's assumptions appear to be satisfied. (Section 15.5 is devoted to examining whether a model meets the regression analysis assumptions.) If the model is unacceptable in any of these areas, you will be forced to revert to the model-specification step and begin again. However, you will be the final judge of whether the model provides acceptable results, and you will always be constrained by time and cost considerations.

You should use the simplest available model that will meet your needs. The objective of model building is to help you make better decisions. You do not need to feel that a sophisticated model is better if a simpler one will provide acceptable results.

**Chapter Outcome 2.**

## How to do it

### Model Specification
**In the context of the statistical models discussed in this chapter, this component involves the following three steps:**

1. Decide what question you want to ask. The question being asked usually indicates the dependent variable. In the previous chapter, we discussed how simple linear regression analysis could be used to describe the relationship between a dependent and an independent variable.

2. List the potential independent variables for your model. Here, your knowledge of the situation you are modeling guides you in identifying potential independent variables.

3. Gather the sample data (observations) for all variables.

## How to do it

### Developing a Multiple Regression Model
**The following steps are employed in developing a multiple regression model:**

1. Specify the model by determining the dependent variable and potential independent variables, and select the sample data.

2. Formulate the model. This is done by computing the correlation coefficients for the dependent variable and each independent variable, and for each independent variable with all other independent variables. The multiple regression equation is also computed. The computations are performed using computer software such as Excel or Minitab.

3. Perform diagnostic checks on the model to determine how well the specified model fits the data and how well the model appears to meet the multiple regression assumptions.

| BUSINESS APPLICATION | **DEVELOPING A MULTIPLE REGRESSION MODEL** |

**First City Real Estate** First City Real Estate executives wish to build a model to predict sales prices for residential property. Such a model will be valuable when working with potential sellers who might list their homes with First City. This can be done using the following steps:

**Step 1    Model Specification.**
The question being asked is how can the real estate firm determine the selling price for a house? Thus, the dependent variable is the sales price. This is what the managers want to be able to predict. The managers met in a brainstorming session to determine a list of possible independent (explanatory) variables. Some variables, such as "condition of the house," were eliminated because of lack of data. Others, such as "curb appeal" (the appeal of the house to people as they drive by), were eliminated because the values for these variables would be too subjective and difficult to quantify. From a wide list of possibilities, the managers selected the following variables as good candidates:

$$x_1 = \text{Home size (in square feet)}$$
$$x_2 = \text{Age of house}$$
$$x_3 = \text{Number of bedrooms}$$
$$x_4 = \text{Number of bathrooms}$$
$$x_5 = \text{Garage size (number of cars)}$$

Data were obtained for a sample of 319 residential properties that had sold within the previous two months in an area served by two of First City's offices. For each house in the sample, the sales price and values for each potential independent variable were collected. The data are in the file **First City**.

**Step 2    Model Building.**
The regression model is developed by including independent variables from among those for which you have complete data. There is no way to determine whether an independent variable will be a good predictor variable by analyzing the individual variable's descriptive statistics, such as the mean and standard deviation. Instead, we need to look at the correlation between the independent

**Correlation Coefficient**

A quantitative measure of the strength of the linear relationship between two variables. The correlation coefficient, $r$, ranges from $-1.0$ to $+1.0$.

**Correlation Matrix**

A table showing the pairwise correlations between all variables (dependent and independent).

variables and the dependent variable, which is measured by the **correlation coefficient**.

When we have multiple independent variables and one dependent variable, we can look at the correlation between all pairs of variables by developing a **correlation matrix**. Each correlation is computed using one of the equations in Equation 15.3. The appropriate formula is determined by whether the correlation is being calculated for an independent variable and the dependent variable or for two independent variables.

---

**Correlation Coefficient**

$$r = \frac{\Sigma(x-\bar{x})(y-\bar{y})}{\sqrt{\Sigma(x-\bar{x})^2 \Sigma(y-\bar{y})^2}} \quad \text{or} \quad r = \frac{\Sigma(x_i-\bar{x}_i)(x_j-\bar{x}_j)}{\sqrt{\Sigma(x_i-\bar{x}_i)^2 \Sigma(x_j-\bar{x}_j)^2}} \quad \textbf{(15.3)}$$

One $x$ variable with $y$      One $x$ variable with another $x$

---

The actual calculations are done using Excel's correlation tool or Minitab's correlation command, and the results are shown in Figure 15.3a and Figure 15.3b. The output provides the correlation between $y$ and each $x$ variable and between each pair of independent variables.[3] Recall that in Chapter 14, a $t$-test (see Equation 14-3) was used to test whether the correlation coefficient is statistically significant.

$$H_0: \rho = 0 \quad H_A: \rho \neq 0$$

We will conduct the test with a significance level of

$$\alpha = 0.05$$

**FIGURE 15.3A**

Excel 2007 Results Showing First City Real Estate Correlation Matrix

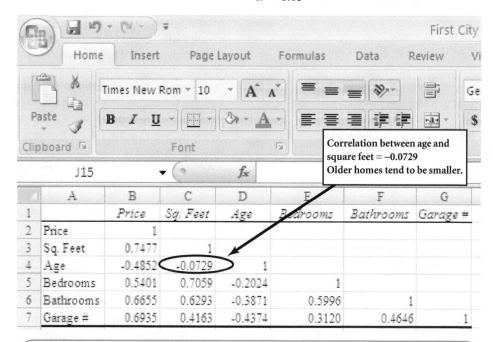

|  | Price | Sq. Feet | Age | Bedrooms | Bathrooms | Garage # |
|---|---|---|---|---|---|---|
| Price | 1 |  |  |  |  |  |
| Sq. Feet | 0.7477 | 1 |  |  |  |  |
| Age | -0.4852 | -0.0729 | 1 |  |  |  |
| Bedrooms | 0.5401 | 0.7059 | -0.2024 | 1 |  |  |
| Bathrooms | 0.6655 | 0.6293 | -0.3871 | 0.5996 | 1 |  |
| Garage # | 0.6935 | 0.4163 | -0.4374 | 0.3120 | 0.4646 | 1 |

Correlation between age and square feet = −0.0729 Older homes tend to be smaller.

**Excel 2007 Instructions:**
1. Open file: First City.xls.
2. Select Home Sample 1 worksheet.
3. Click on **Data > Data Analysis**.
4. Select **Correlation**.
5. Define $y$ variable range (all rows and columns).
6. Click on **Labels**.
7. Click **OK**.

---

[3]Minitab, in addition to providing the correlation matrix, can provide the $p$-values for each correlation. If the $p$-value is less than the specified alpha, the correlation is statistically significant.

**FIGURE 15.3B**

Minitab Results Showing First City Real Estate Correlation Matrix

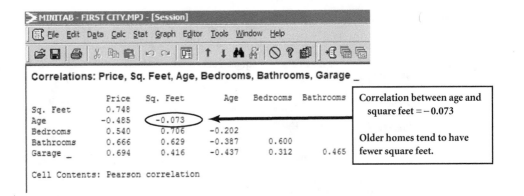

Given degrees of freedom equal to

$$n - 2 = 319 - 2 = 317$$

the critical $t$ (see Appendix E) for a two-tailed test is approximately $\pm 1.96$.[4]

Any correlation coefficient generating a $t$-value greater than 1.96 or less than $-1.96$ is determined to be significant.

For now, we will focus on the correlations in the first column in Figures 15.3a and 15.3b, which measure the strength of the linear relationship between each independent variable and the dependent variable, sales price. For example, the $t$ statistic for price and square feet is

$$t = \frac{r}{\sqrt{\dfrac{1 - r^2}{n - 2}}} = \frac{0.7477}{\sqrt{\dfrac{1 - 0.7477^2}{319 - 2}}} = 20.048$$

Because

$$t = 20.048 > 1.96$$

we reject $H_0$ and conclude that the correlation between sales price and square feet is statistically significant.

Similar calculations for the other independent variables with price show that all variables are statistically correlated with price. This indicates that a significant linear relationship exists between each independent variable and sales price. Variable $x_1$, square feet, has the highest correlation at 0.748. Variable $x_2$, age of the house, has the lowest correlation at $-0.485$. The negative correlation implies that older homes tend to have lower sales prices.

As we discussed in Chapter 14, it is always a good idea to develop scatter plots to visualize the relationship between two variables. Figure 15.4 shows the scatter plots for each independent variable and the dependent variable, sales price. In each case, the plots indicate a linear relationship between the independent variable and the dependent variable. Note that several of the independent variables (bedrooms, bathrooms, garage size) are quantitative but discrete. The scatter plots for these variables show points at each level of the independent variable rather than over a continuum of values.

---

[4]You can use the Excel **TINV** function to get the precise $t$-value, which is 1.967.

**FIGURE 15.4** | First City Real Estate Scatter Plots

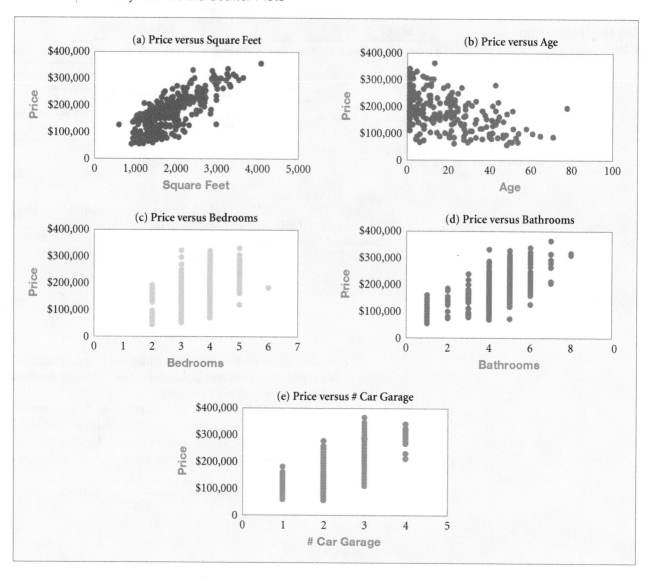

**Chapter Outcome 3.** → **Computing the Regression Equation** First City's goal is to develop a regression model to predict the appropriate selling price for a home, using certain measurable characteristics. The first attempt at developing the model will be to run a multiple regression computer program using all available independent variables. The regression outputs from Excel and Minitab are shown in Figure 15.5a and Figure 15.5b.

The estimate of the multiple regression model given in Figure 15.5a is

$$\hat{y} = 31,127.6 + 63.1(\text{sq. ft.}) - 1,144.4(\text{age}) - 8,410.4(\text{bedrooms})$$
$$+ 3,522.0(\text{bathrooms}) + 28,203.5(\text{garage})$$

The coefficients for each independent variable represent an estimate of the average change in the dependent variable for a 1-unit change in the independent variable, holding all other independent variables constant. For example, for houses of the same age, with the same number of bedrooms, baths, and garages, a 1-square-foot increase in the size of the house is estimated to increase its price by an average of $63.10. Likewise, for houses with the same square feet, bedrooms, bathrooms, and garages, a 1-year increase in the

**FIGURE 15.5A**

Excel 2007 Multiple
Regression Model Results for
First City Real Estate

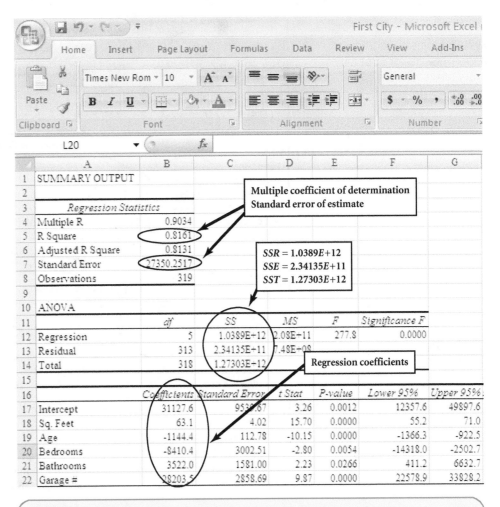

**Excel 2007 Instructions:**
1. Open file: First City.xls.
2. Click on **Data > Data Analysis**.
3. Select **Regression**.
4. Define *y* variable range and the *x* variable range (include labels).
5. Click **Labels**.
6. Click **OK**.

age of the house is estimated to result in an average drop in sales price of $1,144.40. The other coefficients are interpreted in the same way. Note, in each case, we are interpreting the regression coefficient for one independent variable while holding the other variables constant.

To estimate the value of a residential property, First City Real Estate brokers would substitute values for the independent variables into the regression equation. For example, suppose a house with the following characteristics is considered:

$$x_1 = \text{Square feet} = 2,100$$
$$x_2 = \text{Age} = 15$$
$$x_3 = \text{Number of bedrooms} = 4$$
$$x_4 = \text{Number of bathrooms} = 3$$
$$x_5 = \text{Size of garage} = 2$$

The point estimate for the sales price is

$$\hat{y} = 31,127.6 + 63.1\,(2,100) - 1,144.4\,(15) - 8,410.4\,(4) + 3,522.0\,(3) + 28,203.5\,(2)$$

$$\hat{y} = \$179,802.70$$

**FIGURE 15.5B**

Minitab Multiple Regression
Model Results for First City
Real Estate

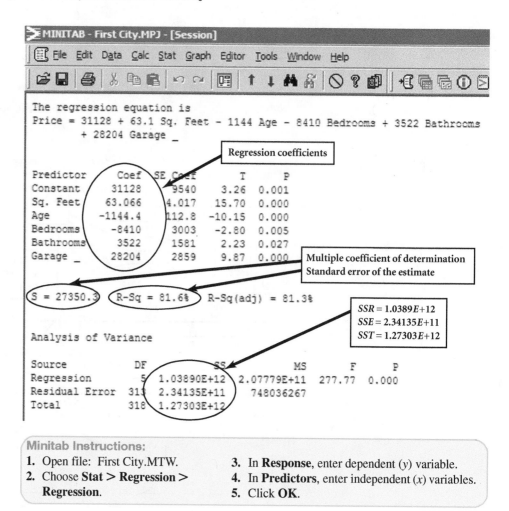

**Minitab Instructions:**

1. Open file: First City.MTW.
2. Choose **Stat > Regression > Regression**.
3. In **Response**, enter dependent (y) variable.
4. In **Predictors**, enter independent (x) variables.
5. Click **OK**.

**The Coefficient of Determination** You learned in Chapter 14 that the *coefficient of determination*, $R^2$, measures the proportion of variation in the dependent variable that can be explained by the dependent variable's relationship to a single independent variable. When there are multiple independent variables in a model, $R^2$ is called the **multiple coefficient of determination** and is used to determine the proportion of variation in the dependent variable that is explained by the dependent variable's relationship to all the independent variables in the model. Equation 15.4 is used to compute $R^2$ for a multiple regression model.

**Multiple coefficient of determination ($R^2$)**

The proportion of the total variation of the dependent variable in a multiple regression model that is explained by its relationship to the independent variables. It is, as is the case in the simple linear model, called *R*-squared and is denoted as $R^2$.

---

**Multiple Coefficient of Determination ($R^2$)**

$$R^2 = \frac{\text{Sum of squares regression}}{\text{Total sum of squares}} = \frac{SSR}{SST} \quad \text{(15.4)}$$

---

As shown in Figure 15.5a, $R^2 = 0.8161$. Both *SSR* and *SST* are also included in the output. Therefore, you can also use Equation 15.4 to get $R^2$, as follows:

$$\frac{SSR}{SST} = \frac{1.0389E+12}{1.27303E+12} = 0.8161$$

More than 81% of the variation in sales price can be explained by the linear relationship of the five independent variables in the regression model to the dependent variable. However, as we shall shortly see, not all independent variables are equally important to the model's ability to explain this variation.

**Model Diagnosis**  Before First City actually uses this regression model to estimate the sales price of a house, there are several questions that should be answered.

1. Is the overall model significant?
2. Are the individual variables significant?
3. Is the standard deviation of the model error too large to provide meaningful results?
4. Is multicollinearity a problem?
5. Have the regression analysis assumptions been satisfied?

We shall answer the first four questions in order. We will have to wait until Section 15.5 before we have the procedures to answer the fifth important question.

**Chapter Outcome 4.** ➤ **Is the Model Significant?**  Because the regression model we constructed is based on a sample of data from the population and is subject to sampling error, we need to test the statistical significance of the overall regression model. The specific null and alternative hypotheses tested for First City Real Estate are

$$H_0: \beta_1 = \beta_2 = \beta_3 = \beta_4 = \beta_5 = 0$$
$$H_A: \text{At least one } \beta_i \neq 0$$

If the null hypothesis is true and all the slope coefficients are simultaneously equal to zero, the overall regression model is not useful for predictive or descriptive purposes.

The *F*-test is a method for testing whether the regression model explains a significant proportion of the variation in the dependent variable (and whether the overall model is significant). The *F*-test statistic for a multiple regression model is shown in Equation 15.5.

---

**F-Test Statistic**

$$F = \frac{\dfrac{SSR}{k}}{\dfrac{SSE}{n-k-1}}$$

(15.5)

where:

$$SSR = \text{Sum of squares regression} = \sum (\hat{y} - \overline{y})^2$$
$$SSE = \text{Sum of squares error} = \sum (y - \hat{y})^2$$
$$n = \text{Sample size}$$
$$k = \text{Number of independent variables}$$
$$\text{Degrees of freedom} = D_1 = k \quad \text{and} \quad D_2 = (n-k-1)$$

---

The ANOVA portion of the output shown in Figure 15.5a contains values for *SSR*, *SSE*, and the *F*-value. The general format of the ANOVA table in a regression analysis is as follows:

**ANOVA**

| Source | df | SS | MS | F | Significance F |
|---|---|---|---|---|---|
| Regression | k | SSR | MSR = SSR/k | MSR/MSE | computed p-value |
| Residual | n − k − 1 | SSE | MSE = SSE/(n − k − 1) | | |
| Total | n − 1 | SST | | | |

The ANOVA portion of the output from Figure 15.5a is as follows:

**ANOVA**

| Source | df | SS | MS | F | Significance F |
|---|---|---|---|---|---|
| Regression | 5 | $1.04E + 12$ | $2.08E + 11$ | 277.8 | 0.0000 |
| Residual | 313 | $2.34E + 11$ | $7.48E + 08$ | | |
| Total | 318 | $1.27303E + 12$ | | | |

We can test the model's significance

$$H_0\text{: } \beta_1 = \beta_2 = \beta_3 = \beta_4 = \beta_5 = 0$$
$$H_A\text{: At least one } \beta_i \neq 0$$

by either comparing the calculated $F$-value, 277.8, with a critical value for a given alpha level

$$\alpha = 0.01$$

and $k = 5$ and $n - k - 1 = 313$ degrees of freedom using Excel's FINV function ($F_{0.01} = 3.079$) or comparing the $p$-value in the output with a specified alpha level. Because

$$F = 277.8 > 3.079\text{, reject } H_0$$

or because

$$p\text{-value} \approx 0.0 < 0.01\text{, reject } H_0$$

we should therefore conclude that the regression model *does* explain a significant proportion of the variation in sales price. Thus, the overall model is statistically significant. This means we can conclude that at least one of the regression slope coefficients is not equal to zero.

Excel and Minitab also provide a measure called the $R$-sq(adj), which is the **adjusted $R$-squared** value (see Figures 15.5a and 15.5b). It is calculated by Equation 15.6.

**Adjusted $R$-squared**

A measure of the percentage of explained variation in the dependent variable in a multiple regression model that takes into account the relationship between the sample size and the number of independent variables in the regression model.

---

### Adjusted $R$-Squared

A measure of the percentage of explained variation in the dependent variable that takes into account the relationship between the sample size and the number of independent variables in the regression model.

$$R\text{-sq(adj)} = R_A^2 = 1 - (1 - R^2)\left(\frac{n-1}{n-k-1}\right) \tag{15.6}$$

where:

$n$ = Sample size
$k$ = Number of independent variables
$R^2$ = Coefficient of determination

---

Adding independent variables to the regression model will always increase $R^2$, even if these variables have no relationship to the dependent variable. Therefore, as the number of independent variables is increased (regardless of the quality of the variables), $R^2$ will increase. However, each additional variable results in the loss of one degree of freedom. This is viewed as part of the cost of adding the specified variable. The addition to $R^2$ may not justify the reduction in degrees of freedom. The $R_A^2$ value takes into account this cost and adjusts the $R_A^2$ value accordingly. $R_A^2$ will always be less than $R^2$. When a variable is added that does not contribute its fair share to the explanation of the variation in the dependent variable, the $R_A^2$ value may actually decline, even though $R^2$ will always increase. The adjusted $R$-squared is a particularly important measure when the number of independent variables is large relative to the sample size. It takes into account the relationship between sample size and number of variables. $R^2$ may appear artificially high if the number of variables is large compared with the sample size.

In this example, in which the sample size is quite large relative to the number of independent variables, the adjusted $R$-squared is 81.3%, only slightly less than $R^2 = 81.6\%$.

**Chapter Outcome 4.** → **Are the Individual Variables Significant?** We have concluded that the overall model is significant. This means *at least* one independent variable explains a significant proportion of the variation in sales price. This does not mean that *all* the variables are significant, however. To determine which variables are significant, we test the following hypotheses:

$$H_0: \beta_j = 0$$
$$H_A: \beta_j \neq 0 \quad \text{for all } j$$

We can test the significance of each independent variable using significance level

$$\alpha = 0.05$$

and a *t*-test, as discussed in Chapter 14. The calculated *t*-values should be compared to the critical *t*-value with

$$n - k - 1 = 319 - 5 - 1 = 313$$

degrees of freedom, which is approximately

$$t_{0.025} \approx 1.97$$

for $\alpha = 0.05$. The calculated *t*-value for each variable is provided on the computer printout in Figures 15.5a and 15.5b. Recall that the *t* statistic is determined by dividing the regression coefficient by the estimator of the standard deviation of the regression coefficient, as shown in Equation 15.7.

---

**t-Test for Significance of Each Regression Coefficient**

$$t = \frac{b_j - 0}{s_{b_j}} \qquad df = n - k - 1 \qquad \text{(15.7)}$$

where:

$b_j$ = Sample slope coefficient for the *j*th independent variable

$s_{b_j}$ = Estimate of the standard error for the *j*th sample slope coefficient

---

For example, the *t*-value for square feet shown in Figure 15.5a is 15.70. This was computed using Equation 15.7, as follows:

$$t = \frac{b_j - 0}{s_{b_j}} = \frac{63.1 - 0}{4.02} = 15.70$$

Because

$$t = 15.70 > 1.97, \text{ we reject } H_0,$$

and conclude that, given the other independent variables in the model, the regression slope for square feet is not zero.

We can also look at the Excel or Minitab output and compare the *p*-value for each regression slope coefficient with alpha. If the *p*-value is less than alpha, we reject the null hypothesis and conclude that the independent variable is statistically significant in the model. Both the *t*-test and the *p*-value techniques will give the same results.

You should consider that these *t*-tests are *conditional* tests. This means that the null hypothesis is *the value of each slope coefficient is 0, given that the other independent variables are already in the model*.[5] Figure 15.6 shows the hypothesis tests for each independent

---

[5]Note that the *t*-tests may be affected if the independent variables in the model are themselves correlated. A procedure known as the *sum of squares drop F-test*, discussed by Kutner et al. in *Applied Linear Statistical Models*, should be used in this situation. Each *t*-test considers only the marginal contribution of the independent variables and may indicate that none of the variables in the model are significant, even though the ANOVA procedure indicates otherwise.

**FIGURE 15.6**

Significance Tests for Each Independent Variable in the First City Real Estate Example

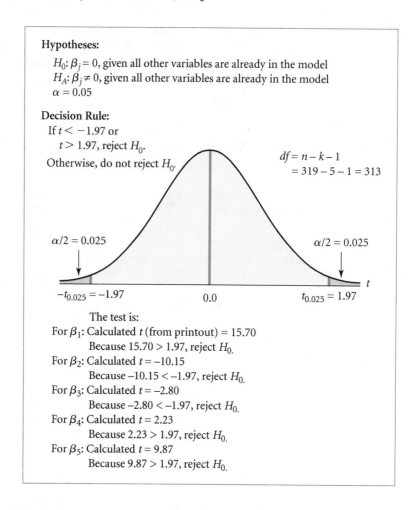

**Hypotheses:**

$H_0: \beta_j = 0$, given all other variables are already in the model
$H_A: \beta_j \neq 0$, given all other variables are already in the model
$\alpha = 0.05$

**Decision Rule:**
If $t < -1.97$ or
$t > 1.97$, reject $H_0$.
Otherwise, do not reject $H_0$.

$df = n - k - 1$
$= 319 - 5 - 1 = 313$

$\alpha/2 = 0.025$          $\alpha/2 = 0.025$

$-t_{0.025} = -1.97$          $0.0$          $t_{0.025} = 1.97$          $t$

The test is:
For $\beta_1$: Calculated $t$ (from printout) = 15.70
 Because 15.70 > 1.97, reject $H_0$.
For $\beta_2$: Calculated $t = -10.15$
 Because $-10.15 < -1.97$, reject $H_0$.
For $\beta_3$: Calculated $t = -2.80$
 Because $-2.80 < -1.97$, reject $H_0$.
For $\beta_4$: Calculated $t = 2.23$
 Because 2.23 > 1.97, reject $H_0$.
For $\beta_5$: Calculated $t = 9.87$
 Because 9.87 > 1.97, reject $H_0$.

variable using a 0.05 significance level. We conclude that all five independent variables in the model are significant. When a regression model is to be used for prediction, the model should contain no insignificant variables. If insignificant variables are present, they should be dropped and a new regression equation obtained before the model is used for prediction purposes. We will have more to say about this later.

**Is the Standard Deviation of the Regression Model Too Large?** The purpose of developing the First City regression model is to be able to determine values of the dependent variable when corresponding values of the independent variables are known. An indication of how good the regression model is can be found by looking at the relationship between the measured values of the dependent variable and those values that would be predicted by the regression model. The standard deviation of the regression model (also called the *standard error of the estimate*), measures the dispersion of observed home sale values, *y*, around values predicted by the regression model. The standard error of the estimate is shown in Figure 15.5a and can be computed using Equation 15.8.

**Standard Error of the Estimate**

$$s_\varepsilon = \sqrt{\frac{SSE}{n - k - 1}} = \sqrt{MSE} \qquad (15.8)$$

where:

$SSE$ = Sum of squares error (residual)
$n$ = Sample size
$k$ = Number of independent variables

Examining Equation 15.8 closely, we see that this standard error of the estimate is the square root of the mean square error of the residuals found in the analysis of variance table.

Sometimes, even though a model has a high $R^2$, the standard error of the estimate will be too large to provide adequate precision for confidence and prediction intervals. A rule of thumb that we have found useful is to examine the range $\pm 2s_e$. Taking into account the mean value of the dependent variable, if this range is acceptable from a practical viewpoint, the standard error of the estimate might be considered acceptable.[6]

In this First City Real Estate Company example, the standard error, shown in Figure 15.5a, is $27,350. Thus, the rough prediction range for the price of an individual home is

$$\pm 2(\$27,350) = \pm\$54,700$$

Considering that the mean price of homes in this study is in the low $200,000s, a potential error of $54,700 high or low is probably not acceptable. Not many homeowners would be willing to have their appraisal value set by a model with a possible error this large. Even though the model is statistically significant, the company needs to take steps to reduce the standard deviation of the estimate. Subsequent sections of this chapter discuss some ways we can attempt to reduce it.

**Chapter Outcome 5.** ➤ **Is Multicollinearity a Problem?** Even if the overall regression model is significant and each independent variable is significant, decision makers should still examine the regression model to determine whether it appears reasonable. This is referred to as checking for *face validity*. Specifically, you should check to see that signs on the regression coefficients are consistent with the signs on the correlation coefficients between the independent variables and the dependent variable. Does any regression coefficient have an unexpected sign?

Before answering this question for the First City Real Estate example, we should review what the regression coefficients mean. First, the constant term, $b_0$, is the estimate of the model's $y$ intercept. If the data used to develop the regression model contain values of $x_1$, $x_2$, $x_3$, $x_4$, and $x_5$ that are simultaneously 0 (such as would be the case for vacant land), $b_0$ is the mean value of $y$, given that $x_1$, $x_2$, $x_3$, $x_4$, and $x_5$ all equal 0. Under these conditions $b_0$ would estimate the average value of a vacant lot. However, in the First City example, no vacant land was in the sample, so $b_0$ has no particular meaning.

The coefficient for square feet, $b_1$, estimates the average change in sales price corresponding to a change in house size of 1 square foot, holding the other independent variables constant. The value shown in Figure 15.5a for $b_1$ is 63.1. The coefficient is positive, indicating that an increase in square footage is associated with an increase in sales price. This relationship is expected. All other things being equal, bigger houses should sell for more money.

Likewise, the coefficient for $x_5$, the size of the garage, is positive, indicating that an increase in size is also associated with an increase in price. This is expected. The coefficient for $x_2$, the age of the house, is negative, indicating that an older house is worth less than a similar younger house. This also seems reasonable. Finally, variable $x_4$ for bathrooms has the expected positive sign. However, the coefficient for variable $x_3$, the number of bedrooms, is $-\$8,410.4$, meaning that if we hold the other variables constant but increase the number of bedrooms by one, the average price will *drop* by $8,410.40. Does this seem reasonable?

Referring to the correlation matrix that was shown earlier in Figure 15.3, the correlation between variable $x_3$, bedrooms, and $y$, the sales price, is $+0.540$. This indicates that without considering the other independent variables, the linear relationship between number of bedrooms and sales price is positive. But why does the regression coefficient for variable $x_3$ turn out to be negative in the model? The answer lies in what is called **multicollinearity**.

Multicollinearity occurs when independent variables are correlated with each other and therefore overlap with respect to the information they provide in explaining the variation in

**Multicollinearity**

A high correlation between two independent variables such that the two variables contribute redundant information to the model. When highly correlated independent variables are included in the regression model, they can adversely affect the regression results.

---

[6]The actual confidence interval for prediction of a new observation requires the use of matrix algebra. However, when the sample size is large and dependent variable values near the means of the dependent variables are used, the rule of thumb given here is a close approximation. Refer to *Applied Linear Statistical Models* by Kutner et al. for further discussion.

the dependent variable. For example, $x_3$ and the other independent variables have the following correlations (see Figure 15.3b):

$$r_{x_3, x_1} = 0.706$$
$$r_{x_3, x_2} = -0.202$$
$$r_{x_3, x_4} = 0.600$$
$$r_{x_3, x_5} = 0.312$$

All four correlations have $t$-values indicating a significant linear relationship. Refer to the correlation matrix in Figure 15.3 to see that other independent variables are also correlated with each other.

The problems caused by multicollinearity, and how to deal with them, continue to be of prime concern to statisticians. From a decision maker's viewpoint, you should be aware that multicollinearity can (and often does) exist and recognize the basic problems it can cause. The following are some of the most obvious problems and indications of severe multicollinearity:

1. Unexpected, therefore potentially incorrect, signs on the coefficients
2. A sizable change in the values of the previously estimated coefficients when a new variable is added to the model
3. A variable that was previously significant in the regression model becomes insignificant when a new independent variable is added.
4. The estimate of the standard deviation of the model error increases when a variable is added to the model.

Mathematical approaches exist for dealing with multicollinearity and reducing its impact. Although these procedures are beyond the scope of this text, one suggestion is to eliminate the variables that are the chief cause of the multicollinearity problems.

If the independent variables in a regression model are correlated and multicollinearity is present, another potential problem is that the $t$-tests for the significance of the individual independent variables may be misleading. That is, a $t$-test may indicate that the variable is not statistically significant when in fact it is.

**Variance Inflation Factor**

A measure of how much the variance of an estimated regression coefficient increases if the independent variables are correlated. A $VIF$ equal to 1.0 for a given independent variable indicates that this independent variable is not correlated with the remaining independent variables in the model. The greater the multicollinearity, the larger the $VIF$.

One method of measuring multicollinearity is known as the **variance inflation factor** (**VIF**). Equation 15.9 is used to compute the $VIF$ for each independent variable.

---

**Variance Inflation Factor**

$$VIF = \frac{1}{(1 - R_j^2)} \qquad (15.9)$$

where:

$R_j^2 = $ Coefficient of determination when the $j$th independent variable is regressed against the remaining $k - 1$ independent variables

---

Both the PHStat add-ins to Excel and Minitab contain options that provide $VIF$ values.[7]

Figure 15.7 shows the Excel (PHStat) output of the $VIF$s for the First City Real Estate example. The effect of multicollinearity is to decrease the test statistic, thus reducing the probability that the variable will be declared significant. A related impact is to increase the width of the confidence interval estimate of the slope coefficient in the regression model. Generally, if the $VIF < 5$ for a particular independent variable, multicollinearity is not considered a problem for that variable. $VIF$ values $\geq 5$ imply that the correlation between the independent variables is too extreme and should be dealt with by dropping variables from the

---

[7]Excel's Regression procedure in the Data Analysis Tools area does not provide $VIF$ values directly. Without PHStat, you would need to compute each regression analysis individually and record the $R$-squared value to compute the $VIF$.

**FIGURE 15.7**

Excel 2007 (PHStat) Multiple
Regression Model Results for
First City Real Estate with
Variance Inflation Factors

**FIGURE 15.7**

Excel 2007 (PHStat) Multiple
Regression Model Results for
First City Real Estate with
Variance Inflation Factors

**Excel 2007 Instructions:**
1. Open file: First City.xls.
2. Click on **Add-Ins PHStat**.
3. Select **Regression > Multiple Regression**.
4. Define *y* variable range and the *x* variable range.
5. Select **Regression Statistics Table** and **ANOVA** and **Coefficients Table**.
6. Select **Variance Inflation Factor (VIF)**.
7. Click **OK**. Note VIFs consolidated to one page for display in Figure 15.7.

**Minitab Instructions (for similar result):**
1. Open file: First City.MTW.
2. Choose **Stat > Regression > Regression**.
3. In **Response** enter dependent (*y*) variable.
4. In **Predictors**, enter independent (*x*) variables.
5. Click **Options**.
6. In **Display**, select Variance Inflation factors.
7. Click **OK. OK.**

model. As Figure 15.7 illustrates, the *VIF* values for each independent variable are less than 5, so based on variance inflation factors, even though the sign on the variable, bedrooms, has switched from positive to negative, the other multicollinearity issues do not exist among these independent variables.

**Confidence Interval Estimation for Regression Coefficients** Previously, we showed how to determine whether the regression coefficients are statistically significant. This was necessary because the estimates of the regression coefficients are developed from sample data and are subject to sampling error. The issue of sampling error also comes into play when interpreting the slope coefficients.

Consider again the regression models for First City Real Estate shown in Figures 15.8a and 15.8b. The regression coefficients shown are *point estimates* for the true regression coefficients. For example, the coefficient for the variable square feet is $b_1 = 63.1$. We interpret this to mean that, holding the other variables constant, for each increase in the size of a home by 1 square foot, the price of a house is estimated to increase by \$63.1. But like all point estimates, this is subject to sampling error. In Chapter 14 you were introduced to the concept of confidence interval estimates for the regression coefficients. That same concept applies in multiple

**FIGURE 15.8A**

Excel 2007 Multiple
Regression Model Results for
First City Real Estate

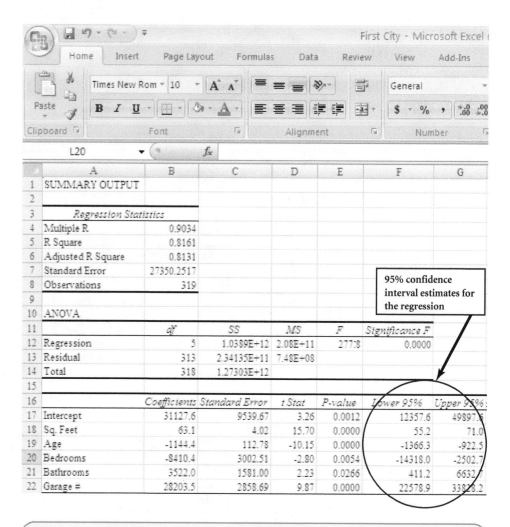

**Excel 2007 Instructions:**
1. Open file: First City.xls.
2. Click on **Data > Data Analysis**.
3. Select **Regression**.
4. Define $y$ variable range and the $x$ variable range (include labels).
5. Click **Labels**.
6. Click **OK**.

regression models. Equation 15.10 is used to develop the confidence interval estimate for the regression coefficients.

**Confidence Interval Estimate for the Regression Slope**

$$b_j \pm t s_{b_j} \tag{15.10}$$

where:

$b_j$ = Point estimate for the regression coefficient for $x_j$

$t$ = Critical $t$-value for the specified confidence level

$s_{b_j}$ = The standard error of the $j$th regression coefficient

The Excel output in Figure 15.8a provides the confidence interval estimates for each regression coefficient. For example, the 95% interval estimate for square feet is

$$\$55.2 \text{ —— } \$71.0$$

Minitab does not have a command to generate confidence intervals for the individual regression parameters. However, statistical quantities are provided on the Minitab output in Figure 15.8b to allow the manual calculation of these confidence intervals. As an example,

**FIGURE 15.8B**

Minitab Multiple Regression Model Results for First City Real Estate

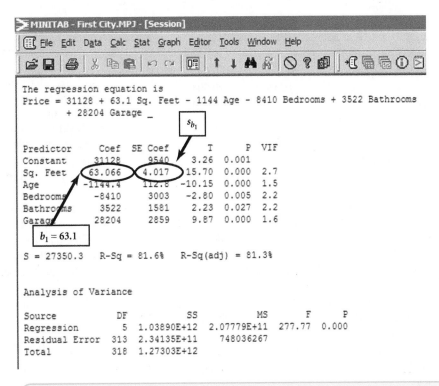

```
MINITAB - First City.MPJ - [Session]
File  Edit  Data  Calc  Stat  Graph  Editor  Tools  Window  Help

The regression equation is
Price = 31128 + 63.1 Sq. Feet - 1144 Age - 8410 Bedrooms + 3522 Bathrooms
         + 28204 Garage
                                          s_b1

Predictor      Coef   SE Coef       T      P   VIF
Constant      31128      9540    3.26  0.001
Sq. Feet     63.066     4.017   15.70  0.000   2.7
Age         -1144.4     112.8  -10.15  0.000   1.5
Bedrooms      -8410      3003   -2.80  0.005   2.2
Bathrooms      3522      1581    2.23  0.027   2.2
Garage        28204      2859    9.87  0.000   1.6

b_1 = 63.1

S = 27350.3    R-Sq = 81.6%    R-Sq(adj) = 81.3%


Analysis of Variance

Source          DF           SS           MS       F      P
Regression       5  1.03890E+12  2.07779E+11  277.77  0.000
Residual Error 313  2.34135E+11    748036267
Total          318  1.27303E+12
```

**Minitab Instructions:**
1. Open file: First City.MTW.
2. Choose **Stat > Regression > Regression**.
3. In **Response**, enter dependent ($y$) variable.
4. In **Predictors**, enter independent ($x$) variable.
5. Click **OK**.

the confidence interval for the coefficient associated with the square feet variable can be computed using Equation 15.10 as[8]

$$b_1 \pm ts_{b_1}$$
$$63.1 \pm 1.967(4.017)$$
$$63.1 \pm 7.90$$
$$\$55.2 \text{———} \$71.0$$

We interpret this interval as follows: Holding the other variables constant, using a 95% confidence level, a change in square feet by 1 foot is estimated to generate an average change in home price of between $55.20 and $71.00. Each of the other regression coefficients can be interpreted in the same manner.

---

[8]Note, we used Excel's **TINV** function to get the precise $t$-value of 1.967.

*MyStatLab*

# 15-1: Exercises

## Skill Development

**15-1.** The following output is associated with a multiple regression model with three independent variables:

|            | df | SS         | MS        | F     | Significance F |
|------------|----|------------|-----------|-------|----------------|
| Regression | 3  | 16,646.091 | 5,548.697 | 5.328 | 0.007          |
| Residual   | 21 | 21,871.669 | 1,041.508 |       |                |
| Total      | 24 | 38,517.760 |           |       |                |

|           | Coefficients | Standard Error | t Stat | p-value |
|-----------|--------------|----------------|--------|---------|
| Intercept | 87.790       | 25.468         | 3.447  | 0.002   |
| $x_1$     | −0.970       | 0.586          | −1.656 | 0.113   |
| $x_2$     | 0.002        | 0.001          | 3.133  | 0.005   |
| $x_3$     | −8.723       | 7.495          | −1.164 | 0.258   |

|  | Lower 95% | Upper 95% | Lower 90% | Upper 90% |
|---|---|---|---|---|
| Intercept | 34.827 | 140.753 | 43.966 | 131.613 |
| $x_1$ | $-2.189$ | 0.248 | $-1.979$ | 0.038 |
| $x_2$ | 0.001 | 0.004 | 0.001 | 0.004 |
| $x_3$ | $-24.311$ | 6.864 | $-21.621$ | 4.174 |

a. What is the regression model associated with these data?

b. Is the model statistically significant?

c. How much of the variation in the dependent variable can be explained by the model?

d. Are all of the independent variables in the model significant? If not, which are not and how can you tell?

e. How much of a change in the dependent variable will be associated with a one-unit change in $x_2$? In $x_3$?

f. Do any of the 95% confidence interval estimates of the slope coefficients contain zero? If so, what does this indicate?

**15-2.** You are given the following estimated regression equation involving a dependent and two independent variables:

$$\hat{y} = 12.67 + 4.14x_1 + 8.72x_2$$

a. Interpret the values of the slope coefficients in the equation.

b. Estimate the value of the dependent variable when $x_1 = 4$ and $x_2 = 9$.

**15-3.** In working for a local retail store you have developed the following estimated regression equation:

$$\hat{y} = 22,167 - 412x_1 + 818x_2 - 93x_3 - 71x_4$$

where:

$y$ = Weekly sales
$x_1$ = Local unemployment rate
$x_2$ = Weekly average high temperature
$x_3$ = Number of activities in the local community
$x_4$ = Average gasoline price

a. Interpret the values of $b_1$, $b_2$, $b_3$, and $b_4$ in this estimated regression equation.

b. What is the estimated sales if the unemployment rate is 5.7%, the average high temperature is 61°, there are 14 activities, and gasoline average price is $1.39?

**15-4.** The following correlation matrix is associated with the same data used to build the regression model in Problem 15-1:

|  | $y$ | $x_1$ | $x_2$ | $x_3$ |
|---|---|---|---|---|
| $y$ | 1 |  |  |  |
| $x_1$ | $-0.406$ | 1 |  |  |
| $x_2$ | 0.459 | 0.051 | 1 |  |
| $x_3$ | $-0.244$ | 0.504 | 0.272 | 1 |

Does this output indicate any potential multicollinearity problems with the analysis?

**15-5.** Consider the following set of data:

| $x_1$ | 29 | 48 | 28 | 22 | 28 | 42 | 33 | 26 | 48 | 44 |
|---|---|---|---|---|---|---|---|---|---|---|
| $x_2$ | 15 | 37 | 24 | 32 | 47 | 13 | 43 | 12 | 58 | 19 |
| $y$ | 16 | 46 | 34 | 26 | 49 | 11 | 41 | 13 | 47 | 16 |

a. Obtain the estimated regression equation.

b. Develop the correlation matrix for this set of data. Select the independent variable whose correlation magnitude is the smallest with the dependent variable. Determine if its correlation with the dependent variable is significant.

c. Determine if the overall model is significant. Use a significance level of 0.05.

d. Calculate the variance inflation factor for each of the independent variables. Indicate if multicollinearity exists between the two independent variables.

**15-6.** Consider the following set of data:

| $x_2$ | 10 | 8 | 11 | 7 | 10 | 11 | 6 |
|---|---|---|---|---|---|---|---|
| $x_1$ | 50 | 45 | 37 | 32 | 44 | 51 | 42 |
| $y$ | 103 | 85 | 115 | 73 | 97 | 102 | 65 |

a. Obtain the estimated regression equation.

b. Examine the coefficient of determination and the adjusted coefficient of determination. Does it seem that either of the independent variables' addition to $R^2$ does not justify the reduction in degrees of freedom that results from its addition to the regression model? Support your assertions.

c. Conduct a hypothesis test to determine if the dependent variable increases when $x_2$ increases. Use a significance level of 0.025 and the $p$-value approach.

d. Construct a 95% confidence interval for the coefficient of $x_1$.

## Computer Database Exercises

**15-7.** An investment analyst collected data about 20 randomly chosen companies. The data consisted of the 52-week-high stock prices, price-to-earnings (PE) ratio, and the market value of the company. These data are in the file entitled **Investment**.

a. Produce a regression equation to predict the market value using the 52-week-high stock price and the PE ratio of the company.

b. Determine if the overall model is significant. Use a significance level of 0.05.

c. OmniVision Technologies (Sunnyvale, CA) in April 2006 had a 52-week-high stock price of 31 and a PE ratio of 19. Estimate its market value for that time period. (*Note*: Its actual market value for that time period was $1,536.)

**15-8.** An article in *BusinessWeek* presents a list of the 100 companies perceived as having "hot growth" characteristics. A company's rank on the list is the sum of 0.5 times its rank in return on total capital and 0.25 times its sales and profit-growth ranks. The file entitled **Growth** contains sales ($million), sales increase (%), return on capital, market value ($million), and recent stock price of the top 20 ranked companies.

a. Produce a correlation matrix for the variables contained in the file entitled **Growth**.

b. Select the two variables that are most highly correlated with the recent stock price and produce the regression equation to predict the recent stock price as a function of the two variables you chose.

c. Determine if the overall model is significant. Use a significance level of 0.10.

d. Examine the coefficient of determination and the adjusted coefficient of determination. Does it seem that either of the independent variables' addition to $R^2$ does not justify the reduction in degrees of freedom that results from its addition to the regression model? Support your assertions.

e. Select the variable that is most correlated with the stock price and test to see if it is a significant predictor of the stock price. Use a significance level of 0.10 and the $p$-value approach.

**15-9.** Refer to Exercise 15-8, which referenced a list of the 100 companies perceived as having "hot growth" characteristics. The file entitled **Logrowth** contains sales ($million), sales increase (%), return on capital, market value ($million), and recent stock price of the companies ranked from 81 to 100. In Exercise 15-8, stock prices were the focus. Examine the sales of the companies.

a. Produce a regression equation that will predict the sales as a function of the other variables.

b. Determine if the overall model is significant. Use a significance level of 0.05.

c. Conduct a test of hypothesis to discover if market value should be removed from this model.

d. To see that a variable can be insignificant in one model but very significant in another, construct a regression equation in which sales is the dependent variable and market value is the independent variable. Test the hypothesis that market value is a significant predictor of sales for those companies ranked from 81 to 100. Use a significance level of 0.05 and the $p$-value approach.

**15-10.** The National Association of Theatre Owners is the largest exhibition trade organization in the world, representing more than 26,000 movie screens in all 50 states and in more than 20 countries worldwide. Its membership includes the largest cinema chains and hundreds of independent theatre owners. It publishes statistics concerning the movie sector of the economy. The file entitled **Flicks** contains data on total U.S. box office grosses ($billion), total number of admissions (billion), average U.S. ticket price ($), and number of movie screens.

a. Construct a regression equation in which total U.S. box office grosses are predicted using the other variables.

b. Determine if the overall model is significant. Use a significance level of 0.05.

c. Determine the range of plausible values for the change in box office grosses if the average ticket price were to be increased by $1. Use a confidence level of 95%.

d. Calculate the variance inflation factor for each of the independent variables. Indicate if multicollinearity exists between any two independent variables.

e. Produce the regression equation suggested by your answer to part d.

**15-11.** The athletic director of State University is interested in developing a multiple regression model that might be used to explain the variation in attendance at football games at his school. A sample of 16 games was selected from home games played during the past 10 seasons. Data for the following factors were determined:

$y$ = Game attendance
$x_1$ = Team win/loss percentage to date
$x_2$ = Opponent win/loss percentage to date
$x_3$ = Games played this season
$x_4$ = Temperature at game time
The data collected are in the file called **Football**.

a. Produce scatter plots for each independent variable versus the dependent variable. Based on the scatter plots, produce a model that you believe represents the relationship between the dependent variable and the group of predictor variables represented in the scatter plots.

b. Based on the correlation matrix developed from these data, comment on whether you think a multiple regression model will be effectively developed from these data.

c. Use the sample data to estimate the multiple regression model that contains all four independent variables.

d. What percentage of the total variation in the dependent variable is explained by the four independent variables in the model?

e. Test to determine whether the overall model is statistically significant. Use $\alpha = 0.05$.

f. Which, if any, of the independent variables is statistically significant? Use a significance level of $\alpha = 0.08$ and the $p$-value approach to conduct these tests.

g. Estimate the standard deviation of the model error and discuss whether this regression model is acceptable as a means of predicting the football attendance at State University at any given game.

h. Define the term *multicollinearity* and indicate the potential problems that multicollinearity can cause for this model. Indicate what, if any, evidence there is of multicollinearity problems with this regression model. Use the variance inflation factor to assist you in this analysis.

i. Develop a 95% confidence interval estimate for each of the regression coefficients and interpret each estimate. Comment on whether the interpretation of the intercept is relevant in this situation.

Chapter Outcome 6. ➤ ## 15.2 Using Qualitative Independent Variables

In Example 15-1 involving the First City Real Estate Company, the independent variables were quantitative and ratio level. However, you will encounter many situations in which you may wish to use a qualitative, lower level variable as an explanatory variable.

If a variable is nominal, and numerical codes are assigned to the categories, you already know not to perform mathematical calculations using those data. The results would be meaningless. Yet, we may wish to use a variable such as marital status, gender, or geographical location as an independent variable in a regression model. If the variable of interest is coded as an ordinal variable, such as education level or job performance ranking, computing means and variances is also inappropriate. Then how are these variables incorporated into a multiple regression analysis? The answer lies in using what are called **dummy** (or indicator) **variables**.

**Dummy Variable**

A variable that is assigned a value equal to either 0 or 1, depending on whether the observation possesses a given characteristic.

For instance, consider the variable gender, which can take on two possible values: male or female. Gender can be converted to a dummy variable as follows:

$$x_1 = 1 \text{ if female}$$
$$x_1 = 0 \text{ if male}$$

Thus, a data set consisting of males and females will have corresponding values for $x_1$ equal to $0$s and $1$s, respectively. Note that it makes no difference which gender is coded $1$ and which is coded $0$.

If a categorical variable has more than two mutually exclusive outcome possibilities, multiple dummy variables must be created. Consider the variable marital status, with the following possible outcomes:

never married    married    divorced    widowed

In this case, marital status has four values. To account for all the possibilities, you would create three dummy variables, one less than the number of possible outcomes for the original variable. They could be coded as follows:

$$x_1 = 1 \text{ if never married, 0 if not}$$
$$x_2 = 1 \text{ if married, 0 if not}$$
$$x_3 = 1 \text{ if divorced, 0 if not}$$

Note that we don't need the fourth variable because we would know that a person is widowed if $x_1 = 0$, $x_2 = 0$, and $x_3 = 0$. If the person isn't single, married, or divorced, he or she must be widowed. *Always use one fewer dummy variables than categories.* The mathematical reason that the number of dummy variables must be one less than the number of possible responses is called the *dummy variable trap*. Perfect multicollinearity is introduced, and the least squares regression estimates cannot be obtained, if the number of dummy variables equals the number of possible categories.

**EXAMPLE 15-1**   **INCORPORATING DUMMY VARIABLES**

**Business Executive Salaries**   To illustrate the effect of incorporating dummy variables into a regression model, consider the sample data displayed in the scatter plot in Figure 15.9. The population from which the sample was selected consists of executives between the ages of 24 and 60 who are working in U.S. manufacturing businesses. Data for annual salary ($y$) and age ($x_1$) are available. The objective is to determine whether a model can be generated to explain the variation in annual salary for business executives. Even though age and annual salary are significantly correlated ($r = 0.686$) at the $\alpha = 0.05$ level, the coefficient of determination is only 47%. Therefore, we would likely search for other independent variables that could help us to further explain the variation in annual salary.

Suppose we can determine which of the 16 people in the sample had a master of business administration (MBA) degree. Figure 15.10 shows the scatter plot for these same data, with

**FIGURE 15.9**

Executive Salary
Data—Scatter Plot

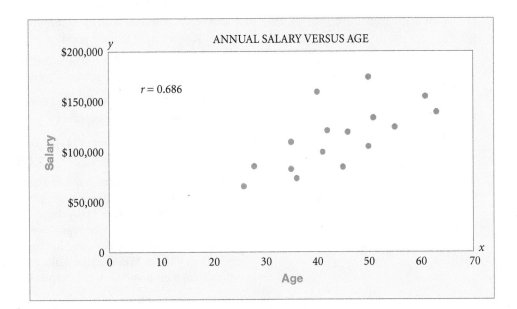

**TABLE 15.2** | **Executive Salary Data Including MBA Variable**

| Salary($) | Age | MBA |
|-----------|-----|-----|
| 65,000 | 26 | 0 |
| 85,000 | 28 | 1 |
| 74,000 | 36 | 0 |
| 83,000 | 35 | 0 |
| 110,000 | 35 | 1 |
| 160,000 | 40 | 1 |
| 100,000 | 41 | 0 |
| 122,000 | 42 | 1 |
| 85,000 | 45 | 0 |
| 120,000 | 46 | 1 |
| 105,000 | 50 | 0 |
| 135,000 | 51 | 1 |
| 125,000 | 55 | 0 |
| 175,000 | 50 | 1 |
| 156,000 | 61 | 1 |
| 140,000 | 63 | 0 |

the MBA data represented by triangles. To incorporate a qualitative variable into the analysis, use the following steps:

**Step 1**  **Code the qualitative variable as a dummy variable.**
Create a new variable, $x_2$, which is a dummy variable coded as

$$x_2 = 1 \text{ if MBA, 0 if not}$$

The data with the new variable are shown in Table 15.2.

**Step 2**  **Develop a multiple regression model with the dummy variables incorporated as independent variables.**
The two-variable population multiple regression model has the following form:

$$y = \beta_0 + \beta_1 x_1 + \beta_2 x_2 + \varepsilon$$

Using either Excel or Minitab, we get the following regression equation as an estimate of the population model:

$$\hat{y} = 6{,}974 + 2{,}055 x_1 + 35{,}236 x_2$$

Because the dummy variable, $x_2$, has been coded 0 or 1 depending on MBA status, incorporating it into the regression model is like having two simple

**FIGURE 15.10**

Impact of a Dummy Variable

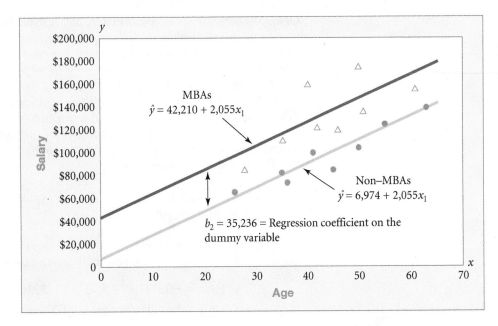

linear regression lines with the same slopes, but different intercepts. For instance, when $x_2 = 0$, the regression equation is

$$\hat{y} = 6,974 + 2,055x_1 + 35,236(0)$$
$$= 6,974 + 2,055x_1$$

This line is shown in Figure 15.10. However, when $x_2 = 1$ (the executive has an MBA), the regression equation is

$$\hat{y} = 6,974 + 2,055x_1 + 35,236(1)$$
$$= 42,210 + 2,055x_1$$

This regression line is also shown in Figure 15.10. As you can see, incorporating the dummy variable affects the regression intercept. In this case, the intercept for executives with an MBA degree is $35,236 higher than for those without an MBA. We interpret the regression coefficient on this dummy variable as follows: Based on these data, and holding age ($x_1$) constant, we estimate that executives with an MBA degree make an average of $35,236 per year more in salary than their non–MBA counterparts.

>>**END EXAMPLE**

**TRY PROBLEM** 15-17 (pg. 659)

**BUSINESS APPLICATION** **REGRESSION MODELS USING DUMMY VARIABLES**

**FIRST CITY REAL ESTATE (*CONTINUED*)** The regression model developed in Example 15-l for First City Real Estate showed potential because the overall model was statistically significant. Looking back at Figure 15.8, we see that the model explained nearly 82% of the variation in sales prices for the homes in the sample. All of the independent variables were significant, given that the other independent variables were in the model. However, the standard error of the estimate is $27,350.

**Excel and Minitab Tutorial**

The managers have decided to try to improve the model. First, they have decided to add a new variable: area. However, at this point, the only area variable they have access to defines whether the home is in the foothills. Because this is a categorical variable with two possible outcomes (foothills or not foothills), a dummy variable can be created as follows:

$$x_6 \text{ (area)} = 1 \text{ if foothills, 0 if not}$$

Of the 319 homes in the sample, 249 were homes in the foothills and 70 were not. Figure 15.11 shows the revised Minitab multiple regression with the variable, area, added. This model is an improvement over the original model because the adjusted $R$-squared has increased from 81.3% to 90.2% and the standard error of the estimate has decreased from $27,350 to $19,828. The conditional $t$-tests show that all of the regression models' slope coefficients, except that for the variable bathrooms, differ significantly from 0. The Minitab output shows that the variance inflation factors are all less than 5.0, so we don't need to be too concerned about the $t$-tests understating the significance of the regression coefficients. (See the Excel Tutorial for this example to get the full *VIF* output from PHStat.)

The resulting regression model is

$$\hat{y} = -6,817 + 63.3(\text{sq. ft.}) - 334(\text{age}) - 8,445(\text{bedrooms}) - 949(\text{bathrooms})$$
$$+ 26,246(\text{garage}) + 62,041(\text{area})$$

Because the variable bathrooms is not significant in the presence of the other variables, we can remove the variable and rerun the multiple regression. The resulting model is

$$\text{Price} = -7,050 + 62.5(\text{sq. ft.}) - 322(\text{age}) - 8,830(\text{bedrooms})$$
$$+ 26,054(\text{garage}) + 61,370(\text{area})$$

**FIGURE 15.11**

Minitab Output—First City Real Estate Revised Regression Model

**Minitab Instructions:**
1. Open file: First City. MTW.
2. Choose **Stat > Regression > Regression**.
3. In **Response**, enter dependent (*y*) variable.
4. In **Predictors**, enter independent (*x*) variables.
5. Click **Options**.
6. In **Display**, select **Variance inflation Factors**.
7. Click **OK. OK.**

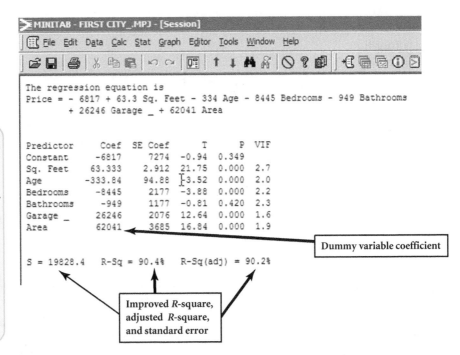

Based on the sample data and this regression model, we estimate that a house with the same characteristics (square feet, age, bedrooms, and garages) is worth an average of $61,370 more if it is located in the foothills (based on how the dummy variable was coded).

There are still signals of multicollinearity problems. The coefficient on the independent variable bedrooms is negative, when we might expect homes with more bedrooms to sell for more. Also, the standard error of the estimate is still very large ($19,817) and does not provide the precision the managers need to set prices for homes. More work needs to be done before the model is complete.

**Possible Improvements to the First City Appraisal Model** Because the standard error of the estimate is still too high, we look to improve the model. We could start by identifying possible problems:

1. We may be missing useful independent variables.
2. Independent variables may have been included that should not have been included.

There is no sure way of determining the correct model specification. However, a recommended approach is for the decision maker to try adding variables or removing variables from the model.

We begin by removing the bedrooms variable, which has an unexpected sign on the regression slope coefficient. (*Note*: If the regression model's sole purpose is for prediction, independent variables with unexpected signs do not automatically pose a problem and do not necessarily need to be deleted. However, insignificant variables should be deleted.) The resulting model is shown in Figures 15.12a and 15.12b. Now, all the variables in the model have the expected signs. However, the standard error of the estimate has increased slightly.

Adding other explanatory variables might help. For instance, consider whether the house has central air conditioning, which might affect sales. If we can identify whether a house has air conditioning, we could add a dummy variable coded as follows:

$$\text{If air conditioning, } x_7 = 1$$
$$\text{If no air conditioning, } x_7 = 0$$

Other potential independent variables might include a more detailed location variable, a measure of the physical condition, or whether the house has one or two stories. Can you think of others?

**FIGURE 15.12A**

Excel 2007 Output for the
First City Real Estate Revised
Model

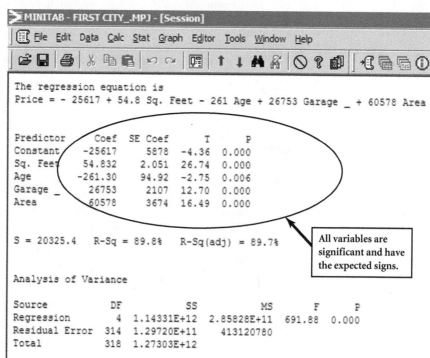

**Excel 2007 Instructions:**
1. Open file: First City.xls (worksheet: Homes-Sample-2).
2. Click on **Data** tab—then click on **Data Analysis**.
3. Select **Regression**.
4. Define *y* variable range and *x* variables range.
5. Click **OK**.

The First City example illustrates that even though a regression model may pass the statistical tests of significance, it may not be functional. Good appraisal models can be developed using multiple regression analysis, provided more detail is available about such characteristics as finish quality, landscaping, location, neighborhood characteristics, and so forth. The cost and effort required to obtain these data can be relatively high.

Developing a multiple regression model is more of an art than a science. The real decisions revolve around how to select the best set of independent variables for the model.

**FIGURE 15.12B**

Minitab Output for the First
City Real Estate Revised
Model

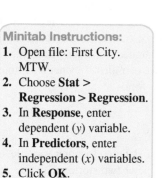

**Minitab Instructions:**
1. Open file: First City. MTW.
2. Choose **Stat > Regression > Regression**.
3. In **Response**, enter dependent (*y*) variable.
4. In **Predictors**, enter independent (*x*) variables.
5. Click **OK**.

## 15-2: Exercises

### Skill Development

**15-12.** Consider the following regression model:

$$y = \beta_0 + \beta_1 x_1 + \beta_2 x_2 + \varepsilon$$

where:

$x_1$ = A quantitative variable

$$x_2 = \begin{cases} 1 \text{ if } x_1 < 20 \\ 0 \text{ if } x_1 \geq 20 \end{cases}$$

The following estimated regression equation was obtained from a sample of 30 observations:

$$\hat{y} = 24.1 + 5.8x_1 + 7.9x_2$$

a. Provide the estimated regression equation for instances in which $x_1 < 20$.

b. Determine the value of $\hat{y}$ when $x_1 = 10$.

c. Provide the estimated regression equation for instances in which $x_1 > 20$.

d. Determine the value of $\hat{y}$ when $x_1 = 30$.

**15-13.** You are considering developing a regression equation relating a dependent variable to two independent variables. One of the variables can be measured on a ratio scale, but the other is a categorical variable with two possible levels.

a. Write a multiple regression equation relating the dependent variable to the independent variables.

b. Interpret the meaning of the coefficients in the regression equation.

**15-14.** You are considering developing a regression equation relating a dependent variable to two independent variables. One of the variables can be measured on a ratio scale, but the other is a categorical variable with four possible levels.

a. How many dummy variables are needed to represent the categorical variable?

b. Write a multiple regression equation relating the dependent variable to the independent variables.

c. Interpret the meaning of the coefficients in the regression equation.

**15-15.** A real estate agent wishes to estimate the monthly rental for apartments based on the size (square feet) and the location of the apartments. She chose the following model:

$$y = \beta_0 + \beta_1 x_1 + \beta_2 x_2 + \varepsilon$$

where:

$x_1$ = Square footage of the apartment

$$x_2 = \begin{cases} 1 \text{ if located in town center} \\ 0 \text{ if not located in town center} \end{cases}$$

This linear regression model was fitted to a sample of size 50 to produce the following regression equation:

$$\hat{y} = 145 + 1.2x_1 + 300x_2$$

a. Predict the average monthly rent for an apartment located in the town center that has 1,500 square feet.

b. Predict the average monthly rent for an apartment located in the suburbs that has 1,500 square feet.

c. Interpret $b_2$ in the context of this exercise.

### Business Applications

**15-16.** The Polk Utility Corporation is developing a multiple regression model that it plans to use to predict customers' utility usage. The analyst currently has three quantitative variables ($x_1$, $x_2$, and $x_3$) in the model, but she is dissatisfied with the $R$-squared and the estimate of the standard deviation of the model's error. Two variables she thinks might be useful are whether the house has a gas water heater or an electric water heater and whether the house was constructed after the 1974 energy crisis or before.

Provide the model she should use to predict customers' utility usage. Specify the dummy variables to be used, the values these variables could assume, and what each value will represent.

**15-17.** A study was recently performed by the American Automobile Association in which it attempted to develop a regression model to explain variation in Environmental Protection Agency (EPA) mileage ratings of new cars. At one stage of the analysis, the estimate of the model took the following form:

$$\hat{y} = 34.20 - 0.003x_1 + 4.56x_2$$

where:

$x_1$ = Vehicle weight

$$x_2 = \begin{cases} 1, \text{ if standard transmission} \\ 0, \text{ if automatic transmission} \end{cases}$$

a. Interpret the regression coefficient for variable $x_1$.

b. Interpret the regression coefficient for variable $x_2$.

c. Present an estimate of a model that would predict the average EPA mileage rating for an automobile with standard transmission as a function of the vehicle's weight.

d. Cadillac's STS-V with automatic transmission weighs approximately 4,394 pounds. Provide an estimate of the average highway mileage you would expect to obtain from this model.

e. Discuss the effect of a dummy variable being incorporated in a regression equation like this one. Use a graph if it is helpful.

**15-18.** A real estate agent wishes to determine the selling price of residences using the size (square feet) and whether the residence is a condominium or a .

single-family home. A sample of 20 residences was obtained with the following results:

| Price($) | Type | Square Feet | Price($) | Type | Square Feet |
|---|---|---|---|---|---|
| 199,700 | Family | 1,500 | 200,600 | Condo | 1,375 |
| 211,800 | Condo | 2,085 | 208,000 | Condo | 1,825 |
| 197,100 | Family | 1,450 | 210,500 | Family | 1,650 |
| 228,400 | Family | 1,836 | 233,300 | Family | 1,960 |
| 215,800 | Family | 1,730 | 187,200 | Condo | 1,360 |
| 190,900 | Condo | 1,726 | 185,200 | Condo | 1,200 |
| 312,200 | Family | 2,300 | 284,100 | Family | 2,000 |
| 313,600 | Condo | 1,650 | 207,200 | Family | 1,755 |
| 239,000 | Family | 1,950 | 258,200 | Family | 1,850 |
| 184,400 | Condo | 1,545 | 203,100 | Family | 1,630 |

a. Produce a regression equation to predict the selling price for residences using a model of the following form:

$$y_i = \beta_0 + \beta_1 x_1 + \beta_2 x_2 + \varepsilon$$

where:

$x_1 = $ Square footage and $x_2 = \begin{cases} 1 \text{ if a condo} \\ 0 \text{ if a single-family home} \end{cases}$

b. Interpret the parameters $\beta_1$ and $\beta_2$ in the model given in part a.

c. Produce an equation that describes the relationship between the selling price and the square footage of (1) condominiums and (2) single-family homes.

d. Conduct a test of hypothesis to determine if the relationship between the selling price and the square footage is different between condominiums and single-family homes.

**15-19.** When cars from Korean automobile manufacturers started coming to the United States they were given very poor quality ratings. That started changing several years ago. J.D. Power and Associates generates a widely respected report on initial quality. The improved quality started being seen in the 2004 Initial Quality Study. Results were based on responses from more than 62,000 purchasers and lessors of new-model-year cars and trucks, who were surveyed after 90 days of ownership. Initial quality is measured by the number of problems per 100 vehicles (PP100). The PP100 data from the interval 1998–2004 follow:

| | 1998 | 1999 | 2000 | 2001 | 2002 | 2003 | 2004 |
|---|---|---|---|---|---|---|---|
| Korean | 272 | 227 | 222 | 214 | 172 | 152 | 117 |
| Domestic | 182 | 177 | 164 | 153 | 137 | 135 | 123 |
| European | 158 | 171 | 154 | 141 | 137 | 136 | 122 |

a. Produce a regression equation to predict the PP100 for vehicles in the model

$$y_i = \beta_0 + \beta_1 x_1 + \beta_2 x_2 + \varepsilon$$

where

$x_1 = \begin{cases} 1 \text{ if Domestic} \\ 0 \text{ if not Domestic} \end{cases}$ and $x_2 = \begin{cases} 1 \text{ if European} \\ 0 \text{ if not European} \end{cases}$

b. Interpret the parameters $\beta_0$, $\beta_1$, and $\beta_2$ in the model given in part a.

c. Conduct a test of hypothesis using the model in part a to determine if the average PP100 is the same for the three international automobile production regions.

## Computer Database **Exercises**

**15-20.** The Energy Information Administration (EIA), created by Congress in 1977, is a statistical agency of the U.S. Department of Energy. It provides data, forecasts, and analyses to promote sound policymaking and public understanding regarding energy and its interaction with the economy and the environment. One of the most important areas of analysis is petroleum. The file entitled **Crude** contains data for the period 1991–2006 concerning the price, supply, and demand for fuel. It has been conjectured that the pricing structure of gasoline changed at the turn of the century.

a. Produce a regression equation to predict the selling price of gasoline:

$$y_i = \beta_0 + \beta_1 x_1 + \varepsilon$$

where:

$x_1 = \begin{cases} 1 \text{ if in twenty-first century} \\ 0 \text{ if in twentieth century} \end{cases}$

b. Conduct a hypothesis test to address the conjecture. Use a significance level of 0.05 and the test statistic approach.

c. Produce a 95% confidence interval to estimate the change of the average selling price of gasoline between the twentieth and the twenty-first centuries.

**15-21.** The Gilmore Accounting firm, in an effort to explain variation in client profitability, collected the data found in the file called **Gilmore**, where:

$y = $ Net profit earned from the client

$x_1 = $ Number of hours spent working with the client

$x_2 = $ Type of client:
 1, if manufacturing
 2, if service
 3, if governmental

a. Develop a scatter plot of each independent variable against the client income variable. Comment on what, if any, relationship appears to exist in each case.

b. Run a simple linear regression analysis using only variable $x_1$ as the independent variable. Describe the resulting estimate fully.

c. Test to determine if the number of hours spent working with the client is useful in predicting client profitability.

**15-22.** Using the data from the Gilmore Accounting firm found in the data file **Gilmore** (see Exercise 15-21),

   a. Incorporate the client type into the regression analysis using dummy variables. Describe the resulting multiple regression estimate.

   b. Test to determine if this model is useful in predicting the net profit earned from the client.

   c. Test to determine if the number of hours spent working with the client is useful in this model in predicting the net profit earned from a client.

   d. Considering the tests you have performed, construct a model and its estimate for predicting the net profit earned from the client.

   e. Predict the average difference in profit if the client is governmental versus one in manufacturing. Also state this in terms of a 95% confidence interval estimate.

**15-23.** Several previous problems have dealt with the College Board changing the format of the SAT test taken by many entering college freshmen. Many reasons were given for changing the format. The class of 2005 was the last to take the former version of the SAT, featuring math and verbal sections. There had been conjecture about whether a relationship between the average math SAT score and the average verbal SAT score and the gender of the student taking the SAT examination existed. Consider the following relationship:

$$y_i = \beta_0 + \beta_1 x_1 + \beta_2 x_2 + \varepsilon$$

where:

$$x_1 = \text{Average verbal SAT score} \quad \text{and} \quad x_2 = \begin{cases} 1 \text{ if female} \\ 0 \text{ if male} \end{cases}$$

   a. Use the file **MathSAT** to compute the linear regression equation to predict the average math SAT score using the gender and the average verbal SAT score of the students taking the SAT examination.

   b. Interpret the parameters in the model.

   c. Conduct a hypothesis test to determine if the gender of the student taking the SAT examination is a significant predictor of the student's average math SAT score for a given average verbal SAT score.

   d. Predict the average math SAT score of female students with an average verbal SAT score of 500.

**END EXERCISES 15-2**

---

Chapter Outcome 7. → # 15.3 Working with Nonlinear Relationships

Section 14.1 in Chapter 14 showed there are a variety of ways in which two variables can be related. Correlation and regression analysis techniques are tools for measuring and modeling linear relationships between variables. Many situations in business have a linear relationship between two variables, and regression equations that model that relationship will be appropriate to use in these situations. However, there are also many instances in which the relationship between two variables will be curvilinear, rather than linear. For instance, demand for electricity has grown at an almost exponential rate relative to the population growth in some areas. Advertisers believe that a diminishing returns relationship will occur between sales and advertising if advertising is allowed to grow too large. These two situations are shown in Figures 15.13 and 15.14, respectively. They represent just two of the great many possible curvilinear relationships that could exist between two variables.

As you will soon see, models with nonlinear relationships become more complicated than models showing only linear relationships. Although complicated models are sometimes

**FIGURE 15.13**

Exponential Relationship of Increased Demand for Electricity versus Population Growth

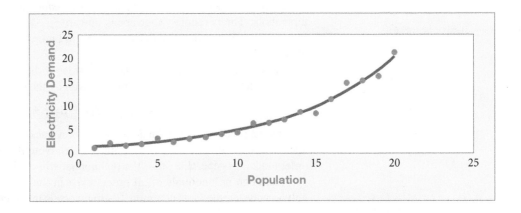

**FIGURE 15.14**

Diminishing Returns
Relationship of Advertising
versus Sales

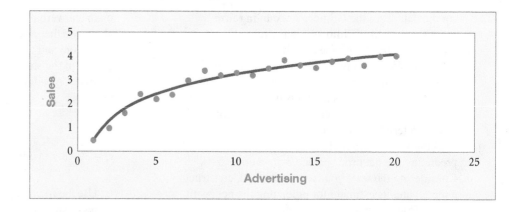

necessary, decision makers should use them with caution for several reasons. First, management researchers and authors have written that people use decision aids they understand and don't use those they don't understand. So, the more complicated a model is, the less likely it is to be used. Second, the scientific principle of parsimony suggests using the simplest model possible that provides a reasonable fit of the data, because complex models typically do not reflect the underlying phenomena that produce the data in the first place.

This section provides a brief introduction to how linear regression analysis can be used in dealing with curvilinear relationships. To model such curvilinear relationships, we must incorporate terms into the multiple regression model that will create "curves" in the model we are building. Including terms whose independent variable has an exponent larger than 1 generates these curves. When a model possesses such terms we refer to it as a *polynomial model*. The general equation for a polynomial with one independent variable is given in Equation 15.11.

---

**Polynomial Population Regression Model**

$$y = \beta_0 + \beta_1 x + \beta_2 x^2 + \cdots + \beta_p x^p + \varepsilon \qquad \textbf{(15.11)}$$

where:

$\beta_0$ = Population regression's constant
$\beta_j$ = Population's regression coefficient for variable $x^j$; $j = 1, 2, \ldots, p$
$p$ = Order (or degree) of the polynomial
$\varepsilon$ = Model error

---

The order, or degree, of the model is determined by the largest exponent of the independent variable in the model. For instance, the model

$$y = \beta_0 + \beta_1 x + \beta_2 x^2 + \varepsilon$$

is a second-order polynomial because the largest exponent in any term of the polynomial is 2. You will note that this model contains terms of all orders less than or equal to 2. A polynomial with this property is said to be a *complete* polynomial. Therefore, the previous model would be referred to as a complete *second-order regression model*. A second-order model produces a parabola. The parabola either opens upward ($\beta_2 > 0$) or downward ($\beta_2 < 0$), shown in Figure 15.15. You will notice that the models in Figures 15.13, 15.14, and 15.15 possess a single curve.

As more curves appear in the data, the order of the polynomial must be increased. A general (complete) third-order polynomial is given by the equation

$$y = \beta_0 + \beta_1 x + \beta_2 x^2 + \beta_3 x^3 + \varepsilon$$

This model produces a curvilinear model that reverses the direction of the initial curve to produce a second curve, as shown in Figure 15.16. Note that there are two curves in the third-order model. In general, a *p*th-order polynomial will exhibit $p - 1$ curves.

Although polynomials of all orders exist in the business sector, perhaps second-order polynomials are the most common. Sharp reversals in the curvature of a relationship between

**FIGURE 15.15** |

Second-Order Regression
Models

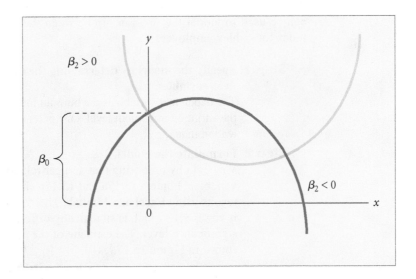

variables in the business environment usually point to some unexpected or, perhaps severe, changes that were not foreseen. The vast majority of organizations try to avoid such reverses. For this reason, and the fact that this is an introductory business statistics course, we will direct most of our attention to second-order polynomials.

The following examples illustrate two of the most common instances in which curvilinear relationships can be used in decision making. They should give you an idea of how to approach similar situations.

Chapter Outcome 7. ➔ | EXAMPLE 15-2 | **MODELING CURVILINEAR RELATIONSHIPS**

**Ashley Investment Services** Ashley Investment Services was severely shaken by the downturn in the stock market during the summer and fall of 2008. To maintain profitability and save as many jobs as possible, since then everyone has been extra busy analyzing new investment opportunities. The director of personnel has noticed an increased number of people suffering from "burnout," in which physical and emotional fatigue hurt job performance. Although he cannot change the job's pressures, he has read that the more time a person spends socializing with coworkers away from the job, the more likely there is to be a higher degree of burnout. With the help of the human resources lab at the local university, the personnel director has administered a questionnaire to company employees. A burnout index has been computed from the responses to the survey. Likewise, the survey responses are used to determine quantitative measures of socialization. Sample data from questionnaires are contained in the file **Ashley**. The following steps

**FIGURE 15.16** |

Third-Order Regression
Models

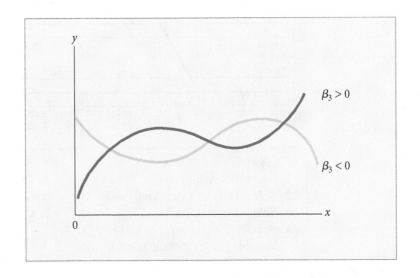

can be used to model the relationship between the socialization index and the burnout index for Ashley employees:

**Step 1**   **Specify the model by determining the dependent and potential independent variables.**

The dependent variable is the burnout index. The company wishes to explain the variation in burnout level. One potential independent variable is the socialization index.

**Step 2**   **Formulate the model.**

We begin by proposing that a linear relationship exists between the two variables. Figures 15.17a and 15.17b show the linear regression analysis results using Excel and Minitab. The correlation between the two variables is $r = 0.818$, which is statistically different from zero at any reasonable significance level. The estimate of the population linear regression model shown in Figure 15.17a is

$$\hat{y} = -66.164 + 9.589x$$

**Step 3**   **Perform diagnostic checks on the model.**

The sample data and the regression line are plotted in Figure 15.18. The line appears to fit the data. However, a closer inspection reveals instances where

**FIGURE 15.17A**

Excel 2007 Output of a Simple Linear Regression for Ashley Investment Services

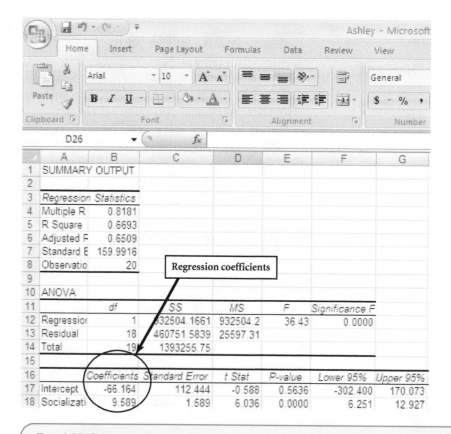

Excel 2007 Instructions:
1. Open file: Ashley.xls.
2. Select **Data > Data Analysis**.
3. Select **Regression**.
4. Specify *y* variable range and *x* variable range (include labels).
5. Check **Labels** option.
6. Specify output location.
7. Click **OK**.

**FIGURE 15.17B**

Minitab Output of a Simple Linear Regression for Ashley Investment Services

**Minitab Instructions:**
1. Open file: Ashley.MTW.
2. Choose **Stat > Regression > Regression**.
3. In **Response**, enter the *y* variable column.
4. In **Predictors**, enter the *x* variable column.
5. Click **OK**.

several consecutive points lie above or below the line. The points are not randomly dispersed around the regression line, as should be the case given the regression analysis assumptions.

As you will recall from earlier discussions, we can use an *F*-test to test whether a regression model explains a significant amount of variation in the dependent variable.

$$H_0: \rho^2 = 0$$
$$H_A: \rho^2 > 0$$

From the output in Figure 15.17a,

$$F = 36.43$$

which has a *p*-value $\approx 0.0000$.

Thus, we conclude that the simple linear model is statistically significant. However, we should also examine the data to determine if any curvilinear relationships may be present.

**FIGURE 15.18**

Plot of Regression Line for the Ashley Investment Services Example

**FIGURE 15.19A**

Excel 2007 Output of a
Second-Order Polynomial Fit
for Ashley Investment

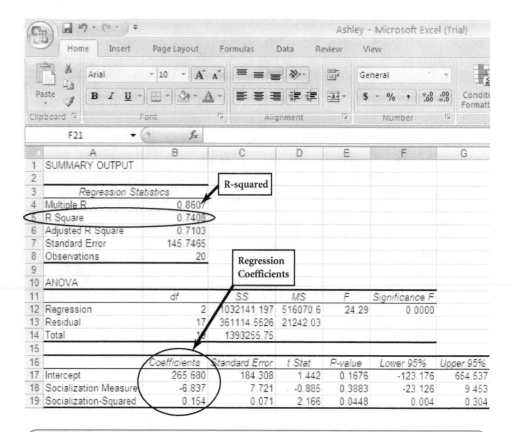

**Excel 2007 Instructions:**
1. Open file: Ashley.xls.
2. Use Excel equations to create the new variable in column C (i.e. for the first data value use = A2^2. Then copy down).
3. Select **Data > Data Analysis**.
4. Select **Regression**.
5. Specify *y* variable range and *x* variable range (include the new variable and the labels).
6. Check **Labels** option.
7. Specify ouput location.
8. Click **OK**.

**FIGURE 15.19B**

Minitab Output of a Second-
Order Polynomial Fit for
Ashley Investment

**Minitab Instructions:**
1. Open file: Ashley.MTW.
2. Use *Calc > Calculator* to create socialization column
3. Choose **Stat > Regression > Fitted Line Plot**.
4. In **Response**, enter *y* variable.
5. In **Predictor**, enter *x* variables.
6. Under **Type of Regression Model**, choose **Quadratic**.
7. Click **OK**.

Step 4  **Model the curvilinear relationship.**
Finding instances of nonrandom patterns in the residuals for a regression model indicates the possibility of using a curvilinear relationship rather than a linear one. One possible approach to modeling the curvilinear nature of the data in the Ashley Investments example is with the use of polynomials. From Figure 15.18, we can see that there appears to be one curve in the data. This suggests fitting the second-order polynomial

$$y = \beta_0 + \beta_1 x + \beta_2 x^2 + \varepsilon$$

Before fitting the estimate for this population model, you will need to create the new independent variable by squaring the socialization measure variable. In Excel use the formula option or in Minitab use the **Calc > Calculator** command to create the new variable. Figures 15.19a and 15.19b show the output after fitting this second-order polynomial model.

Step 5  **Perform diagnostics on the revised curvilinear model.**
Notice the second-order polynomial provides a model whose estimated regression equation has an $R^2$ of 74.1%. This is higher than the $R^2$ of 66.9% for the linear model. Figure 15.20 shows the plot of the second-order polynomial model. Comparing Figure 15.20 with Figure 15.18, we can see that the polynomial model does appear to fit the sample data better than the linear model.

>>**END EXAMPLE**

**TRY PROBLEM** 15-24 (pg. 675)

## Analyzing Interaction Effects

BUSINESS APPLICATION   **DEALING WITH INTERACTION**

**ASHLEY INVESTMENT SERVICES (*CONTINUED*)** Referring to Example 15-3 involving Ashley Investment Services, the director of personnel wondered if the effects of burnout differ among male and female workers. He therefore identified the gender of the previously surveyed employees (see file **Ashley-2**). A multiple scatter plot of the data appears as Figure 15.21.

The personnel director tried to determine the relationship between the burnout index and socialization measure for men and women. The graphical result is presented in Figure 15.21. Note that both relationships appear to be curvilinear, with a similarly shaped curve. As we showed earlier, curvilinear shapes often can be modeled by the second-order polynomial

$$\hat{y} = b_0 + b_1 x_1 + b_2 x_1^2$$

**Excel and Minitab Tutorial**

**FIGURE 15.20**

Plot of Second-Order Polynomial Model for Ashley Investment

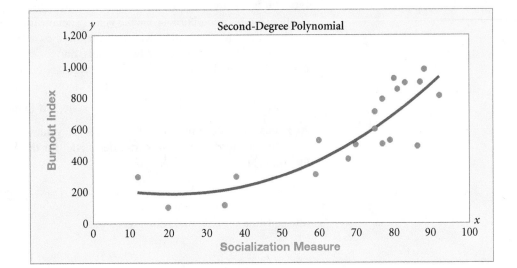

**FIGURE 15.21** |

Excel 2007 Multiple Scatter Plot for Ashley Investment Services

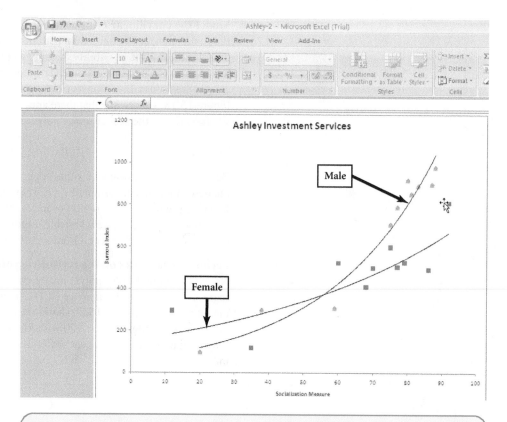

**Excel 2007 Instructions:**
1. Open file: Ashley-2.xls.
2. Select the Socialization Measure and Burnout Index columns.
3. Select the **Insert** tab.
4. Select the **XY (Scatter)**.
5. Select **Chart** and click the right mouse button—choose **Select Data**.
6. Click on **Add** on the **Legend Entry (Series)** section.
7. Enter **Series Name**—(Females)—for **Series X Values** select data from Socialization column for row

corresponding to females (rows 2–11). For **Series Y Values** select data from the Burnout column corresponding to females (rows 2–11).
8. Repeat step 7 for males.
9. Click on **layout** tab to remove legend and to add chart and axis titles.
10. Select data points for males—right click and select **Add Trendline > Exponential**.
11. Repeat step 10 for females.

However, the regression equations that estimate this second-order polynomial for men and women are not the same. The two equations seem to have different locations and different rates of curvature. Whether an employee is a man or woman seems to change the basic relationship between burnout index ($y$) and socialization measure ($x_1$). To represent this difference, the equation's coefficients $b_0$, $b_1$, and $b_2$ must be different for male and female employees. Thus, we could use two models, one for each gender. Alternatively, we could use one model for both male and female employees by incorporating a dummy independent variable with two levels, which is shown as

$$x_2 = 1 \text{ if male, } 0 \text{ if female}$$

As $x_2$ changes values from 0 to 1, it affects the values of the coefficients $b_0$, $b_1$, and $b_2$. Suppose the director fitted the second-order model for the female employees only. He obtained the following regression equation:

$$\hat{y} = 291.70 - 4.62x_1 + 0.102x_1^2$$

The equation for only male employees was

$$\hat{y} = 149.59 - 4.40x_1 + 0.160x_1^2$$

**Interaction**

The case in which one independent variable (such as $x_2$) affects the relationship between another independent variable ($x_1$) and the dependent variable ($y$).

To explain how a change in gender can cause this kind of change, we must introduce **interaction**. In our example, gender ($x_2$) interacts with the relationship between socialization measure ($x_1$) and burnout index ($y$). The question is how do we obtain the interaction terms to model such a relationship? To answer this question, we first obtain the model for the basic relationship between the $x_1$ and the $y$ variables. The population model is

$$y = \beta_0 + \beta_1 x_1 + \beta_2 x_1^2 + \varepsilon$$

To obtain the interaction terms, multiply the terms on the right-hand side of this model by the variable that is interacting with this relationship between $y$ and $x_1$. In this case, that interacting variable is $x_2$. Then the interaction terms would be

$$\beta_3 x_2 + \beta_4 x_1 x_2 + \beta_5 x_1^2 x_2$$

**Composite Model**

The model that contains both the basic terms and the interaction terms.

Notice that we have changed the coefficient subscripts so we do not duplicate those in the original model. Then the interaction terms are added to the original model to produce the **composite model**.

$$y = \beta_0 + \beta_1 x_1 + \beta_2 x_1^2 + \beta_3 x_2 + \beta_4 x_1 x_2 + \beta_5 x_1^2 x_2 + \varepsilon$$

Note, the model for women is obtained by substituting $x_2 = 0$ into the composite model. This gives

$$y = \beta_0 + \beta_1 x_1 + \beta_2 x_1^2 + \beta_3(0) + \beta_4 x_1(0) + \beta_5 x_1^2(0) + \varepsilon$$
$$= \beta_0 + \beta_1 x_1 + \beta_2 x_1^2 + \varepsilon$$

Similarly, for men we substitute the value of $x_2 = 1$. The model then becomes

$$y = \beta_0 + \beta_1 x_1 + \beta_2 x_1^2 + \beta_3(1) + \beta_4 x_1(1) + \beta_5 x_1^2(1) + \varepsilon$$
$$= (\beta_0 + \beta_3) + (\beta_1 + \beta_4)x_1 + (\beta_2 + \beta_5)x_1^2 + \varepsilon$$

This illustrates how the coefficients are changed for different values of $x_2$ and, therefore, how $x_2$ is interacting with the relationship between $x_1$ and $y$. Once we know $\beta_3$, $\beta_4$, and $\beta_5$, we know the effect of the interaction of gender on the original relationship between the burnout index ($y$) and the socialization measure ($x_1$). To estimate the composite model, we need to

**FIGURE 15.22**

Excel 2007 Data Preparation for Estimating Interactive Effects for Second-Order Model for Ashley Investment

| | A | B | C | D | E | F |
|---|---|---|---|---|---|---|
| 1 | Socialization Measure $x_1$ | Burnout Index $y$ | Socialization Squared $x_1^2$ | Gender $x_2$ | $x_1 x_2$ | $x_1^2 x_2$ |
| 2 | 12 | 296 | 144 | 0 | 0 | 0 |
| 3 | 35 | 120 | 1225 | 0 | 0 | 0 |
| 4 | 60 | 525 | 3600 | 0 | 0 | 0 |
| 5 | 68 | 410 | 4624 | 0 | 0 | 0 |
| 6 | 70 | 501 | 4900 | 0 | 0 | 0 |
| 7 | 75 | 600 | 5625 | 0 | 0 | 0 |
| 8 | 77 | 506 | 5929 | 0 | 0 | 0 |
| 9 | 79 | 527 | 6241 | 0 | 0 | 0 |
| 10 | 86 | 493 | 7396 | 0 | 0 | 0 |
| 11 | 92 | 810 | 8464 | 0 | 0 | 0 |
| 12 | 20 | 100 | 400 | 1 | 20 | 400 |
| 13 | 38 | 300 | 1444 | 1 | 38 | 1444 |
| 14 | 59 | 310 | 3481 | 1 | 59 | 3481 |
| 15 | 75 | 709 | 5625 | 1 | 75 | 5625 |
| 16 | 77 | 791 | 5929 | 1 | 77 | 5929 |
| 17 | 80 | 920 | 6400 | 1 | 80 | 6400 |
| 18 | 81 | 855 | 6561 | 1 | 81 | 6561 |
| 19 | 83 | 892 | 6889 | 1 | 83 | 6889 |
| 20 | 87 | 900 | 7569 | 1 | 87 | 7569 |
| 21 | 88 | 980 | 7744 | 1 | 88 | 7744 |

**Excel 2007 Instructions:**

1. Open file: Ashley-2.xls.
2. Use Excel formulas to create new variables in columns C, E, and F.

**FIGURE 15.23A**

Excel 2007 Composite Model for Ashley Investment Services

**Excel 2007 Instructions:**
1. Open file: Ashley-2.xls.
2. Create new variables (see Figure 15.22 Excel 2007 Instructions).
3. Rearrange columns so all *x* variables are contiguous.
4. Select **Data > Data Analysis**.
5. Select **Regression**.
6. Specify *y* variable range and *x* variable range (include the new variables and the labels).
7. Check **Labels** option.
8. Specify output location.
9. Click **OK**.

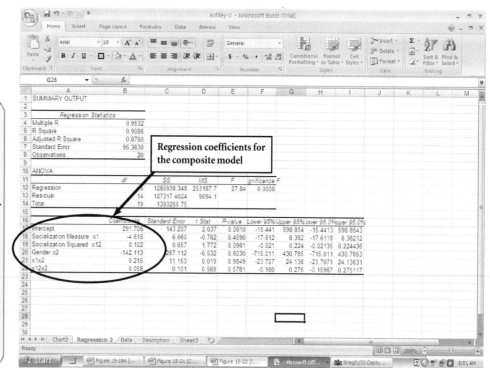

create the required variables, as shown in Figure 15.22. Figures 15.23a and 15.23b show the regression for the composite model. The estimate for the composite model is

$$\hat{y} = 291.706 - 4.615x_1 + 0.102x_1^2 - 142.113x_2 + 0.215x_1x_2 + 0.058x_1^2x_2$$

We obtain the model for females by substituting $x_2 = 0$, giving

$$\hat{y} = 291.706 - 4.615x_1 + 0.102x_1^2 - 142.113(0) + 0.215x_1(0) + 0.058x_1^2(0)$$
$$\hat{y} = 291.706 - 4.615x_1 + 0.102x_1^2$$

**FIGURE 15.23B**

Minitab Composite Model for Ashley Investment Services

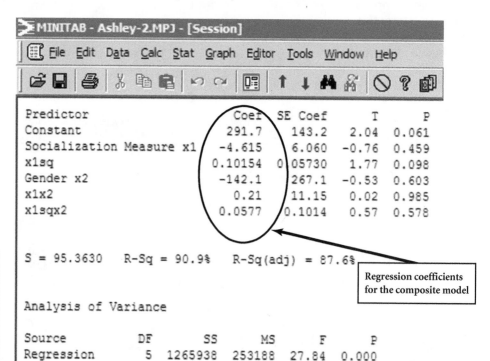

**Minitab Instructions:**
1. Continue from Figure 15.19b.
2. Choose **Stat > Regression > Regression**.
3. In **Response**, enter dependent (*y*) variable.
4. In **Predictors**, enter independent (*x*) variables.
5. Click **OK**.

For males, we substitute $x_2 = 1$, giving

$$\hat{y} = 291.706 - 4.615x_1 + 0.102x_1^2 - 142.113(1) + 0.215x_1(1) + 0.058x_1^2(1)$$
$$\hat{y} = 149.593 - 4.40x_1 + 0.160x_1^2$$

Note that these equations for male and female employees are the same as those we found earlier when we generated two separate regression models, one for each gender.

In this example we have looked at a case in which a dummy variable interacts with the relationship between another independent variable and the dependent variable. However, the interacting variable need not be a dummy variable. It can be any independent variable. Also, strictly speaking, interaction is not said to exist if the only effect of the interaction variable is to change the $y$ intercept of the equation relating another independent variable to the dependent variable. Therefore, when you examine a scatter plot to detect interaction, you are trying to determine if the relationships produced, when the interaction variable changes values, are parallel or not. If the relationships are parallel, that indicates that only the $y$ intercept is being affected by the change of the interacting variable and that interaction does not exist. Figure 15.24 demonstrates this concept graphically.

## The Partial-*F* Test

So far you have been given the procedures required to test the significance of either one or all of the coefficients in a regression model. For instance, in Example 15-3 a hypothesis test was used to determine that a second-order model involving the socialization measure fit the sample data better than the linear model. Testing $H_0: \beta_2 = 0$ was the mechanism used to establish this. We could have determined whether both the linear and quadratic components were useful in predicting the burnout index level by testing the hypothesis $H_0: \beta_1 = \beta_2 = 0$. However, more complex models occur. The interaction model involving Ashley Investment Services containing five predictor variables was

$$y_i = \beta_0 + \beta_1 x_{1i} + \beta_2 x_{1i}^2 + \beta_3 x_{2i} + \beta_4 x_{1i} x_{2i} + \beta_5 x_{1i}^2 x_{2i} + \varepsilon$$

**FIGURE 15.24** | Graphical Evidence of Interaction

(a) First-order polynomial without interaction

(b) First-order polynomial with interaction

(c) Second-order polynomial without interaction

(d) Second-order polynomial with interaction

Two of these predictor variables (i.e., $x_{1i}x_{2i}$ and $x_{1i}^2 x_{2i}$) existing in the model would indicate interaction is evident in this regression model. If the two interaction variables were absent, the model would be

$$y_i = \beta_0 + \beta_1 x_{1i} + \beta_2 x_{1i}^2 + \beta_3 x_{2i} + \varepsilon$$

To determine whether there is statistical evidence of interaction, we must determine if the coefficients of the interaction terms are all equal to 0. If they are, there is no interaction. Otherwise, at least some interaction exists. For the Ashley Investment example, we test the hypotheses

$$H_0: \beta_4 = \beta_5 = 0$$
$$H_A: \text{At least one of the } \beta_i\text{s} \neq 0$$

Earlier in this chapter we introduced procedures for testing whether all of the coefficients of a model equaled 0. In that case, you use the analysis of variance $F$-test found on both Excel and Minitab output. However, to test whether there is significant interaction, we must test more than one but fewer than all the regression coefficients. The method for doing this is the *partial-F test*. This test relies on the fact that if given a choice between two models, one model is a better fit if its sum of squares of error (*SSE*) is significantly smaller than for the other model. Therefore, to determine if interaction exists in our model, we must obtain the *SSE* for the model with the interaction terms and for the model without the interaction terms. The model without the interaction terms is called the *reduced model*. The model containing the interaction terms is called the *complete model*. We will denote the respective sum of squares as $SSE_R$ and $SSE_C$.

It is important to note that the procedure is appropriate to test any subset greater than one but less than all of the model's coefficients. We use the interaction terms in this example just as one such procedure. There are many models not containing interaction terms in which the partial-F test is applicable.

The test is based on the concept that the *SSE* will be significantly reduced if not all of the regression coefficients being tested equal zero. Of course if the *SSE* is significantly reduced, then $SSE_R - SSE_C$ must be significantly different from zero. To determine if this difference is significantly different from zero we use the partial-F test statistic given by Equation 15.12.

---

**Partial-F Test Statistic**

$$F = \frac{(SSE_R - SSE_C)/(c-r)}{MSE_C}$$

(15.12)

where:

$MSE_C$ = Mean square error for the complete model
  = $SSE_C / (n - c - 1)$
$r$ = The number of coefficients in the reduced model
$c$ = The number of coefficients in the complete model
$n$ = Sample size

---

The numerator of this test statistic is basically the average *SSE* per degree of freedom reduced by including the coefficients being tested in the model. This is compared to the average *SSE* per degree of freedom for the complete model. If these averages are significantly different, then the null hypothesis is rejected. This test statistic has an $F$-distribution whose numerator degrees of freedom equals the number of parameters being tested $(c - r)$ and whose denominator degrees of freedom equals the degrees of freedom for the complete model $(n - c - 1)$.

We are now prepared to determine if the director's data indicate a significant interaction between gender and the relationship between the Socialization Measure and the Burnout Index. In order to conduct the test of hypothesis, the director produced regression equations

**FIGURE 15.25A** | Sum of Squares for the Complete Model

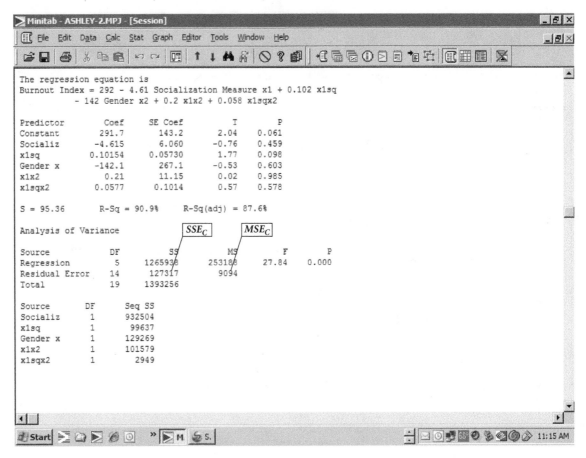

for both models (Figures 15.25a and 15.25b). He obtained the $SSE_C$, $MSE_C$ from Figure 15.25a, and $SSE_R$ from Figure 15.25c. He was then able to conduct the hypothesis test to determine if there was any interaction. Figure 15.25c displays this test.

Since the null hypothesis was rejected we can conclude that interaction does exist in this model. Apparently, gender of the employee does affect the relationship between the Burnout Index and the Socialization Measure. The relationship between the Burnout Index and the Socialization Measure is different within men and women.

You must be very careful with interpretations of regression coefficients when interaction exists. Notice that the equation that contains interaction terms is given by

$$\hat{y}_i = 292 - 4.61x_{1i} + 0.102x_{1i}^2 - 142x_{2i} + 0.2x_{1i}x_{2i} + 0.058x_{1i}^2x_{2i}$$

When interpreting the coefficient $b_1$, you may be tempted to say that the Burnout Index will decrease by an average of 4.61 units for every unit the Socialization Measure $(x_{1i})$ increases, *holding all other predictor variables constant*. However, this is not true, there are three other components of this regression equation that contain $x_{1i}$. When $x_{1i}$ increases by one unit $x_{1i}^2$ will also increase. In addition, the interaction terms also contain $x_{1i}$, and therefore, those terms will change as well. This being the case, every time the variable $x_2$ changes, the rate of change of the interaction terms are also affected. Perhaps you will see this more clearly if we rewrite the equation as

$$\hat{y}_i = (292 - 142x_{2i}) + (0.2x_{2i} - 4.61)x_{1i} + (0.102 + 0.058x_{2i})\,x_{1i}^2$$

In this form you can see that the coefficients of $x_{1i}$ and $x_{1i}^2$ change whenever $x_2$ changes. Thus, the interpretation of any of these components depends on the value $x_2$, as well as $x_{1i}$. Whenever interaction or higher order components are present you should be very careful in your attempts to interpret the results of your regression analysis.

**FIGURE 15.25B** | Sum of Squares for the Reduced Model

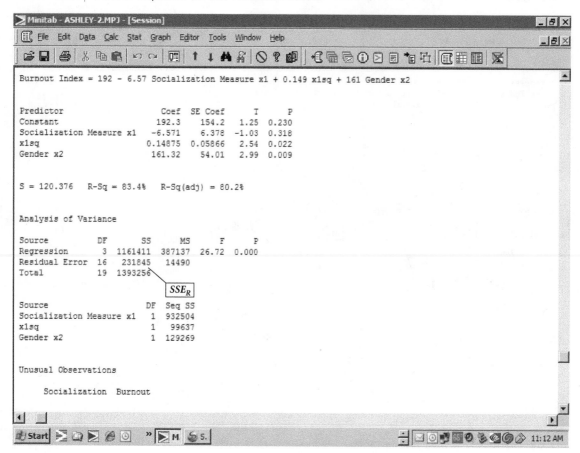

**FIGURE 15.25C**

Partial-$F$ Hypothesis Test for Interaction

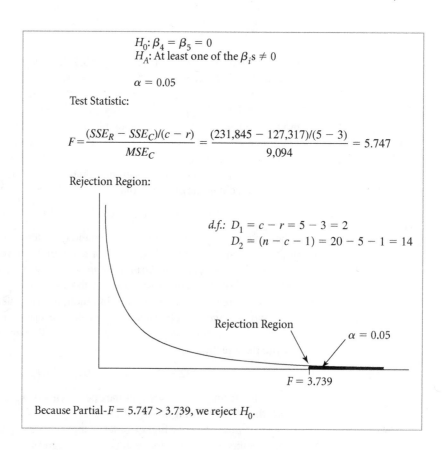

$H_0: \beta_4 = \beta_5 = 0$
$H_A:$ At least one of the $\beta_i$s $\neq 0$

$\alpha = 0.05$

Test Statistic:

$$F = \frac{(SSE_R - SSE_C)/(c - r)}{MSE_C} = \frac{(231{,}845 - 127{,}317)/(5 - 3)}{9{,}094} = 5.747$$

Rejection Region:

$d.f.:\ D_1 = c - r = 5 - 3 = 2$
$\qquad D_2 = (n - c - 1) = 20 - 5 - 1 = 14$

Rejection Region

$\alpha = 0.05$

$F = 3.739$

Because Partial-$F = 5.747 > 3.739$, we reject $H_0$.

MyStatLab

# 15-3: Exercises

## Skill Development

**15-24.** Consider the following values for the dependent and independent variables:

| x | y | x | y |
|---|---|---|---|
| 5 | 10 | 50 | 44 |
| 15 | 15 | 60 | 79 |
| 40 | 25 | 80 | 112 |

a. Develop a scatter plot of the data. Does the plot suggest a linear or nonlinear relationship between the dependent and independent variables?

b. Develop an estimated linear regression equation for the data. Is the relationship significant? Test at an $\alpha = 0.05$ level.

c. Develop a regression equation of the form $\hat{y} = b_0 + b_1x + b_2x^2$. Does this equation provide a better fit to the data than that found in part b?

**15-25.** Consider the following values for the dependent and independent variables:

| x | y | x | y |
|---|---|---|---|
| 6 | 5 | 18 | 30 |
| 9 | 20 | 22 | 33 |
| 14 | 28 | 27 | 35 |

a. Develop a scatter plot of the data. Does the plot suggest a linear or nonlinear relationship between the dependent and independent variables?

b. Develop an estimated linear regression equation for the data. Is the relationship significant? Test at an $\alpha = 0.05$ level.

c. Develop a regression equation of the form $\hat{y} = b_0 + b_1 \ln(x)$. Does this equation provide a better fit to the data than that found in part b?

**15-26.** Examine the following data:

| x | 2 | 8 | 9 | 12 | 15 | 22 | 21 | 25 | 37 | 39 |
|---|---|---|---|----|----|----|----|----|----|----|
| y | 4 | 75 | 175 | 415 | 620 | 7,830 | 7,551 | 7,850 | 11,112 | 11,617 |

a. Construct a scatter plot of the data. Determine the order of the polynomial that is represented by the data.

b. Obtain an estimate of the model identified in part a.

c. Conduct a test of hypothesis to determine if a third-order, as opposed to a second-order, polynomial is a better representation of the relationship between y and x. Use a significance level of 0.05 and the p-value approach.

**15-27.** Examine the following two sets of data:

| When $x_2 = 1$ | | When $x_2 = 2$ | |
|----------------|-----|----------------|-----|
| $x_1$ | y | $x_1$ | y |
| 1 | 2 | 2 | 3 |
| 4 | 15 | 3 | 9 |
| 5 | 23 | 6 | 5 |
| 7 | 52 | 7 | 10 |
| 8 | 60 | 9 | 48 |
| 12 | 154 | 10 | 50 |
| 11 | 122 | 14 | 87 |
| 14 | 200 | 13 | 51 |
| 19 | 381 | 16 | 63 |
| 20 | 392 | 21 | 202 |

a. Produce a distinguishable scatter plot for each of the data sets on the same graph. Does it appear that there is interaction between $x_2$ and the relationship between y and $x_1$? Support your assertions.

b. Consider the following model to represent the relationship among y, $x_1$, and $x_2$:

$$y_i = \beta_0 + \beta_1 x_1 + \beta_2 x_1^2 + \beta_3 x_1 x_2 + \beta_4 x_1^2 x_2 + \varepsilon$$

Produce the estimated regression equation for this model.

c. Conduct a test of hypothesis for each interaction term. Use a significance level of 0.05 and the p-value approach.

d. Based on the two hypothesis tests in part c, does it appear that there is interaction between $x_2$ and the relationship between y and $x_1$? Support your assertions.

**15-28.** Consider the following data:

| x | 1 | 4 | 5 | 7 | 8 | 12 | 11 | 14 | 19 | 20 |
|---|---|---|---|---|---|----|----|----|----|----|
| y | 1 | 54 | 125 | 324 | 512 | 5,530 | 5,331 | 5,740 | 7,058 | 7,945 |

a. Construct a scatter plot of the data. Determine the order of the polynomial that is represented by this data.

b. Obtain an estimate of the model identified in part a.

c. Conduct a test of hypothesis to determine if a third-order, as opposed to a first-order, polynomial is a better representation of the relationship between y and x. Use a significance level of 0.05 and the p-value approach.

**15-29.** A regression equation to be used to predict a dependent variable with four independent variables is developed from a sample of size 10. The resulting equation is

$$\hat{y} = 32.8 + 0.470x_1 + 0.554x_2 - 4.77x_3 + 0.929x_4$$

Two other equations are developed from the sample:

$$\hat{y} = 12.4 + 0.60x_1 + 1.60x_2$$

and

$$\hat{y} = 49.7 - 5.38x_3 + 1.35x_4$$

The respective sum of squares errors for the three equations are 201.72, 1,343, and 494.6.

a. Use the summary information to determine if the independent variables $x_3$ and $x_4$ belong in the complete regression model. Use a significance level of 0.05.

b. Repeat part a for the independent variables $x_1$ and $x_2$. Use the $p$-value approach and a significance level of 0.05.

## Computer Database **Exercises**

15-30. In a bit of good news for male students, American men have closed the gap with women on life span, according to a *USA Today* article. Male life expectancy attained a record 75.2 years, and women's reached 80.4. The National Center for Health Statistics provided the data given in the file entitled **Life**.

a. Produce a scatter plot depicting the relationship between the life expectancy of women and men.

b. Determine the order of the polynomial that is represented on the scatter plot obtained in part a. Produce the estimated regression equation that represents this relationship.

c. Determine if women's average life expectancy can be used in a second-order polynomial to predict the average life expectancy of men. Use a significance level of 0.05.

d. Use the estimated regression equation computed in part b to predict the average length of life of men when women's length of life equals 100. What does this tell you about the wisdom (or lack thereof) of extrapolation in regression models?

15-31. The Gilmore Accounting firm previously mentioned, in an effort to explain variation in client profitability, collected the data found in the file called **Gilmore**, where:

$y$ = Net profit earned from the client
$x_1$ = Number of hours spent working with the client
$x_2$ = Type of client:
    1, if manufacturing
    2, if service
    3, if governmental

Gilmore has asked if it needs the client type in addition to the number of hours spent working with the client to predict the net profit earned from the client. You are asked to provide this information.

a. Fit a model to the data that incorporates the number of hours spent working with the client and the type of client as independent variables. (*Hint*: Client type has three levels.)

b. Fit a second-order model to the data, again using dummy variables for client type. Does this model provide a better fit than that found in part a? Which model would you recommend be used?

15-32. McCullom's International Grains is constantly searching out areas in which to expand its market. Such markets present different challenges since tastes in the international market are often different from domestic tastes. India is one country on which McCullom's has recently focused. Paddy is a grain used widely in India, but its characteristics are unknown to McCullom's. Charles Walters has been assigned to take charge of the handling of this grain. He has researched its various characteristics. During his research he came across an article, "Determination of Biological Maturity and Effect of Harvesting and Drying Conditions on Milling Quality of Paddy" [*Journal of Agricultural Engineering Research* (1975), pp. 353–361], which examines the relationship between $y$, the yield (kg/ha) of paddy, as a function of $x$, and the number of days after flowering at which harvesting took place. The accompanying data appeared in the article and are in a file called **Paddy**.

| $y$ | $x$ | $y$ | $x$ |
|-----|-----|-----|-----|
| 2,508 | 16 | 3,823 | 32 |
| 2,518 | 18 | 3,646 | 34 |
| 3,304 | 20 | 3,708 | 36 |
| 3,423 | 22 | 3,333 | 38 |
| 3,057 | 24 | 3,517 | 40 |
| 3,190 | 26 | 3,241 | 42 |
| 3,500 | 28 | 3,103 | 44 |
| 3,883 | 30 | 2,776 | 46 |

a. Construct a scatter plot of the yield (kg/ha) of paddy as a function of the number of days after flowering at which harvesting took place. Display at least two models that would explain the relationship you see in the scatter plot.

b. Conduct tests of hypotheses to determine if the models you selected are useful in predicting the yield of paddy.

c. Consider the model that includes the second-order term $x^2$. Would a simple linear regression model be preferable to the model containing the second-order term? Conduct a hypothesis test using the $p$-value approach to arrive at your answer.

d. Which model should Charles use to predict the yield of paddy? Explain your answer.

15-33. The National Association of Realtors Existing-Home Sales Series provides a measurement of the residential real estate market. One of the measurements it produces is the Housing Affordability Index (HAI). It is a measure of the financial ability of U.S. families to buy a house: 100 means that families earning the national median income have just the amount of money needed to qualify for a mortgage on a median-priced home; higher than 100 means they have more than enough, and lower than 100 means they have less than enough. The file entitled **Index** contains the HAI and associated variables.

a. Construct a scatter plot relating the HAI to the median family income.
b. Determine the order of the polynomial that is suggested by the scatter plot produced in part a. Obtain the estimated regression equation of the polynomial selected.
c. Determine if monthly principle and interest interacts with the relationship between the HAI and the median family income indicated in part b. (*Hint*: You may need to conduct more than one hypothesis test.) Use a significance level of 0.05 and the *p*-value approach.

**15-34.** Badeaux Brothers Louisiana Treats ships packages of Louisiana coffee, cakes, and Cajun spices to individual customers around the United States. The cost to ship these products depends primarily on the weight of the package being shipped. Badeaux charges the customers for shipping and then ships the product itself. As a part of a study of whether it is economically feasible to continue to ship products itself, Badeaux sampled 20 recent shipments to determine what, if any, relationship exists between shipping costs and package weight. These data are in the file called **Badeaux**.

a. Develop a scatter plot of the data with the dependent variable, cost, on the vertical axis and the independent variable, weight, on the horizontal axis. Does there appear to be a relationship between the two variables? Is the relationship linear?
b. Compute the sample correlation coefficient between the two variables. Conduct a test, using a significance level of 0.05, to determine whether the population correlation coefficient is significantly different from zero.
c. Badeaux Brothers has been using a simple linear regression equation to predict the cost of shipping various items. Would you recommend it use a second-order polynomial model instead? Is the second-order polynomial model a significant improvement on the simple linear regression equation?
d. Badeaux Brothers has made a decision to stop shipping products if the shipping charges exceed $100. The company has asked you to determine the maximum weight for future shipments. Do this for both the first- and second-order models you have developed.

**15-35.** The National Association of Theatre Owners is the largest exhibition trade organization in the world, representing more than 26,000 movie screens in all 50 states and in more than 20 countries worldwide. Its membership includes the largest cinema chains and hundreds of independent theater owners. It publishes statistics concerning the movie sector of the economy. The file entitled **Flicks** contains data on total U.S. box

office grosses ($billion), total number of admissions (billion), average U.S. ticket price ($), and number of movie screens. One concern is the effect the increasing ticket prices have on the number of individuals who go to the theaters to view movies.

a. Construct a scatter plot depicting the relationship between the total number of admissions and the U.S. ticket price.
b. Determine the order of the polynomial that is suggested by the scatter plot produced in part a. Obtain the estimated regression equation of the polynomial selected.
c. Examine the *p*-value associated with the *F*-test for the polynomial you have selected in part a. Relate these results to those of the *t*-tests for the individual parameters and the adjusted coefficient of determination. To what is this attributed?
d. Conduct *t*-tests to remove higher order components until no components can be removed.

**15-36.** The Energy Information Administration (EIA), created by Congress in 1977, is a statistical agency of the U.S. Department of Energy. It provides data, forecasts, and analyses to promote sound policymaking and public understanding regarding energy and its interaction with the economy and the environment. One of the most important areas of analysis is petroleum. The file entitled **Crude** contains data for the period 1991–2006 concerning the price, supply, and demand for fuel. One concern has been the increase in imported oil into the United States.

a. Examine the relationship between price of gasoline and the annual amount of imported crude oil. Construct a scatter plot depicting this relationship.
b. Determine the order of the polynomial that would fit the data displayed in part a. Express "Imports" in millions of gallons, i.e., 3,146,454/1,000,000 = 3.146454. Produce an estimate of this polynomial.
c. Is a linear or quadratic model more appropriate for predicting the price of gasoline using the annual quantity of imported oil? Conduct the appropriate hypothesis test to substantiate your answer.

**15-37.** The National Association of Realtors Existing-Home Sales Series provides a measurement of the residential real estate market. One of the measurements it produces is the Housing Affordability Index (HAI). It is a measure of the financial ability of U.S. families to buy a house. A value of 100 means that families earning the national median income have just the amount of money needed to qualify for a mortgage on a median-priced home; higher than 100 means they have more than enough and lower than 100 means they have less than enough. The file entitled **INDEX** contains the HAI and associated variables.

a. Construct a second order of the polynomial relating the HAI to the median family income.
b. Conduct a test of hypothesis to determine if this polynomial is useful in predicting the HAI. Use a *p*-value approach and a significance level of 0.01.

c. Determine if monthly principle and interest interacts with the relationship between the HAI and the median family income indicated in part b. Use a significance level of 0.01. *Hint:* You must produce another regression equation with the interaction terms inserted. You must then use the appropriate test to determine if the interaction terms belong in this latter model.

**15.38.** An investment analyst collected data of 20 randomly chosen companies. The data consisted of the 52-week-high stock prices, PE ratio, and the market value of the company. These data are in the file entitled **INVESTMENT**. The analyst wishes to produce a

regression equation to predict the market value using the 52-week-high stock price and the PE ratio of the company. He creates a complete second-degree polynomial.

a. Construct an estimate of the regression equation using the indicated variables.
b. Determine if any of the quadratic terms are useful in predicting the average market value. Use a *p*-value approach with a significance level of 0.10.
c. Determine if any of the PE ratio terms are useful in predicting the average market value. Use a test statistic approach with a significance level of 0.05.

**Chapter Outcome 8.** → ## 15.4  Stepwise Regression

One option in regression analysis is to bring all possible independent variables into the model in one step. This is what we have done in the previous sections. We use the term *full regression* to describe this approach. Another method for developing a regression model is called *stepwise regression*. Stepwise regression, as the name implies, develops the least squares regression equation in steps, either through *forward selection, backward elimination,* or *standard stepwise* regression.

### Forward Selection

The forward selection procedure begins (Step 1) by selecting a single independent variable from all those available. The independent variable selected at Step 1 is the variable that is most highly correlated with the dependent variable. A *t*-test is used to determine if this variable explains a significant amount of the variation in the dependent variable. At Step 1, if the variable does explain a significant amount of the dependent variable's variation, it is selected to be part of the final model used to predict the dependent variable. If it does not, the process is terminated. If no variables are found to be significant, the researcher will have to search for different independent variables than the ones already tested.

In the next step (Step 2), a second independent variable is selected based on its ability to explain the remaining unexplained variation in the dependent variable. The independent variable selected in the second, and each subsequent, step is the variable with the highest **coefficient of partial determination**.

**Coefficient of Partial Determination**

The measure of the marginal contribution of each independent variable, given that other independent variables are in the model.

Recall that the coefficient of determination ($R^2$) measures the proportion of variation explained by all of the independent variables in the model. Thus, after the first variable (say, $x_1$) is selected, $R^2$ will indicate the percentage of variation explained by this variable. The forward selection routine will then compute all possible two-variable regression models, with $x_1$ included, and determine the $R^2$ for each model. The coefficient of partial determination at Step 2 is the proportion of the as yet unexplained variation (after $x_1$ is in the model) that is explained by the additional variable. The independent variable that adds the most to $R^2$, given the variable(s) already in the model, is the one selected. Then, a *t*-test is conducted to determine if the newly added variable is significant. This process continues until either all independent variables have been entered or the remaining independent variables do not add appreciably to $R^2$. For the forward selection procedure, the model begins with no variables. Variables are entered one at a time, and after a variable is entered, it cannot be removed.

# Backward Elimination

Backward elimination is just the reverse of the forward selection procedure. In the backward elimination procedure, all variables are forced into the model to begin the process. Variables are removed one at a time until no more insignificant variables are found. Once a variable has been removed from the model, it cannot be re-entered.

---

| **EXAMPLE 15-3** | **APPLYING FORWARD SELECTION STEPWISE REGRESSION ANALYSIS** |
|---|---|

---

**B. T. Longmont Company**  The B. T. Longmont Company operates a large retail department store in Macon, Georgia. Like other department stores, Longmont has incurred heavy losses due to shoplifting and employee pilferage. The store's security manager wants to develop a regression model to explain the monthly dollar loss. The following steps can be used when developing a multiple regression model using stepwise regression:

**Step 1  Specify the model by determining the dependent variable and potential independent variables.**

The dependent variable ($y$) is the monthly dollar losses due to shoplifting and pilferage. The security manager has identified the following potential independent variables:

$x_1$ = Average monthly temperature (degrees Fahrenheit)
$x_2$ = Number of sales transactions
$x_3$ = Dummy variable for holiday month (1 if holiday during month, 0 if not)
$x_4$ = Number of persons on the store's monthly payroll

The data are contained in the file **Longmont**.

**Step 2  Formulate the regression model.**

The correlation matrix for the data is presented in Figure 15.26. The forward selection procedure will select the independent variable most highly correlated with the dependent variable. By examining the bottom row in the correlation matrix in Figure 15.26, you can see the variable $x_2$, number of sales transactions, is most highly correlated ($r = 0.6307$) with dollars lost. Once this variable is entered into the model, the remaining independent variables will be entered based on their ability to explain the remaining variation in the dependent variable.

**FIGURE 15.26**

Excel 2007 Correlation Matrix Output for the B.T. Longmont Company

| | A | B | C | D | E | F |
|---|---|---|---|---|---|---|
| 1 | | Average Temperature | Number of Sales Transactions | Holiday | Employees | Shoplifting Loss |
| 2 | Average Temperature | 1 | | | | |
| 3 | Number of Sales Transactions | -0.0241 | 1 | | | |
| 4 | Holiday | -0.1432 | 0.0626 | 1 | | |
| 5 | Employees | -0.0821 | 0.9185 | -0.1966 | 1 | |
| 6 | Shoplifting Loss | 0.2858 | 0.6307 | 0.1361 | 0.4132 | 1 |

**Excel 2007 Instructions:**
1. Open file: Longmont.xls.
2. Select **Data tab**.
3. Select **Data Analysis > Correlation**.
4. Specify data range (include labels).
5. Click **Labels**.
6. Specify output location.
7. Click **OK**.

**FIGURE 15.27A**

Excel 2007 (PHStat) Forward Selection Results for the B.T. Longmont Company—Step 1

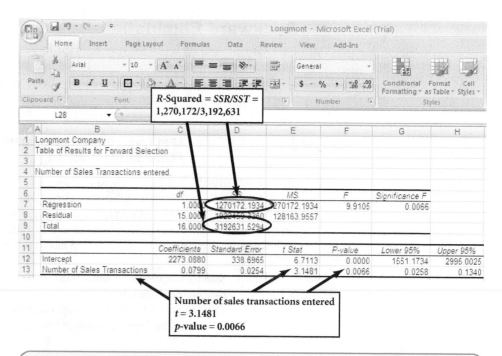

**Excel 2007 (PHStat) Instructions:**

1. Open file: Longmont.xls.
2. Select **Add-Ins**.
3. Select **PHStat**.
4. Select **Regression > Stepwise Regression**.
5. Define data range for *y* variable and data range for *x* variables.
6. Check *p*-value criteria.
7. Select **Forward Selection**.
8. Click **OK**.

Figure 15.27a shows the PHStat stepwise regression output, and Figure 15.27b shows the Minitab output. At Step 1 of the process, variable $x_2$, number of monthly sales transactions, enters the model.

**Step 3** **Perform diagnostic checks on the model.**

Although PHStat does not provide $R^2$ or the standard error of the estimate directly, they can be computed from the output in the ANOVA section of the printout. Recall from Chapter 14 that $R^2$ is computed as

$$R^2 = \frac{SSR}{SST} = \frac{1,270,172.193}{3,192,631.529} = 0.398$$

This single independent variable explains 39.8% ($R^2 = 0.398$) of the variation in the dependent variable. The standard error of the estimate is the square root of the mean square residual:

$$s_\varepsilon = \sqrt{MSE} = \sqrt{MS \text{ residual}} = \sqrt{128,163.96} = 358$$

Now at Step 1, we test the following:

$$H_0: \beta_2 = 0 \text{ (slope for variable } x_2 = 0)$$
$$H_A: \beta_2 \neq 0$$
$$\alpha = 0.05$$

As shown in Figure 15.27a, the calculated *t*-value is 3.1481. We compare this to the critical value from the *t*-distribution for $\alpha/2 = (0.05/2) = 0.025$ and degrees of freedom equal to

$$n - k - 1 = 17 - 1 - 1 = 15$$

**FIGURE 15.27B**

Minitab Forward Selection
Results for the B.T. Longmont
Company—Step 1

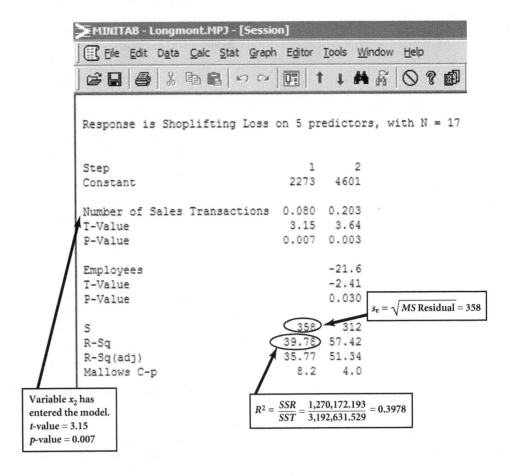

Minitab Instructions:
1. Open file: Longmont.MTW.
2. Choose **Stat > Regression > Stepwise**.
3. In **Response**, enter dependent variable (*y*).
4. In **Predictors**, enter independent variable (*x*).
5. Select **Methods**.
6. Select **Forward selection**, enter $\alpha$ in **Alpha to enter** and $F$ in **F to enter**.
7. Click **OK**.

This critical value is

$$t_{0.025} = 2.1315$$

Because

$$t = 3.1481 > 2.1315$$

we reject the null hypothesis and conclude that the regression slope coefficient for the variable, number of sales transactions, is not zero. Note also, because the

$$p\text{-value} = 0.0066 < \alpha = 0.05$$

we would reject the null hypothesis.[9]

---

[9]Some authors use an *F*-distribution to perform these tests. This is possible since squaring a random variable that has a *t*-distribution produces a random variable that has an *F*-distribution with one degree of freedom in the numerator and the same number of degrees as the *t*-distribution in the denominator.

**Step 4**    **Continue to formulate and diagnose the model by adding other independent variables.**

The next variable to be selected will be the one that can do the most to increase $R^2$. If you were doing this manually, you would try each variable to see which one yields the highest $R^2$, given that the transactions variable is already in the model. Both the PHStat add-in software and Minitab do this automatically. As shown in Figure 15.27b and Figure 15.28, the variable selected in Step 2 of the process is $x_4$, number of employees. Using the ANOVA section, we can determine $R^2$ and $s_\varepsilon$ as before.

$$R^2 = \frac{SSR}{SST} = \frac{1,833,270.524}{3,192,631.529} = 0.5742 \quad \text{and}$$

$$s_\varepsilon = \sqrt{MS \ \text{residual}} = \sqrt{97,097.22} = 311.6$$

The model now explains 57.42% of the variation in the dependent variable. The $t$-values for both slope coefficients exceed $t = 2.145$ (the critical value from the $t$-distribution table with a one-tailed area equal to 0.025 and $17 - 2 - 1 = 14$ degrees of freedom), so we conclude that both variables are significant in explaining the variation in the dependent variable, shoplifting loss.

The forward selection routine continues to enter variables as long as each additional variable explains a significant amount of the remaining variation in the dependent variable. Note that PHStat allows you to set the significance level in terms of a $p$-value or in terms of the $t$ statistic. Then, as long as the calculated $p$-value for an incoming variable is less than your limit, the variable is allowed to enter the model. Likewise, if the calculated $t$-statistic exceeds your $t$ limit, the variable is allowed to enter.

In this example, with the $p$-value limit set at 0.05, neither of the two remaining independent variables would explain a significant amount of the remaining variation in the dependent variable. The procedure is, therefore, terminated. The resulting regression equation provided by forward selection is

$$\hat{y} = 4600.8 + 0.203x_2 - 21.57x_4$$

**FIGURE 15.28**

PHStat Forward Selection Results for the B.T. Longmont Company—Step 2

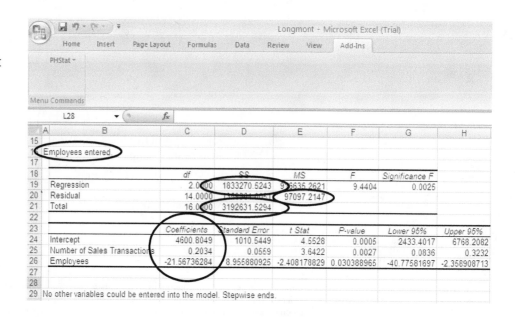

Note that the dummy variables for holiday and temperature did not enter the model. This implies that, given the other variables are already included, knowing whether the month in question has a holiday or knowing its average temperature does not add significantly to the model's ability to explain the variation in the dependent variable.

The B.T. Longmont Company can now use this regression model to explain variation in shoplifting and pilferage losses based on knowing the number of sales transactions and the number of employees.

**>>END EXAMPLE**

**TRY PROBLEM** 15-40 (pg. 687)

## Standard Stepwise Regression

The standard stepwise procedure (sometimes referred to as *forward stepwise regression*—not to be confused with forward selection) combines attributes of both backward elimination and forward selection. The standard stepwise method serves one more important function. If two or more independent variables are correlated, a variable selected in an early step may become insignificant when other variables are added at later steps. The standard stepwise procedure will drop this insignificant variable from the model. Standard stepwise regression also offers a means of observing multicollinearity problems, because we can see how the regression model changes as each new variable is added to it.

The standard stepwise procedure is widely used in decision-making applications and is generally recognized as a useful regression method. However, care should be exercised when using this procedure because it is easy to rely too heavily on the automatic selection process. Remember, the order of variable selection is conditional, based on the variables already in the model. There is no guarantee that stepwise regression will lead you to the best set of independent variables from those available. Decision makers still must use common sense in applying regression analysis to make sure they have usable regression models.

## Best Subsets Regression

Another method for developing multiple regression models is called the *best subsets* method. As the name implies, the best subsets method works by selecting subsets from the chosen possible independent variables to form models. The user can then select the "best" model based on such measures as $R$-squared or the standard error of the estimate. Both Minitab and PHStat contain procedures for performing best subsets regression.

**EXAMPLE 15-4**    **APPLYING BEST SUBSETS REGRESSION**

**Winston Investment Advisors** Charles L. Winston, founder and CEO at Winston Investment Advisors in Burbank, California, is interested in developing a regression model to explain the variation in dividends paid per share by U.S. companies. Such a model would be useful in advising his clients. The following steps show how to develop such a model using the best subsets regression approach:

Step 1   **Specify the model.**
Some publicly traded companies pay higher dividends than others. The CEO is interested in developing a multiple regression model to explain the variation in dividends per share paid to shareholders. The dependent variable will be dividends per share. The CEO met with other analysts in his firm to identify

potential independent variables for which data would be readily available. The following list of potential independent variables was selected:

$x_1$ = Return on equity (net income/equity)

$x_2$ = Earnings per share

$x_3$ = Current assets in millions of dollars

$x_4$ = Year-ending stock price

$x_5$ = Current ratio (current assets/current liabilities)

A random sample of 35 publicly traded U.S. companies was selected. For each company in the sample, the analysis obtained data on the dividend per share paid last year and the year-ending data on the five independent variables. These data are contained in the data file **Company Financials**.

**Step 2** **Formulate the regression model.**

The CEO is interested in developing the "best" regression model for explaining the variation in the dependent variable, dividends per share. The approach taken is to use best subsets, which requires that multiple regression models be developed, each containing a different mix of variables. The models tried will contain from one to five independent variables. The resulting models will be evaluated by comparing values for $R$-squared and the standard error of the estimate. High $R$-squares and low standard errors are desirable. Another statistic, identified as $C_p$, is sometimes used to evaluate regression models. This statistic measures the difference between the estimated model and the true population model. Values of $C_p$ close to $p = k + 1$ ($k$ is the number of independent variables in the model) are preferred.

Both the PHStat Excel add-ins and Minitab can be used to perform best subsets regression analysis. Figure 15.29 shows output from PHStat. Notice that all possible combinations of models with $k = 1$ to $k = 5$ independent variables are included. Several models appear to be good candidates based on $R$-squared, adjusted $R$-squared, standard error of the estimate, and $C_p$ values. These are as follows:

| Model | $C_p$ | $k + 1$ | $R$-square | Adj. $R$-square | Std. Error |
|---|---|---|---|---|---|
| $x_1 x_2 x_3 x_4$ | 4.0 | 5 | 0.628 | 0.579 | 0.496 |
| $x_1 x_2 x_3 x_4 x_5$ | 6.0 | 6 | 0.629 | 0.565 | 0.505 |
| $x_1 x_2 x_3 x_5$ | 5.0 | 5 | 0.615 | 0.564 | 0.505 |
| $x_2 x_3$ | 1.4 | 3 | 0.610 | 0.586 | 0.492 |
| $x_2 x_3 x_4$ | 2.5 | 4 | 0.622 | 0.585 | 0.493 |
| $x_2 x_3 x_4 x_5$ | 4.5 | 5 | 0.622 | 0.572 | 0.500 |
| $x_2 x_3 x_5$ | 3.4 | 4 | 0.610 | 0.573 | 0.500 |

There is little difference in these seven models in terms of the statistics shown. We can examine any of them in more detail by looking at further PHStat output. For instance, the model containing variables $x_1, x_2, x_3$, and $x_5$ is shown in Figure 15.30. Note that although this model is among the best with respect to $R$-squared, adjusted $R$-squared, standard error of the estimate, and $C_p$ value, two of the four variables ($x_1$ = ROE and $x_5$ = Current ratio) have statistically insignificant regression coefficients. Figure 15.31 shows the regression model with the two statistically significant variables remaining. The $R$-squared value is 0.61, the adjusted $R^2$ has increased, and the overall model is statistically significant.

>>END EXAMPLE

TRY PROBLEM 15-43 (pg. 687)

**FIGURE 15.29**

Best Subsets Regression
Output for Winston
Investment Advisors

| | A | B | C | D | E | F |
|---|---|---|---|---|---|---|
| 10 | Model | Cp | k+1 | R Square | Adj. R Square | Std. Error |
| 11 | X1 | 42.306 | 2 | 0.0616 | 0.0331 | 0.7519 |
| 12 | X2 | 20.662 | 2 | 0.3387 | 0.3186 | 0.6312 |
| 13 | X3 | 7.423 | 2 | 0.5081 | 0.4932 | 0.5444 |
| 14 | X4 | 20.684 | 2 | 0.3384 | 0.3183 | 0.6314 |
| 15 | X5 | 46.792 | 2 | 0.0042 | -0.0260 | 0.7746 |
| 16 | X1X2 | 20.853 | 3 | 0.3618 | 0.3219 | 0.6297 |
| 17 | X1X3 | 7.745 | 3 | 0.5296 | 0.5002 | 0.5406 |
| 18 | X1X4 | 22.657 | 3 | 0.3387 | 0.2974 | 0.6410 |
| 19 | X1X5 | 43.934 | 3 | 0.0663 | 0.0080 | 0.7616 |
| 20 | X2X3 | 1.449 | 3 | 0.6102 | 0.5858 | 0.4921 |
| 21 | X2X4 | 17.751 | 3 | 0.4015 | 0.3641 | 0.6098 |
| 22 | X2X5 | 22.434 | 3 | 0.3416 | 0.3004 | 0.6396 |
| 23 | X3X4 | 3.244 | 3 | 0.5872 | 0.5614 | 0.5064 |
| 24 | X3X5 | 9.419 | 3 | 0.5082 | 0.4774 | 0.5528 |
| 25 | X4X5 | 22.464 | 3 | 0.3412 | 0.3000 | 0.6398 |
| 26 | X1X2X3 | 3.054 | 4 | 0.6153 | 0.5780 | 0.4967 |
| 27 | X1X2X4 | 17.690 | 4 | 0.4279 | 0.3725 | 0.6057 |
| 28 | X1X2X5 | 22.670 | 4 | 0.3641 | 0.3026 | 0.6386 |
| 29 | X1X3X4 | 5.197 | 4 | 0.5878 | 0.5480 | 0.5141 |
| 30 | X1X3X5 | 9.735 | 4 | 0.5297 | 0.4842 | 0.5492 |
| 31 | X1X4X5 | 24.414 | 4 | 0.3418 | 0.2781 | 0.6497 |
| 32 | X2X3X4 | 2.543 | 4 | 0.6218 | 0.5852 | 0.4925 |
| 33 | X2X3X5 | 3.438 | 4 | 0.6104 | 0.5726 | 0.4999 |
| 34 | X2X4X5 | 19.741 | 4 | 0.4016 | 0.3437 | 0.6195 |
| 35 | X3X4X5 | 5.080 | 4 | 0.5893 | 0.5496 | 0.5132 |
| 36 | X1X2X3X4 | 4.028 | 5 | 0.6284 | 0.5789 | 0.4963 |
| 37 | X1X2X3X5 | 5.045 | 5 | 0.6154 | 0.5641 | 0.5049 |
| 38 | X1X2X4X5 | 19.661 | 5 | 0.4283 | 0.3521 | 0.6156 |
| 39 | X1X3X4X5 | 7.052 | 5 | 0.5897 | 0.5350 | 0.5215 |
| 40 | X2X3X4X5 | 4.525 | 5 | 0.6220 | 0.5716 | 0.5005 |
| 41 | X1X2X3X4X5 | 6.000 | 6 | 0.6288 | 0.5648 | 0.5045 |

**Excel 2007 (PHStat)**
**Instructions:**
1. Open file: Company Financials.xls.
2. Select **Add-Ins**.
3. Select **PHStat**.
4. Select **Regression > Best Subsets Regression**.
5. Define data range for *y* variable and data range for *x* variables.
6. Click **OK**.

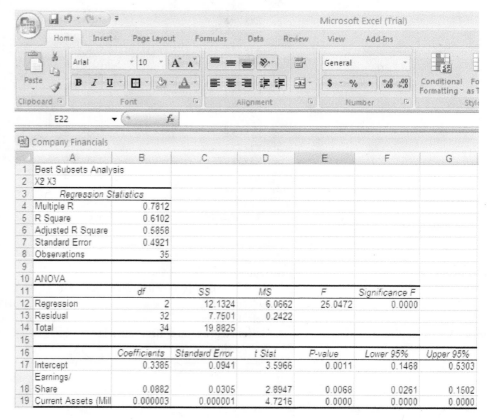

MyStatLab

# 15-4: Exercises

## Skill Development

**15-39.** Suppose you have four potential independent variables, $x_1$, $x_2$, $x_3$, and $x_4$, from which you want to develop a multiple regression model. Using stepwise regression, $x_2$ and $x_4$ entered the model.
  a. Why did only two variables enter the model? Discuss.
  b. Suppose a full regression with only variables $x_2$ and $x_4$ had been run. Would the resulting model be different from the stepwise model that included only these two variables? Discuss.
  c. Now, suppose a full regression model had been developed, with all four independent variables in the model. Which would have the higher $R^2$ value, the full regression model or the stepwise model? Discuss.

**15-40.** You are given the following set of data:

| y | $x_1$ | $x_2$ | $x_3$ | y | $x_1$ | $x_2$ | $x_3$ |
|----|----|-----|----|----|----|-----|----|
| 33 | 9  | 192 | 40 | 45 | 12 | 296 | 52 |
| 44 | 11 | 397 | 47 | 25 | 9  | 235 | 27 |
| 34 | 10 | 235 | 37 | 53 | 10 | 295 | 57 |
| 60 | 13 | 345 | 61 | 45 | 13 | 335 | 50 |
| 20 | 11 | 245 | 23 | 37 | 11 | 243 | 41 |
| 30 | 7  | 235 | 35 | 44 | 13 | 413 | 51 |

  a. Determine the appropriate correlation matrix and use it to predict which variable will enter in the first step of a stepwise regression model.
  b. Use standard stepwise regression to construct a model, entering all significant variables.
  c. Construct a full regression model. What are the differences in the model? Which model explains the most variation in the dependent variable?

**15-41.** You are given the following set of data:

| y | $x_1$ | $x_2$ | $x_3$ | y | $x_1$ | $x_2$ | $x_3$ |
|----|----|----|----|----|----|----|----|
| 45 | 40 | 41 | 39 | 45 | 42 | 39 | 37 |
| 41 | 31 | 41 | 35 | 43 | 37 | 52 | 41 |
| 43 | 45 | 49 | 39 | 34 | 40 | 47 | 40 |
| 38 | 43 | 41 | 41 | 49 | 35 | 44 | 44 |
| 50 | 42 | 42 | 51 | 45 | 39 | 40 | 45 |
| 39 | 48 | 40 | 42 | 40 | 43 | 30 | 42 |
| 50 | 44 | 44 | 41 | 43 | 53 | 34 | 34 |

  a. Determine the appropriate correlation matrix and use it to predict which variable will enter in the first step of a stepwise regression model.

  b. Use standard stepwise regression to construct a model, entering all significant variables.
  c. Construct a full regression model. What are the differences in the model? Which model explains the most variation in the dependent variable?

**15-42.** The following data represent a dependent variable and four independent variables:

| y | $x_1$ | $x_2$ | $x_3$ | $x_4$ | y | $x_1$ | $x_2$ | $x_3$ | $x_4$ |
|----|----|----|----|----|----|----|----|----|----|
| 61 | 37 | 13 | 10 | 21 | 69 | 35 | 19 | 9 | 23 |
| 37 | 25 | 7  | 11 | 32 | 24 | 23 | 14 | 7 | 31 |
| 22 | 23 | 6  | 7  | 18 | 68 | 35 | 17 | 3 | 33 |
| 48 | 12 | 8  | 8  | 30 | 65 | 37 | 11 | 17 | 19 |
| 66 | 34 | 15 | 2  | 33 | 45 | 30 | 9  | 24 | 31 |

  a. Use the standard stepwise regression to produce an estimate of a multiple regression model to predict y. Use 0.15 as the alpha to enter and to remove.
  b. Change the alpha to enter to 0.01. Repeat the standard stepwise procedure.
  c. Change the alpha to remove to 0.35, leaving alpha to enter to be 0.15. Repeat the standard stepwise procedure.
  d. Change the alpha to remove to 0.15, leaving alpha to enter to be 0.05. Repeat the standard stepwise procedure.
  e. Change the alpha to remove and to enter to 0.35. Repeat the standard stepwise procedure.
  f. Compare the estimated regression equations developed in parts a–e.

**15-43.** Consider the following set of data:

| y | $x_1$ | $x_2$ | $x_3$ | $x_4$ | y | $x_1$ | $x_2$ | $x_3$ | $x_4$ |
|----|----|----|----|----|----|----|----|----|----|
| 61 | 37 | 18 | 2 | 13 | 69 | 35 | 21 | 2 | 20 |
| 37 | 25 | 5  | 4 | 10 | 24 | 23 | 7  | 6 | 9  |
| 22 | 23 | 12 | 7 | 4  | 68 | 35 | 15 | 3 | 14 |
| 48 | 12 | 6  | 2 | 15 | 65 | 37 | 19 | 2 | 19 |
| 66 | 34 | 14 | 3 | 25 | 45 | 30 | 12 | 3 | 12 |

  a. Use standard stepwise regression to produce an estimate of a multiple regression model to predict y.
  b. Use forward selection stepwise regression to produce an estimate of a multiple regression model to predict y.

c. Use backwards elimination stepwise regression to produce an estimate of a multiple regression model to predict $y$.

d. Use best subsets regression to produce an estimate of a multiple regression model to predict $y$.

## Computer Database **Exercises**

**15-44.** The U.S. Energy Information Administration publishes summary statistics concerning the energy sector of the U.S. economy. The electric power industry continues to grow. Electricity generation and sales rose to record levels. The file entitled **Energy** presents the revenue from retail sales ($million) and the net generation by energy source for the period 1993–2004.

a. Produce the correlation matrix of all the variables. Predict the variables that will remain in the estimated regression equation if standard stepwise regression is used to predict the revenues from retail sales of energy.

b. Use standard stepwise regression to develop an estimate of a model that is to predict the revenue from retail sales of energy ($million).

c. Compare the results of parts a and b. Explain any difference between the two models.

**15-45.** The Western State Tourist Association gives out pamphlets, maps, and other tourist-related information to people who call a toll-free number and request the information. The association orders the packets of information from a document-printing company and likes to have enough available to meet the immediate need without having too many sitting around taking up space. The marketing manager decided to develop a multiple regression model to be used in predicting the number of calls that will be received in the coming week. A random sample of 12 weeks is selected, with the following variables:

$y$ = Number of calls

$x_1$ = Number of advertisements placed the previous week

$x_2$ = Number of calls received the previous week

$x_3$ = Number of airline tour bookings into Western cities for the current week

These data are in the data file called **Western States**.

a. Develop the multiple regression model for predicting the number of calls received, using backward elimination stepwise regression.

b. At the final step of the analysis, how many variables are in the model?

c. Discuss why the variables were removed from the model in the order shown by the stepwise regression.

**15-46.** Refer to Problem 15-45.

a. Develop the correlation matrix that includes all independent variables and the dependent variable. Predict the order that the variables will be selected into the model if forward selection stepwise regression is used.

b. Use forward selection stepwise regression to develop a model for predicting the number of calls that the company will receive. Write a report that describes what has taken place at each step of the regression process.

c. Compare the forward selection stepwise regression results in part b with the backward elimination results determined in Problem 15-45. Which model would you choose? Explain your answer.

**15-47.** An investment analyst collected data of 20 randomly chosen companies. The data consisted of the 52-week-high stock prices, PE ratios, and the market values of the companies. These data are in the file entitled **Investment**. The analyst wishes to produce a regression equation to predict the market value using the 52-week-high stock price and the PE ratio of the company. He creates a complete second-degree polynomial.

a. Produce two scatter plots: (1) market value versus stock price and (2) market value versus PE ratio. Do the scatter plots support the analyst's decision to produce a second-order polynomial? Support your assertion with statistical reasoning.

b. Use forward selection stepwise regression to eliminate any unneeded components from the analyst's model.

c. Does forward selection stepwise regression support the analyst's decision to produce a second-order polynomial? Support your assertion with statistical reasoning.

**15-48.** A variety of sources suggest that individuals assess their health, at least in part, by estimating their percentage of body fat. A widely accepted measure of body fat uses an underwater weighing technique. There are, however, more convenient methods using only a scale and a measuring tape. An article in the *Journal of Statistics Education* by Roger W. Johnson explored regression models to predict body fat. The file entitled **Bodyfat** lists a portion of the data presented in the cited article.

a. Use best subsets stepwise regression to establish the relationship between body fat and the variables in the specified file.

b. Predict the body fat of an individual whose age is 21, weight is 170 pounds, height is 70 inches, chest circumference is 100 centimeters, abdomen is 90 centimeters, hip is 105 centimeters, and thigh is 60 centimeters around.

**15-49.** The consumer price index (CPI) is a measure of the average change in prices over time in a fixed market basket of goods and services typically purchased by consumers. One of the items in this market basket that affects the CPI is the price of oil and its derivatives. The file entitled **Consumer** contains the price of the derivatives of oil and the CPI adjusted to 2005 levels.

a. Use backward elimination stepwise regression to determine which combination of the oil derivative prices drive the CPI. If you encounter difficulties in completing this task, explain what caused the difficulties.

b. Eliminate the source of the difficulties in part a by producing a correlation matrix to determine where the difficulty lies.

c. Delete one of the variables indicated in part b and complete the instructions in part a.

**END EXERCISES 15-4**

## 15.5 Determining the Aptness of the Model

In Section 15.1 we discussed the basic steps involved in building a multiple regression model. These are as follows:

1. Specify the model.
2. Build the model.
3. Perform diagnostic checks on the model.

The final step is the diagnostic step in which you examine the model to determine how well it performs. In Section 15.2, we discussed several statistics that you need to consider when performing the diagnostic step, including analyzing $R^2$, adjusted $R^2$, and the standard error of the estimate. In addition, we discussed the concept of multicollinearity and the impacts that can occur when multicollinearity is present. Section 15.3 introduced another diagnostic step that involves looking for potential curvilinear relationships between the independent variables and the dependent variable. We presented some basic data transformation techniques for dealing with curvilinear situations. However, a major part of the diagnostic process involves an analysis of how well the model fits the regression analysis assumptions.

The assumptions required to use multiple regression include the following:

**Assumptions**

1. Individual model errors, $\varepsilon$, are statistically independent of one another, and these values represent a random sample from the population of possible residuals at each level of $x$.
2. For a given value of $x$ there can exist many values of $y$, and therefore many possible values for $\varepsilon$. Further, the distribution of possible $\varepsilon$-values for any level of $x$ is normally distributed.
3. The distributions of possible $\varepsilon$-values have equal variances at each level of $x$.
4. The means of the dependent variable, $y$, for all specified values of $x$ can be connected with a line called the population regression model.

The degree to which a regression model satisfies these assumptions is called *aptness*.

### Analysis of Residuals

**Residual**

The difference between the actual value of the dependent variable and the value predicted by the regression model.

The **residual** is computed using Equation 15.13.

**Residual**

$$e_i = y_i - \hat{y}_i \tag{15.13}$$

A residual value can be computed for each observation in the data set. A great deal can be learned about the aptness of the regression model by analyzing the residuals. The principal means of residual analysis is a study of residual plots. The following problems can be inferred through graphical analysis of residuals:

1. The regression function is not linear.
2. The residuals do not have a constant variance.
3. The residuals are not independent.
4. The residual terms are not normally distributed.

We will address each of these in order. The regression options in both Minitab and Excel provide extensive residual analysis.

**Checking for Linearity** A plot of the residuals (on the vertical axis) against the independent variable (on the horizontal axis) is useful for detecting whether a linear function is the appropriate regression function. Figure 15.32 illustrates two different residual plots. Figure 15.32a shows residuals that systematically depart from 0. When $x$ is small the residuals are negative. When $x$ is in the midrange the residuals are positive, and for large $x$-values the residuals are negative again. This type of plot suggests that the relationship between $y$ and $x$ is nonlinear. Figure 15.32b shows a plot in which residuals do not show a systematic variation around 0, implying that the relationship between $x$ and $y$ is linear.

If a linear model is appropriate, we expect the residuals to band around 0 with no systematic pattern displayed. If the residual plot shows a systematic pattern, it may be possible to transform the independent variable (refer to Section 15.3) so that the revised model will produce residual plots that will not systematically vary from 0.

| BUSINESS APPLICATION | RESIDUAL ANALYSIS |

**FIRST CITY REAL ESTATE (CONTINUED)** We have been using First City Real Estate to introduce multiple regression tools throughout this chapter. Remember, the managers wish to develop a multiple regression model for predicting the sales prices of homes in their market. Suppose that the most current model (**First city-3**) incorporates a transformation of the lot size variable as log of lot size. The output for this model is shown in Figure 15.33. Notice the model now has a $R^2$ value of 96.9%.

There are currently four independent variables in the model: square feet, bedrooms, garage, and the log of lot size. Both Minitab and Excel provide procedures for automatically producing residual plots. Figure 15.34 shows the plots of the residuals against each

**Excel and Minitab Tutorial**

**FIGURE 15.32**

Residual Plots Showing Linear and Nonlinear Patterns

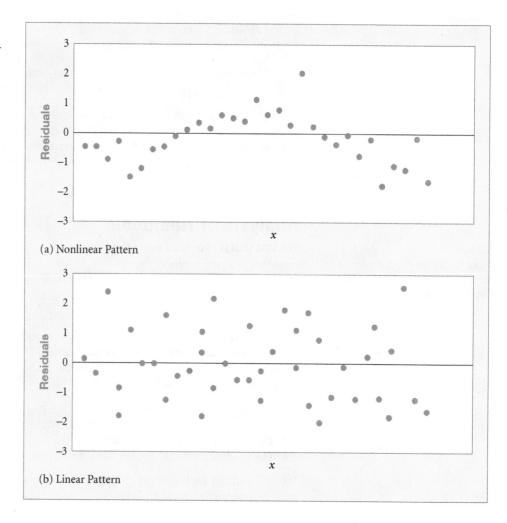

**FIGURE 15.33**

Minitab Output of First City
Real Estate Appraisal Model

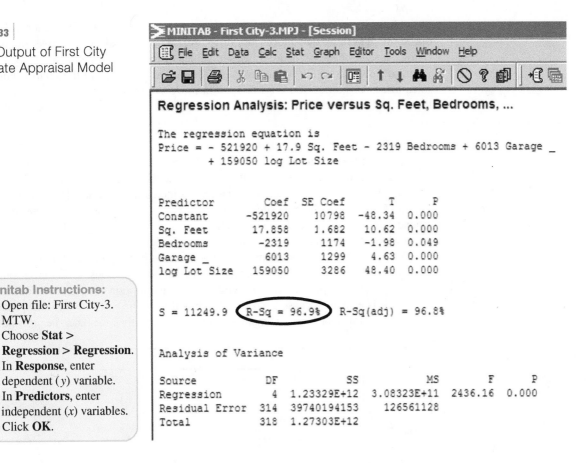

**Minitab Instructions:**
1. Open file: First City-3. MTW.
2. Choose **Stat > Regression > Regression**.
3. In **Response**, enter dependent (*y*) variable.
4. In **Predictors**, enter independent (*x*) variables.
5. Click **OK**.

**FIGURE 15.34** | First City Real Estate Residual Plots versus the Independent Variables

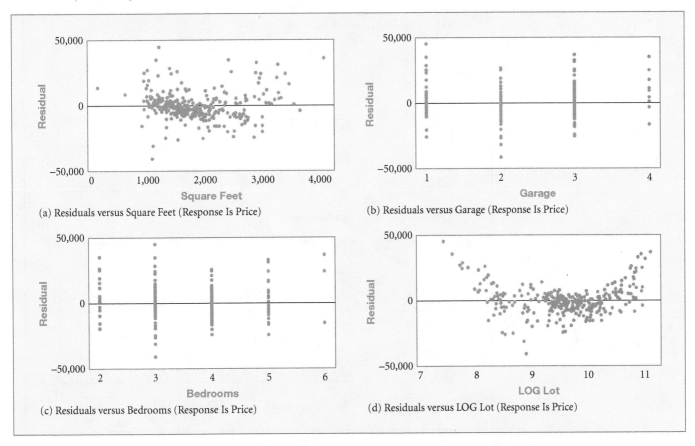

(a) Residuals versus Square Feet (Response Is Price)

(b) Residuals versus Garage (Response Is Price)

(c) Residuals versus Bedrooms (Response Is Price)

(d) Residuals versus LOG Lot (Response Is Price)

of the independent variables. The transformed variable, log lot size, has a residual pattern that shows a systematic pattern (Figure 15.34d). The residuals are positive for small values of log lot size, negative for intermediate values of log lot size, and positive again for large values of log lot size. This pattern suggests that the curvature of the relationship between sales prices of homes and lot size is even more pronounced than the logarithm implies. Potentially, a second- or third-degree polynomial in the lot size should be pursued.

**Do the Residuals Have Equal Variances at all Levels of Each $x$ Variable?**    Residual plots also can be used to determine whether the residuals have a constant variance. Consider Figure 15.35, in which the residuals are plotted against an independent variable. The plot in Figure 15.35a shows an example in which as $x$ increases the residuals become less variable. Figure 15.35b shows the opposite situation. When $x$ is small, the residuals are tightly packed around 0, but as $x$ increases the residuals become more variable. Figure 15.35c shows an example in which the residuals exhibit a constant variance around the zero mean.

When a multiple regression model has been developed, we can analyze the equal variance assumption by plotting the residuals against the fitted ($\hat{y}$) values. When the residual plot is cone-shaped, as in Figure 15.36, it suggests that the assumption of equal variance has been violated. This is evident because the residuals are wider on one end than the other. That indicates that the standard error of the estimate is larger on one end than the other, i.e., it is not constant.

**FIGURE 15.35**

Residual Plots Showing Constant and Nonconstant Variances

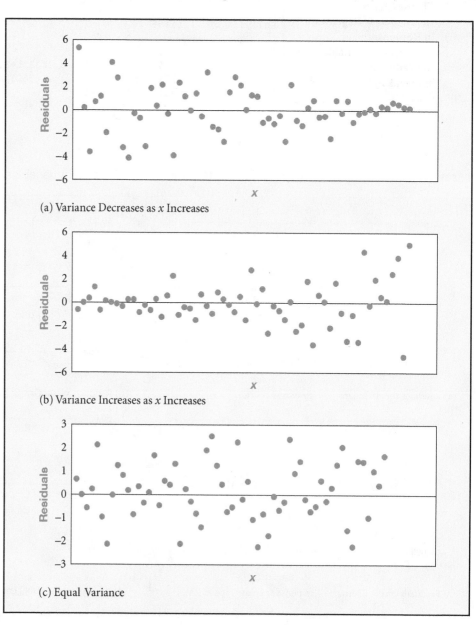

(a) Variance Decreases as $x$ Increases

(b) Variance Increases as $x$ Increases

(c) Equal Variance

**FIGURE 15.36**

Residual Plots against the
Fitted ($\hat{y}$) Values

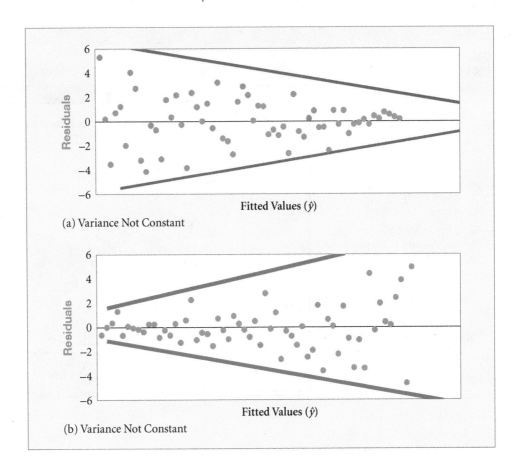

(a) Variance Not Constant

(b) Variance Not Constant

Figure 15.37 shows the residuals plotted against the $\hat{y}$-values for First City Real Estate's appraisal model. We have drawn a band around the residuals that shows that the variance of the residuals stays quite constant over the range of the fitted values.

**Are the Residuals Independent?** If the data used to develop the regression model are measured over time, a plot of the residuals against time is used to determine whether the residuals are correlated. Figure 15.38a shows an example in which the residual plot against time suggests independence. The residuals in Figure 15.38a appear to be randomly distributed around the mean of zero over time. However, in Figure 15.38b, the plot suggests that the residuals are not independent, because in the early time periods the residuals are negative and in later time periods the residuals are positive. This, or any other nonrandom pattern in the residuals over time, indicates that the assumption of independent residuals has been violated. Generally, this means some variable associated with the passage of time has been omitted from the model. Often, time is used as a surrogate for other time-related variables in a regression model. Chapter 16 will discuss time-series data analysis and forecasting techniques in more detail and will address the issue of incorporating the time variable into the model. In Chapter 16, we introduce a procedure called the Durbin-Watson test to determine whether residuals are correlated over time.

**Checking for Normally Distributed Error Terms** The need for normally distributed model errors occurs when we want to test a hypothesis about the regression model. Small departures from normality do not cause serious problems. However, if the model errors depart dramatically from a normal distribution, there is cause for concern. Examining the sample residuals will allow us to detect such dramatic departures. One method for graphically analyzing the residuals is to form a frequency histogram of the residuals to determine whether the general shape is normal. The chi-square goodness-of-fit test presented in Chapter 13 can be used to test whether the residuals fit a normal distribution.

**FIGURE 15.37**

Minitab Plot of Residuals versus Fitted Values for First City Real Estate

**Minitab Instructions:**
1. Open file: First City-3. MTW.
2. Choose **Stat > Regression > Regression**.
3. In **Response**, enter dependent (y) variable.
4. In **Predictors**, enter independent (x) variables.
5. Choose **Graphs**.
6. Under **Residual Plots**, select **Residuals versus fits**.
7. Click **OK. OK.**

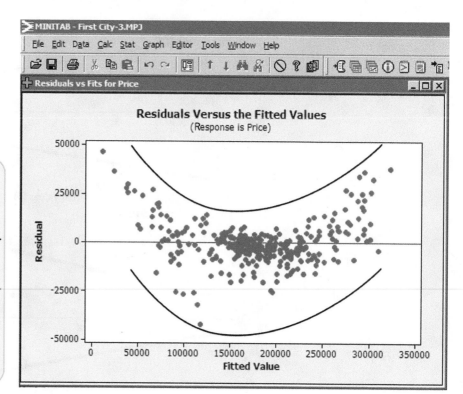

**FIGURE 15.38**

Plot of Residuals against Time

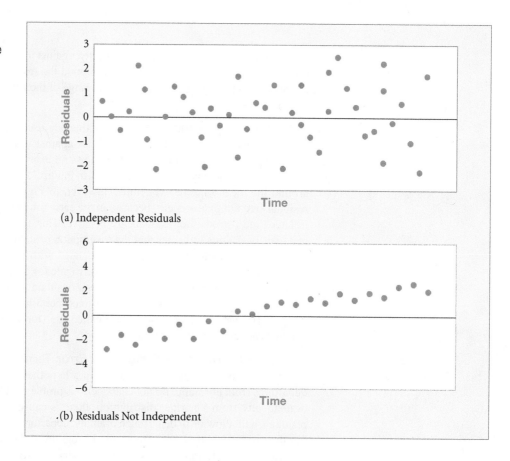

(a) Independent Residuals

.(b) Residuals Not Independent

Another method for determining normality is to calculate and plot the *standardized residuals*. In Chapter 3 you learned that a random variable is standardized by subtracting its mean and dividing the result by its standard deviation. The mean of the residuals is zero. Therefore, dividing each residual by an estimate of its standard deviation gives the standardized residual.[10] Although the proof is beyond the scope of this text, it can be shown that the standardized residual for any particular observation for a simple linear regression model is found using Equation 15.14.

---

### Standardized Residual for Linear Regression

$$s_{e_i} = \frac{e_i}{s_\varepsilon \sqrt{1 + \frac{1}{n} + \frac{(x_i - \bar{x})^2}{\sum x^2 - \frac{(\sum x)^2}{n}}}}$$

(15.14)

where:

$e_i$ = $i$th residual value
$s_\varepsilon$ = Standard error of the estimate
$x_i$ = Value of $x$ used to generate the predicted $y$-value for the $i$th observation

---

Computing the standardized residual for an observation in a multiple regression model is too complicated to be done by hand. However, the standardized residuals are generated from most statistical software, including Minitab and Excel. The Excel and Minitab tutorials illustrate the methods required to generate the standardized residuals and residual plots. Because other problems such as nonconstant variance and nonindependent residuals can result in residuals that seem to be abnormal, you should check these other factors before addressing the normality assumption.

Recall that for a normal distribution, approximately 68% of the values will fall within 1 standard deviation of the mean, 95% will fall within 2 standard deviations of the mean, and virtually all values will fall within 3 standard deviations of the mean.

Figure 15.39 illustrates the histogram of the residuals for the First City Real Estate example. The distribution of residuals looks to be close to a normal distribution. Figure 15.40 shows the

**FIGURE 15.39**

Minitab Histogram of Residuals for First City Real Estate

**Minitab Instructions:**

1. Open file: First City-3. MTW.
2. Choose **Stat > Regression > Regression**.
3. In **Response**, enter dependent ($y$) variable.
4. In **Predictors**, enter independent ($x$) variables.
5. Choose **Graphs**.
6. Under **Residual Plots**, select **Histogram of residuals**.
7. Click **OK. OK.**

---

[10]The standardized residual is also referred to as the *studentized residual*.

**FIGURE 15.40**

Minitab Histogram of
Standardized Residuals for
First City Real Estate

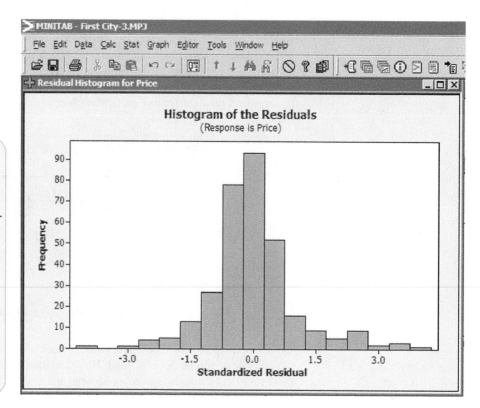

**Minitab Instructions:**

1. Open file: First City-3. MTW.
2. Choose **Stat > Regression > Regression**.
3. In **Response**, enter dependent (*y*) variable.
4. In **Predictors**, enter independent (*x*) variables.
5. Choose **Graphs**.
6. Under **Residual for Plots**, select **Standardized**.
7. Under **Residual Plots**, select **Histogram of residuals**.
8. Click **OK. OK.**

histogram for the standardized residuals, which will have the same basic shape as the residual distribution in Figure 15.39.

Another approach for checking for normality of the residuals is to form a *probability plot*. We start by arranging the residuals in numerical order from smallest to largest. The standardized residuals are plotted on the horizontal axis, and the corresponding expected value for the standardized residual is plotted on the vertical axis. Although we won't delve into how the expected value is computed, you can examine the normal probability plot to see whether the plot forms a straight line. The closer the line is to linear, the closer the residuals are to being normally distributed. Figure 15.41 shows the normal probability plot for the First City Real Estate Company example.

**FIGURE 15.41**

Minitab Normal Probability
Plot of Residuals for First City
Real Estate

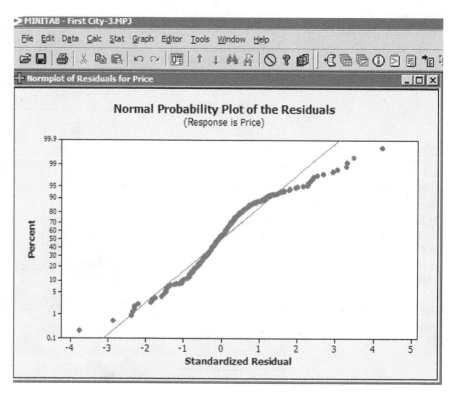

**Minitab Instructions:**

1. Open file: First City-3. MTW.
2. Choose **Stat > Regression > Regression**.
3. In **Response**, enter dependent (*y*) variable.
4. In **Predictors**, enter independent (*x*) variables.
5. Choose **Graphs**.
6. Under **Residual** Plots, select **Normal plot of residuals**.
7. Click **OK.OK.**

You should be aware that Minitab and Excel format their residual plots in a slightly different way. However, the same general information is conveyed, and you can look for the same signs of problems with the regression model.

## Corrective Actions

If, based on analyzing the residuals, you decide the model constructed is not appropriate, but you still want a regression-based model, some corrective action may be warranted. There are three approaches that may work: Transform some of the existing independent variables, remove some variables from the model, or start over in the development of the regression model.

Earlier in this chapter, we discussed a basic approach involved in variable transformation. In general, the transformations of the independent variables (such as raising $x$ to a power, taking the square root of $x$, or taking the log of $x$) are used to make the data better conform to a linear relationship. If the model suffers from nonlinearity and if the residuals have a nonconstant variance, you may want to transform both the independent and dependent variables. In cases in which the normality assumption is not satisfied, transforming the dependent variable is often useful. In many instances, a log transformation works. In some instances, a transformation involving the product of two independent variables will help. A more detailed discussion is beyond the scope of this text. However, you can read more about this subject in the Kutner et al. reference listed at the end of the chapter.

The alternative of using a different regression model means that we respecify the model to include new independent variables or remove existing variables from the model. In most modeling situations, we are in a continual state of model respecification. We are always seeking to improve the regression model by finding new independent variables.

MyStatLab

# 15-5: Exercises

## Skill Development

**15-50.** Consider the following values for an independent and dependent variable:

| x | y |
|----|----|
| 6 | 5 |
| 9 | 20 |
| 14 | 28 |
| 18 | 30 |
| 22 | 33 |
| 27 | 35 |
| 33 | 45 |

a. Determine the estimated linear regression equation relating the dependent and independent variables.
b. Is the regression equation you found significant? Test at the $\alpha = 0.05$ level.
c. Determine both the residuals and standardized residuals. Is there anything about the residuals that

would lead you to question whether the assumptions necessary to use regression analysis are satisfied? Discuss.

**15-51.** Consider the following values for an independent and dependent variable:

| x | y |
|----|----|
| 6 | 5 |
| 9 | 20 |
| 14 | 28 |
| 18 | 15 |
| 22 | 27 |
| 27 | 31 |
| 33 | 32 |
| 50 | 60 |
| 61 | 132 |
| 75 | 160 |

a. Determine the estimated linear regression equation relating the dependent and independent variables.
b. Is the regression equation you found significant? Test at the $\alpha = 0.05$ level.
c. Determine both the residuals and standardized residuals. Is there anything about the residuals that would lead you to question whether the assumptions necessary to use regression analysis are satisfied?

**15-52.** Examine the following data set:

| y | x |
|---|---|
| 25 | 10 |
| 35 | 10 |
| 14 | 10 |
| 45 | 20 |
| 52 | 20 |
| 41 | 20 |
| 65 | 30 |
| 63 | 30 |
| 68 | 30 |

a. Determine the estimated regression equation for this data set.
b. Calculate the residuals for this regression equation.
c. Produce the appropriate residual plot to determine if the linear function is the appropriate regression function for this data set.
d. Use a residual plot to determine if the residuals have a constant variance.
e. Produce a residual plot to determine if the residuals are independent. Assume the order of appearance is the time order of the data.
f. Use a probability plot to determine if the error terms are normally distributed.

**15-53.** Examine the following data set:

| y | $x_1$ | $x_2$ |
|---|---|---|
| 25 | 5 | 25 |
| 35 | 5 | 5 |
| 14 | 5 | 5 |
| 45 | 25 | 40 |
| 52 | 25 | 5 |
| 41 | 25 | 25 |
| 65 | 30 | 30 |
| 63 | 30 | 30 |
| 68 | 30 | 25 |
| 75 | 40 | 30 |

a. Determine the estimated regression equation for this data set.
b. Calculate the residuals and the standardized residuals for this regression equation.

c. Produce the appropriate residual plot to determine if the linear function is the appropriate regression function for this data set.
d. Use a residual plot to determine if the residuals have a constant variance.
e. Produce the appropriate residual plot to determine if the residuals are independent.
f. Construct a probability plot to determine if the error terms are normally distributed.

## Computer Database **Exercises**

**15-54.** Refer to Exercise 15-9, which referenced an article in *Business Week* that presented a list of the 100 companies perceived as having "hot growth" characteristics. The file entitled **Logrowth** contains sales ($million), sales increase (%), return on capital, market value ($million), and recent stock price of the companies ranked from 81 to 100. In Exercise 15-9, a regression equation was constructed in which the sales of the companies was predicted using their market value.
a. Determine the estimated regression equation for this data set.
b. Calculate the residuals and the standardized residuals for this regression equation.
c. Produce the appropriate residual plot to determine if the linear function is the appropriate regression function for this data set.
d. Use a residual plot to determine if the residuals have a constant variance.
e. Produce the appropriate residual plot to determine if the residuals are independent. Assume the data were extracted in the order listed.
f. Construct a probability plot to determine if the error terms are normally distributed.

**15-55.** The White Cover Snowmobile Association promotes snowmobiling in both the Upper Midwest and the Rocky Mountain region. The industry has been affected in the West because of uncertainty associated with conflicting court rulings about the number of snowmobiles allowed in national parks. The Association advertises in outdoor- and tourist-related publications and then sends out pamphlets, maps, and other regional related information to people who call a toll-free number and request the information. The association orders the packets from a document-printing company and likes to have enough available to meet the immediate need without having too many sitting around taking up space. The marketing manager decided to develop a multiple regression model to be used in predicting the number of calls that will be received in the coming week. A random sample of 12 weeks is selected, with the following variables:

$y$ = Number of calls

$x_1$ = Number of advertisements placed the previous week

$x_2$ = Number of calls received the previous week

$x_3$ = Number of airline tour bookings into Western cities for the current week

The data are in the file called **Winter Adventures**.

a. Construct a multiple regression model using all three independent variables. Write a short report discussing the model.

b. Based on the appropriate residual plots, what can you conclude about the constant variance assumption? Discuss.

c. Based on the appropriate residual analysis, does it appear that the residuals are independent? Discuss.

d. Use an appropriate analysis of the residuals to determine whether the regression model meets the assumption of normally distributed error terms. Discuss.

15-56. The athletic director of State University is interested in developing a multiple regression model that might be used to explain the variation in attendance at football games at his school. A sample of 16 games was selected from home games played during the past 10 seasons. Data for the following factors were determined:

$y$ = Game attendance

$x_1$ = Team win/loss percentage to date

$x_2$ = Opponent win/loss percentage to date

$x_3$ = Games played this season

$x_4$ = Temperature at game time

The sample data are in the file called **Football**.

a. Build a multiple regression model using all four independent variables. Write a short report that outlines the characteristics of this model.

b. Develop a table of residuals for this model. What is the average residual value? Why do you suppose it came out to this value? Discuss.

c. Based on the appropriate residual plot, what can you conclude about the constant variance assumption? Discuss.

d. Based on the appropriate residual analysis, does it appear that the model errors are independent? Discuss.

e. Can you conclude, based on the appropriate method of analysis, that the model error terms are approximately normally distributed?

15-57. The consumer price index (CPI) is a measure of the average change in prices over time in a fixed market basket of goods and services typically purchased by consumers. One of the items in this market basket that affects the CPI is the price of oil and its derivatives. The file entitled **Consumer** contains the price of the derivatives of oil and the CPI adjusted to 2005 levels. In Exercise 15-49, backward elimination stepwise regression was used to determine the relationship between CPI and two independent variables: the price of heating oil and of diesel fuel.

a. Construct an estimate of the regression equation using the same variables.

b. Produce the appropriate residual plots to determine if the linear function is the appropriate regression function for this data set.

c. Use a residual plot to determine if the residuals have a constant variance.

d. Produce the appropriate residual plot to determine if the residuals are independent. Assume the data were extracted in the order listed.

e. Construct a probability plot to determine if the error terms are normally distributed.

15-58. In Exercise 15-48 you were asked to use best subsets stepwise regression to establish the relationship between body fat and the independent variables weight, abdomen circumference, and thigh circumference based on data in the file **Bodyfat**. This is an extension of that exercise.

a. Construct an estimate of the regression equation using the same variables.

b. Produce the appropriate residual plots to determine if the linear function is the appropriate regression function for this data set.

c. Use a residual plot to determine if the residuals have a constant variance.

d. Produce the appropriate residual plot to determine if the residuals are independent. Assume the data were extracted in the order listed.

e. Construct a probability plot to determine if the error terms are normally distributed.

15-59. The National Association of Theatre Owners is the largest exhibition trade organization in the world, representing more than 26,000 movie screens in all 50 states and in more than 20 countries worldwide. Its membership includes the largest cinema chains and hundreds of independent theater owners. It publishes statistics concerning the movie sector of the economy. The file entitled **Flicks** contains data on total U.S. box office grosses ($billion), total number of admissions (billion), average U.S. ticket price ($), and number of movie screens.

a. Construct a regression equation in which total U.S. box office grosses are predicted using the other variables.

b. Produce the appropriate residual plots to determine if the linear function is the appropriate regression function for this data set.

c. Square each of the independent variables and add them to the model on which the regression equation in part a was built. Produce the new regression equation.

d. Use a residual plot to determine if the quadratic model in part c alleviates the problem identified in part b.

e. Construct a probability plot to determine if the error terms are normally distributed for the updated model.

# Visual Summary

**Chapter 15:** Chapter 14 introduced linear regression, concentrating on analyzing a linear relationship between two variables. However, business problems are not limited to linear relationships involving only two variables, many situations involve linear and nonlinear relationships among three or more variables. This chapter introduces several extensions of the techniques covered in the last chapter including: multiple linear regression, incorporating qualitative variables in the regression model, working with nonlinear relationships, techniques for determining how "good" the model fits the data, and stepwise regression.

 **15.1** Introduction to Multiple Regression Analysis (pg. 634–653)

### Summary

Multiple linear regression analysis examines the relationship between a dependent and more than one independent variable. Determining the appropriate relationship starts with **model specification**, where the appropriate variables are determined, then moves to **model building**, followed by **model diagnosis**, where the quality of the model built is determined. The purpose of the model is to explain variation in the dependent variable. Useful independent variables are those **highly correlated** with the dependent variable. The percentage of variation in the dependent variable explained by the model is determined by the **coefficient of determination**, $R^2$. The overall model can be tested for significance as can the individual terms in the model. A common problem in multiple regressions models occurs when the independent variable are highly correlated, this is called **multicollinearity**.

**Outcome 1.** Understand the general concepts behind model building using multiple regression analysis.
**Outcome 2.** Apply multiple regression analysis to business decision-making situations.
**Outcome 3.** Analyze the computer output for a multiple regression model and interpret the regression results.
**Outcome 4.** Test hypotheses about the significance of a multiple regression model and test the significance of the independent variables in the model.
**Outcome 5.** Recognize potential problems when using multiple regression analysis and take steps to correct the problems.

 **15.2** Using Qualitative Independent Variables (pg. 654–661)

### Summary

Independent variables are not always quantitative and ratio level. Important independent variables might include determining if someone is married, or not, owns her home, or not, is recently employed and type of car owned. All of these are qualitative, not quantitative, variables and are incorporated into multiple regression analysis using dummy variables. Dummy variables are numerical codes, 0 or 1, depending on whether the observation has the indicated characteristic. Be careful to insure you use one fewer dummy variables than categories to avoid the dummy variable trap.

**Outcome 6.** Incorporate qualitative variables into a regression model by using dummy variables.

 **15.3** Working with Nonlinear Relationships (pg. 661–678)

### Summary

Sometimes business situations involve a nonlinear relationship between the dependent and independent variables. Regression models with nonlinear relationship become more complicated to build and analyze. Start by plotting the data to see the relationships between the dependent variable and independent variable. Exponential, or second or third order polynomial relationships are commonly found. Once the appropriate relationship is determined, the independent variable is modified and used in the model.

**Outcome 7.** Apply regression analysis to situations where the relationship between the independent variable(s) and the dependent variable is nonlinear.

  **15.4** Stepwise Regression (pg. 678–689)

### Summary

Stepwise regression develops the regression equation either through **forward selection**, **backward elimination**, or **standard stepwise regression**. **Forward selection** begins by selecting a single independent variable which is most highly correlated with the dependent variable. Additional variables will be added to the model as long as they reduce a significant amount of the remaining variation in the dependent variable. **Backward elimination** starts with all variables in the model to begin the process. Variables are removed one at a time until no more insignificant variables are found. **Standard stepwise** is similar to forward selection. However, if two or more variables are correlated, a variable selected in an early step may become insignificant when other variables are added at later steps. The standard stepwise procedure will drop this insignificant variable from the model.

**Outcome 8.** Understand the uses of stepwise regression.

 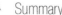 **15.5** Determining the Aptness of the Model (pg. 689–699)

### Summary

Determining the aptness of a model relies on an analysis of **residuals**, the difference between the observed value of the dependent variable and the value predicted by the model. The residuals should be randomly scattered about the regression line with a normal distribution and constant variance. If a plot of the residuals indicates any of the preceding does not occur, corrective action should be taken which might involve transforming some independent variables, dropping some variables or adding new ones, or even starting over with the model building process.

**Outcome 9.** Analyze the extent to which a regression model satisfies the regression assumptions.

 **Conclusion**

Multiple regression uses two or more independent variables to explain the variation in the dependent variable. As a decision maker, you will generally not be required to manually develop the regression model, but you will have to judge its applicability based on a computer printout. Consequently, this chapter has largely involved an analysis of computer printouts. You no doubt will encounter printouts that look somewhat different from those shown in this text and some of the terms used may differ slightly, but Excel and Minitab software we have used are representative of the many software packages that are available.

# Equations

**(15.1)** Population Multiple Regression Model pg. 634

$$y = \beta_0 + \beta_1 x_1 + \beta_2 x_2 + \cdots + \beta_k x_k + \varepsilon$$

**(15.2)** Estimated Multiple Regression Model pg. 634

$$\hat{y} = b_0 + b_1 x_1 + b_2 x_2 + \cdots + b_k x_k$$

**(15.3)** Correlation Coefficient pg. 638

$$r = \frac{\sum (x - \bar{x})(y - \bar{y})}{\sqrt{\sum (x - \bar{x})^2 \sum (y - \bar{y})^2}}$$
One $x$ variable with $y$

or $\quad r = \dfrac{\sum (x_i - \bar{x}_i)(x_j - \bar{x}_j)}{\sqrt{\sum (x_i - \bar{x}_i)^2 \sum (x_j - \bar{x}_j)^2}}$
One $x$ variable with another $x$

**(15.4)** Multiple Coefficient of Determination ($R^2$) pg. 642

$$R^2 = \frac{\text{Sum of squares regression}}{\text{Total sum of squares}} = \frac{SSR}{SST}$$

**(15.5)** $F$-Test Statistic pg. 643

$$F = \frac{\dfrac{SSR}{k}}{\dfrac{SSE}{n-k-1}}$$

**(15.6)** Adjusted $R$-Squared pg. 644

$$R\text{-sq(adj)} = R_A^2 = 1 - (1 - R^2)\left(\frac{n-1}{n-k-1}\right)$$

**(15.7)** $t$-Test for Significance of Each Regression Coefficient pg. 645

$$t = \frac{b_j - 0}{s_{b_j}} \qquad df = n - k - 1$$

**(15.8)** Standard Error of the Estimate pg. 646

$$s_\varepsilon = \sqrt{\frac{SSE}{n - k - 1}} = \sqrt{MSE}$$

**(15.9)** Variance Inflation Factor pg. 648

$$VIF = \frac{1}{(1 - R_j^2)}$$

**(15.10)** Confidence Interval Estimate for the Regression Slope pg. 650

$$b_j \pm t s_{b_j}$$

**(15.11)** Polynomial Population Regression Model pg. 662

$$y = \beta_0 + \beta_1 x + \beta_2 x^2 + \cdots + \beta_p x^p + \varepsilon$$

**(15.12)** Partial-$F$ Test Statistic pg. 672

$$F = \frac{(SSE_R - SSE_C)/(c - r)}{MSE_C}$$

**(15.13)** Residual pg. 689

$$e_i = y_i - \hat{y}_i$$

**(15.14)** Standardized Residual for Linear Regression pg. 695

$$s_{e_i} = \frac{e_i}{s_\varepsilon \sqrt{1 + \dfrac{1}{n} + \dfrac{(x_i - \bar{x})^2}{\sum x^2 - \dfrac{(\sum x)^2}{n}}}}$$

# Key Terms

Adjusted $R$-squared  pg. 644
Coefficient of partial determination
  pg. 678
Composite model  pg. 669
Correlation coefficient  pg. 638

Correlation matrix  pg. 638
Dummy variable  pg. 654
Interaction  pg. 669
Model  pg. 636
Multicollinearity  pg. 647

Multiple coefficient of determination
  ($R^2$) pg. 642
Regression hyperplane  pg. 635
Residual  pg. 689
Variance inflation factor (*VIF*)  pg. 648

# Chapter Exercises

## Conceptual Questions

**15-60.** Go to the library or use the Internet to locate three articles using a regression model with more than one independent variable. For each article write a short summary covering the following points:

Purpose for using the model
How the variables in the model were selected
How the data in the model were selected
Any possible violations of the needed assumptions
The conclusions drawn from using the model

**15-61.** Discuss in your own terms the similarities and differences between simple linear regression analysis and multiple regression analysis.

**15-62.** Discuss what is meant by the least squares criterion as it pertains to multiple regression analysis. Is the least squares criterion any different for simple regression analysis? Discuss.

**15-63.** List the basic assumptions of regression analysis and discuss in your own terms what each means.

**15-64.** What does it mean if we have developed a multiple regression model and have concluded that the model is apt?

**15-65.** Consider the following model:
$$\hat{y} = 5 + 3x_1 + 5x_2$$
a. Provide an interpretation of the coefficient of $x_1$.
b. Is the interpretation provided in part a true regardless of the value of $x_2$? Explain.
c. Now consider the model $\hat{y} = 5 + 3x_1 + 5x_2 + 4x_1x_2$. Let $x_2 = 1$. Give an interpretation of the coefficient of $x_1$ when $x_2 = 1$.
d. Repeat part c when $x_2 = 2$. Is the interpretation provided in part a true regardless of the value of $x_2$? Explain.
e. Considering your answers to parts c and d, what type of regression components has conditional interpretations?

## Computer Database Exercises

**15-66.** Amazon.com has become one of the most successful online merchants. Two measures of its success are sales and net income/loss figures. They are given here.

| Year | Net Income/Loss | Sales |
|------|------|------|
| 1995 | −0.3 | 0.5 |
| 1996 | −5.7 | 15.7 |
| 1997 | −27.5 | 147.7 |
| 1998 | −124.5 | 609.8 |
| 1999 | −719.9 | 1,639.8 |
| 2000 | −1,411.2 | 2,761.9 |
| 2001 | −567.3 | 3,122.9 |
| 2002 | −149.1 | 3,933 |
| 2003 | 35.3 | 5,263.7 |
| 2004 | 588.5 | 6,921 |
| 2005 | 359 | 8,490 |
| 2006 | 190 | 10,711 |
| 2007 | 476 | 14,835 |

a. Produce a scatter plot for Amazon's net income/loss and sales figures for the period 1995 to 2007. Determine the order (or degree) of the polynomial that could be used to predict Amazon's net income/loss using sales figures for the period 1995 to 2007.
b. To simplify the analysis, consider only the values from 1995–2004. Produce the polynomial indicated by this data.
c. Test to determine whether the overall model from part b is statistically significant. Use a significance level of 0.10.
d. Conduct a hypothesis test to determine if curvature exists in the model that predicts Amazon's net income/loss using sales figures from part b. Use a significance level of 0.02 and the test statistic approach.

**The following information applies to Exercises 15-67, 15-68, and 15-69.**

A publishing company in New York is attempting to develop a model that it can use to help predict textbook sales for books it is considering for future publication. The marketing department has collected data on several variables from a random sample of 15 books. These data are given in the file **Textbooks**.

**15-67.** Develop the correlation matrix showing the correlation between all possible pairs of variables. Test statistically to determine which independent variables are significantly correlated with the dependent variable, book sales. Use a significance level of 0.05.

**15-68.** Develop a multiple regression model containing all four independent variables. Show clearly the regression coefficients. Write a short report discussing the model. In your report make sure you cover the following issues:
a. How much of the total variation in book sales can be explained by these four independent variables? Would you conclude that the model is significant at the 0.05 level?
b. Develop a 95% confidence interval for each regression coefficient and interpret these confidence intervals.
c. Which of the independent variables can you conclude to be significant in explaining the variation in book sales? Test using $\alpha = 0.05$.
d. How much of the variation in the dependent variable is explained by the independent variable? Is the model statistically significant at the $\alpha = 0.01$ level? Discuss.
e. How much, if at all, does adding one more page to the book impact the sales volume of the book? Develop and interpret a 95% confidence interval estimate to answer this question.
f. Perform the appropriate analysis to determine the aptness of this regression model. Discuss your results and conclusions.

**15-69.** The publishing company recently came up with some additional data for the 15 books in the original sample. Two new variables, production expenditures ($x_5$) and number of prepublication reviewers ($x_6$), have been added. These additional data are as follows:

| Book | $x_5$ ($) | $x_6$ | Book | $x_5$ ($) | $x_6$ |
|------|-----------|-------|------|-----------|-------|
| 1 | 38,000 | 5 | 9 | 51,000 | 4 |
| 2 | 86,000 | 8 | 10 | 34,000 | 6 |
| 3 | 59,000 | 3 | 11 | 20,000 | 2 |
| 4 | 80,000 | 9 | 12 | 80,000 | 5 |
| 5 | 29,500 | 3 | 13 | 60,000 | 5 |
| 6 | 31,000 | 3 | 14 | 87,000 | 8 |
| 7 | 40,000 | 5 | 15 | 29,000 | 3 |
| 8 | 69,000 | 4 | | | |

Incorporating these additional data, calculate the correlation between each of these additional variables and the dependent variable, book sales.

a. Test the significance of the correlation coefficients, using $\alpha = 0.05$. Comment on your results.

b. Develop a multiple regression model that includes all six independent variables. Which, if any, variables would you recommend be retained if this model is going to be used to predict book sales for the publishing company? For any statistical tests you might perform, use a significance level of 0.05. Discuss your results.

c. Use the $F$-test approach to test the null hypothesis that all slope coefficients are 0. Test with a significance level of 0.05. What do these results mean? Discuss.

d. Do multicollinearity problems appear to be present in the model? Discuss the potential consequences of multicollinearity with respect to the regression model.

e. Discuss whether the standard error of the estimate is small enough to make this model useful for predicting the sales of textbooks.

f. Plot the residuals against the predicted value of $y$ and comment on what this plot means relative to the aptness of the model.

g. Compute the standardized residuals and form these into a frequency histogram. What does this indicate about the normality assumption?

h. Comment on the overall aptness of this model and indicate what might be done to improve the model.

**The following information applies to Exercises 15-70 through 15-79.**

The J. J. McCracken Company has authorized its marketing research department to make a study of customers who have been issued a McCracken charge card. The marketing research department hopes to identify the significant variables that explain the variation in purchases. Once these variables are determined, the department intends to try to attract new customers who would be predicted to make a high volume of purchases.

Twenty-five customers were selected at random, and values for the following variables were recorded in the file called **McCracken**:

$y$ = Average monthly purchases (in dollars) at McCracken

$x_1$ = Customer age

$x_2$ = Customer family income

$x_3$ = Family size

**15-70.** A first step in regression analysis often involves developing a scatter plot of the data. Develop the scatter plots of all the possible pairs of variables, and with a brief statement indicate what each plot says about the relationship between the two variables.

**15-71.** Compute the correlation matrix for these data. Develop the decision rule for testing the significance of each coefficient. Which, if any, correlations are not significant? Use $\alpha = 0.05$.

**15-72.** Use forward selection stepwise regression to develop the multiple regression model. The variable $x_2$, family income, was brought into the model. Discuss why this happened.

**15-73.** Test the significance of the regression model at Step 1 of the process. Justify the significance level you have selected.

**15-74.** Develop a 95% confidence level for the slope coefficient for the family income variable at Step 1 of the model. Be sure to interpret this confidence interval.

**15-75.** Describe the regression model at Step 2 of the analysis. In your discussion, be sure to discuss the effect of adding a new variable on the standard error of the estimate and on $R^2$.

**15-76.** Referring to Problem 15-75, suppose the manager of McCracken's marketing department questions the appropriateness of adding a second variable. How would you respond to her question?

**15-77.** Looking carefully at the stepwise regression model, you can see that the value of the slope coefficient for variable $x_2$, family income, changes as a new variable is added to the regression model. Discuss why this change takes place.

**15-78.** Analyze the stepwise regression model. Write a report to the marketing manager pointing out the strengths and weaknesses of the model. Be sure to comment on the department's goal of being able to use the model to predict which customers will purchase high volumes from McCracken.

**15-79.** Plot the residuals against the predicted value of $y$ and comment on what this plot means relative to the aptness of the model.

a. Compute the standardized residuals and form these in a frequency histogram. What does this indicate about the normality assumption?

b. Comment on the overall aptness of this model and indicate what might be done to improve the model.

**15-80.** The National Association of Realtors Existing-Home Sales Series provides a measurement of the residential real estate market. One of the measurements it produces is the Housing Affordability Index (HAI), which is a measure of the financial ability of U.S. families to buy a house. A value of 100 means that families earning the national median income have just the amount of money needed to qualify for a mortgage on a median-priced home; higher than 100 means they have more than enough, and lower than 100 means they have less than enough. The file entitled **Index** contains the HAI and associated variables.

a. Produce the correlation matrix of all the variables. Predict the variables that will remain in the estimated regression equation if standard stepwise regression is used.

b. Use standard stepwise regression to develop an estimate of a model that is to predict the HAI from the associated variables found in the file entitled **Index**.

c. Compare the results of parts a and b. Explain any difference between the two models.

**15-81.** An investment analyst collected data from 20 randomly chosen companies. The data consisted of the 52-week-high stock prices, PE ratios, and the market values of the companies. This data are in the file entitled **Investment**. The analyst wishes to produce a regression equation to predict the market value using the 52-week-high stock price and the PE ratio of the company. He creates a complete second-degree polynomial.

a. Construct an estimate of the regression equation using the indicated variables.

b. Produce the appropriate residual plots to determine if the polynomial function is the appropriate regression function for this data set.

c. Use a residual plot to determine if the residuals have a constant variance.

d. Produce the appropriate residual plot to determine if the residuals are independent. Assume the data were extracted in the order listed.

e. Construct a probability plot to determine if the error terms are normally distributed.

**15-82.** The consumer price index (CPI) is a measure of the average change in prices over time in a fixed market basket of goods and services typically purchased by consumers. One of the items in this market basket that affects the CPI is the price of oil and its derivatives. The file entitled **Consumer** contains the price of the derivatives of oil and the CPI adjusted to 2005 levels.

a. Produce a multiple regression equation depicting the relationship between the CPI and the price of the derivatives of oil.

b. Conduct a $t$-test on the coefficient that has the highest $p$-value. Use a significance level of 0.02 and the $p$-value approach.

c. Produce a multiple regression equation depicting the relationship between the CPI and the price of the derivatives of oil leaving out the variable tested in part b.

d. Referring to the regression results in part c, repeat the tests indicated in part b.

e. Perform a test of hypothesis to determine if the resulting overall model is statistically significant. Use a significance level of 0.02 and the $p$-value approach.

**15-83.** Badeaux Brothers Louisiana Treats ships packages of Louisiana coffee, cakes, and Cajun spices to individual customers around the United States. The cost to ship these products depends primarily on the weight of the package being shipped. Badeaux charges the customers for shipping and then ships the product itself. As a part of a study of whether it is economically feasible to continue to ship products themselves, Badeaux sampled 20 recent shipments to determine what if any relationship exists between shipping costs and package weight. The data are contained in the file **Badeaux**.

a. Develop a scatter plot of the data with the dependent variable, cost, on the vertical axis and the independent variable, weight, on the horizontal axis. Does there appear to be a relationship between the two variables? Is the relationship linear?

b. Compute the sample correlation coefficient between the two variables. Conduct a test, using an alpha value of 0.05, to determine whether the population correlation coefficient is significantly different from zero.

c. Determine the simple linear regression model for this data. Plot the simple linear regression model together with the data. Would a nonlinear model better fit the sample data?

d. Now develop a nonlinear model and plot the model against the data. Does the nonlinear model provide a better fit than the linear model developed in part c?

**15-84.** The State Tax Commission must download information files each morning. The time to download the files primarily depends on the size of the file. The Tax Commission has asked your computer consulting firm to determine what, if any, relationship exists between download time and size of files. The Tax Commission randomly selected a sample of days and provided the information contained in the file **Tax Commission.**

a. Develop a scatter plot of the data with the dependent variable, download time, on the vertical axis and the independent variable, size, on the horizontal axis. Does there appear to be a relationship between the two variables? Is the relationship linear?

b. Compute the sample correlation coefficient between the two variables. Conduct a test, using an alpha value of 0.05, to determine whether the population correlation coefficient is significantly different from zero.

c. Determine the simple linear regression model for these data. Plot the simple linear regression model together with the data. Would a nonlinear model better fit the sample data?

d. Now determine a nonlinear model and plot the model against the data. Does the nonlinear model provide a better fit than the linear model developed in part c?

**15-85.** Refer to the State Department of Transportation data set called **Liabins**. The department was interested in determining the rate of compliance with the state's mandatory liability insurance law, as well as other things. *Assume the data were collected using a simple random sampling process.* Develop the best possible linear regression model using vehicle year as the dependent variable and any or all of the other variables as potential independent variables. Assume that your objective is to develop a predictive model. Write a report that discusses the steps you took to develop the final model. Include a correlation matrix and all appropriate statistical tests. Use an $\alpha = 0.05$. If you are using a nominal or ordinal variable, remember that you must make sure it is in the form of one or more dummy variables.

# Case 15.1

## Dynamic Scales, Inc.

In 2005, Stanley Ahlon and three financial partners formed Dynamic Scales, Inc. The company was based on an idea Stanley had for developing a scale to weigh trucks in motion and thus eliminate the need for every truck to stop at weigh stations along highways. This dynamic scale would be placed in the highway approximately one-quarter mile from the regular weigh station. The scale would have a minicomputer that would automatically record truck speed, axle weights, and climate variables, including temperature, wind, and moisture. Stanley Ahlon and his partners believed that state transportation departments in the United States would be the primary market for such a scale.

As with many technological advances, developing the dynamic scale has been difficult. When the scale finally proved accurate for trucks traveling 40 miles per hour, it would not perform for trucks traveling at higher speeds. However, eight months ago, Stanley announced that the dynamic scale was ready to be field-tested by the Nebraska State Department of Transportation under a grant from the federal government. Stanley explained to his financial partners, and to Nebraska transportation officials, that the dynamic weight would not exactly equal the static weight (truck weight on a static scale). However, he was sure a statistical relationship between dynamic weight and static weight could be determined, which would make the dynamic scale useful.

Nebraska officials, along with people from Dynamic Scales, installed a dynamic scale on a major highway in Nebraska. Each month for six months data were collected for a random sample of trucks weighed on both the dynamic scale and a static scale. Table 15.3 presents these data.

Once the data were collected, the next step was to determine whether, based on this test, the dynamic scale measurements could be used to predict static weights. A complete report will be submitted to the U.S. government and to Dynamic Scales.

**TABLE 15.3 | Test Data for the Dynamic Scales Example**

| Month | Front-Axle Static Weight (lb.) | Front-Axle Dynamic Weight (lb.) | Truck Speed (mph) | Temperature (°F) | Moisture (%) |
|---|---|---|---|---|---|
| January | 1,800 | 1,625 | 52 | 21 | 0.00 |
| | 1,311 | 1,904 | 71 | 17 | 0.15 |
| | 1,504 | 1,390 | 48 | 13 | 0.40 |
| | 1,388 | 1,402 | 50 | 19 | 0.10 |
| | 1,250 | 1,100 | 61 | 24 | 0.00 |
| February | 2,102 | 1,950 | 55 | 26 | 0.10 |
| | 1,410 | 1,475 | 58 | 32 | 0.20 |
| | 1,000 | 1,103 | 59 | 38 | 0.15 |
| | 1,430 | 1,387 | 43 | 24 | 0.00 |
| | 1,073 | 948 | 59 | 18 | 0.40 |
| March | 1,502 | 1,493 | 62 | 34 | 0.00 |
| | 1,721 | 1,902 | 67 | 36 | 0.00 |
| | 1,113 | 1,415 | 48 | 42 | 0.21 |
| | 978 | 983 | 59 | 29 | 0.32 |
| | 1,254 | 1,149 | 60 | 48 | 0.00 |
| April | 994 | 1,052 | 58 | 37 | 0.00 |
| | 1,127 | 999 | 52 | 34 | 0.21 |
| | 1,406 | 1,404 | 59 | 40 | 0.40 |
| | 875 | 900 | 47 | 48 | 0.00 |
| | 1,350 | 1,275 | 68 | 51 | 0.00 |
| May | 1,102 | 1,120 | 55 | 52 | 0.00 |
| | 1,240 | 1,253 | 57 | 57 | 0.00 |
| | 1,087 | 1,040 | 62 | 63 | 0.00 |
| | 993 | 1,102 | 59 | 62 | 0.10 |
| | 1,408 | 1,400 | 67 | 68 | 0.00 |
| June | 1,420 | 1,404 | 58 | 70 | 0.00 |
| | 1,808 | 1,790 | 54 | 71 | 0.00 |
| | 1,401 | 1,396 | 49 | 83 | 0.00 |
| | 933 | 1,004 | 62 | 88 | 0.40 |
| | 1,150 | 1,127 | 64 | 81 | 0.00 |

# Case 15.2

## Glaser Machine Works

Glaser Machine Works has experienced a significant change in its business operations over the past 50 years. Glaser started business as a machine shop that produced specialty tools and products for the timber and lumber industry. This was a logical fit, given its location in the southern part of the United States. However, over the years Glaser looked to expand its offerings beyond the lumber and timber industry. Initially, its small size coupled with its rural location made it difficult to attract the attention of large companies that could use its products. All of that began to change as Glaser developed the ability not only to fabricate parts and tools but also to assemble products for customers who needed special components in large quantities. Glaser's business really took off when first foreign, and then domestic, automakers began to build automobile plants in the southern United States. Glaser was able to provide quality parts quickly for firms that expected high quality and responsive delivery. Many of Glaser's customers operated with little inventory and required that suppliers be able to provide shipments with short lead times.

As part of its relationship with the automobile industry, Glaser was expected to buy into the lean manufacturing and quality improvement initiatives of its customers. Glaser had always prided itself on its quality, but as the number and variety of its products increased, along with ever higher expectations by its customers, Glaser knew that it would have to respond by ensuring its quality and operations were continually improving. Of recent concern was the performance of its manufacturing line 107B. This line produced a component part for a Japanese automobile company. The Japanese firm had initially been pleased with Glaser's performance, but lately the number of defects was approaching an unacceptable level. Managers of the 107B line knew the line and its workers had been asked to ramp up production to meet increased demand and that some workers were concerned with the amount of overtime being required. There was also concern about the second shift now being run at 107B. Glaser had initially run only one shift, but when demand for its product became so high that there was not sufficient capacity with one shift, additional workers were hired to operate a night shift.

Management was wondering if the new shift had been stretched beyond its capabilities. Glaser plant management asked Kristi Johnson, the assistant production supervisor for line 107B, to conduct an analysis of product defects for the line. Kristi randomly selected several days of output and counted the number of defective parts produced on the 107B line. This information, along with other data, is contained in the file **Glaser Machine Works**. Kristi promised to have a full report for the management team by the end of the month.

### Required Tasks:

1. Identify the primary issue of the case.
2. Identify a statistical model you might use to help analyze the case.
3. Develop a multiple regression model that can be used to help Kristi Johnson analyze the product defects for line 107B. Be sure to carefully specify the dependent variable and the independent variables.
4. Discuss how the variables overtime hours, supervisor training, and shift will be modeled.
5. Run the regression model you developed and interpret the results.
6. Which variables are significant?
7. Provide a short report that describes your analysis and explains in managerial terms the findings of your model. Be sure to explain which variables, if any, are significant explanatory variables. Provide a recommendation to management.

# Case 15.3

## Hawlins Manufacturing

Ross Hawlins had done it all at Hawlins Manufacturing, a company founded by his grandfather 63 years ago. Among his many duties, Ross oversaw all the plant's operations, a task that had grown in responsibility given the company's rapid growth over the past three decades. When Ross's grandfather founded the company, there were only two manufacturing sites. Expansion and acquisition of competitors over the years had caused that number to grow to over 50 manufacturing plants in 18 states.

Hawlins had a simple process that produced only two products, but the demand for these products was strong and Ross had spent millions of dollars upgrading his facilities over the past decade. Consequently, most of the company's equipment was less than 10 years old on average. Hawlins's two products were produced for local markets, as prohibitive shipping costs prevented shipping the product long distances. Product demand was sufficiently strong to support two manufacturing shifts (day and night) at every plant, and every plant had the capability to produce both products sold by Hawlins. Recently, the management team at Hawlins noticed that there were differences in output levels across the various plants. They were uncertain what, if anything, might explain these differences. Clearly, if some plants were more productive than others, there might be some meaningful insights that could be standardized across plants to boost overall productivity.

Ross Hawlins asked Lisa Chandler, an industrial engineer at the company's headquarters, to conduct a study of the plant's productivity. Lisa randomly sampled 159 weeks of output from various plants together with the number of plant employees working that week, the plants' average age in years, the product mix produced that week (either product A or B), and whether the output was from the day or night shift. The sampled data are contained in the file **Hawlins Manufacturing**. The Hawlins management team is expecting a written report and a presentation by Lisa when it meets again next Tuesday.

## Required Tasks:

1. Identify the primary issue of the case.
2. Identify a statistical model you might use to help analyze the case.
3. Develop a multiple regression model for Lisa Chandler. Be sure to carefully specify the dependent variable and the independent variables.
4. Discuss how the type of product (A or B) and the shift (Day or Night) can be included in the regression model.
5. Run the regression model you developed and interpret the results.
6. Which variables are significant?
7. Provide a short report that describes your analysis and explains in management terms the findings of your model. Be sure to explain which variables, if any, are significant explanatory variables. Provide a recommendation to management.

# Case 15.4

## Sapphire Coffee—Part 2

Jennie Garcia could not believe that her career had moved so far so fast. When she left graduate school with a master's degree in anthropology, she intended to work at a local coffee shop until something else came along that was more related to her academic background. But after a few months, she came to enjoy the business, and in a little over a year she was promoted to store manager. When the company for whom she worked continued to grow, Jennie was given oversight of a few stores.

Now, eight years after she started as a barista, Jennie is in charge of operations and planning for the company's southern region. As a part of her responsibilities, Jennie tracks store revenues and forecasts coffee demand. Historically, Sapphire Coffee would base its demand forecast on the number of stores, believing that each store sold approximately the same amount of coffee. This approach seemed to work well when the company had shops of similar size and layout, but as the company grew, stores became more varied. Now, some stores have drive-thru windows, a feature that top management added to some stores believing that it would increase coffee sales for customers who wanted a cup of coffee on their way to work but who were too rushed to park and enter the store.

Jennie noticed that weekly sales seemed to be more variable across stores in her region and was wondering what, if anything, might explain the differences. The company's financial vice president had also noticed the increased differences in sales across stores and was wondering what might be happening. In an e-mail to Jennie he stated that weekly store sales are expected to average $5.00 per square foot. Thus, a 1,000-square-foot store would have average weekly sales of $5,000. He asked that Jennie analyze the stores in her region to see if this rule of thumb was a reliable measure of a store's performance.

Jennie had been in the business long enough to know that a store's size, although an important factor, was not the only thing that might influence sales. She had never been convinced of the efficacy of the drive-thru window, believing that it detracted from the coffee house experience that so many of Sapphire Coffee customers had come to expect. The VP of finance was expecting the analysis to be completed by the weekend. Jennie decided to randomly select weekly sales records for 53 stores, along with each store's size, whether it was located close to a college, and whether it had a drive-thru window. The data are in the file **Sapphire Coffee-2**. A full analysis would need to be sent to the corporate office by Friday.

# Case 15.5

## Wendell Motors

Wendell Motors manufactures and ships small electric motors and drives to a variety of industrial and commercial customers in and around St. Louis. Wendell is a small operation with a single manufacturing plant. Wendell's products are different from other motor and drive manufacturers because Wendell only produces small motors (25 horsepower or less) and because its products are used in a variety of industries and businesses that appreciate Wendell's quality and speed of delivery. Because it has only one plant, Wendell ships motors directly from the plant to its customers. Wendell's reputation for quality and speed of delivery allows it to maintain low inventories of motors and to ship make-to-order products directly.

As part of its ongoing commitment to lean manufacturing and continuous process improvement, Wendell carefully monitors the cost associated with both production and shipping. The manager of shipping for Wendell, Tyler Jenkins, regularly reports the shipping

costs to Wendell's management team. Because few finished goods inventories are maintained, competitive delivery times often require that Wendell expedite shipments. This is almost always the case for those customers who operate their business around the clock every day of the week. Such customers might maintain their own backup safety stock of a particular motor or drive, but circumstances often result in cases where replacement products have to be rushed through production and then expedited to the customer.

Wendell's management team wondered if these special orders were too expensive to handle in this way and if it might be less expensive to produce and hold certain motors as finished goods inventory, enabling off-the-shelf delivery using less expensive modes of shipping. This might especially be true for orders that must be filled on a holiday, incurring an additional shipping charge. At the last meeting of the management team, Tyler Jenkins was asked to analyze expedited shipping costs and to develop a model that could be used to estimate the cost of expediting a customer's order.

Donna Layton, an industrial engineer in the plant, was asked to prepare an inventory cost analysis to determine the expenses of holding additional finished goods inventory. Tyler began his analysis by randomly selecting 45 expedited shipping records. The sampled data can be found in the file **Wendell Motors**.

The management team expects a full report in five days. Tyler knew he would need a model for explaining shipping costs for expedited orders and that he would also need to answer the questions as to what effect, if any, shipping on a holiday had on costs.

# References

Berenson, Mark L., and David M. Levine, *Basic Business Statistics: Concepts and Applications*, 11th ed. (Upper Saddle River, NJ: Prentice Hall, 2009).

Bowerman, Bruce L., and Richard T. O'Connell, *Linear Statistical Models: An Applied Approach*, 2nd ed. (Belmont, CA: Duxbury Press, 1990).

Cryer, Jonathan D., and Robert B. Miller, *Statistics for Business: Data Analysis and Modeling*, 2nd ed. (Belmont, CA: Duxbury Press, 1994).

Demmert, Henry, and Marshall Medoff, "Game-Specific Factors and Major League Baseball Attendance: An Econometric Study," *Santa Clara Business Review* (1977), pp. 49–56.

Dielman, Terry E., *Applied Regression Analysis: A Second Course in Business and Economic Statistics*, 4th ed. (Belmont, CA: Duxbury Press, 2005).

Draper, Norman R., and Harry Smith, *Applied Regression Analysis*, 3rd ed. (New York City: John Wiley and Sons, 1998).

Frees, Edward W., *Data Analysis Using Regression Models: The Business Perspective* (Upper Saddle River, NJ: Prentice Hall, 1996).

Gloudemans, Robert J., and Dennis Miller, "Multiple Regression Analysis Applied to Residential Properties." *Decision Sciences* 7 (April 1976), pp. 294–304.

Kleinbaum, David G., Lawrence L. Kupper, Azhar Nizam, and Keith E. Muller, *Applied Regression Analysis and Multivariable Methods*, 4th ed. (Florence, KY: Cengage Learning, 2008).

Kutner, Michael H., Christopher J. Nachtsheim, John Neter, and William Li, *Applied Linear Statistical Models*, 5th ed. (New York City: McGraw-Hill Irwin, 2005).

*Microsoft Excel 2007* (Redmond, WA: Microsoft Corp. 2007).

*Minitab for Windows Version 15* (State College, PA: Minitab, 2007).

**Chapter 16** Quick Prep Links

- **Review** the steps used to develop a line chart discussed in Chapter 2.

- **Make sure** you understand the steps necessary to construct and interpret linear and nonlinear regression models in Chapters 14 and 15.

- **Review** the concepts and properties associated with means discussed in Chapter 3.

chapter 16

# Analyzing and Forecasting Time-Series Data

# Why you need to know

No organization, large or small, can function effectively without a forecast for the goods or services it provides. A retail clothing store must forecast the demand for the shirts it sells by shirt size. The concessionaire at Dodger Stadium in Los Angeles must forecast each game's attendance to determine how many soft drinks and Dodger dogs to have on hand. Your state's elected officials must forecast tax revenues in order to establish a budget each year. These are only a few of the instances in which forecasting is required. For many organizations, the success of the forecasting effort will play a major role in determining the general success of the organization.

When you graduate and join an organization in the public or private sectors, you will almost certainly be required to prepare forecasts or to use forecasts provided by someone else in the organization. You won't have access to a crystal ball on which to rely for an accurate prediction of the future. Fortunately, if you have learned the material presented in this chapter, you will have a basic understanding of forecasting and of how and when to apply various forecasting techniques. We urge you to focus on the material and take with you the tools that will give you a competitive advantage over those who are not familiar with forecasting techniques.

# 16.1 Introduction to Forecasting, Time-Series Data, and Index Numbers

Decision makers often confuse forecasting and planning. Planning is the process of determining how to deal with the future. On the other hand, *forecasting* is the process of predicting what the future will be like. Forecasts are used as inputs for the planning process.

Experts agree that good planning is essential for an organization to be effective. Because forecasts are an important part of the planning process, you need to be familiar with forecasting methods. There are two broad categories of forecasting techniques: qualitative and quantitative. *Qualitative forecasting* techniques are based on expert opinion and judgment. *Quantitative forecasting* techniques are based on statistical methods for analyzing quantitative historical data. This chapter focuses on quantitative forecasting techniques.

In general, quantitative forecasting techniques are used whenever the following conditions are true: Historical data relating to the variable to be forecast exist, the historical data can be quantified, and you are willing to assume that the historical pattern will continue into the future.

## General Forecasting Issues

Decision makers who are actively involved in forecasting frequently say that forecasting is both an art and a science. Operationally, the forecaster is engaged in the process of modeling a real-world system. Determining the appropriate forecasting model is a challenging task, but it can be made manageable by employing the same model-building process discussed in Chapter 15 consisting of **model specification**, **model fitting**, and **model diagnosis**. As we will point out in later sections, guidelines exist for determining which techniques may be more appropriate than others in certain situations. However, you may have to specify (and try) several model forms for a given situation before deciding on one that is acceptable. The idea is that if the future tends to look like the past, a model should adequately fit the past data to have a reasonable chance of forecasting the future. As a forecaster, you will spend much time selecting a model's specification and estimating its parameters to reach an acceptable fit of the past data. You will need to determine how well a model fits past data, how well it performs in mock forecasting trials, and how well its assumptions appear to be satisfied. If the model is unacceptable in any of these areas, you will be forced to revert to the model specification step and begin again.

An important consideration when you are developing a forecasting model is to use the simplest available model that will meet your forecasting needs. The objective of forecasting is to provide good forecasts. You do not need to feel that a sophisticated approach is better if a simpler one will provide acceptable forecasts. As in football, in which some players specialize in defense and others in offense, forecasting techniques have been developed for special situations, which are generally dependent on the **forecasting horizon**. For the purpose of categorizing forecasting techniques in most business situations, the forecast horizon, or lead time, is typically divided into four categories:

1. Immediate term—less than one month
2. Short term—one to three months
3. Medium term—three months to two years
4. Long term—two years or more

As we introduce various forecasting techniques, we will indicate the forecasting horizon(s) for which each is typically best suited.

In addition to determining the desired forecasting horizon, the forecaster must determine the **forecasting period**. For instance, the forecasting period might be a day, a week, a month, a quarter, or a year. Thus, the forecasting horizon consists of one or more forecasting periods. If quantitative forecasting techniques are to be employed, historical quantitative data must be available for a similar period. If we want weekly forecasts, weekly historical data must be available. The **forecasting interval** is generally the same length as the forecast period. That is, if the forecast period is one week, then we will provide a new forecast each week.

**Model Specification**

The process of selecting the forecasting technique to be used in a particular situation.

**Model Fitting**

The process of estimating the specified model's parameters to achieve an adequate fit of the historical data.

**Model Diagnosis**

The process of determining how well a model fits past data and how well the model's assumptions appear to be satisfied.

**Forecasting Horizon**

The number of future periods covered by a forecast. It is sometimes referred to as *forecast lead time*.

**Forecasting Period**

The unit of time for which forecasts are to be made.

**Forecasting Interval**

The frequency with which new forecasts are prepared.

# Components of a Time Series

Quantitative forecasting models have one factor in common: They use past measurements of the variable of interest to generate a forecast of the future. The past data, measured over time, are called *time-series data*. The decision maker who plans to develop a quantitative forecasting model must analyze the relevant time-series data.

**Chapter Outcome 1.→** | BUSINESS APPLICATION | **IDENTIFYING TIME-SERIES COMPONENTS**

 **WEB SITE DESIGN AND CONSULTING** For the past four years, White-Space, Inc., has been helping firms to design and implement Web sites. The owners need to forecast revenues in order to make sure they have ample cash flows to operate the business. In forecasting this company's revenue for next year, they plan to consider the historical pattern over the prior four years. They want to know whether demand for consulting services has tended to increase or decrease and whether there have been particular times during the year when demand was typically higher than at other times. The forecasters can perform a time-series analysis of the historical sales.

Table 16.1 presents the time-series data for the revenue generated by the firm's sales for the four-year period. An effective means for analyzing these data is to develop a *time-series plot*, or line chart, as shown in Figure 16.1. By graphing the data, much can be observed about the firm's revenue over the past four years. The time-series plot is an important tool in identifying the time-series components. All time-series data exhibit one or more of the following:

1. Trend component
2. Seasonal component
3. Cyclical component
4. Random component

**Trend Component** A *trend* is the long-term increase or decrease in a variable being measured over time. Figure 16.1 shows that White-Space's revenues exhibited an upward trend over the four-year period. In other situations, the time series may exhibit a downward trend.

Trends can be classified as **linear** or nonlinear. A trend can be observed when a time series is measured in any time increment, such as years, quarters, months, or days. Figure 16.1 shows a good example of a positive linear trend. Time-series data that exhibit a linear trend will tend to increase or decrease at a fairly constant rate. However, not all trends are linear.

**Linear Trend**

A long-term increase or decrease in a time series in which the rate of change is relatively constant.

**TABLE 16.1** | **Time-Series Data for Sales Revenues (Thousands of Dollars)**

| | Billing Total | | | |
|---|---|---|---|---|
| Month | 2006 | 2007 | 2008 | 2009 |
| January | 170 | 390 | 500 | 750 |
| February | 200 | 350 | 470 | 700 |
| March | 190 | 300 | 510 | 680 |
| April | 220 | 320 | 480 | 710 |
| May | 180 | 310 | 530 | 710 |
| June | 230 | 350 | 500 | 660 |
| July | 220 | 380 | 540 | 630 |
| August | 260 | 420 | 580 | 670 |
| September | 300 | 460 | 630 | 700 |
| October | 330 | 500 | 690 | 720 |
| November | 370 | 540 | 770 | 850 |
| December | 390 | 560 | 760 | 880 |

**FIGURE 16.1**

Time-Series Plot for
White-Space Billing Data

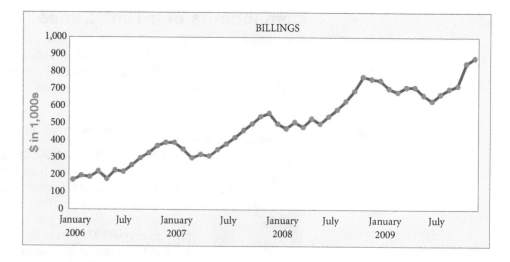

Many time series will show a *nonlinear trend*. For instance in the 8 years between 2001 and 2008, total annual game attendance for the New York Yankees Major League baseball team is shown in Figure 16.2. Attendance was fairly flat between 2001 and 2003, increased dramatically between 2003 and 2006, and then slowed down again through 2008.

**Seasonal Component** Another component that may be present in time-series data is the **seasonal component**. Many time series show a repeating pattern over time. For instance, Figure 16.1 showed a time series that exhibits a wavelike pattern. This pattern repeats itself throughout the time series. Web site consulting revenues reach an annual maximum around January and then decline to an annual minimum around April. This pattern repeats itself every 12 months. The shortest period of repetition for a pattern is known as its *recurrence period*. A seasonal component's recurrence period is at most one year. If the time series exhibits a repetitious pattern with a recurrence period longer than a year, the time series is said to exhibit a cyclical effect—a concept to be explored shortly.

In analyzing past sales data for a retail toy store, we would expect to see sales increase in the months leading into Christmas and then substantially decrease after Christmas. Automobile

**Seasonal Component**

A wavelike pattern that is repeated throughout a time series and has a recurrence period of at most one year.

**FIGURE 16.2**

New York Yankees Annual
Attendance Showing a
Nonlinear Trend

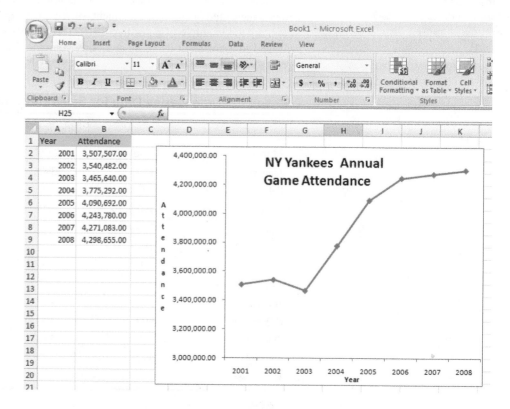

**FIGURE 16.3**

Hotel Sales by Quarter

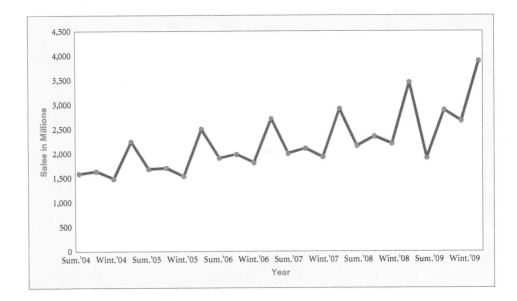

gasoline sales might show a seasonal increase during the summer months, when people drive more, and a decrease during the cold winter months. These predictable highs and lows at specific times during the year indicate seasonality in data.

To view seasonality in a time series, the data must be measured quarterly, monthly, weekly, or daily. Annual data will not show seasonal patterns of highs and lows. Figure 16.3 shows quarterly sales data for a major hotel chain from June 2004 through December 2009. Notice that the data exhibit a definite seasonal pattern. The local maximums occur in the spring. The recurrence period of the component in the time series is, therefore, one year. The winter quarter tends to be low, whereas the following quarter (spring) is the high quarter each year.

Seasonality can be observed in time-series data measured over time periods shorter than a year. For example, the number of checks processed daily by a bank may show predictable highs and lows at certain times during a month. The pattern of customers arriving at the bank during any hour may be "seasonal" within a day, with more customers arriving near opening time, around the lunch hour, and near closing time.

**Cyclical Component**

A wavelike pattern within the time series that repeats itself throughout the time series and has a recurrence period of more than one year.

**Cyclical Component** If you observe time-series data over a long enough time span, you may see sustained periods of high values followed by periods of lower values. If the recurrence period of these fluctuations is larger than a year, the data are said to contain a **cyclical component**.

National economic measures such as the unemployment rate, gross national product, stock market indexes, and personal saving rates tend to cycle. The cycles vary in length and magnitude. That is, some cyclical time series may have longer runs of high and low values than others. Also, some time series may exhibit deeper troughs and higher crests than others. Figure 16.4 shows quarterly housing starts in the United States between 1995 and 2006. Note the definite cyclical pattern, with low periods in 1995, 1997, and 2000. Although the pattern resembles the shape of a seasonal component, the length of the recurrence period identifies this pattern as being the result of a cyclical component.

**Random Component**

Changes in time-series data that are unpredictable and cannot be associated with a trend, seasonal, or cyclical component.

**Random Component** Although not all time series possess a trend, seasonal, or cyclical component, virtually all time series will have a **random component**. The random component is often referred to as "noise" in the data. A time series with no identifiable pattern is completely random and contains only noise. In addition to other components, each of the time series in Figures 16.1 through 16.4 contains random fluctuations.

In the following sections of this chapter, you will see how various forecasting techniques deal with the time-series components. An important first step in forecasting is to identify which components are present in the time series to be analyzed. As we have shown, constructing a time-series plot is the first step in this process.

**FIGURE 16.4** |

Time-Series Plot of Housing
Starts

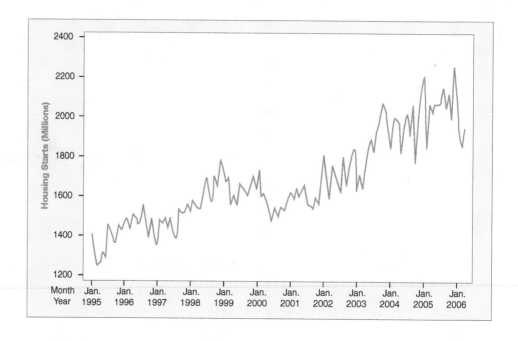

Chapter Outcome 2.➤ # Introduction to Index Numbers

When analyzing time-series data, decision makers must often compare one value measured at one point in time with other values measured at different points in time. For example, a real estate broker may wish to compare house prices in 2009 with house prices in previous years. A common procedure for making relative comparisons is to begin by determining a **base period index** to which all other data values can be fairly compared.

**Base Period Index**

The time-series value to which all other values in the time series are compared. The index number for the base period is defined as 100.

Equation 16.1 is used to make relative comparisons for data found in different periods by calculating a *simple index number*.

---

**Simple Index Number**

$$I_t = \frac{y_t}{y_0} 100 \qquad \text{(16.1)}$$

where:

$I_t$ = Index number at time period $t$
$y_t$ = Value of the time series at time $t$
$y_0$ = Value of the time series at the index base period

---

**EXAMPLE 16-1**    **COMPUTING SIMPLE INDEX NUMBERS**

**Wilson Windows, Inc.** The managers at Wilson Windows, Inc., are considering the purchase of a window and door plant in Wisconsin. The current owners of the window and door plant have touted their company's rapid sales growth over the past 10 years as a reason for their asking price. Wilson executives wish to convert the company's sales data to index numbers. The following steps can be used to do this:

Step 1   **Obtain the time-series data.**
         The company has sales data for each of the 10 years since 2000.

Step 2   **Select a base period.**
         Wilson managers have selected 2000 as the index base period. Sales in 2000 were $14.0 million.

**Step 3** **Compute the simple index numbers for each year using Equation 16.1.**
For instance, sales in 2001 were $15.2 million. Using Equation 16.1, the index for 2001 is

$$I_t = \frac{y_t}{y_0} 100$$

$$I_{2001} = \frac{15.2}{14.0} 100 = 108.6$$

For the 10 years, we get:

| Year | Sales ($ millions) | Index |
|------|--------------------|-------|
| 2000 | 14.0 | 100.0 |
| 2001 | 15.2 | 108.6 |
| 2002 | 17.8 | 127.1 |
| 2003 | 21.4 | 152.9 |
| 2004 | 24.6 | 175.7 |
| 2005 | 30.5 | 217.9 |
| 2006 | 29.8 | 212.9 |
| 2007 | 32.4 | 231.4 |
| 2008 | 37.2 | 265.7 |
| 2009 | 39.1 | 279.3 |

**>> END EXAMPLE**

**TRY PROBLEM** 16-8 (pg. 722)

Referring to Example 16-1, we can use the index numbers to determine the percentage change any year is from the base year. For instance, sales in 2007 have an index of 231.4. This means that sales in 2007 are 131.4% above sales in the base year of 2000. Sales in 2009 are 179.3% higher than they were in 2000.

Note that although you can use the index number to compare values between any one time period and the base period and can express the difference in percentage-change terms, you cannot compare period-to-period changes by subtracting the index numbers. For instance, in Example 16-1, when comparing sales for 2008 and 2009, we cannot say that the growth has been

$$279.3 - 265.7 = 13.6\%$$

To determine the actual percentage growth, we do the following:

$$\frac{279.3 - 265.7}{265.7} 100 = 5.1\%$$

Thus, the sales growth rate between 2008 and 2009 has been 5.1%, not 13.6%.

## Aggregate Price Indexes

"The dollar's not worth what it once was" is a saying that everyone has heard. The problem is that nothing is worth what it used to be; sometimes it is worth more, and other times it is worth less. The simple index shown in Equation 16.1 works well for comparing prices when we wish to analyze the price of a single item over time. For instance, we could use the simple index to analyze how apartment rents have changed over time or how college tuition has increased over time. However, if we wish to compare prices of a group of items, we might construct an **aggregate price index**.

**Aggregate Price Index**
An index that is used to measure the rate of change from a base period for a group of two or more items.

Equation 16.2 is used to compute an unweighted aggregate price index.

### Unweighted Aggregate Price Index

$$I_t = \frac{\sum p_t}{\sum p_0}(100)$$

(16.2)

where:

$I_t$ = Unweighted aggregate index at time period $t$
$p_t$ = Sum of the prices for the group of items at time period $t$
$p_0$ = Sum of the prices for the group of items at base time period

---

**EXAMPLE 16-2**   COMPUTING AN UNWEIGHTED AGGREGATE PRICE INDEX

**College Costs** There have been many news stories recently discussing the rate of growth of college and university costs. One university is interested in analyzing the growth in the total costs for students over the past five years. The university wishes to consider three main costs: tuition and fees, room and board, and books and supplies. Rather than analyzing these factors individually using three simple indexes, an unweighted aggregate price index can be developed using the following steps:

**Step 1**   **Define the variables to be included in the index and gather the time-series data.**

The university has identified three main categories of costs: tuition fees, room and board, and books and supplies. Data for the past five years have been collected. Full-time tuition and fees for two semesters are used. The full dorm-and-meal package offered by the university is priced for the room-and-board variable, and the books-and-supplies cost for a "typical" student are used for that component of the total costs.

**Step 2**   **Select a base period.**

The base period for this study will be the 2004–2005 academic year.

**Step 3**   **Use Equation 16.2 to compute the unweighted aggregate price index.**

The equation is

$$I_t = \frac{\sum p_t}{\sum p_0}(100)$$

The sum of the prices for the three components during the base academic year of 2004–2005 is $13,814. The sum of the prices in the 2008–2009 academic year is $19,492. Applying Equation 16.2, the unweighted aggregate price index is

$$I_{2008-2009} = \frac{\$19,492}{\$13,814}(100) = 141.1$$

This means, as a group, the components making up the cost of attending this university have increased by 41.1% since the 2004–2005 academic year. The indexes for the other years are shown as follows:

| Academic Year | Tuition & Fees ($) | Room & Board ($) | Books & Supplies ($) | $\sum p_t$ ($) | Index |
|---|---|---|---|---|---|
| 2004–2005 | 7,300 | 5,650 | 864 | 13,814 | 100.0 |
| 2005–2006 | 7,720 | 5,980 | 945 | 14,645 | 106.0 |
| 2006–2007 | 8,560 | 6,350 | 1,067 | 15,977 | 115.7 |
| 2007–2008 | 9,430 | 6,590 | 1,234 | 17,254 | 124.9 |
| 2008–2009 | 10,780 | 7,245 | 1,467 | 19,492 | 141.1 |

**>> END EXAMPLE**

**TRY PROBLEM** 16-9 (pg. 722)

# Weighted Aggregate Price Indexes

Example 16-2 utilized an unweighted aggregate price index to determine the change in university costs. This was appropriate because each student would incur the same set of three costs. However, in some situations, the items composing a total cost are not equally weighted. For instance, in a consumer price study of a "market basket" of 10 food items, a typical household will not use the same number (or volume) of each item. During a week, a typical household might use three gallons of milk, but only two loaves of bread. In these types of situations, we need to compute a weighted aggregate price index to account for the different levels of use. Two common weighted indexes are the Paasche Index and the Laspeyres Index.

**The Paasche Index** Equation 16.3 is used to compute a Paasche Index. Note that the weighting percentage in Equation 16.3 for the Paasche Index is always the percentage for the time period for which the index is being computed. The idea is that the prices in the base period should be weighted relative to their current use, not to what that use level was in other periods.

---

### Paasche Index

$$I_t = \frac{\sum q_t p_t}{\sum q_t p_0} (100)$$

(16.3)

where:

$q_t$ = Weighting percentage at time $t$
$p_t$ = Price in time period $t$
$p_0$ = Price in the base period

---

**EXAMPLE 16-3** | **COMPUTING THE PAASCHE INDEX**

**Wage Rates** Before a company makes a decision to locate a new manufacturing plant in a community, the managers will be interested in knowing how the wage rates have changed. Two categories of wages are to be analyzed as a package: production hourly wages and administrative/clerical hourly wages. Annual data showing the average hourly wage rates since 2000 are available. Each year, the makeup of the labor market differs in terms of the percentage of employees in the two categories. To compute a Paasche Index, use the following steps:

**Step 1 Define the variables to be included in the index and gather the time-series data.**
The variables are the mean hourly price for production workers and the mean average price for administrative/clerical workers. Data are collected for the 10-year period through 2009.

**Step 2 Select the base period.**
Because similar data for another community are available only back to 2003, the company will use 2003 as the base period to make comparisons between the two communities easier.

**Step 3 Use Equation 16.3 to compute the Paasche Index.**
The equation is

$$I_t = \frac{\sum q_t p_t}{\sum q_t p_0} (100)$$

The hourly wage rate for production workers in the base year 2003 was $10.80, whereas the average hourly administrative/clerical rate was $10.25.

In 2009, the production hourly rate had increased to $15.45, and the administrative/clerical rate was $13.45. In 2009, 60% of the employees in the community were designated as working in production and 40% were administrative/clerical. Equation 16.3 is used to compute the Paasche Index for 2009, as follows:

$$I_{2009} = \frac{(0.60)(\$15.45) + (0.40)(\$13.45)}{(0.60)(\$10.80) + (0.40)(\$10.25)}(100) = 138.5$$

This means that, overall, the wage rates in this community have increased by 38.5% since the base year of 2003. The following table shows the Paasche Indexes for all years.

| Year | Production Wage Rate ($) | Percent Production | Administrative/Clerical Wage Rate ($) | Percent Admin./Clerical | Paasche Index |
|------|------|------|------|------|------|
| 2000 | 8.50 | 0.78 | 9.10 | 0.22 | 80.8 |
| 2001 | 9.10 | 0.73 | 9.45 | 0.27 | 86.3 |
| 2002 | 10.00 | 0.69 | 9.80 | 0.31 | 93.5 |
| 2003 | 10.80 | 0.71 | 10.25 | 0.29 | 100.0 |
| 2004 | 11.55 | 0.68 | 10.60 | 0.32 | 105.9 |
| 2005 | 12.15 | 0.67 | 10.95 | 0.33 | 110.7 |
| 2006 | 12.85 | 0.65 | 11.45 | 0.35 | 116.5 |
| 2007 | 13.70 | 0.65 | 11.90 | 0.35 | 123.2 |
| 2008 | 14.75 | 0.62 | 12.55 | 0.38 | 131.4 |
| 2009 | 15.45 | 0.60 | 13.45 | 0.40 | 138.5 |

**>> END EXAMPLE**

**TRY PROBLEM** 16-12 (pg. 723)

**The Laspeyres Index** The Paasche Index is computed using the logic that the index for the current period should be compared to a base period with the current period weightings. An alternate index, called the Laspeyres Index, uses the base-period weighting in its computation, as shown in Equation 16.4.

**Laspeyres Index**

$$I_t = \frac{\sum q_0 p_t}{\sum q_0 p_0}(100) \qquad \textbf{(16.4)}$$

where:

$q_0$ = Weighting percentage at base period
$p_t$ = Price in time period $t$
$p_0$ = Price in base period

**EXAMPLE 16-4** **COMPUTING THE LASPEYRES INDEX**

**Wage Rates** Refer to Example 16-3, in which the managers of a company are interested in knowing how the wage rates have changed in the community in which they are considering building a plant. Two categories of wages are to be analyzed as a package: production hourly wages and administrative/clerical hourly wages. Annual data showing the average hourly wage rate since

2000 are available. Each year, the makeup of the labor market differs in terms of the percentage of employees in the two categories. To compute a Laspeyres Index, use the following steps:

Step 1 **Define the variables to be included in the index and gather the time-series data.**
The variables are the mean hourly price for production workers and the mean average price for administrative/clerical workers. Data are collected for the 10-year period through 2009.

Step 2 **Select the base period.**
Because similar data for another community are available only back to 2003, the company will use 2003 as the base period to make comparisons between the two communities easier.

Step 3 **Use Equation 16.4 to compute the Laspeyres Index.**
The equation is

$$I_t = \frac{\sum q_0 p_t}{\sum q_0 p_0} (100)$$

The hourly wage rate for production workers in the base year of 2003 was $10.80, whereas the average hourly administrative/clerical rate was $10.25. In that year, 71% of the workers were classified as production. In 2009, the production hourly rate had increased to $15.45, and the administrative/clerical rate was at $13.45. Equation 16.4 is used to compute the Laspeyres Index for 2009, as follows:

$$I_{2009} = \frac{(0.71)(\$15.45) + (0.29)(\$13.45)}{(0.71)(\$10.80) + (0.29)(\$10.25)} (100) = 139.7$$

This means that, overall, the wage rates in this community have increased by 39.7% since the base year of 2003. The following table shows the Laspeyres Indexes for all years.

| Year | Production Wage Rate ($) | Percent Production | Administrative/Clerical Wage Rate ($) | Percent Admin./Clerical | Laspeyres Index |
|------|--------------------------|--------------------|---------------------------------------|--------------------------|-----------------|
| 2000 | 8.50  | 0.78 | 9.10  | 0.22 | 81.5  |
| 2001 | 9.10  | 0.73 | 9.45  | 0.27 | 86.5  |
| 2002 | 10.00 | 0.69 | 9.80  | 0.31 | 93.4  |
| 2003 | 10.80 | 0.71 | 10.25 | 0.29 | 100.0 |
| 2004 | 11.55 | 0.68 | 10.60 | 0.32 | 106.0 |
| 2005 | 12.15 | 0.67 | 10.95 | 0.33 | 110.9 |
| 2006 | 12.85 | 0.65 | 11.45 | 0.35 | 116.9 |
| 2007 | 13.70 | 0.65 | 11.90 | 0.35 | 123.8 |
| 2008 | 14.75 | 0.62 | 12.55 | 0.38 | 132.6 |
| 2009 | 15.45 | 0.60 | 13.45 | 0.40 | 139.7 |

**>> END EXAMPLE**

**TRY PROBLEM** 16-13 (pg. 723)

# Commonly Used Index Numbers

In addition to converting time-series data to index numbers, you will encounter a variety of indexes in your professional and personal life.

**Consumer Price Index** To most of us, inflation has come to mean increased prices and less purchasing power for our dollar. The Consumer Price Index (CPI) attempts to measure the overall changes in retail prices for goods and services. The CPI, originally published in

**TABLE 16.2**  |  **CPI Index (1996 to 2008)**

| Year | 1996 | 1997 | 1998 | 1999 | 2000 | 2001 | 2002 | 2003 | 2004 | 2005 | 2006 | 2007 | 2008 |
|------|------|------|------|------|------|------|------|------|------|------|------|------|------|
| CPI | 156.9 | 157.0 | 160.5 | 166.6 | 172.2 | 177.1 | 179.9 | 184.0 | 188.9 | 195.3 | 201.6 | 207.3 | 215.3 |

Base = 1982 to 1984 (Index = 100)
*Source:* Bureau of Labor Statistics: http://www.bls.gov/cpi/home.htm#data

1913 by the U.S. Department of Labor, uses a "market basket" of goods and services purchased by a typical wage earner living in a city. The CPI, a weighted aggregate index similar to a Laspeyres Index, is based on items grouped into seven categories, including food, housing, clothing, transportation, medical care, entertainment, and miscellaneous items. The items in the market basket have changed over time to keep pace with the buying habits of our society and as new products and services have become available.

Since 1945, the base period used to construct the CPI has been updated. Currently, the base period, 1982 to 1984, has an index of 100. Table 16.2 shows the CPI index values for 1996 to 2008. For instance, the index for 2005 is 195.3, which means that the price of the market basket of goods increased 95.3% between 1984 and 2005. Remember also that you cannot determine the inflation rate by subtracting index values for successive years. Instead, you must divide the difference by the earlier year's index. For instance, the rate of inflation between 2004 and 2005 was

$$\text{Inflation rate} = \frac{195.3 - 188.9}{188.9}(100) = 3.39\%$$

Thus, in general terms, if your income did not increase by at least 3.39% between 2004 and 2005, you failed to keep pace with inflation and your purchasing power was reduced.

**Producer Price Index**  The U.S. Bureau of Labor Statistics publishes the *Producer Price Index* (PPI) on a monthly basis to measure the rate of change in nonretail prices. Like the CPI, the PPI is a Laspeyres weighted aggregate index. This index is used as a leading indicator of upcoming changes in the CPI. Table 16.3 shows the PPI between 1996 and 2005.

## Stock Market Indexes

Every night on the national and local TV news, reporters tell us what happened on the stock market that day by reporting on the *Dow Jones Industrial Average* (DJIA). The Dow, as this index is commonly referred to, is not the same type of index as the CPI or PPI, in that it is not a percentage of a base year. Rather, the DJIA is the sum of the stock prices for 30 large industrial companies whose stocks trade on the New York Stock Exchange divided by a factor that is adjusted for stock splits. Many analysts use the DJIA, which is computed daily, as a measure of the health of the stock market. Other analysts prefer other indexes, such as the *Standard and Poor's 500* (S&P 500). The S&P 500 includes stock prices for 500 companies and is thought by some to be more representative of the broader market.

**TABLE 16.3**  |  **PPI Index (1996 to 2005)**

| Year | 1996 | 1997 | 1998 | 1999 | 2000 | 2001 | 2002 | 2003 | 2004 | 2005 |
|------|------|------|------|------|------|------|------|------|------|------|
| PPI | 127.7 | 127.6 | 124.4 | 125.5 | 132.7 | 134.2 | 131.1 | 138.1 | 142.7 | 157.4 |

Base = 1984 (Index = 100)
*Source:* Bureau of Labor Statistics: http://www.bls.gov/ppi/home.htm#data

The *NASDAQ* is an index made up of stocks on the NASDAQ exchange and is heavily influenced by technology-based companies that are traded on this exchange. Publications such as *The Wall Street Journal* and *Barrons* publish all these indexes and others every day for investors to use in their investing decisions.

# Using Index Numbers to Deflate a Time Series

A common use of index numbers is to convert values measured at different times into more directly comparable values. For instance, if your wages increase, but at a rate less than inflation, you will in fact be earning less in "real terms." A company experiencing increasing sales at a rate of increase less than inflation is actually not increasing in "real terms."

**BUSINESS APPLICATION**    **DEFLATING TIME-SERIES VALUES USING INDEX VALUES**

**WYMAN-GORMAN COMPANY**   The Wyman-Gorman Company, located in Massachusetts, designs and produces forgings, primarily for internal combustion engines. The company has recently been experiencing some financial difficulty and has discontinued its agricultural and earthmoving divisions. Table 16.4 shows sales in millions of dollars for the company since 1996. Also shown is the PPI (Producer Price Index) for the same years. Finally, sales, adjusted to 1984 dollars, are also shown.

Equation 16.5 is used to determine the adjusted time-series values.

---

**Deflation Formula**

$$y_{adj_t} = \frac{y_t}{I_t}(100)$$                    (16.5)

where:

$y_{adj_t}$ = Deflated time-series value at time $t$
$y_t$ = Actual value of the time series at time $t$
$I_t$ = Index (such as CPI or PPI) at time $t$

---

For instance, in 1996 sales were \$610.3 million. The PPI for that year was 127.7. The sales, adjusted to 1984 dollars, is

$$y_{adj_{1996}} = \frac{610.3}{127.7}(100) = \$477.9$$

**TABLE 16.4** | **Deflated Sales Data—Using Producer Price Index (PPI)**

| Year | Sales ($ millions) | PPI (Base = 1984) | Sales ($ millions, adjusted to 1984 dollars) |
|------|--------------------|--------------------|----------------------------------------------|
| 1996 | 610.3 | 127.7 | 477.9 |
| 1997 | 473.1 | 127.6 | 370.8 |
| 1998 | 383.5 | 124.4 | 308.3 |
| 1999 | 425.5 | 125.5 | 339.0 |
| 2000 | 384.1 | 132.7 | 289.4 |
| 2001 | 341.1 | 134.2 | 254.2 |
| 2002 | 310.3 | 131.1 | 236.7 |
| 2003 | 271.6 | 138.1 | 196.7 |
| 2004 | 371.6 | 142.7 | 260.4 |
| 2005 | 390.2 | 157.4 | 247.9 |

# 16-1: Exercises

## Skill Development

**16-1.** What is meant by time-series data? Give an example.

**16-2.** Explain the difference between time-series data and cross-sectional data. Are these two types of data sets mutually exclusive? What do they have in common? How do they differ?

**16-3.** What are the differences between quantitative and qualitative forecasting techniques? Under what conditions is it appropriate to use a quantitative technique?

**16-4.** Provide an example of a business decision that requires (1) a short-term forecast, (2) a medium-term forecast, and (3) a long-term forecast.

**16-5.** What is meant by the trend component of a time series? How is a linear trend different from a nonlinear trend?

**16-6.** Must a seasonal component be associated with the seasons (fall, spring, summer, winter) of the year? Provide an example of a seasonal effect that is not associated with the seasons of the year.

**16-7.** A Greek entrepreneur followed the olive harvests. He noted that olives ripen in September. Each March he would try to determine if the upcoming olive harvest would be especially bountiful. If his analysis indicated it would, he would enter into agreements with the owners of all the olive oil presses in the region. In exchange for a small deposit months ahead of the harvest, he would obtain the right to lease the presses at market prices during the harvest. If he was correct about the harvest and demand for olive oil presses boomed, he could make a great deal of money. Identify the following quantities in the context of this scenario:
   a. forecasting horizon
   b. category that applies to the forecasting horizon identified in part a
   c. forecasting period
   d. forecasting interval

**16-8.** Consider the following median selling prices ($thousands) for homes in a community:

| Year | Price |
|------|-------|
| 1 | 320 |
| 2 | 334 |
| 3 | 329 |
| 4 | 344 |
| 5 | 358 |
| 6 | 347 |
| 7 | 383 |
| 8 | 404 |
| 9 | 397 |
| 10 | 411 |

   a. Use year 1 as a base year and construct a simple index number to show how the median selling price has increased.

   b. Determine the actual percentage growth in the median selling price between the base year and year 10.
   c. Determine the actual percentage growth in the median selling price between the base year and year 5.
   d. Determine the actual percentage growth in the median selling price between year 5 and year 10.

**16-9.** The following values represent advertising rates paid by a regional catalog retailer that advertises either on radio or in newspapers:

| Year | Radio Rates ($) | Newspaper Rates ($) |
|------|-----------------|---------------------|
| 1 | 300 | 400 |
| 2 | 310 | 420 |
| 3 | 330 | 460 |
| 4 | 346 | 520 |
| 5 | 362 | 580 |
| 6 | 380 | 640 |
| 7 | 496 | 660 |

   a. Determine a relative index for each type of advertisement using year 1 as the base year.
   b. Determine an unweighted aggregate index for the two types of advertisement.
   c. In year 1 the retailer spent 30% of the advertisement budget on radio advertising. Construct a Laspeyres index for the data.
   d. Using year 1 as the base, construct a Paasche index for the same data.

## Business Applications

Problems 16-10 through 16-13 refer to Gallup Construction and Paving, a company whose primary business has been constructing homes in planned communities in the upper Midwest. The company has kept a record of the relative cost of labor and materials in its market areas for the last 11 years. These data are as follows:

| Year | Hourly Wages ($) | Average Material Cost ($) |
|------|------------------|---------------------------|
| 1999 | 30.10 | 66,500 |
| 2000 | 30.50 | 68,900 |
| 2001 | 31.70 | 70,600 |
| 2002 | 32.50 | 70,900 |
| 2003 | 34.00 | 71,200 |
| 2004 | 35.50 | 71,700 |
| 2005 | 35.10 | 72,500 |
| 2006 | 35.05 | 73,700 |
| 2007 | 34.90 | 73,400 |
| 2008 | 33.80 | 74,100 |
| 2009 | 34.20 | 74,000 |

**16-10.** Using 1999 as the base year, construct a separate index for each component in the construction of a house.

**16-11.** Plot both series of data and comment on the trend you see in both plots.

**16-12.** Construct a Paasche index for 2004 using the data. Use 1999 as the base year and assume that in 2004 60% of the cost of a townhouse was in materials.

**16-13.** Construct a Laspeyres index using the data, assuming that in 1999, 40% of the cost of a townhouse was labor.

**16-14.** Retail Forward, Inc., is a global management consulting and market research firm specializing in retail intelligence and strategies. One of its press releases (*June Consumer Outlook: Spending Plans Show Resilience*, June 1, 2006) divulged the result of the Retail Forward ShopperScape™ survey conducted each month from a sample of 4,000 U.S. primary household shoppers. A measure of consumer spending is represented by the figure at the top of the page:

a. Describe the type of index used by Retail Forward to explore consumer spending.

b. Determine the actual percentage change in the Future Spending Index between December 2005 and June 2006.

c. Determine the actual percentage change in the Future Spending Index between June 2005 and June 2006.

## Computer Database **Exercises**

**16-15.** The Energy Information Administration (EIA), created by Congress in 1977, is a statistical agency of the U.S. Department of Energy. It provides data, forecasts, and analyses to promote sound policymaking and public understanding regarding energy and its interaction with the economy and the environment. The price of the sources of energy is becoming more and more important as our natural resources are consumed. The file entitled **Prices** contains data for the period

1993–2008 concerning the price of gasoline ($/gal.), natural gas ($/cu. ft.), and electricity (cents/kilowatt hr.).

a. Using 1993 as the base, calculate an aggregate energy price index for these three energy costs.

b. Determine the actual percentage change in the aggregate energy prices between 1993 and 2008.

c. Determine the actual percentage change in the aggregate energy prices between 1998 and 2008.

**16-16.** The federal funds rate is the interest rate charged by banks when banks borrow "overnight" from each other. The funds rate fluctuates according to supply and demand and is not under the direct control of the Federal Reserve Board, but is strongly influenced by the Fed's actions. The file entitled **The Fed** contains the federal funds rates for the period 1955–2008.

a. Construct a time-series plot for the federal funds rate for the period 1955–2008.

b. Describe the time-series components that are present in the data set.

c. Indicate the recurrence periods for any seasonal or cyclical components.

**16-17.** The Census Bureau of the Department of Commerce released the U.S. retail e-commerce sales for the period Fourth Quarter 1999–Fourth Quarter 2008. The file entitled **E-Commerce** contains that data.

a. Using the fourth quarter of 1999 as the base, calculate a Laspeyres Index for the retail sales for the period of Fourth Quarter 1999–Fourth Quarter 2008.

b. Determine the actual percentage change in the retail sales for the period Fourth Quarter 1999–First Quarter 2004.

c. Determine the actual percentage change in the retail sales for the period First Quarter 2004–First Quarter 2006.

# 16.2 Trend-Based Forecasting Techniques

As we discussed in Section 16.1, some time series exhibit an increasing or decreasing trend. Further, the trend may be linear or nonlinear. A plot of the data will be very helpful in identifying which, if any, of these trends exist.

## Developing a Trend-Based Forecasting Model

In this section, we introduce *trend-based forecasting techniques*. As the name implies, these techniques are used to identify the presence of a trend and to model that trend. Once the trend model has been defined, it is used to provide forecasts for future time periods.

**Chapter Outcomes 3 and 4.→** | BUSINESS APPLICATION | LINEAR TREND FORECASTING

**THE TAFT ICE CREAM COMPANY** The Taft Ice Cream Company is a family-operated company selling gourmet ice cream to resort areas, primarily on the North Carolina coast. Figure 16.5 displays the annual sales data for the 10-year period 1997–2006 and shows the time-series plot illustrating that sales have trended up in the 10-year period. These data are in a file called **Taft**.

Taft's owners are considering expanding their ice cream manufacturing facilities. As part of the bank's financing requirements, the managers are asked to supply a forecast of future sales. Recall from our earlier discussions that the forecasting process has three steps: (1) model specification, (2) model fitting, and (3) model diagnosis.

**Excel and Minitab Tutorial**

**Step 1   Model Specification**
The time-series plot in Figure 16.5 indicates that sales have exhibited a linear growth pattern. A possible forecasting tool is a linear trend (straight-line) model.

**Step 2   Model-Fitting**
Because we have specified a linear trend model, the process of fitting can be accomplished using least squares regression analysis of a form described by Equation 16.6.

**FIGURE 16.5**

Excel 2007 Output Showing Taft Ice Cream Sales Trend Line

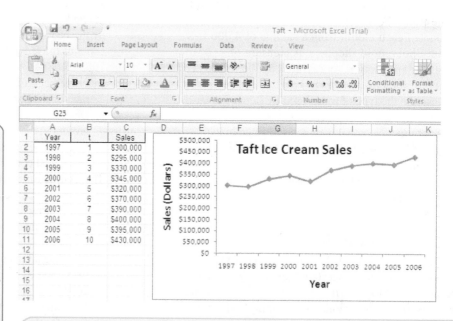

**Excel 2007 Instructions:**
1. Open file: Taft.xls.
2. Select data in the Sales data column.
3. Click on **Insert > Line Chart**.
4. Click on **Select Data**.
5. Under **Horizontal (categories) Axis Labels**, select data in Year column.
6. Click on **Layout > Chart Title** and enter desired title.
7. Click on **Layout > Axis Titles** and enter horizontal and vertical axis titles.

**Minitab Instructions (for similar results):**
1. Open file: Taft.MTW.
2. Choose **Graph > Time Series Plot**.
3. Select **Simple**.
4. Under **Series**, enter time series' column.
5. Click **Time/Scale**.
6. Under **Time Scale** select **Calendar** and **Year**.
7. Under **Start Values**, insert the starting year.
8. Click **OK. OK.**

---

**Linear Trend Model**

$$y_t = \beta_0 + \beta_1 t + \varepsilon_t \qquad \text{(16.6)}$$

where:

$$y_t = \text{Value of the trend at time } t$$
$$\beta_0 = y \text{ intercept of the trend line}$$
$$\beta_1 = \text{Slope of the trend line}$$
$$t = \text{Time period } (t = 1, 2, \ldots)$$
$$\varepsilon_t = \text{Model error at time } t$$

---

We let the first period in the time series be $t = 1$, the second period be $t = 2$, and so forth. The values for time form the independent variable, with sales being the dependent variable. Referring to Chapter 14, the least squares regression equations for the slope and intercept are estimated by Equations 16.7 and 16.8. Here the sums are taken over the values of $t$ ($t = 1, 2 \ldots$).

---

**Least Squares Equations Estimates**

$$b_1 = \frac{\sum t y_t - \dfrac{\sum t \sum y_t}{n}}{\sum t^2 - \dfrac{(\sum t)^2}{n}} \qquad \text{(16.7)}$$

$$b_0 = \frac{\sum y_t}{n} - b_1 \frac{\sum t}{n} \qquad \text{(16.8)}$$

where:

$$n = \text{Number of periods in the time series}$$
$$t = \text{Time period (independent variable)}$$
$$y_t = \text{Dependent variable at time } t$$

---

The linear regression procedures in either Excel or Minitab can be used to compute the least squares trend model. Figure 16.6 shows the Excel output for the Taft Ice Cream Company example. The least squares trend model for the Taft Company is

$$\hat{y}_t = b_0 + b_1 t$$
$$\hat{y}_t = 277,333.33 + 14,575.76(t)$$

For a forecast, we use $F_t$ as the forecast value or predicted value at time period $t$. Thus,

$$F_t = 277,333.33 + 14,575.76(t)$$

**Step 3   Model Diagnosis**

The linear trend regression output in Figure 16.6 offers some conclusions about the potential capabilities of our model. The $R$-squared $= 0.9123$ shows that for these 10 years of data, the linear trend model explains more than 91% of the variation in sales. The $p$-value for the regression slope coefficient to four decimal places is 0.0000. This means that time ($t$) can be used to explain a significant portion of the variation in sales. Figure 16.7 shows the plot of the trend line through the data. You can see the trend model fits the historical data quite closely. Although these results are a good sign, the model diagnosis step requires further analysis.

**FIGURE 16.6**

Excel 2007 Output for Taft Ice Cream Trend Model

**Excel 2007 Instructions:**
1. Open file: Taft.xls.
2. Select **Data > Data Analysis**.
3. Click on **Regression**.
4. Enter range for the *y* variable (*Sales*).
5. Enter range for the *x* variable ($t = 1, 2 \ldots$).
6. Specify output location.
7. Click on **Labels**.

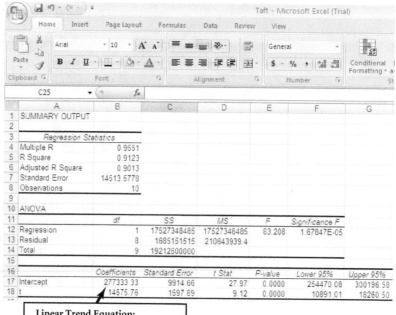

**Linear Trend Equation:**
Sales = 277,333.33 + 14,575.76($t$)

**Minitab Instructions (for similar results):**
1. Open file: Taft.MTW.
2. Choose **Stat > Regression > Regression**.
3. In **Response**, enter the time series column, *Sales*.
4. In **Predictors**, enter the time variable column, *t*.
5. Click **OK**.

**FIGURE 16.7**

Excel 2007 Output for Taft Ice Cream Trend Line

**Excel 2007 Instructions:**
1. Open file: Taft.xls.
2. Select the *Sales* data.
3. Click on **Insert > Line Chart**.
4. Click on Select **Data**.
5. Under **Horizontal (categories) Axis Labels**, select data in *Year* column.
6. Click on **Layout > Chart Title** and enter desired title.
7. Click on **Layout > Axis Titles** and enter horizontal and vertical axes titles.
8. Select the data.
9. Right-click and select **Add Trendline > Linear**.
10. To set color, go to **Trend Line Options** (see step 9).

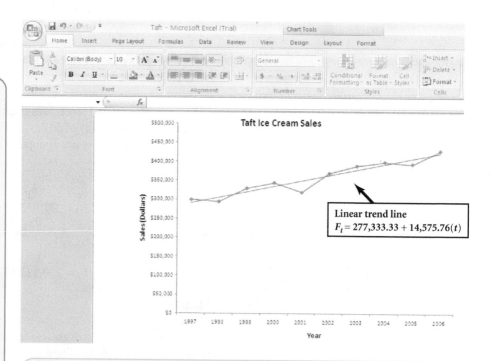

Linear trend line
$F_t = 277,333.33 + 14,575.76(t)$

**Minitab Instructions (for similar results):**
1. Open file: Taft.MTW.
2. Choose **Stat > Time Series > Trend Analysis**.
3. In **Variable**, enter the time series column.
4. Under **Model Type** choose **Linear**.
5. Click **OK**.

# Comparing the Forecast Values to the Actual Data

The slope of the trend line indicates the Taft Ice Cream Company has experienced an average increase in sales of $14,575.76 per year over the 10-year period. The linear trend model's fitted sales values for periods $t = 1$ through $t = 10$ can be found by substituting for $t$ in the following forecast equation:

$$F_t = 277,333.33 + 14,575.76(t)$$

For example, for $t = 1$, we get

$$F_t = 277,333.33 + 14,575.76(1)$$
$$= \$291,909.09$$

Note that the actual sales figure, $y_1$, for period 1 was $300,000. The difference between the actual sales in time $t$ and the forecast values in time $t$, found using the trend model, is called the *forecast error* or the *residual*. Figure 16.8 shows the forecasts for periods 1 through 10 and the forecast errors at each period.

Computing the forecast error by comparing the trend-line values with actual past data is an important part of the model diagnosis step. The errors measure how closely the model fits the actual data at each point. A perfect fit would lead to residuals of 0 each time. We would like to see small residuals and an overall good fit. Two commonly used measures of fit are mean squared residual, or *mean squared error* (*MSE*), and *mean absolute deviation* (*MAD*). These measures are computed using Equations 16.9 and 16.10, respectively. *MAD* measures the average magnitude of the forecast errors. *MSE* is a measure of the variability in the forecast errors. The forecast error is the observed value, $y_t$, minus the predicted value, $F_t$.

| **Mean Squared Error** | | **Mean Absolute Deviation** | |
|---|---|---|---|
| $MSE = \dfrac{\Sigma(y_t - F_t)^2}{n}$ | **(16.9)** | $MAD = \dfrac{\Sigma |y_t - F_t|}{n}$ | **(16.10)** |

where:

$y_t$ = Actual value at time $t$
$F_t$ = Predicted value at time $t$
$n$ = Number of time periods

**FIGURE 16.8**

Excel 2007 Residual Output for Taft Ice Cream

**Excel 2007 Instructions:**
1. Follow Figure 16.6 Excel Instructions.
2. In **Regression** procedure, click on **Residuals**.

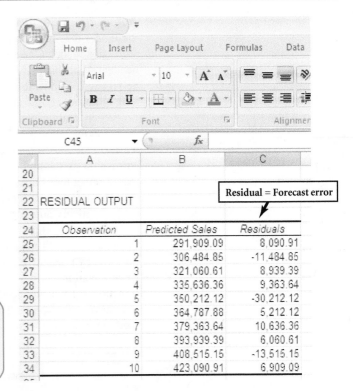

| Observation | Predicted Sales | Residuals |
|---|---|---|
| 1 | 291,909.09 | 8,090.91 |
| 2 | 306,484.85 | -11,484.85 |
| 3 | 321,060.61 | 8,939.39 |
| 4 | 335,636.36 | 9,363.64 |
| 5 | 350,212.12 | -30,212.12 |
| 6 | 364,787.88 | 5,212.12 |
| 7 | 379,363.64 | 10,636.36 |
| 8 | 393,939.39 | 6,060.61 |
| 9 | 408,515.15 | -13,515.15 |
| 10 | 423,090.91 | 6,909.09 |

Residual = Forecast error

**FIGURE 16.9**

Excel 2007 MSE and MAD
Computations for Taft Ice
Cream

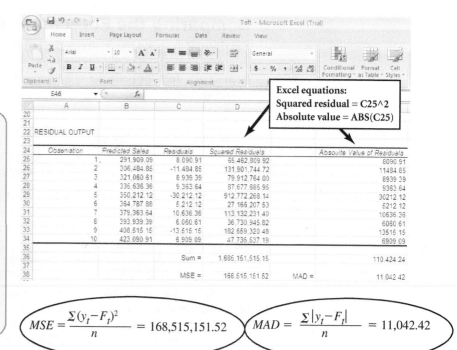

**Excel 2007 Instructions:**
1. Follow Figure 16.6 Excel Instructions.
2. In **Regression** procedure, click on **Residuals**.
3. Create a new column of squared residuals.
4. Create a column of absolute values of the residuals using the **ABS** function in Excel.
5. Use Equations 16.9 and 16.10 to calculate *MSE* and *MAD*.

**Excel equations:**
Squared residual = C25^2
Absolute value = ABS(C25)

| Observation | Predicted Sales | Residuals | Squared Residuals | Absolute Value of Residuals |
|---|---|---|---|---|
| 1 | 291,909.09 | 8,090.91 | 65,462,809.92 | 8090.91 |
| 2 | 306,484.85 | -11,484.85 | 131,901,744.72 | 11484.85 |
| 3 | 321,060.61 | 8,939.39 | 79,912,764.00 | 8939.39 |
| 4 | 335,636.36 | 9,363.64 | 87,677,685.95 | 9363.64 |
| 5 | 350,212.12 | -30,212.12 | 912,772,268.14 | 30212.12 |
| 6 | 364,787.88 | 5,212.12 | 27,166,207.53 | 5212.12 |
| 7 | 379,363.64 | 10,636.36 | 113,132,231.40 | 10636.36 |
| 8 | 393,939.39 | 6,060.61 | 36,730,945.82 | 6060.61 |
| 9 | 408,515.15 | -13,515.15 | 182,659,320.48 | 13515.15 |
| 10 | 423,090.91 | 6,909.09 | 47,735,537.19 | 6909.09 |
| | | Sum = | 1,685,151,515.15 | 110,424.24 |
| | | MSE = | 166,515,151.52 | MAD = 11,042.42 |

$$MSE = \frac{\Sigma(y_t - F_t)^2}{n} = 168,515,151.52 \qquad MAD = \frac{\Sigma|y_t - F_t|}{n} = 11,042.42$$

Figure 16.9 shows the *MSE* and *MAD* calculations using Excel for the Taft Ice Cream example. The *MAD* value of $11,042 indicates the linear trend model has an average absolute error of $11,042 per period. The *MSE* (in squared units) equals 168,515,151.52. The square root of the *MSE* (often referred to as *RMSE*, root mean square error) is $12,981.34, and although it is not equal to the *MAD* value, it does provide similar information about the relationship between the forecast values and the actual values of the time series.[1]

These error measures are particularly helpful when comparing two or more forecasting techniques. We can compute the *MSE* and/or the *MAD* for each forecasting technique. The forecasting technique that gives the smallest *MSE* or *MAD* is generally considered to provide the best fit.

**Autocorrelation** In addition to examining the fit of the forecasts to the actual time series, the model-diagnosis step also should examine how a model meets the assumptions of the regression model. One regression assumption is that the error terms are uncorrelated, or independent. When using regression with time-series data, the assumption of independence could be violated. That is, the error terms may be correlated over time. We call this *serial correlation*, or **autocorrelation**.

**Autocorrelation**

Correlation of the error terms (residuals) occurs when the residuals at points in time are related.

When dealing with a time-series variable, the value of *y* at time period *t* is commonly related to the value of *y* at previous time periods. If a relationship between $y_t$ and $y_{t-1}$ exists, we conclude that first-order autocorrelation exists. If $y_t$ is related to $y_{t-2}$, second-order autocorrelation exists, and so forth. If the time-series values are autocorrelated, the assumption that the error terms are independent is violated.

The autocorrelation can be positive or negative. For instance, when the values are first-order positively autocorrelated, we expect a positive residual to be followed by a positive residual in the next period, and we expect a negative residual to be followed by another negative residual. With negative first-order autocorrelation, we expect a positive residual to be followed by a negative residual, followed by a positive residual, and so on. The presence of autocorrelation can have adverse consequences on tests of statistical significance in a regression model. Thus, you need to be able to detect the presence of autocorrelation and take action to remove the problem. The *Durbin-Watson statistic*, which is shown in Equation 16.11, is used to test whether residuals are autocorrelated.

---

[1]Technically this is the square root of the average squared distance between the forecasts and the observed data values. Algebraically, of course, this is not the same as the average forecast error, but it is comparable.

**Durbin-Watson Statistic**

$$d = \frac{\sum\limits_{t=2}^{n}(e_t - e_{t-1})^2}{\sum\limits_{t=1}^{n} e_t^2}$$   (16.11)

where:

$d$ = Durbin-Watson test statistic

$e_t = (y_t - \hat{y}_t)$ = Residual at time $t$

$n$ = Number of time periods in the time series

Figure 16.10 shows the Minitab output providing the Durbin-Watson statistic for the Taft Ice Cream data, as follows:

$$d = \frac{\sum\limits_{t=2}^{n}(e_t - e_{t-1})^2}{\sum\limits_{t=1}^{n} e_t^2} = 2.65$$

Examining Equation 16.11, we see that if successive values of the residual are close in value, the Durbin-Watson $d$ statistic will be small. This situation would describe one in which residuals are positively correlated.

The Durbin-Watson statistic can have a value ranging from 0 to 4. A value of 2 indicates no autocorrelation. However, like any other statistics computed from a sample, the Durbin-Watson $d$ is subject to sampling error. We may wish to test formally to determine whether positive autocorrelation exists.

$$H_0: \rho = 0$$
$$H_A: \rho > 0$$

**FIGURE 16.10**

Minitab Output—Durbin-Watson Statistic: Taft Ice Cream Company Example

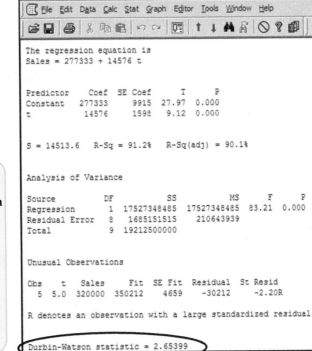

**Minitab Instructions:**
1. Open file: Taft.MTW.
2. Choose **Stat > Regression > Regression**.
3. In **Response**, enter the time series column, *Sales*.
4. In **Predictors**, enter the time variable column, *t*.
5. Select **Options**.
6. Under **Display**, select **Durbin-Watson statistic**.
8. Click **OK. OK.**

**Excel 2007 Instructions (for similar results):**
1. Open file: Taft.xls.
2. Click on **Add-Ins**.
3. Select **PHStat**.
4. Select **Regression > Simple Linear Regression**.
5. Define *y* variable.
6. Define *x* variable.
7. Check box for **Durbin-Watson statistic**.
8. Click **OK**.

If the $d$ statistic is too small, we will reject the null hypothesis and conclude that positive autocorrelation exists. If the $d$ statistic is too large, we will not reject and will not be able to conclude that positive autocorrelation exists. Appendix O contains a table of one-tailed Durbin-Watson critical values for $\alpha = 0.05$ and $\alpha = 0.01$ levels. (*Note*: The critical values in Appendix O are for one-tailed tests with $\alpha = 0.05$ or $0.01$. For a two-tailed test, the alpha is doubled.) The Durbin-Watson table provides two critical values: $d_L$ and $d_U$. In this test for positive autocorrelation, the decision rule is

If $d < d_L$, reject $H_0$ and conclude that positive autocorrelation exists.
If $d > d_U$, do not reject $H_0$ and conclude that no positive autocorrelation exists.
If $d_L < d < d_U$, the test is inconclusive.

The Durbin-Watson test is not reliable for sample sizes smaller than 15. Therefore, for the Taft Ice Cream Company application, we are unable to conduct the hypothesis test for autocorrelation. However, Example 16-5 shows a Durbin-Watson test carried out.

---

**EXAMPLE 16-5**    **TESTING FOR AUTOCORRELATION**

**Banion Automotive, Inc.** Banion Automotive, Inc., has supplied parts to General Motors since the company was founded in 1992. During this time, revenues from the General Motors account have grown steadily. Figure 16.11 displays the data in a time-series plot. The data are in a file called **Banion Automotive**.

Recently the managers of the company developed a linear trend regression model they hope to use to forecast revenue for the next two years to determine whether they can support adding another production line to their Ohio factory. They are now interested in determining whether the linear model is subject to positive autocorrelation. To test for this, the following steps can be used:

Step 1  **Specify the model.**
Based on a study of the line chart, the forecasting model is to be a simple linear trend regression model, with revenue as the dependent variable and time ($t$) as the independent variable.

Step 2  **Fit the model.**
Because we have specified a linear trend model, the process of fitting can be accomplished using least squares regression analysis and Excel or Minitab to

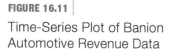

**FIGURE 16.11**

Time-Series Plot of Banion Automotive Revenue Data

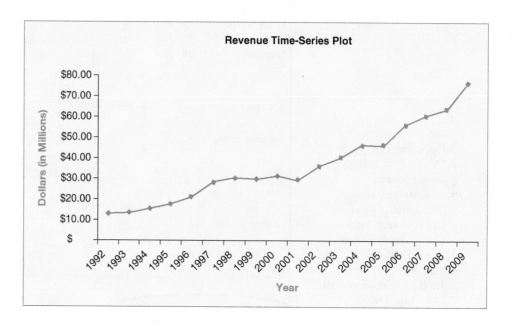

estimate the slope and intercept for the model. Fitting the 18 data points with a least squares line, we find the following:

$$F_t = 5.0175 + 3.3014(t)$$

**Step 3 Diagnose the model.**
The following values were also found:

$$R^2 = 0.935$$
$$F\text{-statistic} = 230.756$$
$$\text{Standard error} = 4.78$$

The large $F$-statistic indicates that the model explains a significant amount of variation in revenue over time. However, looking at a plot of the trend line shown in Figure 16.12, we see a pattern of actual revenue values first above, and then below, the trend line. This pattern indicates possible autocorrelation among the error terms. We will test for autocorrelation by calculating the Durbin-Watson $d$ statistic. Both Minitab and the PHStat add-ins for Excel have the option to generate the Durbin-Watson statistic. The output is shown in Figure 16.13.

Figure 16.13 shows the Durbin-Watson $d$ statistic as

$$d = 0.661$$

The null and alternative hypotheses for testing for positive autocorrelation are

$$H_0: \rho = 0$$
$$H_A: \rho > 0$$

We next go to the Durbin-Watson table (Appendix O) for $\alpha = 0.05$, sample size 18, and number of independent variables, $p = 1$. The values from the table for $d_L$ and $d_U$ are

$$d_L = 1.16 \quad \text{and} \quad d_U = 1.39$$

The decision rule for testing whether we have positive autocorrelation is

If $d < 1.16$, reject $H_0$ and conclude that positive autocorrelation exists.
If $d > 1.39$, conclude that no positive autocorrelation exists.
If $1.16 < d < 1.39$, the test is inconclusive.

**FIGURE 16.12**

Banion Automotive Trend Line

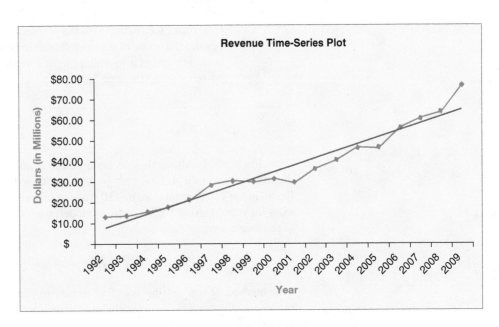

**FIGURE 16.13**

Excel 2007 (PHStat) Output—Durbin-Watson Statistic for Banion Automotive

**Excel 2007 Instructions:**

1. Open file: Banion Automotive.xls.
2. Select **Add-Ins**.
3. Select **PHStat**.
4. Select **Regression > Simple Linear Regression**.
5. Define *y* variable data range.
6. Specify *x* variable data range (time = *t* values).
7. Click on **Durbin-Watson Statistic**.
8. Click **OK**.

**Minitab Instructions (for similar results):**

1. Open file: Banion Automotive.MTW.
2. Choose **Stat > Regression > Regression**.
3. In **Response**, enter the time series column, *Revenue*.
4. In **Predictors**, enter the time variable column, *t*.
5. Select **Options**.
6. Under **Display**, select **Durbin-Watson statistic**.
7. Click **OK. OK**.

Because $d = 0.661 < d_L = 1.16$, we must reject the null hypothesis and conclude that significant positive autocorrelation exists in the regression model. This means that the assumption of uncorrelated error terms has been violated in this case. Thus, the linear trend model is not the appropriate model to provide the annual revenue forecasts for the next two years. There are several techniques for dealing with the problem of autocorrelation. Some of these are beyond the scope of this text. (Refer to books by Nelson and Wonnacott.) However, one option is to attempt to fit a nonlinear trend to the data, which is discussed starting on page 734.

**>> END EXAMPLE**

**TRY PROBLEM** 16-18 (pg. 747)

**True Forecasts** Although a decision maker is interested in how well a forecasting technique can fit historical data, the real test comes with how well it forecasts future values. Recall in the Taft example, we had 10 years of historical data. If we wish to forecast ice cream sales for year 11 using the linear trend model, we substitute $t = 11$ into the forecast equation to produce a forecast as follows:

$$F_{11} = 277,333.33 + 14,575.76(11) = \$437,666.69$$

This method of forecasting is called *trend projection*. To determine how well our trend model actually forecasts, we would have to wait until the actual sales amount for period 11 is known.

As we just indicated, a model's true forecasting ability is determined by how well it forecasts future values, not by how well it fits historical values. However, having to wait until after the forecast period to know how effective a forecast is doesn't help us assess a model's effectiveness ahead of time. This problem can be partially overcome by using *split samples*, which involves dividing a time series into two groups. You put the first ($n_1$) periods of historical data in the first group. These ($n_1$) periods will be used to develop the forecasting model. The second group contains the remaining ($n_2$) periods of historical data, which will be used to test the model's forecasting ability. These data are called the *holdout data*. Usually, three to five periods are held out, depending on the total number of periods in the time series.

In the Taft Ice Cream business application, we have only 10 years of historical data, so we will hold out the last three periods and use the first seven periods to develop the linear trend model. The computations are performed as before, using Excel or Minitab or Equations 16.7 and 16.8. Because we are using a different data set to develop the linear equation, we get a slightly different trend line than when all 10 periods were used. The new trend line is

$$F_t = 277{,}142.85 + 14{,}642.85(t)$$

This model is now used to provide forecasts for periods 8 through 10 by using trend projection. These forecasts are

| Year | Actual | Forecast | Error |
|------|--------|----------|-------|
| $t$  | $y_t$  | $F_t$    | $(y_t - F_t)$ |
| 8    | 400,000 | 394,285.65 | 5,714.35 |
| 9    | 395,000 | 408,928.50 | −13,928.50 |
| 10   | 430,000 | 423,571.35 | 6,428.65 |

Then we can compute the *MSE* and the *MAD* values for periods 8 through 10.

$$MSE = \frac{[(5{,}714.35)^2 + (-13{,}928.50)^2 + (6{,}428.65)^2]}{3} = 89{,}328{,}149.67$$

and

$$MAD = \frac{(|5{,}714.35| + |-13{,}928.50| + |6{,}428.65|)}{3} = 8{,}690.50$$

These values could be compared with those produced using other forecasting techniques or evaluated against the forecaster's own standards. Smaller values are preferred. Other factors should also be considered. For instance, in some cases, the forecast values might tend to be higher (or lower) than the actual values. This may imply the linear trend model isn't the best model to use. Forecasting models that tend to over- or underforecast are said to contain *forecast bias*. Equation 16.12 is used as an estimator of the bias.

---

### Forecast Bias

$$\text{Forecast bias} = \frac{\Sigma(y_t - F_t)}{n} \tag{16.12}$$

---

The forecast bias can be either positive or negative. A positive value indicates a tendency to underforecast. A negative value indicates a tendency to overforecast. The estimated bias taken from the forecasts for periods 8 through 10 in our example is

$$\text{Forecast bias} = \frac{[(5{,}714.35) + (-13{,}928.50) + (6{,}428.65)]}{3} = -595.17$$

This means that, on average, the model overforecasts sales by $595.17.

Suppose that on the basis of our bias estimate we judge that the linear trend model does an acceptable job in forecasting. Then all available data (periods 1 through 10) would be used to develop a linear trend model (see Figure 16.6), and a trend projection would be used to forecast for future time periods by substituting appropriate values for $t$ into the trend model.

$$F_t = 277,333.33 + 14,575.76(t)$$

However, if the linear model is judged to be unacceptable, the forecaster will need to try a different technique. For the purpose of the bank loan application, the Taft Ice Cream Company needs to forecast sales for the next three years (periods 11 through 13). Assuming the linear trend model is acceptable, these forecasts are

$$F_{11} = 277,333.33 + 14,575.76(11) = \$437,666.69$$
$$F_{12} = 277,333.33 + 14,575.76(12) = \$452,242.45$$
$$F_{13} = 277,333.33 + 14,575.76(13) = \$466,818.21$$

# Nonlinear Trend Forecasting

As we indicated earlier, you may encounter a time series that exhibits a nonlinear trend. Figure 16.2 showed an example of a nonlinear trend. When the historical data show a nonlinear trend, you should consider using a nonlinear trend forecasting model. A common method for dealing with nonlinear trends is to use an extension of the linear trend method. This extension calls for making a data transformation before applying the least squares regression analysis.

**Excel and Minitab Tutorial**

**BUSINESS APPLICATION**    **FORECASTING NONLINEAR TRENDS**

**HARRISON EQUIPMENT COMPANY** Consider Harrison Equipment Company, which leases large construction equipment to contractors in the Southwest. The lease arrangements call for Harrison to perform all repairs and maintenance on this equipment. Figure 16.14 shows a line chart for the repair costs for a crawler tractor leased to a contractor in Phoenix for the past 20 quarters. The data are contained in the file **Harrison**.

**FIGURE 16.14**

Excel 2007 Time-Series Plot for Harrison Equipment Repair Costs

**Excel 2007 Instructions:**
1. Open file: Harrison.xls.
2. Select data in the *Repair Costs* data column.
3. Click on **Insert > Line Chart**.
4. Click on **Select Data**.
5. Under **Horizontal (categories) Axis Labels**, select data in *year* and *quarter* columns.
6. Click on **Layout > Chart Title** and enter desired title.
7. Click on **Layout > Axis Titles** and enter horizontal and vertical axes titles.

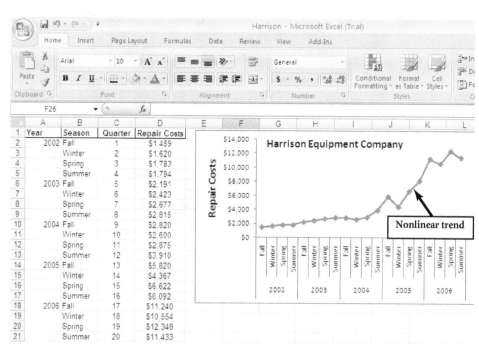

**Minitab Instructions (for similar results):**
1. Open file: Harrison.MTW.
2. Select **Graph > Time Series Plot**.
3. Select **Simple**.
4. Under **Series**, enter time series column.
5. Click **Time/Scale**.
6. Under **Time Scale** select **Calendar** and **Quarter Year**.
7. Under **Start Values**, insert the starting quarter and year.
8. Click **OK. OK**.

**Chapter Outcome 4.** ➞ **Model Specification**

Harrison Equipment is interested in forecasting future repair costs for the crawler tractor. Recall that the first step in forecasting is model specification. Even though the plot in Figure 16.14 indicates a sharp upward nonlinear trend, the forecaster may start by specifying a linear trend model.

**Model Fitting**

As a part of the model-fitting step, the forecaster could use Excel's or Minitab's regression procedure to obtain the linear forecasting model shown in Figure 16.15. As shown the linear trend model is

$$F_t = -1,022.7 + 570.9(t)$$

**Model Diagnosis**

The fit is pretty good with an $R$-squared = 0.8214 and a standard error of 1,618.5. But we need to look closer. Figure 16.15 shows a plot of the trend line compared with the actual data. A close inspection indicates the linear trend model may not be best for this case. Notice that the linear model underforecasts, then overforecasts, then underforecasts again. From this we might suspect positive autocorrelation.

We can establish the following null and alternative hypotheses:

$$H_0: \rho = 0$$
$$H_A: \rho > 0$$

Equation 16.11 could be used to manually compute the Durbin-Watson $d$ statistic, or more likely, we would use either PHStat or Minitab. The calculated Durbin-Watson is

$$d = 0.505$$

**FIGURE 16.15**

Excel 2007 (PHStat) Output for the Harrison Equipment Company Linear Trend Model

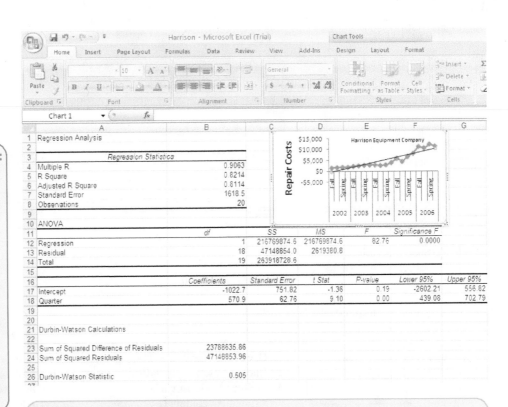

**Excel 2007 Instructions:**
1. Open file: Harrison.xls.
2. Select **Add-Ins**.
3. Select **PHStat**.
4. Select **Regression > Simple Linear Regression**.
5. Specify *y* variable data range.
6. Specify *x* variable data range (time = *t* values).
7. Check box for **Durbin-Watson Statistic**.
8. Copy Figure 16.14 line chart onto output—add linear trend line.
9. Click **OK**.

**Minitab Instructions (for similar results):**
1. Open file: Harrison.MTW.
2. Follow Minitab instructions in Figure 16.13.
3. Choose **Stat > Time Series > Trend Analysis**.
4. In **Variable**, enter time-series column.
5. Under **Model Type**, Choose **Linear**.
6. Click **OK**.

The $d_L$ critical value from the Durbin-Watson table in Appendix O for $\alpha = 0.05$ and a sample size of $n = 20$ and $p = 1$ independent variable is 1.20.

Because $d = 0.505 < d_L = 1.20$, we reject the null hypothesis.

We conclude that the error terms are significantly positively autocorrelated. The model-building process needs to be repeated.

### Model Specification

After examining Figure 16.15 and determining the results of the test for positive autocorrelation, a nonlinear trend will likely provide a better fit for these data. To account for the nonlinear growth trend, which starts out slowly and then builds rapidly, the forecaster might consider transforming the time variable by squaring $t$ to form a model of the form

$$y = \beta_0 + \beta_1 t + \beta_2 t^2 + \varepsilon$$

This transformation is suggested because the growth in costs appears to be increasing at an increasing rate. Other nonlinear trends may require different types of transformations, such as taking a square root or natural log. Each situation must be analyzed separately. (See the reference by Kutner et al. for further discussion of transformations.)

### Model Fitting

Figure 16.16 shows the Excel regression results, and Figure 16.17 shows the revised time-series plot using the polynomial transformation. The resulting nonlinear trend regression model is

$$F_t = 2,318.7 - 340.4(t) + 43.4(t^2)$$

**FIGURE 16.16**

Excel 2007 (PHStat) Transformed Regression Model for Harrison Equipment

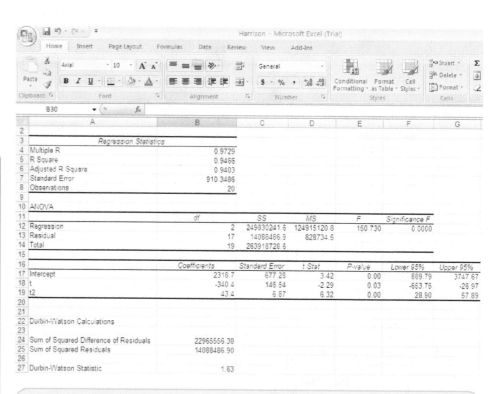

**Excel 2007 (PHStat) Instructions:**

1. Open data file: Harrison.xls.
2. Select **Add-Ins**.
3. Select **PHStat**.
4. Select **Regression > Multiple Regression**.
6. Specify *y* variable data range.
7. Specify *x* variable data range (time = *t* values and $t^2$ = squared values).
8. Check on **Residuals table** (output not shown here).
9. Check box for **Durbin-Watson Statistic**.
10. Click **OK**.

**Minitab Instructions (for similar results):**

1. Open File: Harrison.MTW.
2. Choose **Calc > Calculator**.
3. In **Store result in variable**, enter destination column *Qrt square*.
4. With cursor in **Expressions**, enter *Quarter* column then **2.
5. Click **OK**.
6. Choose **Stat > Regression > Regression**.
7. In **Response**, enter *Repair Costs*. In **Predictors**, enter *Qrt square*.
8. Click **Storage**.
9. Under **Diagnostic Measures**, select **Residuals**. Under **Characteristics of Estimated Equation**, select **Fits**.
10. Click **OK. OK.**

**FIGURE 16.17**

Excel 2007 Transformed
Model for Harrison Equipment
Company

**Excel 2007 (PHStat)
Instructions:**
1. Open data file:
   Harrison.xls.
2. Follow Figure 16.14
   instruction to generate
   line chart.
3. Select **Add-Ins**.
4. Select **PHStat**.
5. Select **Regression >
   Multiple Regression**.
6. Specify $y$ variable data
   range.
7. Specify $x$ variable data
   range (time = $t$ values
   and $t$-squared values).
8. Click on **Residuals table**
   (output not shown here).
9. Paste **Predicted Values**
   on the line chart.

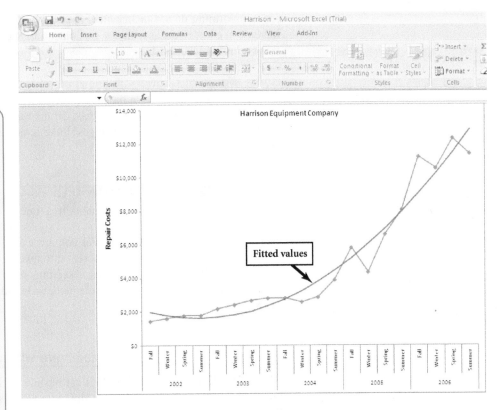

**Model Diagnosis**

Visually, the transformed model now looks more appropriate. The fit is much better as the $R$-squared value is increased to 0.9466 and the standard error is reduced to 910.35. The null and alternative hypotheses for testing whether positive autocorrelation exists are

$$H_0: \rho = 0$$
$$H_A: \rho > 0$$

As seen in Figure 16.16, the calculated Durbin-Watson statistic is

$$d = 1.63$$

The $d_L$ and $d_U$ critical values from the Durbin-Watson table in Appendix O for $\alpha = 0.05$ and a sample size of $n = 20$ and $p = 2$ independent variables are 1.10 and 1.54, respectively.

Because $d = 1.63 > 1.54$, the Durbin-Watson test indicates that there is no positive autocorrelation. Given this result and the improvements to $R$-squared and the standard error of the estimate, the nonlinear model is judged superior to the original linear model.

Forecasts for periods 21 and 22, using this latest model, are obtained using the trend projection method.

For period $t = 21$:

$$F_{21} = 2{,}318.7 - 340.4(21) + 43.4(21^2) = \$14{,}310$$

For period $t = 22$:

$$F_{22} = 2{,}318.7 - 340.4(22) + 43.4(22^2) = \$15{,}836$$

Using transformations often provides a very effective way of improving the fit of a time series. However, a forecaster should be careful not to get caught up in an exercise of "curve-fitting." One suggestion is that only explainable terms—terms that can be justified—be used for transforming data. For instance, in our example, we might well expect repair costs to increase at a faster rate as a tractor gets older and begins wearing out. Thus, the $t^2$ transformation seems to make sense.

**Some Words of Caution** The trend projection method relies on the future behaving in a manner similar to the past. In the previous example, if equipment repair costs continue to follow the pattern displayed over the past 20 quarters, these forecasts may prove acceptable. However, if the future pattern changes, there is no reason to believe these forecasts will be close to actual costs.

## Adjusting for Seasonality

In Section 16.1, we discussed seasonality in a time series. The seasonal component represents those changes (highs and lows) in the time series that occur at approximately the same time every period. If the forecasting model you are using does not already explicitly account for seasonality, you should adjust your forecast to take into account the seasonal component. The linear and nonlinear trend models discussed thus far do not automatically incorporate the seasonal component. Forecasts using these models should be adjusted as illustrated in the following application.

**Excel and Minitab Tutorial**

**BUSINESS APPLICATION** FORECASTING WITH SEASONAL DATA

**BIG MOUNTAIN SKI RESORT** Most businesses in the tourist industry know that sales are seasonal. For example, at the Big Mountain Ski Resort, business peaks at two times during the year: winter for skiing and summer for golf and tennis. These peaks can be identified in a time series if the sales data are measured on at least a quarterly basis. Figure 16.18 shows the quarterly sales data for the past four years in spreadsheet form. The line chart for these data is also shown. The data are in the file **Big Mountain**. The time-series plot clearly shows that the summer and winter quarters are the busy times. There has also been a slightly increasing linear trend in sales over the four years.

**FIGURE 16.18**

Excel 2007 Big Mountain Resort Quarterly Sales Data

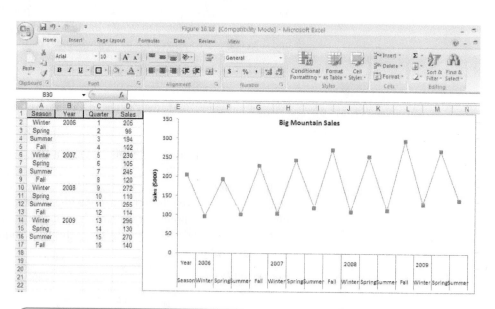

**Excel 2007 Instructions:**
1. Open file: Big Mountain.xls.
2. Select data in the Sales data column.
3. Click on **Insert > Line Chart**.
4. Click on **Select Data**.
5. Under **Horizontal (categories) Axis**

**Labels**, select data in *Year* and *Season* columns.
6. Click on **Layout > Chart Title** and enter desired title.
7. Click on **Layout > Axis Titles** and enter horizontal and vertical axes titles.

Big Mountain Resort wants to forecast sales for each quarter of the coming year, and it hopes to use a linear trend model. When the historical data show a trend and seasonality, the trend-based forecasting model needs to be adjusted to incorporate the seasonality. One method for doing this involves computing **seasonal indexes**.

**Seasonal Index**

A number used to quantify the effect of seasonality in time-series data.

For instance, when we have quarterly data, we can develop four seasonal indexes, one each for winter, spring, summer, and fall. A seasonal index below 1.00 indicates that the quarter has a value that is typically below the average value for the year. On the other hand, an index greater than 1.00 indicates that the quarter's value is typically higher than the yearly average.

**Computing Seasonal Indexes** Although there are several methods for computing the seasonal indexes, the procedure introduced here is the *ratio-to-moving-average method*. This method assumes that the actual time-series data can be represented as a product of the four time-series components—trend, seasonal, cyclical, and random—which produces the multiplicative model shown in Equation 16.13.

---

**Multiplicative Time-Series Model**

$$y_t = T_t \times S_t \times C_t \times I_t \tag{16.13}$$

where:

$y_t$ = Value of the time series at time $t$
$T_t$ = Trend value at time $t$
$S_t$ = Seasonal value at time $t$
$C_t$ = Cyclical value at time $t$
$I_t$ = Irregular or random value at time $t$

---

The ratio-to-moving-average method begins by removing the seasonal and irregular components, $S_t$ and $I_t$, from the data, leaving the combined trend and cyclical components, $T_t$ and $C_t$. This is done by first computing successive four-period moving averages for the time series. A moving average is the average of $n$ consecutive values of a time series. Using the Big Mountain sales data in Figure 16.19, we find that the **moving average** using the first four quarters is

**Moving Average**

The successive averages of $n$ consecutive values in a time series.

$$\frac{205 + 96 + 194 + 102}{4} = 149.25$$

**FIGURE 16.19**

Excel 2007 Seasonal Index— Step 1: Moving Average Values for Big Mountain Resort

**Excel 2007 Instructions:**
1. Open file: Big Mountain. xls.
2. Create a new column of 4-period moving averages using Excel's **AVERAGE** function. The first moving average is placed in cell E3 and the equation is =**AVERAGE(D2:D5)**.
3. Copy the equation down to cell E15.

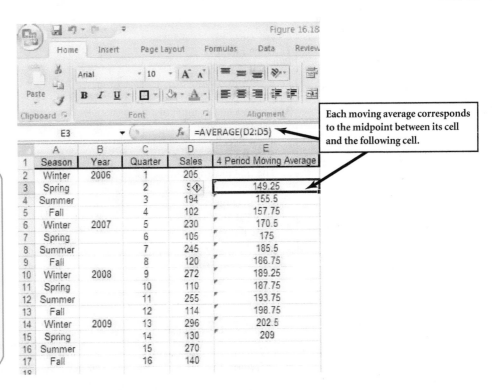

This moving average is associated with the middle time period of the data values in the moving average. The middle period of the first four quarters is 2.5 (between quarter 2 and quarter 3).

The second moving average is found by dropping the value from period 1 and adding the value from period 5, as follows:

$$\frac{96 + 194 + 102 + 230}{4} = 155.50$$

This moving average is associated with time period 3.5, the middle period between quarters 3 and 4.

Figure 16.19 shows the moving averages for the Big Mountain sales data in Excel spreadsheet form.[2] We selected 4 data values for the moving average because we have quarterly data; with monthly data, 12 data values would have been used.

The next step is to compute the *centered moving averages* by averaging each successive pair of moving averages. Centering the moving averages is necessary so that the resulting moving average will be associated with one of the data set's original time periods. In this example, Big Mountain is interested in quarterly sales data—that is, time periods 1, 2, 3, etc. Therefore, the moving averages we have representing time periods 2.5, 3.5, and so forth are not of interest to Big Mountain. Centering these averaged time series values, however, produces moving averages for the (quarterly) time periods of interest. For example, the first two moving averages are averaged to produce the first centered moving average. We get

$$\frac{149.25 + 155.5}{2} = 152.38$$

This centered moving average is associated with quarter 3. The centered moving averages are shown in Figure 16.20.[3] These values estimate the $T_t \times C_t$ value.

**FIGURE 16.20**

Excel 2007 Seasonal Index—Step 2: Big Mountain Resort Centered Moving Averages

**Excel 2007 Instructions:**
1. Open File: Big Mountain.xls.
2. Follow instructions in Figure 16.19.
3. Create a new column of centered moving averages using Excel's **AVERAGE** function. The first moving average is placed in cell F4 and the equation is =**AVERAGE (E3:E4)**.
4. Copy the equation down to cell F15.

| | A | B | C | D | E | F |
|---|---|---|---|---|---|---|
| 1 | Season | Year | Quarter | Sales | 4 Period Moving Average | Centered Moving Average |
| 2 | Winter | 2006 | 1 | 205 | | |
| 3 | Spring | | 2 | 96 | 149.25 | |
| 4 | Summer | | 3 | 194 | 155.5 | 152.38 |
| 5 | Fall | | 4 | 102 | 157.75 | 156.63 |
| 6 | Winter | 2007 | 5 | 230 | 170.5 | 164.13 |
| 7 | Spring | | 6 | 105 | 175 | 172.75 |
| 8 | Summer | | 7 | 245 | 185.5 | 180.25 |
| 9 | Fall | | 8 | 120 | 186.75 | 186.13 |
| 10 | Winter | 2008 | 9 | 272 | 189.25 | 188.00 |
| 11 | Spring | | 10 | 110 | 187.75 | 188.50 |
| 12 | Summer | | 11 | 255 | 193.75 | 190.75 |
| 13 | Fall | | 12 | 114 | 198.75 | 196.25 |
| 14 | Winter | 2009 | 13 | 296 | 202.5 | 200.63 |
| 15 | Spring | | 14 | 130 | 209 | 205.75 |
| 16 | Summer | | 15 | 270 | | |
| 17 | Fall | | 16 | 140 | | |

fx =AVERAGE(E3:E4)

---

[2]The Excel process illustrated by Figures 16.19 through 16.23 is also accomplished using Minitab's **Time Series >. Decomposition** command, which is illustrated by Figure 16.25 on page 744.
[3]Excel's tabular format does not allow the uncentered moving averages to be displayed with their "interquarter" time periods. That is, 149.25 is associated with time period 2.5, 155.50 with time period 3.5, and so forth.

If the number of data values used for a moving average is odd, the moving average will be associated with the time period of the middle observation. In such cases, we would not have to center the moving average, as we did in Figure 16.20, because the moving averages would already be associated with one of the time periods from the original time series.

Next, we estimate the $S_t \times I_t$ value. Dividing the actual sales value for each quarter by the corresponding centered moving average, as in Equation 16.14, does this. As an example, we examine the third time period: summer of 2006. The sales value of 194 is divided by the centered moving average of 152.38, to produce 1.273. This value is called the *ratio-to-moving-average*. Figure 16.21 shows these values for the Big Mountain data.

### Ratio-to-Moving-Average

$$S_t \times I_t = \frac{y_t}{T_t \times C_t} \qquad (16.14)$$

The final step in determining the seasonal indexes is to compute the mean ratio-to-moving-average value for each season. Each quarter's ratio-to-moving-average is averaged over the years to produce the *seasonal index* for that quarter. Figure 16.22 shows the seasonal indexes. The seasonal index for the winter quarter is 1.441. This indicates that sales for Big Mountain during the winter are 44.1% above the average for the year. Also, sales in the spring quarter are only 60.8% of the average for the year.

One important point about the seasonal indexes is that the sum of the indexes is equal to the number of seasonal indexes. That is, the average of all seasonal indexes equals 1.0. In the Big Mountain Resort example, we find

| Summer | | Fall | | Winter | | Spring | | |
|---|---|---|---|---|---|---|---|---|
| 1.323 | + | 0.626 | + | 1.441 | + | 0.608 | = | 3.998 (difference from 4 due to rounding) |

Likewise, in an example with monthly data instead of quarterly data, we would generate 12 seasonal indexes, one for each month. The sum of these indexes should be 12.

**The Need to Normalize the Indexes** If the sum of the seasonal indexes does not equal the number of time periods in the recurrence period of the time series, an adjustment is necessary. In the Big Mountain Resort example, the sum of the four seasonal indexes may have

**FIGURE 16.21**

Excel 2007 Seasonal Index—Step 3: Big Mountain Resort Ratio-to-Moving-Averages

**Excel 2007 Instructions:**
1. Open File: Big Mountain.xls.
2. Follow instructions in Figures 16.19 and 16.20.
3. Create a new column of ratio-to-moving-averages using an Excel equation (e.g., **=D4/F4**).
4. Copy the equation down to cell G15.

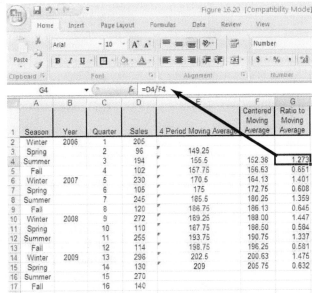

**FIGURE 16.22**

Excel 2007 Seasonal Index—
Step 4: Big Mountain Resort
Mean Ratios

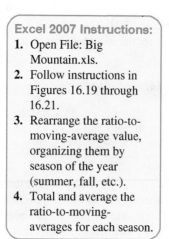

been something other than 4 (the recurrence period). In such cases, we must adjust the seasonal indexes by multiplying each by the number of time periods in the recurrence period over the sum of the unadjusted seasonal indexes. For quarterly data such as the Big Mountain Resort example, we would multiply each seasonal index by 4/(Sum of the unadjusted seasonal indexes). Performing this multiplication will *normalize* the seasonal indexes. This adjustment is necessary if the seasonal adjustments are going to even out over the recurrence period.

**Deseasonalizing**  A strong seasonal component may partially mask a trend in the time-series data. Consequently, to identify the trend you should first remove the effect of the seasonal component. This is called *deseasonalizing* the time series.

Again, assume that the multiplicative model shown previously in Equation 16.13 is appropriate:

$$y_t = T_t \times S_t \times C_t \times I_t$$

Deseasonalizing is accomplished by dividing $y_t$ by the appropriate seasonal index, $S_t$, as shown in Equation 16.15.

---

### Deseasonalization

$$T_t \times C_t \times I_t = \frac{y_t}{S_t} \qquad \textbf{(16.15)}$$

---

For time period 1, which is the winter quarter, the seasonal index is 1.441. The deseasonalized value for $y_1$ is

$$205/1.441 = 142.26$$

Figure 16.23 presents the deseasonalized values and the graph of these deseasonalized sales data for the Big Mountain example. This shows that there has been a gentle upward trend over the four years.

Once the data have been deseasonalized, the next step is to determine the trend based on the deseasonalized data. As in the previous examples of trend estimation, you can use either

**FIGURE 16.23**

Excel 2007 Deseasonalized Time Series for Big Mountain Sales Data

**Excel 2007 Instructions:**

1. Open File: Big Mountain.xls.
2. Follow instructions for Figures 16.18 through 16.22.
3. Create a new column containing the deseasonalized values. Use Excel equations and Equation 16.15.
4. Select the new deseasonalized data and paste onto the line graph.

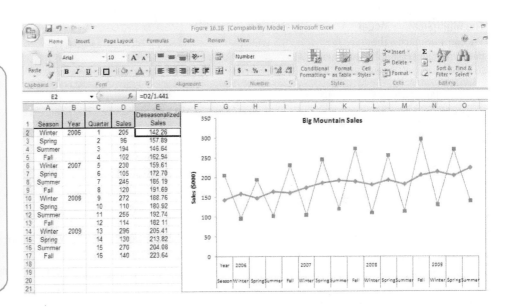

Excel or Minitab to develop the linear model for the deseasonalized data. The results are shown in Figure 16.24. The linear regression trend line equation is

$$F_t = 142.113 + 4.686(t)$$

You can use this trend line and the trend projection method to forecast sales for period $t = 17$:

$$F_{17} = 142.113 + 4.686(17) = 221.775 = \$221,775$$

**Seasonally Unadjusted Forecast**

A forecast made for seasonal data that does not include an adjustment for the seasonal component in the time series.

This is a **seasonally unadjusted forecast**, because the time-series data used in developing the trend line were deseasonalized.

Now we need to adjust the forecast for period 17 to reflect the quarterly fluctuations. We do this by multiplying the unadjusted forecast values by the appropriate seasonal index. In this case, period 17 corresponds to the winter quarter. The winter quarter has a seasonal index of 1.441, indicating a high sales period. The adjusted forecast is

$$F_{17} = (221.775)(1.441) = 319.578, \text{ or } \$319,578$$

**FIGURE 16.24**

Excel 2007 Regression Trend Line of Big Mountain Deseasonalized Data

**Excel 2007 Instructions:**

1. Open File: Big Mountain.xls.
2. Follow instructions in Figures 16.19 through 16.23.
3. Click on **Data**.
4. Select **Data Analysis > Regression**.
5. Specify *y* variable range (deseasonalized variable) and *x* variable range (time variable).
6. Click **OK**.

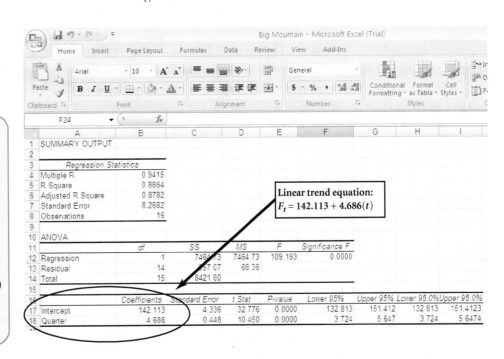

## How to do it

### The Seasonal Adjustment Process: The Multiplicative Model

**We can summarize the steps for performing a seasonal adjustment to a trend-based forecast as follows:**

1. Compute each moving average from the $k$ appropriate consecutive data values, where $k$ is the number of values in one period of the time series.
2. Compute the centered moving averages.
3. Isolate the seasonal component by computing the ratio-to-moving-average values.
4. Compute the seasonal indexes by averaging the ratio-to-moving-average values for comparable periods.
5. Normalize the seasonal indexes (if necessary).
6. Deseasonalize the time series by dividing the actual data by the appropriate seasonal index.
7. Use least squares regression to develop the trend line using the deseasonalized data.
8. Develop the unadjusted forecasts using trend projection.
9. Seasonally adjust the forecasts by multiplying the unadjusted forecasts by the appropriate seasonal index.

The seasonally adjusted forecasts for each quarter in 2010 are as follows:

| Quarter (2010) | $t$ | Unadjusted Forecast | Index | Adjusted Forecast |
|---|---|---|---|---|
| Winter | 17 | 221.775 | 1.441 | 319.578 = $319,578 |
| Spring | 18 | 226.461 | 0.608 | 137.688 = $137,688 |
| Summer | 19 | 231.147 | 1.323 | 305.807 = $305,807 |
| Fall | 20 | 235.833 | 0.626 | 147.631 = $147,631 |

You can use the seasonally adjusted trend model when a time series exhibits both a trend and seasonality. This process allows for a better identification of the trend and produces forecasts that are more sensitive to seasonality in the data.

Minitab contains a procedure for generating seasonal indexes and seasonally adjusted forecasts. Figure 16.25 shows the Minitab results for the Big Mountain Ski Resort example. Notice that the forecast option in Minitab gives different forecasts than we showed earlier. This is because Minitab generates the linear trend model using original sales data rather than deseasonalized data. Our suggestion is to use Minitab to generate the seasonal indexes, but then follow our outline to generate seasonally adjusted forecasts.[4]

**Using Dummy Variables to Represent Seasonality** The multiplicative model approach for dealing with seasonal data in a time-series forecasting application is one method that is commonly used by forecasters. Another method used to incorporate the seasonal component into a linear trend forecast involves the use of dummy variables. To illustrate, we again use the Big Mountain example, which had four years of quarterly data. Because of quarterly data, start by constructing 3 dummy variables (one less than the number of data values in the

**FIGURE 16.25**

Minitab Output Showing Big Mountain Seasonal Indexes

Minitab Instructions:
1. Open file: Big Mountain. MTW.
2. Select **Stat > Time Series > Decomposition**.
3. In **Variable** enter time series column.
4. In **Seasonal length**, enter number of time periods in season.
5. Under **Model Type**, choose **Multiplicative**.
6. Under **Model Components**, choose **Trend plus seasonal**.
7. Select **Generate forecasts**, for **Number of forecasts** insert *4*: for **Starting with origin** insert the last time series time period:*16*.
8. Click **OK**.

---

[4]Neither Excel nor PHStat offers a procedure for automatically generating seasonal indexes. However, as shown in the Big Mountain example, you can use the spreadsheet formulas to do this. See the Excel Tutorial that accompanies this text.

**TABLE 16.5** | **Big Mountain Sales Output Using Dummy Variables**

| Season | Year | $y$ Sales | Quarter = $t$ | $x_1$ Winter Dummy | $x_2$ Spring Dummy | $x_3$ Summer Dummy |
|---|---|---|---|---|---|---|
| Winter | 2006 | 205 | 1 | 1 | 0 | 0 |
| Spring | | 96 | 2 | 0 | 1 | 0 |
| Summer | | 194 | 3 | 0 | 0 | 1 |
| Fall | | 102 | 4 | 0 | 0 | 0 |
| Winter | 2007 | 230 | 5 | 1 | 0 | 0 |
| Spring | | 105 | 6 | 0 | 1 | 0 |
| Summer | | 245 | 7 | 0 | 0 | 1 |
| Fall | | 120 | 8 | 0 | 0 | 0 |
| Winter | 2008 | 272 | 9 | 1 | 0 | 0 |
| Spring | | 110 | 10 | 0 | 1 | 0 |
| Summer | | 255 | 11 | 0 | 0 | 1 |
| Fall | | 114 | 12 | 0 | 0 | 0 |
| Winter | 2009 | 296 | 13 | 1 | 0 | 0 |
| Spring | | 130 | 14 | 0 | 1 | 0 |
| Summer | | 270 | 15 | 0 | 0 | 1 |
| Fall | | 140 | 16 | 0 | 0 | 0 |

year; if you have monthly data, construct 11 dummy variables). Form dummy variables as follows:

$x_1 = 1$ if season is winter      $x_1 = 0$ if not winter
$x_2 = 1$ if season is spring      $x_2 = 0$ if not spring
$x_3 = 1$ if season is summer      $x_3 = 0$ if not summer

Table 16.5 shows the revised data set for the Big Mountain Company.

Next form a multiple regression model:

$$F_t = \beta_0 + \beta_1 t + \beta_2 x_1 + \beta_3 x_2 + \beta_4 x_3 + \varepsilon$$

Note, this model formulation is an extension of the linear trend model where the seasonality is accounted for by adding the regression coefficient for the season to the linear trend fitted value.

Figure 16.26 shows the Excel multiple regression output. The regression equation is

$$F_t = 71.0 + 4.8t + 146.2(x_1) + 0.9(x_2) + 126.8(x_3)$$

The $R$-square value is very high at 0.9710, indicating the regression model fits the historical data quite well. The $F$-ratio of 92.07 is significant at any reasonable level of significance, indicating the overall regression model is statistically significant. However, the $p$-value for $x_2$, the spring dummy variable, is 0.9359, indicating that variable is insignificant. Consequently, we will drop this variable and rerun the regression analysis with only three independent variables. The resulting model is

$$F_t = 71.5 + 4.8t + 145.7x_1 + 126.4x_3$$

This overall model is significant, and all three variables are statistically significant at any reasonable level of alpha. The coefficients on the two dummy variables can be interpreted as the seasonal indexes for winter and summer. The indexes for spring and fall are incorporated into the intercept value. We can now use this model to develop forecasts for year 5 (periods 17–20) as follows:

Winter ($t = 17$): $F_t = 71.5 + 4.8(17) + 145.7(1) + 126.4(0) = 298.80 = \$298,800$
Spring ($t = 18$): $F_t = 71.5 + 4.8(18) + 145.7(0) + 126.4(0) = 157.90 = \$157,900$
Summer ($t = 19$): $F_t = 71.5 + 4.8(19) + 145.7(0) + 126.4(1) = 289.10 = \$289,100$
Fall ($t = 20$): $F_t = 71.5 + 4.8(20) + 145.7(0) + 126.4(0) = 167.50 = \$167,500$

**FIGURE 16.26**

Excel 2007 Regression
Output with Dummy Variables
Included—Big Mountain
Example

**Excel 2007 Instructions:**
1. Open File: Big Mountain. xls.
2. Create three dummy variables for winter, spring, and summer.
3. Click on **Data**.
4. Select **Data Analysis > Regression**.
5. Specify *y* variable range and *x* variable range (time variable plus three dummies).
6. Click **OK**.

| | A | B | C | D | E | F | G |
|---|---|---|---|---|---|---|---|
| 1 | SUMMARY OUTPUT | | | | | | |
| 2 | | | | | | | |
| 3 | *Regression Statistics* | | | | | | |
| 4 | Multiple R | 0.9854 | | | | | |
| 5 | R Square | 0.9710 | | | | | |
| 6 | Adjusted R Square | 0.9604 | | | | | |
| 7 | Standard Error | 14.4244 | | | | | |
| 8 | Observations | 16 | | | | | |
| 9 | | | | | | | |
| 10 | ANOVA | | | | | | |
| 11 | | *df* | *SS* | *MS* | *F* | *Significance F* | |
| 12 | Regression | 4 | 76622.3 | 19155.6 | 92.07 | 0.0000 | |
| 13 | Residual | 11 | 2288.7 | 208.1 | | | |
| 14 | Total | 15 | 78911 | | | | |
| 15 | | | | | | | |
| 16 | | *Coefficients* | *Standard Error* | *t Stat* | *P-value* | *Lower 95%* | *Upper 95%* |
| 17 | Intercept | 71.0 | 10.82 | 6.563 | 0.0000 | 47.2 | 94.8 |
| 18 | Time = t | 4.8 | 0.81 | 5.953 | 0.0001 | 3.0 | 6.6 |
| 19 | Winter Dummy | 146.2 | 10.48 | 13.942 | 0.0000 | 123.1 | 169.2 |
| 20 | Spring Dummy | 0.9 | 10.33 | 0.082 | 0.9359 | -21.9 | 23.6 |
| 21 | Summer Dummy | 126.8 | 10.23 | 12.393 | 0.0000 | 104.3 | 149.3 |

If you compare these forecasts to the ones we previously obtained using the multiplicative model approach, the forecasts for winter and summer are lower with the dummy variable model but higher for spring and fall. You could use the split-sample approach to test the two alternative approaches to see which, in this case, seems to provide more accurate forecasts based on *MAD* and *MSE* calculations.

Both the multiplicative and the dummy variable approach have their advantages and both methods are commonly used by business forecasters.

# 16-2: **Exercises**

## Skill **Development**

Problems 16-18 to 16-22 refer to Tran's Furniture Store, which has maintained monthly sales records for the past 48 months, with the following results:

| Month | Sales ($) | Month | Sales ($) |
|---|---|---|---|
| 1 (Jan.) | 23,500 | 11 | 39,500 |
| 2 | 21,700 | 12 | 43,400 |
| 3 | 18,750 | 13 (Jan.) | 23,500 |
| 4 | 22,000 | 14 | 23,400 |
| 5 | 23,000 | 15 | 21,400 |
| 6 | 26,200 | 16 | 24,200 |
| 7 | 27,300 | 17 | 26,900 |
| 8 | 29,300 | 18 | 29,700 |
| 9 | 31,200 | 19 | 31,100 |
| 10 | 34,200 | 20 | 32,400 |

| Month | Sales ($) | Month | Sales ($) |
|---|---|---|---|
| 21 | 34,500 | 35 | 43,600 |
| 22 | 35,700 | 36 | 47,400 |
| 23 | 42,000 | 37 (Jan) | 32,400 |
| 24 | 42,600 | 38 | 35,600 |
| 25 (Jan.) | 31,000 | 39 | 31,200 |
| 26 | 30,400 | 40 | 34,600 |
| 27 | 29,800 | 41 | 36,800 |
| 28 | 32,500 | 42 | 35,700 |
| 29 | 34,500 | 43 | 37,500 |
| 30 | 33,800 | 44 | 40,000 |
| 31 | 34,200 | 45 | 43,200 |
| 32 | 36,700 | 46 | 46,700 |
| 33 | 39,700 | 47 | 50,100 |
| 34 | 42,400 | 48 | 52,100 |

**16-18.** Based on the Durbin-Watson statistic, is there evidence of autocorrelation in these data? Use a linear trend model.

**16-19.** Using the multiplicative model, estimate the $T \times C$ portion by computing a 12-month moving average and then the centered 12-month moving average.

**16-20.** Estimate the $S \times I$ portion of the multiplicative model by finding the ratio-to-moving-averages for the time-series data. Determine whether these ratio-to-moving-averages are stable from year to year.

**16-21.** Extract the irregular component by taking the normalized average of the ratio-to-moving-averages. Make a table that shows the normalized seasonal indexes. Interpret what the index for January means relative to the index for July.

**16-22.** Based on your work in the previous three problems,
   a. Determine a seasonally adjusted linear trend forecasting model. Compare this model with an unadjusted linear trend model. Use both models to forecast Tran's sales for period 49.
   b. Which of the two models developed has the lower *MAD* and lower *MSE*?

**16-23.** Consider the following set of sales data, given in millions of dollars:

| 2006 | 2008 |
|---|---|
| 1st quarter 152 | 1st quarter 217 |
| 2nd quarter 162 | 2nd quarter 209 |
| 3rd quarter 157 | 3rd quarter 202 |
| 4th quarter 167 | 4th quarter 221 |

| 2007 | 2009 |
|---|---|
| 1st quarter 182 | 1st quarter 236 |
| 2nd quarter 192 | 2nd quarter 242 |
| 3rd quarter 191 | 3rd quarter 231 |
| 4th quarter 197 | 4th quarter 224 |

   a. Plot these data. Based on your visual observations, what time-series components are present in the data?
   b. Determine the seasonal index for each quarter.
   c. Fit a linear trend model to the data and determine the *MAD* and *MSE* values. Comment on the adequacy of the linear trend model based on these measures of forecast error.
   d. Provide a seasonally unadjusted forecast using the linear trend model for each quarter of the year 2010.
   e. Use the seasonal index values computed in part b to provide seasonal adjusted forecasts for each quarter of 2010.

**16-24.** Examine the following time series:

| $t$ | 1 | 2 | 3 | 4 | 5 | 6 | 7 | 8 | 9 | 10 |
|---|---|---|---|---|---|---|---|---|---|---|
| $y_t$ | 52 | 72 | 58 | 66 | 68 | 60 | 46 | 43 | 17 | 3 |

   a. Produce a scatter plot of this time series. Indicate the appropriate forecasting model for this time series.
   b. Construct the equation for the forecasting model identified in part a.
   c. Produce forecasts for time periods 11, 12, 13, and 14.
   d. Obtain the forecast bias for the forecasts produced in part c if the actual time series values are −35, −41, −79, and −100 for periods 11–14, respectively.

**16-25.** Examine the following quarterly data:

| $t$ | 1 | 2 | 3 | 4 | 5 | 6 | 7 | 8 | 9 | 10 | 11 | 12 |
|---|---|---|---|---|---|---|---|---|---|---|---|---|
| $y_t$ | 2 | 12 | 23 | 20 | 18 | 32 | 48 | 41 | 35 | 52 | 79 | 63 |

   a. Compute the four-period moving averages for this set of data.
   b. Compute the centered moving averages from the moving averages of part a.
   c. Compute the ratio-to-moving-averages values.
   d. Calculate the seasonal indexes. Normalize them if necessary.
   e. Deseasonalize the time series.
   f. Produce the trend line using the deseasonalized data.
   g. Produce seasonally adjusted forecasts for each of the time periods 13, 14, 15, and 16.

## Business Applications

**16-26.** "The average college senior graduated this year with more than $19,000 in debt" was the beginning sentence of a recent article in *USA Today*. The majority of students have loans that are not due until the student leaves school. This can result in the student ignoring the size of debt that piles up. Federal loans obtained to finance college education are steadily mounting. The data given here show the amount of loans ($million) for the last 13 academic years, with year 20 being the most recent.

| Year | Amount | Year | Amount | Year | Amount |
|---|---|---|---|---|---|
| 1 | 9,914 | 8 | 16,221 | 15 | 37,228 |
| 2 | 10,182 | 9 | 22,557 | 16 | 39,101 |
| 3 | 12,493 | 10 | 26,011 | 17 | 42,761 |
| 4 | 13,195 | 11 | 28,737 | 18 | 49,360 |
| 5 | 13,414 | 12 | 31,906 | 19 | 57,463 |
| 6 | 13,890 | 13 | 33,930 | 20 | 62,614 |
| 7 | 15,232 | 14 | 34,376 | | |

   a. Produce a time-series plot of these data. Indicate the time-series components that exist in the data.

b. Conduct a test of hypothesis to determine if there exists a linear trend in these data. Use a significance level of 0.10 and the *p*-value approach.

c. Provide a 90% prediction interval for the amount of federal loans for the 26th academic year.

**16-27.** The average monthly price of regular gasoline in Southern California is monitored by the Automobile Club of Southern California's monthly Fuel Gauge Report. The prices of the time period July 2004 to June 2006 are given here.

| Month | Price ($) | Month | Price ($) | Month | Price ($) |
|-------|-----------|-------|-----------|-------|-----------|
| 7/04  | 2.247     | 5/05  | 2.532     | 3/06  | 2.626     |
| 8/04  | 2.108     | 6/05  | 2.375     | 4/06  | 2.903     |
| 9/04  | 2.111     | 7/05  | 2.592     | 5/06  | 3.417     |
| 10/04 | 2.352     | 8/05  | 2.774     | 6/06  | 3.301     |
| 11/04 | 2.374     | 9/05  | 3.031     |       |           |
| 12/04 | 2.192     | 10/05 | 2.943     |       |           |
| 1/05  | 1.989     | 11/05 | 2.637     |       |           |
| 2/05  | 2.130     | 12/05 | 2.289     |       |           |
| 3/05  | 2.344     | 1/06  | 2.357     |       |           |
| 4/05  | 2.642     | 2/06  | 2.628     |       |           |

a. Produce a time-series plot of the average price of regular gas in Southern California. Identify any time-series components that exist in the data.

b. Identify the recurrence period of the time series. Determine the seasonal index for each month within the recurrence period.

c. Fit a linear trend model to the deseasonalized data.

d. Provide a seasonally adjusted forecast using the linear trend model for July 2006 and July 2010.

**16-28.** Manuel Gutierrez correctly predicted the increasing need for home health care services due to the country's aging population. Five years ago, he started a company offering meal delivery, physical therapy, and minor housekeeping services in the Galveston area. Since that time he has opened offices in seven additional Gulf State cities. Manuel is currently analyzing the revenue data from his first location for the first five years of operation.

**Revenue ($10,000s)**

| | 2005 | 2006 | 2007 | 2008 | 2009 |
|-----------|------|------|------|------|------|
| January   | 23   | 67   | 72   | 76   | 81   |
| February  | 34   | 63   | 64   | 75   | 72   |
| March     | 45   | 65   | 64   | 77   | 71   |
| April     | 48   | 71   | 77   | 81   | 83   |
| May       | 46   | 75   | 79   | 86   | 85   |
| June      | 49   | 70   | 72   | 75   | 77   |
| July      | 60   | 72   | 71   | 80   | 79   |
| August    | 65   | 75   | 77   | 82   | 84   |
| September | 67   | 80   | 79   | 86   | 91   |
| October   | 60   | 78   | 78   | 87   | 86   |
| November  | 71   | 89   | 87   | 91   | 94   |
| December  | 76   | 94   | 92   | 96   | 99   |

a. Plot these data. Based on your visual observations, what time-series components are present in the data?

b. Determine the seasonal index for each month.

c. (1) Fit a linear trend model to the deseasonalized data for the years 2005–2009 and determine the *MAD* and *MSE* for forecasts for each of the months in 2010. (2) Conduct a test of hypothesis to determine if the linear trend model fits the existing data. (3) Comment on the adequacy of the linear trend model based on the measures of forecast error and the hypothesis test you conducted.

d. Manuel had hoped to reach $2,000,000 in revenue by the time he had been in business for 10 years. From the results in part c, is this a feasible goal based on the historical data provided? Consider and comment on the size of the standard error for this prediction. What makes this value so large? How does it affect your conclusion?

e. Use the seasonal index values computed in part b to provide seasonal adjusted forecasts for each month of the year 2010.

**16-29.** A major brokerage company has an office in Miami, Florida. The manager of the office is evaluated based on the number of new clients generated each quarter. The following data reflect the number of new customers added during each quarter between 2006 and 2009.

| 2006 | 2007 |
|------|------|
| 1st quarter 218 | 1st quarter 250 |
| 2nd quarter 190 | 2nd quarter 220 |
| 3rd quarter 236 | 3rd quarter 265 |
| 4th quarter 218 | 4th quarter 241 |

| 2008 | 2009 |
|------|------|
| 1st quarter 244 | 1st quarter 229 |
| 2nd quarter 228 | 2nd quarter 221 |
| 3rd quarter 263 | 3rd quarter 248 |
| 4th quarter 240 | 4th quarter 231 |

a. Plot the time series and discuss the components that are present in the data.

b. Referring to part a, fit the linear trend model to the data for the years 2006–2008. Then use the resulting model to forecast the number of new brokerage customers for each quarter in the year 2009. Compute the *MAD* and *MSE* for these forecasts and discuss the results.

c. Using the data for the years 2006–2008, determine the seasonal indexes for each quarter.

d. Develop a seasonally unadjusted forecast for the four quarters of year 2009.

e. Using the seasonal indexes computed in part d, determine the seasonally adjusted forecast for each quarter for the year 2009. Compute the *MAD* and *MSE* for these forecasts.

f. Examine the values for the *MAD* and *MSE* in parts b and e. Which of the two forecasting techniques would you recommend the manager use to forecast the number of new clients generated each quarter? Support your choice by giving your rationale.

## Computer Database **Exercises**

**16-30.** Logan Pickens is a plan/build construction company specializing in resort area construction projects. Plan/build companies typically have a cash flow problem since they tend to be paid in lump sums when projects are completed or hit milestones. However, their expenses, such as payroll, must be paid regularly. Consequently, such companies need bank lines of credit to finance their initial costs, but in 2009 lines of credit were difficult to negotiate. The data file **Logan-Pickens** contains month-end cash balances for the past 16 months.

  a. Plot the data as a time-series graph. Discuss what the graph implies concerning the relationship between cash balance and the time variable, month.

  b. Fit a linear trend model to the data. Compute the coefficient of determination for this model and show the trend line on the time-series graph. Discuss the appropriateness of the linear trend model. What are the strengths and weaknesses of the model?

  c. Referring to part b, compute the *MAD* and *MSE* for the 16 data points.

  d. Use the $t^2$ transformation approach and recompute the linear model using the transformed time variable. Plot the new trend line against the transformed data. Discuss whether this model appears to provide a better fit than did the model without the transformation. Compare the coefficients of determination for the two models. Which model seems to be superior, using the coefficient of determination as the criterion?

  e. Refer to part d. Compute the *MAD* and *MSE* for the 16 data values. Discuss how these compare to those that were computed in part c, prior to transformation. Do the measures of fit ($R^2$, *MSE*, or *MAD*) agree on the best model to use for forecasting purposes?

**16-31.** Refer to Problem 16-30.

  a. Use the linear trend model (without transformation) for the first 15 months and provide a cash balance forecast for month 16. Then make

the $t^2$ transformation and develop a new linear trend forecasting model based on months 1–15. Forecast the cash balance for month 16. Now compare the accuracy of the forecasts with and without the transformation. Which of the two forecast models would you prefer? Explain your answer.

  b. Provide a 95% prediction interval for the cash balance forecast for month 16 using the linear trend model both with and without the transformation. Which interval has the widest width? On this basis, which procedure would you choose?

**16-32.** The federal funds rate is the interest rate charged by banks when banks borrow "overnight" from each other. The funds rate fluctuates according to supply and demand and is not under the direct control of the Federal Reserve Board, but is strongly influenced by the Fed's actions. The file entitled **The Fed** contains the federal funds rates for the period 1955–2008.

  a. Produce a scatter plot of the federal funds rate for the period 1955–2008. Identify any time-series components that exist in the data.

  b. Identify the recurrence period of the time series. Determine the seasonal index for each month within the recurrence period.

  c. Fit a nonlinear trend model that uses coded years and coded years squared as predictors for the deseasonalized data.

  d. Provide a seasonally adjusted forecast using the nonlinear trend model for 2010 and 2012.

  e. Diagnose the model.

**16-33.** The Census Bureau of the Department of Commerce released the U.S. retail e-commerce sales ("Quarterly Retail E-Commerce Sales 1st Quarter 2006," May 18, 2006) for the period of Fourth Quarter 1999–Fourth Quarter 2008. The file entitled **E-Commerce** contains those data.

  a. Produce a time-series plot of this data. Indicate the time-series components that exist in the data.

  b. Conduct a test of hypothesis to determine if there exists a linear trend in these data. Use a significance level of 0.10 and the *p*-value approach.

  c. Provide forecasts for the e-commerce retail sales for the next four quarters.

  d. Presume the next four quarters exhibit e-commerce retail sales of 35,916, 36,432, 35,096, and 36,807, respectively. Produce the forecast bias. Interpret this number in the context of this exercise.

## 16.3 Forecasting Using Smoothing Methods

The trend-based forecasting technique introduced in the previous section is widely used and can be very effective in many situations. However, it has a disadvantage in that it gives as much weight to the earliest data in the time series as it does to the data that are close to the period for which the forecast is required. Also, this trend approach does not provide an opportunity for the model to "learn" or "adjust" to changes in the time series.

A class of forecasting techniques called *smoothing models* is widely used to overcome these problems and to provide forecasts in situations in which there is no pronounced trend in the data. These models attempt to "smooth out" the random or irregular component in the time series by an averaging process. In this section we introduce two frequently used smoothing-based forecasting techniques: single exponential smoothing and double exponential smoothing. Double exponential smoothing offers a modification to the single exponential smoothing model that specifically deals with trends.

**Chapter Outcome 5.** ➤ ## Exponential Smoothing

The trend-based forecasting methods discussed in Section 16.2 are used in many forecasting situations. As we showed, the least squares trend line is computed using all available historical data. Each observation is given equal input in establishing the trend line, thus allowing the trend line to reflect all the past data. If the future pattern looks like the past, the forecast should be reasonably accurate.

However, in many situations involving time-series data, the more recent the observation, the more indicative it is of possible future values. For example, this month's sales are probably a better indicator of next month's sales than would be sales from 20 months ago. However, the regression analysis approach to trend-based forecasting does not take this fact into account. The data from 20 periods ago will be given the same weight as data from the most current period in developing a forecasting model. This equal valuation can be a drawback to the trend-based forecasting approach.

**Exponential Smoothing**

A time-series and forecasting technique that produces an exponentially weighted moving average in which each smoothing calculation or forecast is dependent on all previous observed values.

With **exponential smoothing**, current observations can be weighted more heavily than older observations in determining the forecast. Therefore, if in recent periods the time-series values are much higher (or lower) than those in earlier periods, the forecast can be made to reflect this difference. The extent to which the forecast reflects the current data depends on the weights assigned by the decision maker.

We will introduce two classes of exponential smoothing models: single exponential smoothing and double exponential smoothing. Double smoothing is used when a time series exhibits a linear trend. Single smoothing is used when no linear trend is present in the time series. Both single and double exponential smoothing are appropriate for short-term forecasting and for time series that are not seasonal.

**Single Exponential Smoothing** Just as its name implies, single exponential smoothing uses a single smoothing constant. Equations 16.16 and 16.17 represent two equivalent methods for forecasting using single exponential smoothing.

---

**Exponential Smoothing Model**

$$F_{t+1} = F_t + \alpha(y_t - F_t) \tag{16.16}$$

or

$$F_{t+1} = \alpha y_t + (1 - \alpha)F_t \tag{16.17}$$

where:

$F_{t+1}$ = Forecast value for period $t + 1$
$y_t$ = Actual value of the time series at time $t$
$F_t$ = Forecast value for period $t$
$\alpha$ = Alpha (smoothing constant $0 \leq \alpha \leq 1$)

---

The logic of the exponential smoothing model is that the forecast made for the next period will equal the forecast made for the current period, plus or minus some adjustment factor. The adjustment factor is determined by the difference between this period's forecast and the actual value $(y_t - F_t)$, multiplied by the smoothing constant, $\alpha$. The idea is that if we forecast low, we will adjust next period's forecast upward, by an amount determined by the smoothing constant.

---

| **EXAMPLE 16-6** | **DEVELOPING A SINGLE EXPONENTIAL SMOOTHING MODEL** |

**Dawson Graphic Design** Consider the past 10 weeks of potential incoming customer sale calls for Dawson Graphic Design located in Orlando, Florida. These data and their line graph are shown in Figure 16.27. The data showing the number of incoming calls from potential customers are in the file **Dawson**. Suppose the current time period is the end of week 10 and we wish to forecast the number of incoming calls for week 11 using a single exponential smoothing model. The following steps can be used:

**Step 1** **Specify the model.**

Because the data do not exhibit a pronounced trend and because we are interested in a short-term forecast (one period ahead), the single exponential smoothing model with a single smoothing constant can be used.

**Step 2** **Fit the model.**

We start by selecting a value for $\alpha$, the smoothing constant, between 0.0 and 1.0. The closer $\alpha$ is to 0.0, the less influence the current observations have in determining the forecast. Small $\alpha$ values will result in greater smoothing of the time series. Likewise, when $\alpha$ is near 1.0, the current observations have greater impact in determining the forecast and less smoothing will occur. There is no firm rule for selecting the value for the smoothing constant. However, in general, if the time series is quite stable, a small $\alpha$ should be used to lessen the impact of random or irregular fluctuations. Because the time series shown in Figure 16.27 appears to be relatively stable, we will use $\alpha = 0.20$ in this example.

**Excel and Minitab Tutorial**

**FIGURE 16.27**

Incoming Customer Sale Calls Data and Line Graph for Dawson Graphic Design

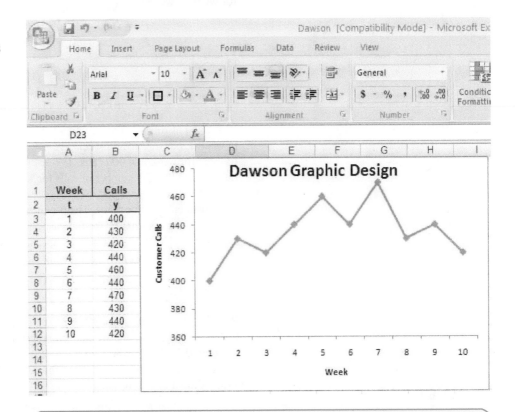

**Excel 2007 Instructions:**

1. Open data file: Dawson.xls.
2. Select the *Calls* data.
3. Click on **Insert > Line**.
4. Click on **Layout**.
5. Use **Chart Titles** and **Axis Titles** to provide appropriate labels.

The forecast value for period $t = 11$ is found using Equation 16.17, as follows:

$$F_{11} = 0.20y_{10} + (1 - 0.20)F_{10}$$

This demonstrates that the forecast for period 11 is a weighted average of the actual number of calls in period 10 and the forecast for period 10. Although we know the number of calls for period 10, we don't know the forecast for period 10. However, we can determine it by

$$F_{10} = 0.20y_9 + (1 - 0.20)F_9$$

Again, this forecast is a weighted average of the actual number of calls in period 9 and the forecast calls for period 9. We would continue in this manner until we get to

$$F_2 = 0.20y_1 + (1 - 0.20)F_1$$

This requires a forecast for period 1. Because we have no data before period 1 from which to develop a forecast, a rule often used is to assume that $F_1 = y_1$.[5]

#### Forecast for period 1 = Actual value in period 1

Because setting the starting value is somewhat arbitrary, you should obtain as much historical data as possible to "warm" the model and dampen out the effect of the starting value. In our example, we have 10 periods of data to warm the model before the forecast for period 11 is made. Note that when using an exponential smoothing model, the effect of the initial forecast is reduced by $(1 - \alpha)$ in the forecast for period 2, then reduced again for period 3, and so on. After sufficient periods, any error due to the arbitrary initial forecast should be very small.

Figure 16.28 shows the results of using the single exponential smoothing equation and Excel for weeks 1 through 10. For week 1, $F_1 = y_1 = 400$. Then, for week 2, we get

$$F_2 = 0.20y_1 + (1 - 0.20)F_1$$
$$F_2 = (0.20)400 + (1 - 0.20)400.00 = 400.00$$

For week 3,

$$F_3 = 0.20y_2 + (1 - 0.20)F_2$$
$$F_3 = (0.20)430 + (1 - 0.20)400.00 = 406.00$$

At the end of week 2, after seeing what actually happened to the number of calls in week 2, our forecast for week 3 is 406 calls. This is a 6-unit increase over the forecast for week 2 of 400 calls. The actual number of calls in week 2 was 430, rather than 400. The number of calls for week 2 was 30 units higher than the forecast for that time period. Because the actual calls were larger than the forecast, an adjustment must be made. The 6-unit adjustment is determined by multiplying the smoothing constant by the forecast error $[0.20(30) = 6]$, as specified in Equation 16.16. The adjustment compensates for the forecast error in week 2.

Continuing for week 4 again using Equation 16.17,

$$F_4 = 0.20y_3 + (1 - 0.20)F_3$$
$$F_4 = (0.20)420 + (1 - 0.20)406.00 = 408.80$$

Recall that our forecast for week 3 was 406. However, actual calls were higher than forecast at 420, and we underforecast by 14 calls. The adjustment for week 4 is then $0.20(14) = 2.80$, and the forecast for week 4 is $406 + 2.80 = 408.80$.

This process continues through the data until we are ready to forecast week 11, as shown in Figure 16.28.

$$F_{11} = 0.20y_{10} + (1 - 0.20)F_{10}$$
$$F_{11} = (0.20)420 + (1 - 0.20)435.70 = 432.56$$

---

[5]Another approach for establishing the starting value, $F_1$, is to use the mean value for some portion of the available data. Regardless of the method used, the quantity of available data should be large enough to dampen out the impact of the starting value.

FIGURE 16.28

Dawson Graphic Design
Single Exponential
Smoothing—Excel
Spreadsheet

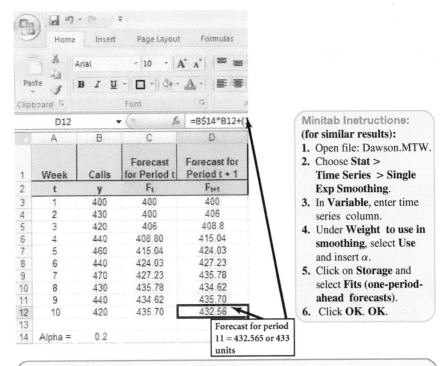

**Minitab Instructions:**
**(for similar results):**
1. Open file: Dawson.MTW.
2. Choose **Stat >**
   **Time Series > Single**
   **Exp Smoothing**.
3. In **Variable**, enter time
   series column.
4. Under **Weight to use in**
   **smoothing**, select **Use**
   and insert $\alpha$.
5. Click on **Storage** and
   select **Fits (one-period-**
   **ahead forecasts)**.
6. Click **OK. OK**.

Forecast for period
11 = 432.565 or 433
units

**Excel 2007 Instructions:**
1. Open data file: Dawson.xls.
2. Create and label two new columns.
3. Enter the smoothing constant in an
   empty cell (e.g. B14).
4. Enter initial forecast for period 1 in
   C3 (400).
5. Use Equation 16.17 to create forecast for
   period $t + 1$ in D2.
6. Forecast for period $t$ is set equal to
   forecast for period $t + 1$ from previous
   period.
7. Copy equations down.

Dawson Graphic Design managers would forecast incoming customer calls for
week 11 of 432. If we wished to forecast week 12 calls, we would either use
the week 11 forecast or wait until the actual week 11 calls are known and then
update the smoothing equations to get a new forecast for week 12.

**Step 3    Diagnose the model.**
However, before we actually use the exponential smoothing forecast for
decision-making purposes, we need to determine how successfully the model
fits the historical data. Unlike the trend-based forecast, which uses least
squares regression, there is no need to use split samples to test the forecasting
ability of an exponential smoothing model, because the forecasts are "true
forecasts." The forecast for a given period is made before considering the
actual value for that period.

Figure 16.29 shows the *MAD* for the forecast model with $\alpha = 0.20$ and a
plot of the forecast values versus the actual call values. This plot shows the
smoothing that has occurred. Note, we don't include period 1 in the *MAD*
calculation since the forecast is set equal to the actual value.

Our next step would be to try different smoothing constants and find the
*MAD* for each new $\alpha$. The forecast for period 11 would be made using the
smoothing constant that generates the smallest *MAD*.

Both Excel and Minitab have single exponential smoothing procedures,
although Minitab's procedure is much more extensive. Refer to the Excel and
Minitab tutorials for instructions on each. Minitab provides optional methods for
determining the initial forecast value for period 1 and a variety of useful graphs.
Minitab also has an option for determining the optimal smoothing constant
value.[6] Figure 16.30 shows the output generated using Minitab. This shows that

---
[6]The solver in Excel can be used to determine the optimal alpha level to minimize the *MAD*.

**FIGURE 16.29**

Excel 2007 Output for Dawson Graphic Design *MAD* Computation for Single Exponential Smoothing, $\alpha = 0.20$

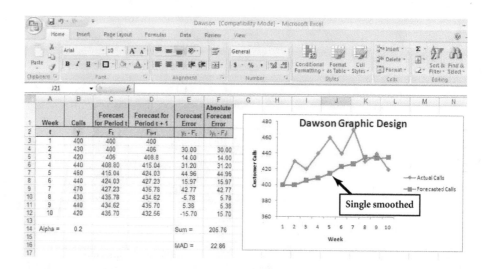

**Excel 2007 Instructions:**
1. Open data file: Dawson.xls.
2. Select the *Calls* data.
3. Click on **Insert > Line**.
4. Click on **Layout**.
5. Use **Chart Titles** and **Axis Titles** to provide appropriate labels.
6. Follow directions for Figure 16.28.
7. Select the Forecast values ($F_t$) and copy and paste onto the line chart.
8. Create a column of forecast errors using an Excel equation.
9. Create a column of absolute forecast errors using Excel's **ABS** function.
10. Compute the *MAD* by using the **AVERAGE** function for the absolute errors.

**FIGURE 16.30**

Minitab Output for Dawson Graphic Design Single Exponential Smoothing Model

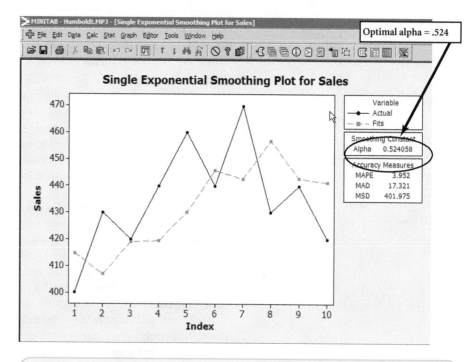

**Minitab Instructions:**
1. Open file: Humboldt.MTW.
2. Choose **Stat >Time Series > Single Exp Smoothing**.
3. In **Variable**, enter time series column.
4. Under **Weight to Use in Smoothing**, select **Optimal ARIMA**.
5. Click **OK**.

the best forecast is found using an $\alpha = 0.524$. Note, *MAD* is decreased from 20.86 (when $\alpha = 0.20$) to 17.321 when the optimal smoothing constant is used.

>>**END EXAMPLE**

**TRY PROBLEM** 16-34 (pg. 759)

A major advantage of the single exponential smoothing model is that it is easy to update. In Example 16-6, the forecast for week 12 using this model is found by simply plugging the actual data value for week 11, once it is known, into the smoothing formula.

$$F_{12} = \alpha y_{11} + (1 - \alpha)F_{11}$$

We do not need to go back and recompute the entire model, as would have been necessary with a trend-based regression model.

**Chapter Outcome 5.** → **Double Exponential Smoothing** When the time series has an increasing or decreasing trend, a modification to the single exponential smoothing model is used to explicitly account for the trend. The resulting technique is called *double exponential smoothing*. The double exponential smoothing model is often referred to as *exponential smoothing with trend*. In double exponential smoothing, a second smoothing constant, beta ($\beta$), is included to account for the trend. Equations 16.18, 16.19, and 16.20 are needed to provide the forecasts.

---

**Double Exponential Smoothing Model**

$$C_t = \alpha y_t + (1 - \alpha)(C_{t-1} + T_{t-1}) \tag{16.18}$$
$$T_t = \beta(C_t - C_{t-1}) + (1 - \beta)T_{t-1} \tag{16.19}$$
$$F_{t+1} = C_t + T_t \tag{16.20}$$

where:

$y_t$ = Value of the time series at time $t$
$\alpha$ = Constant-process smoothing constant
$\beta$ = Trend-smoothing constant
$C_t$ = Smoothed constant-process value for period $t$
$T_t$ = Smoothed trend value for period $t$
$F_{t+1}$ = Forecast value for period $t + 1$
$t$ = Current time period

Equation 16.18 is used to smooth the time-series data; Equation 16.19 is used to smooth the trend; and Equation 16.20 combines the two smoothed values to form the forecast for period $t + 1$.

---

**EXAMPLE 16-7** | **DOUBLE EXPONENTIAL SMOOTHING**

**Excel and Minitab Tutorial**

**Billingsley Insurance Company** The Billingsley Insurance Company has maintained data on the number of automobile claims filed at its Denver office over the past 12 months. These data, which are in the file **Billingsley**, are listed and graphed in Figure 16.31. The claims manager wants to forecast claims for month 13. A double exponential smoothing model can be developed using the following steps:

**Step 1 Specify the model.**
The time series contains a strong upward trend, so a double exponential smoothing model might be selected.

As was the case with single exponential smoothing, we must select starting values. In the case of the double exponential smoothing model, we must select initial values for $C_0$, $T_0$, and the smoothing constants $\alpha$ and $\beta$. The choice of smoothing constant values ($\alpha$ and $\beta$) depends on the same issues as those discussed earlier for single exponential smoothing. That is, use larger smoothing constants when less smoothing is desired and values closer to 0 when more smoothing is desired. The larger the smoothing constant value, the more impact that current data will have on the forecast. Suppose we use $\alpha = 0.20$ and $\beta = 0.30$ in this example. There are several approaches for

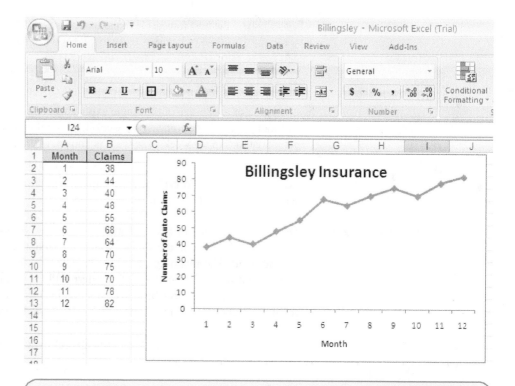

**Excel 2007 Instructions:**
1. Open file: Billingsley.xls.
2. Select *Claims* data.
3. Click on **Insert > Line Chart**.

4. Click on **Layout > Chart Title** and enter desired title.
5. Click on **Layout > Axis Titles** and enter horizontal and vertical axes titles.

selecting starting values for $C_0$ and $T_0$. The method we use here is to fit the least squares trend to the historical data,

$$\hat{y}_t = b_0 + b_1 t$$

where the y intercept, $b_0$, is used as the starting value, $C_0$, and the slope, $b_1$, is used as the starting value for the trend, $T_0$. We can use the regression procedure in Excel or Minitab to perform these calculations, giving

$$\hat{y}_t = 34.273 + 4.1119(t)$$

So,

$$C_0 = 34.273 \quad \text{and} \quad T_0 = 4.1119$$

Keep in mind that these are arbitrary starting values, and as with single exponential smoothing, their effect will be dampened out as you proceed through the sample data to the current period. The more historical data you have, the less impact the starting values will have in the forecast.

**Step 2** **Fit the model.**

The forecast for period 1 made at the beginning of period 1 is

$$F_1 = C_0 + T_0$$
$$F_1 = 34.273 + 4.1119 = 38.385$$

At the close of period 1, in which actual claims were 38, the smoothing equations are updated as follows.

$$C_1 = 0.20(38) + (1 - 0.20)(34.273 + 4.1119) = 38.308$$
$$T_1 = 0.30(38.308 - 34.273) + (1 - 0.30)(4.1119) = 4.089$$

Next, the forecast for period 2 is

$$F_2 = 38.308 + 4.089 = 42.397$$

We then repeat the process through period 12 to find the forecast for period 13.

**Step 3    Diagnose the model.**

Figures 16.32 and 16.33 show the results of the computations and the *MAD* value. The forecast for period 13 is

$$F_{13} = C_{12} + T_{12}$$
$$F_{13} = 83.867 + 3.908 = 87.775$$

Based on this double exponential smoothing model, the number of claims for period 13 is forecast to be about 88. However, before settling on this forecast, we should try different smoothing constants to determine whether a smaller *MAD* can be found.

>>**END EXAMPLE**

**TRY PROBLEM** 16-39 (pg. 760)

As you can see, the computations required for double exponential smoothing are somewhat tedious and are ideally suited for your computer. Although Excel does not have a double exponential smoothing procedure, in Figure 16.32 we have used Excel formulas to develop

**FIGURE 16.32**

Excel 2007 Double Exponential Smoothing Spreadsheet for Billingsley Insurance

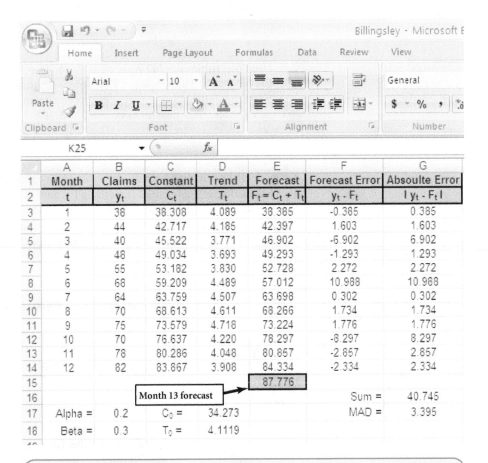

| | A | B | C | D | E | F | G |
|---|---|---|---|---|---|---|---|
| 1 | Month | Claims | Constant | Trend | Forecast | Forecast Error | Absoulte Error |
| 2 | t | $y_t$ | $C_t$ | $T_t$ | $F_t = C_t + T_t$ | $y_t - F_t$ | $\mid y_t - F_t \mid$ |
| 3 | 1 | 38 | 38.308 | 4.089 | 38.385 | -0.385 | 0.385 |
| 4 | 2 | 44 | 42.717 | 4.185 | 42.397 | 1.603 | 1.603 |
| 5 | 3 | 40 | 45.522 | 3.771 | 46.902 | -6.902 | 6.902 |
| 6 | 4 | 48 | 49.034 | 3.693 | 49.293 | -1.293 | 1.293 |
| 7 | 5 | 55 | 53.182 | 3.830 | 52.728 | 2.272 | 2.272 |
| 8 | 6 | 68 | 59.209 | 4.489 | 57.012 | 10.988 | 10.988 |
| 9 | 7 | 64 | 63.759 | 4.507 | 63.698 | 0.302 | 0.302 |
| 10 | 8 | 70 | 68.613 | 4.611 | 68.266 | 1.734 | 1.734 |
| 11 | 9 | 75 | 73.579 | 4.718 | 73.224 | 1.776 | 1.776 |
| 12 | 10 | 70 | 76.637 | 4.220 | 78.297 | -8.297 | 8.297 |
| 13 | 11 | 78 | 80.286 | 4.048 | 80.857 | -2.857 | 2.857 |
| 14 | 12 | 82 | 83.867 | 3.908 | 84.334 | -2.334 | 2.334 |
| 15 | | | | | 87.776 | | |
| 16 | | | Month 13 forecast | | | Sum = | 40.745 |
| 17 | Alpha = | 0.2 | $C_0 =$ | 34.273 | | MAD = | 3.395 |
| 18 | Beta = | 0.3 | $T_0 =$ | 4.1119 | | | |

**Excel 2007 Instructions:**

1. Open File: Billingsley.xls.
2. Create five new column headings as shown in Figure 16.32.
3. Place the smoothing constants (alpha and beta) in empty cells (B17 and B18).
4. Place the starting values for the constant process and the trend in empty cells (D17 and D18).
5. Use Equations 16.18 and 16.19 to create process columns.
6. Use Equation 16.19 to create the forecast values in the forecast column.
7. Calculate the forecast error by subtracting the forecast column values from the *y* column values.
8. Calculate the absolute forecast errors using the Excel **ABS** function.
9. Calculate the *MAD* by using the Excel **AVERAGE** function.

**FIGURE 16.33**

Minitab Double Exponential Smoothing Spreadsheet for Billingsley Insurance

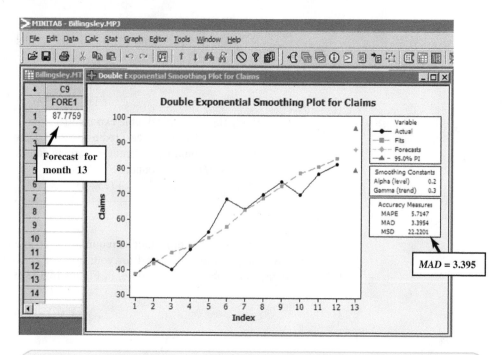

**Minitab Instructions:**

1. Open file: Billingsley.MTW.
2. Choose **Stat > Time Series > Double Exp Smoothing**.
3. In **Variable**, enter time series column.
4. Check **Generate forecasts** and enter 1 in **Number of forecasts** and 12 in **Starting from origin**.
5. Click **OK**.

our model in conjunction with the regression tool for determining the starting values. Minitab does have a double exponential smoothing routine, as illustrated in Figure 16.33.

The *MAPE* on the Minitab output is the *Mean Absolute Percent Error*, which is computed using Equation 16.21. The *MAPE* = 5.7147, indicating that on average, the double exponential smoothing model produced a forecast that differed from the actual claims by 5.7%.

**Mean Absolute Percent Error**

$$MAPE = \frac{\sum \dfrac{|y_t - F_t|}{y_t}(100)}{n} \qquad (16.21)$$

where:

$y_t$ = Value of time series in time $t$

$F_t$ = Forecast value for time period $t$

$n$ = Number of periods of available data

*MyStatLab*

# 16-3: Exercises

## Skill Development

**16-34.** The following table represents two years of data:

| Year 1 | | Year 2 | |
|---|---|---|---|
| 1st quarter | 242 | 1st quarter | 272 |
| 2nd quarter | 252 | 2nd quarter | 267 |
| 3rd quarter | 257 | 3rd quarter | 276 |
| 4th quarter | 267 | 4th quarter | 281 |

a. Prepare a single exponential smoothing forecast for the first quarter of year 3 using an alpha value of 0.10. Let the initial forecast value for quarter 1 of year 1 be 250.
b. Prepare a single exponential smoothing forecast for the first quarter of year 3 using an alpha value of 0.25. Let the initial forecast value for quarter 1 of year 1 be 250.
c. Calculate the *MAD* value for the forecasts you generated in parts a and b. Which alpha value provides the smaller *MAD* value at the end of the 4th quarter in year 2?

**16-35.** The following data represent enrollment in a major at your university for the past six semesters (*Note*: semester 1 is the oldest data; semester 6 is the most recent data):

| Semester | Enrollment |
|---|---|
| 1 | 87 |
| 2 | 110 |
| 3 | 123 |
| 4 | 127 |
| 5 | 145 |
| 6 | 160 |

a. Prepare a graph of enrollment for the six semesters.
b. Based on the graph you prepared in part a, does it appear that a trend is present in the enrollment figures?
c. Prepare a single exponential smoothing forecast for semester 7 using an alpha value of 0.35. Assume that the initial forecast for semester 1 is 90.
d. Prepare a double exponential smoothing forecast for semester 7 using an alpha value of 0.20 and a beta value of 0.25. Assume that the initial smoothed constant value for semester 1 is 80 and the initial smoothed trend value for semester 1 is 10.
e. Calculate the *MAD* values for the simple exponential smoothing model and the double exponential smoothing model at the end of semester 6. Which

model appears to be doing the better job of forecasting course enrollment? Don't include period 1 in the calculation.

**16-36.** The following data represent the average number of employees in outlets of a large consumer electronics retailer:

| Year | 2001 | 2002 | 2003 | 2004 | 2005 | 2006 | 2007 | 2008 | 2009 | 2010 |
|---|---|---|---|---|---|---|---|---|---|---|
| Number | 20.6 | 17.3 | 18.6 | 21.5 | 23.2 | 19.9 | 18.7 | 15.6 | 19.7 | 20.4 |

a. Construct a time-series plot of this time series. Does it appear that a linear trend exists in the time series?
b. Calculate forecasts for each of the years in the time series. Use a smoothing constant of 0.25 and single exponential smoothing.
c. Calculate the *MAD* value for the forecasts you generated in part b.
d. Construct a single exponential smoothing forecast for 2011. Use a smoothing constant of 0.25.

**16-37.** A brokerage company is interested in forecasting the number of new accounts the office will obtain next month. It has collected the following data for the past 12 months:

| Month | Accounts |
|---|---|
| 1 | 19 |
| 2 | 20 |
| 3 | 21 |
| 4 | 25 |
| 5 | 26 |
| 6 | 24 |
| 7 | 24 |
| 8 | 21 |
| 9 | 27 |
| 10 | 30 |
| 11 | 24 |
| 12 | 30 |

a. Produce a time-series plot for these data. Specify the exponential forecasting model that should be used to obtain next month's forecast.
b. Assuming a double exponential smoothing model, fit the least squares trend to the historical data, to determine the smoothed constant-process value and the smoothed trend value for period 0.
c. Produce the forecasts for periods 1 through 12 using $\alpha = 0.15$, $\beta = 0.25$. Indicate the number of new accounts the company may expect to receive next month based on the forecast model.
d. Calculate the *MAD* for this model.

## Business Applications

**16-38.** With tax revenues declining in many states, school districts have been searching for methods of cutting costs without affecting classroom academics. One district has been looking at the cost of extracurricular activities ranging from band trips to athletics. The district business manager has gathered the past six months' costs for these activities as shown here.

| Month | Expenditures ($) |
|---|---|
| September | 23,586.41 |
| October | 23,539.22 |
| November | 23,442.06 |
| December | 23,988.71 |
| January | 23,727.13 |
| February | 23,799.69 |

Using this past history, prepare a single exponential smoothing forecast for March using an $\alpha$ value of 0.25.

**16-39.** "The average college senior graduated this year with more than $19,000 in debt" was the beginning sentence of a recent article in *USA Today*. The majority of students have loans that are not due until the student leaves school. This can result in the student ignoring the size of debt that piles up. Federal loans obtained to finance college education are steadily mounting. The data given here show the amount of loans ($million) for the last 20 academic years, with year 20 being the most recent.

| Year | Amount | Year | Amount | Year | Amount |
|---|---|---|---|---|---|
| 1 | 9,914 | 8 | 16,221 | 15 | 37,228 |
| 2 | 10,182 | 9 | 22,557 | 16 | 39,101 |
| 3 | 12,493 | 10 | 26,011 | 17 | 42,761 |
| 4 | 13,195 | 11 | 28,737 | 18 | 49,360 |
| 5 | 13,414 | 12 | 31,906 | 19 | 57,463 |
| 6 | 13,890 | 13 | 33,930 | 20 | 62,614 |
| 7 | 15,232 | 14 | 34,376 | | |

a. Produce a time-series plot for these data. Specify the exponential forecasting model that should be used to obtain next year's forecast.
b. Assuming a double exponential smoothing model, fit the least squares trend to the historical data to determine the smoothed constant-process value and the smoothed trend value for period 0.
c. Using data for periods 1 through 20 and using $\alpha = 0.20$ and $\beta = 0.30$, forecast the total student loan volume for the year 21.
d. Calculate the *MAD* for this model.

**16-40.** The human resources manager for a medium-sized business is interested in predicting the dollar value of medical expenditures filed by employees of her company for the year 2011. From her company's database she has collected the following information showing the dollar value of medical expenditures made by employees for the previous seven years:

| Year | Medical Claims |
|---|---|
| 2004 | $405,642.43 |
| 2005 | $407,180.60 |
| 2006 | $408,203.30 |
| 2007 | $410,088.03 |
| 2008 | $411,085.64 |
| 2009 | $412,200.39 |
| 2010 | $414,043.90 |

a. Prepare a graph of medical expenditures for the years 2004–2010. Which forecasting technique do you think is most appropriate for this time series, single exponential smoothing or double exponential smoothing? Why?
b. Use an $\alpha$ value of 0.25 and a $\beta$ value of 0.15 to produce a double exponential forecast for the medical claims data. Use linear trend analysis to obtain the starting values for $C_0$ and $T_0$.
c. Compute the *MAD* value for your model for the years 2004 to 2010. Also produce a graph of your forecast values.

**16-41.** Retail Forward, Inc., is a global management consulting and market research firm specializing in retail intelligence and strategies. One of its press releases (*June Consumer Outlook: Spending Plans Show Resilience*, June 1, 2006) divulged the result of the Retail Forward ShopperScape™ survey conducted each month from a sample of 4,000 U.S. primary household shoppers. A measure of consumer spending is represented by the following figure:

a. Construct a time-series plot of these data. Does it appear that a linear trend exists in the time series?

b. Calculate forecasts for each of the months in the time series. Use a smoothing constant of 0.25.

c. Calculate the *MAD* value for the forecasts you generated in part b.

d. Construct a single exponential smoothing forecast for July 2006. Use a smoothing constant of 0.25.

## Computer Database **Exercises**

**16-42.** The National Association of Theatre Owners is the largest exhibition trade organization in the world, representing more than 26,000 movie screens in all 50 states and in more than 20 countries worldwide. Its membership includes the largest cinema chains and hundreds of independent theater owners. It publishes statistics concerning the movie sector of the economy. The file entitled **Flicks** contains data on average U.S. ticket prices ($). One concern is the rapidly increasing price of tickets.

a. Produce a time-series plot for these data. Specify the exponential forecasting model that should be used to obtain next year's forecast.

b. Assuming a double exponential smoothing model, fit the least squares trend to the historical data to determine the smoothed constant-process value and the smoothed trend value for period 0.

c. Use $\alpha = 0.20$ and $\beta = 0.30$ to forecast the average yearly ticket price for the year 2010.

d. Calculate the *MAD* for this model.

**16-43.** Inflation is a fall in the market value or purchasing power of money. Measurements of inflation are prepared and published by the Bureau of Labor Statistics of the Department of Labor, which measures average changes in prices of goods and services. The file entitled **CPI** contains the monthly CPI and inflation rate for the period January 2000–December 2005.

a. Construct a plot of this time series. Does it appear that a linear trend exists in the time series? Specify the exponential forecasting model that should be used to obtain next month's forecast.

b. Assuming a single exponential smoothing model, calculate forecasts for each of the months in the time series. Use a smoothing constant of 0.15.

c. Calculate the *MAD* value for the forecasts you generated in part b.

d. Construct a single exponential smoothing forecast for January 2006. Use a smoothing constant of 0.15.

**16-44.** The sales manager at Grossmieller Importers in New York City needs to determine a monthly forecast for the number of men's golf sweaters that will be sold so that he can order an appropriate amount of packing boxes. Grossmieller ships sweaters to retail stores throughout the United States and Canada. Shirts are packed six to a box. Data for the past 12 months are contained in the data file called **Grossmieller**.

a. Plot the sales data using a time-series plot. Based on the graph, what time series components are present? Discuss.

b. (1) Use a single exponential smoothing model with $\alpha = 0.30$ to forecast sales for month 17. Assume that the initial forecast for period 1 is 36,000. (2) Compute the *MAD* for this model. (3) Graph the smoothing-model-fitted values on the time-series plot.

c. (1) Referring to part b, try different alpha levels to determine which smoothing constant value you would recommend. (2) Indicate why you have selected this value and then develop the forecast for month 17. (3) Compare this to the forecast you got using $\alpha = 0.30$ in part b.

**16-45.** Referring to Problem 16-44, in which the sales manager for Grossmieller Imports of New York City needs to forecast monthly sales,

a. Discuss why a double exponential smoothing model might be preferred over a single exponential smoothing model.

b. (1) Develop a double exponential smoothing model using $\alpha = 0.20$ and $\beta = 0.30$ as smoothing constants. To obtain the starting values, use the regression trend line approach discussed in this section. (2) Determine the forecast for month 17. (3) Also compute the *MAD* for this model. (4) Graph the fitted values on the time-series graph.

c. Compare the results for this double exponential smoothing model with the "best" single exponential smoothing model developed in part c of Exercise 16-44. Discuss which model is preferred.

d. Referring to part b, try different alpha and beta values in an attempt to determine an improved forecast model for monthly sales. For each model, show the forecast for period 17 and the *MAD*. Write a short report that compares the different models.

e. Referring to part d and to part c for Exercise 16-44, write a report to the Grossmieller sales manager that indicates your choice for the forecasting model, complete with your justification for the selection.

# Visual Summary

**Chapter 16:** Organizations must operate effectively in the environment they face today, but also plan to continue to effectively operate in the future. To plan for the future organizations must **forecast**. This chapter introduces the two basic types of forecasting: qualitative forecasting and quantitative forecasting. Qualitative forecasting techniques are based on expert opinion and judgment. **Quantitative forecasting** techniques are based on statistical methods for analyzing quantitative historical data. The chapter focuses on **quantitative forecasting** techniques. Numerous techniques exist, often determined by the **forecasting horizon**. Forecasts are often divided into four phases, **immediate forecasts** of one month or less, **short term** of one to three months, **medium term** of three months to two years and **long term** of two years of more. The forecasting technique used is often determined by the length of the forecast, called the forecasting horizon. The model building issues discussed in Chapter 15 involving **model specification**, **model fitting**, and **model diagnosis** also apply to forecasting models.

 **16.1** Introduction to Forecasting, Time-Series Data, and Index Numbers (pg. 710–723)

## Summary

Quantitative forecasting techniques rely on data gathered in the past to forecast what will happen in the future. **Time series** analysis is a commonly used quantitative forecasting technique. Time series analysis involves looking for patterns in the past data that will hopefully continue into the future. It involves looking for four components, trend, seasonal, cyclical and random. A **trend** is the long-term increase or decrease in a variable being measured over time and can be linear or nonlinear. A **seasonal component** is present if the data shows a repeating pattern over time. If when observing time-series data you see sustained periods of high values followed by periods of lower values and the recurrence period of these fluctuations is larger than a year, the data are said to contain a **cyclical component**. Although not all time series possess a trend, seasonal, or cyclical component, virtually all time series will have a random component. The **random component** is often referred to as "noise" in the data. When analyzing time-series data, you will often compare one value measured at one point in time with other values measured at different points in time. A common procedure for making relative comparisons is to begin by determining a **base period index** to which all other data values can be fairly compared. The simplest index is an **unweighted aggregate index**. More complicated weighted indexes include the **Paasche** and **Lespeyres** indexes.

> **Outcome 1.** Identify the components present in a time series.
> **Outcome 2.** Understand and compute basic index numbers.

 **16.2** Trend-Based Forecasting Techniques (pg. 724–749)

## Summary

**Trend-based forecasting techniques** begin by identifying and modeling that trend. Once the trend model has been defined, it is used to provide forecasts for future time periods. Regression analysis is often used to identify the trend component. How well the trend fits the actual data can be determined by the **Mean Squared Error (MSE)** or **Mean Absolute Deviation (MAD)**. In general the smaller the MSE and MAD the better the model fits the actual data. Using regression analysis to determine the trend carries some risk, one of which is that the error terms in the analysis are not independent. Related error terms indicate autocorrelation in the data and is tested for using the **Durbin-Watson Statistic**. Seasonality is often found in trend based forecasting models and if found is dealt with by computing seasonal indexes. While alternate methods are used to compute **seasonal indexes** this section concentrates on the **ratio-to-moving-average method**. Once the seasonal indexes are determined, they are used to deseasonalize the data to allow for a better trend forecast. The indexes are then used to determine a **seasonally adjusted forecast**. Determining the trend and seasonal components to a time series model allows the cyclical and random components to be better determined.

> **Outcome 3.** Apply the fundamental steps in developing and implementing forecasting models.
> **Outcome 4.** Apply trend-based forecasting models, including linear trend, nonlinear trend, and seasonally adjusted trend.

 **16.3** Forecasting Using Smoothing Methods (pg. 750–761)

## Summary

A disadvantage of trend based forecasting is that it gives as much weight to the earliest data in the time series as it does to the data that are close to the period for which the forecast is required. It does not therefore allow model to "learn" or "adjust" to changes in the time series. This section introduces exponential smoothing models. With **exponential smoothing**, current observations can be weighted more heavily than older observations in determining the forecast. Therefore, if in recent periods the time-series values are much higher (or lower) than those in earlier periods, the forecast can be made to reflect this difference. The section discusses **single exponential smoothing** models and double exponential smoothing models. **Single exponential smoothing** models are used when only random fluctuations are seen in the data while **double exponential smoothing** models are used if the data seems to combine both random variations with a trend. Both models weigh recent data more heavily than past data. As with all forecast models the basic steps of model building: specification, fitting and diagnosing the model are followed.

> **Outcome 5.** Use smoothing-based forecasting models, including single and double exponential smoothing

 **Conclusion**

While both qualitative and quantitative forecasting techniques are used, this chapter has emphasized quantitative techniques. Quantitative forecasting techniques require historical data for the variable to be forecasted. The success of a quantitative model is determined by how well the model fits the historical time-series data and how closely the future resembles the past. Forecasting is as much an art as it is a science. The more experience you have in a given situation, the more effective you likely will be at identifying and applying the appropriate forecasting tool. You will find that the techniques introduced in this chapter are used frequently as an initial basis for a forecast. However, in most cases, the decision maker will modify the forecast based on personal judgment and other qualitative inputs that are not considered by the quantitative model.

# Equations

**(16.1)** Simple Index Number pg. 714

$$I_t = \frac{y_t}{y_0} 100$$

**(16.2)** Unweighted Aggregate Price Index pg. 716

$$I_t = \frac{\sum p_t}{\sum p_0}(100)$$

**(16.3)** The Paasche Index pg. 717

$$I_t = \frac{\sum q_t p_t}{\sum q_t p_0}(100)$$

**(16.4)** Laspeyres Index pg. 718

$$I_t = \frac{\sum q_0 p_t}{\sum q_0 p_0}(100)$$

**(16.5)** Deflation Formula pg. 721

$$y_{adj_t} = \frac{y_t}{I_t}(100)$$

**(16.6)** Linear Trend Model pg. 725

$$y_t = \beta_0 + \beta_1 t + \varepsilon_t$$

**(16.7)** Least Squares Equations Estimates pg. 725

$$b_1 = \frac{\sum t y_t - \dfrac{\sum t \sum y_t}{n}}{\sum t^2 - \dfrac{(\sum t)^2}{n}}$$

**(16.8)**

$$b_0 = \frac{\sum y_t}{n} - b_1 \frac{\sum t}{n}$$

**(16.9)** Mean Squared Error pg. 727

$$MSE = \frac{\sum(y_t - F_t)^2}{n}$$

**(16.10)** Mean Absolute Deviation pg. 727

$$MAD = \frac{\sum |y_t - F_t|}{n}$$

**(16.11)** Durbin-Watson Statistic pg. 729

$$d = \frac{\displaystyle\sum_{t=2}^{n}(e_t - e_{t-1})^2}{\displaystyle\sum_{t=1}^{n} e_t^2}$$

**(16.12)** Forecast Bias pg. 733

$$\text{Forecast bias} = \frac{\sum(y_t - F_t)}{n}$$

**(16.13)** Multiplicative Time-Series Model pg. 739

$$y_t = T_t \times S_t \times C_t \times I_t$$

**(16.14)** Ratio-to-Moving-Average pg. 741

$$S_t \times I_t = \frac{y_t}{T_t \times C_t}$$

**(16.15)** Deseasonalization pg. 742

$$T_t \times C_t \times I_t = \frac{y_t}{S_t}$$

**(16.16)** Exponential Smoothing Model pg. 750

$$F_{t+1} = F_t + \alpha(y_t - F_t)$$

or

**(16.17)** $$F_{t+1} = \alpha y_t + (1 - \alpha)F_t$$

**(16.18)** Double Exponential Smoothing Model pg. 755

$$C_t = \alpha y_t + (1 - \alpha)(C_{t-1} + T_{t-1})$$

**(16.19)** $$T_t = \beta(C_t - C_{t-1}) + (1 - \beta)T_{t-1}$$

**(16.20)** $$F_{t+1} = C_t + T_t$$

**(16.21)** Mean Absolute Percent Error pg. 758

$$MAPE = \frac{\sum \dfrac{|y_t - F_t|}{y_t}(100)}{n}$$

# Key Terms

Aggregate price index pg. 715
Autocorrelation pg. 728
Base period index pg. 714
Cyclical component pg. 713
Exponential smoothing pg. 750
Forecasting horizon pg. 710

Forecasting interval pg. 710
Forecasting period pg. 710
Linear trend pg. 711
Model diagnosis pg. 710
Model fitting pg. 710
Model specification pg. 710

Moving average pg. 739
Random component pg. 713
Seasonal component pg. 712
Seasonal index pg. 739
Seasonally unadjusted forecast pg. 743

# Chapter Exercises

## Conceptual Questions

**16-46.** Go to the library or use the Internet to find data showing your state's population for the past 20 years. Plot these data and indicate which of the time-series components are present.

**16-47.** A time series exhibits the pattern stated below. Indicate the type of time-series component described.
   a. The pattern is "wavelike" with a recurrence period of nine months.
   b. The time series is steadily increasing.
   c. The pattern is "wavelike" with a recurrence period of two years.
   d. The pattern is unpredictable.
   e. The pattern steadily decreases, with a "wavelike" shape which reoccurs every 10 years.

**16-48.** Identify the businesses in your community that might be expected to have sales that exhibit a seasonal component. Discuss.

**16-49.** Discuss the difference between a cyclical component and a seasonal component. Which component is more predictable, seasonal or cyclical? Discuss and illustrate with examples.

**16-50.** In the simple linear regression model, confidence and prediction intervals are utilized to provide interval estimates for an average and a particular value, respectively, of the dependent variable. The linear trend model in time series is an application of simple linear regression. This being said, discuss whether a confidence or a prediction interval is the relevant interval estimate for a linear trend model's forecast.

## Business Applications

Problems 16-51 through 16-54 refer to Malcar Autoparts Company, which has started producing replacement control microcomputers for automobiles. This has been a growth industry since the first control units were introduced in 1985. Sales data since 1994 are as follows:

| Year | Sales ($) | Year | Sales ($) |
|------|-----------|------|-----------|
| 1994 | 240,000 | 2002 | 1,570,000 |
| 1995 | 218,000 | 2003 | 1,947,000 |
| 1996 | 405,000 | 2004 | 2,711,000 |
| 1997 | 587,000 | 2005 | 3,104,000 |
| 1998 | 795,000 | 2006 | 2,918,000 |
| 1999 | 762,000 | 2007 | 4,606,000 |
| 2000 | 998,000 | 2008 | 5,216,000 |
| 2001 | 1,217,000 | 2009 | 5,010,000 |

**16-51.** As a start in analyzing these data,
   a. Graph these data and indicate whether they appear to have a linear trend.
   b. Develop a simple linear regression model with time as the independent variable. Using this regression model, describe the trend and the strength of the linear trend over the 16 years. Is the trend line statistically significant? Plot the trend line against the actual data.
   c. Compute the *MAD* value for this model.
   d. Provide the Malcar Autoparts Company an estimate of its expected sales for the next 5 years.
   e. Provide the maximum and minimum sales Malcar can expect with 90% confidence for the year 2014.

**16-52.** Develop a single exponential smoothing model using $\alpha = 0.20$. Use as a starting value the average of the first 6 years' data. Determine the forecasted value for year 2010.
   a. Compute the *MAD* for this model.
   b. Plot the forecast values against the actual data.
   c. Use the same starting value but try different smoothing constants (say, 0.05, 0.10, 0.25, and 0.30) in an effort to reduce the *MAD* value.
   d. Is it possible to answer part d of Problem 16.51 using this forecasting technique? Explain your answer.

**16-53.** Develop a double exponential smoothing model using smoothing constants $\alpha = 0.20$ and $\beta = 0.40$. As starting values, use the least squares trend line slope and intercept values.
   a. Compute the *MAD* for this model.
   b. Plot the forecast values against the actual data.
   c. Use the same starting values but try different smoothing constants [say, $(\alpha, \beta) = (0.10, 0.50)$, $(0.30, 0.30)$, and $(0.40, 0.20)$] in an effort to reduce the *MAD* value.

**16-54.** Using whatever diagnostic tools you are familiar with, determine which of the three forecasting methods utilized to forecast sales for Malcar Autoparts Company in the previous three problems provides superior forecasts. Explain the reasons for your choice.

**16-55.** Amazon.com has become one of the most successful online merchants. Two measures of its success are sales and net income/loss figures. They are given here.

| Year | Net Income/Loss | Sales |
|------|-----------------|-------|
| 1995 | −0.3 | 0.5 |
| 1996 | −5.7 | 15.7 |
| 1997 | −27.5 | 147.7 |
| 1998 | −124.5 | 609.8 |
| 1999 | −719.9 | 1,639.8 |
| 2000 | −1,411.2 | 2,761.9 |
| 2001 | −567.3 | 3,122.9 |
| 2002 | −149.1 | 3,933 |
| 2003 | 35.3 | 5,263.7 |
| 2004 | 588.5 | 6,921 |
| 2005 | 359 | 8,490 |
| 2006 | 190 | 10,711 |
| 2007 | 476 | 14,835 |

a. Produce a time-series plot for these data. Specify the exponential forecasting model that should be used to obtain the following years' forecasts.

b. Assuming a double exponential smoothing model, fit the least squares trend to the historical data to determine the smoothed constant-process value and the smoothed trend value for period 0.

c. Produce the forecasts for periods 1 through 13 using $\alpha = 0.10$ and $\beta = 0.20$. Indicate the sales Amazon should expect for 2008 based on the forecast model.

d. Calculate the MAD for this model.

**16-56.** College tuition has risen at a pace faster than inflation for more than two decades, according to an article in *USA Today*. The following data indicate the average college tuition (in 2003 dollars) for public colleges:

| Period | 1983–1984 | 1988–1989 | 1993–1994 | 1998–1999 | 2003–2004 | 2008–2009 |
|--------|-----------|-----------|-----------|-----------|-----------|-----------|
| Public | 2,074 | 2,395 | 3,188 | 3,632 | 4,694 | 5,652 |

a. Produce a time-series plot of these data. Indicate the time-series components that exist in the data.

b. Provide a forecast for the average tuition for public colleges in the academic year 2013–2014. (*Hint:* One time-series time period represents five academic years.)

c. Provide an interval of plausible values for the average tuition change after five academic periods have gone by. Use a confidence level of 0.90.

## Computer Database Exercises

**16-57.** HSH® Associates, financial publishers, is the nation's largest publisher of mortgage and consumer loan information. Every week it collects current data from 2,000 mortgage lenders across the nation. It tracks a variety of adjustable rate mortgage (ARM) indexes and makes them available on its Web site. The file **ARM**

contains the national monthly average one-year ARM for the time period January 2004 to December 2008.

a. Produce a scatter plot of the federal ARM for the time period January 2004 to December 2008. Identify any time-series components that exist in the data.

b. Identify the recurrence period of the time series. Determine the seasonal index for each month within the recurrence period.

c. Fit a nonlinear trend model containing coded years and coded years squared as predictors for the deseasonalized data.

d. Provide a seasonally adjusted forecast using the nonlinear trend model for January 2009.

e. Diagnose the model.

**16-58.** DataNet is an Internet service where clients can find information and purchase various items such as airline tickets, stereo equipment, and listed stocks. DataNet has been in operation for four years. Data on monthly calls for service for the time that the company has been in business are in the data file called **DataNet**.

a. Plot these data in a time-series graph. Based on the graph, what time-series components are present in the data?

b. Develop the seasonal indexes for each month. Describe what the seasonal index for August means.

c. Fit a linear trend model to the deseasonalized data for months 1–48 and determine the MAD value. Comment on the adequacy of the linear trend model based on these measures of forecast error.

d. Provide a seasonally unadjusted forecast using the linear trend model for each month of the year.

e. Use the seasonal index values computed in part b to provide seasonal adjusted forecasts for months 49–52.

**16-59.** Referring to Problem 16-58, the managers of DataNet, the Internet company where users can purchase products like airline tickets, need to forecast monthly call volumes in order to have sufficient capacity. Develop a single exponential smoothing model using $\alpha = 0.30$. Use as a starting value the average of the first six months' data.

a. Compute the MAD for this model.

b. Plot the forecast values against the actual data.

c. Use the same starting value but try different smoothing constants (say, 0.10, 0.20, 0.40, and 0.50) in an effort to reduce the MAD value.

d. Reflect on the type of time series for which the single exponential smoothing model is designed to provide forecasts. Does it surprise you that the MAD for this method is relatively large for these data? Explain your reasoning.

**16-60.** Continuing with the DataNet forecasting problems, develop a double exponential smoothing model using smoothing constants $\alpha = 0.20$ and $\beta = 0.20$. As starting values, use the least squares trend line slope and intercept values.

a. Compute the *MAD* for this model.

b. Plot the forecast values against the actual data.

c. Compare this with a linear trend model. Which forecast method would you use? Explain your rationale.

d. Use the same starting values but try different smoothing constants [say, $(\alpha, \beta) = (0.10, 0.30)$, $(0.15, 0.25)$, and $(0.30, 0.10)$] in an effort to reduce the *MAD* value. Prepare a short report that summarizes your efforts.

16-61. The College Board, administrator of the SAT test for college entrants, has made several changes to the test in recent years. One recent change occurred between years 2005 and 2006. In a press release the College Board announced SAT scores for students in the class of 2005, the last to take the former version of the SAT featuring math and verbal sections. The board indicated that for the class of 2005, the average SAT

math scores continued their strong upward trend, increasing from 518 in 2004 to 520 in 2005, 14 points higher than 10 years ago and an all-time high. The file entitled **MathSAT** contains the math SAT scores for the interval 1967 to 2005.

a. Produce a time-series plot for the combined gender math SAT scores for the period 1980 to 2005. Indicate the time-series components that exist in the data.

b. Conduct a test of hypothesis to determine if the average SAT math scores of students continued to increase in the period indicated in part a. Use a significance level of 0.10 and the test statistic approach.

c. Produce a forecast for the average SAT math scores for 2010.

d. Beginning with the March 12, 2005, administration of the exam, the SAT Reasoning Test, was modified and lengthened. How does this affect the forecast produced in part c? What statistical concept is exhibited by producing the forecast in part c?

# Video Case 2

## Restaurant Location and Re-imaging Decisions @ McDonald's

In the early days of his restaurant company's growth, McDonald's founder Ray Kroc knew that finding the right location was key. He had a keen eye for prime real estate locations. Today, the company is more than 30,000 restaurants strong. When it comes to picking prime real estate locations for its restaurants and making the most of them, McDonald's is way ahead of the competition. In fact, when it comes to global real estate holdings, no corporate entity has more.

From urban office and airport locations, to Wal-Mart stores and the busiest street corner in your town, McDonald's has grown to become one of the world's most recognized brands. Getting there hasn't been just a matter of buying all available real estate on the market. Instead, the company has used the basic principles and process Ray Kroc believed in to investigate and secure the best possible sites for its restaurants. Factors such as neighborhood demographics, traffic patterns, competitor proximity, workforce, and retail shopping center locations all play a role.

Many of the company's restaurant locations have been in operation for decades. And although the restaurants have adapted to changing times—including diet fads and reporting nutrition information, staff uniform updates, and menu innovations such as Happy Meals, Chicken McNuggets, and premium salads—there's more to bringing customers back time and again than an updated menu and a good location. Those same factors that played a role in the original location decision need to be periodically examined to learn what's changed and, as a result, what changes the local McDonald's needs to consider.

Beginning in 2003, McDonald's started work on "re-imaging" its existing restaurants while continuing to expand the brand

globally. More than 6,000 restaurants have been re-imaged to date. Sophia Galassi, vice president of U.S. Restaurant Development, is responsible for the new look nationwide. According to Sophia, re-imaging is more than new landscaping and paint. In some cases, the entire store is torn down and rebuilt with redesigned drive-thru lanes to speed customers through faster, interiors with contemporary colors and coffee-house seating, and entertainment zones with televisions, and free Wi-Fi.

"We work very closely with our owner/operators to collect solid data about their locations, and then help analyze them so we can present the business case to them," says Sophia. Charts and graphs, along with the detailed statistical results, are vital to the decision process.

One recent project provides a good example of how statistics supported the re-imaging decision. Dave Traub, owner/operator, had been successfully operating a restaurant in Midlothian, Virginia, for more than 30 years. The location was still prime, but the architecture and décor hadn't kept up with changing times. After receiving the statistical analysis on the location from McDonald's, Dave had the information he needed to make the decision to invest in re-imaging the restaurant. With revenues and customer traffic up, he has no regrets. "We've become the community's gathering place. The local senior citizens group now meets here regularly in the mornings," he says.

The re-imaging effort doesn't mean the end to new restaurant development for the company. "As long as new communities are developed and growth continues in neighborhoods across the country, we'll be analyzing data about them to be sure our restaurants are positioned in the best possible locations," states Sophia. Ray Kroc would be proud.

## Discussion Questions:

1. Sophia Galassi, vice president of U.S. Restaurant Development for McDonald's, indicated that she and her staff work very closely with owner/operators to collect data about McDonald's restaurant locations. Describe some of the kinds of data that Sophia's staff would collect and the respective types of charts that could be used to present their findings to the owner/operators.

2. At the end of 2001, Sophia Galassi and her team led a remodel and re-imaging effort for the McDonald's franchises in a major U.S. city. This entailed a total change in store layout and design and a renewed emphasis on customer service. Once this work had been completed, the company put in place a comprehensive customer satisfaction data collection and tracking system. The data in the file called **McDonald's Customer Satisfaction** consist of the overall percentage of customers at the franchise McDonald's in this city who have rated the customer service as Excellent or Very Good during each quarter since the re-imaging and remodeling was completed. Develop a line chart and discuss what time-series components appear to be contained in these data.

3. Referring to question 2, based on the available historical data, develop a seasonally adjusted forecast for the percentage of customers who will rate the stores as Excellent or Very Good for Quarter 3 and Quarter 4 of 2006. Discuss the process you used to arrive at these forecasts.

4. Referring to questions 2 and 3, use any other forecasting method discussed in this chapter to arrive at a forecast for Quarters 3 and 4 of 2006. Compare your chosen model with the seasonally adjusted forecast model specified in question 3. Use appropriate measures of forecast error. Prepare a short report outlining your forecasting attempts along with your recommendation of which method McDonald's should use in this case.

5. Prior to remodeling or re-imaging a McDonald's store, extensive research is conducted. This includes the use of "mystery shoppers," who are people hired by McDonald's to go to stores as customers to observe various attributes of the store and the service being provided. The file called **McDonald's Mystery Shopper** contains data pertaining to the "cleanliness" rating provided by the mystery shoppers who visited a particular McDonald's location each month between January 2004 and June 2006. The values represent the average rating on a 0–100 percent scale provided by five shoppers. A score of 100% is considered perfect. Using these time-series data, develop a line chart and discuss what time-series components are present in these data.

6. Referring to question 5, develop a double exponential smoothing model to forecast the rating for July 2006 (use alpha = 0.20 and beta = 0.30 smoothing constants.) Compare the results of this forecasting approach with a simple linear trend forecasting approach. Write a short report describing the methods you have used and the results. Use linear trend analysis to obtain the starting values for $C_0$ and $T_0$.

# Case 16.1

## Park Falls Chamber of Commerce

Masao Sugiyama is the recently elected president of the Chamber of Commerce in Park Falls, Wisconsin. He is the long-time owner of the only full-service hardware store in this small farming town. Being president of the Chamber of Commerce has been considered largely a ceremonial post because business conditions have not changed in Park Falls for as long as anyone can remember. However, Masao has just read an article in *The Wall Street Journal* that has made him think he needs to take a more active interest in the business conditions of his town.

The article concerned Wal-Mart, the largest retailer in the United States. Wal-Mart has expanded primarily by locating in small towns and avoiding large suburban areas. The Park Falls merchants have not had to deal with either Lowes or Home Depot because these companies have located primarily in large urban centers. In addition, a supplier has recently told Masao that both Lowes and Home Depot are considering locating stores in smaller towns. Sugiyama knows that Wal-Mart has moved into the outskirts of metropolitan areas and now is considering stores for smaller, untapped markets. He also has heard that Lowes and Home Depot have recently had difficulty.

Masao decided he needs to know more about all three retailers. He asked the son of a friend to locate the following sales data, which are also in a file called **Park Falls**.

| | | Quarterly Sales Values in Millions of Dollars | | |
|---|---|---|---|---|
| | | Lowes | Home Depot | Wal-Mart |
| Fiscal 1999 | Q1 | $ 3,772 | $ 8,952 | $29,819 |
| | Q2 | $ 4,435 | $10,431 | $33,521 |
| | Q3 | $ 3,909 | $ 9,877 | $33,509 |
| | Q4 | $ 3,789 | $ 9,174 | $40,785 |
| Fiscal 2000 | Q1 | $ 4,467 | $11,112 | $34,717 |
| | Q2 | $ 5,264 | $12,618 | $38,470 |
| | Q3 | $ 4,504 | $11,545 | $40,432 |
| | Q4 | $ 4,543 | $10,463 | $51,394 |
| Fiscal 2001 | Q1 | $ 5,276 | $12,200 | $42,985 |
| | Q2 | $ 6,127 | $14,576 | $46,112 |
| | Q3 | $ 5,455 | $13,289 | $45,676 |
| | Q4 | $ 5,253 | $13,488 | $56,556 |
| Fiscal 2002 | Q1 | $ 6,470 | $14,282 | $48,052 |
| | Q2 | $ 7,488 | $16,277 | $52,799 |
| | Q3 | $ 6,415 | $14,475 | $52,738 |
| | Q4 | $ 6,118 | $13,213 | $64,210 |

(continued)

| | | Quarterly Sales Values in Millions of Dollars | | |
|---|---|---|---|---|
| | | Lowes | Home Depot | Wal-Mart |
| Fiscal 2003 | Q1 | $ 7,118 | $15,104 | $51,705 |
| | Q2 | $ 8,666 | $17,989 | $56,271 |
| | Q3 | $ 7,802 | $16,598 | $55,241 |
| | Q4 | $ 7,252 | $15,125 | $66,400 |
| Fiscal 2004 | Q1 | $ 8,681 | $17,550 | $56,718 |
| | Q2 | $10,169 | $19,960 | $62,637 |
| | Q3 | $ 9,064 | $18,772 | $62,480 |
| | Q4 | $ 8,550 | $16,812 | $74,494 |

| | | Quarterly Sales Values in Millions of Dollars | | |
|---|---|---|---|---|
| | | Lowes | Home Depot | Wal-Mart |
| Fiscal 2005 | Q1 | $ 9,913 | $18,973 | $64,763 |
| | Q2 | $11,929 | $22,305 | $69,722 |
| | Q3 | $10,592 | $30,744 | $68,520 |
| | Q4 | $10,808 | $19,489 | $82,216 |

Masao is interested in what all these data tell him. How much faster has Wal-Mart grown than the other two firms? Is there any evidence Wal-Mart's growth has leveled off? Does Lowes seem to be rebounding, based on sales? Are seasonal fluctuations an issue in these sales figures? Is there any evidence that one firm is more affected by the cyclical component than the others? He needs some help in analyzing these data.

# Case 16.2

## The St. Louis Companies

An irritated Roger Hatton finds himself sitting in the St. Louis airport after hearing that his flight to Chicago has been delayed—and, if the storm in Chicago continues, possibly cancelled. Because he must get to Chicago if at all possible, Roger is stuck at the airport. He decides he might as well try to get some work done, so he opens his laptop computer and calls up the **Claimnum** file.

Roger was recently assigned as an analyst in the worker's compensation section of the St. Louis Companies, one of the biggest issuers of worker's compensation insurance in the country. Until this year, the revenues and claim costs for all parts of the company were grouped together to determine any yearly profit or loss. Therefore, no one really knew if an individual department was profitable. Now, however, the new president is looking at each part of the company as a profit center. The clear implication is that money-losing departments may not have a future unless they develop a clear plan to become profitable.

When Roger asked the accounting department for a listing, by client, of all policy payments and claims filed and paid, he was told that the information is available but he may have to wait two or three months to get it. He was able to determine, however, that the department has been keeping track of the clients who file frequent (at least one a month) claims and the total number of firms that

purchase workers' compensation insurance. Using the data from this report, Roger divides the number of clients filing frequent claims by the corresponding number of clients. These ratios, in the file **Claimnum**, are as follows:

| Year | Ratio (%) | Year | Ratio (%) |
|---|---|---|---|
| 1 | 3.8 | 12 | 6.1 |
| 2 | 3.6 | 13 | 7.8 |
| 3 | 3.5 | 14 | 7.1 |
| 4 | 4.9 | 15 | 7.6 |
| 5 | 5.9 | 16 | 9.7 |
| 6 | 5.6 | 17 | 9.6 |
| 7 | 4.9 | 18 | 7.5 |
| 8 | 5.6 | 19 | 7.9 |
| 9 | 8.5 | 20 | 8.3 |
| 10 | 7.7 | 21 | 8.4 |
| 11 | 7.1 | | |

Staring at these figures, Roger feels there should be some way to use them to project what the next several years may hold if the company doesn't change its underwriting policies.

# Case 16.3

## Wagner Machine Works

Mary Lindsey has recently agreed to leave her upper-level management job at a major paper manufacturing firm and return to her hometown to take over the family machine-products business. The U.S. machine-products industry had a strong position of world dominance until recently, when it was devastated by foreign competition, particularly from Germany and Japan. Among the many problems facing the American industry is that it is made up of many small firms that must compete with foreign industrial giants.

Wagner Machine Works, the company Mary is taking over, is one of the few survivors in its part of the state, but it, too, faces increasing competitive pressure. Mary's father let the business slide as he approached retirement, and Mary sees the need for an immediate modernization of their plant. She has arranged for a loan from the local bank, but now she must forecast sales for the next three years to ensure that the company has enough cash flow to repay the debt. Surprisingly, Mary finds that her father has no forecasting system in place, and she cannot afford the time, or money, to install a system like that used at her previous company.

Wagner Machine Works' quarterly sales (in millions of dollars) for the past 15 years are as follows:

| Year | Quarter 1 | Quarter 2 | Quarter 3 | Quarter 4 |
|------|-----------|-----------|-----------|-----------|
| 1995 | 10,490 | 11,130 | 10,005 | 11,058 |
| 1996 | 11,424 | 12,550 | 10,900 | 12,335 |
| 1997 | 12,835 | 13,100 | 11,660 | 13,767 |
| 1998 | 13,877 | 14,100 | 12,780 | 14,738 |
| 1999 | 14,798 | 15,210 | 13,785 | 16,218 |
| 2000 | 16,720 | 17,167 | 14,785 | 17,725 |
| 2001 | 18,348 | 18,951 | 16,554 | 19,889 |
| 2002 | 20,317 | 21,395 | 19,445 | 22,816 |
| 2003 | 23,335 | 24,179 | 22,548 | 25,029 |
| 2004 | 25,729 | 27,778 | 23,391 | 27,360 |
| 2005 | 28,886 | 30,125 | 26,049 | 30,300 |
| 2006 | 30,212 | 33,702 | 27,907 | 31,096 |
| 2007 | 31,715 | 35,720 | 28,554 | 34,326 |
| 2008 | 35,533 | 39,447 | 30,046 | 37,587 |
| 2009 | 39,093 | 44,650 | 30,046 | 37,587 |

While looking at these data, Mary wonders whether they can be used to forecast sales for the next three years. She wonders how much, if any, confidence she can have in a forecast made with these data. She also wonders if the recent increase in sales is due to growing business or just to inflationary price increases in the national economy.

## Required Tasks:

1. Identify the central issue in the case.
2. Plot the quarterly sales for the past 15 years for Wagner Machine Works.
3. Identify any patterns that are evident in the quarterly sales data.
4. If a seasonal pattern is identified, estimate quarterly seasonal factors.
5. Deseasonalize the data using the quarterly seasonal factors developed.
6. Run a regression model on the deseasonalized data using the time period as the independent variable.
7. Develop a seasonally adjusted forecast for the next three years.
8. Prepare a report that includes graphs and analysis.

# References

Armstrong, J. Scott, "Forecasting by Extrapolation: Conclusions from 25 Years of Research." *Interfaces*, 14, no. 6 (1984).

Bails, Dale G., and Larry C. Peppers, *Business Fluctuations: Forecasting Techniques and Applications*, 2nd ed. (Englewood Cliffs, NJ: Prentice Hall, 1992).

Berenson, Mark L., and David M. Levine, *Basic Business Statistics: Concepts and Applications*, 11th ed. (Upper Saddle River, NJ: Prentice Hall, 2009).

Bowerman, Bruce L., and Richard T. O'Connell, *Forecasting and Time Series: An Applied Approach*, 4th ed. (North Scituate, MA: Duxbury Press, 1993).

Brandon, Charles, R. Fritz, and J. Xander, "Econometric Forecasts: Evaluation and Revision." *Applied Economics*, 15, no. 2 (1983).

Cryer, Jonathan D., *Time Series Analysis* (Boston: Duxbury Press, 1986).

Frees, Edward W., *Data Analysis Using Regression Models: The Business Perspective* (Englewood Cliffs, NJ: Prentice Hall, 1996).

Granger, C. W. G., *Forecasting in Business and Economics*, 2nd ed. (New York: Academic Press, 1989).

Kutner, Michael H., Christopher J. Nachtshein, John Neter, and William Li, *Applied Linear Statistical Models*, 5th ed. (New York: McGraw-Hill Irwin, 2005).

Makridakis, Spyros, Steven C. Wheelwright, and Rob J. Hyndman, *Forecasting: Methods and Applications*, 3rd ed. (New York: John Wiley & Sons, 1998).

McLaughlin, Robert L., "Forecasting Models: Sophisticated or Naive?" *Journal of Forecasting*, 2, no. 3 (1983).

*Microsoft Excel 2007* (Redmond, WA: Microsoft Corp., 2007).

*Minitab for Windows Version 15* (State College, PA: Minitab, 2007).

Montgomery, Douglas C., and Lynwood A. Johnson, *Forecasting and Time Series Analysis*, 2nd ed. (New York: McGraw-Hill, 1990).

Nelson, C. R., *Applied Time Series Analysis for Managerial Forecasting* (San Francisco: Holdon-Day, 1983).

The Ombudsman: "Research on Forecasting—A Quarter-Century Review, 1960–1984." *Interfaces*, 16, no. 1 (1986).

Willis, R. E., *A Guide to Forecasting for Planners* (Englewood Cliffs, NJ: Prentice Hall, 1987).

Wonnacott, T. H., and R. J. Wonnacott, *Econometrics*, 2nd ed. (New York: John Wiley & Sons, 1979).

# List of **Appendix Tables**

| | | | | | | | | |
|---|---|---|---|---|---|---|---|---|
| 1511 | 4745 | 8716 | 2793 | 9142 | 4958 | 5245 | 8312 | 8925 |
| 6249 | 7073 | 0460 | 0819 | 0729 | 6806 | 2713 | 6595 | 5149 |
| 2587 | 4800 | 3455 | 7565 | 1196 | 7768 | 6137 | 4941 | 0488 |
| 0168 | 1379 | 7838 | 7487 | 7420 | 5285 | 8045 | 6679 | 1361 |
| 9664 | 9021 | 4990 | 5570 | 4697 | 7939 | 5842 | 5353 | 7503 |
| 1384 | 4981 | 2708 | 6437 | 2298 | 6230 | 7443 | 9425 | 5384 |
| 6390 | 8953 | 4292 | 7372 | 7197 | 2121 | 6538 | 2093 | 7629 |
| 6944 | 8134 | 0704 | 8500 | 6996 | 3492 | 4397 | 8802 | 3253 |
| 3610 | 3119 | 7442 | 6218 | 7623 | 0546 | 8394 | 3286 | 4463 |
| 9865 | 0028 | 1783 | 9029 | 2858 | 8737 | 7023 | 0444 | 8575 |
| 7044 | 6712 | 7530 | 0018 | 0945 | 8803 | 4467 | 0979 | 1342 |
| 9304 | 4857 | 5476 | 8386 | 1540 | 5760 | 9815 | 7191 | 3291 |
| 1717 | 8278 | 0072 | 2636 | 3217 | 1693 | 6081 | 1330 | 3458 |
| 2461 | 3598 | 5173 | 9666 | 6165 | 7438 | 6805 | 2357 | 6994 |
| 8240 | 9856 | 0075 | 7599 | 8468 | 7653 | 6272 | 0573 | 4344 |
| 1697 | 6805 | 1386 | 2340 | 6694 | 9786 | 0536 | 6423 | 1083 |
| 4695 | 2251 | 8962 | 5638 | 9459 | 5578 | 0676 | 2276 | 4724 |
| 3056 | 8558 | 3020 | 7509 | 5105 | 4283 | 5390 | 5715 | 8405 |
| 6887 | 9035 | 8520 | 6571 | 3233 | 7175 | 2859 | 1615 | 3349 |
| 1267 | 8824 | 5588 | 2821 | 1247 | 0967 | 4355 | 1385 | 0727 |
| 4369 | 9267 | 9377 | 8205 | 6479 | 7002 | 0649 | 4731 | 7086 |
| 2888 | 0333 | 5347 | 4849 | 5526 | 2975 | 5295 | 5071 | 6011 |
| 9893 | 7251 | 6243 | 4617 | 9256 | 4039 | 4800 | 9393 | 3263 |
| 8927 | 3977 | 6054 | 5979 | 8566 | 8120 | 2566 | 4449 | 2414 |
| 2676 | 7064 | 2198 | 3234 | 3796 | 5506 | 4462 | 5121 | 9052 |
| 0775 | 7316 | 2249 | 5606 | 9411 | 3818 | 5268 | 7652 | 6098 |
| 3828 | 9178 | 3726 | 0743 | 4075 | 3560 | 9542 | 3922 | 7688 |
| 3281 | 3419 | 6660 | 7968 | 1238 | 2246 | 2164 | 4567 | 1801 |
| 0328 | 7471 | 5352 | 2019 | 5842 | 1665 | 5939 | 6337 | 9102 |
| 8406 | 1826 | 8437 | 3078 | 9068 | 1425 | 1232 | 0573 | 7751 |
| 7076 | 8418 | 6778 | 1292 | 2019 | 3506 | 7474 | 0141 | 6544 |
| 0446 | 8641 | 3249 | 5431 | 4068 | 6045 | 1939 | 5626 | 1867 |
| 3719 | 9712 | 7472 | 1517 | 8850 | 6862 | 6990 | 5475 | 6227 |
| 5648 | 0563 | 6346 | 1981 | 9512 | 0659 | 5694 | 6668 | 2563 |
| 3694 | 8582 | 3434 | 4052 | 8392 | 3883 | 5126 | 0477 | 4034 |
| 3554 | 9876 | 4249 | 9473 | 9085 | 6594 | 2434 | 9453 | 8883 |
| 4934 | 8446 | 4646 | 2054 | 1136 | 1023 | 6295 | 6483 | 9915 |
| 7835 | 1506 | 0019 | 5011 | 0563 | 4450 | 1466 | 6334 | 2606 |
| 1098 | 2113 | 8287 | 3487 | 8250 | 2269 | 1876 | 3684 | 8856 |
| 1186 | 2685 | 7225 | 8311 | 3835 | 8059 | 9163 | 2539 | 6487 |
| 4618 | 1522 | 0627 | 0448 | 0669 | 4086 | 4083 | 0881 | 4270 |
| 5529 | 4173 | 5711 | 7419 | 2535 | 5876 | 8435 | 2564 | 3031 |
| 0754 | 5808 | 8458 | 2218 | 9180 | 6213 | 5280 | 4753 | 0696 |
| 5865 | 0806 | 2070 | 7986 | 4800 | 3076 | 2866 | 0515 | 7417 |
| 6168 | 8963 | 0235 | 1514 | 7875 | 2176 | 3095 | 1171 | 7892 |
| 7479 | 4144 | 6697 | 2255 | 5465 | 7233 | 4981 | 3553 | 8144 |
| 4608 | 6576 | 9422 | 4198 | 2578 | 1701 | 4764 | 7460 | 3509 |
| 0654 | 2483 | 6001 | 4486 | 4941 | 1500 | 3502 | 9693 | 1956 |
| 3000 | 9694 | 6616 | 5599 | 7759 | 1581 | 9896 | 2312 | 8140 |
| 2686 | 3675 | 5760 | 2918 | 0185 | 7364 | 9985 | 5930 | 9869 |
| 4713 | 4121 | 5144 | 5164 | 8104 | 0403 | 4984 | 3877 | 8772 |
| 9281 | 6522 | 7916 | 8941 | 6710 | 1670 | 1399 | 5961 | 4714 |
| 5736 | 9419 | 5022 | 6955 | 3356 | 5732 | 1042 | 0527 | 7441 |
| 2383 | 0408 | 2821 | 7313 | 5781 | 6951 | 7181 | 0608 | 2864 |
| 8740 | 8038 | 7284 | 6054 | 2246 | 1674 | 9984 | 0355 | 0775 |

## APPENDIX B

Cumulative
Binomial
Distribution Table

$$P(x \le X) = \sum_{i=0}^{X} \frac{n!}{i!(n-i)!} \, p^i (1-p)^{n-i}$$

### n = 1

| x | p = 0.01 | p = 0.02 | p = 0.03 | p = 0.04 | p = 0.05 | p = 0.06 | p = 0.07 | p = 0.08 | p = 0.09 |
|---|---|---|---|---|---|---|---|---|---|
| 0 | 0.9900 | 0.9800 | 0.9700 | 0.9600 | 0.9500 | 0.9400 | 0.9300 | 0.9200 | 0.9100 |
| 1 | 1.0000 | 1.0000 | 1.0000 | 1.0000 | 1.0000 | 1.0000 | 1.0000 | 1.0000 | 1.0000 |
| x | p = 0.10 | p = 0.15 | p = 0.20 | p = 0.25 | p = 0.30 | p = 0.35 | p = 0.40 | p = 0.45 | p = 0.50 |
| 0 | 0.9000 | 0.8500 | 0.8000 | 0.7500 | 0.7000 | 0.6500 | 0.6000 | 0.5500 | 0.5000 |
| 1 | 1.0000 | 1.0000 | 1.0000 | 1.0000 | 1.0000 | 1.0000 | 1.0000 | 1.0000 | 1.0000 |
| x | p = 0.55 | p = 0.60 | p = 0.65 | p = 0.70 | p = 0.75 | p = 0.80 | p = 0.85 | p = 0.90 | p = 0.91 |
| 0 | 0.4500 | 0.4000 | 0.3500 | 0.3000 | 0.2500 | 0.2000 | 0.1500 | 0.1000 | 0.0900 |
| 1 | 1.0000 | 1.0000 | 1.0000 | 1.0000 | 1.0000 | 1.0000 | 1.0000 | 1.0000 | 1.0000 |
| x | p = 0.92 | p = 0.93 | p = 0.94 | p = 0.95 | p = 0.96 | p = 0.97 | p = 0.98 | p = 0.99 | p = 1.00 |
| 0 | 0.0800 | 0.0700 | 0.0600 | 0.0500 | 0.0400 | 0.0300 | 0.0200 | 0.0100 | 0.0000 |
| 1 | 1.0000 | 1.0000 | 1.0000 | 1.0000 | 1.0000 | 1.0000 | 1.0000 | 1.0000 | 1.0000 |

### n = 2

| x | p = 0.01 | p = 0.02 | p = 0.03 | p = 0.04 | p = 0.05 | p = 0.06 | p = 0.07 | p = 0.08 | p = 0.09 |
|---|---|---|---|---|---|---|---|---|---|
| 0 | 0.9801 | 0.9604 | 0.9409 | 0.9216 | 0.9025 | 0.8836 | 0.8649 | 0.8464 | 0.8281 |
| 1 | 0.9999 | 0.9996 | 0.9991 | 0.9984 | 0.9975 | 0.9964 | 0.9951 | 0.9936 | 0.9919 |
| 2 | 1.0000 | 1.0000 | 1.0000 | 1.0000 | 1.0000 | 1.0000 | 1.0000 | 1.0000 | 1.0000 |
| x | p = 0.10 | p = 0.15 | p = 0.20 | p = 0.25 | p = 0.30 | p = 0.35 | p = 0.40 | p = 0.45 | p = 0.50 |
| 0 | 0.8100 | 0.7225 | 0.6400 | 0.5625 | 0.4900 | 0.4225 | 0.3600 | 0.3025 | 0.2500 |
| 1 | 0.9900 | 0.9775 | 0.9600 | 0.9375 | 0.9100 | 0.8775 | 0.8400 | 0.7975 | 0.7500 |
| 2 | 1.0000 | 1.0000 | 1.0000 | 1.0000 | 1.0000 | 1.0000 | 1.0000 | 1.0000 | 1.0000 |
| x | p = 0.55 | p = 0.60 | p = 0.65 | p = 0.70 | p = 0.75 | p = 0.80 | p = 0.85 | p = 0.90 | p = 0.91 |
| 0 | 0.2025 | 0.1600 | 0.1225 | 0.0900 | 0.0625 | 0.0400 | 0.0225 | 0.0100 | 0.0081 |
| 1 | 0.6975 | 0.6400 | 0.5775 | 0.5100 | 0.4375 | 0.3600 | 0.2775 | 0.1900 | 0.1719 |
| 2 | 1.0000 | 1.0000 | 1.0000 | 1.0000 | 1.0000 | 1.0000 | 1.0000 | 1.0000 | 1.0000 |
| x | p = 0.92 | p = 0.93 | p = 0.94 | p = 0.95 | p = 0.96 | p = 0.97 | p = 0.98 | p = 0.99 | p = 1.00 |
| 0 | 0.0064 | 0.0049 | 0.0036 | 0.0025 | 0.0016 | 0.0009 | 0.0004 | 0.0001 | 0.0000 |
| 1 | 0.1536 | 0.1351 | 0.1164 | 0.0975 | 0.0784 | 0.0591 | 0.0396 | 0.0199 | 0.0000 |
| 2 | 1.0000 | 1.0000 | 1.0000 | 1.0000 | 1.0000 | 1.0000 | 1.0000 | 1.0000 | 1.0000 |

### n = 3

| x | p = 0.01 | p = 0.02 | p = 0.03 | p = 0.04 | p = 0.05 | p = 0.06 | p = 0.07 | p = 0.08 | p = 0.09 |
|---|---|---|---|---|---|---|---|---|---|
| 0 | 0.9703 | 0.9412 | 0.9127 | 0.8847 | 0.8574 | 0.8306 | 0.8044 | 0.7787 | 0.7536 |
| 1 | 0.9997 | 0.9988 | 0.9974 | 0.9953 | 0.9928 | 0.9896 | 0.9860 | 0.9818 | 0.9772 |
| 2 | 1.0000 | 1.0000 | 1.0000 | 0.9999 | 0.9999 | 0.9998 | 0.9997 | 0.9995 | 0.9993 |
| 3 | 1.0000 | 1.0000 | 1.0000 | 1.0000 | 1.0000 | 1.0000 | 1.0000 | 1.0000 | 1.0000 |
| x | p = 0.10 | p = 0.15 | p = 0.20 | p = 0.25 | p = 0.30 | p = 0.35 | p = 0.40 | p = 0.45 | p = 0.50 |
| 0 | 0.7290 | 0.6141 | 0.5120 | 0.4219 | 0.3430 | 0.2746 | 0.2160 | 0.1664 | 0.1250 |
| 1 | 0.9720 | 0.9393 | 0.8960 | 0.8438 | 0.7840 | 0.7183 | 0.6480 | 0.5748 | 0.5000 |
| 2 | 0.9990 | 0.9966 | 0.9920 | 0.9844 | 0.9730 | 0.9571 | 0.9360 | 0.9089 | 0.8750 |
| 3 | 1.0000 | 1.0000 | 1.0000 | 1.0000 | 1.0000 | 1.0000 | 1.0000 | 1.0000 | 1.0000 |
| x | p = 0.55 | p = 0.60 | p = 0.65 | p = 0.70 | p = 0.75 | p = 0.80 | p = 0.85 | p = 0.90 | p = 0.91 |
| 0 | 0.0911 | 0.0640 | 0.0429 | 0.0270 | 0.0156 | 0.0080 | 0.0034 | 0.0010 | 0.0007 |
| 1 | 0.4253 | 0.3520 | 0.2818 | 0.2160 | 0.1563 | 0.1040 | 0.0608 | 0.0280 | 0.0228 |
| 2 | 0.8336 | 0.7840 | 0.7254 | 0.6570 | 0.5781 | 0.4880 | 0.3859 | 0.2710 | 0.2464 |
| 3 | 1.0000 | 1.0000 | 1.0000 | 1.0000 | 1.0000 | 1.0000 | 1.0000 | 1.0000 | 1.0000 |
| x | p = 0.92 | p = 0.93 | p = 0.94 | p = 0.95 | p = 0.96 | p = 0.97 | p = 0.98 | p = 0.99 | p = 1.00 |
| 0 | 0.0005 | 0.0003 | 0.0002 | 0.0001 | 0.0001 | 0.0000 | 0.0000 | 0.0000 | 0.0000 |
| 1 | 0.0182 | 0.0140 | 0.0104 | 0.0073 | 0.0047 | 0.0026 | 0.0012 | 0.0003 | 0.0000 |
| 2 | 0.2213 | 0.1956 | 0.1694 | 0.1426 | 0.1153 | 0.0873 | 0.0588 | 0.0297 | 0.0000 |
| 3 | 1.0000 | 1.0000 | 1.0000 | 1.0000 | 1.0000 | 1.0000 | 1.0000 | 1.0000 | 1.0000 |

### n = 4

| x | p = 0.01 | p = 0.02 | p = 0.03 | p = 0.04 | p = 0.05 | p = 0.06 | p = 0.07 | p = 0.08 | p = 0.09 |
|---|---|---|---|---|---|---|---|---|---|
| 0 | 0.9606 | 0.9224 | 0.8853 | 0.8493 | 0.8145 | 0.7807 | 0.7481 | 0.7164 | 0.6857 |
| 1 | 0.9994 | 0.9977 | 0.9948 | 0.9909 | 0.9860 | 0.9801 | 0.9733 | 0.9656 | 0.9570 |
| 2 | 1.0000 | 1.0000 | 0.9999 | 0.9998 | 0.9995 | 0.9992 | 0.9987 | 0.9981 | 0.9973 |
| 3 | 1.0000 | 1.0000 | 1.0000 | 1.0000 | 1.0000 | 1.0000 | 1.0000 | 1.0000 | 0.9999 |
| 4 | 1.0000 | 1.0000 | 1.0000 | 1.0000 | 1.0000 | 1.0000 | 1.0000 | 1.0000 | 1.0000 |

| x | p = 0.10 | p = 0.15 | p = 0.20 | p = 0.25 | p = 0.30 | p = 0.35 | p = 0.40 | p = 0.45 | p = 0.50 |
|---|---|---|---|---|---|---|---|---|---|
| 0 | 0.6561 | 0.5220 | 0.4096 | 0.3164 | 0.2401 | 0.1785 | 0.1296 | 0.0915 | 0.0625 |
| 1 | 0.9477 | 0.8905 | 0.8192 | 0.7383 | 0.6517 | 0.5630 | 0.4752 | 0.3910 | 0.3125 |
| 2 | 0.9963 | 0.9880 | 0.9728 | 0.9492 | 0.9163 | 0.8735 | 0.8208 | 0.7585 | 0.6875 |
| 3 | 0.9999 | 0.9995 | 0.9984 | 0.9961 | 0.9919 | 0.9850 | 0.9744 | 0.9590 | 0.9375 |
| 4 | 1.0000 | 1.0000 | 1.0000 | 1.0000 | 1.0000 | 1.0000 | 1.0000 | 1.0000 | 1.0000 |

| x | p = 0.55 | p = 0.60 | p = 0.65 | p = 0.70 | p = 0.75 | p = 0.80 | p = 0.85 | p = 0.90 | p = 0.91 |
|---|---|---|---|---|---|---|---|---|---|
| 0 | 0.0410 | 0.0256 | 0.0150 | 0.0081 | 0.0039 | 0.0016 | 0.0005 | 0.0001 | 0.0001 |
| 1 | 0.2415 | 0.1792 | 0.1265 | 0.0837 | 0.0508 | 0.0272 | 0.0120 | 0.0037 | 0.0027 |
| 2 | 0.6090 | 0.5248 | 0.4370 | 0.3483 | 0.2617 | 0.1808 | 0.1095 | 0.0523 | 0.0430 |
| 3 | 0.9085 | 0.8704 | 0.8215 | 0.7599 | 0.6836 | 0.5904 | 0.4780 | 0.3439 | 0.3143 |
| 4 | 1.0000 | 1.0000 | 1.0000 | 1.0000 | 1.0000 | 1.0000 | 1.0000 | 1.0000 | 1.0000 |

| x | p = 0.92 | p = 0.93 | p = 0.94 | p = 0.95 | p = 0.96 | p = 0.97 | p = 0.98 | p = 0.99 | p = 1.00 |
|---|---|---|---|---|---|---|---|---|---|
| 0 | 0.0000 | 0.0000 | 0.0000 | 0.0000 | 0.0000 | 0.0000 | 0.0000 | 0.0000 | 0.0000 |
| 1 | 0.0019 | 0.0013 | 0.0008 | 0.0005 | 0.0002 | 0.0001 | 0.0000 | 0.0000 | 0.0000 |
| 2 | 0.0344 | 0.0267 | 0.0199 | 0.0140 | 0.0091 | 0.0052 | 0.0023 | 0.0006 | 0.0000 |
| 3 | 0.2836 | 0.2519 | 0.2193 | 0.1855 | 0.1507 | 0.1147 | 0.0776 | 0.0394 | 0.0000 |
| 4 | 1.0000 | 1.0000 | 1.0000 | 1.0000 | 1.0000 | 1.0000 | 1.0000 | 1.0000 | 1.0000 |

### n = 5

| x | p = 0.01 | p = 0.02 | p = 0.03 | p = 0.04 | p = 0.05 | p = 0.06 | p = 0.07 | p = 0.08 | p = 0.09 |
|---|---|---|---|---|---|---|---|---|---|
| 0 | 0.9510 | 0.9039 | 0.8587 | 0.8154 | 0.7738 | 0.7339 | 0.6957 | 0.6591 | 0.6240 |
| 1 | 0.9990 | 0.9962 | 0.9915 | 0.9852 | 0.9774 | 0.9681 | 0.9575 | 0.9456 | 0.9326 |
| 2 | 1.0000 | 0.9999 | 0.9997 | 0.9994 | 0.9988 | 0.9980 | 0.9969 | 0.9955 | 0.9937 |
| 3 | 1.0000 | 1.0000 | 1.0000 | 1.0000 | 1.0000 | 0.9999 | 0.9999 | 0.9998 | 0.9997 |
| 4 | 1.0000 | 1.0000 | 1.0000 | 1.0000 | 1.0000 | 1.0000 | 1.0000 | 1.0000 | 1.0000 |
| 5 | 1.0000 | 1.0000 | 1.0000 | 1.0000 | 1.0000 | 1.0000 | 1.0000 | 1.0000 | 1.0000 |

| x | p = 0.10 | p = 0.15 | p = 0.20 | p = 0.25 | p = 0.30 | p = 0.35 | p = 0.40 | p = 0.45 | p = 0.50 |
|---|---|---|---|---|---|---|---|---|---|
| 0 | 0.5905 | 0.4437 | 0.3277 | 0.2373 | 0.1681 | 0.1160 | 0.0778 | 0.0503 | 0.0313 |
| 1 | 0.9185 | 0.8352 | 0.7373 | 0.6328 | 0.5282 | 0.4284 | 0.3370 | 0.2562 | 0.1875 |
| 2 | 0.9914 | 0.9734 | 0.9421 | 0.8965 | 0.8369 | 0.7648 | 0.6826 | 0.5931 | 0.5000 |
| 3 | 0.9995 | 0.9978 | 0.9933 | 0.9844 | 0.9692 | 0.9460 | 0.9130 | 0.8688 | 0.8125 |
| 4 | 1.0000 | 0.9999 | 0.9997 | 0.9990 | 0.9976 | 0.9947 | 0.9898 | 0.9815 | 0.9688 |
| 5 | 1.0000 | 1.0000 | 1.0000 | 1.0000 | 1.0000 | 1.0000 | 1.0000 | 1.0000 | 1.0000 |

| x | p = 0.55 | p = 0.60 | p = 0.65 | p = 0.70 | p = 0.75 | p = 0.80 | p = 0.85 | p = 0.90 | p = 0.91 |
|---|---|---|---|---|---|---|---|---|---|
| 0 | 0.0185 | 0.0102 | 0.0053 | 0.0024 | 0.0010 | 0.0003 | 0.0001 | 0.0000 | 0.0000 |
| 1 | 0.1312 | 0.0870 | 0.0540 | 0.0308 | 0.0156 | 0.0067 | 0.0022 | 0.0005 | 0.0003 |
| 2 | 0.4069 | 0.3174 | 0.2352 | 0.1631 | 0.1035 | 0.0579 | 0.0266 | 0.0086 | 0.0063 |
| 3 | 0.7438 | 0.6630 | 0.5716 | 0.4718 | 0.3672 | 0.2627 | 0.1648 | 0.0815 | 0.0674 |
| 4 | 0.9497 | 0.9222 | 0.8840 | 0.8319 | 0.7627 | 0.6723 | 0.5563 | 0.4095 | 0.3760 |
| 5 | 1.0000 | 1.0000 | 1.0000 | 1.0000 | 1.0000 | 1.0000 | 1.0000 | 1.0000 | 1.0000 |

| x | p = 0.92 | p = 0.93 | p = 0.94 | p = 0.95 | p = 0.96 | p = 0.97 | p = 0.98 | p = 0.99 | p = 1.00 |
|---|---|---|---|---|---|---|---|---|---|
| 0 | 0.0000 | 0.0000 | 0.0000 | 0.0000 | 0.0000 | 0.0000 | 0.0000 | 0.0000 | 0.0000 |
| 1 | 0.0002 | 0.0001 | 0.0001 | 0.0000 | 0.0000 | 0.0000 | 0.0000 | 0.0000 | 0.0000 |
| 2 | 0.0045 | 0.0031 | 0.0020 | 0.0012 | 0.0006 | 0.0003 | 0.0001 | 0.0000 | 0.0000 |
| 3 | 0.0544 | 0.0425 | 0.0319 | 0.0226 | 0.0148 | 0.0085 | 0.0038 | 0.0010 | 0.0000 |
| 4 | 0.3409 | 0.3043 | 0.2661 | 0.2262 | 0.1846 | 0.1413 | 0.0961 | 0.0490 | 0.0000 |
| 5 | 1.0000 | 1.0000 | 1.0000 | 1.0000 | 1.0000 | 1.0000 | 1.0000 | 1.0000 | 1.0000 |

### n = 6

| x | p = 0.01 | p = 0.02 | p = 0.03 | p = 0.04 | p = 0.05 | p = 0.06 | p = 0.07 | p = 0.08 | p = 0.09 |
|---|---|---|---|---|---|---|---|---|---|
| 0 | 0.9415 | 0.8858 | 0.8330 | 0.7828 | 0.7351 | 0.6899 | 0.6470 | 0.6064 | 0.5679 |
| 1 | 0.9985 | 0.9943 | 0.9875 | 0.9784 | 0.9672 | 0.9541 | 0.9392 | 0.9227 | 0.9048 |
| 2 | 1.0000 | 0.9998 | 0.9995 | 0.9988 | 0.9978 | 0.9962 | 0.9942 | 0.9915 | 0.9882 |
| 3 | 1.0000 | 1.0000 | 1.0000 | 1.0000 | 0.9999 | 0.9998 | 0.9997 | 0.9995 | 0.9992 |
| 4 | 1.0000 | 1.0000 | 1.0000 | 1.0000 | 1.0000 | 1.0000 | 1.0000 | 1.0000 | 1.0000 |

(continued)

| 5 | 1.0000 | 1.0000 | 1.0000 | 1.0000 | 1.0000 | 1.0000 | 1.0000 | 1.0000 | 1.0000 |
| 6 | 1.0000 | 1.0000 | 1.0000 | 1.0000 | 1.0000 | 1.0000 | 1.0000 | 1.0000 | 1.0000 |

| $x$ | $p = 0.10$ | $p = 0.15$ | $p = 0.20$ | $p = 0.25$ | $p = 0.30$ | $p = 0.35$ | $p = 0.40$ | $p = 0.45$ | $p = 0.50$ |
|---|---|---|---|---|---|---|---|---|---|
| 0 | 0.5314 | 0.3771 | 0.2621 | 0.1780 | 0.1176 | 0.0754 | 0.0467 | 0.0277 | 0.0156 |
| 1 | 0.8857 | 0.7765 | 0.6554 | 0.5339 | 0.4202 | 0.3191 | 0.2333 | 0.1636 | 0.1094 |
| 2 | 0.9842 | 0.9527 | 0.9011 | 0.8306 | 0.7443 | 0.6471 | 0.5443 | 0.4415 | 0.3438 |
| 3 | 0.9987 | 0.9941 | 0.9830 | 0.9624 | 0.9295 | 0.8826 | 0.8208 | 0.7447 | 0.6563 |
| 4 | 0.9999 | 0.9996 | 0.9984 | 0.9954 | 0.9891 | 0.9777 | 0.9590 | 0.9308 | 0.8906 |
| 5 | 1.0000 | 1.0000 | 0.9999 | 0.9998 | 0.9993 | 0.9982 | 0.9959 | 0.9917 | 0.9844 |
| 6 | 1.0000 | 1.0000 | 1.0000 | 1.0000 | 1.0000 | 1.0000 | 1.0000 | 1.0000 | 1.0000 |

| $x$ | $p = 0.55$ | $p = 0.60$ | $p = 0.65$ | $p = 0.70$ | $p = 0.75$ | $p = 0.80$ | $p = 0.85$ | $p = 0.90$ | $p = 0.91$ |
|---|---|---|---|---|---|---|---|---|---|
| 0 | 0.0083 | 0.0041 | 0.0018 | 0.0007 | 0.0002 | 0.0001 | 0.0000 | 0.0000 | 0.0000 |
| 1 | 0.0692 | 0.0410 | 0.0223 | 0.0109 | 0.0046 | 0.0016 | 0.0004 | 0.0001 | 0.0000 |
| 2 | 0.2553 | 0.1792 | 0.1174 | 0.0705 | 0.0376 | 0.0170 | 0.0059 | 0.0013 | 0.0008 |
| 3 | 0.5585 | 0.4557 | 0.3529 | 0.2557 | 0.1694 | 0.0989 | 0.0473 | 0.0159 | 0.0118 |
| 4 | 0.8364 | 0.7667 | 0.6809 | 0.5798 | 0.4661 | 0.3446 | 0.2235 | 0.1143 | 0.0952 |
| 5 | 0.9723 | 0.9533 | 0.9246 | 0.8824 | 0.8220 | 0.7379 | 0.6229 | 0.4686 | 0.4321 |
| 6 | 1.0000 | 1.0000 | 1.0000 | 1.0000 | 1.0000 | 1.0000 | 1.0000 | 1.0000 | 1.0000 |

| $x$ | $p = 0.92$ | $p = 0.93$ | $p = 0.94$ | $p = 0.95$ | $p = 0.96$ | $p = 0.97$ | $p = 0.98$ | $p = 0.99$ | $p = 1.00$ |
|---|---|---|---|---|---|---|---|---|---|
| 0 | 0.0000 | 0.0000 | 0.0000 | 0.0000 | 0.0000 | 0.0000 | 0.0000 | 0.0000 | 0.0000 |
| 1 | 0.0000 | 0.0000 | 0.0000 | 0.0000 | 0.0000 | 0.0000 | 0.0000 | 0.0000 | 0.0000 |
| 2 | 0.0005 | 0.0003 | 0.0002 | 0.0001 | 0.0000 | 0.0000 | 0.0000 | 0.0000 | 0.0000 |
| 3 | 0.0085 | 0.0058 | 0.0038 | 0.0022 | 0.0012 | 0.0005 | 0.0002 | 0.0000 | 0.0000 |
| 4 | 0.0773 | 0.0608 | 0.0459 | 0.0328 | 0.0216 | 0.0125 | 0.0057 | 0.0015 | 0.0000 |
| 5 | 0.3936 | 0.3530 | 0.3101 | 0.2649 | 0.2172 | 0.1670 | 0.1142 | 0.0585 | 0.0000 |
| 6 | 1.0000 | 1.0000 | 1.0000 | 1.0000 | 1.0000 | 1.0000 | 1.0000 | 1.0000 | 1.0000 |

$$n = 7$$

| $x$ | $p = 0.01$ | $p = 0.02$ | $p = 0.03$ | $p = 0.04$ | $p = 0.05$ | $p = 0.06$ | $p = 0.07$ | $p = 0.08$ | $p = 0.09$ |
|---|---|---|---|---|---|---|---|---|---|
| 0 | 0.9321 | 0.8681 | 0.8080 | 0.7514 | 0.6983 | 0.6485 | 0.6017 | 0.5578 | 0.5168 |
| 1 | 0.9980 | 0.9921 | 0.9829 | 0.9706 | 0.9556 | 0.9382 | 0.9187 | 0.8974 | 0.8745 |
| 2 | 1.0000 | 0.9997 | 0.9991 | 0.9980 | 0.9962 | 0.9937 | 0.9903 | 0.9860 | 0.9807 |
| 3 | 1.0000 | 1.0000 | 1.0000 | 0.9999 | 0.9998 | 0.9996 | 0.9993 | 0.9988 | 0.9982 |
| 4 | 1.0000 | 1.0000 | 1.0000 | 1.0000 | 1.0000 | 1.0000 | 1.0000 | 0.9999 | 0.9999 |
| 5 | 1.0000 | 1.0000 | 1.0000 | 1.0000 | 1.0000 | 1.0000 | 1.0000 | 1.0000 | 1.0000 |
| 6 | 1.0000 | 1.0000 | 1.0000 | 1.0000 | 1.0000 | 1.0000 | 1.0000 | 1.0000 | 1.0000 |
| 7 | 1.0000 | 1.0000 | 1.0000 | 1.0000 | 1.0000 | 1.0000 | 1.0000 | 1.0000 | 1.0000 |

| $x$ | $p = 0.10$ | $p = 0.15$ | $p = 0.20$ | $p = 0.25$ | $p = 0.30$ | $p = 0.35$ | $p = 0.40$ | $p = 0.45$ | $p = 0.50$ |
|---|---|---|---|---|---|---|---|---|---|
| 0 | 0.4783 | 0.3206 | 0.2097 | 0.1335 | 0.0824 | 0.0490 | 0.0280 | 0.0152 | 0.0078 |
| 1 | 0.8503 | 0.7166 | 0.5767 | 0.4449 | 0.3294 | 0.2338 | 0.1586 | 0.1024 | 0.0625 |
| 2 | 0.9743 | 0.9262 | 0.8520 | 0.7564 | 0.6471 | 0.5323 | 0.4199 | 0.3164 | 0.2266 |
| 3 | 0.9973 | 0.9879 | 0.9667 | 0.9294 | 0.8740 | 0.8002 | 0.7102 | 0.6083 | 0.5000 |
| 4 | 0.9998 | 0.9988 | 0.9953 | 0.9871 | 0.9712 | 0.9444 | 0.9037 | 0.8471 | 0.7734 |
| 5 | 1.0000 | 0.9999 | 0.9996 | 0.9987 | 0.9962 | 0.9910 | 0.9812 | 0.9643 | 0.9375 |
| 6 | 1.0000 | 1.0000 | 1.0000 | 0.9999 | 0.9998 | 0.9994 | 0.9984 | 0.9963 | 0.9922 |
| 7 | 1.0000 | 1.0000 | 1.0000 | 1.0000 | 1.0000 | 1.0000 | 1.0000 | 1.0000 | 1.0000 |

| $x$ | $p = 0.55$ | $p = 0.60$ | $p = 0.65$ | $p = 0.70$ | $p = 0.75$ | $p = 0.80$ | $p = 0.85$ | $p = 0.90$ | $p = 0.91$ |
|---|---|---|---|---|---|---|---|---|---|
| 0 | 0.0037 | 0.0016 | 0.0006 | 0.0002 | 0.0001 | 0.0000 | 0.0000 | 0.0000 | 0.0000 |
| 1 | 0.0357 | 0.0188 | 0.0090 | 0.0038 | 0.0013 | 0.0004 | 0.0001 | 0.0000 | 0.0000 |
| 2 | 0.1529 | 0.0963 | 0.0556 | 0.0288 | 0.0129 | 0.0047 | 0.0012 | 0.0002 | 0.0001 |
| 3 | 0.3917 | 0.2898 | 0.1998 | 0.1260 | 0.0706 | 0.0333 | 0.0121 | 0.0027 | 0.0018 |
| 4 | 0.6836 | 0.5801 | 0.4677 | 0.3529 | 0.2436 | 0.1480 | 0.0738 | 0.0257 | 0.0193 |
| 5 | 0.8976 | 0.8414 | 0.7662 | 0.6706 | 0.5551 | 0.4233 | 0.2834 | 0.1497 | 0.1255 |
| 6 | 0.9848 | 0.9720 | 0.9510 | 0.9176 | 0.8665 | 0.7903 | 0.6794 | 0.5217 | 0.4832 |
| 7 | 1.0000 | 1.0000 | 1.0000 | 1.0000 | 1.0000 | 1.0000 | 1.0000 | 1.0000 | 1.0000 |

| $x$ | $p = 0.92$ | $p = 0.93$ | $p = 0.94$ | $p = 0.95$ | $p = 0.96$ | $p = 0.97$ | $p = 0.98$ | $p = 0.99$ | $p = 1.00$ |
|---|---|---|---|---|---|---|---|---|---|
| 0 | 0.0000 | 0.0000 | 0.0000 | 0.0000 | 0.0000 | 0.0000 | 0.0000 | 0.0000 | 0.0000 |
| 1 | 0.0000 | 0.0000 | 0.0000 | 0.0000 | 0.0000 | 0.0000 | 0.0000 | 0.0000 | 0.0000 |
| 2 | 0.0001 | 0.0000 | 0.0000 | 0.0000 | 0.0000 | 0.0000 | 0.0000 | 0.0000 | 0.0000 |
| 3 | 0.0012 | 0.0007 | 0.0004 | 0.0002 | 0.0001 | 0.0000 | 0.0000 | 0.0000 | 0.0000 |
| 4 | 0.0140 | 0.0097 | 0.0063 | 0.0038 | 0.0020 | 0.0009 | 0.0003 | 0.0000 | 0.0000 |
| 5 | 0.1026 | 0.0813 | 0.0618 | 0.0444 | 0.0294 | 0.0171 | 0.0079 | 0.0020 | 0.0000 |
| 6 | 0.4422 | 0.3983 | 0.3515 | 0.3017 | 0.2486 | 0.1920 | 0.1319 | 0.0679 | 0.0000 |
| 7 | 1.0000 | 1.0000 | 1.0000 | 1.0000 | 1.0000 | 1.0000 | 1.0000 | 1.0000 | 1.0000 |

$n = 8$

| x | p = 0.01 | p = 0.02 | p = 0.03 | p = 0.04 | p = 0.05 | p = 0.06 | p = 0.07 | p = 0.08 | p = 0.09 |
|---|---|---|---|---|---|---|---|---|---|
| 0 | 0.9227 | 0.8508 | 0.7837 | 0.7214 | 0.6634 | 0.6096 | 0.5596 | 0.5132 | 0.4703 |
| 1 | 0.9973 | 0.9897 | 0.9777 | 0.9619 | 0.9428 | 0.9208 | 0.8965 | 0.8702 | 0.8423 |
| 2 | 0.9999 | 0.9996 | 0.9987 | 0.9969 | 0.9942 | 0.9904 | 0.9853 | 0.9789 | 0.9711 |
| 3 | 1.0000 | 1.0000 | 0.9999 | 0.9998 | 0.9996 | 0.9993 | 0.9987 | 0.9978 | 0.9966 |
| 4 | 1.0000 | 1.0000 | 1.0000 | 1.0000 | 1.0000 | 1.0000 | 0.9999 | 0.9999 | 0.9997 |
| 5 | 1.0000 | 1.0000 | 1.0000 | 1.0000 | 1.0000 | 1.0000 | 1.0000 | 1.0000 | 1.0000 |
| 6 | 1.0000 | 1.0000 | 1.0000 | 1.0000 | 1.0000 | 1.0000 | 1.0000 | 1.0000 | 1.0000 |
| 7 | 1.0000 | 1.0000 | 1.0000 | 1.0000 | 1.0000 | 1.0000 | 1.0000 | 1.0000 | 1.0000 |
| 8 | 1.0000 | 1.0000 | 1.0000 | 1.0000 | 1.0000 | 1.0000 | 1.0000 | 1.0000 | 1.0000 |

| x | p = 0.10 | p = 0.15 | p = 0.20 | p = 0.25 | p = 0.30 | p = 0.35 | p = 0.40 | p = 0.45 | p = 0.50 |
|---|---|---|---|---|---|---|---|---|---|
| 0 | 0.4305 | 0.2725 | 0.1678 | 0.1001 | 0.0576 | 0.0319 | 0.0168 | 0.0084 | 0.0039 |
| 1 | 0.8131 | 0.6572 | 0.5033 | 0.3671 | 0.2553 | 0.1691 | 0.1064 | 0.0632 | 0.0352 |
| 2 | 0.9619 | 0.8948 | 0.7969 | 0.6785 | 0.5518 | 0.4278 | 0.3154 | 0.2201 | 0.1445 |
| 3 | 0.9950 | 0.9786 | 0.9437 | 0.8862 | 0.8059 | 0.7064 | 0.5941 | 0.4770 | 0.3633 |
| 4 | 0.9996 | 0.9971 | 0.9896 | 0.9727 | 0.9420 | 0.8939 | 0.8263 | 0.7396 | 0.6367 |
| 5 | 1.0000 | 0.9998 | 0.9988 | 0.9958 | 0.9887 | 0.9747 | 0.9502 | 0.9115 | 0.8555 |
| 6 | 1.0000 | 1.0000 | 0.9999 | 0.9996 | 0.9987 | 0.9964 | 0.9915 | 0.9819 | 0.9648 |
| 7 | 1.0000 | 1.0000 | 1.0000 | 1.0000 | 0.9999 | 0.9998 | 0.9993 | 0.9983 | 0.9961 |
| 8 | 1.0000 | 1.0000 | 1.0000 | 1.0000 | 1.0000 | 1.0000 | 1.0000 | 1.0000 | 1.0000 |

| x | p = 0.55 | p = 0.60 | p = 0.65 | p = 0.70 | p = 0.75 | p = 0.80 | p = 0.85 | p = 0.90 | p = 0.91 |
|---|---|---|---|---|---|---|---|---|---|
| 0 | 0.0017 | 0.0007 | 0.0002 | 0.0001 | 0.0000 | 0.0000 | 0.0000 | 0.0000 | 0.0000 |
| 1 | 0.0181 | 0.0085 | 0.0036 | 0.0013 | 0.0004 | 0.0001 | 0.0000 | 0.0000 | 0.0000 |
| 2 | 0.0885 | 0.0498 | 0.0253 | 0.0113 | 0.0042 | 0.0012 | 0.0002 | 0.0000 | 0.0000 |
| 3 | 0.2604 | 0.1737 | 0.1061 | 0.0580 | 0.0273 | 0.0104 | 0.0029 | 0.0004 | 0.0003 |
| 4 | 0.5230 | 0.4059 | 0.2936 | 0.1941 | 0.1138 | 0.0563 | 0.0214 | 0.0050 | 0.0034 |
| 5 | 0.7799 | 0.6846 | 0.5722 | 0.4482 | 0.3215 | 0.2031 | 0.1052 | 0.0381 | 0.0289 |
| 6 | 0.9368 | 0.8936 | 0.8309 | 0.7447 | 0.6329 | 0.4967 | 0.3428 | 0.1869 | 0.1577 |
| 7 | 0.9916 | 0.9832 | 0.9681 | 0.9424 | 0.8999 | 0.8322 | 0.7275 | 0.5695 | 0.5297 |
| 8 | 1.0000 | 1.0000 | 1.0000 | 1.0000 | 1.0000 | 1.0000 | 1.0000 | 1.0000 | 1.0000 |

| x | p = 0.92 | p = 0.93 | p = 0.94 | p = 0.95 | p = 0.96 | p = 0.97 | p = 0.98 | p = 0.99 | p = 1.00 |
|---|---|---|---|---|---|---|---|---|---|
| 0 | 0.0000 | 0.0000 | 0.0000 | 0.0000 | 0.0000 | 0.0000 | 0.0000 | 0.0000 | 0.0000 |
| 1 | 0.0000 | 0.0000 | 0.0000 | 0.0000 | 0.0000 | 0.0000 | 0.0000 | 0.0000 | 0.0000 |
| 2 | 0.0000 | 0.0000 | 0.0000 | 0.0000 | 0.0000 | 0.0000 | 0.0000 | 0.0000 | 0.0000 |
| 3 | 0.0001 | 0.0001 | 0.0000 | 0.0000 | 0.0000 | 0.0000 | 0.0000 | 0.0000 | 0.0000 |
| 4 | 0.0022 | 0.0013 | 0.0007 | 0.0004 | 0.0002 | 0.0001 | 0.0000 | 0.0000 | 0.0000 |
| 5 | 0.0211 | 0.0147 | 0.0096 | 0.0058 | 0.0031 | 0.0013 | 0.0004 | 0.0001 | 0.0000 |
| 6 | 0.1298 | 0.1035 | 0.0792 | 0.0572 | 0.0381 | 0.0223 | 0.0103 | 0.0027 | 0.0000 |
| 7 | 0.4868 | 0.4404 | 0.3904 | 0.3366 | 0.2786 | 0.2163 | 0.1492 | 0.0773 | 0.0000 |
| 8 | 1.0000 | 1.0000 | 1.0000 | 1.0000 | 1.0000 | 1.0000 | 1.0000 | 1.0000 | 1.0000 |

$n = 9$

| x | p = 0.01 | p = 0.02 | p = 0.03 | p = 0.04 | p = 0.05 | p = 0.06 | p = 0.07 | p = 0.08 | p = 0.09 |
|---|---|---|---|---|---|---|---|---|---|
| 0 | 0.9135 | 0.8337 | 0.7602 | 0.6925 | 0.6302 | 0.5730 | 0.5204 | 0.4722 | 0.4279 |
| 1 | 0.9966 | 0.9869 | 0.9718 | 0.9522 | 0.9288 | 0.9022 | 0.8729 | 0.8417 | 0.8088 |
| 2 | 0.9999 | 0.9994 | 0.9980 | 0.9955 | 0.9916 | 0.9862 | 0.9791 | 0.9702 | 0.9595 |
| 3 | 1.0000 | 1.0000 | 0.9999 | 0.9997 | 0.9994 | 0.9987 | 0.9977 | 0.9963 | 0.9943 |
| 4 | 1.0000 | 1.0000 | 1.0000 | 1.0000 | 1.0000 | 0.9999 | 0.9998 | 0.9997 | 0.9995 |
| 5 | 1.0000 | 1.0000 | 1.0000 | 1.0000 | 1.0000 | 1.0000 | 1.0000 | 1.0000 | 1.0000 |
| 6 | 1.0000 | 1.0000 | 1.0000 | 1.0000 | 1.0000 | 1.0000 | 1.0000 | 1.0000 | 1.0000 |
| 7 | 1.0000 | 1.0000 | 1.0000 | 1.0000 | 1.0000 | 1.0000 | 1.0000 | 1.0000 | 1.0000 |
| 8 | 1.0000 | 1.0000 | 1.0000 | 1.0000 | 1.0000 | 1.0000 | 1.0000 | 1.0000 | 1.0000 |
| 9 | 1.0000 | 1.0000 | 1.0000 | 1.0000 | 1.0000 | 1.0000 | 1.0000 | 1.0000 | 1.0000 |

| x | p = 0.10 | p = 0.15 | p = 0.20 | p = 0.25 | p = 0.30 | p = 0.35 | p = 0.40 | p = 0.45 | p = 0.50 |
|---|---|---|---|---|---|---|---|---|---|
| 0 | 0.3874 | 0.2316 | 0.1342 | 0.0751 | 0.0404 | 0.0207 | 0.0101 | 0.0046 | 0.0020 |
| 1 | 0.7748 | 0.5995 | 0.4362 | 0.3003 | 0.1960 | 0.1211 | 0.0705 | 0.0385 | 0.0195 |
| 2 | 0.9470 | 0.8591 | 0.7382 | 0.6007 | 0.4628 | 0.3373 | 0.2318 | 0.1495 | 0.0898 |
| 3 | 0.9917 | 0.9661 | 0.9144 | 0.8343 | 0.7297 | 0.6089 | 0.4826 | 0.3614 | 0.2539 |
| 4 | 0.9991 | 0.9944 | 0.9804 | 0.9511 | 0.9012 | 0.8283 | 0.7334 | 0.6214 | 0.5000 |
| 5 | 0.9999 | 0.9994 | 0.9969 | 0.9900 | 0.9747 | 0.9464 | 0.9006 | 0.8342 | 0.7461 |
| 6 | 1.0000 | 1.0000 | 0.9997 | 0.9987 | 0.9957 | 0.9888 | 0.9750 | 0.9502 | 0.9102 |
| 7 | 1.0000 | 1.0000 | 1.0000 | 0.9999 | 0.9996 | 0.9986 | 0.9962 | 0.9909 | 0.9805 |
| 8 | 1.0000 | 1.0000 | 1.0000 | 1.0000 | 1.0000 | 0.9999 | 0.9997 | 0.9992 | 0.9980 |
| 9 | 1.0000 | 1.0000 | 1.0000 | 1.0000 | 1.0000 | 1.0000 | 1.0000 | 1.0000 | 1.0000 |

(continued)

| x | p = 0.55 | p = 0.60 | p = 0.65 | p = 0.70 | p = 0.75 | p = 0.80 | p = 0.85 | p = 0.90 | p = 0.91 |
|---|---|---|---|---|---|---|---|---|---|
| 0 | 0.0008 | 0.0003 | 0.0001 | 0.0000 | 0.0000 | 0.0000 | 0.0000 | 0.0000 | 0.0000 |
| 1 | 0.0091 | 0.0038 | 0.0014 | 0.0004 | 0.0001 | 0.0000 | 0.0000 | 0.0000 | 0.0000 |
| 2 | 0.0498 | 0.0250 | 0.0112 | 0.0043 | 0.0013 | 0.0003 | 0.0000 | 0.0000 | 0.0000 |
| 3 | 0.1658 | 0.0994 | 0.0536 | 0.0253 | 0.0100 | 0.0031 | 0.0006 | 0.0001 | 0.0000 |
| 4 | 0.3786 | 0.2666 | 0.1717 | 0.0988 | 0.0489 | 0.0196 | 0.0056 | 0.0009 | 0.0005 |
| 5 | 0.6386 | 0.5174 | 0.3911 | 0.2703 | 0.1657 | 0.0856 | 0.0339 | 0.0083 | 0.0057 |
| 6 | 0.8505 | 0.7682 | 0.6627 | 0.5372 | 0.3993 | 0.2618 | 0.1409 | 0.0530 | 0.0405 |
| 7 | 0.9615 | 0.9295 | 0.8789 | 0.8040 | 0.6997 | 0.5638 | 0.4005 | 0.2252 | 0.1912 |
| 8 | 0.9954 | 0.9899 | 0.9793 | 0.9596 | 0.9249 | 0.8658 | 0.7684 | 0.6126 | 0.5721 |
| 9 | 1.0000 | 1.0000 | 1.0000 | 1.0000 | 1.0000 | 1.0000 | 1.0000 | 1.0000 | 1.0000 |

| x | p = 0.92 | p = 0.93 | p = 0.94 | p = 0.95 | p = 0.96 | p = 0.97 | p = 0.98 | p = 0.99 | p = 1.00 |
|---|---|---|---|---|---|---|---|---|---|
| 0 | 0.0000 | 0.0000 | 0.0000 | 0.0000 | 0.0000 | 0.0000 | 0.0000 | 0.0000 | 0.0000 |
| 1 | 0.0000 | 0.0000 | 0.0000 | 0.0000 | 0.0000 | 0.0000 | 0.0000 | 0.0000 | 0.0000 |
| 2 | 0.0000 | 0.0000 | 0.0000 | 0.0000 | 0.0000 | 0.0000 | 0.0000 | 0.0000 | 0.0000 |
| 3 | 0.0000 | 0.0000 | 0.0000 | 0.0000 | 0.0000 | 0.0000 | 0.0000 | 0.0000 | 0.0000 |
| 4 | 0.0003 | 0.0002 | 0.0001 | 0.0000 | 0.0000 | 0.0000 | 0.0000 | 0.0000 | 0.0000 |
| 5 | 0.0037 | 0.0023 | 0.0013 | 0.0006 | 0.0003 | 0.0001 | 0.0000 | 0.0000 | 0.0000 |
| 6 | 0.0298 | 0.0209 | 0.0138 | 0.0084 | 0.0045 | 0.0020 | 0.0006 | 0.0001 | 0.0000 |
| 7 | 0.1583 | 0.1271 | 0.0978 | 0.0712 | 0.0478 | 0.0282 | 0.0131 | 0.0034 | 0.0000 |
| 8 | 0.5278 | 0.4796 | 0.4270 | 0.3698 | 0.3075 | 0.2398 | 0.1663 | 0.0865 | 0.0000 |
| 9 | 1.0000 | 1.0000 | 1.0000 | 1.0000 | 1.0000 | 1.0000 | 1.0000 | 1.0000 | 1.0000 |

$$n = 10$$

| x | p = 0.01 | p = 0.02 | p = 0.03 | p = 0.04 | p = 0.05 | p = 0.06 | p = 0.07 | p = 0.08 | p = 0.09 |
|---|---|---|---|---|---|---|---|---|---|
| 0 | 0.9044 | 0.8171 | 0.7374 | 0.6648 | 0.5987 | 0.5386 | 0.4840 | 0.4344 | 0.3894 |
| 1 | 0.9957 | 0.9838 | 0.9655 | 0.9418 | 0.9139 | 0.8824 | 0.8483 | 0.8121 | 0.7746 |
| 2 | 0.9999 | 0.9991 | 0.9972 | 0.9938 | 0.9885 | 0.9812 | 0.9717 | 0.9599 | 0.9460 |
| 3 | 1.0000 | 1.0000 | 0.9999 | 0.9996 | 0.9990 | 0.9980 | 0.9964 | 0.9942 | 0.9912 |
| 4 | 1.0000 | 1.0000 | 1.0000 | 1.0000 | 0.9999 | 0.9998 | 0.9997 | 0.9994 | 0.9990 |
| 5 | 1.0000 | 1.0000 | 1.0000 | 1.0000 | 1.0000 | 1.0000 | 1.0000 | 1.0000 | 0.9999 |
| 6 | 1.0000 | 1.0000 | 1.0000 | 1.0000 | 1.0000 | 1.0000 | 1.0000 | 1.0000 | 1.0000 |
| 7 | 1.0000 | 1.0000 | 1.0000 | 1.0000 | 1.0000 | 1.0000 | 1.0000 | 1.0000 | 1.0000 |
| 8 | 1.0000 | 1.0000 | 1.0000 | 1.0000 | 1.0000 | 1.0000 | 1.0000 | 1.0000 | 1.0000 |
| 9 | 1.0000 | 1.0000 | 1.0000 | 1.0000 | 1.0000 | 1.0000 | 1.0000 | 1.0000 | 1.0000 |
| 10 | 1.0000 | 1.0000 | 1.0000 | 1.0000 | 1.0000 | 1.0000 | 1.0000 | 1.0000 | 1.0000 |

| x | p = 0.10 | p = 0.15 | p = 0.20 | p = 0.25 | p = 0.30 | p = 0.35 | p = 0.40 | p = 0.45 | p = 0.50 |
|---|---|---|---|---|---|---|---|---|---|
| 0 | 0.3487 | 0.1969 | 0.1074 | 0.0563 | 0.0282 | 0.0135 | 0.0060 | 0.0025 | 0.0010 |
| 1 | 0.7361 | 0.5443 | 0.3758 | 0.2440 | 0.1493 | 0.0860 | 0.0464 | 0.0233 | 0.0107 |
| 2 | 0.9298 | 0.8202 | 0.6778 | 0.5256 | 0.3828 | 0.2616 | 0.1673 | 0.0996 | 0.0547 |
| 3 | 0.9872 | 0.9500 | 0.8791 | 0.7759 | 0.6496 | 0.5138 | 0.3823 | 0.2660 | 0.1719 |
| 4 | 0.9984 | 0.9901 | 0.9672 | 0.9219 | 0.8497 | 0.7515 | 0.6331 | 0.5044 | 0.3770 |
| 5 | 0.9999 | 0.9986 | 0.9936 | 0.9803 | 0.9527 | 0.9051 | 0.8338 | 0.7384 | 0.6230 |
| 6 | 1.0000 | 0.9999 | 0.9991 | 0.9965 | 0.9894 | 0.9740 | 0.9452 | 0.8980 | 0.8281 |
| 7 | 1.0000 | 1.0000 | 0.9999 | 0.9996 | 0.9984 | 0.9952 | 0.9877 | 0.9726 | 0.9453 |
| 8 | 1.0000 | 1.0000 | 1.0000 | 1.0000 | 0.9999 | 0.9995 | 0.9983 | 0.9955 | 0.9893 |
| 9 | 1.0000 | 1.0000 | 1.0000 | 1.0000 | 1.0000 | 1.0000 | 0.9999 | 0.9997 | 0.9990 |
| 10 | 1.0000 | 1.0000 | 1.0000 | 1.0000 | 1.0000 | 1.0000 | 1.0000 | 1.0000 | 1.0000 |

| x | p = 0.55 | p = 0.60 | p = 0.65 | p = 0.70 | p = 0.75 | p = 0.80 | p = 0.85 | p = 0.90 | p = 0.91 |
|---|---|---|---|---|---|---|---|---|---|
| 0 | 0.0003 | 0.0001 | 0.0000 | 0.0000 | 0.0000 | 0.0000 | 0.0000 | 0.0000 | 0.0000 |
| 1 | 0.0045 | 0.0017 | 0.0005 | 0.0001 | 0.0000 | 0.0000 | 0.0000 | 0.0000 | 0.0000 |
| 2 | 0.0274 | 0.0123 | 0.0048 | 0.0016 | 0.0004 | 0.0001 | 0.0000 | 0.0000 | 0.0000 |
| 3 | 0.1020 | 0.0548 | 0.0260 | 0.0106 | 0.0035 | 0.0009 | 0.0001 | 0.0000 | 0.0000 |
| 4 | 0.2616 | 0.1662 | 0.0949 | 0.0473 | 0.0197 | 0.0064 | 0.0014 | 0.0001 | 0.0001 |
| 5 | 0.4956 | 0.3669 | 0.2485 | 0.1503 | 0.0781 | 0.0328 | 0.0099 | 0.0016 | 0.0010 |
| 6 | 0.7340 | 0.6177 | 0.4862 | 0.3504 | 0.2241 | 0.1209 | 0.0500 | 0.0128 | 0.0088 |
| 7 | 0.9004 | 0.8327 | 0.7384 | 0.6172 | 0.4744 | 0.3222 | 0.1798 | 0.0702 | 0.0540 |
| 8 | 0.9767 | 0.9536 | 0.9140 | 0.8507 | 0.7560 | 0.6242 | 0.4557 | 0.2639 | 0.2254 |
| 9 | 0.9975 | 0.9940 | 0.9865 | 0.9718 | 0.9437 | 0.8926 | 0.8031 | 0.6513 | 0.6106 |
| 10 | 1.0000 | 1.0000 | 1.0000 | 1.0000 | 1.0000 | 1.0000 | 1.0000 | 1.0000 | 1.0000 |

| x | p = 0.92 | p = 0.93 | p = 0.94 | p = 0.95 | p = 0.96 | p = 0.97 | p = 0.98 | p = 0.99 | p = 1.00 |
|---|---|---|---|---|---|---|---|---|---|
| 0 | 0.0000 | 0.0000 | 0.0000 | 0.0000 | 0.0000 | 0.0000 | 0.0000 | 0.0000 | 0.0000 |
| 1 | 0.0000 | 0.0000 | 0.0000 | 0.0000 | 0.0000 | 0.0000 | 0.0000 | 0.0000 | 0.0000 |
| 2 | 0.0000 | 0.0000 | 0.0000 | 0.0000 | 0.0000 | 0.0000 | 0.0000 | 0.0000 | 0.0000 |

| | | | | | | | | | |
|---|---|---|---|---|---|---|---|---|---|
| 3 | 0.0000 | 0.0000 | 0.0000 | 0.0000 | 0.0000 | 0.0000 | 0.0000 | 0.0000 | 0.0000 |
| 4 | 0.0000 | 0.0000 | 0.0000 | 0.0000 | 0.0000 | 0.0000 | 0.0000 | 0.0000 | 0.0000 |
| 5 | 0.0006 | 0.0003 | 0.0002 | 0.0001 | 0.0000 | 0.0000 | 0.0000 | 0.0000 | 0.0000 |
| 6 | 0.0058 | 0.0036 | 0.0020 | 0.0010 | 0.0004 | 0.0001 | 0.0000 | 0.0000 | 0.0000 |
| 7 | 0.0401 | 0.0283 | 0.0188 | 0.0115 | 0.0062 | 0.0028 | 0.0009 | 0.0001 | 0.0000 |
| 8 | 0.1879 | 0.1517 | 0.1176 | 0.0861 | 0.0582 | 0.0345 | 0.0162 | 0.0043 | 0.0000 |
| 9 | 0.5656 | 0.5160 | 0.4614 | 0.4013 | 0.3352 | 0.2626 | 0.1829 | 0.0956 | 0.0000 |
| 10 | 1.0000 | 1.0000 | 1.0000 | 1.0000 | 1.0000 | 1.0000 | 1.0000 | 1.0000 | 1.0000 |

### $n = 11$

| x | $p = 0.01$ | $p = 0.02$ | $p = 0.03$ | $p = 0.04$ | $p = 0.05$ | $p = 0.06$ | $p = 0.07$ | $p = 0.08$ | $p = 0.09$ |
|---|---|---|---|---|---|---|---|---|---|
| 0 | 0.8953 | 0.8007 | 0.7153 | 0.6382 | 0.5688 | 0.5063 | 0.4501 | 0.3996 | 0.3544 |
| 1 | 0.9948 | 0.9805 | 0.9587 | 0.9308 | 0.8981 | 0.8618 | 0.8228 | 0.7819 | 0.7399 |
| 2 | 0.9998 | 0.9988 | 0.9963 | 0.9917 | 0.9848 | 0.9752 | 0.9630 | 0.9481 | 0.9305 |
| 3 | 1.0000 | 1.0000 | 0.9998 | 0.9993 | 0.9984 | 0.9970 | 0.9947 | 0.9915 | 0.9871 |
| 4 | 1.0000 | 1.0000 | 1.0000 | 1.0000 | 0.9999 | 0.9997 | 0.9995 | 0.9990 | 0.9983 |
| 5 | 1.0000 | 1.0000 | 1.0000 | 1.0000 | 1.0000 | 1.0000 | 1.0000 | 0.9999 | 0.9998 |
| 6 | 1.0000 | 1.0000 | 1.0000 | 1.0000 | 1.0000 | 1.0000 | 1.0000 | 1.0000 | 1.0000 |
| 7 | 1.0000 | 1.0000 | 1.0000 | 1.0000 | 1.0000 | 1.0000 | 1.0000 | 1.0000 | 1.0000 |
| 8 | 1.0000 | 1.0000 | 1.0000 | 1.0000 | 1.0000 | 1.0000 | 1.0000 | 1.0000 | 1.0000 |
| 9 | 1.0000 | 1.0000 | 1.0000 | 1.0000 | 1.0000 | 1.0000 | 1.0000 | 1.0000 | 1.0000 |
| 10 | 1.0000 | 1.0000 | 1.0000 | 1.0000 | 1.0000 | 1.0000 | 1.0000 | 1.0000 | 1.0000 |
| 11 | 1.0000 | 1.0000 | 1.0000 | 1.0000 | 1.0000 | 1.0000 | 1.0000 | 1.0000 | 1.0000 |

| x | $p = 0.10$ | $p = 0.15$ | $p = 0.20$ | $p = 0.25$ | $p = 0.30$ | $p = 0.35$ | $p = 0.40$ | $p = 0.45$ | $p = 0.50$ |
|---|---|---|---|---|---|---|---|---|---|
| 0 | 0.3138 | 0.1673 | 0.0859 | 0.0422 | 0.0198 | 0.0088 | 0.0036 | 0.0014 | 0.0005 |
| 1 | 0.6974 | 0.4922 | 0.3221 | 0.1971 | 0.1130 | 0.0606 | 0.0302 | 0.0139 | 0.0059 |
| 2 | 0.9104 | 0.7788 | 0.6174 | 0.4552 | 0.3127 | 0.2001 | 0.1189 | 0.0652 | 0.0327 |
| 3 | 0.9815 | 0.9306 | 0.8389 | 0.7133 | 0.5696 | 0.4256 | 0.2963 | 0.1911 | 0.1133 |
| 4 | 0.9972 | 0.9841 | 0.9496 | 0.8854 | 0.7897 | 0.6683 | 0.5328 | 0.3971 | 0.2744 |
| 5 | 0.9997 | 0.9973 | 0.9883 | 0.9657 | 0.9218 | 0.8513 | 0.7535 | 0.6331 | 0.5000 |
| 6 | 1.0000 | 0.9997 | 0.9980 | 0.9924 | 0.9784 | 0.9499 | 0.9006 | 0.8262 | 0.7256 |
| 7 | 1.0000 | 1.0000 | 0.9998 | 0.9988 | 0.9957 | 0.9878 | 0.9707 | 0.9390 | 0.8867 |
| 8 | 1.0000 | 1.0000 | 1.0000 | 0.9999 | 0.9994 | 0.9980 | 0.9941 | 0.9852 | 0.9673 |
| 9 | 1.0000 | 1.0000 | 1.0000 | 1.0000 | 1.0000 | 0.9998 | 0.9993 | 0.9978 | 0.9941 |
| 10 | 1.0000 | 1.0000 | 1.0000 | 1.0000 | 1.0000 | 1.0000 | 1.0000 | 0.9998 | 0.9995 |
| 11 | 1.0000 | 1.0000 | 1.0000 | 1.0000 | 1.0000 | 1.0000 | 1.0000 | 1.0000 | 1.0000 |

| x | $p = 0.55$ | $p = 0.60$ | $p = 0.65$ | $p = 0.70$ | $p = 0.75$ | $p = 0.80$ | $p = 0.85$ | $p = 0.90$ | $p = 0.91$ |
|---|---|---|---|---|---|---|---|---|---|
| 0 | 0.0002 | 0.0000 | 0.0000 | 0.0000 | 0.0000 | 0.0000 | 0.0000 | 0.0000 | 0.0000 |
| 1 | 0.0022 | 0.0007 | 0.0002 | 0.0000 | 0.0000 | 0.0000 | 0.0000 | 0.0000 | 0.0000 |
| 2 | 0.0148 | 0.0059 | 0.0020 | 0.0006 | 0.0001 | 0.0000 | 0.0000 | 0.0000 | 0.0000 |
| 3 | 0.0610 | 0.0293 | 0.0122 | 0.0043 | 0.0012 | 0.0002 | 0.0000 | 0.0000 | 0.0000 |
| 4 | 0.1738 | 0.0994 | 0.0501 | 0.0216 | 0.0076 | 0.0020 | 0.0003 | 0.0000 | 0.0000 |
| 5 | 0.3669 | 0.2465 | 0.1487 | 0.0782 | 0.0343 | 0.0117 | 0.0027 | 0.0003 | 0.0002 |
| 6 | 0.6029 | 0.4672 | 0.3317 | 0.2103 | 0.1146 | 0.0504 | 0.0159 | 0.0028 | 0.0017 |
| 7 | 0.8089 | 0.7037 | 0.5744 | 0.4304 | 0.2867 | 0.1611 | 0.0694 | 0.0185 | 0.0129 |
| 8 | 0.9348 | 0.8811 | 0.7999 | 0.6873 | 0.5448 | 0.3826 | 0.2212 | 0.0896 | 0.0695 |
| 9 | 0.9861 | 0.9698 | 0.9394 | 0.8870 | 0.8029 | 0.6779 | 0.5078 | 0.3026 | 0.2601 |
| 10 | 0.9986 | 0.9964 | 0.9912 | 0.9802 | 0.9578 | 0.9141 | 0.8327 | 0.6862 | 0.6456 |
| 11 | 1.0000 | 1.0000 | 1.0000 | 1.0000 | 1.0000 | 1.0000 | 1.0000 | 1.0000 | 1.0000 |

| x | $p = 0.92$ | $p = 0.93$ | $p = 0.94$ | $p = 0.95$ | $p = 0.96$ | $p = 0.97$ | $p = 0.98$ | $p = 0.99$ | $p = 1.00$ |
|---|---|---|---|---|---|---|---|---|---|
| 0 | 0.0000 | 0.0000 | 0.0000 | 0.0000 | 0.0000 | 0.0000 | 0.0000 | 0.0000 | 0.0000 |
| 1 | 0.0000 | 0.0000 | 0.0000 | 0.0000 | 0.0000 | 0.0000 | 0.0000 | 0.0000 | 0.0000 |
| 2 | 0.0000 | 0.0000 | 0.0000 | 0.0000 | 0.0000 | 0.0000 | 0.0000 | 0.0000 | 0.0000 |
| 3 | 0.0000 | 0.0000 | 0.0000 | 0.0000 | 0.0000 | 0.0000 | 0.0000 | 0.0000 | 0.0000 |
| 4 | 0.0000 | 0.0000 | 0.0000 | 0.0000 | 0.0000 | 0.0000 | 0.0000 | 0.0000 | 0.0000 |
| 5 | 0.0001 | 0.0000 | 0.0000 | 0.0000 | 0.0000 | 0.0000 | 0.0000 | 0.0000 | 0.0000 |
| 6 | 0.0010 | 0.0005 | 0.0003 | 0.0001 | 0.0000 | 0.0000 | 0.0000 | 0.0000 | 0.0000 |
| 7 | 0.0085 | 0.0053 | 0.0030 | 0.0016 | 0.0007 | 0.0002 | 0.0000 | 0.0000 | 0.0000 |
| 8 | 0.0519 | 0.0370 | 0.0248 | 0.0152 | 0.0083 | 0.0037 | 0.0012 | 0.0002 | 0.0000 |
| 9 | 0.2181 | 0.1772 | 0.1382 | 0.1019 | 0.0692 | 0.0413 | 0.0195 | 0.0052 | 0.0000 |
| 10 | 0.6004 | 0.5499 | 0.4937 | 0.4312 | 0.3618 | 0.2847 | 0.1993 | 0.1047 | 0.0000 |
| 11 | 1.0000 | 1.0000 | 1.0000 | 1.0000 | 1.0000 | 1.0000 | 1.0000 | 1.0000 | 1.0000 |

*(continued)*

$n = 12$

| x | p = 0.01 | p = 0.02 | p = 0.03 | p = 0.04 | p = 0.05 | p = 0.06 | p = 0.07 | p = 0.08 | p = 0.09 |
|---|---|---|---|---|---|---|---|---|---|
| 0 | 0.8864 | 0.7847 | 0.6938 | 0.6127 | 0.5404 | 0.4759 | 0.4186 | 0.3677 | 0.3225 |
| 1 | 0.9938 | 0.9769 | 0.9514 | 0.9191 | 0.8816 | 0.8405 | 0.7967 | 0.7513 | 0.7052 |
| 2 | 0.9998 | 0.9985 | 0.9952 | 0.9893 | 0.9804 | 0.9684 | 0.9532 | 0.9348 | 0.9134 |
| 3 | 1.0000 | 0.9999 | 0.9997 | 0.9990 | 0.9978 | 0.9957 | 0.9925 | 0.9880 | 0.9820 |
| 4 | 1.0000 | 1.0000 | 1.0000 | 0.9999 | 0.9998 | 0.9996 | 0.9991 | 0.9984 | 0.9973 |
| 5 | 1.0000 | 1.0000 | 1.0000 | 1.0000 | 1.0000 | 1.0000 | 0.9999 | 0.9998 | 0.9997 |
| 6 | 1.0000 | 1.0000 | 1.0000 | 1.0000 | 1.0000 | 1.0000 | 1.0000 | 1.0000 | 1.0000 |
| 7 | 1.0000 | 1.0000 | 1.0000 | 1.0000 | 1.0000 | 1.0000 | 1.0000 | 1.0000 | 1.0000 |
| 8 | 1.0000 | 1.0000 | 1.0000 | 1.0000 | 1.0000 | 1.0000 | 1.0000 | 1.0000 | 1.0000 |
| 9 | 1.0000 | 1.0000 | 1.0000 | 1.0000 | 1.0000 | 1.0000 | 1.0000 | 1.0000 | 1.0000 |
| 10 | 1.0000 | 1.0000 | 1.0000 | 1.0000 | 1.0000 | 1.0000 | 1.0000 | 1.0000 | 1.0000 |
| 11 | 1.0000 | 1.0000 | 1.0000 | 1.0000 | 1.0000 | 1.0000 | 1.0000 | 1.0000 | 1.0000 |
| 12 | 1.0000 | 1.0000 | 1.0000 | 1.0000 | 1.0000 | 1.0000 | 1.0000 | 1.0000 | 1.0000 |

| x | p = 0.10 | p = 0.15 | p = 0.20 | p = 0.25 | p = 0.30 | p = 0.35 | p = 0.40 | p = 0.45 | p = 0.50 |
|---|---|---|---|---|---|---|---|---|---|
| 0 | 0.2824 | 0.1422 | 0.0687 | 0.0317 | 0.0138 | 0.0057 | 0.0022 | 0.0008 | 0.0002 |
| 1 | 0.6590 | 0.4435 | 0.2749 | 0.1584 | 0.0850 | 0.0424 | 0.0196 | 0.0083 | 0.0032 |
| 2 | 0.8891 | 0.7358 | 0.5583 | 0.3907 | 0.2528 | 0.1513 | 0.0834 | 0.0421 | 0.0193 |
| 3 | 0.9744 | 0.9078 | 0.7946 | 0.6488 | 0.4925 | 0.3467 | 0.2253 | 0.1345 | 0.0730 |
| 4 | 0.9957 | 0.9761 | 0.9274 | 0.8424 | 0.7237 | 0.5833 | 0.4382 | 0.3044 | 0.1938 |
| 5 | 0.9995 | 0.9954 | 0.9806 | 0.9456 | 0.8822 | 0.7873 | 0.6652 | 0.5269 | 0.3872 |
| 6 | 0.9999 | 0.9993 | 0.9961 | 0.9857 | 0.9614 | 0.9154 | 0.8418 | 0.7393 | 0.6128 |
| 7 | 1.0000 | 0.9999 | 0.9994 | 0.9972 | 0.9905 | 0.9745 | 0.9427 | 0.8883 | 0.8062 |
| 8 | 1.0000 | 1.0000 | 0.9999 | 0.9996 | 0.9983 | 0.9944 | 0.9847 | 0.9644 | 0.9270 |
| 9 | 1.0000 | 1.0000 | 1.0000 | 1.0000 | 0.9998 | 0.9992 | 0.9972 | 0.9921 | 0.9807 |
| 10 | 1.0000 | 1.0000 | 1.0000 | 1.0000 | 1.0000 | 0.9999 | 0.9997 | 0.9989 | 0.9968 |
| 11 | 1.0000 | 1.0000 | 1.0000 | 1.0000 | 1.0000 | 1.0000 | 1.0000 | 0.9999 | 0.9998 |
| 12 | 1.0000 | 1.0000 | 1.0000 | 1.0000 | 1.0000 | 1.0000 | 1.0000 | 1.0000 | 1.0000 |

| x | p = 0.55 | p = 0.60 | p = 0.65 | p = 0.70 | p = 0.75 | p = 0.80 | p = 0.85 | p = 0.90 | p = 0.91 |
|---|---|---|---|---|---|---|---|---|---|
| 0 | 0.0001 | 0.0000 | 0.0000 | 0.0000 | 0.0000 | 0.0000 | 0.0000 | 0.0000 | 0.0000 |
| 1 | 0.0011 | 0.0003 | 0.0001 | 0.0000 | 0.0000 | 0.0000 | 0.0000 | 0.0000 | 0.0000 |
| 2 | 0.0079 | 0.0028 | 0.0008 | 0.0002 | 0.0000 | 0.0000 | 0.0000 | 0.0000 | 0.0000 |
| 3 | 0.0356 | 0.0153 | 0.0056 | 0.0017 | 0.0004 | 0.0001 | 0.0000 | 0.0000 | 0.0000 |
| 4 | 0.1117 | 0.0573 | 0.0255 | 0.0095 | 0.0028 | 0.0006 | 0.0001 | 0.0000 | 0.0000 |
| 5 | 0.2607 | 0.1582 | 0.0846 | 0.0386 | 0.0143 | 0.0039 | 0.0007 | 0.0001 | 0.0000 |
| 6 | 0.4731 | 0.3348 | 0.2127 | 0.1178 | 0.0544 | 0.0194 | 0.0046 | 0.0005 | 0.0003 |
| 7 | 0.6956 | 0.5618 | 0.4167 | 0.2763 | 0.1576 | 0.0726 | 0.0239 | 0.0043 | 0.0027 |
| 8 | 0.8655 | 0.7747 | 0.6533 | 0.5075 | 0.3512 | 0.2054 | 0.0922 | 0.0256 | 0.0180 |
| 9 | 0.9579 | 0.9166 | 0.8487 | 0.7472 | 0.6093 | 0.4417 | 0.2642 | 0.1109 | 0.0866 |
| 10 | 0.9917 | 0.9804 | 0.9576 | 0.9150 | 0.8416 | 0.7251 | 0.5565 | 0.3410 | 0.2948 |
| 11 | 0.9992 | 0.9978 | 0.9943 | 0.9862 | 0.9683 | 0.9313 | 0.8578 | 0.7176 | 0.6775 |
| 12 | 1.0000 | 1.0000 | 1.0000 | 1.0000 | 1.0000 | 1.0000 | 1.0000 | 1.0000 | 1.0000 |

| x | p = 0.92 | p = 0.93 | p = 0.94 | p = 0.95 | p = 0.96 | p = 0.97 | p = 0.98 | p = 0.99 | p = 1.00 |
|---|---|---|---|---|---|---|---|---|---|
| 0 | 0.0000 | 0.0000 | 0.0000 | 0.0000 | 0.0000 | 0.0000 | 0.0000 | 0.0000 | 0.0000 |
| 1 | 0.0000 | 0.0000 | 0.0000 | 0.0000 | 0.0000 | 0.0000 | 0.0000 | 0.0000 | 0.0000 |
| 2 | 0.0000 | 0.0000 | 0.0000 | 0.0000 | 0.0000 | 0.0000 | 0.0000 | 0.0000 | 0.0000 |
| 3 | 0.0000 | 0.0000 | 0.0000 | 0.0000 | 0.0000 | 0.0000 | 0.0000 | 0.0000 | 0.0000 |
| 4 | 0.0000 | 0.0000 | 0.0000 | 0.0000 | 0.0000 | 0.0000 | 0.0000 | 0.0000 | 0.0000 |
| 5 | 0.0000 | 0.0000 | 0.0000 | 0.0000 | 0.0000 | 0.0000 | 0.0000 | 0.0000 | 0.0000 |
| 6 | 0.0002 | 0.0001 | 0.0000 | 0.0000 | 0.0000 | 0.0000 | 0.0000 | 0.0000 | 0.0000 |
| 7 | 0.0016 | 0.0009 | 0.0004 | 0.0002 | 0.0001 | 0.0000 | 0.0000 | 0.0000 | 0.0000 |
| 8 | 0.0120 | 0.0075 | 0.0043 | 0.0022 | 0.0010 | 0.0003 | 0.0001 | 0.0000 | 0.0000 |
| 9 | 0.0652 | 0.0468 | 0.0316 | 0.0196 | 0.0107 | 0.0048 | 0.0015 | 0.0002 | 0.0000 |
| 10 | 0.2487 | 0.2033 | 0.1595 | 0.1184 | 0.0809 | 0.0486 | 0.0231 | 0.0062 | 0.0000 |
| 11 | 0.6323 | 0.5814 | 0.5241 | 0.4596 | 0.3873 | 0.3062 | 0.2153 | 0.1136 | 0.0000 |
| 12 | 1.0000 | 1.0000 | 1.0000 | 1.0000 | 1.0000 | 1.0000 | 1.0000 | 1.0000 | 1.0000 |

$n = 13$

| x | p = 0.01 | p = 0.02 | p = 0.03 | p = 0.04 | p = 0.05 | p = 0.06 | p = 0.07 | p = 0.08 | p = 0.09 |
|---|---|---|---|---|---|---|---|---|---|
| 0 | 0.8775 | 0.7690 | 0.6730 | 0.5882 | 0.5133 | 0.4474 | 0.3893 | 0.3383 | 0.2935 |
| 1 | 0.9928 | 0.9730 | 0.9436 | 0.9068 | 0.8646 | 0.8186 | 0.7702 | 0.7206 | 0.6707 |
| 2 | 0.9997 | 0.9980 | 0.9938 | 0.9865 | 0.9755 | 0.9608 | 0.9422 | 0.9201 | 0.8946 |
| 3 | 1.0000 | 0.9999 | 0.9995 | 0.9986 | 0.9969 | 0.9940 | 0.9897 | 0.9837 | 0.9758 |

| x | 1.0000 | 1.0000 | 1.0000 | 0.9999 | 0.9997 | 0.9993 | 0.9987 | 0.9976 | 0.9959 |
|---|---|---|---|---|---|---|---|---|---|
| 4 | 1.0000 | 1.0000 | 1.0000 | 0.9999 | 0.9997 | 0.9993 | 0.9987 | 0.9976 | 0.9959 |
| 5 | 1.0000 | 1.0000 | 1.0000 | 1.0000 | 1.0000 | 0.9999 | 0.9999 | 0.9997 | 0.9995 |
| 6 | 1.0000 | 1.0000 | 1.0000 | 1.0000 | 1.0000 | 1.0000 | 1.0000 | 1.0000 | 0.9999 |
| 7 | 1.0000 | 1.0000 | 1.0000 | 1.0000 | 1.0000 | 1.0000 | 1.0000 | 1.0000 | 1.0000 |
| 8 | 1.0000 | 1.0000 | 1.0000 | 1.0000 | 1.0000 | 1.0000 | 1.0000 | 1.0000 | 1.0000 |
| 9 | 1.0000 | 1.0000 | 1.0000 | 1.0000 | 1.0000 | 1.0000 | 1.0000 | 1.0000 | 1.0000 |
| 10 | 1.0000 | 1.0000 | 1.0000 | 1.0000 | 1.0000 | 1.0000 | 1.0000 | 1.0000 | 1.0000 |
| 11 | 1.0000 | 1.0000 | 1.0000 | 1.0000 | 1.0000 | 1.0000 | 1.0000 | 1.0000 | 1.0000 |
| 12 | 1.0000 | 1.0000 | 1.0000 | 1.0000 | 1.0000 | 1.0000 | 1.0000 | 1.0000 | 1.0000 |
| 13 | 1.0000 | 1.0000 | 1.0000 | 1.0000 | 1.0000 | 1.0000 | 1.0000 | 1.0000 | 1.0000 |

| x | $p = 0.10$ | $p = 0.15$ | $p = 0.20$ | $p = 0.25$ | $p = 0.30$ | $p = 0.35$ | $p = 0.40$ | $p = 0.45$ | $p = 0.50$ |
|---|---|---|---|---|---|---|---|---|---|
| 0 | 0.2542 | 0.1209 | 0.0550 | 0.0238 | 0.0097 | 0.0037 | 0.0013 | 0.0004 | 0.0001 |
| 1 | 0.6213 | 0.3983 | 0.2336 | 0.1267 | 0.0637 | 0.0296 | 0.0126 | 0.0049 | 0.0017 |
| 2 | 0.8661 | 0.6920 | 0.5017 | 0.3326 | 0.2025 | 0.1132 | 0.0579 | 0.0269 | 0.0112 |
| 3 | 0.9658 | 0.8820 | 0.7473 | 0.5843 | 0.4206 | 0.2783 | 0.1686 | 0.0929 | 0.0461 |
| 4 | 0.9935 | 0.9658 | 0.9009 | 0.7940 | 0.6543 | 0.5005 | 0.3530 | 0.2279 | 0.1334 |
| 5 | 0.9991 | 0.9925 | 0.9700 | 0.9198 | 0.8346 | 0.7159 | 0.5744 | 0.4268 | 0.2905 |
| 6 | 0.9999 | 0.9987 | 0.9930 | 0.9757 | 0.9376 | 0.8705 | 0.7712 | 0.6437 | 0.5000 |
| 7 | 1.0000 | 0.9998 | 0.9988 | 0.9944 | 0.9818 | 0.9538 | 0.9023 | 0.8212 | 0.7095 |
| 8 | 1.0000 | 1.0000 | 0.9998 | 0.9990 | 0.9960 | 0.9874 | 0.9679 | 0.9302 | 0.8666 |
| 9 | 1.0000 | 1.0000 | 1.0000 | 0.9999 | 0.9993 | 0.9975 | 0.9922 | 0.9797 | 0.9539 |
| 10 | 1.0000 | 1.0000 | 1.0000 | 1.0000 | 0.9999 | 0.9997 | 0.9987 | 0.9959 | 0.9888 |
| 11 | 1.0000 | 1.0000 | 1.0000 | 1.0000 | 1.0000 | 1.0000 | 0.9999 | 0.9995 | 0.9983 |
| 12 | 1.0000 | 1.0000 | 1.0000 | 1.0000 | 1.0000 | 1.0000 | 1.0000 | 1.0000 | 0.9999 |
| 13 | 1.0000 | 1.0000 | 1.0000 | 1.0000 | 1.0000 | 1.0000 | 1.0000 | 1.0000 | 1.0000 |

| x | $p = 0.55$ | $p = 0.60$ | $p = 0.65$ | $p = 0.70$ | $p = 0.75$ | $p = 0.80$ | $p = 0.85$ | $p = 0.90$ | $p = 0.91$ |
|---|---|---|---|---|---|---|---|---|---|
| 0 | 0.0000 | 0.0000 | 0.0000 | 0.0000 | 0.0000 | 0.0000 | 0.0000 | 0.0000 | 0.0000 |
| 1 | 0.0005 | 0.0001 | 0.0000 | 0.0000 | 0.0000 | 0.0000 | 0.0000 | 0.0000 | 0.0000 |
| 2 | 0.0041 | 0.0013 | 0.0003 | 0.0001 | 0.0000 | 0.0000 | 0.0000 | 0.0000 | 0.0000 |
| 3 | 0.0203 | 0.0078 | 0.0025 | 0.0007 | 0.0001 | 0.0000 | 0.0000 | 0.0000 | 0.0000 |
| 4 | 0.0698 | 0.0321 | 0.0126 | 0.0040 | 0.0010 | 0.0002 | 0.0000 | 0.0000 | 0.0000 |
| 5 | 0.1788 | 0.0977 | 0.0462 | 0.0182 | 0.0056 | 0.0012 | 0.0002 | 0.0000 | 0.0000 |
| 6 | 0.3563 | 0.2288 | 0.1295 | 0.0624 | 0.0243 | 0.0070 | 0.0013 | 0.0001 | 0.0001 |
| 7 | 0.5732 | 0.4256 | 0.2841 | 0.1654 | 0.0802 | 0.0300 | 0.0075 | 0.0009 | 0.0005 |
| 8 | 0.7721 | 0.6470 | 0.4995 | 0.3457 | 0.2060 | 0.0991 | 0.0342 | 0.0065 | 0.0041 |
| 9 | 0.9071 | 0.8314 | 0.7217 | 0.5794 | 0.4157 | 0.2527 | 0.1180 | 0.0342 | 0.0242 |
| 10 | 0.9731 | 0.9421 | 0.8868 | 0.7975 | 0.6674 | 0.4983 | 0.3080 | 0.1339 | 0.1054 |
| 11 | 0.9951 | 0.9874 | 0.9704 | 0.9363 | 0.8733 | 0.7664 | 0.6017 | 0.3787 | 0.3293 |
| 12 | 0.9996 | 0.9987 | 0.9963 | 0.9903 | 0.9762 | 0.9450 | 0.8791 | 0.7458 | 0.7065 |
| 13 | 1.0000 | 1.0000 | 1.0000 | 1.0000 | 1.0000 | 1.0000 | 1.0000 | 1.0000 | 1.0000 |

| x | $p = 0.92$ | $p = 0.93$ | $p = 0.94$ | $p = 0.95$ | $p = 0.96$ | $p = 0.97$ | $p = 0.98$ | $p = 0.99$ | $p = 1.00$ |
|---|---|---|---|---|---|---|---|---|---|
| 0 | 0.0000 | 0.0000 | 0.0000 | 0.0000 | 0.0000 | 0.0000 | 0.0000 | 0.0000 | 0.0000 |
| 1 | 0.0000 | 0.0000 | 0.0000 | 0.0000 | 0.0000 | 0.0000 | 0.0000 | 0.0000 | 0.0000 |
| 2 | 0.0000 | 0.0000 | 0.0000 | 0.0000 | 0.0000 | 0.0000 | 0.0000 | 0.0000 | 0.0000 |
| 3 | 0.0000 | 0.0000 | 0.0000 | 0.0000 | 0.0000 | 0.0000 | 0.0000 | 0.0000 | 0.0000 |
| 4 | 0.0000 | 0.0000 | 0.0000 | 0.0000 | 0.0000 | 0.0000 | 0.0000 | 0.0000 | 0.0000 |
| 5 | 0.0000 | 0.0000 | 0.0000 | 0.0000 | 0.0000 | 0.0000 | 0.0000 | 0.0000 | 0.0000 |
| 6 | 0.0000 | 0.0000 | 0.0000 | 0.0000 | 0.0000 | 0.0000 | 0.0000 | 0.0000 | 0.0000 |
| 7 | 0.0003 | 0.0001 | 0.0001 | 0.0000 | 0.0000 | 0.0000 | 0.0000 | 0.0000 | 0.0000 |
| 8 | 0.0024 | 0.0013 | 0.0007 | 0.0003 | 0.0001 | 0.0000 | 0.0000 | 0.0000 | 0.0000 |
| 9 | 0.0163 | 0.0103 | 0.0060 | 0.0031 | 0.0014 | 0.0005 | 0.0001 | 0.0000 | 0.0000 |
| 10 | 0.0799 | 0.0578 | 0.0392 | 0.0245 | 0.0135 | 0.0062 | 0.0020 | 0.0003 | 0.0000 |
| 11 | 0.2794 | 0.2298 | 0.1814 | 0.1354 | 0.0932 | 0.0564 | 0.0270 | 0.0072 | 0.0000 |
| 12 | 0.6617 | 0.6107 | 0.5526 | 0.4867 | 0.4118 | 0.3270 | 0.2310 | 0.1225 | 0.0000 |
| 13 | 1.0000 | 1.0000 | 1.0000 | 1.0000 | 1.0000 | 1.0000 | 1.0000 | 1.0000 | 1.0000 |

$$n = 14$$

| x | $p = 0.01$ | $p = 0.02$ | $p = 0.03$ | $p = 0.04$ | $p = 0.05$ | $p = 0.06$ | $p = 0.07$ | $p = 0.08$ | $p = 0.09$ |
|---|---|---|---|---|---|---|---|---|---|
| 0 | 0.8687 | 0.7536 | 0.6528 | 0.5647 | 0.4877 | 0.4205 | 0.3620 | 0.3112 | 0.2670 |
| 1 | 0.9916 | 0.9690 | 0.9355 | 0.8941 | 0.8470 | 0.7963 | 0.7436 | 0.6900 | 0.6368 |
| 2 | 0.9997 | 0.9975 | 0.9923 | 0.9833 | 0.9699 | 0.9522 | 0.9302 | 0.9042 | 0.8745 |
| 3 | 1.0000 | 0.9999 | 0.9994 | 0.9981 | 0.9958 | 0.9920 | 0.9864 | 0.9786 | 0.9685 |
| 4 | 1.0000 | 1.0000 | 1.0000 | 0.9998 | 0.9996 | 0.9990 | 0.9980 | 0.9965 | 0.9941 |
| 5 | 1.0000 | 1.0000 | 1.0000 | 1.0000 | 1.0000 | 0.9999 | 0.9998 | 0.9996 | 0.9992 |
| 6 | 1.0000 | 1.0000 | 1.0000 | 1.0000 | 1.0000 | 1.0000 | 1.0000 | 1.0000 | 0.9999 |

*(continued)*

| x | | | | | | | | | |
|---|---|---|---|---|---|---|---|---|---|
| 7 | 1.0000 | 1.0000 | 1.0000 | 1.0000 | 1.0000 | 1.0000 | 1.0000 | 1.0000 | 1.0000 |
| 8 | 1.0000 | 1.0000 | 1.0000 | 1.0000 | 1.0000 | 1.0000 | 1.0000 | 1.0000 | 1.0000 |
| 9 | 1.0000 | 1.0000 | 1.0000 | 1.0000 | 1.0000 | 1.0000 | 1.0000 | 1.0000 | 1.0000 |
| 10 | 1.0000 | 1.0000 | 1.0000 | 1.0000 | 1.0000 | 1.0000 | 1.0000 | 1.0000 | 1.0000 |
| 11 | 1.0000 | 1.0000 | 1.0000 | 1.0000 | 1.0000 | 1.0000 | 1.0000 | 1.0000 | 1.0000 |
| 12 | 1.0000 | 1.0000 | 1.0000 | 1.0000 | 1.0000 | 1.0000 | 1.0000 | 1.0000 | 1.0000 |
| 13 | 1.0000 | 1.0000 | 1.0000 | 1.0000 | 1.0000 | 1.0000 | 1.0000 | 1.0000 | 1.0000 |
| 14 | 1.0000 | 1.0000 | 1.0000 | 1.0000 | 1.0000 | 1.0000 | 1.0000 | 1.0000 | 1.0000 |

| x | $p = 0.10$ | $p = 0.15$ | $p = 0.20$ | $p = 0.25$ | $p = 0.30$ | $p = 0.35$ | $p = 0.40$ | $p = 0.45$ | $p = 0.50$ |
|---|---|---|---|---|---|---|---|---|---|
| 0 | 0.2288 | 0.1028 | 0.0440 | 0.0178 | 0.0068 | 0.0024 | 0.0008 | 0.0002 | 0.0001 |
| 1 | 0.5846 | 0.3567 | 0.1979 | 0.1010 | 0.0475 | 0.0205 | 0.0081 | 0.0029 | 0.0009 |
| 2 | 0.8416 | 0.6479 | 0.4481 | 0.2811 | 0.1608 | 0.0839 | 0.0398 | 0.0170 | 0.0065 |
| 3 | 0.9559 | 0.8535 | 0.6982 | 0.5213 | 0.3552 | 0.2205 | 0.1243 | 0.0632 | 0.0287 |
| 4 | 0.9908 | 0.9533 | 0.8702 | 0.7415 | 0.5842 | 0.4227 | 0.2793 | 0.1672 | 0.0898 |
| 5 | 0.9985 | 0.9885 | 0.9561 | 0.8883 | 0.7805 | 0.6405 | 0.4859 | 0.3373 | 0.2120 |
| 6 | 0.9998 | 0.9978 | 0.9884 | 0.9617 | 0.9067 | 0.8164 | 0.6925 | 0.5461 | 0.3953 |
| 7 | 1.0000 | 0.9997 | 0.9976 | 0.9897 | 0.9685 | 0.9247 | 0.8499 | 0.7414 | 0.6047 |
| 8 | 1.0000 | 1.0000 | 0.9996 | 0.9978 | 0.9917 | 0.9757 | 0.9417 | 0.8811 | 0.7880 |
| 9 | 1.0000 | 1.0000 | 1.0000 | 0.9997 | 0.9983 | 0.9940 | 0.9825 | 0.9574 | 0.9102 |
| 10 | 1.0000 | 1.0000 | 1.0000 | 1.0000 | 0.9998 | 0.9989 | 0.9961 | 0.9886 | 0.9713 |
| 11 | 1.0000 | 1.0000 | 1.0000 | 1.0000 | 1.0000 | 0.9999 | 0.9994 | 0.9978 | 0.9935 |
| 12 | 1.0000 | 1.0000 | 1.0000 | 1.0000 | 1.0000 | 1.0000 | 0.9999 | 0.9997 | 0.9991 |
| 13 | 1.0000 | 1.0000 | 1.0000 | 1.0000 | 1.0000 | 1.0000 | 1.0000 | 1.0000 | 0.9999 |
| 14 | 1.0000 | 1.0000 | 1.0000 | 1.0000 | 1.0000 | 1.0000 | 1.0000 | 1.0000 | 1.0000 |

| x | $p = 0.55$ | $p = 0.60$ | $p = 0.65$ | $p = 0.70$ | $p = 0.75$ | $p = 0.80$ | $p = 0.85$ | $p = 0.90$ | $p = 0.91$ |
|---|---|---|---|---|---|---|---|---|---|
| 0 | 0.0000 | 0.0000 | 0.0000 | 0.0000 | 0.0000 | 0.0000 | 0.0000 | 0.0000 | 0.0000 |
| 1 | 0.0003 | 0.0001 | 0.0000 | 0.0000 | 0.0000 | 0.0000 | 0.0000 | 0.0000 | 0.0000 |
| 2 | 0.0022 | 0.0006 | 0.0001 | 0.0000 | 0.0000 | 0.0000 | 0.0000 | 0.0000 | 0.0000 |
| 3 | 0.0114 | 0.0039 | 0.0011 | 0.0002 | 0.0000 | 0.0000 | 0.0000 | 0.0000 | 0.0000 |
| 4 | 0.0426 | 0.0175 | 0.0060 | 0.0017 | 0.0003 | 0.0000 | 0.0000 | 0.0000 | 0.0000 |
| 5 | 0.1189 | 0.0583 | 0.0243 | 0.0083 | 0.0022 | 0.0004 | 0.0000 | 0.0000 | 0.0000 |
| 6 | 0.2586 | 0.1501 | 0.0753 | 0.0315 | 0.0103 | 0.0024 | 0.0003 | 0.0000 | 0.0000 |
| 7 | 0.4539 | 0.3075 | 0.1836 | 0.0933 | 0.0383 | 0.0116 | 0.0022 | 0.0002 | 0.0001 |
| 8 | 0.6627 | 0.5141 | 0.3595 | 0.2195 | 0.1117 | 0.0439 | 0.0115 | 0.0015 | 0.0008 |
| 9 | 0.8328 | 0.7207 | 0.5773 | 0.4158 | 0.2585 | 0.1298 | 0.0467 | 0.0092 | 0.0059 |
| 10 | 0.9368 | 0.8757 | 0.7795 | 0.6448 | 0.4787 | 0.3018 | 0.1465 | 0.0441 | 0.0315 |
| 11 | 0.9830 | 0.9602 | 0.9161 | 0.8392 | 0.7189 | 0.5519 | 0.3521 | 0.1584 | 0.1255 |
| 12 | 0.9971 | 0.9919 | 0.9795 | 0.9525 | 0.8990 | 0.8021 | 0.6433 | 0.4154 | 0.3632 |
| 13 | 0.9998 | 0.9992 | 0.9976 | 0.9932 | 0.9822 | 0.9560 | 0.8972 | 0.7712 | 0.7330 |
| 14 | 1.0000 | 1.0000 | 1.0000 | 1.0000 | 1.0000 | 1.0000 | 1.0000 | 1.0000 | 1.0000 |

| x | $p = 0.92$ | $p = 0.93$ | $p = 0.94$ | $p = 0.95$ | $p = 0.96$ | $p = 0.97$ | $p = 0.98$ | $p = 0.99$ | $p = 1.00$ |
|---|---|---|---|---|---|---|---|---|---|
| 0 | 0.0000 | 0.0000 | 0.0000 | 0.0000 | 0.0000 | 0.0000 | 0.0000 | 0.0000 | 0.0000 |
| 1 | 0.0000 | 0.0000 | 0.0000 | 0.0000 | 0.0000 | 0.0000 | 0.0000 | 0.0000 | 0.0000 |
| 2 | 0.0000 | 0.0000 | 0.0000 | 0.0000 | 0.0000 | 0.0000 | 0.0000 | 0.0000 | 0.0000 |
| 3 | 0.0000 | 0.0000 | 0.0000 | 0.0000 | 0.0000 | 0.0000 | 0.0000 | 0.0000 | 0.0000 |
| 4 | 0.0000 | 0.0000 | 0.0000 | 0.0000 | 0.0000 | 0.0000 | 0.0000 | 0.0000 | 0.0000 |
| 5 | 0.0000 | 0.0000 | 0.0000 | 0.0000 | 0.0000 | 0.0000 | 0.0000 | 0.0000 | 0.0000 |
| 6 | 0.0000 | 0.0000 | 0.0000 | 0.0000 | 0.0000 | 0.0000 | 0.0000 | 0.0000 | 0.0000 |
| 7 | 0.0000 | 0.0000 | 0.0000 | 0.0000 | 0.0000 | 0.0000 | 0.0000 | 0.0000 | 0.0000 |
| 8 | 0.0004 | 0.0002 | 0.0001 | 0.0000 | 0.0000 | 0.0000 | 0.0000 | 0.0000 | 0.0000 |
| 9 | 0.0035 | 0.0020 | 0.0010 | 0.0004 | 0.0002 | 0.0000 | 0.0000 | 0.0000 | 0.0000 |
| 10 | 0.0214 | 0.0136 | 0.0080 | 0.0042 | 0.0019 | 0.0006 | 0.0001 | 0.0000 | 0.0000 |
| 11 | 0.0958 | 0.0698 | 0.0478 | 0.0301 | 0.0167 | 0.0077 | 0.0025 | 0.0003 | 0.0000 |
| 12 | 0.3100 | 0.2564 | 0.2037 | 0.1530 | 0.1059 | 0.0645 | 0.0310 | 0.0084 | 0.0000 |
| 13 | 0.6888 | 0.6380 | 0.5795 | 0.5123 | 0.4353 | 0.3472 | 0.2464 | 0.1313 | 0.0000 |
| 14 | 1.0000 | 1.0000 | 1.0000 | 1.0000 | 1.0000 | 1.0000 | 1.0000 | 1.0000 | 1.0000 |

$$n = 15$$

| x | $p = 0.01$ | $p = 0.02$ | $p = 0.03$ | $p = 0.04$ | $p = 0.05$ | $p = 0.06$ | $p = 0.07$ | $p = 0.08$ | $p = 0.09$ |
|---|---|---|---|---|---|---|---|---|---|
| 0 | 0.8601 | 0.7386 | 0.6333 | 0.5421 | 0.4633 | 0.3953 | 0.3367 | 0.2863 | 0.2430 |
| 1 | 0.9904 | 0.9647 | 0.9270 | 0.8809 | 0.8290 | 0.7738 | 0.7168 | 0.6597 | 0.6035 |
| 2 | 0.9996 | 0.9970 | 0.9906 | 0.9797 | 0.9638 | 0.9429 | 0.9171 | 0.8870 | 0.8531 |
| 3 | 1.0000 | 0.9998 | 0.9992 | 0.9976 | 0.9945 | 0.9896 | 0.9825 | 0.9727 | 0.9601 |

| | | | | | | | | |
|---|---|---|---|---|---|---|---|---|
| 4 | 1.0000 | 1.0000 | 0.9999 | 0.9998 | 0.9994 | 0.9986 | 0.9972 | 0.9950 | 0.9918 |
| 5 | 1.0000 | 1.0000 | 1.0000 | 1.0000 | 0.9999 | 0.9999 | 0.9997 | 0.9993 | 0.9987 |
| 6 | 1.0000 | 1.0000 | 1.0000 | 1.0000 | 1.0000 | 1.0000 | 1.0000 | 0.9999 | 0.9998 |
| 7 | 1.0000 | 1.0000 | 1.0000 | 1.0000 | 1.0000 | 1.0000 | 1.0000 | 1.0000 | 1.0000 |
| 8 | 1.0000 | 1.0000 | 1.0000 | 1.0000 | 1.0000 | 1.0000 | 1.0000 | 1.0000 | 1.0000 |
| 9 | 1.0000 | 1.0000 | 1.0000 | 1.0000 | 1.0000 | 1.0000 | 1.0000 | 1.0000 | 1.0000 |
| 10 | 1.0000 | 1.0000 | 1.0000 | 1.0000 | 1.0000 | 1.0000 | 1.0000 | 1.0000 | 1.0000 |
| 11 | 1.0000 | 1.0000 | 1.0000 | 1.0000 | 1.0000 | 1.0000 | 1.0000 | 1.0000 | 1.0000 |
| 12 | 1.0000 | 1.0000 | 1.0000 | 1.0000 | 1.0000 | 1.0000 | 1.0000 | 1.0000 | 1.0000 |
| 13 | 1.0000 | 1.0000 | 1.0000 | 1.0000 | 1.0000 | 1.0000 | 1.0000 | 1.0000 | 1.0000 |
| 14 | 1.0000 | 1.0000 | 1.0000 | 1.0000 | 1.0000 | 1.0000 | 1.0000 | 1.0000 | 1.0000 |
| 15 | 1.0000 | 1.0000 | 1.0000 | 1.0000 | 1.0000 | 1.0000 | 1.0000 | 1.0000 | 1.0000 |

| $x$ | $p = 0.10$ | $p = 0.15$ | $p = 0.20$ | $p = 0.25$ | $p = 0.30$ | $p = 0.35$ | $p = 0.40$ | $p = 0.45$ | $p = 0.50$ |
|---|---|---|---|---|---|---|---|---|---|
| 0 | 0.2059 | 0.0874 | 0.0352 | 0.0134 | 0.0047 | 0.0016 | 0.0005 | 0.0001 | 0.0000 |
| 1 | 0.5490 | 0.3186 | 0.1671 | 0.0802 | 0.0353 | 0.0142 | 0.0052 | 0.0017 | 0.0005 |
| 2 | 0.8159 | 0.6042 | 0.3980 | 0.2361 | 0.1268 | 0.0617 | 0.0271 | 0.0107 | 0.0037 |
| 3 | 0.9444 | 0.8227 | 0.6482 | 0.4613 | 0.2969 | 0.1727 | 0.0905 | 0.0424 | 0.0176 |
| 4 | 0.9873 | 0.9383 | 0.8358 | 0.6865 | 0.5155 | 0.3519 | 0.2173 | 0.1204 | 0.0592 |
| 5 | 0.9978 | 0.9832 | 0.9389 | 0.8516 | 0.7216 | 0.5643 | 0.4032 | 0.2608 | 0.1509 |
| 6 | 0.9997 | 0.9964 | 0.9819 | 0.9434 | 0.8689 | 0.7548 | 0.6098 | 0.4522 | 0.3036 |
| 7 | 1.0000 | 0.9994 | 0.9958 | 0.9827 | 0.9500 | 0.8868 | 0.7869 | 0.6535 | 0.5000 |
| 8 | 1.0000 | 0.9999 | 0.9992 | 0.9958 | 0.9848 | 0.9578 | 0.9050 | 0.8182 | 0.6964 |
| 9 | 1.0000 | 1.0000 | 0.9999 | 0.9992 | 0.9963 | 0.9876 | 0.9662 | 0.9231 | 0.8491 |
| 10 | 1.0000 | 1.0000 | 1.0000 | 0.9999 | 0.9993 | 0.9972 | 0.9907 | 0.9745 | 0.9408 |
| 11 | 1.0000 | 1.0000 | 1.0000 | 1.0000 | 0.9999 | 0.9995 | 0.9981 | 0.9937 | 0.9824 |
| 12 | 1.0000 | 1.0000 | 1.0000 | 1.0000 | 1.0000 | 0.9999 | 0.9997 | 0.9989 | 0.9963 |
| 13 | 1.0000 | 1.0000 | 1.0000 | 1.0000 | 1.0000 | 1.0000 | 1.0000 | 0.9999 | 0.9995 |
| 14 | 1.0000 | 1.0000 | 1.0000 | 1.0000 | 1.0000 | 1.0000 | 1.0000 | 1.0000 | 1.0000 |
| 15 | 1.0000 | 1.0000 | 1.0000 | 1.0000 | 1.0000 | 1.0000 | 1.0000 | 1.0000 | 1.0000 |

| $x$ | $p = 0.55$ | $p = 0.60$ | $p = 0.65$ | $p = 0.70$ | $p = 0.75$ | $p = 0.80$ | $p = 0.85$ | $p = 0.90$ | $p = 0.91$ |
|---|---|---|---|---|---|---|---|---|---|
| 0 | 0.0000 | 0.0000 | 0.0000 | 0.0000 | 0.0000 | 0.0000 | 0.0000 | 0.0000 | 0.0000 |
| 1 | 0.0001 | 0.0000 | 0.0000 | 0.0000 | 0.0000 | 0.0000 | 0.0000 | 0.0000 | 0.0000 |
| 2 | 0.0011 | 0.0003 | 0.0001 | 0.0000 | 0.0000 | 0.0000 | 0.0000 | 0.0000 | 0.0000 |
| 3 | 0.0063 | 0.0019 | 0.0005 | 0.0001 | 0.0000 | 0.0000 | 0.0000 | 0.0000 | 0.0000 |
| 4 | 0.0255 | 0.0093 | 0.0028 | 0.0007 | 0.0001 | 0.0000 | 0.0000 | 0.0000 | 0.0000 |
| 5 | 0.0769 | 0.0338 | 0.0124 | 0.0037 | 0.0008 | 0.0001 | 0.0000 | 0.0000 | 0.0000 |
| 6 | 0.1818 | 0.0950 | 0.0422 | 0.0152 | 0.0042 | 0.0008 | 0.0001 | 0.0000 | 0.0000 |
| 7 | 0.3465 | 0.2131 | 0.1132 | 0.0500 | 0.0173 | 0.0042 | 0.0006 | 0.0000 | 0.0000 |
| 8 | 0.5478 | 0.3902 | 0.2452 | 0.1311 | 0.0566 | 0.0181 | 0.0036 | 0.0003 | 0.0002 |
| 9 | 0.7392 | 0.5968 | 0.4357 | 0.2784 | 0.1484 | 0.0611 | 0.0168 | 0.0022 | 0.0013 |
| 10 | 0.8796 | 0.7827 | 0.6481 | 0.4845 | 0.3135 | 0.1642 | 0.0617 | 0.0127 | 0.0082 |
| 11 | 0.9576 | 0.9095 | 0.8273 | 0.7031 | 0.5387 | 0.3518 | 0.1773 | 0.0556 | 0.0399 |
| 12 | 0.9893 | 0.9729 | 0.9383 | 0.8732 | 0.7639 | 0.6020 | 0.3958 | 0.1841 | 0.1469 |
| 13 | 0.9983 | 0.9948 | 0.9858 | 0.9647 | 0.9198 | 0.8329 | 0.6814 | 0.4510 | 0.3965 |
| 14 | 0.9999 | 0.9995 | 0.9984 | 0.9953 | 0.9866 | 0.9648 | 0.9126 | 0.7941 | 0.7570 |
| 15 | 1.0000 | 1.0000 | 1.0000 | 1.0000 | 1.0000 | 1.0000 | 1.0000 | 1.0000 | 1.0000 |

| $x$ | $p = 0.92$ | $p = 0.93$ | $p = 0.94$ | $p = 0.95$ | $p = 0.96$ | $p = 0.97$ | $p = 0.98$ | $p = 0.99$ | $p = 1.00$ |
|---|---|---|---|---|---|---|---|---|---|
| 0 | 0.0000 | 0.0000 | 0.0000 | 0.0000 | 0.0000 | 0.0000 | 0.0000 | 0.0000 | 0.0000 |
| 1 | 0.0000 | 0.0000 | 0.0000 | 0.0000 | 0.0000 | 0.0000 | 0.0000 | 0.0000 | 0.0000 |
| 2 | 0.0000 | 0.0000 | 0.0000 | 0.0000 | 0.0000 | 0.0000 | 0.0000 | 0.0000 | 0.0000 |
| 3 | 0.0000 | 0.0000 | 0.0000 | 0.0000 | 0.0000 | 0.0000 | 0.0000 | 0.0000 | 0.0000 |
| 4 | 0.0000 | 0.0000 | 0.0000 | 0.0000 | 0.0000 | 0.0000 | 0.0000 | 0.0000 | 0.0000 |
| 5 | 0.0000 | 0.0000 | 0.0000 | 0.0000 | 0.0000 | 0.0000 | 0.0000 | 0.0000 | 0.0000 |
| 6 | 0.0000 | 0.0000 | 0.0000 | 0.0000 | 0.0000 | 0.0000 | 0.0000 | 0.0000 | 0.0000 |
| 7 | 0.0000 | 0.0000 | 0.0000 | 0.0000 | 0.0000 | 0.0000 | 0.0000 | 0.0000 | 0.0000 |
| 8 | 0.0001 | 0.0000 | 0.0000 | 0.0000 | 0.0000 | 0.0000 | 0.0000 | 0.0000 | 0.0000 |
| 9 | 0.0007 | 0.0003 | 0.0001 | 0.0001 | 0.0000 | 0.0000 | 0.0000 | 0.0000 | 0.0000 |
| 10 | 0.0050 | 0.0028 | 0.0014 | 0.0006 | 0.0002 | 0.0001 | 0.0000 | 0.0000 | 0.0000 |
| 11 | 0.0273 | 0.0175 | 0.0104 | 0.0055 | 0.0024 | 0.0008 | 0.0002 | 0.0000 | 0.0000 |
| 12 | 0.1130 | 0.0829 | 0.0571 | 0.0362 | 0.0203 | 0.0094 | 0.0030 | 0.0004 | 0.0000 |
| 13 | 0.3403 | 0.2832 | 0.2262 | 0.1710 | 0.1191 | 0.0730 | 0.0353 | 0.0096 | 0.0000 |
| 14 | 0.7137 | 0.6633 | 0.6047 | 0.5367 | 0.4579 | 0.3667 | 0.2614 | 0.1399 | 0.0000 |
| 15 | 1.0000 | 1.0000 | 1.0000 | 1.0000 | 1.0000 | 1.0000 | 1.0000 | 1.0000 | 1.0000 |

*(continued)*

$n = 20$

| x | p = 0.01 | p = 0.02 | p = 0.03 | p = 0.04 | p = 0.05 | p = 0.06 | p = 0.07 | p = 0.08 | p = 0.09 |
|---|---|---|---|---|---|---|---|---|---|
| 0 | 0.8179 | 0.6676 | 0.5438 | 0.4420 | 0.3585 | 0.2901 | 0.2342 | 0.1887 | 0.1516 |
| 1 | 0.9831 | 0.9401 | 0.8802 | 0.8103 | 0.7358 | 0.6605 | 0.5869 | 0.5169 | 0.4516 |
| 2 | 0.9990 | 0.9929 | 0.9790 | 0.9561 | 0.9245 | 0.8850 | 0.8390 | 0.7879 | 0.7334 |
| 3 | 1.0000 | 0.9994 | 0.9973 | 0.9926 | 0.9841 | 0.9710 | 0.9529 | 0.9294 | 0.9007 |
| 4 | 1.0000 | 1.0000 | 0.9997 | 0.9990 | 0.9974 | 0.9944 | 0.9893 | 0.9817 | 0.9710 |
| 5 | 1.0000 | 1.0000 | 1.0000 | 0.9999 | 0.9997 | 0.9991 | 0.9981 | 0.9962 | 0.9932 |
| 6 | 1.0000 | 1.0000 | 1.0000 | 1.0000 | 1.0000 | 0.9999 | 0.9997 | 0.9994 | 0.9987 |
| 7 | 1.0000 | 1.0000 | 1.0000 | 1.0000 | 1.0000 | 1.0000 | 1.0000 | 0.9999 | 0.9998 |
| 8 | 1.0000 | 1.0000 | 1.0000 | 1.0000 | 1.0000 | 1.0000 | 1.0000 | 1.0000 | 1.0000 |
| 9 | 1.0000 | 1.0000 | 1.0000 | 1.0000 | 1.0000 | 1.0000 | 1.0000 | 1.0000 | 1.0000 |
| 10 | 1.0000 | 1.0000 | 1.0000 | 1.0000 | 1.0000 | 1.0000 | 1.0000 | 1.0000 | 1.0000 |
| 11 | 1.0000 | 1.0000 | 1.0000 | 1.0000 | 1.0000 | 1.0000 | 1.0000 | 1.0000 | 1.0000 |
| 12 | 1.0000 | 1.0000 | 1.0000 | 1.0000 | 1.0000 | 1.0000 | 1.0000 | 1.0000 | 1.0000 |
| 13 | 1.0000 | 1.0000 | 1.0000 | 1.0000 | 1.0000 | 1.0000 | 1.0000 | 1.0000 | 1.0000 |
| 14 | 1.0000 | 1.0000 | 1.0000 | 1.0000 | 1.0000 | 1.0000 | 1.0000 | 1.0000 | 1.0000 |
| 15 | 1.0000 | 1.0000 | 1.0000 | 1.0000 | 1.0000 | 1.0000 | 1.0000 | 1.0000 | 1.0000 |
| 16 | 1.0000 | 1.0000 | 1.0000 | 1.0000 | 1.0000 | 1.0000 | 1.0000 | 1.0000 | 1.0000 |
| 17 | 1.0000 | 1.0000 | 1.0000 | 1.0000 | 1.0000 | 1.0000 | 1.0000 | 1.0000 | 1.0000 |
| 18 | 1.0000 | 1.0000 | 1.0000 | 1.0000 | 1.0000 | 1.0000 | 1.0000 | 1.0000 | 1.0000 |
| 19 | 1.0000 | 1.0000 | 1.0000 | 1.0000 | 1.0000 | 1.0000 | 1.0000 | 1.0000 | 1.0000 |
| 20 | 1.0000 | 1.0000 | 1.0000 | 1.0000 | 1.0000 | 1.0000 | 1.0000 | 1.0000 | 1.0000 |

| x | p = 0.10 | p = 0.15 | p = 0.20 | p = 0.25 | p = 0.30 | p = 0.35 | p = 0.40 | p = 0.45 | p = 0.50 |
|---|---|---|---|---|---|---|---|---|---|
| 0 | 0.1216 | 0.0388 | 0.0115 | 0.0032 | 0.0008 | 0.0002 | 0.0000 | 0.0000 | 0.0000 |
| 1 | 0.3917 | 0.1756 | 0.0692 | 0.0243 | 0.0076 | 0.0021 | 0.0005 | 0.0001 | 0.0000 |
| 2 | 0.6769 | 0.4049 | 0.2061 | 0.0913 | 0.0355 | 0.0121 | 0.0036 | 0.0009 | 0.0002 |
| 3 | 0.8670 | 0.6477 | 0.4114 | 0.2252 | 0.1071 | 0.0444 | 0.0160 | 0.0049 | 0.0013 |
| 4 | 0.9568 | 0.8298 | 0.6296 | 0.4148 | 0.2375 | 0.1182 | 0.0510 | 0.0189 | 0.0059 |
| 5 | 0.9887 | 0.9327 | 0.8042 | 0.6172 | 0.4164 | 0.2454 | 0.1256 | 0.0553 | 0.0207 |
| 6 | 0.9976 | 0.9781 | 0.9133 | 0.7858 | 0.6080 | 0.4166 | 0.2500 | 0.1299 | 0.0577 |
| 7 | 0.9996 | 0.9941 | 0.9679 | 0.8982 | 0.7723 | 0.6010 | 0.4159 | 0.2520 | 0.1316 |
| 8 | 0.9999 | 0.9987 | 0.9900 | 0.9591 | 0.8867 | 0.7624 | 0.5956 | 0.4143 | 0.2517 |
| 9 | 1.0000 | 0.9998 | 0.9974 | 0.9861 | 0.9520 | 0.8782 | 0.7553 | 0.5914 | 0.4119 |
| 10 | 1.0000 | 1.0000 | 0.9994 | 0.9961 | 0.9829 | 0.9468 | 0.8725 | 0.7507 | 0.5881 |
| 11 | 1.0000 | 1.0000 | 0.9999 | 0.9991 | 0.9949 | 0.9804 | 0.9435 | 0.8692 | 0.7483 |
| 12 | 1.0000 | 1.0000 | 1.0000 | 0.9998 | 0.9987 | 0.9940 | 0.9790 | 0.9420 | 0.8684 |
| 13 | 1.0000 | 1.0000 | 1.0000 | 1.0000 | 0.9997 | 0.9985 | 0.9935 | 0.9786 | 0.9423 |
| 14 | 1.0000 | 1.0000 | 1.0000 | 1.0000 | 1.0000 | 0.9997 | 0.9984 | 0.9936 | 0.9793 |
| 15 | 1.0000 | 1.0000 | 1.0000 | 1.0000 | 1.0000 | 1.0000 | 0.9997 | 0.9985 | 0.9941 |
| 16 | 1.0000 | 1.0000 | 1.0000 | 1.0000 | 1.0000 | 1.0000 | 1.0000 | 0.9997 | 0.9987 |
| 17 | 1.0000 | 1.0000 | 1.0000 | 1.0000 | 1.0000 | 1.0000 | 1.0000 | 1.0000 | 0.9998 |
| 18 | 1.0000 | 1.0000 | 1.0000 | 1.0000 | 1.0000 | 1.0000 | 1.0000 | 1.0000 | 1.0000 |
| 19 | 1.0000 | 1.0000 | 1.0000 | 1.0000 | 1.0000 | 1.0000 | 1.0000 | 1.0000 | 1.0000 |
| 20 | 1.0000 | 1.0000 | 1.0000 | 1.0000 | 1.0000 | 1.0000 | 1.0000 | 1.0000 | 1.0000 |

| x | p = 0.55 | p = 0.60 | p = 0.65 | p = 0.70 | p = 0.75 | p = 0.80 | p = 0.85 | p = 0.90 | p = 0.91 |
|---|---|---|---|---|---|---|---|---|---|
| 0 | 0.0000 | 0.0000 | 0.0000 | 0.0000 | 0.0000 | 0.0000 | 0.0000 | 0.0000 | 0.0000 |
| 1 | 0.0000 | 0.0000 | 0.0000 | 0.0000 | 0.0000 | 0.0000 | 0.0000 | 0.0000 | 0.0000 |
| 2 | 0.0000 | 0.0000 | 0.0000 | 0.0000 | 0.0000 | 0.0000 | 0.0000 | 0.0000 | 0.0000 |
| 3 | 0.0003 | 0.0000 | 0.0000 | 0.0000 | 0.0000 | 0.0000 | 0.0000 | 0.0000 | 0.0000 |
| 4 | 0.0015 | 0.0003 | 0.0000 | 0.0000 | 0.0000 | 0.0000 | 0.0000 | 0.0000 | 0.0000 |
| 5 | 0.0064 | 0.0016 | 0.0003 | 0.0000 | 0.0000 | 0.0000 | 0.0000 | 0.0000 | 0.0000 |
| 6 | 0.0214 | 0.0065 | 0.0015 | 0.0003 | 0.0000 | 0.0000 | 0.0000 | 0.0000 | 0.0000 |
| 7 | 0.0580 | 0.0210 | 0.0060 | 0.0013 | 0.0002 | 0.0000 | 0.0000 | 0.0000 | 0.0000 |
| 8 | 0.1308 | 0.0565 | 0.0196 | 0.0051 | 0.0009 | 0.0001 | 0.0000 | 0.0000 | 0.0000 |
| 9 | 0.2493 | 0.1275 | 0.0532 | 0.0171 | 0.0039 | 0.0006 | 0.0000 | 0.0000 | 0.0000 |
| 10 | 0.4086 | 0.2447 | 0.1218 | 0.0480 | 0.0139 | 0.0026 | 0.0002 | 0.0000 | 0.0000 |
| 11 | 0.5857 | 0.4044 | 0.2376 | 0.1133 | 0.0409 | 0.0100 | 0.0013 | 0.0001 | 0.0000 |
| 12 | 0.7480 | 0.5841 | 0.3990 | 0.2277 | 0.1018 | 0.0321 | 0.0059 | 0.0004 | 0.0002 |
| 13 | 0.8701 | 0.7500 | 0.5834 | 0.3920 | 0.2142 | 0.0867 | 0.0219 | 0.0024 | 0.0013 |
| 14 | 0.9447 | 0.8744 | 0.7546 | 0.5836 | 0.3828 | 0.1958 | 0.0673 | 0.0113 | 0.0068 |
| 15 | 0.9811 | 0.9490 | 0.8818 | 0.7625 | 0.5852 | 0.3704 | 0.1702 | 0.0432 | 0.0290 |
| 16 | 0.9951 | 0.9840 | 0.9556 | 0.8929 | 0.7748 | 0.5886 | 0.3523 | 0.1330 | 0.0993 |
| 17 | 0.9991 | 0.9964 | 0.9879 | 0.9645 | 0.9087 | 0.7939 | 0.5951 | 0.3231 | 0.2666 |
| 18 | 0.9999 | 0.9995 | 0.9979 | 0.9924 | 0.9757 | 0.9308 | 0.8244 | 0.6083 | 0.5484 |
| 19 | 1.0000 | 1.0000 | 0.9998 | 0.9992 | 0.9968 | 0.9885 | 0.9612 | 0.8784 | 0.8484 |
| 20 | 1.0000 | 1.0000 | 1.0000 | 1.0000 | 1.0000 | 1.0000 | 1.0000 | 1.0000 | 1.0000 |

| x | p = 0.92 | p = 0.93 | p = 0.94 | p = 0.95 | p = 0.96 | p = 0.97 | p = 0.98 | p = 0.99 | p = 1.00 |
|---|---|---|---|---|---|---|---|---|---|
| 0 | 0.0000 | 0.0000 | 0.0000 | 0.0000 | 0.0000 | 0.0000 | 0.0000 | 0.0000 | 0.0000 |
| 1 | 0.0000 | 0.0000 | 0.0000 | 0.0000 | 0.0000 | 0.0000 | 0.0000 | 0.0000 | 0.0000 |
| 2 | 0.0000 | 0.0000 | 0.0000 | 0.0000 | 0.0000 | 0.0000 | 0.0000 | 0.0000 | 0.0000 |
| 3 | 0.0000 | 0.0000 | 0.0000 | 0.0000 | 0.0000 | 0.0000 | 0.0000 | 0.0000 | 0.0000 |
| 4 | 0.0000 | 0.0000 | 0.0000 | 0.0000 | 0.0000 | 0.0000 | 0.0000 | 0.0000 | 0.0000 |
| 5 | 0.0000 | 0.0000 | 0.0000 | 0.0000 | 0.0000 | 0.0000 | 0.0000 | 0.0000 | 0.0000 |
| 6 | 0.0000 | 0.0000 | 0.0000 | 0.0000 | 0.0000 | 0.0000 | 0.0000 | 0.0000 | 0.0000 |
| 7 | 0.0000 | 0.0000 | 0.0000 | 0.0000 | 0.0000 | 0.0000 | 0.0000 | 0.0000 | 0.0000 |
| 8 | 0.0000 | 0.0000 | 0.0000 | 0.0000 | 0.0000 | 0.0000 | 0.0000 | 0.0000 | 0.0000 |
| 9 | 0.0000 | 0.0000 | 0.0000 | 0.0000 | 0.0000 | 0.0000 | 0.0000 | 0.0000 | 0.0000 |
| 10 | 0.0000 | 0.0000 | 0.0000 | 0.0000 | 0.0000 | 0.0000 | 0.0000 | 0.0000 | 0.0000 |
| 11 | 0.0000 | 0.0000 | 0.0000 | 0.0000 | 0.0000 | 0.0000 | 0.0000 | 0.0000 | 0.0000 |
| 12 | 0.0001 | 0.0000 | 0.0000 | 0.0000 | 0.0000 | 0.0000 | 0.0000 | 0.0000 | 0.0000 |
| 13 | 0.0006 | 0.0003 | 0.0001 | 0.0000 | 0.0000 | 0.0000 | 0.0000 | 0.0000 | 0.0000 |
| 14 | 0.0038 | 0.0019 | 0.0009 | 0.0003 | 0.0001 | 0.0000 | 0.0000 | 0.0000 | 0.0000 |
| 15 | 0.0183 | 0.0107 | 0.0056 | 0.0026 | 0.0010 | 0.0003 | 0.0000 | 0.0000 | 0.0000 |
| 16 | 0.0706 | 0.0471 | 0.0290 | 0.0159 | 0.0074 | 0.0027 | 0.0006 | 0.0000 | 0.0000 |
| 17 | 0.2121 | 0.1610 | 0.1150 | 0.0755 | 0.0439 | 0.0210 | 0.0071 | 0.0010 | 0.0000 |
| 18 | 0.4831 | 0.4131 | 0.3395 | 0.2642 | 0.1897 | 0.1198 | 0.0599 | 0.0169 | 0.0000 |
| 19 | 0.8113 | 0.7658 | 0.7099 | 0.6415 | 0.5580 | 0.4562 | 0.3324 | 0.1821 | 0.0000 |
| 20 | 1.0000 | 1.0000 | 1.0000 | 1.0000 | 1.0000 | 1.0000 | 1.0000 | 1.0000 | 1.0000 |

### n = 25

| x | p = 0.01 | p = 0.02 | p = 0.03 | p = 0.04 | p = 0.05 | p = 0.06 | p = 0.07 | p = 0.08 | p = 0.09 |
|---|---|---|---|---|---|---|---|---|---|
| 0 | 0.7778 | 0.6035 | 0.4670 | 0.3604 | 0.2774 | 0.2129 | 0.1630 | 0.1244 | 0.0946 |
| 1 | 0.9742 | 0.9114 | 0.8280 | 0.7358 | 0.6424 | 0.5527 | 0.4696 | 0.3947 | 0.3286 |
| 2 | 0.9980 | 0.9868 | 0.9620 | 0.9235 | 0.8729 | 0.8129 | 0.7466 | 0.6768 | 0.6063 |
| 3 | 0.9999 | 0.9986 | 0.9938 | 0.9835 | 0.9659 | 0.9402 | 0.9064 | 0.8649 | 0.8169 |
| 4 | 1.0000 | 0.9999 | 0.9992 | 0.9972 | 0.9928 | 0.9850 | 0.9726 | 0.9549 | 0.9314 |
| 5 | 1.0000 | 1.0000 | 0.9999 | 0.9996 | 0.9988 | 0.9969 | 0.9935 | 0.9877 | 0.9790 |
| 6 | 1.0000 | 1.0000 | 1.0000 | 1.0000 | 0.9998 | 0.9995 | 0.9987 | 0.9972 | 0.9946 |
| 7 | 1.0000 | 1.0000 | 1.0000 | 1.0000 | 1.0000 | 0.9999 | 0.9998 | 0.9995 | 0.9989 |
| 8 | 1.0000 | 1.0000 | 1.0000 | 1.0000 | 1.0000 | 1.0000 | 1.0000 | 0.9999 | 0.9998 |
| 9 | 1.0000 | 1.0000 | 1.0000 | 1.0000 | 1.0000 | 1.0000 | 1.0000 | 1.0000 | 1.0000 |
| 10 | 1.0000 | 1.0000 | 1.0000 | 1.0000 | 1.0000 | 1.0000 | 1.0000 | 1.0000 | 1.0000 |
| 11 | 1.0000 | 1.0000 | 1.0000 | 1.0000 | 1.0000 | 1.0000 | 1.0000 | 1.0000 | 1.0000 |
| 12 | 1.0000 | 1.0000 | 1.0000 | 1.0000 | 1.0000 | 1.0000 | 1.0000 | 1.0000 | 1.0000 |
| 13 | 1.0000 | 1.0000 | 1.0000 | 1.0000 | 1.0000 | 1.0000 | 1.0000 | 1.0000 | 1.0000 |
| 14 | 1.0000 | 1.0000 | 1.0000 | 1.0000 | 1.0000 | 1.0000 | 1.0000 | 1.0000 | 1.0000 |
| 15 | 1.0000 | 1.0000 | 1.0000 | 1.0000 | 1.0000 | 1.0000 | 1.0000 | 1.0000 | 1.0000 |
| 16 | 1.0000 | 1.0000 | 1.0000 | 1.0000 | 1.0000 | 1.0000 | 1.0000 | 1.0000 | 1.0000 |
| 17 | 1.0000 | 1.0000 | 1.0000 | 1.0000 | 1.0000 | 1.0000 | 1.0000 | 1.0000 | 1.0000 |
| 18 | 1.0000 | 1.0000 | 1.0000 | 1.0000 | 1.0000 | 1.0000 | 1.0000 | 1.0000 | 1.0000 |
| 19 | 1.0000 | 1.0000 | 1.0000 | 1.0000 | 1.0000 | 1.0000 | 1.0000 | 1.0000 | 1.0000 |
| 20 | 1.0000 | 1.0000 | 1.0000 | 1.0000 | 1.0000 | 1.0000 | 1.0000 | 1.0000 | 1.0000 |
| 21 | 1.0000 | 1.0000 | 1.0000 | 1.0000 | 1.0000 | 1.0000 | 1.0000 | 1.0000 | 1.0000 |
| 22 | 1.0000 | 1.0000 | 1.0000 | 1.0000 | 1.0000 | 1.0000 | 1.0000 | 1.0000 | 1.0000 |
| 23 | 1.0000 | 1.0000 | 1.0000 | 1.0000 | 1.0000 | 1.0000 | 1.0000 | 1.0000 | 1.0000 |
| 24 | 1.0000 | 1.0000 | 1.0000 | 1.0000 | 1.0000 | 1.0000 | 1.0000 | 1.0000 | 1.0000 |
| 25 | 1.0000 | 1.0000 | 1.0000 | 1.0000 | 1.0000 | 1.0000 | 1.0000 | 1.0000 | 1.0000 |

| x | p = 0.10 | p = 0.15 | p = 0.20 | p = 0.25 | p = 0.30 | p = 0.35 | p = 0.40 | p = 0.45 | p = 0.50 |
|---|---|---|---|---|---|---|---|---|---|
| 0 | 0.0718 | 0.0172 | 0.0038 | 0.0008 | 0.0001 | 0.0000 | 0.0000 | 0.0000 | 0.0000 |
| 1 | 0.2712 | 0.0931 | 0.0274 | 0.0070 | 0.0016 | 0.0003 | 0.0001 | 0.0000 | 0.0000 |
| 2 | 0.5371 | 0.2537 | 0.0982 | 0.0321 | 0.0090 | 0.0021 | 0.0004 | 0.0001 | 0.0000 |
| 3 | 0.7636 | 0.4711 | 0.2340 | 0.0962 | 0.0332 | 0.0097 | 0.0024 | 0.0005 | 0.0001 |
| 4 | 0.9020 | 0.6821 | 0.4207 | 0.2137 | 0.0905 | 0.0320 | 0.0095 | 0.0023 | 0.0005 |
| 5 | 0.9666 | 0.8385 | 0.6167 | 0.3783 | 0.1935 | 0.0826 | 0.0294 | 0.0086 | 0.0020 |
| 6 | 0.9905 | 0.9305 | 0.7800 | 0.5611 | 0.3407 | 0.1734 | 0.0736 | 0.0258 | 0.0073 |
| 7 | 0.9977 | 0.9745 | 0.8909 | 0.7265 | 0.5118 | 0.3061 | 0.1536 | 0.0639 | 0.0216 |
| 8 | 0.9995 | 0.9920 | 0.9532 | 0.8506 | 0.6769 | 0.4668 | 0.2735 | 0.1340 | 0.0539 |
| 9 | 0.9999 | 0.9979 | 0.9827 | 0.9287 | 0.8106 | 0.6303 | 0.4246 | 0.2424 | 0.1148 |
| 10 | 1.0000 | 0.9995 | 0.9944 | 0.9703 | 0.9022 | 0.7712 | 0.5858 | 0.3843 | 0.2122 |
| 11 | 1.0000 | 0.9999 | 0.9985 | 0.9893 | 0.9558 | 0.8746 | 0.7323 | 0.5426 | 0.3450 |
| 12 | 1.0000 | 1.0000 | 0.9996 | 0.9966 | 0.9825 | 0.9396 | 0.8462 | 0.6937 | 0.5000 |
| 13 | 1.0000 | 1.0000 | 0.9999 | 0.9991 | 0.9940 | 0.9745 | 0.9222 | 0.8173 | 0.6550 |

(continued)

| x | | | | | | | | | |
|---|---|---|---|---|---|---|---|---|---|
| 14 | 1.0000 | 1.0000 | 1.0000 | 0.9998 | 0.9982 | 0.9907 | 0.9656 | 0.9040 | 0.7878 |
| 15 | 1.0000 | 1.0000 | 1.0000 | 1.0000 | 0.9995 | 0.9971 | 0.9868 | 0.9560 | 0.8852 |
| 16 | 1.0000 | 1.0000 | 1.0000 | 1.0000 | 0.9999 | 0.9992 | 0.9957 | 0.9826 | 0.9461 |
| 17 | 1.0000 | 1.0000 | 1.0000 | 1.0000 | 1.0000 | 0.9998 | 0.9988 | 0.9942 | 0.9784 |
| 18 | 1.0000 | 1.0000 | 1.0000 | 1.0000 | 1.0000 | 1.0000 | 0.9997 | 0.9984 | 0.9927 |
| 19 | 1.0000 | 1.0000 | 1.0000 | 1.0000 | 1.0000 | 1.0000 | 0.9999 | 0.9996 | 0.9980 |
| 20 | 1.0000 | 1.0000 | 1.0000 | 1.0000 | 1.0000 | 1.0000 | 1.0000 | 0.9999 | 0.9995 |
| 21 | 1.0000 | 1.0000 | 1.0000 | 1.0000 | 1.0000 | 1.0000 | 1.0000 | 1.0000 | 0.9999 |
| 22 | 1.0000 | 1.0000 | 1.0000 | 1.0000 | 1.0000 | 1.0000 | 1.0000 | 1.0000 | 1.0000 |
| 23 | 1.0000 | 1.0000 | 1.0000 | 1.0000 | 1.0000 | 1.0000 | 1.0000 | 1.0000 | 1.0000 |
| 24 | 1.0000 | 1.0000 | 1.0000 | 1.0000 | 1.0000 | 1.0000 | 1.0000 | 1.0000 | 1.0000 |
| 25 | 1.0000 | 1.0000 | 1.0000 | 1.0000 | 1.0000 | 1.0000 | 1.0000 | 1.0000 | 1.0000 |

| x | $p = 0.55$ | $p = 0.60$ | $p = 0.65$ | $p = 0.70$ | $p = 0.75$ | $p = 0.80$ | $p = 0.85$ | $p = 0.90$ | $p = 0.91$ |
|---|---|---|---|---|---|---|---|---|---|
| 0 | 0.0000 | 0.0000 | 0.0000 | 0.0000 | 0.0000 | 0.0000 | 0.0000 | 0.0000 | 0.0000 |
| 1 | 0.0000 | 0.0000 | 0.0000 | 0.0000 | 0.0000 | 0.0000 | 0.0000 | 0.0000 | 0.0000 |
| 2 | 0.0000 | 0.0000 | 0.0000 | 0.0000 | 0.0000 | 0.0000 | 0.0000 | 0.0000 | 0.0000 |
| 3 | 0.0000 | 0.0000 | 0.0000 | 0.0000 | 0.0000 | 0.0000 | 0.0000 | 0.0000 | 0.0000 |
| 4 | 0.0001 | 0.0000 | 0.0000 | 0.0000 | 0.0000 | 0.0000 | 0.0000 | 0.0000 | 0.0000 |
| 5 | 0.0004 | 0.0001 | 0.0000 | 0.0000 | 0.0000 | 0.0000 | 0.0000 | 0.0000 | 0.0000 |
| 6 | 0.0016 | 0.0003 | 0.0000 | 0.0000 | 0.0000 | 0.0000 | 0.0000 | 0.0000 | 0.0000 |
| 7 | 0.0058 | 0.0012 | 0.0002 | 0.0000 | 0.0000 | 0.0000 | 0.0000 | 0.0000 | 0.0000 |
| 8 | 0.0174 | 0.0043 | 0.0008 | 0.0001 | 0.0000 | 0.0000 | 0.0000 | 0.0000 | 0.0000 |
| 9 | 0.0440 | 0.0132 | 0.0029 | 0.0005 | 0.0000 | 0.0000 | 0.0000 | 0.0000 | 0.0000 |
| 10 | 0.0960 | 0.0344 | 0.0093 | 0.0018 | 0.0002 | 0.0000 | 0.0000 | 0.0000 | 0.0000 |
| 11 | 0.1827 | 0.0778 | 0.0255 | 0.0060 | 0.0009 | 0.0001 | 0.0000 | 0.0000 | 0.0000 |
| 12 | 0.3063 | 0.1538 | 0.0604 | 0.0175 | 0.0034 | 0.0004 | 0.0000 | 0.0000 | 0.0000 |
| 13 | 0.4574 | 0.2677 | 0.1254 | 0.0442 | 0.0107 | 0.0015 | 0.0001 | 0.0000 | 0.0000 |
| 14 | 0.6157 | 0.4142 | 0.2288 | 0.0978 | 0.0297 | 0.0056 | 0.0005 | 0.0000 | 0.0000 |
| 15 | 0.7576 | 0.5754 | 0.3697 | 0.1894 | 0.0713 | 0.0173 | 0.0021 | 0.0001 | 0.0000 |
| 16 | 0.8660 | 0.7265 | 0.5332 | 0.3231 | 0.1494 | 0.0468 | 0.0080 | 0.0005 | 0.0002 |
| 17 | 0.9361 | 0.8464 | 0.6939 | 0.4882 | 0.2735 | 0.1091 | 0.0255 | 0.0023 | 0.0011 |
| 18 | 0.9742 | 0.9264 | 0.8266 | 0.6593 | 0.4389 | 0.2200 | 0.0695 | 0.0095 | 0.0054 |
| 19 | 0.9914 | 0.9706 | 0.9174 | 0.8065 | 0.6217 | 0.3833 | 0.1615 | 0.0334 | 0.0210 |
| 20 | 0.9977 | 0.9905 | 0.9680 | 0.9095 | 0.7863 | 0.5793 | 0.3179 | 0.0980 | 0.0686 |
| 21 | 0.9995 | 0.9976 | 0.9903 | 0.9668 | 0.9038 | 0.7660 | 0.5289 | 0.2364 | 0.1831 |
| 22 | 0.9999 | 0.9996 | 0.9979 | 0.9910 | 0.9679 | 0.9018 | 0.7463 | 0.4629 | 0.3937 |
| 23 | 1.0000 | 0.9999 | 0.9997 | 0.9984 | 0.9930 | 0.9726 | 0.9069 | 0.7288 | 0.6714 |
| 24 | 1.0000 | 1.0000 | 1.0000 | 0.9999 | 0.9992 | 0.9962 | 0.9828 | 0.9282 | 0.9054 |
| 25 | 1.0000 | 1.0000 | 1.0000 | 1.0000 | 1.0000 | 1.0000 | 1.0000 | 1.0000 | 1.0000 |

| x | $p = 0.92$ | $p = 0.93$ | $p = 0.94$ | $p = 0.95$ | $p = 0.96$ | $p = 0.97$ | $p = 0.98$ | $p = 0.99$ | $p = 1.00$ |
|---|---|---|---|---|---|---|---|---|---|
| 0 | 0.0000 | 0.0000 | 0.0000 | 0.0000 | 0.0000 | 0.0000 | 0.0000 | 0.0000 | 0.0000 |
| 1 | 0.0000 | 0.0000 | 0.0000 | 0.0000 | 0.0000 | 0.0000 | 0.0000 | 0.0000 | 0.0000 |
| 2 | 0.0000 | 0.0000 | 0.0000 | 0.0000 | 0.0000 | 0.0000 | 0.0000 | 0.0000 | 0.0000 |
| 3 | 0.0000 | 0.0000 | 0.0000 | 0.0000 | 0.0000 | 0.0000 | 0.0000 | 0.0000 | 0.0000 |
| 4 | 0.0000 | 0.0000 | 0.0000 | 0.0000 | 0.0000 | 0.0000 | 0.0000 | 0.0000 | 0.0000 |
| 5 | 0.0000 | 0.0000 | 0.0000 | 0.0000 | 0.0000 | 0.0000 | 0.0000 | 0.0000 | 0.0000 |
| 6 | 0.0000 | 0.0000 | 0.0000 | 0.0000 | 0.0000 | 0.0000 | 0.0000 | 0.0000 | 0.0000 |
| 7 | 0.0000 | 0.0000 | 0.0000 | 0.0000 | 0.0000 | 0.0000 | 0.0000 | 0.0000 | 0.0000 |
| 8 | 0.0000 | 0.0000 | 0.0000 | 0.0000 | 0.0000 | 0.0000 | 0.0000 | 0.0000 | 0.0000 |
| 9 | 0.0000 | 0.0000 | 0.0000 | 0.0000 | 0.0000 | 0.0000 | 0.0000 | 0.0000 | 0.0000 |
| 10 | 0.0000 | 0.0000 | 0.0000 | 0.0000 | 0.0000 | 0.0000 | 0.0000 | 0.0000 | 0.0000 |
| 11 | 0.0000 | 0.0000 | 0.0000 | 0.0000 | 0.0000 | 0.0000 | 0.0000 | 0.0000 | 0.0000 |
| 12 | 0.0000 | 0.0000 | 0.0000 | 0.0000 | 0.0000 | 0.0000 | 0.0000 | 0.0000 | 0.0000 |
| 13 | 0.0000 | 0.0000 | 0.0000 | 0.0000 | 0.0000 | 0.0000 | 0.0000 | 0.0000 | 0.0000 |
| 14 | 0.0000 | 0.0000 | 0.0000 | 0.0000 | 0.0000 | 0.0000 | 0.0000 | 0.0000 | 0.0000 |
| 15 | 0.0000 | 0.0000 | 0.0000 | 0.0000 | 0.0000 | 0.0000 | 0.0000 | 0.0000 | 0.0000 |
| 16 | 0.0001 | 0.0000 | 0.0000 | 0.0000 | 0.0000 | 0.0000 | 0.0000 | 0.0000 | 0.0000 |
| 17 | 0.0005 | 0.0002 | 0.0001 | 0.0000 | 0.0000 | 0.0000 | 0.0000 | 0.0000 | 0.0000 |
| 18 | 0.0028 | 0.0013 | 0.0005 | 0.0002 | 0.0000 | 0.0000 | 0.0000 | 0.0000 | 0.0000 |
| 19 | 0.0123 | 0.0065 | 0.0031 | 0.0012 | 0.0004 | 0.0001 | 0.0000 | 0.0000 | 0.0000 |
| 20 | 0.0451 | 0.0274 | 0.0150 | 0.0072 | 0.0028 | 0.0008 | 0.0001 | 0.0000 | 0.0000 |
| 21 | 0.1351 | 0.0936 | 0.0598 | 0.0341 | 0.0165 | 0.0062 | 0.0014 | 0.0001 | 0.0000 |
| 22 | 0.3232 | 0.2534 | 0.1871 | 0.1271 | 0.0765 | 0.0380 | 0.0132 | 0.0020 | 0.0000 |
| 23 | 0.6053 | 0.5304 | 0.4473 | 0.3576 | 0.2642 | 0.1720 | 0.0886 | 0.0258 | 0.0000 |
| 24 | 0.8756 | 0.8370 | 0.7871 | 0.7226 | 0.6396 | 0.5330 | 0.3965 | 0.2222 | 0.0000 |
| 25 | 1.0000 | 1.0000 | 1.0000 | 1.0000 | 1.0000 | 1.0000 | 1.0000 | 1.0000 | 1.0000 |

## APPENDIX C

Cumulative Poisson
Probability
Distribution Table

$$P(x \le X) = \sum_{i=0}^{X} \frac{(\lambda t)^i e^{-\lambda t}}{i!}$$

$\lambda t$

| x | 0.005 | 0.01 | 0.02 | 0.03 | 0.04 | 0.05 | 0.06 | 0.07 | 0.08 | 0.09 |
|---|-------|------|------|------|------|------|------|------|------|------|
| 0 | 0.9950 | 0.9900 | 0.9802 | 0.9704 | 0.9608 | 0.9512 | 0.9418 | 0.9324 | 0.9231 | 0.9139 |
| 1 | 1.0000 | 1.0000 | 0.9998 | 0.9996 | 0.9992 | 0.9988 | 0.9983 | 0.9977 | 0.9970 | 0.9962 |
| 2 | 1.0000 | 1.0000 | 1.0000 | 1.0000 | 1.0000 | 1.0000 | 1.0000 | 0.9999 | 0.9999 | 0.9999 |
| 3 | 1.0000 | 1.0000 | 1.0000 | 1.0000 | 1.0000 | 1.0000 | 1.0000 | 1.0000 | 1.0000 | 1.0000 |

$\lambda t$

| x | 0.10 | 0.20 | 0.30 | 0.40 | 0.50 | 0.60 | 0.70 | 0.80 | 0.90 | 1.00 |
|---|------|------|------|------|------|------|------|------|------|------|
| 0 | 0.9048 | 0.8187 | 0.7408 | 0.6703 | 0.6065 | 0.5488 | 0.4966 | 0.4493 | 0.4066 | 0.3679 |
| 1 | 0.9953 | 0.9825 | 0.9631 | 0.9384 | 0.9098 | 0.8781 | 0.8442 | 0.8088 | 0.7725 | 0.7358 |
| 2 | 0.9998 | 0.9989 | 0.9964 | 0.9921 | 0.9856 | 0.9769 | 0.9659 | 0.9526 | 0.9371 | 0.9197 |
| 3 | 1.0000 | 0.9999 | 0.9997 | 0.9992 | 0.9982 | 0.9966 | 0.9942 | 0.9909 | 0.9865 | 0.9810 |
| 4 | 1.0000 | 1.0000 | 1.0000 | 0.9999 | 0.9998 | 0.9996 | 0.9992 | 0.9986 | 0.9977 | 0.9963 |
| 5 | 1.0000 | 1.0000 | 1.0000 | 1.0000 | 1.0000 | 1.0000 | 0.9999 | 0.9998 | 0.9997 | 0.9994 |
| 6 | 1.0000 | 1.0000 | 1.0000 | 1.0000 | 1.0000 | 1.0000 | 1.0000 | 1.0000 | 1.0000 | 0.9999 |
| 7 | 1.0000 | 1.0000 | 1.0000 | 1.0000 | 1.0000 | 1.0000 | 1.0000 | 1.0000 | 1.0000 | 1.0000 |

$\lambda t$

| x | 1.10 | 1.20 | 1.30 | 1.40 | 1.50 | 1.60 | 1.70 | 1.80 | 1.90 | 2.00 |
|---|------|------|------|------|------|------|------|------|------|------|
| 0 | 0.3329 | 0.3012 | 0.2725 | 0.2466 | 0.2231 | 0.2019 | 0.1827 | 0.1653 | 0.1496 | 0.1353 |
| 1 | 0.6990 | 0.6626 | 0.6268 | 0.5918 | 0.5578 | 0.5249 | 0.4932 | 0.4628 | 0.4337 | 0.4060 |
| 2 | 0.9004 | 0.8795 | 0.8571 | 0.8335 | 0.8088 | 0.7834 | 0.7572 | 0.7306 | 0.7037 | 0.6767 |
| 3 | 0.9743 | 0.9662 | 0.9569 | 0.9463 | 0.9344 | 0.9212 | 0.9068 | 0.8913 | 0.8747 | 0.8571 |
| 4 | 0.9946 | 0.9923 | 0.9893 | 0.9857 | 0.9814 | 0.9763 | 0.9704 | 0.9636 | 0.9559 | 0.9473 |
| 5 | 0.9990 | 0.9985 | 0.9978 | 0.9968 | 0.9955 | 0.9940 | 0.9920 | 0.9896 | 0.9868 | 0.9834 |
| 6 | 0.9999 | 0.9997 | 0.9996 | 0.9994 | 0.9991 | 0.9987 | 0.9981 | 0.9974 | 0.9966 | 0.9955 |
| 7 | 1.0000 | 1.0000 | 0.9999 | 0.9999 | 0.9998 | 0.9997 | 0.9996 | 0.9994 | 0.9992 | 0.9989 |
| 8 | 1.0000 | 1.0000 | 1.0000 | 1.0000 | 1.0000 | 1.0000 | 0.9999 | 0.9999 | 0.9998 | 0.9998 |
| 9 | 1.0000 | 1.0000 | 1.0000 | 1.0000 | 1.0000 | 1.0000 | 1.0000 | 1.0000 | 1.0000 | 1.0000 |

$\lambda t$

| x | 2.10 | 2.20 | 2.30 | 2.40 | 2.50 | 2.60 | 2.70 | 2.80 | 2.90 | 3.00 |
|---|------|------|------|------|------|------|------|------|------|------|
| 0 | 0.1225 | 0.1108 | 0.1003 | 0.0907 | 0.0821 | 0.0743 | 0.0672 | 0.0608 | 0.0550 | 0.0498 |
| 1 | 0.3796 | 0.3546 | 0.3309 | 0.3084 | 0.2873 | 0.2674 | 0.2487 | 0.2311 | 0.2146 | 0.1991 |
| 2 | 0.6496 | 0.6227 | 0.5960 | 0.5697 | 0.5438 | 0.5184 | 0.4936 | 0.4695 | 0.4460 | 0.4232 |
| 3 | 0.8386 | 0.8194 | 0.7993 | 0.7787 | 0.7576 | 0.7360 | 0.7141 | 0.6919 | 0.6696 | 0.6472 |
| 4 | 0.9379 | 0.9275 | 0.9162 | 0.9041 | 0.8912 | 0.8774 | 0.8629 | 0.8477 | 0.8318 | 0.8153 |
| 5 | 0.9796 | 0.9751 | 0.9700 | 0.9643 | 0.9580 | 0.9510 | 0.9433 | 0.9349 | 0.9258 | 0.9161 |
| 6 | 0.9941 | 0.9925 | 0.9906 | 0.9884 | 0.9858 | 0.9828 | 0.9794 | 0.9756 | 0.9713 | 0.9665 |
| 7 | 0.9985 | 0.9980 | 0.9974 | 0.9967 | 0.9958 | 0.9947 | 0.9934 | 0.9919 | 0.9901 | 0.9881 |
| 8 | 0.9997 | 0.9995 | 0.9994 | 0.9991 | 0.9989 | 0.9985 | 0.9981 | 0.9976 | 0.9969 | 0.9962 |
| 9 | 0.9999 | 0.9999 | 0.9999 | 0.9998 | 0.9997 | 0.9996 | 0.9995 | 0.9993 | 0.9991 | 0.9989 |
| 10 | 1.0000 | 1.0000 | 1.0000 | 1.0000 | 0.9999 | 0.9999 | 0.9999 | 0.9998 | 0.9998 | 0.9997 |
| 11 | 1.0000 | 1.0000 | 1.0000 | 1.0000 | 1.0000 | 1.0000 | 1.0000 | 1.0000 | 0.9999 | 0.9999 |
| 12 | 1.0000 | 1.0000 | 1.0000 | 1.0000 | 1.0000 | 1.0000 | 1.0000 | 1.0000 | 1.0000 | 1.0000 |

(*continued*)

λt

| x | 3.10 | 3.20 | 3.30 | 3.40 | 3.50 | 3.60 | 3.70 | 3.80 | 3.90 | 4.00 |
|---|------|------|------|------|------|------|------|------|------|------|
| 0 | 0.0450 | 0.0408 | 0.0369 | 0.0334 | 0.0302 | 0.0273 | 0.0247 | 0.0224 | 0.0202 | 0.0183 |
| 1 | 0.1847 | 0.1712 | 0.1586 | 0.1468 | 0.1359 | 0.1257 | 0.1162 | 0.1074 | 0.0992 | 0.0916 |
| 2 | 0.4012 | 0.3799 | 0.3594 | 0.3397 | 0.3208 | 0.3027 | 0.2854 | 0.2689 | 0.2531 | 0.2381 |
| 3 | 0.6248 | 0.6025 | 0.5803 | 0.5584 | 0.5366 | 0.5152 | 0.4942 | 0.4735 | 0.4532 | 0.4335 |
| 4 | 0.7982 | 0.7806 | 0.7626 | 0.7442 | 0.7254 | 0.7064 | 0.6872 | 0.6678 | 0.6484 | 0.6288 |
| 5 | 0.9057 | 0.8946 | 0.8829 | 0.8705 | 0.8576 | 0.8441 | 0.8301 | 0.8156 | 0.8006 | 0.7851 |
| 6 | 0.9612 | 0.9554 | 0.9490 | 0.9421 | 0.9347 | 0.9267 | 0.9182 | 0.9091 | 0.8995 | 0.8893 |
| 7 | 0.9858 | 0.9832 | 0.9802 | 0.9769 | 0.9733 | 0.9692 | 0.9648 | 0.9599 | 0.9546 | 0.9489 |
| 8 | 0.9953 | 0.9943 | 0.9931 | 0.9917 | 0.9901 | 0.9883 | 0.9863 | 0.9840 | 0.9815 | 0.9786 |
| 9 | 0.9986 | 0.9982 | 0.9978 | 0.9973 | 0.9967 | 0.9960 | 0.9952 | 0.9942 | 0.9931 | 0.9919 |
| 10 | 0.9996 | 0.9995 | 0.9994 | 0.9992 | 0.9990 | 0.9987 | 0.9984 | 0.9981 | 0.9977 | 0.9972 |
| 11 | 0.9999 | 0.9999 | 0.9998 | 0.9998 | 0.9997 | 0.9996 | 0.9995 | 0.9994 | 0.9993 | 0.9991 |
| 12 | 1.0000 | 1.0000 | 1.0000 | 0.9999 | 0.9999 | 0.9999 | 0.9999 | 0.9998 | 0.9998 | 0.9997 |
| 13 | 1.0000 | 1.0000 | 1.0000 | 1.0000 | 1.0000 | 1.0000 | 1.0000 | 1.0000 | 0.9999 | 0.9999 |
| 14 | 1.0000 | 1.0000 | 1.0000 | 1.0000 | 1.0000 | 1.0000 | 1.0000 | 1.0000 | 1.0000 | 1.0000 |

λt

| x | 4.10 | 4.20 | 4.30 | 4.40 | 4.50 | 4.60 | 4.70 | 4.80 | 4.90 | 5.00 |
|---|------|------|------|------|------|------|------|------|------|------|
| 0 | 0.0166 | 0.0150 | 0.0136 | 0.0123 | 0.0111 | 0.0101 | 0.0091 | 0.0082 | 0.0074 | 0.0067 |
| 1 | 0.0845 | 0.0780 | 0.0719 | 0.0663 | 0.0611 | 0.0563 | 0.0518 | 0.0477 | 0.0439 | 0.0404 |
| 2 | 0.2238 | 0.2102 | 0.1974 | 0.1851 | 0.1736 | 0.1626 | 0.1523 | 0.1425 | 0.1333 | 0.1247 |
| 3 | 0.4142 | 0.3954 | 0.3772 | 0.3594 | 0.3423 | 0.3257 | 0.3097 | 0.2942 | 0.2793 | 0.2650 |
| 4 | 0.6093 | 0.5898 | 0.5704 | 0.5512 | 0.5321 | 0.5132 | 0.4946 | 0.4763 | 0.4582 | 0.4405 |
| 5 | 0.7693 | 0.7531 | 0.7367 | 0.7199 | 0.7029 | 0.6858 | 0.6684 | 0.6510 | 0.6335 | 0.6160 |
| 6 | 0.8786 | 0.8675 | 0.8558 | 0.8436 | 0.8311 | 0.8180 | 0.8046 | 0.7908 | 0.7767 | 0.7622 |
| 7 | 0.9427 | 0.9361 | 0.9290 | 0.9214 | 0.9134 | 0.9049 | 0.8960 | 0.8867 | 0.8769 | 0.8666 |
| 8 | 0.9755 | 0.9721 | 0.9683 | 0.9642 | 0.9597 | 0.9549 | 0.9497 | 0.9442 | 0.9382 | 0.9319 |
| 9 | 0.9905 | 0.9889 | 0.9871 | 0.9851 | 0.9829 | 0.9805 | 0.9778 | 0.9749 | 0.9717 | 0.9682 |
| 10 | 0.9966 | 0.9959 | 0.9952 | 0.9943 | 0.9933 | 0.9922 | 0.9910 | 0.9896 | 0.9880 | 0.9863 |
| 11 | 0.9989 | 0.9986 | 0.9983 | 0.9980 | 0.9976 | 0.9971 | 0.9966 | 0.9960 | 0.9953 | 0.9945 |
| 12 | 0.9997 | 0.9996 | 0.9995 | 0.9993 | 0.9992 | 0.9990 | 0.9988 | 0.9986 | 0.9983 | 0.9980 |
| 13 | 0.9999 | 0.9999 | 0.9998 | 0.9998 | 0.9997 | 0.9997 | 0.9996 | 0.9995 | 0.9994 | 0.9993 |
| 14 | 1.0000 | 1.0000 | 1.0000 | 0.9999 | 0.9999 | 0.9999 | 0.9999 | 0.9999 | 0.9998 | 0.9998 |
| 15 | 1.0000 | 1.0000 | 1.0000 | 1.0000 | 1.0000 | 1.0000 | 1.0000 | 1.0000 | 0.9999 | 0.9999 |
| 16 | 1.0000 | 1.0000 | 1.0000 | 1.0000 | 1.0000 | 1.0000 | 1.0000 | 1.0000 | 1.0000 | 1.0000 |

λt

| x | 5.10 | 5.20 | 5.30 | 5.40 | 5.50 | 5.60 | 5.70 | 5.80 | 5.90 | 6.00 |
|---|------|------|------|------|------|------|------|------|------|------|
| 0 | 0.0061 | 0.0055 | 0.0050 | 0.0045 | 0.0041 | 0.0037 | 0.0033 | 0.0030 | 0.0027 | 0.0025 |
| 1 | 0.0372 | 0.0342 | 0.0314 | 0.0289 | 0.0266 | 0.0244 | 0.0224 | 0.0206 | 0.0189 | 0.0174 |
| 2 | 0.1165 | 0.1088 | 0.1016 | 0.0948 | 0.0884 | 0.0824 | 0.0768 | 0.0715 | 0.0666 | 0.0620 |
| 3 | 0.2513 | 0.2381 | 0.2254 | 0.2133 | 0.2017 | 0.1906 | 0.1800 | 0.1700 | 0.1604 | 0.1512 |
| 4 | 0.4231 | 0.4061 | 0.3895 | 0.3733 | 0.3575 | 0.3422 | 0.3272 | 0.3127 | 0.2987 | 0.2851 |
| 5 | 0.5984 | 0.5809 | 0.5635 | 0.5461 | 0.5289 | 0.5119 | 0.4950 | 0.4783 | 0.4619 | 0.4457 |
| 6 | 0.7474 | 0.7324 | 0.7171 | 0.7017 | 0.6860 | 0.6703 | 0.6544 | 0.6384 | 0.6224 | 0.6063 |
| 7 | 0.8560 | 0.8449 | 0.8335 | 0.8217 | 0.8095 | 0.7970 | 0.7841 | 0.7710 | 0.7576 | 0.7440 |
| 8 | 0.9252 | 0.9181 | 0.9106 | 0.9027 | 0.8944 | 0.8857 | 0.8766 | 0.8672 | 0.8574 | 0.8472 |
| 9 | 0.9644 | 0.9603 | 0.9559 | 0.9512 | 0.9462 | 0.9409 | 0.9352 | 0.9292 | 0.9228 | 0.9161 |
| 10 | 0.9844 | 0.9823 | 0.9800 | 0.9775 | 0.9747 | 0.9718 | 0.9686 | 0.9651 | 0.9614 | 0.9574 |
| 11 | 0.9937 | 0.9927 | 0.9916 | 0.9904 | 0.9890 | 0.9875 | 0.9859 | 0.9841 | 0.9821 | 0.9799 |
| 12 | 0.9976 | 0.9972 | 0.9967 | 0.9962 | 0.9955 | 0.9949 | 0.9941 | 0.9932 | 0.9922 | 0.9912 |
| 13 | 0.9992 | 0.9990 | 0.9988 | 0.9986 | 0.9983 | 0.9980 | 0.9977 | 0.9973 | 0.9969 | 0.9964 |
| 14 | 0.9997 | 0.9997 | 0.9996 | 0.9995 | 0.9994 | 0.9993 | 0.9991 | 0.9990 | 0.9988 | 0.9986 |
| 15 | 0.9999 | 0.9999 | 0.9999 | 0.9998 | 0.9998 | 0.9998 | 0.9997 | 0.9996 | 0.9996 | 0.9995 |
| 16 | 1.0000 | 1.0000 | 1.0000 | 0.9999 | 0.9999 | 0.9999 | 0.9999 | 0.9999 | 0.9999 | 0.9998 |
| 17 | 1.0000 | 1.0000 | 1.0000 | 1.0000 | 1.0000 | 1.0000 | 1.0000 | 1.0000 | 1.0000 | 0.9999 |
| 18 | 1.0000 | 1.0000 | 1.0000 | 1.0000 | 1.0000 | 1.0000 | 1.0000 | 1.0000 | 1.0000 | 1.0000 |

$\lambda t$

| x | 6.10 | 6.20 | 6.30 | 6.40 | 6.50 | 6.60 | 6.70 | 6.80 | 6.90 | 7.00 |
|---|------|------|------|------|------|------|------|------|------|------|
| 0 | 0.0022 | 0.0020 | 0.0018 | 0.0017 | 0.0015 | 0.0014 | 0.0012 | 0.0011 | 0.0010 | 0.0009 |
| 1 | 0.0159 | 0.0146 | 0.0134 | 0.0123 | 0.0113 | 0.0103 | 0.0095 | 0.0087 | 0.0080 | 0.0073 |
| 2 | 0.0577 | 0.0536 | 0.0498 | 0.0463 | 0.0430 | 0.0400 | 0.0371 | 0.0344 | 0.0320 | 0.0296 |
| 3 | 0.1425 | 0.1342 | 0.1264 | 0.1189 | 0.1118 | 0.1052 | 0.0988 | 0.0928 | 0.0871 | 0.0818 |
| 4 | 0.2719 | 0.2592 | 0.2469 | 0.2351 | 0.2237 | 0.2127 | 0.2022 | 0.1920 | 0.1823 | 0.1730 |
| 5 | 0.4298 | 0.4141 | 0.3988 | 0.3837 | 0.3690 | 0.3547 | 0.3406 | 0.3270 | 0.3137 | 0.3007 |
| 6 | 0.5902 | 0.5742 | 0.5582 | 0.5423 | 0.5265 | 0.5108 | 0.4953 | 0.4799 | 0.4647 | 0.4497 |
| 7 | 0.7301 | 0.7160 | 0.7017 | 0.6873 | 0.6728 | 0.6581 | 0.6433 | 0.6285 | 0.6136 | 0.5987 |
| 8 | 0.8367 | 0.8259 | 0.8148 | 0.8033 | 0.7916 | 0.7796 | 0.7673 | 0.7548 | 0.7420 | 0.7291 |
| 9 | 0.9090 | 0.9016 | 0.8939 | 0.8858 | 0.8774 | 0.8686 | 0.8596 | 0.8502 | 0.8405 | 0.8305 |
| 10 | 0.9531 | 0.9486 | 0.9437 | 0.9386 | 0.9332 | 0.9274 | 0.9214 | 0.9151 | 0.9084 | 0.9015 |
| 11 | 0.9776 | 0.9750 | 0.9723 | 0.9693 | 0.9661 | 0.9627 | 0.9591 | 0.9552 | 0.9510 | 0.9467 |
| 12 | 0.9900 | 0.9887 | 0.9873 | 0.9857 | 0.9840 | 0.9821 | 0.9801 | 0.9779 | 0.9755 | 0.9730 |
| 13 | 0.9958 | 0.9952 | 0.9945 | 0.9937 | 0.9929 | 0.9920 | 0.9909 | 0.9898 | 0.9885 | 0.9872 |
| 14 | 0.9984 | 0.9981 | 0.9978 | 0.9974 | 0.9970 | 0.9966 | 0.9961 | 0.9956 | 0.9950 | 0.9943 |
| 15 | 0.9994 | 0.9993 | 0.9992 | 0.9990 | 0.9988 | 0.9986 | 0.9984 | 0.9982 | 0.9979 | 0.9976 |
| 16 | 0.9998 | 0.9997 | 0.9997 | 0.9996 | 0.9996 | 0.9995 | 0.9994 | 0.9993 | 0.9992 | 0.9990 |
| 17 | 0.9999 | 0.9999 | 0.9999 | 0.9999 | 0.9998 | 0.9998 | 0.9998 | 0.9997 | 0.9997 | 0.9996 |
| 18 | 1.0000 | 1.0000 | 1.0000 | 1.0000 | 0.9999 | 0.9999 | 0.9999 | 0.9999 | 0.9999 | 0.9999 |
| 19 | 1.0000 | 1.0000 | 1.0000 | 1.0000 | 1.0000 | 1.0000 | 1.0000 | 1.0000 | 1.0000 | 1.0000 |
| 20 | 1.0000 | 1.0000 | 1.0000 | 1.0000 | 1.0000 | 1.0000 | 1.0000 | 1.0000 | 1.0000 | 1.0000 |

$\lambda t$

| x | 7.10 | 7.20 | 7.30 | 7.40 | 7.50 | 7.60 | 7.70 | 7.80 | 7.90 | 8.00 |
|---|------|------|------|------|------|------|------|------|------|------|
| 0 | 0.0008 | 0.0007 | 0.0007 | 0.0006 | 0.0006 | 0.0005 | 0.0005 | 0.0004 | 0.0004 | 0.0003 |
| 1 | 0.0067 | 0.0061 | 0.0056 | 0.0051 | 0.0047 | 0.0043 | 0.0039 | 0.0036 | 0.0033 | 0.0030 |
| 2 | 0.0275 | 0.0255 | 0.0236 | 0.0219 | 0.0203 | 0.0188 | 0.0174 | 0.0161 | 0.0149 | 0.0138 |
| 3 | 0.0767 | 0.0719 | 0.0674 | 0.0632 | 0.0591 | 0.0554 | 0.0518 | 0.0485 | 0.0453 | 0.0424 |
| 4 | 0.1641 | 0.1555 | 0.1473 | 0.1395 | 0.1321 | 0.1249 | 0.1181 | 0.1117 | 0.1055 | 0.0996 |
| 5 | 0.2881 | 0.2759 | 0.2640 | 0.2526 | 0.2414 | 0.2307 | 0.2203 | 0.2103 | 0.2006 | 0.1912 |
| 6 | 0.4349 | 0.4204 | 0.4060 | 0.3920 | 0.3782 | 0.3646 | 0.3514 | 0.3384 | 0.3257 | 0.3134 |
| 7 | 0.5838 | 0.5689 | 0.5541 | 0.5393 | 0.5246 | 0.5100 | 0.4956 | 0.4812 | 0.4670 | 0.4530 |
| 8 | 0.7160 | 0.7027 | 0.6892 | 0.6757 | 0.6620 | 0.6482 | 0.6343 | 0.6204 | 0.6065 | 0.5925 |
| 9 | 0.8202 | 0.8096 | 0.7988 | 0.7877 | 0.7764 | 0.7649 | 0.7531 | 0.7411 | 0.7290 | 0.7166 |
| 10 | 0.8942 | 0.8867 | 0.8788 | 0.8707 | 0.8622 | 0.8535 | 0.8445 | 0.8352 | 0.8257 | 0.8159 |
| 11 | 0.9420 | 0.9371 | 0.9319 | 0.9265 | 0.9208 | 0.9148 | 0.9085 | 0.9020 | 0.8952 | 0.8881 |
| 12 | 0.9703 | 0.9673 | 0.9642 | 0.9609 | 0.9573 | 0.9536 | 0.9496 | 0.9454 | 0.9409 | 0.9362 |
| 13 | 0.9857 | 0.9841 | 0.9824 | 0.9805 | 0.9784 | 0.9762 | 0.9739 | 0.9714 | 0.9687 | 0.9658 |
| 14 | 0.9935 | 0.9927 | 0.9918 | 0.9908 | 0.9897 | 0.9886 | 0.9873 | 0.9859 | 0.9844 | 0.9827 |
| 15 | 0.9972 | 0.9969 | 0.9964 | 0.9959 | 0.9954 | 0.9948 | 0.9941 | 0.9934 | 0.9926 | 0.9918 |
| 16 | 0.9989 | 0.9987 | 0.9985 | 0.9983 | 0.9980 | 0.9978 | 0.9974 | 0.9971 | 0.9967 | 0.9963 |
| 17 | 0.9996 | 0.9995 | 0.9994 | 0.9993 | 0.9992 | 0.9991 | 0.9989 | 0.9988 | 0.9986 | 0.9984 |
| 18 | 0.9998 | 0.9998 | 0.9998 | 0.9997 | 0.9997 | 0.9996 | 0.9996 | 0.9995 | 0.9994 | 0.9993 |
| 19 | 0.9999 | 0.9999 | 0.9999 | 0.9999 | 0.9999 | 0.9999 | 0.9998 | 0.9998 | 0.9998 | 0.9997 |
| 20 | 1.0000 | 1.0000 | 1.0000 | 1.0000 | 1.0000 | 1.0000 | 0.9999 | 0.9999 | 0.9999 | 0.9999 |
| 21 | 1.0000 | 1.0000 | 1.0000 | 1.0000 | 1.0000 | 1.0000 | 1.0000 | 1.0000 | 1.0000 | 1.0000 |

*(continued)*

|   | $\lambda t$ | | | | | | | | | |
|---|---|---|---|---|---|---|---|---|---|---|
| $x$ | 8.10 | 8.20 | 8.30 | 8.40 | 8.50 | 8.60 | 8.70 | 8.80 | 8.90 | 9.00 |
| 0 | 0.0003 | 0.0003 | 0.0002 | 0.0002 | 0.0002 | 0.0002 | 0.0002 | 0.0002 | 0.0001 | 0.0001 |
| 1 | 0.0028 | 0.0025 | 0.0023 | 0.0021 | 0.0019 | 0.0018 | 0.0016 | 0.0015 | 0.0014 | 0.0012 |
| 2 | 0.0127 | 0.0118 | 0.0109 | 0.0100 | 0.0093 | 0.0086 | 0.0079 | 0.0073 | 0.0068 | 0.0062 |
| 3 | 0.0396 | 0.0370 | 0.0346 | 0.0323 | 0.0301 | 0.0281 | 0.0262 | 0.0244 | 0.0228 | 0.0212 |
| 4 | 0.0940 | 0.0887 | 0.0837 | 0.0789 | 0.0744 | 0.0701 | 0.0660 | 0.0621 | 0.0584 | 0.0550 |
| 5 | 0.1822 | 0.1736 | 0.1653 | 0.1573 | 0.1496 | 0.1422 | 0.1352 | 0.1284 | 0.1219 | 0.1157 |
| 6 | 0.3013 | 0.2896 | 0.2781 | 0.2670 | 0.2562 | 0.2457 | 0.2355 | 0.2256 | 0.2160 | 0.2068 |
| 7 | 0.4391 | 0.4254 | 0.4119 | 0.3987 | 0.3856 | 0.3728 | 0.3602 | 0.3478 | 0.3357 | 0.3239 |
| 8 | 0.5786 | 0.5647 | 0.5507 | 0.5369 | 0.5231 | 0.5094 | 0.4958 | 0.4823 | 0.4689 | 0.4557 |
| 9 | 0.7041 | 0.6915 | 0.6788 | 0.6659 | 0.6530 | 0.6400 | 0.6269 | 0.6137 | 0.6006 | 0.5874 |
| 10 | 0.8058 | 0.7955 | 0.7850 | 0.7743 | 0.7634 | 0.7522 | 0.7409 | 0.7294 | 0.7178 | 0.7060 |
| 11 | 0.8807 | 0.8731 | 0.8652 | 0.8571 | 0.8487 | 0.8400 | 0.8311 | 0.8220 | 0.8126 | 0.8030 |
| 12 | 0.9313 | 0.9261 | 0.9207 | 0.9150 | 0.9091 | 0.9029 | 0.8965 | 0.8898 | 0.8829 | 0.8758 |
| 13 | 0.9628 | 0.9595 | 0.9561 | 0.9524 | 0.9486 | 0.9445 | 0.9403 | 0.9358 | 0.9311 | 0.9261 |
| 14 | 0.9810 | 0.9791 | 0.9771 | 0.9749 | 0.9726 | 0.9701 | 0.9675 | 0.9647 | 0.9617 | 0.9585 |
| 15 | 0.9908 | 0.9898 | 0.9887 | 0.9875 | 0.9862 | 0.9848 | 0.9832 | 0.9816 | 0.9798 | 0.9780 |
| 16 | 0.9958 | 0.9953 | 0.9947 | 0.9941 | 0.9934 | 0.9926 | 0.9918 | 0.9909 | 0.9899 | 0.9889 |
| 17 | 0.9982 | 0.9979 | 0.9977 | 0.9973 | 0.9970 | 0.9966 | 0.9962 | 0.9957 | 0.9952 | 0.9947 |
| 18 | 0.9992 | 0.9991 | 0.9990 | 0.9989 | 0.9987 | 0.9985 | 0.9983 | 0.9981 | 0.9978 | 0.9976 |
| 19 | 0.9997 | 0.9997 | 0.9996 | 0.9995 | 0.9995 | 0.9994 | 0.9993 | 0.9992 | 0.9991 | 0.9989 |
| 20 | 0.9999 | 0.9999 | 0.9998 | 0.9998 | 0.9998 | 0.9998 | 0.9997 | 0.9997 | 0.9996 | 0.9996 |
| 21 | 1.0000 | 1.0000 | 0.9999 | 0.9999 | 0.9999 | 0.9999 | 0.9999 | 0.9999 | 0.9998 | 0.9998 |
| 22 | 1.0000 | 1.0000 | 1.0000 | 1.0000 | 1.0000 | 1.0000 | 1.0000 | 1.0000 | 0.9999 | 0.9999 |
| 23 | 1.0000 | 1.0000 | 1.0000 | 1.0000 | 1.0000 | 1.0000 | 1.0000 | 1.0000 | 1.0000 | 1.0000 |

|   | $\lambda t$ | | | | | | | | | |
|---|---|---|---|---|---|---|---|---|---|---|
| $x$ | 9.10 | 9.20 | 9.30 | 9.40 | 9.50 | 9.60 | 9.70 | 9.80 | 9.90 | 10.00 |
| 0 | 0.0001 | 0.0001 | 0.0001 | 0.0001 | 0.0001 | 0.0001 | 0.0001 | 0.0001 | 0.0001 | 0.0000 |
| 1 | 0.0011 | 0.0010 | 0.0009 | 0.0009 | 0.0008 | 0.0007 | 0.0007 | 0.0006 | 0.0005 | 0.0005 |
| 2 | 0.0058 | 0.0053 | 0.0049 | 0.0045 | 0.0042 | 0.0038 | 0.0035 | 0.0033 | 0.0030 | 0.0028 |
| 3 | 0.0198 | 0.0184 | 0.0172 | 0.0160 | 0.0149 | 0.0138 | 0.0129 | 0.0120 | 0.0111 | 0.0103 |
| 4 | 0.0517 | 0.0486 | 0.0456 | 0.0429 | 0.0403 | 0.0378 | 0.0355 | 0.0333 | 0.0312 | 0.0293 |
| 5 | 0.1098 | 0.1041 | 0.0986 | 0.0935 | 0.0885 | 0.0838 | 0.0793 | 0.0750 | 0.0710 | 0.0671 |
| 6 | 0.1978 | 0.1892 | 0.1808 | 0.1727 | 0.1649 | 0.1574 | 0.1502 | 0.1433 | 0.1366 | 0.1301 |
| 7 | 0.3123 | 0.3010 | 0.2900 | 0.2792 | 0.2687 | 0.2584 | 0.2485 | 0.2388 | 0.2294 | 0.2202 |
| 8 | 0.4426 | 0.4296 | 0.4168 | 0.4042 | 0.3918 | 0.3796 | 0.3676 | 0.3558 | 0.3442 | 0.3328 |
| 9 | 0.5742 | 0.5611 | 0.5479 | 0.5349 | 0.5218 | 0.5089 | 0.4960 | 0.4832 | 0.4705 | 0.4579 |
| 10 | 0.6941 | 0.6820 | 0.6699 | 0.6576 | 0.6453 | 0.6329 | 0.6205 | 0.6080 | 0.5955 | 0.5830 |
| 11 | 0.7932 | 0.7832 | 0.7730 | 0.7626 | 0.7520 | 0.7412 | 0.7303 | 0.7193 | 0.7081 | 0.6968 |
| 12 | 0.8684 | 0.8607 | 0.8529 | 0.8448 | 0.8364 | 0.8279 | 0.8191 | 0.8101 | 0.8009 | 0.7916 |
| 13 | 0.9210 | 0.9156 | 0.9100 | 0.9042 | 0.8981 | 0.8919 | 0.8853 | 0.8786 | 0.8716 | 0.8645 |
| 14 | 0.9552 | 0.9517 | 0.9480 | 0.9441 | 0.9400 | 0.9357 | 0.9312 | 0.9265 | 0.9216 | 0.9165 |
| 15 | 0.9760 | 0.9738 | 0.9715 | 0.9691 | 0.9665 | 0.9638 | 0.9609 | 0.9579 | 0.9546 | 0.9513 |
| 16 | 0.9878 | 0.9865 | 0.9852 | 0.9838 | 0.9823 | 0.9806 | 0.9789 | 0.9770 | 0.9751 | 0.9730 |
| 17 | 0.9941 | 0.9934 | 0.9927 | 0.9919 | 0.9911 | 0.9902 | 0.9892 | 0.9881 | 0.9870 | 0.9857 |
| 18 | 0.9973 | 0.9969 | 0.9966 | 0.9962 | 0.9957 | 0.9952 | 0.9947 | 0.9941 | 0.9935 | 0.9928 |
| 19 | 0.9988 | 0.9986 | 0.9985 | 0.9983 | 0.9980 | 0.9978 | 0.9975 | 0.9972 | 0.9969 | 0.9965 |
| 20 | 0.9995 | 0.9994 | 0.9993 | 0.9992 | 0.9991 | 0.9990 | 0.9989 | 0.9987 | 0.9986 | 0.9984 |
| 21 | 0.9998 | 0.9998 | 0.9997 | 0.9997 | 0.9996 | 0.9996 | 0.9995 | 0.9995 | 0.9994 | 0.9993 |
| 22 | 0.9999 | 0.9999 | 0.9999 | 0.9999 | 0.9999 | 0.9998 | 0.9998 | 0.9998 | 0.9997 | 0.9997 |
| 23 | 1.0000 | 1.0000 | 1.0000 | 1.0000 | 0.9999 | 0.9999 | 0.9999 | 0.9999 | 0.9999 | 0.9999 |
| 24 | 1.0000 | 1.0000 | 1.0000 | 1.0000 | 1.0000 | 1.0000 | 1.0000 | 1.0000 | 1.0000 | 1.0000 |

$\lambda t$

| $x$ | 11.00 | 12.00 | 13.00 | 14.00 | 15.00 | 16.00 | 17.00 | 18.00 | 19.00 | 20.00 |
|---|---|---|---|---|---|---|---|---|---|---|
| 0 | 0.0000 | 0.0000 | 0.0000 | 0.0000 | 0.0000 | 0.0000 | 0.0000 | 0.0000 | 0.0000 | 0.0000 |
| 1 | 0.0002 | 0.0001 | 0.0000 | 0.0000 | 0.0000 | 0.0000 | 0.0000 | 0.0000 | 0.0000 | 0.0000 |
| 2 | 0.0012 | 0.0005 | 0.0002 | 0.0001 | 0.0000 | 0.0000 | 0.0000 | 0.0000 | 0.0000 | 0.0000 |
| 3 | 0.0049 | 0.0023 | 0.0011 | 0.0005 | 0.0002 | 0.0001 | 0.0000 | 0.0000 | 0.0000 | 0.0000 |
| 4 | 0.0151 | 0.0076 | 0.0037 | 0.0018 | 0.0009 | 0.0004 | 0.0002 | 0.0001 | 0.0000 | 0.0000 |
| 5 | 0.0375 | 0.0203 | 0.0107 | 0.0055 | 0.0028 | 0.0014 | 0.0007 | 0.0003 | 0.0002 | 0.0001 |
| 6 | 0.0786 | 0.0458 | 0.0259 | 0.0142 | 0.0076 | 0.0040 | 0.0021 | 0.0010 | 0.0005 | 0.0003 |
| 7 | 0.1432 | 0.0895 | 0.0540 | 0.0316 | 0.0180 | 0.0100 | 0.0054 | 0.0029 | 0.0015 | 0.0008 |
| 8 | 0.2320 | 0.1550 | 0.0998 | 0.0621 | 0.0374 | 0.0220 | 0.0126 | 0.0071 | 0.0039 | 0.0021 |
| 9 | 0.3405 | 0.2424 | 0.1658 | 0.1094 | 0.0699 | 0.0433 | 0.0261 | 0.0154 | 0.0089 | 0.0050 |
| 10 | 0.4599 | 0.3472 | 0.2517 | 0.1757 | 0.1185 | 0.0774 | 0.0491 | 0.0304 | 0.0183 | 0.0108 |
| 11 | 0.5793 | 0.4616 | 0.3532 | 0.2600 | 0.1848 | 0.1270 | 0.0847 | 0.0549 | 0.0347 | 0.0214 |
| 12 | 0.6887 | 0.5760 | 0.4631 | 0.3585 | 0.2676 | 0.1931 | 0.1350 | 0.0917 | 0.0606 | 0.0390 |
| 13 | 0.7813 | 0.6815 | 0.5730 | 0.4644 | 0.3632 | 0.2745 | 0.2009 | 0.1426 | 0.0984 | 0.0661 |
| 14 | 0.8540 | 0.7720 | 0.6751 | 0.5704 | 0.4657 | 0.3675 | 0.2808 | 0.2081 | 0.1497 | 0.1049 |
| 15 | 0.9074 | 0.8444 | 0.7636 | 0.6694 | 0.5681 | 0.4667 | 0.3715 | 0.2867 | 0.2148 | 0.1565 |
| 16 | 0.9441 | 0.8987 | 0.8355 | 0.7559 | 0.6641 | 0.5660 | 0.4677 | 0.3751 | 0.2920 | 0.2211 |
| 17 | 0.9678 | 0.9370 | 0.8905 | 0.8272 | 0.7489 | 0.6593 | 0.5640 | 0.4686 | 0.3784 | 0.2970 |
| 18 | 0.9823 | 0.9626 | 0.9302 | 0.8826 | 0.8195 | 0.7423 | 0.6550 | 0.5622 | 0.4695 | 0.3814 |
| 19 | 0.9907 | 0.9787 | 0.9573 | 0.9235 | 0.8752 | 0.8122 | 0.7363 | 0.6509 | 0.5606 | 0.4703 |
| 20 | 0.9953 | 0.9884 | 0.9750 | 0.9521 | 0.9170 | 0.8682 | 0.8055 | 0.7307 | 0.6472 | 0.5591 |
| 21 | 0.9977 | 0.9939 | 0.9859 | 0.9712 | 0.9469 | 0.9108 | 0.8615 | 0.7991 | 0.7255 | 0.6437 |
| 22 | 0.9990 | 0.9970 | 0.9924 | 0.9833 | 0.9673 | 0.9418 | 0.9047 | 0.8551 | 0.7931 | 0.7206 |
| 23 | 0.9995 | 0.9985 | 0.9960 | 0.9907 | 0.9805 | 0.9633 | 0.9367 | 0.8989 | 0.8490 | 0.7875 |
| 24 | 0.9998 | 0.9993 | 0.9980 | 0.9950 | 0.9888 | 0.9777 | 0.9594 | 0.9317 | 0.8933 | 0.8432 |
| 25 | 0.9999 | 0.9997 | 0.9990 | 0.9974 | 0.9938 | 0.9869 | 0.9748 | 0.9554 | 0.9269 | 0.8878 |
| 26 | 1.0000 | 0.9999 | 0.9995 | 0.9987 | 0.9967 | 0.9925 | 0.9848 | 0.9718 | 0.9514 | 0.9221 |
| 27 | 1.0000 | 0.9999 | 0.9998 | 0.9994 | 0.9983 | 0.9959 | 0.9912 | 0.9827 | 0.9687 | 0.9475 |
| 28 | 1.0000 | 1.0000 | 0.9999 | 0.9997 | 0.9991 | 0.9978 | 0.9950 | 0.9897 | 0.9805 | 0.9657 |
| 29 | 1.0000 | 1.0000 | 1.0000 | 0.9999 | 0.9996 | 0.9989 | 0.9973 | 0.9941 | 0.9882 | 0.9782 |
| 30 | 1.0000 | 1.0000 | 1.0000 | 0.9999 | 0.9998 | 0.9994 | 0.9986 | 0.9967 | 0.9930 | 0.9865 |
| 31 | 1.0000 | 1.0000 | 1.0000 | 1.0000 | 0.9999 | 0.9997 | 0.9993 | 0.9982 | 0.9960 | 0.9919 |
| 32 | 1.0000 | 1.0000 | 1.0000 | 1.0000 | 1.0000 | 0.9999 | 0.9996 | 0.9990 | 0.9978 | 0.9953 |
| 33 | 1.0000 | 1.0000 | 1.0000 | 1.0000 | 1.0000 | 0.9999 | 0.9998 | 0.9995 | 0.9988 | 0.9973 |
| 34 | 1.0000 | 1.0000 | 1.0000 | 1.0000 | 1.0000 | 1.0000 | 0.9999 | 0.9998 | 0.9994 | 0.9985 |
| 35 | 1.0000 | 1.0000 | 1.0000 | 1.0000 | 1.0000 | 1.0000 | 1.0000 | 0.9999 | 0.9997 | 0.9992 |
| 36 | 1.0000 | 1.0000 | 1.0000 | 1.0000 | 1.0000 | 1.0000 | 1.0000 | 0.9999 | 0.9998 | 0.9996 |
| 37 | 1.0000 | 1.0000 | 1.0000 | 1.0000 | 1.0000 | 1.0000 | 1.0000 | 1.0000 | 0.9999 | 0.9998 |
| 38 | 1.0000 | 1.0000 | 1.0000 | 1.0000 | 1.0000 | 1.0000 | 1.0000 | 1.0000 | 1.0000 | 0.9999 |
| 39 | 1.0000 | 1.0000 | 1.0000 | 1.0000 | 1.0000 | 1.0000 | 1.0000 | 1.0000 | 1.0000 | 0.9999 |
| 40 | 1.0000 | 1.0000 | 1.0000 | 1.0000 | 1.0000 | 1.0000 | 1.0000 | 1.0000 | 1.0000 | 1.0000 |

## APPENDIX D

### Standard Normal Distribution Table

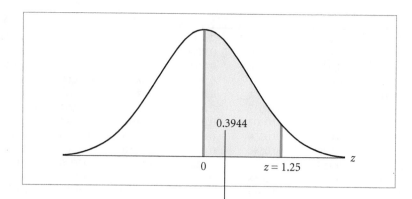

| z | 0 | 0.01 | 0.02 | 0.03 | 0.04 | 0.05 | 0.06 | 0.07 | 0.08 | 0.09 |
|---|---|------|------|------|------|------|------|------|------|------|
| 0.0 | 0.0000 | 0.0040 | 0.0080 | 0.0120 | 0.0160 | 0.0199 | 0.0239 | 0.0279 | 0.0319 | 0.0359 |
| 0.1 | 0.0398 | 0.0438 | 0.0478 | 0.0517 | 0.0557 | 0.0596 | 0.0636 | 0.0675 | 0.0714 | 0.0753 |
| 0.2 | 0.0793 | 0.0832 | 0.0871 | 0.0910 | 0.0948 | 0.0987 | 0.1026 | 0.1064 | 0.1103 | 0.1141 |
| 0.3 | 0.1179 | 0.1217 | 0.1255 | 0.1293 | 0.1331 | 0.1368 | 0.1406 | 0.1443 | 0.1480 | 0.1517 |
| 0.4 | 0.1554 | 0.1591 | 0.1628 | 0.1664 | 0.1700 | 0.1736 | 0.1772 | 0.1808 | 0.1844 | 0.1879 |
| 0.5 | 0.1915 | 0.1950 | 0.1985 | 0.2019 | 0.2054 | 0.2088 | 0.2123 | 0.2157 | 0.2190 | 0.2224 |
| 0.6 | 0.2257 | 0.2291 | 0.2324 | 0.2357 | 0.2389 | 0.2422 | 0.2454 | 0.2486 | 0.2517 | 0.2549 |
| 0.7 | 0.2580 | 0.2611 | 0.2642 | 0.2673 | 0.2704 | 0.2734 | 0.2764 | 0.2794 | 0.2823 | 0.2852 |
| 0.8 | 0.2881 | 0.2910 | 0.2939 | 0.2967 | 0.2995 | 0.3023 | 0.3051 | 0.3078 | 0.3106 | 0.3133 |
| 0.9 | 0.3159 | 0.3186 | 0.3212 | 0.3238 | 0.3264 | 0.3289 | 0.3315 | 0.3340 | 0.3365 | 0.3389 |
| 1.0 | 0.3413 | 0.3438 | 0.3461 | 0.3485 | 0.3508 | 0.3531 | 0.3554 | 0.3577 | 0.3599 | 0.3621 |
| 1.1 | 0.3643 | 0.3665 | 0.3686 | 0.3708 | 0.3729 | 0.3749 | 0.3770 | 0.3790 | 0.3810 | 0.3830 |
| 1.2 | 0.3849 | 0.3869 | 0.3888 | 0.3907 | 0.3925 | 0.3944 | 0.3962 | 0.3980 | 0.3997 | 0.4015 |
| 1.3 | 0.4032 | 0.4049 | 0.4066 | 0.4082 | 0.4099 | 0.4115 | 0.4131 | 0.4147 | 0.4162 | 0.4177 |
| 1.4 | 0.4192 | 0.4207 | 0.4222 | 0.4236 | 0.4251 | 0.4265 | 0.4279 | 0.4292 | 0.4306 | 0.4319 |
| 1.5 | 0.4332 | 0.4345 | 0.4357 | 0.4370 | 0.4382 | 0.4394 | 0.4406 | 0.4418 | 0.4429 | 0.4441 |
| 1.6 | 0.4452 | 0.4463 | 0.4474 | 0.4484 | 0.4495 | 0.4505 | 0.4515 | 0.4525 | 0.4535 | 0.4545 |
| 1.7 | 0.4554 | 0.4564 | 0.4573 | 0.4582 | 0.4591 | 0.4599 | 0.4608 | 0.4616 | 0.4625 | 0.4633 |
| 1.8 | 0.4641 | 0.4649 | 0.4656 | 0.4664 | 0.4671 | 0.4678 | 0.4686 | 0.4693 | 0.4699 | 0.4706 |
| 1.9 | 0.4713 | 0.4719 | 0.4726 | 0.4732 | 0.4738 | 0.4744 | 0.4750 | 0.4756 | 0.4761 | 0.4767 |
| 2.0 | 0.4772 | 0.4778 | 0.4783 | 0.4788 | 0.4793 | 0.4798 | 0.4803 | 0.4808 | 0.4812 | 0.4817 |
| 2.1 | 0.4821 | 0.4826 | 0.4830 | 0.4834 | 0.4838 | 0.4842 | 0.4846 | 0.4850 | 0.4854 | 0.4857 |
| 2.2 | 0.4861 | 0.4864 | 0.4868 | 0.4871 | 0.4875 | 0.4878 | 0.4881 | 0.4884 | 0.4887 | 0.4890 |
| 2.3 | 0.4893 | 0.4896 | 0.4898 | 0.4901 | 0.4904 | 0.4906 | 0.4909 | 0.4911 | 0.4913 | 0.4916 |
| 2.4 | 0.4918 | 0.4920 | 0.4922 | 0.4925 | 0.4927 | 0.4929 | 0.4931 | 0.4932 | 0.4934 | 0.4936 |
| 2.5 | 0.4938 | 0.4940 | 0.4941 | 0.4943 | 0.4945 | 0.4946 | 0.4948 | 0.4949 | 0.4951 | 0.4952 |
| 2.6 | 0.4953 | 0.4955 | 0.4956 | 0.4957 | 0.4959 | 0.4960 | 0.4961 | 0.4962 | 0.4963 | 0.4964 |
| 2.7 | 0.4965 | 0.4966 | 0.4967 | 0.4968 | 0.4969 | 0.4970 | 0.4971 | 0.4972 | 0.4973 | 0.4974 |
| 2.8 | 0.4974 | 0.4975 | 0.4976 | 0.4977 | 0.4977 | 0.4978 | 0.4979 | 0.4979 | 0.4980 | 0.4981 |
| 2.9 | 0.4981 | 0.4982 | 0.4982 | 0.4983 | 0.4984 | 0.4984 | 0.4985 | 0.4985 | 0.4986 | 0.4986 |
| 3.0 | 0.4987 | 0.4987 | 0.4987 | 0.4988 | 0.4988 | 0.4989 | 0.4989 | 0.4989 | 0.4990 | 0.4990 |

Exponential
Distribution Table

**Values of $e^{-\lambda a}$**

| $\lambda a$ | $e^{-\lambda a}$ | $\lambda a$ | $e^{-\lambda a}$ | $\lambda a$ | $e^{-\lambda a}$ | $\lambda a$ | $e^{-\lambda a}$ | $\lambda a$ | $e^{-\lambda a}$ |
|---|---|---|---|---|---|---|---|---|---|
| 0.00 | 1.0000 | 2.05 | 0.1287 | 4.05 | 0.0174 | 6.05 | 0.0024 | 8.05 | 0.0003 |
| 0.05 | 0.9512 | 2.10 | 0.1225 | 4.10 | 0.0166 | 6.10 | 0.0022 | 8.10 | 0.0003 |
| 0.10 | 0.9048 | 2.15 | 0.1165 | 4.15 | 0.0158 | 6.15 | 0.0021 | 8.15 | 0.0003 |
| 0.15 | 0.8607 | 2.20 | 0.1108 | 4.20 | 0.0150 | 6.20 | 0.0020 | 8.20 | 0.0003 |
| 0.20 | 0.8187 | 2.25 | 0.1054 | 4.25 | 0.0143 | 6.25 | 0.0019 | 8.25 | 0.0003 |
| 0.25 | 0.7788 | 2.30 | 0.1003 | 4.30 | 0.0136 | 6.30 | 0.0018 | 8.30 | 0.0002 |
| 0.30 | 0.7408 | 2.35 | 0.0954 | 4.35 | 0.0129 | 6.35 | 0.0017 | 8.35 | 0.0002 |
| 0.35 | 0.7047 | 2.40 | 0.0907 | 4.40 | 0.0123 | 6.40 | 0.0017 | 8.40 | 0.0002 |
| 0.40 | 0.6703 | 2.45 | 0.0863 | 4.45 | 0.0117 | 6.45 | 0.0016 | 8.45 | 0.0002 |
| 0.45 | 0.6376 | 2.50 | 0.0821 | 4.50 | 0.0111 | 6.50 | 0.0015 | 8.50 | 0.0002 |
| 0.50 | 0.6065 | 2.55 | 0.0781 | 4.55 | 0.0106 | 6.55 | 0.0014 | 8.55 | 0.0002 |
| 0.55 | 0.5769 | 2.60 | 0.0743 | 4.60 | 0.0101 | 6.60 | 0.0014 | 8.60 | 0.0002 |
| 0.60 | 0.5488 | 2.65 | 0.0707 | 4.65 | 0.0096 | 6.65 | 0.0013 | 8.65 | 0.0002 |
| 0.65 | 0.5220 | 2.70 | 0.0672 | 4.70 | 0.0091 | 6.70 | 0.0012 | 8.70 | 0.0002 |
| 0.70 | 0.4966 | 2.75 | 0.0639 | 4.75 | 0.0087 | 6.75 | 0.0012 | 8.75 | 0.0002 |
| 0.75 | 0.4724 | 2.80 | 0.0608 | 4.80 | 0.0082 | 6.80 | 0.0011 | 8.80 | 0.0002 |
| 0.80 | 0.4493 | 2.85 | 0.0578 | 4.85 | 0.0078 | 6.85 | 0.0011 | 8.85 | 0.0001 |
| 0.85 | 0.4274 | 2.90 | 0.0550 | 4.90 | 0.0074 | 6.90 | 0.0010 | 8.90 | 0.0001 |
| 0.90 | 0.4066 | 2.95 | 0.0523 | 4.95 | 0.0071 | 6.95 | 0.0010 | 8.95 | 0.0001 |
| 0.95 | 0.3867 | 3.00 | 0.0498 | 5.00 | 0.0067 | 7.00 | 0.0009 | 9.00 | 0.0001 |
| 1.00 | 0.3679 | 3.05 | 0.0474 | 5.05 | 0.0064 | 7.05 | 0.0009 | 9.05 | 0.0001 |
| 1.05 | 0.3499 | 3.10 | 0.0450 | 5.10 | 0.0061 | 7.10 | 0.0008 | 9.10 | 0.0001 |
| 1.10 | 0.3329 | 3.15 | 0.0429 | 5.15 | 0.0058 | 7.15 | 0.0008 | 9.15 | 0.0001 |
| 1.15 | 0.3166 | 3.20 | 0.0408 | 5.20 | 0.0055 | 7.20 | 0.0007 | 9.20 | 0.0001 |
| 1.20 | 0.3012 | 3.25 | 0.0388 | 5.25 | 0.0052 | 7.25 | 0.0007 | 9.25 | 0.0001 |
| 1.25 | 0.2865 | 3.30 | 0.0369 | 5.30 | 0.0050 | 7.30 | 0.0007 | 9.30 | 0.0001 |
| 1.30 | 0.2725 | 3.35 | 0.0351 | 5.35 | 0.0047 | 7.35 | 0.0006 | 9.35 | 0.0001 |
| 1.35 | 0.2592 | 3.40 | 0.0334 | 5.40 | 0.0045 | 7.40 | 0.0006 | 9.40 | 0.0001 |
| 1.40 | 0.2466 | 3.45 | 0.0317 | 5.45 | 0.0043 | 7.45 | 0.0006 | 9.45 | 0.0001 |
| 1.45 | 0.2346 | 3.50 | 0.0302 | 5.50 | 0.0041 | 7.50 | 0.0006 | 9.50 | 0.0001 |
| 1.50 | 0.2231 | 3.55 | 0.0287 | 5.55 | 0.0039 | 7.55 | 0.0005 | 9.55 | 0.0001 |
| 1.55 | 0.2122 | 3.60 | 0.0273 | 5.60 | 0.0037 | 7.60 | 0.0005 | 9.60 | 0.0001 |
| 1.60 | 0.2019 | 3.65 | 0.0260 | 5.65 | 0.0035 | 7.65 | 0.0005 | 9.65 | 0.0001 |
| 1.65 | 0.1920 | 3.70 | 0.0247 | 5.70 | 0.0033 | 7.70 | 0.0005 | 9.70 | 0.0001 |
| 1.70 | 0.1827 | 3.75 | 0.0235 | 5.75 | 0.0032 | 7.75 | 0.0004 | 9.75 | 0.0001 |
| 1.75 | 0.1738 | 3.80 | 0.0224 | 5.80 | 0.0030 | 7.80 | 0.0004 | 9.80 | 0.0001 |
| 1.80 | 0.1653 | 3.85 | 0.0213 | 5.85 | 0.0029 | 7.85 | 0.0004 | 9.85 | 0.0001 |
| 1.85 | 0.1572 | 3.90 | 0.0202 | 5.90 | 0.0027 | 7.90 | 0.0004 | 9.90 | 0.0001 |
| 1.90 | 0.1496 | 3.95 | 0.0193 | 5.95 | 0.0026 | 7.95 | 0.0004 | 9.95 | 0.0000 |
| 1.95 | 0.1423 | 4.00 | 0.0183 | 6.00 | 0.0025 | 8.00 | 0.0003 | 10.00 | 0.0000 |
| 2.00 | 0.1353 | | | | | | | | |

## APPENDIX F

Values of *t*
for Selected
Probabilities

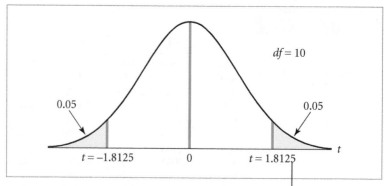

PROBABILITIES (OR AREAS UNDER *t*-DISTRIBUTION CURVE)

| Conf. Level | 0.1 | 0.3 | 0.5 | 0.7 | 0.8 | 0.9 | 0.95 | 0.98 | 0.99 |
|---|---|---|---|---|---|---|---|---|---|
| One Tail | 0.45 | 0.35 | 0.25 | 0.15 | 0.1 | 0.05 | 0.025 | 0.01 | 0.005 |
| Two Tails | 0.9 | 0.7 | 0.5 | 0.3 | 0.2 | 0.1 | 0.05 | 0.02 | 0.01 |
| *df* | | | | | Values of *t* | | | | |
| 1 | 0.1584 | 0.5095 | 1.0000 | 1.9626 | 3.0777 | 6.3137 | 12.7062 | 31.8210 | 63.6559 |
| 2 | 0.1421 | 0.4447 | 0.8165 | 1.3862 | 1.8856 | 2.9200 | 4.3027 | 6.9645 | 9.9250 |
| 3 | 0.1366 | 0.4242 | 0.7649 | 1.2498 | 1.6377 | 2.3534 | 3.1824 | 4.5407 | 5.8408 |
| 4 | 0.1338 | 0.4142 | 0.7407 | 1.1896 | 1.5332 | 2.1318 | 2.7765 | 3.7469 | 4.6041 |
| 5 | 0.1322 | 0.4082 | 0.7267 | 1.1558 | 1.4759 | 2.0150 | 2.5706 | 3.3649 | 4.0321 |
| 6 | 0.1311 | 0.4043 | 0.7176 | 1.1342 | 1.4398 | 1.9432 | 2.4469 | 3.1427 | 3.7074 |
| 7 | 0.1303 | 0.4015 | 0.7111 | 1.1192 | 1.4149 | 1.8946 | 2.3646 | 2.9979 | 3.4995 |
| 8 | 0.1297 | 0.3995 | 0.7064 | 1.1081 | 1.3968 | 1.8595 | 2.3060 | 2.8965 | 3.3554 |
| 9 | 0.1293 | 0.3979 | 0.7027 | 1.0997 | 1.3830 | 1.8331 | 2.2622 | 2.8214 | 3.2498 |
| 10 | 0.1289 | 0.3966 | 0.6998 | 1.0931 | 1.3722 | 1.8125 | 2.2281 | 2.7638 | 3.1693 |
| 11 | 0.1286 | 0.3956 | 0.6974 | 1.0877 | 1.3634 | 1.7959 | 2.2010 | 2.7181 | 3.1058 |
| 12 | 0.1283 | 0.3947 | 0.6955 | 1.0832 | 1.3562 | 1.7823 | 2.1788 | 2.6810 | 3.0545 |
| 13 | 0.1281 | 0.3940 | 0.6938 | 1.0795 | 1.3502 | 1.7709 | 2.1604 | 2.6503 | 3.0123 |
| 14 | 0.1280 | 0.3933 | 0.6924 | 1.0763 | 1.3450 | 1.7613 | 2.1448 | 2.6245 | 2.9768 |
| 15 | 0.1278 | 0.3928 | 0.6912 | 1.0735 | 1.3406 | 1.7531 | 2.1315 | 2.6025 | 2.9467 |
| 16 | 0.1277 | 0.3923 | 0.6901 | 1.0711 | 1.3368 | 1.7459 | 2.1199 | 2.5835 | 2.9208 |
| 17 | 0.1276 | 0.3919 | 0.6892 | 1.0690 | 1.3334 | 1.7396 | 2.1098 | 2.5669 | 2.8982 |
| 18 | 0.1274 | 0.3915 | 0.6884 | 1.0672 | 1.3304 | 1.7341 | 2.1009 | 2.5524 | 2.8784 |
| 19 | 0.1274 | 0.3912 | 0.6876 | 1.0655 | 1.3277 | 1.7291 | 2.0930 | 2.5395 | 2.8609 |
| 20 | 0.1273 | 0.3909 | 0.6870 | 1.0640 | 1.3253 | 1.7247 | 2.0860 | 2.5280 | 2.8453 |
| 21 | 0.1272 | 0.3906 | 0.6864 | 1.0627 | 1.3232 | 1.7207 | 2.0796 | 2.5176 | 2.8314 |
| 22 | 0.1271 | 0.3904 | 0.6858 | 1.0614 | 1.3212 | 1.7171 | 2.0739 | 2.5083 | 2.8188 |
| 23 | 0.1271 | 0.3902 | 0.6853 | 1.0603 | 1.3195 | 1.7139 | 2.0687 | 2.4999 | 2.8073 |
| 24 | 0.1270 | 0.3900 | 0.6848 | 1.0593 | 1.3178 | 1.7109 | 2.0639 | 2.4922 | 2.7970 |
| 25 | 0.1269 | 0.3898 | 0.6844 | 1.0584 | 1.3163 | 1.7081 | 2.0595 | 2.4851 | 2.7874 |
| 26 | 0.1269 | 0.3896 | 0.6840 | 1.0575 | 1.3150 | 1.7056 | 2.0555 | 2.4786 | 2.7787 |
| 27 | 0.1268 | 0.3894 | 0.6837 | 1.0567 | 1.3137 | 1.7033 | 2.0518 | 2.4727 | 2.7707 |
| 28 | 0.1268 | 0.3893 | 0.6834 | 1.0560 | 1.3125 | 1.7011 | 2.0484 | 2.4671 | 2.7633 |
| 29 | 0.1268 | 0.3892 | 0.6830 | 1.0553 | 1.3114 | 1.6991 | 2.0452 | 2.4620 | 2.7564 |
| 30 | 0.1267 | 0.3890 | 0.6828 | 1.0547 | 1.3104 | 1.6973 | 2.0423 | 2.4573 | 2.7500 |
| 40 | 0.1265 | 0.3881 | 0.6807 | 1.0500 | 1.3031 | 1.6839 | 2.0211 | 2.4233 | 2.7045 |
| 50 | 0.1263 | 0.3875 | 0.6794 | 1.0473 | 1.2987 | 1.6759 | 2.0086 | 2.4033 | 2.6778 |
| 60 | 0.1262 | 0.3872 | 0.6786 | 1.0455 | 1.2958 | 1.6706 | 2.0003 | 2.3901 | 2.6603 |
| 70 | 0.1261 | 0.3869 | 0.6780 | 1.0442 | 1.2938 | 1.6669 | 1.9944 | 2.3808 | 2.6479 |
| 80 | 0.1261 | 0.3867 | 0.6776 | 1.0432 | 1.2922 | 1.6641 | 1.9901 | 2.3739 | 2.6387 |
| 90 | 0.1260 | 0.3866 | 0.6772 | 1.0424 | 1.2910 | 1.6620 | 1.9867 | 2.3685 | 2.6316 |
| 100 | 0.1260 | 0.3864 | 0.6770 | 1.0418 | 1.2901 | 1.6602 | 1.9840 | 2.3642 | 2.6259 |
| 250 | 0.1258 | 0.3858 | 0.6755 | 1.0386 | 1.2849 | 1.6510 | 1.9695 | 2.3414 | 2.5956 |
| 500 | 0.1257 | 0.3855 | 0.6750 | 1.0375 | 1.2832 | 1.6479 | 1.9647 | 2.3338 | 2.5857 |
| ∞ | 0.1257 | 0.3853 | 0.6745 | 1.0364 | 1.2816 | 1.6449 | 1.9600 | 2.3263 | 2.5758 |

Values of $\chi^2$
for Selected
Probabilities

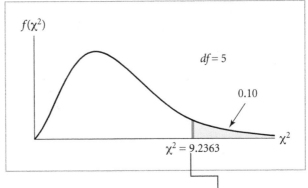

PROBABILITIES (OR AREAS UNDER CHI-SQUARE DISTRIBUTION CURVE
ABOVE GIVEN CHI-SQUARE VALUES)

| | 0.995 | 0.99 | 0.975 | 0.95 | 0.90 | 0.10 | 0.05 | 0.025 | 0.01 | 0.005 |
|---|---|---|---|---|---|---|---|---|---|---|
| df | | | | | | *Values of Chi-Squared* | | | | |
| 1 | 0.0000 | 0.0002 | 0.0010 | 0.0039 | 0.0158 | 2.7055 | 3.8415 | 5.0239 | 6.6349 | 7.8794 |
| 2 | 0.0100 | 0.0201 | 0.0506 | 0.1026 | 0.2107 | 4.6052 | 5.9915 | 7.3778 | 9.2104 | 10.5965 |
| 3 | 0.0717 | 0.1148 | 0.2158 | 0.3518 | 0.5844 | 6.2514 | 7.8147 | 9.3484 | 11.3449 | 12.8381 |
| 4 | 0.2070 | 0.2971 | 0.4844 | 0.7107 | 1.0636 | 7.7794 | 9.4877 | 11.1433 | 13.2767 | 14.8602 |
| 5 | 0.4118 | 0.5543 | 0.8312 | 1.1455 | 1.6103 | 9.2363 | 11.0705 | 12.8325 | 15.0863 | 16.7496 |
| 6 | 0.6757 | 0.8721 | 1.2373 | 1.6354 | 2.2041 | 10.6446 | 12.5916 | 14.4494 | 16.8119 | 18.5475 |
| 7 | 0.9893 | 1.2390 | 1.6899 | 2.1673 | 2.8331 | 12.0170 | 14.0671 | 16.0128 | 18.4753 | 20.2777 |
| 8 | 1.3444 | 1.6465 | 2.1797 | 2.7326 | 3.4895 | 13.3616 | 15.5073 | 17.5345 | 20.0902 | 21.9549 |
| 9 | 1.7349 | 2.0879 | 2.7004 | 3.3251 | 4.1682 | 14.6837 | 16.9190 | 19.0228 | 21.6660 | 23.5893 |
| 10 | 2.1558 | 2.5582 | 3.2470 | 3.9403 | 4.8652 | 15.9872 | 18.3070 | 20.4832 | 23.2093 | 25.1881 |
| 11 | 2.6032 | 3.0535 | 3.8157 | 4.5748 | 5.5778 | 17.2750 | 19.6752 | 21.9200 | 24.7250 | 26.7569 |
| 12 | 3.0738 | 3.5706 | 4.4038 | 5.2260 | 6.3038 | 18.5493 | 21.0261 | 23.3367 | 26.2170 | 28.2997 |
| 13 | 3.5650 | 4.1069 | 5.0087 | 5.8919 | 7.0415 | 19.8119 | 22.3620 | 24.7356 | 27.6882 | 29.8193 |
| 14 | 4.0747 | 4.6604 | 5.6287 | 6.5706 | 7.7895 | 21.0641 | 23.6848 | 26.1189 | 29.1412 | 31.3194 |
| 15 | 4.6009 | 5.2294 | 6.2621 | 7.2609 | 8.5468 | 22.3071 | 24.9958 | 27.4884 | 30.5780 | 32.8015 |
| 16 | 5.1422 | 5.8122 | 6.9077 | 7.9616 | 9.3122 | 23.5418 | 26.2962 | 28.8453 | 31.9999 | 34.2671 |
| 17 | 5.6973 | 6.4077 | 7.5642 | 8.6718 | 10.0852 | 24.7690 | 27.5871 | 30.1910 | 33.4087 | 35.7184 |
| 18 | 6.2648 | 7.0149 | 8.2307 | 9.3904 | 10.8649 | 25.9894 | 28.8693 | 31.5264 | 34.8052 | 37.1564 |
| 19 | 6.8439 | 7.6327 | 8.9065 | 10.1170 | 11.6509 | 27.2036 | 30.1435 | 32.8523 | 36.1908 | 38.5821 |
| 20 | 7.4338 | 8.2604 | 9.5908 | 10.8508 | 12.4426 | 28.4120 | 31.4104 | 34.1696 | 37.5663 | 39.9969 |
| 21 | 8.0336 | 8.8972 | 10.2829 | 11.5913 | 13.2396 | 29.6151 | 32.6706 | 35.4789 | 38.9322 | 41.4009 |
| 22 | 8.6427 | 9.5425 | 10.9823 | 12.3380 | 14.0415 | 30.8133 | 33.9245 | 36.7807 | 40.2894 | 42.7957 |
| 23 | 9.2604 | 10.1957 | 11.6885 | 13.0905 | 14.8480 | 32.0069 | 35.1725 | 38.0756 | 41.6383 | 44.1814 |
| 24 | 9.8862 | 10.8563 | 12.4011 | 13.8484 | 15.6587 | 33.1962 | 36.4150 | 39.3641 | 42.9798 | 45.5584 |
| 25 | 10.5196 | 11.5240 | 13.1197 | 14.6114 | 16.4734 | 34.3816 | 37.6525 | 40.6465 | 44.3140 | 46.9280 |
| 26 | 11.1602 | 12.1982 | 13.8439 | 15.3792 | 17.2919 | 35.5632 | 38.8851 | 41.9231 | 45.6416 | 48.2898 |
| 27 | 11.8077 | 12.8785 | 14.5734 | 16.1514 | 18.1139 | 36.7412 | 40.1133 | 43.1945 | 46.9628 | 49.6450 |
| 28 | 12.4613 | 13.5647 | 15.3079 | 16.9279 | 18.9392 | 37.9159 | 41.3372 | 44.4608 | 48.2782 | 50.9936 |
| 29 | 13.1211 | 14.2564 | 16.0471 | 17.7084 | 19.7677 | 39.0875 | 42.5569 | 45.7223 | 49.5878 | 52.3355 |
| 30 | 13.7867 | 14.9535 | 16.7908 | 18.4927 | 20.5992 | 40.2560 | 43.7730 | 46.9792 | 50.8922 | 53.6719 |

## APPENDIX H

*F*-Distribution
Table: Upper 5%
Probability (or 5%
Area) under
*F*-Distribution
Curve

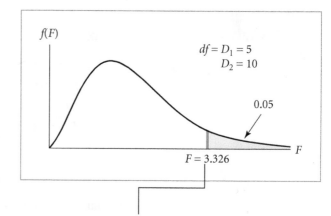

**DENOMINATOR**

$df = D_2$            NUMERATOR $df = D_1$

| | 1 | 2 | 3 | 4 | 5 | 6 | 7 | 8 | 9 | 10 |
|---|---|---|---|---|---|---|---|---|---|---|
| 1 | 161.446 | 199.499 | 215.707 | 224.583 | 230.160 | 233.988 | 236.767 | 238.884 | 240.543 | 241.882 |
| 2 | 18.513 | 19.000 | 19.164 | 19.247 | 19.296 | 19.329 | 19.353 | 19.371 | 19.385 | 19.396 |
| 3 | 10.128 | 9.552 | 9.277 | 9.117 | 9.013 | 8.941 | 8.887 | 8.845 | 8.812 | 8.785 |
| 4 | 7.709 | 6.944 | 6.591 | 6.388 | 6.256 | 6.163 | 6.094 | 6.041 | 5.999 | 5.964 |
| 5 | 6.608 | 5.786 | 5.409 | 5.192 | 5.050 | 4.950 | 4.876 | 4.818 | 4.772 | 4.735 |
| 6 | 5.987 | 5.143 | 4.757 | 4.534 | 4.387 | 4.284 | 4.207 | 4.147 | 4.099 | 4.060 |
| 7 | 5.591 | 4.737 | 4.347 | 4.120 | 3.972 | 3.866 | 3.787 | 3.726 | 3.677 | 3.637 |
| 8 | 5.318 | 4.459 | 4.066 | 3.838 | 3.688 | 3.581 | 3.500 | 3.438 | 3.388 | 3.347 |
| 9 | 5.117 | 4.256 | 3.863 | 3.633 | 3.482 | 3.374 | 3.293 | 3.230 | 3.179 | 3.137 |
| 10 | 4.965 | 4.103 | 3.708 | 3.478 | 3.326 | 3.217 | 3.135 | 3.072 | 3.020 | 2.978 |
| 11 | 4.844 | 3.982 | 3.587 | 3.357 | 3.204 | 3.095 | 3.012 | 2.948 | 2.896 | 2.854 |
| 12 | 4.747 | 3.885 | 3.490 | 3.259 | 3.106 | 2.996 | 2.913 | 2.849 | 2.796 | 2.753 |
| 13 | 4.667 | 3.806 | 3.411 | 3.179 | 3.025 | 2.915 | 2.832 | 2.767 | 2.714 | 2.671 |
| 14 | 4.600 | 3.739 | 3.344 | 3.112 | 2.958 | 2.848 | 2.764 | 2.699 | 2.646 | 2.602 |
| 15 | 4.543 | 3.682 | 3.287 | 3.056 | 2.901 | 2.790 | 2.707 | 2.641 | 2.588 | 2.544 |
| 16 | 4.494 | 3.634 | 3.239 | 3.007 | 2.852 | 2.741 | 2.657 | 2.591 | 2.538 | 2.494 |
| 17 | 4.451 | 3.592 | 3.197 | 2.965 | 2.810 | 2.699 | 2.614 | 2.548 | 2.494 | 2.450 |
| 18 | 4.414 | 3.555 | 3.160 | 2.928 | 2.773 | 2.661 | 2.577 | 2.510 | 2.456 | 2.412 |
| 19 | 4.381 | 3.522 | 3.127 | 2.895 | 2.740 | 2.628 | 2.544 | 2.477 | 2.423 | 2.378 |
| 20 | 4.351 | 3.493 | 3.098 | 2.866 | 2.711 | 2.599 | 2.514 | 2.447 | 2.393 | 2.348 |
| 24 | 4.260 | 3.403 | 3.009 | 2.776 | 2.621 | 2.508 | 2.423 | 2.355 | 2.300 | 2.255 |
| 30 | 4.171 | 3.316 | 2.922 | 2.690 | 2.534 | 2.421 | 2.334 | 2.266 | 2.211 | 2.165 |
| 40 | 4.085 | 3.232 | 2.839 | 2.606 | 2.449 | 2.336 | 2.249 | 2.180 | 2.124 | 2.077 |
| 50 | 4.034 | 3.183 | 2.790 | 2.557 | 2.400 | 2.286 | 2.199 | 2.130 | 2.073 | 2.026 |
| 100 | 3.936 | 3.087 | 2.696 | 2.463 | 2.305 | 2.191 | 2.103 | 2.032 | 1.975 | 1.927 |
| 200 | 3.888 | 3.041 | 2.650 | 2.417 | 2.259 | 2.144 | 2.056 | 1.985 | 1.927 | 1.878 |
| 300 | 3.873 | 3.026 | 2.635 | 2.402 | 2.244 | 2.129 | 2.040 | 1.969 | 1.911 | 1.862 |

**DENOMINATOR**

$df = D_2$            NUMERATOR $df = D_1$

| | 11 | 12 | 13 | 14 | 15 | 16 | 17 | 18 | 19 | 20 |
|---|---|---|---|---|---|---|---|---|---|---|
| 1 | 242.981 | 243.905 | 244.690 | 245.363 | 245.949 | 246.466 | 246.917 | 247.324 | 247.688 | 248.016 |
| 2 | 19.405 | 19.412 | 19.419 | 19.424 | 19.429 | 19.433 | 19.437 | 19.440 | 19.443 | 19.446 |
| 3 | 8.763 | 8.745 | 8.729 | 8.715 | 8.703 | 8.692 | 8.683 | 8.675 | 8.667 | 8.660 |
| 4 | 5.936 | 5.912 | 5.891 | 5.873 | 5.858 | 5.844 | 5.832 | 5.821 | 5.811 | 5.803 |
| 5 | 4.704 | 4.678 | 4.655 | 4.636 | 4.619 | 4.604 | 4.590 | 4.579 | 4.568 | 4.558 |
| 6 | 4.027 | 4.000 | 3.976 | 3.956 | 3.938 | 3.922 | 3.908 | 3.896 | 3.884 | 3.874 |
| 7 | 3.603 | 3.575 | 3.550 | 3.529 | 3.511 | 3.494 | 3.480 | 3.467 | 3.455 | 3.445 |
| 8 | 3.313 | 3.284 | 3.259 | 3.237 | 3.218 | 3.202 | 3.187 | 3.173 | 3.161 | 3.150 |
| 9 | 3.102 | 3.073 | 3.048 | 3.025 | 3.006 | 2.989 | 2.974 | 2.960 | 2.948 | 2.936 |
| 10 | 2.943 | 2.913 | 2.887 | 2.865 | 2.845 | 2.828 | 2.812 | 2.798 | 2.785 | 2.774 |
| 11 | 2.818 | 2.788 | 2.761 | 2.739 | 2.719 | 2.701 | 2.685 | 2.671 | 2.658 | 2.646 |
| 12 | 2.717 | 2.687 | 2.660 | 2.637 | 2.617 | 2.599 | 2.583 | 2.568 | 2.555 | 2.544 |
| 13 | 2.635 | 2.604 | 2.577 | 2.554 | 2.533 | 2.515 | 2.499 | 2.484 | 2.471 | 2.459 |
| 14 | 2.565 | 2.534 | 2.507 | 2.484 | 2.463 | 2.445 | 2.428 | 2.413 | 2.400 | 2.388 |
| 15 | 2.507 | 2.475 | 2.448 | 2.424 | 2.403 | 2.385 | 2.368 | 2.353 | 2.340 | 2.328 |
| 16 | 2.456 | 2.425 | 2.397 | 2.373 | 2.352 | 2.333 | 2.317 | 2.302 | 2.288 | 2.276 |

DENOMINATOR

$df = D_2$

NUMERATOR $df = D_1$

| | 11 | 12 | 13 | 14 | 15 | 16 | 17 | 18 | 19 | 20 |
|---|---|---|---|---|---|---|---|---|---|---|
| 17 | 2.413 | 2.381 | 2.353 | 2.329 | 2.308 | 2.289 | 2.272 | 2.257 | 2.243 | 2.230 |
| 18 | 2.374 | 2.342 | 2.314 | 2.290 | 2.269 | 2.250 | 2.233 | 2.217 | 2.203 | 2.191 |
| 19 | 2.340 | 2.308 | 2.280 | 2.256 | 2.234 | 2.215 | 2.198 | 2.182 | 2.168 | 2.155 |
| 20 | 2.310 | 2.278 | 2.250 | 2.225 | 2.203 | 2.184 | 2.167 | 2.151 | 2.137 | 2.124 |
| 24 | 2.216 | 2.183 | 2.155 | 2.130 | 2.108 | 2.088 | 2.070 | 2.054 | 2.040 | 2.027 |
| 30 | 2.126 | 2.092 | 2.063 | 2.037 | 2.015 | 1.995 | 1.976 | 1.960 | 1.945 | 1.932 |
| 40 | 2.038 | 2.003 | 1.974 | 1.948 | 1.924 | 1.904 | 1.885 | 1.868 | 1.853 | 1.839 |
| 50 | 1.986 | 1.952 | 1.921 | 1.895 | 1.871 | 1.850 | 1.831 | 1.814 | 1.798 | 1.784 |
| 100 | 1.886 | 1.850 | 1.819 | 1.792 | 1.768 | 1.746 | 1.726 | 1.708 | 1.691 | 1.676 |
| 200 | 1.837 | 1.801 | 1.769 | 1.742 | 1.717 | 1.694 | 1.674 | 1.656 | 1.639 | 1.623 |
| 300 | 1.821 | 1.785 | 1.753 | 1.725 | 1.700 | 1.677 | 1.657 | 1.638 | 1.621 | 1.606 |

DENOMINATOR

$df = D_2$

NUMERATOR $df = D_1$

| | 24 | 30 | 40 | 50 | 100 | 200 | 300 |
|---|---|---|---|---|---|---|---|
| 1 | 249.052 | 250.096 | 251.144 | 251.774 | 253.043 | 253.676 | 253.887 |
| 2 | 19.454 | 19.463 | 19.471 | 19.476 | 19.486 | 19.491 | 19.492 |
| 3 | 8.638 | 8.617 | 8.594 | 8.581 | 8.554 | 8.540 | 8.536 |
| 4 | 5.774 | 5.746 | 5.717 | 5.699 | 5.664 | 5.646 | 5.640 |
| 5 | 4.527 | 4.496 | 4.464 | 4.444 | 4.405 | 4.385 | 4.378 |
| 6 | 3.841 | 3.808 | 3.774 | 3.754 | 3.712 | 3.690 | 3.683 |
| 7 | 3.410 | 3.376 | 3.340 | 3.319 | 3.275 | 3.252 | 3.245 |
| 8 | 3.115 | 3.079 | 3.043 | 3.020 | 2.975 | 2.951 | 2.943 |
| 9 | 2.900 | 2.864 | 2.826 | 2.803 | 2.756 | 2.731 | 2.723 |
| 10 | 2.737 | 2.700 | 2.661 | 2.637 | 2.588 | 2.563 | 2.555 |
| 11 | 2.609 | 2.570 | 2.531 | 2.507 | 2.457 | 2.431 | 2.422 |
| 12 | 2.505 | 2.466 | 2.426 | 2.401 | 2.350 | 2.323 | 2.314 |
| 13 | 2.420 | 2.380 | 2.339 | 2.314 | 2.261 | 2.234 | 2.225 |
| 14 | 2.349 | 2.308 | 2.266 | 2.241 | 2.187 | 2.159 | 2.150 |
| 15 | 2.288 | 2.247 | 2.204 | 2.178 | 2.123 | 2.095 | 2.085 |
| 16 | 2.235 | 2.194 | 2.151 | 2.124 | 2.068 | 2.039 | 2.030 |
| 17 | 2.190 | 2.148 | 2.104 | 2.077 | 2.020 | 1.991 | 1.981 |
| 18 | 2.150 | 2.107 | 2.063 | 2.035 | 1.978 | 1.948 | 1.938 |
| 19 | 2.114 | 2.071 | 2.026 | 1.999 | 1.940 | 1.910 | 1.899 |
| 20 | 2.082 | 2.039 | 1.994 | 1.966 | 1.907 | 1.875 | 1.865 |
| 24 | 1.984 | 1.939 | 1.892 | 1.863 | 1.800 | 1.768 | 1.756 |
| 30 | 1.887 | 1.841 | 1.792 | 1.761 | 1.695 | 1.660 | 1.647 |
| 40 | 1.793 | 1.744 | 1.693 | 1.660 | 1.589 | 1.551 | 1.537 |
| 50 | 1.737 | 1.687 | 1.634 | 1.599 | 1.525 | 1.484 | 1.469 |
| 100 | 1.627 | 1.573 | 1.515 | 1.477 | 1.392 | 1.342 | 1.323 |
| 200 | 1.572 | 1.516 | 1.455 | 1.415 | 1.321 | 1.263 | 1.240 |
| 300 | 1.554 | 1.497 | 1.435 | 1.393 | 1.296 | 1.234 | 1.210 |

(*continued*)

## APPENDIX H (continued)

F-Distribution
Table: Upper 2.5%
Probability (or 2.5%
Area) under
F-Distribution
Curve

DENOMINATOR

| $df = D_2$ | NUMERATOR $df = D_1$ | | | | | | | | | | |
|---|---|---|---|---|---|---|---|---|---|---|---|
| | 1 | 2 | 3 | 4 | 5 | 6 | 7 | 8 | 9 | 10 | 11 |
| 1 | 647.793 | 799.482 | 864.151 | 899.599 | 921.835 | 937.114 | 948.203 | 956.643 | 963.279 | 968.634 | 973.028 |
| 2 | 38.506 | 39.000 | 39.166 | 39.248 | 39.298 | 39.331 | 39.356 | 39.373 | 39.387 | 39.398 | 39.407 |
| 3 | 17.443 | 16.044 | 15.439 | 15.101 | 14.885 | 14.735 | 14.624 | 14.540 | 14.473 | 14.419 | 14.374 |
| 4 | 12.218 | 10.649 | 9.979 | 9.604 | 9.364 | 9.197 | 9.074 | 8.980 | 8.905 | 8.844 | 8.794 |
| 5 | 10.007 | 8.434 | 7.764 | 7.388 | 7.146 | 6.978 | 6.853 | 6.757 | 6.681 | 6.619 | 6.568 |
| 6 | 8.813 | 7.260 | 6.599 | 6.227 | 5.988 | 5.820 | 5.695 | 5.600 | 5.523 | 5.461 | 5.410 |
| 7 | 8.073 | 6.542 | 5.890 | 5.523 | 5.285 | 5.119 | 4.995 | 4.899 | 4.823 | 4.761 | 4.709 |
| 8 | 7.571 | 6.059 | 5.416 | 5.053 | 4.817 | 4.652 | 4.529 | 4.433 | 4.357 | 4.295 | 4.243 |
| 9 | 7.209 | 5.715 | 5.078 | 4.718 | 4.484 | 4.320 | 4.197 | 4.102 | 4.026 | 3.964 | 3.912 |
| 10 | 6.937 | 5.456 | 4.826 | 4.468 | 4.236 | 4.072 | 3.950 | 3.855 | 3.779 | 3.717 | 3.665 |
| 11 | 6.724 | 5.256 | 4.630 | 4.275 | 4.044 | 3.881 | 3.759 | 3.664 | 3.588 | 3.526 | 3.474 |
| 12 | 6.554 | 5.096 | 4.474 | 4.121 | 3.891 | 3.728 | 3.607 | 3.512 | 3.436 | 3.374 | 3.321 |
| 13 | 6.414 | 4.965 | 4.347 | 3.996 | 3.767 | 3.604 | 3.483 | 3.388 | 3.312 | 3.250 | 3.197 |
| 14 | 6.298 | 4.857 | 4.242 | 3.892 | 3.663 | 3.501 | 3.380 | 3.285 | 3.209 | 3.147 | 3.095 |
| 15 | 6.200 | 4.765 | 4.153 | 3.804 | 3.576 | 3.415 | 3.293 | 3.199 | 3.123 | 3.060 | 3.008 |
| 16 | 6.115 | 4.687 | 4.077 | 3.729 | 3.502 | 3.341 | 3.219 | 3.125 | 3.049 | 2.986 | 2.934 |
| 17 | 6.042 | 4.619 | 4.011 | 3.665 | 3.438 | 3.277 | 3.156 | 3.061 | 2.985 | 2.922 | 2.870 |
| 18 | 5.978 | 4.560 | 3.954 | 3.608 | 3.382 | 3.221 | 3.100 | 3.005 | 2.929 | 2.866 | 2.814 |
| 19 | 5.922 | 4.508 | 3.903 | 3.559 | 3.333 | 3.172 | 3.051 | 2.956 | 2.880 | 2.817 | 2.765 |
| 20 | 5.871 | 4.461 | 3.859 | 3.515 | 3.289 | 3.128 | 3.007 | 2.913 | 2.837 | 2.774 | 2.721 |
| 24 | 5.717 | 4.319 | 3.721 | 3.379 | 3.155 | 2.995 | 2.874 | 2.779 | 2.703 | 2.640 | 2.586 |
| 30 | 5.568 | 4.182 | 3.589 | 3.250 | 3.026 | 2.867 | 2.746 | 2.651 | 2.575 | 2.511 | 2.458 |
| 40 | 5.424 | 4.051 | 3.463 | 3.126 | 2.904 | 2.744 | 2.624 | 2.529 | 2.452 | 2.388 | 2.334 |
| 50 | 5.340 | 3.975 | 3.390 | 3.054 | 2.833 | 2.674 | 2.553 | 2.458 | 2.381 | 2.317 | 2.263 |
| 100 | 5.179 | 3.828 | 3.250 | 2.917 | 2.696 | 2.537 | 2.417 | 2.321 | 2.244 | 2.179 | 2.124 |
| 200 | 5.100 | 3.758 | 3.182 | 2.850 | 2.630 | 2.472 | 2.351 | 2.256 | 2.178 | 2.113 | 2.058 |
| 300 | 5.075 | 3.735 | 3.160 | 2.829 | 2.609 | 2.451 | 2.330 | 2.234 | 2.156 | 2.091 | 2.036 |

DENOMINATOR

| $df = D_2$ | NUMERATOR $df = D_1$ | | | | | | | | | | |
|---|---|---|---|---|---|---|---|---|---|---|---|
| | 12 | 13 | 14 | 15 | 16 | 17 | 18 | 19 | 20 | 24 | 30 |
| 1 | 976.725 | 979.839 | 982.545 | 984.874 | 986.911 | 988.715 | 990.345 | 991.800 | 993.081 | 997.272 | 1001.405 |
| 2 | 39.415 | 39.421 | 39.427 | 39.431 | 39.436 | 39.439 | 39.442 | 39.446 | 39.448 | 39.457 | 39.465 |
| 3 | 14.337 | 14.305 | 14.277 | 14.253 | 14.232 | 14.213 | 14.196 | 14.181 | 14.167 | 14.124 | 14.081 |
| 4 | 8.751 | 8.715 | 8.684 | 8.657 | 8.633 | 8.611 | 8.592 | 8.575 | 8.560 | 8.511 | 8.461 |
| 5 | 6.525 | 6.488 | 6.456 | 6.428 | 6.403 | 6.381 | 6.362 | 6.344 | 6.329 | 6.278 | 6.227 |
| 6 | 5.366 | 5.329 | 5.297 | 5.269 | 5.244 | 5.222 | 5.202 | 5.184 | 5.168 | 5.117 | 5.065 |
| 7 | 4.666 | 4.628 | 4.596 | 4.568 | 4.543 | 4.521 | 4.501 | 4.483 | 4.467 | 4.415 | 4.362 |
| 8 | 4.200 | 4.162 | 4.130 | 4.101 | 4.076 | 4.054 | 4.034 | 4.016 | 3.999 | 3.947 | 3.894 |
| 9 | 3.868 | 3.831 | 3.798 | 3.769 | 3.744 | 3.722 | 3.701 | 3.683 | 3.667 | 3.614 | 3.560 |
| 10 | 3.621 | 3.583 | 3.550 | 3.522 | 3.496 | 3.474 | 3.453 | 3.435 | 3.419 | 3.365 | 3.311 |
| 11 | 3.430 | 3.392 | 3.359 | 3.330 | 3.304 | 3.282 | 3.261 | 3.243 | 3.226 | 3.173 | 3.118 |
| 12 | 3.277 | 3.239 | 3.206 | 3.177 | 3.152 | 3.129 | 3.108 | 3.090 | 3.073 | 3.019 | 2.963 |
| 13 | 3.153 | 3.115 | 3.082 | 3.053 | 3.027 | 3.004 | 2.983 | 2.965 | 2.948 | 2.893 | 2.837 |
| 14 | 3.050 | 3.012 | 2.979 | 2.949 | 2.923 | 2.900 | 2.879 | 2.861 | 2.844 | 2.789 | 2.732 |
| 15 | 2.963 | 2.925 | 2.891 | 2.862 | 2.836 | 2.813 | 2.792 | 2.773 | 2.756 | 2.701 | 2.644 |
| 16 | 2.889 | 2.851 | 2.817 | 2.788 | 2.761 | 2.738 | 2.717 | 2.698 | 2.681 | 2.625 | 2.568 |

DENOMINATOR
$df = D_2$

| | | | | | NUMERATOR $df = D_1$ | | | | | | |
|---|---|---|---|---|---|---|---|---|---|---|---|
| | **12** | **13** | **14** | **15** | **16** | **17** | **18** | **19** | **20** | **24** | **30** |
| 17 | 2.825 | 2.786 | 2.753 | 2.723 | 2.697 | 2.673 | 2.652 | 2.633 | 2.616 | 2.560 | 2.502 |
| 18 | 2.769 | 2.730 | 2.696 | 2.667 | 2.640 | 2.617 | 2.596 | 2.576 | 2.559 | 2.503 | 2.445 |
| 19 | 2.720 | 2.681 | 2.647 | 2.617 | 2.591 | 2.567 | 2.546 | 2.526 | 2.509 | 2.452 | 2.394 |
| 20 | 2.676 | 2.637 | 2.603 | 2.573 | 2.547 | 2.523 | 2.501 | 2.482 | 2.464 | 2.408 | 2.349 |
| 24 | 2.541 | 2.502 | 2.468 | 2.437 | 2.411 | 2.386 | 2.365 | 2.345 | 2.327 | 2.269 | 2.209 |
| 30 | 2.412 | 2.372 | 2.338 | 2.307 | 2.280 | 2.255 | 2.233 | 2.213 | 2.195 | 2.136 | 2.074 |
| 40 | 2.288 | 2.248 | 2.213 | 2.182 | 2.154 | 2.129 | 2.107 | 2.086 | 2.068 | 2.007 | 1.943 |
| 50 | 2.216 | 2.176 | 2.140 | 2.109 | 2.081 | 2.056 | 2.033 | 2.012 | 1.993 | 1.931 | 1.866 |
| 100 | 2.077 | 2.036 | 2.000 | 1.968 | 1.939 | 1.913 | 1.890 | 1.868 | 1.849 | 1.784 | 1.715 |
| 200 | 2.010 | 1.969 | 1.932 | 1.900 | 1.870 | 1.844 | 1.820 | 1.798 | 1.778 | 1.712 | 1.640 |
| 300 | 1.988 | 1.947 | 1.910 | 1.877 | 1.848 | 1.821 | 1.797 | 1.775 | 1.755 | 1.688 | 1.616 |

DENOMINATOR
$df = D_2$

| | | | NUMERATOR $df = D_1$ | | |
|---|---|---|---|---|---|
| | **40** | **50** | **100** | **200** | **300** |
| 1 | 1005.596 | 1008.098 | 1013.163 | 1015.724 | 1016.539 |
| 2 | 39.473 | 39.478 | 39.488 | 39.493 | 39.495 |
| 3 | 14.036 | 14.010 | 13.956 | 13.929 | 13.920 |
| 4 | 8.411 | 8.381 | 8.319 | 8.288 | 8.278 |
| 5 | 6.175 | 6.144 | 6.080 | 6.048 | 6.037 |
| 6 | 5.012 | 4.980 | 4.915 | 4.882 | 4.871 |
| 7 | 4.309 | 4.276 | 4.210 | 4.176 | 4.165 |
| 8 | 3.840 | 3.807 | 3.739 | 3.705 | 3.693 |
| 9 | 3.505 | 3.472 | 3.403 | 3.368 | 3.357 |
| 10 | 3.255 | 3.221 | 3.152 | 3.116 | 3.104 |
| 11 | 3.061 | 3.027 | 2.956 | 2.920 | 2.908 |
| 12 | 2.906 | 2.871 | 2.800 | 2.763 | 2.750 |
| 13 | 2.780 | 2.744 | 2.671 | 2.634 | 2.621 |
| 14 | 2.674 | 2.638 | 2.565 | 2.526 | 2.513 |
| 15 | 2.585 | 2.549 | 2.474 | 2.435 | 2.422 |
| 16 | 2.509 | 2.472 | 2.396 | 2.357 | 2.343 |
| 17 | 2.442 | 2.405 | 2.329 | 2.289 | 2.275 |
| 18 | 2.384 | 2.347 | 2.269 | 2.229 | 2.215 |
| 19 | 2.333 | 2.295 | 2.217 | 2.176 | 2.162 |
| 20 | 2.287 | 2.249 | 2.170 | 2.128 | 2.114 |
| 24 | 2.146 | 2.107 | 2.024 | 1.981 | 1.966 |
| 30 | 2.009 | 1.968 | 1.882 | 1.835 | 1.819 |
| 40 | 1.875 | 1.832 | 1.741 | 1.691 | 1.673 |
| 50 | 1.796 | 1.752 | 1.656 | 1.603 | 1.584 |
| 100 | 1.640 | 1.592 | 1.483 | 1.420 | 1.397 |
| 200 | 1.562 | 1.511 | 1.393 | 1.320 | 1.293 |
| 300 | 1.536 | 1.484 | 1.361 | 1.285 | 1.255 |

*(continued)*

## APPENDIX H (continued)

*F*-Distribution
Table: Upper 1%
Probability (or 1%
Area) under
*F*-Distribution
Curve

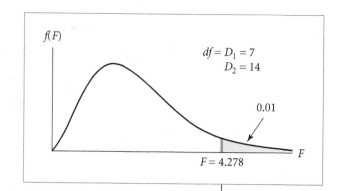

DENOMINATOR
*df* = $D_2$

NUMERATOR *df* = $D_1$

| | 1 | 2 | 3 | 4 | 5 | 6 | 7 | 8 | 9 | 10 | 11 |
|---|---|---|---|---|---|---|---|---|---|---|---|
| 1 | 4052.185 | 4999.340 | 5403.534 | 5624.257 | 5763.955 | 5858.950 | 5928.334 | 5980.954 | 6022.397 | 6055.925 | 6083.399 |
| 2 | 98.502 | 99.000 | 99.164 | 99.251 | 99.302 | 99.331 | 99.357 | 99.375 | 99.390 | 99.397 | 99.408 |
| 3 | 34.116 | 30.816 | 29.457 | 28.710 | 28.237 | 27.911 | 27.671 | 27.489 | 27.345 | 27.228 | 27.132 |
| 4 | 21.198 | 18.000 | 16.694 | 15.977 | 15.522 | 15.207 | 14.976 | 14.799 | 14.659 | 14.546 | 14.452 |
| 5 | 16.258 | 13.274 | 12.060 | 11.392 | 10.967 | 10.672 | 10.456 | 10.289 | 10.158 | 10.051 | 9.963 |
| 6 | 13.745 | 10.925 | 9.780 | 9.148 | 8.746 | 8.466 | 8.260 | 8.102 | 7.976 | 7.874 | 7.790 |
| 7 | 12.246 | 9.547 | 8.451 | 7.847 | 7.460 | 7.191 | 6.993 | 6.840 | 6.719 | 6.620 | 6.538 |
| 8 | 11.259 | 8.649 | 7.591 | 7.006 | 6.632 | 6.371 | 6.178 | 6.029 | 5.911 | 5.814 | 5.734 |
| 9 | 10.562 | 8.022 | 6.992 | 6.422 | 6.057 | 5.802 | 5.613 | 5.467 | 5.351 | 5.257 | 5.178 |
| 10 | 10.044 | 7.559 | 6.552 | 5.994 | 5.636 | 5.386 | 5.200 | 5.057 | 4.942 | 4.849 | 4.772 |
| 11 | 9.646 | 7.206 | 6.217 | 5.668 | 5.316 | 5.069 | 4.886 | 4.744 | 4.632 | 4.539 | 4.462 |
| 12 | 9.330 | 6.927 | 5.953 | 5.412 | 5.064 | 4.821 | 4.640 | 4.499 | 4.388 | 4.296 | 4.220 |
| 13 | 9.074 | 6.701 | 5.739 | 5.205 | 4.862 | 4.620 | 4.441 | 4.302 | 4.191 | 4.100 | 4.025 |
| 14 | 8.862 | 6.515 | 5.564 | 5.035 | 4.695 | 4.456 | 4.278 | 4.140 | 4.030 | 3.939 | 3.864 |
| 15 | 8.683 | 6.359 | 5.417 | 4.893 | 4.556 | 4.318 | 4.142 | 4.004 | 3.895 | 3.805 | 3.730 |
| 16 | 8.531 | 6.226 | 5.292 | 4.773 | 4.437 | 4.202 | 4.026 | 3.890 | 3.780 | 3.691 | 3.616 |
| 17 | 8.400 | 6.112 | 5.185 | 4.669 | 4.336 | 4.101 | 3.927 | 3.791 | 3.682 | 3.593 | 3.518 |
| 18 | 8.285 | 6.013 | 5.092 | 4.579 | 4.248 | 4.015 | 3.841 | 3.705 | 3.597 | 3.508 | 3.434 |
| 19 | 8.185 | 5.926 | 5.010 | 4.500 | 4.171 | 3.939 | 3.765 | 3.631 | 3.523 | 3.434 | 3.360 |
| 20 | 8.096 | 5.849 | 4.938 | 4.431 | 4.103 | 3.871 | 3.699 | 3.564 | 3.457 | 3.368 | 3.294 |
| 24 | 7.823 | 5.614 | 4.718 | 4.218 | 3.895 | 3.667 | 3.496 | 3.363 | 3.256 | 3.168 | 3.094 |
| 30 | 7.562 | 5.390 | 4.510 | 4.018 | 3.699 | 3.473 | 3.305 | 3.173 | 3.067 | 2.979 | 2.906 |
| 40 | 7.314 | 5.178 | 4.313 | 3.828 | 3.514 | 3.291 | 3.124 | 2.993 | 2.888 | 2.801 | 2.727 |
| 50 | 7.171 | 5.057 | 4.199 | 3.720 | 3.408 | 3.186 | 3.020 | 2.890 | 2.785 | 2.698 | 2.625 |
| 100 | 6.895 | 4.824 | 3.984 | 3.513 | 3.206 | 2.988 | 2.823 | 2.694 | 2.590 | 2.503 | 2.430 |
| 200 | 6.763 | 4.713 | 3.881 | 3.414 | 3.110 | 2.893 | 2.730 | 2.601 | 2.497 | 2.411 | 2.338 |
| 300 | 6.720 | 4.677 | 3.848 | 3.382 | 3.079 | 2.862 | 2.699 | 2.571 | 2.467 | 2.380 | 2.307 |

DENOMINATOR
*df* = $D_2$

NUMERATOR *df* = $D_1$

| | 12 | 13 | 14 | 15 | 16 | 17 | 18 | 19 | 20 | 24 | 30 |
|---|---|---|---|---|---|---|---|---|---|---|---|
| 1 | 6106.682 | 6125.774 | 6143.004 | 6156.974 | 6170.012 | 6181.188 | 6191.432 | 6200.746 | 6208.662 | 6234.273 | 6260.350 |
| 2 | 99.419 | 99.422 | 99.426 | 99.433 | 99.437 | 99.441 | 99.444 | 99.448 | 99.448 | 99.455 | 99.466 |
| 3 | 27.052 | 26.983 | 26.924 | 26.872 | 26.826 | 26.786 | 26.751 | 26.719 | 26.690 | 26.597 | 26.504 |
| 4 | 14.374 | 14.306 | 14.249 | 14.198 | 14.154 | 14.114 | 14.079 | 14.048 | 14.019 | 13.929 | 13.838 |
| 5 | 9.888 | 9.825 | 9.770 | 9.722 | 9.680 | 9.643 | 9.609 | 9.580 | 9.553 | 9.466 | 9.379 |
| 6 | 7.718 | 7.657 | 7.605 | 7.559 | 7.519 | 7.483 | 7.451 | 7.422 | 7.396 | 7.313 | 7.229 |
| 7 | 6.469 | 6.410 | 6.359 | 6.314 | 6.275 | 6.240 | 6.209 | 6.181 | 6.155 | 6.074 | 5.992 |
| 8 | 5.667 | 5.609 | 5.559 | 5.515 | 5.477 | 5.442 | 5.412 | 5.384 | 5.359 | 5.279 | 5.198 |
| 9 | 5.111 | 5.055 | 5.005 | 4.962 | 4.924 | 4.890 | 4.860 | 4.833 | 4.808 | 4.729 | 4.649 |
| 10 | 4.706 | 4.650 | 4.601 | 4.558 | 4.520 | 4.487 | 4.457 | 4.430 | 4.405 | 4.327 | 4.247 |
| 11 | 4.397 | 4.342 | 4.293 | 4.251 | 4.213 | 4.180 | 4.150 | 4.123 | 4.099 | 4.021 | 3.941 |
| 12 | 4.155 | 4.100 | 4.052 | 4.010 | 3.972 | 3.939 | 3.910 | 3.883 | 3.858 | 3.780 | 3.701 |
| 13 | 3.960 | 3.905 | 3.857 | 3.815 | 3.778 | 3.745 | 3.716 | 3.689 | 3.665 | 3.587 | 3.507 |
| 14 | 3.800 | 3.745 | 3.698 | 3.656 | 3.619 | 3.586 | 3.556 | 3.529 | 3.505 | 3.427 | 3.348 |
| 15 | 3.666 | 3.612 | 3.564 | 3.522 | 3.485 | 3.452 | 3.423 | 3.396 | 3.372 | 3.294 | 3.214 |
| 16 | 3.553 | 3.498 | 3.451 | 3.409 | 3.372 | 3.339 | 3.310 | 3.283 | 3.259 | 3.181 | 3.101 |

DENOMINATOR

| $df = D_2$ | NUMERATOR $df = D_1$ | | | | | | | | | | |
|---|---|---|---|---|---|---|---|---|---|---|---|
| | **12** | **13** | **14** | **15** | **16** | **17** | **18** | **19** | **20** | **24** | **30** |
| 17 | 3.455 | 3.401 | 3.353 | 3.312 | 3.275 | 3.242 | 3.212 | 3.186 | 3.162 | 3.083 | 3.003 |
| 18 | 3.371 | 3.316 | 3.269 | 3.227 | 3.190 | 3.158 | 3.128 | 3.101 | 3.077 | 2.999 | 2.919 |
| 19 | 3.297 | 3.242 | 3.195 | 3.153 | 3.116 | 3.018 | 2.989 | 2.962 | 2.938 | 2.859 | 2.778 |
| 20 | 3.231 | 3.177 | 3.130 | 3.088 | 3.051 | 3.018 | 2.789 | 2.762 | 2.738 | 2.659 | 2.577 |
| 24 | 3.032 | 2.977 | 2.930 | 2.889 | 2.852 | 2.819 | 2.600 | 2.573 | 2.549 | 2.469 | 2.386 |
| 30 | 2.843 | 2.789 | 2.742 | 2.700 | 2.663 | 2.630 | 2.421 | 2.394 | 2.369 | 2.288 | 2.203 |
| 40 | 2.665 | 2.611 | 2.563 | 2.522 | 2.484 | 2.451 | 2.318 | 2.290 | 2.265 | 2.183 | 2.098 |
| 50 | 2.563 | 2.508 | 2.461 | 2.419 | 2.382 | 2.348 | 2.120 | 2.092 | 2.067 | 1.983 | 1.893 |
| 100 | 2.368 | 2.313 | 2.265 | 2.223 | 2.185 | 2.151 | 2.026 | 1.997 | 1.971 | 1.886 | 1.794 |
| 200 | 2.275 | 2.220 | 2.172 | 2.129 | 2.091 | 2.057 | 1.995 | 1.966 | 1.940 | 1.854 | 1.761 |
| 300 | 2.244 | 2.190 | 2.142 | 2.099 | 2.061 | 2.026 | 1.995 | 1.966 | 1.940 | 1.854 | 1.761 |

DENOMINATOR

| $df = D_2$ | NUMERATOR $df = D_1$ | | | | |
|---|---|---|---|---|---|
| | **40** | **50** | **100** | **200** | **300** |
| 1 | 6286.427 | 6302.260 | 6333.925 | 6349.757 | 6355.345 |
| 2 | 99.477 | 99.477 | 99.491 | 99.491 | 99.499 |
| 3 | 26.411 | 26.354 | 26.241 | 26.183 | 26.163 |
| 4 | 13.745 | 13.690 | 13.577 | 13.520 | 13.501 |
| 5 | 9.291 | 9.238 | 9.130 | 9.075 | 9.057 |
| 6 | 7.143 | 7.091 | 6.987 | 6.934 | 6.916 |
| 7 | 5.908 | 5.858 | 5.755 | 5.702 | 5.685 |
| 8 | 5.116 | 5.065 | 4.963 | 4.911 | 4.894 |
| 9 | 4.567 | 4.517 | 4.415 | 4.363 | 4.346 |
| 10 | 4.165 | 4.115 | 4.014 | 3.962 | 3.944 |
| 11 | 3.860 | 3.810 | 3.708 | 3.656 | 3.638 |
| 12 | 3.619 | 3.569 | 3.467 | 3.414 | 3.397 |
| 13 | 3.425 | 3.375 | 3.272 | 3.219 | 3.202 |
| 14 | 3.266 | 3.215 | 3.112 | 3.059 | 3.040 |
| 15 | 3.132 | 3.081 | 2.977 | 2.923 | 2.905 |
| 16 | 3.018 | 2.967 | 2.863 | 2.808 | 2.790 |
| 17 | 2.920 | 2.869 | 2.764 | 2.709 | 2.691 |
| 18 | 2.835 | 2.784 | 2.678 | 2.623 | 2.604 |
| 19 | 2.761 | 2.709 | 2.602 | 2.547 | 2.528 |
| 20 | 2.695 | 2.643 | 2.535 | 2.479 | 2.460 |
| 24 | 2.492 | 2.440 | 2.329 | 2.271 | 2.251 |
| 30 | 2.299 | 2.245 | 2.131 | 2.070 | 2.049 |
| 40 | 2.114 | 2.058 | 1.938 | 1.874 | 1.851 |
| 50 | 2.007 | 1.949 | 1.825 | 1.757 | 1.733 |
| 100 | 1.797 | 1.735 | 1.598 | 1.518 | 1.490 |
| 200 | 1.694 | 1.629 | 1.481 | 1.391 | 1.357 |
| 300 | 1.660 | 1.594 | 1.441 | 1.346 | 1.309 |

## APPENDIX I

### Critical Values of Hartley's $F_{max}$ Test

$$F_{max} = \frac{S^2_{largest}}{S^2_{smallest}} \sim F_{max_{1-a(c,v)}}$$

UPPER 5% POINTS ($\alpha = 0.05$)

| $v$ \ $c$ | 2 | 3 | 4 | 5 | 6 | 7 | 8 | 9 | 10 | 11 | 12 |
|---|---|---|---|---|---|---|---|---|---|---|---|
| 2 | 39.0 | 87.5 | 142 | 202 | 266 | 333 | 403 | 475 | 550 | 626 | 704 |
| 3 | 15.4 | 27.8 | 39.2 | 50.7 | 62.0 | 72.9 | 83.5 | 93.9 | 104 | 114 | 124 |
| 4 | 9.60 | 15.5 | 20.6 | 25.2 | 29.5 | 33.6 | 37.5 | 41.1 | 44.6 | 48.0 | 51.4 |
| 5 | 7.15 | 10.8 | 13.7 | 16.3 | 18.7 | 20.8 | 22.9 | 24.7 | 26.5 | 28.2 | 29.9 |
| 6 | 5.82 | 8.38 | 10.4 | 12.1 | 13.7 | 15.0 | 16.3 | 17.5 | 18.6 | 19.7 | 20.7 |
| 7 | 4.99 | 6.94 | 8.44 | 9.70 | 10.8 | 11.8 | 12.7 | 13.5 | 14.3 | 15.1 | 15.8 |
| 8 | 4.43 | 6.00 | 7.18 | 8.12 | 9.03 | 9.78 | 10.5 | 11.1 | 11.7 | 12.2 | 12.7 |
| 9 | 4.03 | 5.34 | 6.31 | 7.11 | 7.80 | 8.41 | 8.95 | 9.45 | 9.91 | 10.3 | 10.7 |
| 10 | 3.72 | 4.85 | 5.67 | 6.34 | 6.92 | 7.42 | 7.87 | 8.28 | 8.66 | 9.01 | 9.34 |
| 12 | 3.28 | 4.16 | 4.79 | 5.30 | 5.72 | 6.09 | 6.42 | 6.72 | 7.00 | 7.25 | 7.48 |
| 15 | 2.86 | 3.54 | 4.01 | 4.37 | 4.68 | 4.95 | 5.19 | 5.40 | 5.59 | 5.77 | 5.93 |
| 20 | 2.46 | 2.95 | 3.29 | 3.54 | 3.76 | 3.94 | 4.10 | 4.24 | 4.37 | 4.49 | 4.59 |
| 30 | 2.07 | 2.40 | 2.61 | 2.78 | 2.91 | 3.02 | 3.12 | 3.21 | 3.29 | 3.36 | 3.39 |
| 60 | 1.67 | 1.85 | 1.96 | 2.04 | 2.11 | 2.17 | 2.22 | 2.26 | 2.30 | 2.33 | 2.36 |
| $\infty$ | 1.00 | 1.00 | 1.00 | 1.00 | 1.00 | 1.00 | 1.00 | 1.00 | 1.00 | 1.00 | 1.00 |

UPPER 1% POINTS ($\alpha = 0.01$)

| $v$ \ $c$ | 2 | 3 | 4 | 5 | 6 | 7 | 8 | 9 | 10 | 11 | 12 |
|---|---|---|---|---|---|---|---|---|---|---|---|
| 2 | 199 | 448 | 729 | 1036 | 1362 | 1705 | 2063 | 2432 | 2813 | 3204 | 3605 |
| 3 | 47.5 | 85 | 120 | 151 | 184 | 21(6) | 24(9) | 28(1) | 31(0) | 33(7) | 36(1) |
| 4 | 23.2 | 37 | 49 | 59 | 69 | 79 | 89 | 97 | 106 | 113 | 120 |
| 5 | 14.9 | 22 | 28 | 33 | 38 | 42 | 46 | 50 | 54 | 57 | 60 |
| 6 | 11.1 | 15.5 | 19.1 | 22 | 25 | 27 | 30 | 32 | 34 | 36 | 37 |
| 7 | 8.89 | 12.1 | 14.5 | 16.5 | 18.4 | 20 | 22 | 23 | 24 | 26 | 27 |
| 8 | 7.50 | 9.9 | 11.7 | 13.2 | 14.5 | 15.8 | 16.9 | 17.9 | 18.9 | 19.8 | 21 |
| 9 | 6.54 | 8.5 | 9.9 | 11.1 | 12.1 | 13.1 | 13.9 | 14.7 | 15.3 | 16.0 | 16.6 |
| 10 | 5.85 | 7.4 | 8.6 | 9.6 | 10.4 | 11.1 | 11.8 | 12.4 | 12.9 | 13.4 | 13.9 |
| 12 | 4.91 | 6.1 | 6.9 | 7.6 | 8.2 | 8.7 | 9.1 | 9.5 | 9.9 | 10.2 | 10.6 |
| 15 | 4.07 | 4.9 | 5.5 | 6.0 | 6.4 | 6.7 | 7.1 | 7.3 | 7.5 | 7.8 | 8.0 |
| 20 | 3.32 | 3.8 | 4.3 | 4.6 | 4.9 | 5.1 | 5.3 | 5.5 | 5.6 | 5.8 | 5.9 |
| 30 | 2.63 | 3.0 | 3.3 | 3.4 | 3.6 | 3.7 | 3.8 | 3.9 | 4.0 | 4.1 | 4.2 |
| 60 | 1.96 | 2.2 | 2.3 | 2.4 | 2.4 | 2.5 | 2.5 | 2.6 | 2.6 | 2.7 | 2.7 |
| $\infty$ | 1.00 | 1.0 | 1.0 | 1.0 | 1.0 | 1.0 | 1.0 | 1.0 | 1.0 | 1.00 | 1.0 |

Note: $S^2_{largest}$ is the largest and the $s^2_{smallest}$ the smallest in a set of $c$ independent mean squares, each based on $v$ degrees of freedom.

Source: Reprinted from E. S. Pearson and H. O. Hartley, eds., *Biometrika Tables for Statisticians*, 3d ed. (New York: Cambridge University Press, 1966), by permission of the Biometrika Trustees.

Distribution of the
Studentized Range
(*q*-values)

$p = 0.95$

| $D_2$\\$D_1$ | 2 | 3 | 4 | 5 | 6 | 7 | 8 | 9 | 10 |
|---|---|---|---|---|---|---|---|---|---|
| 1 | 17.97 | 26.98 | 32.82 | 37.08 | 40.41 | 43.12 | 45.40 | 47.36 | 49.07 |
| 2 | 6.08 | 8.33 | 9.80 | 10.88 | 11.74 | 12.44 | 13.03 | 13.54 | 13.99 |
| 3 | 4.50 | 5.91 | 6.82 | 7.50 | 8.04 | 8.48 | 8.85 | 9.18 | 9.46 |
| 4 | 3.93 | 5.04 | 5.76 | 6.29 | 6.71 | 7.05 | 7.35 | 7.60 | 7.83 |
| 5 | 3.64 | 4.60 | 5.22 | 5.67 | 6.03 | 6.33 | 6.58 | 6.80 | 6.99 |
| 6 | 3.46 | 4.34 | 4.90 | 5.30 | 5.63 | 5.90 | 6.12 | 6.32 | 6.49 |
| 7 | 3.34 | 4.16 | 4.68 | 5.06 | 5.36 | 5.61 | 5.82 | 6.00 | 6.16 |
| 8 | 3.26 | 4.04 | 4.53 | 4.89 | 5.17 | 5.40 | 5.60 | 5.77 | 5.92 |
| 9 | 3.20 | 3.95 | 4.41 | 4.76 | 5.02 | 5.24 | 5.43 | 5.59 | 5.74 |
| 10 | 3.15 | 3.88 | 4.33 | 4.65 | 4.91 | 5.12 | 5.30 | 5.46 | 5.60 |
| 11 | 3.11 | 3.82 | 4.26 | 4.57 | 4.82 | 5.03 | 5.20 | 5.35 | 5.49 |
| 12 | 3.08 | 3.77 | 4.20 | 4.51 | 4.75 | 4.95 | 5.12 | 5.27 | 5.39 |
| 13 | 3.06 | 3.73 | 4.15 | 4.45 | 4.69 | 4.88 | 5.05 | 5.19 | 5.32 |
| 14 | 3.03 | 3.70 | 4.11 | 4.41 | 4.64 | 4.83 | 4.99 | 5.13 | 5.25 |
| 15 | 3.01 | 3.67 | 4.08 | 4.37 | 4.59 | 4.78 | 4.94 | 5.08 | 5.20 |
| 16 | 3.00 | 3.65 | 4.05 | 4.33 | 4.56 | 4.74 | 4.90 | 5.03 | 5.15 |
| 17 | 2.98 | 3.63 | 4.02 | 4.30 | 4.52 | 4.70 | 4.86 | 4.99 | 5.11 |
| 18 | 2.97 | 3.61 | 4.00 | 4.28 | 4.49 | 4.67 | 4.82 | 4.96 | 5.07 |
| 19 | 2.96 | 3.59 | 3.98 | 4.25 | 4.47 | 4.65 | 4.79 | 4.92 | 5.04 |
| 20 | 2.95 | 3.58 | 3.96 | 4.23 | 4.45 | 4.62 | 4.77 | 4.90 | 5.01 |
| 24 | 2.92 | 3.53 | 3.90 | 4.17 | 4.37 | 4.54 | 4.68 | 4.81 | 4.92 |
| 30 | 2.89 | 3.49 | 3.85 | 4.10 | 4.30 | 4.46 | 4.60 | 4.72 | 4.82 |
| 40 | 2.86 | 3.44 | 3.79 | 4.04 | 4.23 | 4.39 | 4.52 | 4.63 | 4.73 |
| 60 | 2.83 | 3.40 | 3.74 | 3.98 | 4.16 | 4.31 | 4.44 | 4.55 | 4.65 |
| 120 | 2.80 | 3.36 | 3.68 | 3.92 | 4.10 | 4.24 | 4.36 | 4.47 | 4.56 |
| ∞ | 2.77 | 3.31 | 3.63 | 3.86 | 4.03 | 4.17 | 4.29 | 4.39 | 4.47 |

| $D_2$\\$D_1$ | 11 | 12 | 13 | 14 | 15 | 16 | 17 | 18 | 19 | 20 |
|---|---|---|---|---|---|---|---|---|---|---|
| 1 | 50.59 | 51.96 | 53.20 | 54.33 | 55.36 | 56.32 | 57.22 | 58.04 | 58.83 | 59.56 |
| 2 | 14.39 | 14.75 | 15.08 | 15.38 | 15.65 | 15.91 | 16.14 | 16.37 | 16.57 | 16.77 |
| 3 | 9.72 | 9.95 | 10.15 | 10.35 | 10.52 | 10.69 | 10.84 | 10.98 | 11.11 | 11.24 |
| 4 | 8.03 | 8.21 | 8.37 | 8.52 | 8.66 | 8.79 | 8.91 | 9.03 | 9.13 | 9.23 |
| 5 | 7.17 | 7.32 | 7.47 | 7.60 | 7.72 | 7.83 | 7.93 | 8.03 | 8.12 | 8.21 |
| 6 | 6.65 | 6.79 | 6.92 | 7.03 | 7.14 | 7.24 | 7.34 | 7.43 | 7.51 | 7.59 |
| 7 | 6.30 | 6.43 | 6.55 | 6.66 | 6.76 | 6.85 | 6.94 | 7.02 | 7.10 | 7.17 |
| 8 | 6.05 | 6.18 | 6.29 | 6.39 | 6.48 | 6.57 | 6.65 | 6.73 | 6.80 | 6.87 |
| 9 | 5.87 | 5.98 | 6.09 | 6.19 | 6.28 | 6.36 | 6.44 | 6.51 | 6.58 | 6.64 |
| 10 | 5.72 | 5.83 | 5.93 | 6.03 | 6.11 | 6.19 | 6.27 | 6.34 | 6.40 | 6.47 |
| 11 | 5.61 | 5.71 | 5.81 | 5.90 | 5.98 | 6.06 | 6.13 | 6.20 | 6.27 | 6.33 |
| 12 | 5.51 | 5.61 | 5.71 | 5.80 | 5.88 | 5.95 | 6.02 | 6.09 | 6.15 | 6.21 |
| 13 | 5.43 | 5.53 | 5.63 | 5.71 | 5.79 | 5.86 | 5.93 | 5.99 | 6.05 | 6.11 |
| 14 | 5.36 | 5.46 | 5.55 | 5.64 | 5.71 | 5.79 | 5.85 | 5.91 | 5.97 | 6.03 |
| 15 | 5.31 | 5.40 | 5.49 | 5.57 | 5.65 | 5.72 | 5.78 | 5.85 | 5.90 | 5.96 |
| 16 | 5.26 | 5.35 | 5.44 | 5.52 | 5.59 | 5.66 | 5.73 | 5.79 | 5.84 | 5.90 |
| 17 | 5.21 | 5.31 | 5.39 | 5.47 | 5.54 | 5.61 | 5.67 | 5.73 | 5.79 | 5.84 |
| 18 | 5.17 | 5.27 | 5.35 | 5.43 | 5.50 | 5.57 | 5.63 | 5.69 | 5.74 | 5.79 |
| 19 | 5.14 | 5.23 | 5.31 | 5.39 | 5.46 | 5.53 | 5.59 | 5.65 | 5.70 | 5.75 |
| 20 | 5.11 | 5.20 | 5.28 | 5.36 | 5.43 | 5.49 | 5.55 | 5.61 | 5.66 | 5.71 |
| 24 | 5.01 | 5.10 | 5.18 | 5.25 | 5.32 | 5.38 | 5.44 | 5.49 | 5.55 | 5.59 |
| 30 | 4.92 | 5.00 | 5.08 | 5.15 | 5.21 | 5.27 | 5.33 | 5.38 | 5.43 | 5.47 |
| 40 | 4.82 | 4.90 | 4.98 | 5.04 | 5.11 | 5.16 | 5.22 | 5.27 | 5.31 | 5.36 |
| 60 | 4.73 | 4.81 | 4.88 | 4.94 | 5.00 | 5.06 | 5.11 | 5.15 | 5.20 | 5.24 |
| 120 | 4.64 | 4.71 | 4.78 | 4.84 | 4.90 | 4.95 | 5.00 | 5.04 | 5.09 | 5.13 |
| ∞ | 4.55 | 4.62 | 4.68 | 4.74 | 4.80 | 4.85 | 4.89 | 4.93 | 4.97 | 5.01 |

*Note:* $D_1 = K$ populations and $D_2 = N - K$.

$p = 0.99$

| $D_2$＼$D_1$ | 2 | 3 | 4 | 5 | 6 | 7 | 8 | 9 | 10 |
|---|---|---|---|---|---|---|---|---|---|
| 1 | 90.03 | 135.0 | 164.3 | 185.6 | 202.2 | 215.8 | 227.2 | 237.0 | 245.6 |
| 2 | 14.04 | 19.02 | 22.29 | 24.72 | 26.63 | 28.20 | 29.53 | 30.68 | 31.69 |
| 3 | 8.26 | 10.62 | 12.17 | 13.33 | 14.24 | 15.00 | 15.64 | 16.20 | 16.69 |
| 4 | 6.51 | 8.12 | 9.17 | 9.96 | 10.58 | 11.10 | 11.55 | 11.93 | 12.27 |
| 5 | 5.70 | 6.98 | 7.80 | 8.42 | 8.91 | 9.32 | 9.67 | 9.97 | 10.24 |
| 6 | 5.24 | 6.33 | 7.03 | 7.56 | 7.97 | 8.32 | 8.61 | 8.87 | 9.10 |
| 7 | 4.95 | 5.92 | 6.54 | 7.01 | 7.37 | 7.68 | 7.94 | 8.17 | 8.37 |
| 8 | 4.75 | 5.64 | 6.20 | 6.62 | 6.96 | 7.24 | 7.47 | 7.68 | 7.86 |
| 9 | 4.60 | 5.43 | 5.96 | 6.35 | 6.66 | 6.91 | 7.13 | 7.33 | 7.49 |
| 10 | 4.48 | 5.27 | 5.77 | 6.14 | 6.43 | 6.67 | 6.87 | 7.05 | 7.21 |
| 11 | 4.39 | 5.15 | 5.62 | 5.97 | 6.25 | 6.48 | 6.67 | 6.84 | 6.99 |
| 12 | 4.32 | 5.05 | 5.50 | 5.84 | 6.10 | 6.32 | 6.51 | 6.67 | 6.81 |
| 13 | 4.26 | 4.96 | 5.40 | 5.73 | 5.98 | 6.19 | 6.37 | 6.53 | 6.67 |
| 14 | 4.21 | 4.89 | 5.32 | 5.63 | 5.88 | 6.08 | 6.26 | 6.41 | 6.54 |
| 15 | 4.17 | 4.84 | 5.25 | 5.56 | 5.80 | 5.99 | 6.16 | 6.31 | 6.44 |
| 16 | 4.13 | 4.79 | 5.19 | 5.49 | 5.72 | 5.92 | 6.08 | 6.22 | 6.35 |
| 17 | 4.10 | 4.74 | 5.14 | 5.43 | 5.66 | 5.85 | 6.01 | 6.15 | 6.27 |
| 18 | 4.07 | 4.70 | 5.09 | 5.38 | 5.60 | 5.79 | 5.94 | 6.08 | 6.20 |
| 19 | 4.05 | 4.67 | 5.05 | 5.33 | 5.55 | 5.73 | 5.89 | 6.02 | 6.14 |
| 20 | 4.02 | 4.64 | 5.02 | 5.29 | 5.51 | 5.69 | 5.84 | 5.97 | 6.09 |
| 24 | 3.96 | 4.55 | 4.91 | 5.17 | 5.37 | 5.54 | 5.69 | 5.81 | 5.92 |
| 30 | 3.89 | 4.45 | 4.80 | 5.05 | 5.24 | 5.40 | 5.54 | 5.65 | 5.76 |
| 40 | 3.82 | 4.37 | 4.70 | 4.93 | 5.11 | 5.26 | 5.39 | 5.50 | 5.60 |
| 60 | 3.76 | 4.28 | 4.59 | 4.82 | 4.99 | 5.13 | 5.25 | 5.36 | 5.45 |
| 120 | 3.70 | 4.20 | 4.50 | 4.71 | 4.87 | 5.01 | 5.12 | 5.21 | 5.30 |
| $\infty$ | 3.64 | 4.12 | 4.40 | 4.60 | 4.76 | 4.88 | 4.99 | 5.08 | 5.16 |

| $D_2$＼$D_1$ | 11 | 12 | 13 | 14 | 15 | 16 | 17 | 18 | 19 | 20 |
|---|---|---|---|---|---|---|---|---|---|---|
| 1 | 253.2 | 260.0 | 266.2 | 271.8 | 277.0 | 281.8 | 286.3 | 290.4 | 294.3 | 298.0 |
| 2 | 32.59 | 33.40 | 34.13 | 34.81 | 35.43 | 36.00 | 36.53 | 37.03 | 37.50 | 37.95 |
| 3 | 17.13 | 17.53 | 17.89 | 18.22 | 18.52 | 18.81 | 19.07 | 19.32 | 19.55 | 19.77 |
| 4 | 12.57 | 12.84 | 13.09 | 13.32 | 13.53 | 13.73 | 13.91 | 14.08 | 14.24 | 14.40 |
| 5 | 10.48 | 10.70 | 10.89 | 11.08 | 11.24 | 11.40 | 11.55 | 11.68 | 11.81 | 11.93 |
| 6 | 9.30 | 9.48 | 9.65 | 9.81 | 9.95 | 10.08 | 10.21 | 10.32 | 10.43 | 10.54 |
| 7 | 8.55 | 8.71 | 8.86 | 9.00 | 9.12 | 9.24 | 9.35 | 9.46 | 9.55 | 9.65 |
| 8 | 8.03 | 8.18 | 8.31 | 8.44 | 8.55 | 8.66 | 8.76 | 8.85 | 8.94 | 9.03 |
| 9 | 7.65 | 7.78 | 7.91 | 8.03 | 8.13 | 8.23 | 8.33 | 8.41 | 8.49 | 8.57 |
| 10 | 7.36 | 7.49 | 7.60 | 7.71 | 7.81 | 7.91 | 7.99 | 8.08 | 8.15 | 8.23 |
| 11 | 7.13 | 7.25 | 7.36 | 7.46 | 7.56 | 7.65 | 7.73 | 7.81 | 7.88 | 7.95 |
| 12 | 6.94 | 7.06 | 7.17 | 7.26 | 7.36 | 7.44 | 7.52 | 7.59 | 7.66 | 7.73 |
| 13 | 6.79 | 6.90 | 7.01 | 7.10 | 7.19 | 7.27 | 7.35 | 7.42 | 7.48 | 7.55 |
| 14 | 6.66 | 6.77 | 6.87 | 6.96 | 7.05 | 7.13 | 7.20 | 7.27 | 7.33 | 7.39 |
| 15 | 6.55 | 6.66 | 6.76 | 6.84 | 6.93 | 7.00 | 7.07 | 7.14 | 7.20 | 7.26 |
| 16 | 6.46 | 6.56 | 6.66 | 6.74 | 6.82 | 6.90 | 6.97 | 7.03 | 7.09 | 7.15 |
| 17 | 6.38 | 6.48 | 6.57 | 6.66 | 6.73 | 6.81 | 6.87 | 6.94 | 7.00 | 7.05 |
| 18 | 6.31 | 6.41 | 6.50 | 6.58 | 6.65 | 6.73 | 6.79 | 6.85 | 6.91 | 6.97 |
| 19 | 6.25 | 6.34 | 6.43 | 6.51 | 6.58 | 6.65 | 6.72 | 6.78 | 6.84 | 6.89 |
| 20 | 6.19 | 6.28 | 6.37 | 6.45 | 6.52 | 6.59 | 6.65 | 6.71 | 6.77 | 6.82 |
| 24 | 6.02 | 6.11 | 6.19 | 6.26 | 6.33 | 6.39 | 6.45 | 6.51 | 6.56 | 6.61 |
| 30 | 5.85 | 5.93 | 6.01 | 6.08 | 6.14 | 6.20 | 6.26 | 6.31 | 6.36 | 6.41 |
| 40 | 5.69 | 5.76 | 5.83 | 5.90 | 5.96 | 6.02 | 6.07 | 6.12 | 6.16 | 6.21 |
| 60 | 5.53 | 5.60 | 5.67 | 5.73 | 5.78 | 5.84 | 5.89 | 5.93 | 5.97 | 6.01 |
| 120 | 5.37 | 5.44 | 5.50 | 5.56 | 5.61 | 5.66 | 5.71 | 5.75 | 5.79 | 5.83 |
| $\infty$ | 5.23 | 5.28 | 5.35 | 5.40 | 5.45 | 5.49 | 5.54 | 5.57 | 5.61 | 5.65 |

*Source:* Reprinted with permission from E. S. Pearson and H. O. Hartley, *Biometrika Tables for Statisticians* (New York: Cambridge University Press, 1954).

## APPENDIX K

Critical Values of *r* in the Runs Test

**a.** Lower Tail: Too Few Runs

| $n_1$ \ $n_2$ | 2 | 3 | 4 | 5 | 6 | 7 | 8 | 9 | 10 | 11 | 12 | 13 | 14 | 15 | 16 | 17 | 18 | 19 | 20 |
|---|---|---|---|---|---|---|---|---|---|---|---|---|---|---|---|---|---|---|---|
| 2 | | | | | | | | | | | 2 | 2 | 2 | 2 | 2 | 2 | 2 | 2 | 2 |
| 3 | | | | 2 | 2 | 2 | 2 | 2 | 2 | 2 | 2 | 2 | 3 | 3 | 3 | 3 | 3 | 3 | 3 |
| 4 | | | 2 | 2 | 2 | 3 | 3 | 3 | 3 | 3 | 3 | 3 | 3 | 3 | 4 | 4 | 4 | 4 | 4 |
| 5 | | 2 | 2 | 3 | 3 | 3 | 3 | 3 | 4 | 4 | 4 | 4 | 4 | 4 | 4 | 4 | 5 | 5 | 5 |
| 6 | 2 | 2 | 3 | 3 | 3 | 3 | 4 | 4 | 4 | 4 | 5 | 5 | 5 | 5 | 5 | 5 | 6 | 6 |
| 7 | 2 | 2 | 3 | 3 | 3 | 4 | 4 | 5 | 5 | 5 | 5 | 5 | 6 | 6 | 6 | 6 | 6 | 6 |
| 8 | 2 | 3 | 3 | 3 | 4 | 4 | 5 | 5 | 5 | 6 | 6 | 6 | 6 | 6 | 7 | 7 | 7 | 7 |
| 9 | 2 | 3 | 3 | 4 | 4 | 5 | 5 | 5 | 6 | 6 | 6 | 7 | 7 | 7 | 7 | 8 | 8 | 8 |
| 10 | 2 | 3 | 3 | 4 | 5 | 5 | 5 | 6 | 6 | 7 | 7 | 7 | 7 | 8 | 8 | 8 | 8 | 9 |
| 11 | 2 | 3 | 4 | 4 | 5 | 5 | 6 | 6 | 7 | 7 | 7 | 8 | 8 | 8 | 9 | 9 | 9 | 9 |
| 12 | 2 | 2 | 3 | 4 | 4 | 5 | 6 | 6 | 7 | 7 | 7 | 8 | 8 | 8 | 9 | 9 | 9 | 10 | 10 |
| 13 | 2 | 2 | 3 | 4 | 5 | 5 | 6 | 6 | 7 | 7 | 8 | 8 | 9 | 9 | 9 | 10 | 10 | 10 | 10 |
| 14 | 2 | 2 | 3 | 4 | 5 | 5 | 6 | 7 | 7 | 8 | 8 | 9 | 9 | 9 | 10 | 10 | 10 | 11 | 11 |
| 15 | 2 | 3 | 3 | 4 | 5 | 6 | 6 | 7 | 7 | 8 | 8 | 9 | 9 | 10 | 10 | 11 | 11 | 11 | 12 |
| 16 | 2 | 3 | 4 | 4 | 5 | 6 | 6 | 7 | 8 | 8 | 9 | 9 | 10 | 10 | 11 | 11 | 11 | 12 | 12 |
| 17 | 2 | 3 | 4 | 4 | 5 | 6 | 7 | 7 | 8 | 9 | 9 | 10 | 10 | 11 | 11 | 11 | 12 | 12 | 13 |
| 18 | 2 | 3 | 4 | 5 | 5 | 6 | 7 | 8 | 8 | 9 | 9 | 10 | 10 | 11 | 11 | 12 | 12 | 13 | 13 |
| 19 | 2 | 3 | 4 | 5 | 6 | 6 | 7 | 8 | 8 | 9 | 10 | 10 | 11 | 11 | 12 | 12 | 13 | 13 | 13 |
| 20 | 2 | 3 | 4 | 5 | 6 | 6 | 7 | 8 | 9 | 9 | 10 | 10 | 11 | 12 | 12 | 13 | 13 | 13 | 14 |

**b.** Upper Tail: Too Many Runs

| $n_1$ \ $n_2$ | 2 | 3 | 4 | 5 | 6 | 7 | 8 | 9 | 10 | 11 | 12 | 13 | 14 | 15 | 16 | 17 | 18 | 19 | 20 |
|---|---|---|---|---|---|---|---|---|---|---|---|---|---|---|---|---|---|---|---|
| 2 | | | | | | | | | | | | | | | | | | | |
| 3 | | | | | | | | | | | | | | | | | | | |
| 4 | | | | 9 | 9 | | | | | | | | | | | | | | |
| 5 | | | 9 | 10 | 10 | 11 | 11 | | | | | | | | | | | | |
| 6 | | | 9 | 10 | 11 | 12 | 12 | 13 | 13 | 13 | 13 | | | | | | | | |
| 7 | | | | 11 | 12 | 13 | 13 | 14 | 14 | 14 | 14 | 15 | 15 | 15 | | | | | |
| 8 | | | | 11 | 12 | 13 | 14 | 14 | 15 | 15 | 16 | 16 | 16 | 16 | 17 | 17 | 17 | 17 | 17 |
| 9 | | | | | 13 | 14 | 14 | 15 | 16 | 16 | 16 | 17 | 17 | 18 | 18 | 18 | 18 | 18 | 18 |
| 10 | | | | | 13 | 14 | 15 | 16 | 16 | 17 | 17 | 18 | 18 | 18 | 19 | 19 | 19 | 20 | 20 |
| 11 | | | | | 13 | 14 | 15 | 16 | 17 | 17 | 18 | 19 | 19 | 19 | 20 | 20 | 20 | 21 | 21 |
| 12 | | | | | 13 | 14 | 16 | 16 | 17 | 18 | 19 | 19 | 20 | 20 | 21 | 21 | 21 | 22 | 22 |
| 13 | | | | | | 15 | 16 | 17 | 18 | 19 | 19 | 20 | 20 | 21 | 21 | 22 | 22 | 23 | 23 |
| 14 | | | | | | 15 | 16 | 17 | 18 | 19 | 20 | 20 | 21 | 22 | 22 | 23 | 23 | 23 | 24 |
| 15 | | | | | | 15 | 16 | 18 | 18 | 19 | 20 | 21 | 22 | 22 | 23 | 23 | 24 | 24 | 25 |
| 16 | | | | | | | 17 | 18 | 19 | 20 | 21 | 21 | 22 | 23 | 23 | 24 | 25 | 25 | 25 |
| 17 | | | | | | | 17 | 18 | 19 | 20 | 21 | 22 | 23 | 23 | 24 | 25 | 25 | 26 | 26 |
| 18 | | | | | | | 17 | 18 | 19 | 20 | 21 | 22 | 23 | 24 | 25 | 25 | 26 | 26 | 27 |
| 19 | | | | | | | 17 | 18 | 20 | 21 | 22 | 23 | 23 | 24 | 25 | 26 | 26 | 27 | 27 |
| 20 | | | | | | | 17 | 18 | 20 | 21 | 22 | 23 | 24 | 25 | 25 | 26 | 27 | 27 | 28 |

*Source:* Adapted from Frieda S. Swed and C. Eisenhart, "Tables for testing randomness of grouping in a sequence of alternatives," *Ann. Math. Statist.* 14 (1943): 83–86, with the permission of the publisher.

## APPENDIX L

Mann-Whitney
$U$ Test Probabilities
$(n < 9)$

### $n_2 = 3$

| $U$ \ $n_1$ | 1 | 2 | 3 |
|---|---|---|---|
| 0 | .250 | .100 | .050 |
| 1 | .500 | .200 | .100 |
| 2 | .750 | .400 | .200 |
| 3 | | .600 | .350 |
| 4 | | | .500 |
| 5 | | | .650 |

### $n_2 = 4$

| $U$ \ $n_1$ | 1 | 2 | 3 | 4 |
|---|---|---|---|---|
| 0 | .200 | .067 | .028 | .014 |
| 1 | .400 | .133 | .057 | .029 |
| 2 | .600 | .267 | .114 | .057 |
| 3 | | .400 | .200 | .100 |
| 4 | | .600 | .314 | .171 |
| 5 | | | .429 | .243 |
| 6 | | | .571 | .343 |
| 7 | | | | .443 |
| 8 | | | | .557 |

### $n_2 = 5$

| $U$ \ $n_1$ | 1 | 2 | 3 | 4 | 5 |
|---|---|---|---|---|---|
| 0 | .167 | .047 | .018 | .008 | .004 |
| 1 | .333 | .095 | .036 | .016 | .008 |
| 2 | .500 | .190 | .071 | .032 | .016 |
| 3 | .667 | .286 | .125 | .056 | .028 |
| 4 | | .429 | .196 | .095 | .048 |
| 5 | | .571 | .286 | .143 | .075 |
| 6 | | | .393 | .206 | .111 |
| 7 | | | .500 | .278 | .155 |
| 8 | | | .607 | .365 | .210 |
| 9 | | | | .452 | .274 |
| 10 | | | | .548 | .345 |
| 11 | | | | | .421 |
| 12 | | | | | .500 |
| 13 | | | | | .579 |

### $n_2 = 6$

| $U$ \ $n_1$ | 1 | 2 | 3 | 4 | 5 | 6 |
|---|---|---|---|---|---|---|
| 0 | .143 | .036 | .012 | .005 | .002 | .001 |
| 1 | .286 | .071 | .024 | .010 | .004 | .002 |
| 2 | .428 | .143 | .048 | .019 | .009 | .004 |
| 3 | .571 | .214 | .083 | .033 | .015 | .008 |
| 4 | | .321 | .131 | .057 | .026 | .013 |
| 5 | | .429 | .190 | .086 | .041 | .021 |
| 6 | | .571 | .274 | .129 | .063 | .032 |
| 7 | | | .357 | .176 | .089 | .047 |
| 8 | | | .452 | .238 | .123 | .066 |
| 9 | | | .548 | .305 | .165 | .090 |
| 10 | | | | .381 | .214 | .120 |
| 11 | | | | .457 | .268 | .155 |
| 12 | | | | .545 | .331 | .197 |
| 13 | | | | | .396 | .242 |
| 14 | | | | | .465 | .294 |
| 15 | | | | | .535 | .350 |
| 16 | | | | | | .409 |
| 17 | | | | | | .469 |
| 18 | | | | | | .531 |

### $n_2 = 7$

| $U$ \ $n_1$ | 1 | 2 | 3 | 4 | 5 | 6 | 7 |
|---|---|---|---|---|---|---|---|
| 0 | .125 | .028 | .008 | .003 | .001 | .001 | .000 |
| 1 | .250 | .056 | .017 | .006 | .003 | .001 | .001 |
| 2 | .375 | .111 | .033 | .012 | .005 | .002 | .001 |
| 3 | .500 | .167 | .058 | .021 | .009 | .004 | .002 |
| 4 | .625 | .250 | .092 | .036 | .015 | .007 | .003 |
| 5 | | .333 | .133 | .055 | .024 | .011 | .006 |
| 6 | | .444 | .192 | .082 | .037 | .017 | .009 |
| 7 | | .556 | .258 | .115 | .053 | .026 | .013 |
| 8 | | | .333 | .158 | .074 | .037 | .019 |
| 9 | | | .417 | .206 | .101 | .051 | .027 |
| 10 | | | .500 | .264 | .134 | .069 | .036 |
| 11 | | | .583 | .324 | .172 | .090 | .049 |
| 12 | | | | .394 | .216 | .117 | .064 |
| 13 | | | | .464 | .265 | .147 | .082 |
| 14 | | | | .538 | .319 | .183 | .104 |
| 15 | | | | | .378 | .223 | .130 |
| 16 | | | | | .438 | .267 | .159 |
| 17 | | | | | .500 | .314 | .191 |
| 18 | | | | | .562 | .365 | .228 |
| 19 | | | | | | .418 | .267 |
| 20 | | | | | | .473 | .310 |
| 21 | | | | | | .527 | .355 |
| 22 | | | | | | | .402 |
| 23 | | | | | | | .451 |
| 24 | | | | | | | .500 |
| 25 | | | | | | | .549 |

$n_2 = 8$

| $U$ \ $n_1$ | 1 | 2 | 3 | 4 | 5 | 6 | 7 | 8 | $t$ | Normal |
|---|---|---|---|---|---|---|---|---|---|---|
| 0 | .111 | .022 | .006 | .002 | .001 | .000 | .000 | .000 | 3.308 | .001 |
| 1 | .222 | .044 | .012 | .004 | .002 | .001 | .000 | .000 | 3.203 | .001 |
| 2 | .333 | .089 | .024 | .008 | .003 | .001 | .001 | .000 | 3.098 | .001 |
| 3 | .444 | .133 | .042 | .014 | .005 | .002 | .001 | .001 | 2.993 | .001 |
| 4 | .556 | .200 | .067 | .024 | .009 | .004 | .002 | .001 | 2.888 | .002 |
| 5 | | .267 | .097 | .036 | .015 | .006 | .003 | .001 | 2.783 | .003 |
| 6 | | .356 | .139 | .055 | .023 | .010 | .005 | .002 | 2.678 | .004 |
| 7 | | .444 | .188 | .077 | .033 | .015 | .007 | .003 | 2.573 | .005 |
| 8 | | .556 | .248 | .107 | .047 | .021 | .010 | .005 | 2.468 | .007 |
| 9 | | | .315 | .141 | .064 | .030 | .014 | .007 | 2.363 | .009 |
| 10 | | | .387 | .184 | .085 | .041 | .020 | .010 | 2.258 | .012 |
| 11 | | | .461 | .230 | .111 | .054 | .027 | .014 | 2.153 | .016 |
| 12 | | | .539 | .285 | .142 | .071 | .036 | .019 | 2.048 | .020 |
| 13 | | | | .341 | .177 | .091 | .047 | .025 | 1.943 | .026 |
| 14 | | | | .404 | .217 | .114 | .060 | .032 | 1.838 | .033 |
| 15 | | | | .467 | .262 | .141 | .076 | .041 | 1.733 | .041 |
| 16 | | | | .533 | .311 | .172 | .095 | .052 | 1.628 | .052 |
| 17 | | | | | .362 | .207 | .116 | .065 | 1.523 | .064 |
| 18 | | | | | .416 | .245 | .140 | .080 | 1.418 | .078 |
| 19 | | | | | .472 | .286 | .168 | .097 | 1.313 | .094 |
| 20 | | | | | .528 | .331 | .198 | .117 | 1.208 | .113 |
| 21 | | | | | | .377 | .232 | .139 | 1.102 | .135 |
| 22 | | | | | | .426 | .268 | .164 | .998 | .159 |
| 23 | | | | | | .475 | .306 | .191 | .893 | .185 |
| 24 | | | | | | .525 | .347 | .221 | .788 | .215 |
| 25 | | | | | | | .389 | .253 | .683 | .247 |
| 26 | | | | | | | .433 | .287 | .578 | .282 |
| 27 | | | | | | | .478 | .323 | .473 | .318 |
| 28 | | | | | | | .522 | .360 | .368 | .356 |
| 29 | | | | | | | | .399 | .263 | .396 |
| 30 | | | | | | | | .439 | .158 | .437 |
| 31 | | | | | | | | .480 | .052 | .481 |
| 32 | | | | | | | | .520 | | |

*Source:* Reproduced from H. B. Mann and D. R. Whitney, "On a test of whether one of two random variables is stochastically larger than the other," *Ann. Math. Statist.* 18 (1947): 52–54, with the permission of the publisher.

## Mann-Whitney $U$ Test Critical Values $(9 \le n \le 20)$

Critical Values of $U$ for a One-Tailed Test at $\alpha = 0.001$ or for a Two-Tailed Test at $\alpha = 0.002$

| $n_1$ \ $n_2$ | 9 | 10 | 11 | 12 | 13 | 14 | 15 | 16 | 17 | 18 | 19 | 20 |
|---|---|---|---|---|---|---|---|---|---|---|---|---|
| 1 | | | | | | | | | | | | |
| 2 | | | | | | | | | | | | |
| 3 | | | | | | | | | 0 | 0 | 0 | 0 |
| 4 | | 0 | 0 | 0 | 1 | 1 | 1 | 2 | 2 | 3 | 3 | 3 |
| 5 | 1 | 1 | 2 | 2 | 3 | 3 | 4 | 5 | 5 | 6 | 7 | 7 |
| 6 | 2 | 3 | 4 | 4 | 5 | 6 | 7 | 8 | 9 | 10 | 11 | 12 |
| 7 | 3 | 5 | 6 | 7 | 8 | 9 | 10 | 11 | 13 | 14 | 15 | 16 |
| 8 | 5 | 6 | 8 | 9 | 11 | 12 | 14 | 15 | 17 | 18 | 20 | 21 |
| 9 | 7 | 8 | 10 | 12 | 14 | 15 | 17 | 19 | 21 | 23 | 25 | 26 |
| 10 | 8 | 10 | 12 | 14 | 17 | 19 | 21 | 23 | 25 | 27 | 29 | 32 |
| 11 | 10 | 12 | 15 | 17 | 20 | 22 | 24 | 27 | 29 | 32 | 34 | 37 |
| 12 | 12 | 14 | 17 | 20 | 23 | 25 | 28 | 31 | 34 | 37 | 40 | 42 |
| 13 | 14 | 17 | 20 | 23 | 26 | 29 | 32 | 35 | 38 | 42 | 45 | 48 |
| 14 | 15 | 19 | 22 | 25 | 29 | 32 | 36 | 39 | 43 | 46 | 50 | 54 |
| 15 | 17 | 21 | 24 | 28 | 32 | 36 | 40 | 43 | 47 | 51 | 55 | 59 |
| 16 | 19 | 23 | 27 | 31 | 35 | 39 | 43 | 48 | 52 | 56 | 60 | 65 |
| 17 | 21 | 25 | 29 | 34 | 38 | 43 | 47 | 52 | 57 | 61 | 66 | 70 |
| 18 | 23 | 27 | 32 | 37 | 42 | 46 | 51 | 56 | 61 | 66 | 71 | 76 |
| 19 | 25 | 29 | 34 | 40 | 45 | 50 | 55 | 60 | 66 | 71 | 77 | 82 |
| 20 | 26 | 32 | 37 | 42 | 48 | 54 | 59 | 65 | 70 | 76 | 82 | 88 |

Critical Values of $U$ for a One-Tailed Test at $\alpha = 0.01$ or for a Two-Tailed Test at $\alpha = 0.02$

| $n_1$ \ $n_2$ | 9 | 10 | 11 | 12 | 13 | 14 | 15 | 16 | 17 | 18 | 19 | 20 |
|---|---|---|---|---|---|---|---|---|---|---|---|---|
| 1 | | | | | | | | | | | | |
| 2 | | | | | 0 | 0 | 0 | 0 | 0 | 0 | 1 | 1 |
| 3 | 1 | 1 | 1 | 2 | 2 | 2 | 3 | 3 | 4 | 4 | 4 | 5 |
| 4 | 3 | 3 | 4 | 5 | 5 | 6 | 7 | 7 | 8 | 9 | 9 | 10 |
| 5 | 5 | 6 | 7 | 8 | 9 | 10 | 11 | 12 | 13 | 14 | 15 | 16 |
| 6 | 7 | 8 | 9 | 11 | 12 | 13 | 15 | 16 | 18 | 19 | 20 | 22 |
| 7 | 9 | 11 | 12 | 14 | 16 | 17 | 19 | 21 | 23 | 24 | 26 | 28 |
| 8 | 11 | 13 | 15 | 17 | 20 | 22 | 24 | 26 | 28 | 30 | 32 | 34 |
| 9 | 14 | 16 | 18 | 21 | 23 | 26 | 28 | 31 | 33 | 36 | 38 | 40 |
| 10 | 16 | 19 | 22 | 24 | 27 | 30 | 33 | 36 | 38 | 41 | 44 | 47 |
| 11 | 18 | 22 | 25 | 28 | 31 | 34 | 37 | 41 | 44 | 47 | 50 | 53 |
| 12 | 21 | 24 | 28 | 31 | 35 | 38 | 42 | 46 | 49 | 53 | 56 | 60 |
| 13 | 23 | 27 | 31 | 35 | 39 | 43 | 47 | 51 | 55 | 59 | 63 | 67 |
| 14 | 26 | 30 | 34 | 38 | 43 | 47 | 51 | 56 | 60 | 65 | 69 | 73 |
| 15 | 28 | 33 | 37 | 42 | 47 | 51 | 56 | 61 | 66 | 70 | 75 | 80 |
| 16 | 31 | 36 | 41 | 46 | 51 | 56 | 61 | 66 | 71 | 76 | 82 | 87 |
| 17 | 33 | 38 | 44 | 49 | 55 | 60 | 66 | 71 | 77 | 82 | 88 | 93 |
| 18 | 36 | 41 | 47 | 53 | 59 | 65 | 70 | 76 | 82 | 88 | 94 | 100 |
| 19 | 38 | 44 | 50 | 56 | 63 | 69 | 75 | 82 | 88 | 94 | 101 | 107 |
| 20 | 40 | 47 | 53 | 60 | 67 | 73 | 80 | 87 | 93 | 100 | 107 | 114 |

Critical Values of $U$ for a One-Tailed Test at $\alpha = 0.025$ or for a Two-Tailed Test at $\alpha = 0.05$

| $n_1$ \ $n_2$ | 9 | 10 | 11 | 12 | 13 | 14 | 15 | 16 | 17 | 18 | 19 | 20 |
|---|---|---|---|---|---|---|---|---|---|---|---|---|
| 1 | | | | | | | | | | | | |
| 2 | 0 | 0 | 0 | 1 | 1 | 1 | 1 | 1 | 2 | 2 | 2 | 2 |
| 3 | 2 | 3 | 3 | 4 | 4 | 5 | 5 | 6 | 6 | 7 | 7 | 8 |
| 4 | 4 | 5 | 6 | 7 | 8 | 9 | 10 | 11 | 11 | 12 | 13 | 13 |
| 5 | 7 | 8 | 9 | 11 | 12 | 13 | 14 | 15 | 17 | 18 | 19 | 20 |
| 6 | 10 | 11 | 13 | 14 | 16 | 17 | 19 | 21 | 22 | 24 | 25 | 27 |
| 7 | 12 | 14 | 16 | 18 | 20 | 22 | 24 | 26 | 28 | 30 | 32 | 34 |
| 8 | 15 | 17 | 19 | 22 | 24 | 26 | 29 | 31 | 34 | 36 | 38 | 41 |
| 9 | 17 | 20 | 23 | 26 | 28 | 31 | 34 | 37 | 39 | 42 | 45 | 48 |
| 10 | 20 | 23 | 26 | 29 | 33 | 36 | 39 | 42 | 45 | 48 | 52 | 55 |
| 11 | 23 | 26 | 30 | 33 | 37 | 40 | 44 | 47 | 51 | 55 | 58 | 62 |
| 12 | 26 | 29 | 33 | 37 | 41 | 45 | 49 | 53 | 57 | 61 | 65 | 69 |
| 13 | 28 | 33 | 37 | 41 | 45 | 50 | 54 | 59 | 63 | 67 | 72 | 76 |
| 14 | 31 | 36 | 40 | 45 | 50 | 55 | 59 | 64 | 67 | 74 | 78 | 83 |
| 15 | 34 | 39 | 44 | 49 | 54 | 59 | 64 | 70 | 75 | 80 | 85 | 90 |
| 16 | 37 | 42 | 47 | 53 | 59 | 64 | 70 | 75 | 81 | 86 | 92 | 98 |
| 17 | 39 | 45 | 51 | 57 | 63 | 67 | 75 | 81 | 87 | 93 | 99 | 105 |
| 18 | 42 | 48 | 55 | 61 | 67 | 74 | 80 | 86 | 93 | 99 | 106 | 112 |
| 19 | 45 | 52 | 58 | 65 | 72 | 78 | 85 | 92 | 99 | 106 | 113 | 119 |
| 20 | 48 | 55 | 62 | 69 | 76 | 83 | 90 | 98 | 105 | 112 | 119 | 127 |

Critical Values of $U$ for a One-Tailed Test at $\alpha = 0.05$ or for a Two-Tailed Test at $\alpha = 0.10$

| $n_1$ \ $n_2$ | 9 | 10 | 11 | 12 | 13 | 14 | 15 | 16 | 17 | 18 | 19 | 20 |
|---|---|---|---|---|---|---|---|---|---|---|---|---|
| 1 | | | | | | | | | | | 0 | 0 |
| 2 | 1 | 1 | 1 | 2 | 2 | 2 | 3 | 3 | 3 | 4 | 4 | 4 |
| 3 | 3 | 4 | 5 | 5 | 6 | 7 | 7 | 8 | 9 | 9 | 10 | 11 |
| 4 | 6 | 7 | 8 | 9 | 10 | 11 | 12 | 14 | 15 | 16 | 17 | 18 |
| 5 | 9 | 11 | 12 | 13 | 15 | 16 | 18 | 19 | 20 | 22 | 23 | 25 |
| 6 | 12 | 14 | 16 | 17 | 19 | 21 | 23 | 25 | 26 | 28 | 30 | 32 |
| 7 | 15 | 17 | 19 | 21 | 24 | 26 | 28 | 30 | 33 | 35 | 37 | 39 |
| 8 | 18 | 20 | 23 | 26 | 28 | 31 | 33 | 36 | 39 | 41 | 44 | 47 |
| 9 | 21 | 24 | 27 | 30 | 33 | 36 | 39 | 42 | 45 | 48 | 51 | 54 |
| 10 | 24 | 27 | 31 | 34 | 37 | 41 | 44 | 48 | 51 | 55 | 58 | 62 |
| 11 | 27 | 31 | 34 | 38 | 42 | 46 | 50 | 54 | 57 | 61 | 65 | 69 |
| 12 | 30 | 34 | 38 | 42 | 47 | 51 | 55 | 60 | 64 | 68 | 72 | 77 |
| 13 | 33 | 37 | 42 | 47 | 51 | 56 | 61 | 65 | 70 | 75 | 80 | 84 |
| 14 | 36 | 41 | 46 | 51 | 56 | 61 | 66 | 71 | 77 | 82 | 87 | 92 |
| 15 | 39 | 44 | 50 | 55 | 61 | 66 | 72 | 77 | 83 | 88 | 94 | 100 |
| 16 | 42 | 48 | 54 | 60 | 65 | 71 | 77 | 83 | 89 | 95 | 101 | 107 |
| 17 | 45 | 51 | 57 | 64 | 70 | 77 | 83 | 89 | 96 | 102 | 109 | 115 |
| 18 | 48 | 55 | 61 | 68 | 75 | 82 | 88 | 95 | 102 | 109 | 116 | 123 |
| 19 | 51 | 58 | 65 | 72 | 80 | 87 | 94 | 101 | 109 | 116 | 123 | 130 |
| 20 | 54 | 62 | 69 | 77 | 84 | 92 | 100 | 107 | 115 | 123 | 130 | 138 |

*Source:* Adapted and abridged from Tables 1, 3, 5, and 7 of D. Auble, "Extended tables for the Mann-Whitney statistic," *Bulletin of the Institute of Educational Research at Indiana University* 1, No. 2 (1953), with the permission of the publisher.

Critical Values of $T$
in the Wilcoxon
Matched-Pairs
Signed-Ranks Test
($n \leq 25$)

| | LEVEL OF SIGNIFICANCE FOR ONE-TAILED TEST | | |
| --- | --- | --- | --- |
| | 0.025 | 0.01 | 0.005 |
| $n$ | LEVEL OF SIGNIFICANCE FOR TWO-TAILED TEST | | |
| | 0.05 | 0.02 | 0.01 |
| 6 | 0 | — | — |
| 7 | 2 | 0 | — |
| 8 | 4 | 2 | 0 |
| 9 | 6 | 3 | 2 |
| 10 | 8 | 5 | 3 |
| 11 | 11 | 7 | 5 |
| 12 | 14 | 10 | 7 |
| 13 | 17 | 13 | 10 |
| 14 | 21 | 16 | 13 |
| 15 | 25 | 20 | 16 |
| 16 | 30 | 24 | 20 |
| 17 | 35 | 28 | 23 |
| 18 | 40 | 33 | 28 |
| 19 | 46 | 38 | 32 |
| 20 | 52 | 43 | 38 |
| 21 | 59 | 49 | 43 |
| 22 | 66 | 56 | 49 |
| 23 | 73 | 62 | 55 |
| 24 | 81 | 69 | 61 |
| 25 | 89 | 77 | 68 |

*Source:* Adapted from Table 1 of F. Wilcoxon, *Some Rapid Approximate Statistical Procedures* (New York: American Cyanamid Company, 1949), 13, with the permission of the publisher.

Critical Values $d_L$ and $d_U$ of the Durbin-Watson Statistic $D$ (Critical Values Are One-Sided)

| | $\alpha = .05$ | | | | | | | | | |
|---|---|---|---|---|---|---|---|---|---|---|
| | $P = 1$ | | $P = 2$ | | $P = 3$ | | $P = 4$ | | $P = 5$ | |
| $n$ | $d_L$ | $d_U$ | $d_L$ | $d_U$ | $d_L$ | $d_U$ | $d_L$ | $d_U$ | $d_L$ | $d_U$ |
| 15 | 1.08 | 1.36 | .95 | 1.54 | .82 | 1.75 | .69 | 1.97 | .56 | 2.21 |
| 16 | 1.10 | 1.37 | .98 | 1.54 | .86 | 1.73 | .74 | 1.93 | .62 | 2.15 |
| 17 | 1.13 | 1.38 | 1.02 | 1.54 | .90 | 1.71 | .78 | 1.90 | .67 | 2.10 |
| 18 | 1.16 | 1.39 | 1.05 | 1.53 | .93 | 1.69 | .82 | 1.87 | .71 | 2.06 |
| 19 | 1.18 | 1.40 | 1.08 | 1.53 | .97 | 1.68 | .86 | 1.85 | .75 | 2.02 |
| 20 | 1.20 | 1.41 | 1.10 | 1.54 | 1.00 | 1.68 | .90 | 1.83 | .79 | 1.99 |
| 21 | 1.22 | 1.42 | 1.13 | 1.54 | 1.03 | 1.67 | .93 | 1.81 | .83 | 1.96 |
| 22 | 1.24 | 1.43 | 1.15 | 1.54 | 1.05 | 1.66 | .96 | 1.80 | .86 | 1.94 |
| 23 | 1.26 | 1.44 | 1.17 | 1.54 | 1.08 | 1.66 | .99 | 1.79 | .90 | 1.92 |
| 24 | 1.27 | 1.45 | 1.19 | 1.55 | 1.10 | 1.66 | 1.01 | 1.78 | .93 | 1.90 |
| 25 | 1.29 | 1.45 | 1.21 | 1.55 | 1.12 | 1.66 | 1.04 | 1.77 | .95 | 1.89 |
| 26 | 1.30 | 1.46 | 1.22 | 1.55 | 1.14 | 1.65 | 1.06 | 1.76 | .98 | 1.88 |
| 27 | 1.32 | 1.47 | 1.24 | 1.56 | 1.16 | 1.65 | 1.08 | 1.76 | 1.01 | 1.86 |
| 28 | 1.33 | 1.48 | 1.26 | 1.56 | 1.18 | 1.65 | 1.10 | 1.75 | 1.03 | 1.85 |
| 29 | 1.34 | 1.48 | 1.27 | 1.56 | 1.20 | 1.65 | 1.12 | 1.74 | 1.05 | 1.84 |
| 30 | 1.35 | 1.49 | 1.28 | 1.57 | 1.21 | 1.65 | 1.14 | 1.74 | 1.07 | 1.83 |
| 31 | 1.36 | 1.50 | 1.30 | 1.57 | 1.23 | 1.65 | 1.16 | 1.74 | 1.09 | 1.83 |
| 32 | 1.37 | 1.50 | 1.31 | 1.57 | 1.24 | 1.65 | 1.18 | 1.73 | 1.11 | 1.82 |
| 33 | 1.38 | 1.51 | 1.32 | 1.58 | 1.26 | 1.65 | 1.19 | 1.73 | 1.13 | 1.81 |
| 34 | 1.39 | 1.51 | 1.33 | 1.58 | 1.27 | 1.65 | 1.21 | 1.73 | 1.15 | 1.81 |
| 35 | 1.40 | 1.52 | 1.34 | 1.58 | 1.28 | 1.65 | 1.22 | 1.73 | 1.16 | 1.80 |
| 36 | 1.41 | 1.52 | 1.35 | 1.59 | 1.29 | 1.65 | 1.24 | 1.73 | 1.18 | 1.80 |
| 37 | 1.42 | 1.53 | 1.36 | 1.59 | 1.31 | 1.66 | 1.25 | 1.72 | 1.19 | 1.80 |
| 38 | 1.43 | 1.54 | 1.37 | 1.59 | 1.32 | 1.66 | 1.26 | 1.72 | 1.21 | 1.79 |
| 39 | 1.43 | 1.54 | 1.38 | 1.60 | 1.33 | 1.66 | 1.27 | 1.72 | 1.22 | 1.79 |
| 40 | 1.44 | 1.54 | 1.39 | 1.60 | 1.34 | 1.66 | 1.29 | 1.72 | 1.23 | 1.79 |
| 45 | 1.48 | 1.57 | 1.43 | 1.62 | 1.38 | 1.67 | 1.34 | 1.72 | 1.29 | 1.78 |
| 50 | 1.50 | 1.59 | 1.46 | 1.63 | 1.42 | 1.67 | 1.38 | 1.72 | 1.34 | 1.77 |
| 55 | 1.53 | 1.60 | 1.49 | 1.64 | 1.45 | 1.68 | 1.41 | 1.72 | 1.38 | 1.77 |
| 60 | 1.55 | 1.62 | 1.51 | 1.65 | 1.48 | 1.69 | 1.44 | 1.73 | 1.41 | 1.77 |
| 65 | 1.57 | 1.63 | 1.54 | 1.66 | 1.50 | 1.70 | 1.47 | 1.73 | 1.44 | 1.77 |
| 70 | 1.58 | 1.64 | 1.55 | 1.67 | 1.52 | 1.70 | 1.49 | 1.74 | 1.46 | 1.77 |
| 75 | 1.60 | 1.65 | 1.57 | 1.68 | 1.54 | 1.71 | 1.51 | 1.74 | 1.49 | 1.77 |
| 80 | 1.61 | 1.66 | 1.59 | 1.69 | 1.56 | 1.72 | 1.53 | 1.74 | 1.51 | 1.77 |
| 85 | 1.62 | 1.67 | 1.60 | 1.70 | 1.57 | 1.72 | 1.55 | 1.75 | 1.52 | 1.77 |
| 90 | 1.63 | 1.68 | 1.61 | 1.70 | 1.59 | 1.73 | 1.57 | 1.75 | 1.54 | 1.78 |
| 95 | 1.64 | 1.69 | 1.62 | 1.71 | 1.60 | 1.73 | 1.58 | 1.75 | 1.56 | 1.78 |
| 100 | 1.65 | 1.69 | 1.63 | 1.72 | 1.61 | 1.74 | 1.59 | 1.76 | 1.57 | 1.78 |

(*continued*)

$n$ = Number of observations; $P$ = Number of independent variables.
*Source:* This table is reproduced from *Biometrika* 41 (1951): 173 and 175, with the permission of the *Biometrika* Trustees.

$$\alpha = .01$$

| n | P = 1 $d_L$ | $d_U$ | P = 2 $d_L$ | $d_U$ | P = 3 $d_L$ | $d_U$ | P = 4 $d_L$ | $d_U$ | P = 5 $d_L$ | $d_U$ |
|---|---|---|---|---|---|---|---|---|---|---|
| 15 | .81 | 1.07 | .70 | 1.25 | .59 | 1.46 | .49 | 1.70 | .39 | 1.96 |
| 16 | .84 | 1.09 | .74 | 1.25 | .63 | 1.44 | .53 | 1.66 | .44 | 1.90 |
| 17 | .87 | 1.10 | .77 | 1.25 | .67 | 1.43 | .57 | 1.63 | .48 | 1.85 |
| 18 | .90 | 1.12 | .80 | 1.26 | .71 | 1.42 | .61 | 1.60 | .52 | 1.80 |
| 19 | .93 | 1.13 | .83 | 1.26 | .74 | 1.41 | .65 | 1.58 | .56 | 1.77 |
| 20 | .95 | 1.15 | .86 | 1.27 | .77 | 1.41 | .68 | 1.57 | .60 | 1.74 |
| 21 | .97 | 1.16 | .89 | 1.27 | .80 | 1.41 | .72 | 1.55 | .63 | 1.71 |
| 22 | 1.00 | 1.17 | .91 | 1.28 | .83 | 1.40 | .75 | 1.54 | .66 | 1.69 |
| 23 | 1.02 | 1.19 | .94 | 1.29 | .86 | 1.40 | .77 | 1.53 | .70 | 1.67 |
| 24 | 1.04 | 1.20 | .96 | 1.30 | .88 | 1.41 | .80 | 1.53 | .72 | 1.66 |
| 25 | 1.05 | 1.21 | .98 | 1.30 | .90 | 1.41 | .83 | 1.52 | .75 | 1.65 |
| 26 | 1.07 | 1.22 | 1.00 | 1.31 | .93 | 1.41 | .85 | 1.52 | .78 | 1.64 |
| 27 | 1.09 | 1.23 | 1.02 | 1.32 | .95 | 1.41 | .88 | 1.51 | .81 | 1.63 |
| 28 | 1.10 | 1.24 | 1.04 | 1.32 | .97 | 1.41 | .90 | 1.51 | .83 | 1.62 |
| 29 | 1.12 | 1.25 | 1.05 | 1.33 | .99 | 1.42 | .92 | 1.51 | .85 | 1.61 |
| 30 | 1.13 | 1.26 | 1.07 | 1.34 | 1.01 | 1.42 | .94 | 1.51 | .88 | 1.61 |
| 31 | 1.15 | 1.27 | 1.08 | 1.34 | 1.02 | 1.42 | .96 | 1.51 | .90 | 1.60 |
| 32 | 1.16 | 1.28 | 1.10 | 1.35 | 1.04 | 1.43 | .98 | 1.51 | .92 | 1.60 |
| 33 | 1.17 | 1.29 | 1.11 | 1.36 | 1.05 | 1.43 | 1.00 | 1.51 | .94 | 1.59 |
| 34 | 1.18 | 1.30 | 1.13 | 1.36 | 1.07 | 1.43 | 1.01 | 1.51 | .95 | 1.59 |
| 35 | 1.19 | 1.31 | 1.14 | 1.37 | 1.08 | 1.44 | 1.03 | 1.51 | .97 | 1.59 |
| 36 | 1.21 | 1.32 | 1.15 | 1.38 | 1.10 | 1.44 | 1.04 | 1.51 | .99 | 1.59 |
| 37 | 1.22 | 1.32 | 1.16 | 1.38 | 1.11 | 1.45 | 1.06 | 1.51 | 1.00 | 1.59 |
| 38 | 1.23 | 1.33 | 1.18 | 1.39 | 1.12 | 1.45 | 1.07 | 1.52 | 1.02 | 1.58 |
| 39 | 1.24 | 1.34 | 1.19 | 1.39 | 1.14 | 1.45 | 1.09 | 1.52 | 1.03 | 1.58 |
| 40 | 1.25 | 1.34 | 1.20 | 1.40 | 1.15 | 1.46 | 1.10 | 1.52 | 1.05 | 1.58 |
| 45 | 1.29 | 1.38 | 1.24 | 1.42 | 1.20 | 1.48 | 1.16 | 1.53 | 1.11 | 1.58 |
| 50 | 1.32 | 1.40 | 1.28 | 1.45 | 1.24 | 1.49 | 1.20 | 1.54 | 1.16 | 1.59 |
| 55 | 1.36 | 1.43 | 1.32 | 1.47 | 1.28 | 1.51 | 1.25 | 1.55 | 1.21 | 1.59 |
| 60 | 1.38 | 1.45 | 1.35 | 1.48 | 1.32 | 1.52 | 1.28 | 1.56 | 1.25 | 1.60 |
| 65 | 1.41 | 1.47 | 1.38 | 1.50 | 1.35 | 1.53 | 1.31 | 1.57 | 1.28 | 1.61 |
| 70 | 1.43 | 1.49 | 1.40 | 1.52 | 1.37 | 1.55 | 1.34 | 1.58 | 1.31 | 1.61 |
| 75 | 1.45 | 1.50 | 1.42 | 1.53 | 1.39 | 1.56 | 1.37 | 1.59 | 1.34 | 1.62 |
| 80 | 1.47 | 1.52 | 1.44 | 1.54 | 1.42 | 1.57 | 1.39 | 1.60 | 1.36 | 1.62 |
| 85 | 1.48 | 1.53 | 1.46 | 1.55 | 1.43 | 1.58 | 1.41 | 1.60 | 1.39 | 1.63 |
| 90 | 1.50 | 1.54 | 1.47 | 1.56 | 1.45 | 1.59 | 1.43 | 1.61 | 1.41 | 1.64 |
| 95 | 1.51 | 1.55 | 1.49 | 1.57 | 1.47 | 1.60 | 1.45 | 1.62 | 1.42 | 1.64 |
| 100 | 1.52 | 1.56 | 1.50 | 1.58 | 1.48 | 1.60 | 1.46 | 1.63 | 1.44 | 1.65 |

$n$ = Number of observations; $P$ = Number of independent variables.

*Source:* This table is reproduced from *Biometrika* 41 (1951): 173 and 175, with the permission of the *Biometrika* Trustees.

Lower and Upper
Critical Values $W$
of Wilcoxon
Signed-Ranks Test

| $n$ | One-Tailed: $\alpha = .05$ / Two-Tailed: $\alpha = .10$ | $\alpha = .025$ / $\alpha = .05$ | $\alpha = .01$ / $\alpha = .02$ | $\alpha = .005$ / $\alpha = .01$ |
|---|---|---|---|---|
| | (Lower, Upper) | | | |
| 5 | 0,15 | —,— | —,— | —,— |
| 6 | 2,19 | 0,21 | —,— | —,— |
| 7 | 3,25 | 2,26 | 0,28 | —,— |
| 8 | 5,31 | 3,33 | 1,35 | 0,36 |
| 9 | 8,37 | 5,40 | 3,42 | 1,44 |
| 10 | 10,45 | 8,47 | 5,50 | 3,52 |
| 11 | 13,53 | 10,56 | 7,59 | 5,61 |
| 12 | 17,61 | 13,65 | 10,68 | 7,71 |
| 13 | 21,70 | 17,74 | 12,79 | 10,81 |
| 14 | 25,80 | 21,84 | 16,89 | 13,92 |
| 15 | 30,90 | 25,95 | 19,101 | 16,104 |
| 16 | 35,101 | 29,107 | 23,113 | 19,117 |
| 17 | 41,112 | 34,119 | 27,126 | 23,130 |
| 18 | 47,124 | 40,131 | 32,139 | 27,144 |
| 19 | 53,137 | 46,144 | 37,153 | 32,158 |
| 20 | 60,150 | 52,158 | 43,167 | 37,173 |

*Source:* Adapted from Table 2 of F. Wilcoxon and R. A. Wilcox, *Some Rapid Approximate Statistical Procedures* (Pearl River, NY: Lederle Laboratories, 1964), with permission of the American Cyanamid Company.

Control Chart
Factors

| Number of Observations in Subgroup | $d_2$ | $d_3$ | $D_3$ | $D_4$ | $A_2$ |
|---|---|---|---|---|---|
| 2 | 1.128 | 0.853 | 0 | 3.267 | 1.880 |
| 3 | 1.693 | 0.888 | 0 | 2.575 | 1.023 |
| 4 | 2.059 | 0.880 | 0 | 2.282 | 0.729 |
| 5 | 2.326 | 0.864 | 0 | 2.114 | 0.577 |
| 6 | 2.534 | 0.848 | 0 | 2.004 | 0.483 |
| 7 | 2.704 | 0.833 | 0.076 | 1.924 | 0.419 |
| 8 | 2.847 | 0.820 | 0.136 | 1.864 | 0.373 |
| 9 | 2.970 | 0.808 | 0.184 | 1.816 | 0.337 |
| 10 | 3.078 | 0.797 | 0.223 | 1.777 | 0.308 |
| 11 | 3.173 | 0.787 | 0.256 | 1.744 | 0.285 |
| 12 | 3.258 | 0.778 | 0.283 | 1.717 | 0.266 |
| 13 | 3.336 | 0.770 | 0.307 | 1.693 | 0.249 |
| 14 | 3.407 | 0.763 | 0.328 | 1.672 | 0.235 |
| 15 | 3.472 | 0.756 | 0.347 | 1.653 | 0.223 |
| 16 | 3.532 | 0.750 | 0.363 | 1.637 | 0.212 |
| 17 | 3.588 | 0.744 | 0.378 | 1.622 | 0.203 |
| 18 | 3.640 | 0.739 | 0.391 | 1.609 | 0.194 |
| 19 | 3.689 | 0.733 | 0.404 | 1.596 | 0.187 |
| 20 | 3.735 | 0.729 | 0.415 | 1.585 | 0.180 |
| 21 | 3.778 | 0.724 | 0.425 | 1.575 | 0.173 |
| 22 | 3.819 | 0.720 | 0.435 | 1.565 | 0.167 |
| 23 | 3.858 | 0.716 | 0.443 | 1.557 | 0.162 |
| 24 | 3.895 | 0.712 | 0.452 | 1.548 | 0.157 |
| 25 | 3.931 | 0.708 | 0.459 | 1.541 | 0.153 |

*Source:* Reprinted from ASTM-STP 15D by kind permission of the American Society for Testing and Materials.

# Answers to Selected Odd-Numbered Problems

This section contains summary answers to most of the odd-numbered problems in the text. The *Student Solutions Manual* contains fully developed solutions to all odd-numbered problems and shows clearly how each answer is determined.

## Chapter 1

**1-1.** Descriptive; use charts, graphs, tables, and numerical measures.

**1-3.** A bar chart is used whenever you want to display data that has already been categorized, while a histogram is used to display data over a range of values for the factor under consideration.

**1-5.** Hypothesis testing uses statistical techniques to validate a claim.

**1-13.** statistical inference, particularly estimation

**1-17.** written survey or telephone survey

**1-19.** An experiment is any process that generates data as its outcome.

**1-23.** internal and external validity

**1-27.** Advantages—low cost, speed of delivery, instant updating of data analysis; disadvantages—low response and potential confusion about questions

**1-29.** personal observation data gathering

**1-33.** Part range $= \dfrac{Population\ size}{Sample\ size} = \dfrac{18,000}{100} = 180$

Thus, the first person selected will come from employees 1–180. Once that person is randomly selected, the second person will be the one numbered 100 higher than the first, and so on.

**1-37.** The census would consist of all items produced on the line in a defined period of time.

**1-41.** parameters, since it would include all U.S. colleges

**1-43.** **a.** stratified random sampling
**b.** simple random sampling or possibly cluster random sampling
**c.** systematic random sampling
**d.** stratified random sampling

**1-49.** **a.** time-series
**b.** cross-sectional
**c.** time-series
**d.** cross-sectional

**1-51.** **a.** ordinal—categories with defined order
**b.** nominal—categories with no defined order
**c.** ratio
**d.** nominal—categories with no defined order

**1-53.** ordinal data

**1-55.** **a.** nominal data
**b.** ratio data
**c.** nominal data
**d.** ratio data
**e.** ratio data
**f.** nominal data
**g.** ratio data

**1-61.** interval or ratio data

**1-67.** **a.** Use a random sample or systematic random sample.
**b.** The product is going to be ruined after testing it. You would not want to ruin the entire product that comes off the assembly line.

## Chapter 2

**2-3.** **a.** $2^k \geq n$ or $2^{10} = 1,024 \geq 1,000$   Thus, use $k = 10$ classes.

**b.** $w = \dfrac{High - Low}{Classes} = \dfrac{2,900 - 300}{10} = \dfrac{2,600}{10} = 260$ (round to 300)

**2-5.** **a.** 2.833, which is rounded to 3.
**b.** Divide the number of occurrences (frequency) in each class by the total number of occurrences.
**c.** Compute a running sum for each class by adding the frequency for that class to the frequencies for all classes above it.
**d.** Classes form the horizontal axis, and the frequency forms the vertical axis. Bars corresponding to the frequency of each class are developed.

**2-7.** **a.** $1 - 0.24 = 0.76$
**b.** $0.56 - 0.08 = 0.48$
**c.** $0.96 - 0.08 = 0.86$

**2-9.** **a.**

| Class | Frequency | Relative Frequency |
|-------|-----------|--------------------|
| 2–3   | 2         | 0.0333             |
| 4–5   | 25        | 0.4167             |
| 6–7   | 26        | 0.4333             |
| 8–9   | 6         | 0.1000             |
| 10–11 | 1         | 0.0167             |

**b.** cumulative frequencies: 2; 27; 53; 59; 60
**c.** cumulative relative frequencies:  0.0333; 0.4500; 0.8833; 0.9833; 1.000
**d.** ogive

**2-13.** **a.** The weights are sorted from smallest to largest to create the data array.

**b.**

| Weight (Classes) | Frequency |
|------------------|-----------|
| 77–81            | 3         |
| 82–86            | 9         |
| 87–91            | 16        |
| 92–96            | 16        |
| 97–101           | 5         |
| Total =          | 49        |

**c.** The histogram can be created from the frequency distribution.
**d.** 10.20%

**2-15.** **a.** $w = \dfrac{Largest - smallest}{number\ of\ classes} = \dfrac{214.4 - 105.0}{11} = 9.945 \rightarrow w = 10.$

**b.** 8 of the 25, or 0.32 of the salaries at least $175,000
**c.** 18 of the 25, or 0.72 having salaries that are at most $205,000 but at least $135,000

**2-19. a.** 9 classes

**b.** $w = \dfrac{\text{High} - \text{Low}}{\text{Classes}} = \dfrac{32 - 10}{9} = \dfrac{22}{9} = 2.44$ (round up to 3.0)

**c.** The frequency distribution with nine classes and a class width of 3.0 will depend on the starting point for the first class. This starting value must be at or below the minimum value of 10.

**d.** The distribution is mound shaped and fairly symmetrical. It appears that the center is between 19 and 22 rounds per year, but the rounds played are quite spread out around the center.

**2-21. a.** $2^5 = 32$ and $2^6 = 64$. Therefore, 6 classes are chosen.

**b.** The class width is 690,189/6 classes = 115,031.5. Rounding up to the nearest 1,000 passengers results in a class width of 116,000.

**c.**

| Classes | Frequency |
|---|---|
| $0 < 116{,}000$ | 29 |
| $116{,}000 < 232{,}000$ | 3 |
| $232{,}000 < 347{,}000$ | 4 |
| $347{,}000 < 462{,}000$ | 1 |
| $462{,}000 < 577{,}000$ | 0 |
| $577{,}000 < 692{,}000$ | 1 |

**d.** More airlines have fewer than 116,000 passengers.

**2-23. a.** Order the observations (coffee consumption) from smallest to largest.

**b.** Using the $2^k > n$ guideline, the number of classes, $k$, would be 0.9 and $w = (10.1 - 3.5)/8 = 0.821$, which is rounded to 0. Most observations fall in the class of 5.3–7.9 kg of coffee.

**c.** The histogram can be created from the frequency distribution. The classes are shown on the horizontal axis and the frequency on the vertical axis.

**2-29. a.** The pie chart categories are the regions and the measure is the region's percentage of total income.

**b.** The bar chart categories are the regions and the measure for each category is the region's percentage of total income.

**c.** The bar chart, however, makes it easier to compare percentages across regions.

**2-31. b.** $= 1 - 0.0985 = 0.9015$

**2-33.** The bar chart is skewed below indicating that the number of $1 million houses is growing rapidly. It also appears that that growth is exponential rather than linear.

**2-35.** A bar chart can be used to make the comparison.

**2-37. a.** The stem unit is 10 and the leaf unit is 1.

**b.** between 70 and 79 seconds

**2-41. a.** Leaf unit = 1.0

**b.** Slightly skewed to the left. The center is between 24 and 26.

**c.** $\bar{x} = \dfrac{2{,}428}{50} = 24.28$

**2-43. a.**

| University Related | Religious Affiliated | Municipally Owned | Privately Held |
|---|---|---|---|
| $6,398 | $3,591 | $4,613 | $5,191 |

**b.** The largest average charges occurs at university-related hospitals and the lowest average appears to be in Religious Affiliated hospitals.

**c.** A pie chart showing how that total is divided among the four hospital types would not be useful or appropriate.

**2-47.** The sales have trended upward over the past 12 months.

**2-49.** The line chart shows that year-end deposits have been increasing since 1997, but have increased more sharply since 2002 and have leveled off between 2006 and 2007.

**2-51. b.** curvilinear

**c.** The largest difference in sales occurred between 2006 and 2007. That difference was $14.835 - 10.711 = 4.124$ ($billions).

**2-55.** positive linear relationship

**2-61. b.** Both relationships seem to be linear in nature.

**c.** This occurred in 1998, 1999, and 2001.

**2-67. b.** It appears that there is a positive linear relationship between the attendance and the year.

**2-73. a.** The independent variable is hours and the dependent variable is sales.

**b.** It appears that there is a positive linear relationship.

## Chapter 3

**3-1.** $Q1 = 4{,}423$; Median = 5,002; $Q3 = 5{,}381$

**3-3.** $Q1 = \dfrac{13.5 + 13.6}{2} = 13.55$

$Q3 = \dfrac{15.5 + 15.9}{2} = 15.7$

**3-7. a.** $(31.2 + 32.2)/2 = 31.7$

**b.** $(26.7 + 31.2)/2 = 28.95$

**c.** $(20.8 + 22.8)/2 = 21.8$

**3-9. a.** Mean = 19; Median = $(19 + 19)/2 = 19$; Mode = 19

**b.** Symmetrical; Mean = Median = Mode

**3-11. a.** 11,213.48

**b.** Use weighted average.

**3-13. a.** Mean = 114.21; Median = 107.50; Mode = 156

**b.** skewed right

**3-15. a.** 562.99

**b.** 551.685

**c.** 562.90

**3-17. a.** FDIC = 768,351,603.83

Bank of America average = 113,595,000

**b.** 768,351,603.83/113,595,000 = 6.76

**3-19.** Mean = 0.33 minutes; Median = 0.31 minutes; Mode = 0.24 minutes; slightly right skewed; 80th percentile = 0.40 minutes

**3-21. a.** $\bar{x} = \dfrac{2{,}448.30}{20} = 122.465$; Median = $(123.2 + 123.7)/2 = 123.45$; left-skewed

**b.** 0.925

**c.** 126.36

**d.** weighted average

**3-25. a.** Range = $8 - 0 = 8$

**b.** 3.99

**c.** 1.998

**3-27. a.** 16.87

**b.** 4.11

**3-29.** Standard deviation = 2.8

**3-31. a.** Standard deviation = 7.21; IQR = $24 - 12 = 12$

**b.** Range = Largest − Smallest = $30 - 6 = 24$; Standard deviation = 6.96; IQR = 12

**c.** $\sigma^2$ is smaller than $s^2$ by a factor of $(N - 1)/N$. $\sigma$ is smaller than $s$ by a factor of $\sqrt{(N - 1)/N}$. The range is not affected.

**3-33. a.** The variance is 815.79 and the standard deviation is 28.56.
  **b.** Interquartile range overcomes the susceptibility of the range to being highly influenced by extreme values.

**3-35. a.** Range $= 33 - 21 = 12$

$$\bar{x} = \frac{\sum\limits_{i=1}^{n} x_i}{n} = 261/10 = 26.1$$

$$S^2 = \frac{\sum\limits_{i=1}^{n} (x - \bar{x})^2}{n-1} = 148.9 / (10-1) = 16.5444;$$

$$S = \sqrt{S^2} = \sqrt{16.5444} = 4.0675$$

Interquartile range $= 28 - 23 = 5$

  **b.** Ages are lower at Whitworth than for the U.S. colleges and universities as a group.

**3-37. a.** The range is 113.0, the IQR is 62.25, the variance is 1,217.14, and the standard deviation is 34.89.
  **b.** No
  **c.** Adding a constant to all the data values leaves the variance unchanged.

**3-39. a.** 2004: Mean $= 0.422$; Variance $= 0.999$;
  Standard deviation $= 1.000$; IQR $= 1.7$
  2005: Mean $= 1.075$; Variance $= 0.396$;
  Standard deviation $= 0.629$; IQR $= 0.75$
  **b.** $\bar{x}_2 = 1.075$ and $\bar{x}_1 = 0.422$
  **c.** $s_1 = 1.000$ and $s_2 = 0.629$

**3-41. a.** Men spent an average of $117, whereas women spent an average of $98 for their phones. The standard deviation for men was nearly twice that for women.
  **b.** Business users spent an average of $166.67 on their phone, whereas home users spent an average of $105.74. The variation in phone costs for the two groups was about equal.

**3-43. a.** The population mean is

$$\mu = \frac{\sum x}{N} = \$178,465$$

  **b.** The population median is
  $\tilde{\mu} = \$173,000$
  **c.** The range is:
  R $=$ High $-$ Low
  R $= \$361,100 - \$54,100$
  $= \$307,000$
  **d.** The population standard deviation is

$$\sigma = \sqrt{\frac{\sum (x - \mu)^2}{N}} = \$63,172$$

**3-47. a.** at least 75% in the range 2,600 to 3,400; $\mu \pm 2(\sigma)$.
  **b.** The range 2,400 to 3,600 should contain at least 89% of the data values.
  **c.** less than 11%.

**3-49. a.** 25.008
  **b.** $CV = 23.55\%$
  **c.** The range from 31.19 to 181.24 should contain at least 89% of the data values.

**3-51.** For Distribution A: $CV = \dfrac{\sigma}{\mu}(100) = \dfrac{100}{500}(100) = 20\%$

For Distribution B: $CV = \dfrac{\sigma}{\mu}(100) = \dfrac{4.0}{10.0}(100) = 40\%$

**3-53. a.** $z = \dfrac{800 - \bar{x}}{s} = \dfrac{800 - 1,000}{250} = -0.80$
  **b.** $z = 0.80$
  **c.** $z = 0.00$

**3-55. a.** $\bar{x} = \dfrac{1,530}{30} = 51$; Variance $= 510.76$; Standard deviation $= 22.60$

  **b.** $51 \pm 22.60$, $51 \pm 2(22.60)$, $51 \pm 3(22.60)$, i.e., (28.4, 73.6), (5.8, 96.2), and (−16.8, 118.8). There are $(19/30)100\% = 63.3\%$ of the data within (28.4, 73.6), $(30/30)100\% = 100\%$ of the data within (5.8, 96.2), $(30/30)100\% = 100\%$ of the data within (−16.8, 118.8).
  **c.** bell-shaped population

**3-57. a.**

|  | Drug A | Drug B |
|---|---|---|
| Mean | 234.75 | 270.92 |
| Standard Deviation | 13.92 | 19.90 |

  **b.** Based on the sample means of the time each drug is effective, Drug B appears to be effective longer than Drug A.
  **c.** Based on the standard deviation of effect time, Drug B exhibits a higher variability in effect time than Drug A.
  **d.** Drug A, $CV = 5.93\%$; Drug B, $CV = 7.35\%$. Drug B has a higher coefficient of variation and the greater relative spread.

**3-59.** Existing supplier: $CV = \dfrac{0.078}{3.75}(100) = 2.08\%$

New supplier: $CV = \dfrac{0.135}{18.029}(100) = 0.75\%$

**3-61.** Anyone scoring below 61.86 (rounded to 62) will be rejected without an interview.
  Anyone scoring higher than 91.98 (rounded to 92) will be sent directly to the company.

**3-63.** $CV = \dfrac{3,083.45}{11,144.48}(100) = 27.67\%$

At least 75% of CPA firms will compute a tax owed between $4,977.58 ———— $17,311.38

**3-65. a.**

| Varibale | Mean | StDev | Variance | Q1 | Median | Q3 | IQR |
|---|---|---|---|---|---|---|---|
| Scores | 94.780 | 4.130 | 17.056 | 93.000 | 96.000 | 98.000 | 5.000 |

  **b.** Tchebysheff's Theorem would be preferable.
  **c.** 99

**3-73.** The mode is a useful measure of location of a set of data if the data set is large and involves nominal or ordinal data.

**3-75. a.** 0.34
  **b.** 0.34
  **c.** 0.16

**3-77. a.** 364.42
  **b.** Variance $= 16,662.63$; Standard deviation $= 129.08$

**3-81. a.** Comparing only the mean bushels/acre you would say that Seed Type C produces the greatest average yield per acre.
  **b.** $CV$ of Seed Type A $= 25/88 = 0.2841$ or $28.41\%$
  $CV$ of Seed Type B $= 15/56 = 0.2679$ or $26.79\%$
  $CV$ of Seed Type C $= 16/100 = 0.1600$ or $16\%$
  Seed Type C shows the least relative variability.
  **c.** Seed Type A: 68% between 63 to 113
  95% between 38 to 138
  approximately 100% between 13 to 163
  Seed Type B: 68% between 41 to 71
  95% between 26 to 86
  approximately 100% between 11 to 101

Seed Type C: 68% between 84 to 116
95% between 68 to 132
approximately 100% between 52 to 148

**d.** Seed Type A
**e.** Seed type C

**3-87. a.**

| Variable | Mean | StDev |
|----------|------|-------|
| Price | 22.000 | 3.813 |

**b.** $\bar{x} \pm 1s = 22 \pm (3.813) = (18.187, 25.813)$; $\bar{x} \pm 2s =$ $(14.374, 29.626)$; $\bar{x} \pm 3s = (10.561, 33.439)$

**c.** The Empirical Rule indicates that 95% of the data is contained within $\bar{x} \pm 2s$. This would mean that each tail has $(1 - 0.95)/2 = 0.025$ of the data. Therefore, the costume should be priced at $14.37.

**3-89. a.**

| Variable | Mean | StDev | Median |
|----------|------|-------|--------|
| Close-Open | −0.0354 | 0.2615 | −0.0600 |

**b.** It means that the closing price for GE stock is an average of approximately four ($0.0354) cents lower than the opening price.

**c.**

| Variable | Mean | StDev | Median |
|----------|------|-------|--------|
| Open | 33.947 | 0.503 | 33.980 |
| Close-Open | −0.0354 | 0.2615 | −0.0600 |

# Chapter 4

**4-1.** independent events

**4-3.** V, V    V, C    V, S    C, V    C, C    C, S
S, V    S, C    S, S

**4-5. a.** subjective probability based on expert opinion
**b.** relative frequency based on previous customer return history
**c.** $1/5 = 0.20$

**4-7.** $1/3 = 0.333333$

**4-9. a.** $P(\text{Brown}) = \#\text{Brown}/\text{Total} = 310/982 = 0.3157$
**b.** $P(\text{YZ-99}) = \#\text{YZ-99}/\text{Total} = 375/982 = 0.3819$
**c.** $P(\text{YZ-99 and Brown}) = 205/982 = 0.2088$
**d.** not mutually exclusive since their joint probability is 0.1324

**4-11.** 0.375

**4-15.**

| Type of Ad | Occurrences |
|------------|-------------|
| Help Wanted Ad | 204 |
| Real Estate Ad | 520 |
| Other Ad | 306 |
| Total | 1,030 |

**a.** 0.1981
**b.** relative frequency
**c.** yes

**4-17. a.** relative frequency assessment method
**b.** $P(\#1) = \dfrac{4,000}{5,900} = 0.69$

**4-19. a.** $3,122/21,768 = 0.1434$
**b.** relative frequency assessment method

**4-21. a.** $P(Caesarean) = \dfrac{22}{50} = 0.44$
**b.** New births may not exactly match the 50 in this study.

**4-23.** The following joint frequency table (developed using Excel's pivot table feature) summarizes the data.

| | Electrical | Mechanical | Total |
|---|-----------|------------|-------|
| Lincoln | 28 | 39 | *67* |
| Tyler | 64 | 69 | *133* |
| Total | *92* | *108* | *200* |

**a.** $133/200 = 0.665$
**b.** $108/200 = 0.54$
**c.** $28/200 = 0.14$

**4-25. a.** $\dfrac{43}{100} = 0.43$

**b.** $\dfrac{5+6+6}{100} = 0.17$

**c.** For Pepsi, Probability $= \dfrac{5+6+6}{12+12+11} = \dfrac{17}{35} = 0.486$

For Coke, Probability $= \dfrac{6+6+6}{12+12+11} = \dfrac{18}{35} = 0.514$

**d.** For Pepsi, Probability $= \dfrac{7+6+8+5}{19+16+14+16} = \dfrac{26}{65} = 0.4$

For Coke, Probability $= \dfrac{12+10+6+11}{19+16+14+16} = \dfrac{39}{65} = 0.6$

**4-27. a.** $(0.9)(1 - 0.5) = 0.45$
**b.** $(0.6)(0.8) = 0.48$

**4-29.** $P(\text{senior 1 and senior 2}) = \left(\dfrac{5}{10}\right)\left(\dfrac{4}{9}\right) = \dfrac{20}{90} = 0.22$

**4-31. a.** $P(E_1 \text{ and } B) = P(E_1|B)P(B) = 0.25(0.30) = 0.075$
**b.** $P(E_1 \text{ or } B) = P(E_1) + P(B) - P(E_1 \text{ and } B) = 0.35 + 0.30 - 0.075 = 0.575$
**c.** $P(E_1 \text{ and } E_2 \text{ and } E_3) = P(E_1)P(E_2)P(E_3) = 0.35(0.15)(0.40) = 0.021$

**4-33. a.** $P(B) = \dfrac{\text{Number of drives from } B}{\text{Total drives}} = \dfrac{195}{700} = 0.28$

**b.** $P(\text{Defect}) = \dfrac{\text{Number of defective drives}}{\text{Total drives}} = \dfrac{50}{700} = 0.07$

**c.** $P(\text{Defect}|B) = \dfrac{P(\text{Defect and } B)}{P(B)} = \dfrac{0.02}{0.28} = 0.076$

$P(\text{Defect}|B) = \dfrac{\text{Number of defective drives from } B}{\text{Number of drives from } B}$

$= \dfrac{15}{195} = 0.076$

**4-35. a.** 0.61; 0.316
**b.** 0.42; 0.202; 0.518
**c.** 0.39

**4-37.** They cannot get to 99.9% on color copies.

**4-39.** $P(\text{Free gas}) = 0.00015 + 0.00585 + 0.0005 = 0.0065$

**4-40. a.** 0.1667
**b.** 0.0278
**c.** 0.6944
**d.** $(1/6)(5/6) + (5/6)(1/6) = 0.2778$

**4-41. a.** $P(\text{NFL}) = 105/200 = 0.5250$
  **b.** $P(\text{College degree and NBA}) = 40/200 = 0.20$
  **c.** $10/50 = 0.20$
  **d.** The two events are not independent.

**4-43.** $P(\text{Line 1 | Defective}) = (0.05)(0.4)/0.0725 = 0.2759$
  $P(\text{Line 2 | Defective}) = (0.10)(0.35)/0.0725 = 0.4828$
  $P(\text{Line 3 | Defective}) = (0.07)(0.25)/0.0725 = 0.2413$
  The unsealed cans probably came from Line 2.

**4-45.** $P(\text{Supplier A | Defective}) = (0.15)(0.3)/0.115 = 0.3913$
  $P(\text{Supplier B | Defective}) = (0.10)(0.7)/0.115 = 0.6087$
  Supplier B is the most likely to have supplied the defective parts.

**4-47. a.** $P(E_1 \text{ and } E_2) = P(E_1|E_2)P(E_2) = 0.508(0.607) = 0.308$
  **b.** $P(E_1 \text{ and } E_3) = P(E_1|E_3) = 0.607/0.853 = 0.712$

**4-49. a.** 0.76
  **b.** 0.988
  **c.** 0.024
  **d.** 0.9999
**4-51. a.** 0.1856
  **b.** 0.50
  **c.** 0.0323
  **d.** 0.3653
**4-53. a.** 0.119
  **b.** 0.148
  **c.** 0.3814
**4-55. a.** 0.50
  **b.** 0.755
  **c.** 0.269
**4-61. a.** 0.80; 0.40; 0.20; 0.60
  **b.** $A|\bar{B}$ and $\bar{A}|\bar{B}$ are complements.

**4-63. a.** 0.0156
  **b.** 0.1563
  **c.** 0.50
**4-65. a.** 0.149
  **b.** 0.997
  **c.** 0.449
**4-67. a.** the relative frequency assessment approach
  **b.** 0.028
  **c.** 0.349
  **d.** yes
**4-69.** Clerk 1 is most likely responsible for the boxes that raised the complaints.
**4-71. a.** $\dfrac{100}{300} = 0.33$

  **b.** $\dfrac{30}{300} = 0.10$

  **c.** $P(\text{East or } C) = P(\text{East}) + P(C) - P(\text{East and } C) =$
  $0.25 + 0.333 - 0.103 = 0.48$
  **d.** $P(C|\text{East}) = P(C \text{ and East})/P(\text{East}) = 0.103/0.25 = 0.41$
**4-73. a.** 0.3333
  **b.** Boise will get 70.91% of the cost, Salt Lake will get 21.82%, and Toronto will get 7.27% regardless of production volume.

## Chapter 5

**5-1. a.** discrete random variable
  **b.** The possible values for $x$ are $x = \{0, 1, 2, 3, 4, 5, 6\}$
**5-3. a.** number of children under 22 living in a household
  **b.** discrete

**5-5.** 3.7 days
**5-7. a.** 130
  **b.** 412.50
  **c.** $\sqrt{412.50} = 20.31$
**5-9. a.** 15.75
  **b.** 20.75
  **c.** 78.75
  **d.** increases both the expected value by an amount equal to the constant added
  **e.** both the expected value being multiplied by that same constant
**5-11. a.** 3.51
  **b.** $\sigma^2 = 1.6499$; $\sigma = 1.2845$
**5-13. a.** 2.87 days
  **b.** $\sigma = \sqrt{1.4931} = 1.22$
  **c.** 1.65 days to 4.09 days
**5-15. a.** \$58,300
  **b.** \$57,480
**5-17. a.** Small firm profits = \$135,000
  Mid-sized profits = \$155,000
  Large firm profits = \$160,000
  **b.** Small firm: $\sigma = \$30,000$
  Mid-sized firm: $\sigma = \$90,000$
  Large firm: $\sigma = \$156,604.60$
  **c.** The large firm has the largest expected profit.
**5-21. a.**

| $x$ | $P(x)$ | $x$ | $P(x)$ |
|-----|--------|-----|--------|
| 14 | 0.008 | 19 | 0.216 |
| 15 | 0.024 | 20 | 0.240 |
| 16 | 0.064 | 21 | 0.128 |
| 17 | 0.048 | 22 | 0.072 |
| 18 | 0.184 | 23 | 0.016 |

  **b.** 19.168; $\sigma = \sqrt{\sigma^2} = \sqrt{3.1634} = 1.7787$
  **c.** Median is 19 and the quality control department is correct.
**5-23.** 0.2668
**5-25. a.** $P(x = 5) = 0.0746$
  **b.** $P(x \geq 7) = 0.2143$
  **c.** 4
  **d.** $\sigma = \sqrt{npq} = \sqrt{20(.20)(.80)} = 1.7889$
**5-27.** 0.1029
**5-29. a.** 0.1442
  **b.** 0.8002
  **c.** 4.55
**5-31. a.** 0.0688
  **b.** 0.0031
  **c.** 0.1467
  **d.** 0.8470
  **e.** 0.9987
**5-33. a.** 3.2
  **b.** 1.386
  **c.** 0.4060
  **d.** 0.9334
**5-35. a.** 3.08
  **b.** 0.0068
  **c.** 0.0019
  **d.** It is quite unlikely.

**5-37. a.** 0.5580
    **b.** 0.8784
    **c.** An increase in sample size would be required.
**5-39. a.** 2.96
    **b.** Variance = 1.8648; Standard deviation = 1.3656
    **c.** 0.3811
**5-41. a.** 0.3179
    **b.** 0.2174
    **c.** 0.25374
**5-43. a.** 0.051987
    **b.** 0.028989
**5-45. a.** 0.372
    **b.** 12 estimate may be too high.
    **c.** 0.0832
    **d.** 0.0003
    **e.** Redemption rate is lower than either Vericours or TCA Fulfillment estimate.
**5-49. a.** 9 corporations
    **b.** 0.414324
    **c.** 70th percentile is 12.
**5-51. a.** 0.0498
    **b.** 0.1512
**5-53.** 0.175.
**5-55. a.** 0.4242
    **b.** 0.4242
    **c.** 0.4696
**5-57. a.** $P(x = 3) = 0.5$
    **b.** $P(x = 5) = 0$
    **c.** 0.6667
    **d.** Since $0.6667 > 0.25$, then $x' = 2$.
**5-59.** $P(x \geq 10) = 1 - 0.8305 = 0.1695$
**5-61.** 0.0015
**5-63. a.** $P(x = 4) = 0.4696$
    **b.** $P(x = 3) = 0.2167$
    **c.** 0.9680
**5-65. a.** 0.0355
    **b.** 0.0218
    **c.** 0.0709
**5-67. a.** 0.0632
    **b.** 120 Spicy Dogs
**5-69. a.** 0.0274
    **b.** 0.0000
    **c.** 0.0001
**5-71. a.** 8
    **b.** $\lambda t = 1(3) = 3$
    **c.** 0.0119
    **d.** It is very unlikely. Therefore, we believe that the goal has not been met.
**5-75. a.** This means the trials are dependent.
    **b.** does not imply that the trials are independent
**5-77. a.**

| X | P(x) | xP(x) |
|---|------|-------|
| 0 | 0.56 | 0.00 |
| 1 | 0.21 | 0.21 |
| 2 | 0.13 | 0.26 |
| 3 | 0.07 | 0.21 |
| 4 | 0.03 | 0.12 |
|   |      | 0.80 |

    **b.** Standard deviation = 1.0954; Variance = 1.20
**5-79.** 0.0020
**5-81.** 0.6244

**5-83. a.** 2.0
    **b.** 1.4142
    **c.** because outcomes equally likely
**5-85. a.** $E(x) = 750$; $E(y) = 100$
    **b.** StDev(x) = 844.0972; StDev(y) = 717.635
    **c.** $CV(x) = 844.0972/750 = 1.1255$
       $CV(y) = 717.635/100 = 7.1764$
**5-87. a.** 0.3501
    **b.** 0.3250
**5-89. a.** 0.02
    **b.** $E(X) = 0.6261$
    **c.** (0, 2.2783)
    **d.** $1 - 0.9929 = 0.0071$

## Chapter 6

**6-1. a.** $\dfrac{225 - 200}{20} = \dfrac{25}{20} = 1.25$

    **b.** $\dfrac{190 - 200}{20} = \dfrac{-10}{20} = -0.50$

    **c.** $\dfrac{240 - 200}{20} = \dfrac{40}{20} = 2.00$

**6-3. a.** 0.4901
    **b.** 0.6826
    **c.** 0.0279
**6-5. a.** 0.4750
    **b.** 0.05
    **c.** 0.0904
    **d.** 0.97585
    **e.** 0.8513
**6-7. a.** 0.9270
    **b.** 0.6678
    **c.** 0.9260
    **d.** 0.8413
    **e.** 0.3707
**6-9. a.** $x = 1.29(0.50) + 5.5 = 6.145$
    **b.** $\mu = 6.145 - (1.65)(0.50) = 5.32$
**6-11. a.** 0.0027
    **b.** 0.2033
    **c.** 0.1085
**6-13. a.** 0.0668
    **b.** 0.228
    **c.** 0.7745
**6-15. a.** 0.3446
    **b.** 0.673
    **c.** 51.30
    **d.** 0.9732
**6-17. a.** 0.1762
    **b.** 0.3446
    **c.** 0.4401
    **d.** 0.0548
**6-19.** The mean and standard deviation of the random variable are 15,000 and 1,250, respectively.
    **a.** 0.0548
    **b.** 0.0228
    **c.** $\mu = 15,912$ (approximately)
**6-21.** about $3,367.35
**6-23. a.** 0.1949
    **b.** 0.9544
    **c.** Mean = Median; symmetric distribution
**6-25.** $P(x < 1.0) = 0.5000 - 0.4761 = 0.0239$

**6-27. a.** $P(0.747 \leq x \leq 0.753) = 0.6915 - 0.1587 = 0.5328$

 **b.** $\sigma = \dfrac{0.753 - 0.75}{2.33} = 0.001$

**6-31. a.** skewed right
 **b.** approximate normal distribution
 **c.** 0.1230
 **d.** 2.034%
**6-33. a.** 0.75
 **b.** $Q_1 = 4.25/0.0625 = 8$; $Q_2 = 4.50/0.0625 = 12$; $Q_3 = 4.75/0.0625 = 16$
 **c.** 14.43
 **d.** 0.92
**6-35. a.** 0.9179
 **b.** 0.0498
 **c.** 0.0323
 **d.** 0.9502
**6-37. a.** 0.3935
 **b.** 0.2865
**6-39. a.** 0.7143
 **b.** 0.1429
 **c.** 0.0204
**6-41. a.** 0.4084; yes
 **b.** 40,840
**6-43. a.** 0.2939
 **b.** 0.4579
 0.1455
**6-45. a.** 0.0183
 **b.** 0.3679
**6-47. a.** 0.0498
 **b.** 0.4493
 **c.** approximately, $\lambda = 0.08917$
**6-49. a.** positively skewed
 **b. Descriptive Statistics: ATM FEES**

| Variable | Mean | StDev |
|----------|------|-------|
| ATM FEES | 2.907 | 2.555 |

 **c.** $1 - 0.6433 = 0.3567$
**6-55. a.** 0.1353
 **b.** 0.1353
**6-57.** 0.5507
**6-59.** Machine #1: 0.4236
 Machine #2: 0.4772
**6-61. a.** 0.0498
 **b.** 0.0971
 **c.** 0.1354
**6-63. d.** 5
 **e.** 0.25
 **f.** 0.125
 **g.** 0.167
**6-65.** $P(x > 74) = 0.1271$
 $P(x > 90) = 0.011$
**6-67. a.** approximately normally distributed
 **b.** Mean = 2.453; Standard deviation = 4.778
 **c.** 0.0012
 **d.** No
**6-69. a.** The histogram seems to be "bell shaped."
 **b.** The 90th percentile is 540.419.
 **c.** 376.71 is the 43rd percentile.
**6-71. a.** Uniform distribution. Sampling error could account for differences in this sample.

 **b.** $f(x) = \dfrac{1}{b-a} = \dfrac{1}{35 - 24.8} = 0.098$

 **c.** 0.451

## Chapter 7

**7-1.** $-18.50$
**7-3.** $\bar{x} - \mu = 10.17 - 11.38 = -1.21$
**7-5. a.** $-4.125$
 **b.** $-13.458$ to $11.042$
 **c.** $-9.208$ to $9.208$
**7-9.** 0.64
**7-11. a.** $\mu = \dfrac{\sum x}{N} = \dfrac{864}{20} = 43.20$ days

 **b.** $\bar{x} = \dfrac{\sum x}{n} = \dfrac{206}{5} = 41.20$ days;

 Sampling error $= 41.20 - 43.20 = -2$
 **c.** $-28.4$ days to 40.4 days
**7-13. a.** \$3,445.30
 **b.** $-\$29.70$
**7-15. a.** 1,432.08
 **b.** 87.12
 **c.** $-175.937$ to 178.634
**7-17. a.** Mean of Sales
 Mean of sales $= 2,764.83$
 **b.** Mean of Sample
 Mean of sample $= 2,797.16$
 **c.** \$32.33 million
 **d.** Smallest $= -\$170.47$; Largest $= \$218.41$
**7-21. a.** Sampling error $= \bar{x} - \mu = \$15.84 - \$20.00 = -\$4.16$
 **b.** Random and nonrandom samples can produce sampling error and the error is computed the same way.
**7-23.** $P(\bar{x} > 2,100) = 0.5000 - 0.3907 = 0.1093$

**7-25.** $\sigma_{\bar{x}} = \dfrac{\sigma}{\sqrt{n}} = \dfrac{40}{\sqrt{25}} = 8$

**7-27.** 0.0016
**7-29. a.** 0.3936
 **b.** 0.2119
 **c.** 0.1423
 **d.** 0.0918
**7-31. a.** 0.8413
 **b.** 0.1587
**7-33. a.** 0.3830
 **b.** 0.9444
 **c.** 0.9736
**7-35.** $P(\bar{x} \geq 4.2) = 0.5000 - 0.4989 = 0.0011$
**7-37.** $P(\bar{x} \leq 33.5) = 0.5000 - 0.2019 = 0.2981$
**7-39. a. Descriptive Statistics: Video Price**

| Variable | Mean | StDev |
|----------|------|-------|
| Video Price | 45.580 | 2.528 |

 **b. Cumulative Distribution Function**
 Normal with mean = 46 and Standard deviation = 0.179

| $x$ | $P(X \leq x)$ |
|-----|---------------|
| 45.58 | 0.00948 |

 **c. Cumulative Distribution Function**
 Normal with mean = 45.75 and Standard deviation = 0.179

| $x$ | $P(X \leq x)$ |
|-----|---------------|
| 45.58 | 0.171127 |

**7-43. a.** Mean = 55.68; Standard deviation = 6.75

**7-45. a.** 0.8621
   **b.** 0.0146
   **c.** 0.8475
   **d.** 0.7422
**7-47. a.** Sampling error $= p - \pi = 0.65 - 0.70 = -0.05$
   **b.** 0.1379
**7-49. a.** 0.8221
   **b.** 0.6165
**7-51. a.** 0.9015
   **b.** 0.0049
**7-53. a.** $p = \dfrac{x}{n} = \dfrac{27}{60} = 0.45$
   **b.** $P(p \geq 0.45) = 0.5000 - 0.2852 = 0.2148$
**7-55.** $P(p \geq 0.09) = 0.5000 - 0.4838 = 0.0162$
**7-57. a.** 0.1020
   **b.** 0.4522
   **c.** $\approx 0.0$
**7-59. a.** 0.0749
   **b.** 0.0359
   **c.** essentially 0
**7-61. a.** 0.72
   **b.** 0.9448
   **c.** The proportion of on-time arrivals is smaller than in 2004.
**7-63. a.** 131 over \$100,000 and 65 of \$100,000 or less
   **b.** 0.668
   **c.** 0.2981
**7-67.** Sample averages would be less variable than the population.
**7-69. a.** 405.55
   **b.** 159.83
**7-71.** A sample size of 1 would be sufficient.
**7-73. a.** 0.2643
   **b.** 0.3752
   **c.** 0.0951
**7-75. a.** Right skewed distribution; a normal distribution cannot be used.
   **b.** Sampling distribution of the sample means cannot be approximated by a normal distribution.
   **c.** 0.50
**7-77. a.** 0.8660
   **b.** 0.9783
**7-79. a.** $P(x > 16.10) = 0.5000 - 0.1554 = 0.3446$
   **b.** $P(\bar{x} > 16.10) = 0.5000 - 0.4177 = 0.0823$
**7-81.** Note, because of the small population, the finite correction factor is used.
   **a.** 0.1112
   **b.** Either the mean or the standard deviation or both may have changed.
   **c.** 0.2483
**7-83. a.** 0
   **b.** highly unlikely
   **c.** 0.4999
**7-85. a.** 0
   **b.** 0.117
**7-89. a.** 0.216
   **b.** 0.3275
   **c.** Reducing the warranty is a judgment call

## Chapter 8

**8-1.** 15.86 ————— 20.94
**8-3.** 293.18 ————— 306.82
**8-5.** 1,180.10 ————— 1,219.90
**8-7. a.** 1.69 ————— 4.31
   **b.** 1.38 ————— 4.62
**8-9.** 97.62 ——— 106.38

**8-11. a.** 11.6028 ————— 15.1972
   **b.** 29.9590 ————— 32.4410
   **c.** 2.9098 ————— 6.0902
   **d.** 18.3192 ————— 25.0808
**8-13. a.** \$13.945 ————— \$14.515
   **b.** \$7,663.92; \$7,362.96
**8-15. a.** (4,780.25; 5,219.75)
   **b.** 219.75
   **c.** $715.97 \approx 716$
**8-17. a.** \$5.29 ————— \$13.07
   **b.** Sample data do not dispute the American Express study.
**8-19. a.** 83.785
   **b.** (505.415, 567.985)
   **c.** increased since 2007
**8-21. a.** 163.5026 ————— 171.5374
   **b.** Increase the sample size, decrease the level of confidence, decrease the standard deviation.
**8-23. a.** 6.3881 ————— 6.6855
**8-25. a.** $\bar{x} = \dfrac{33.281}{130} = 256.01$; $s$ is 80.68.
   **b.** 242.01 ————— 270.01
   **c.** $\pm 14.00$ seconds
**8-27.** $n = \dfrac{z^2\sigma^2}{e^2} = \dfrac{1.96^2 350^2}{50^2} = 188.24 = 189$
**8-29.** $n = \dfrac{z^2\sigma^2}{e^2} = \left(\dfrac{z\sigma}{e}\right)^2 = \left(\dfrac{(1.96)(680)}{44}\right)^2 = 917.54 \approx 918$
**8-31.** 3,684.21
**8-33. a.** 61.47; $n = 62$
   **b.** 5,725.95; $n = 5726$
   **c.** 1.658; $n = 2$
   **d.** 305.38; $n = 306$
   **e.** 61.47; $n = 62$
**8-35.** $n = 249$
**8-37. a.** 883
   **b.** 1. Reduce the confidence level to something less than 95%.
      2. Increase the margin of error beyond 0.25 pounds.
      3. some combination of decreasing the confidence level and increasing the margin of error
**8-39.** $n = \dfrac{z^2\sigma^2}{e^2} = \left(\dfrac{z\sigma}{e}\right)^2 = \left(\dfrac{(2.575)(1.4)}{0.2}\right)^2 = 324.9 \cong 325$
**8-41. a.** $n = 246$
   **b.** $n = 6{,}147$
   **c.** Margin of error is from \$0.44 to \$0.51.
**8-43. a.** $n = 60$
   **b.** $n = 239$
**8-45. a.** $429 - 137 = 292$ additional
   **b.** $302 - 137 = 165$ additional
**8-47. a.** Net required sample is $1{,}749 - 150 = 1{,}599$.
   **b.** Reduce the confidence level (lowers the $z$-value) or increase the margin of error or some combination of the two.
**8-49.** 1,698
**8-51.** 0.224 ————— 0.336
**8-53. a.** yes
   **b.** (0.286, 0.414)
   **c.** 0.286 ——— 0.414
   **d.** 0.064
**8-55. a.** $p = \dfrac{x}{n} = \dfrac{7}{40} = 0.175$
   **b.** (0.057, 0.293)
   **c.** $n = 888$

**8-57. a.** 0.324 —— 0.436

**b.** 9,604

**8-59. a.** 0.3155 —— 0.3745

**b.** 179.20 —— 212.716

**c.** 0.3692 —— 0.4424

**d.** 1,224.51 = 1,225

**8-61.** 0.895 ————————————— 0.925

**8-63. a.** 0.6627 —— 0.7173

**b.** 2,401

**c.** 0.4871(2) = 0.9742

**8-65. a.** 0.1167

**b.** 0.1131

**c.** (0.0736, 0.1598)

**8-67. a.** 0.7444

**b.** 0.6260 —— 0.8628

**c.** The sample size could be increased.

**8-75. a.** 0.7265 —— 0.7935

**b.** 25,427.50 —— 27,772.50

**8-77. a.** $n = 62 - 40 = 22$ more

**b.** \$620 without pilot; savings of \$1,390 − \$620 = \$770

**8-79. a.** 5.21

**b.** $n = 390$

**c.** 0.25 work days = 2.00 work hours

**8-81. a.** 0.7003 —— 0.7741

**b.** 32,279.4674 —— 33,322.7227

**8-83. a.** 45.23 to 45.93

**b.** is plausible

**c.** $n = 25$

## Chapter 9

**9-1. a.** $z = 1.96$

**b.** $t = -1.6991$

**c.** $t = \pm 2.4033$

**d.** $z = \pm 1.645$

**9-3. a.** $z_\alpha = 1.645$

**b.** $t_{\alpha/2} = \pm 2.5083$

**c.** $z_{\alpha/2} = \pm 2.575$

**d.** $-t_\alpha = -1.5332$

**e.** Invalid

**9-5. a.** Reject the null hypothesis if the calculated value of the test statistic, $z$, is greater than 2.575 or less than −2.575. Otherwise, do not reject.

**b.** $z = -3.111$

**c.** Reject the null hypothesis.

**9-7. a.** Reject the null hypothesis if the calculated value of the test statistic, $t$, is less than the critical value of −2.0639. Otherwise, do not reject.

**b.** $t = -1.875$

**c.** Do not reject the null hypothesis.

**9-9. a.** Reject the null hypothesis if the calculated value of the test statistic, $t$, is greater than 1.3277. Otherwise, do not reject.

**b.** $t = 0.78$

**c.** Do not reject the null hypothesis.

**9-11. a.** Type I error

**b.** Type II error

**c.** Type I error

**d.** No error

**e.** Type II error

**f.** No error

**9-13. a.** $H_0: \mu \geq 30{,}000$

$H_A: \mu < 30{,}000$

**b.** \$30,411.25

**c.** Do not reject.

**d.** Type II

**9-15. a.** $H_0: \mu \geq 3{,}600$

$H_A: \mu < 3{,}600$

**b.** Since $t = -0.85 > -1.8331$, the null hypothesis is not rejected.

**9-17. a.** $H_0: \mu \geq 55$

$H_A: \mu < 55$

**b.** Because $t = -0.93 > -2.4620$, the null hypothesis is not rejected.

**9-19.** The annual average consumer unit spending for food at home in Detroit is less than the 2006 national consumer unit average.

**9-21. a.** Since $t = 0.74 < 2.1604$, we do not reject the null hypothesis.

**b.** Type II error

**9-23. a.** $z = 1.96$

**b.** $z = -1.645$

**c.** $z = \pm 2.33$

**d.** $z = \pm 1.645$

**9-25.** Since $-2.17 > -2.33$, don't reject.

**9-27. a.** Reject the null hypothesis if the calculated value of the test statistic, $z$, is less than the critical value of the test statistic $z = -1.96$. Otherwise, do not reject.

**b.** $z = -2.0785$

**c.** reject

**9-29. a.** $p$-value = 0.05

**b.** $p$-value = 0.5892

**c.** $p$-value = 0.1902

**d.** $p$-value = 0.0292

**9-31.** Because $z = -3.145$ is less than $-2.055$, reject $H_0$.

**9-33.** Since $z = 0.97 < 1.645$, we do not reject the null hypothesis.

**9-35.** Because $z = 1.543$ is less than 1.96, do not reject $H_0$. $p$-value $= 0.50 - 0.4382 = 0.0618$

**9-37. a.** $H_0: \pi \leq 0.40$

$H_A: \pi > 0.40$

**b.** Since $z = 1.43 < 1.645$, we do not reject the null hypothesis.

**9-39. a.** $H_0: \pi \leq 0.10$

$H_A: \pi > 0.10$

**b.** Since the $p$-value = 0.1736 is greater than 0.05, don't reject.

**9-41. a.** Since $z = 3.8824 > 1.96$, reject $H_0$.

**b.** $p$-value $= 2(0.5 - 0.5) = 0.0$

**9-43.** Because $z = 0.5155$ is neither less than $-1.645$ nor greater than 1.645, do not reject $H_0$.

**9-45. a.** $H_0: \pi \geq 0.50$

$H_A: \pi < 0.50$

**b.** Since $z = -6.08 < -2.05$, we reject the null hypothesis.

**9-47. a.** The appropriate null and alternative hypotheses are

$H_0: \pi \geq 0.95$

$H_A: \pi < 0.95$

**b.** Since $z = -4.85 < -1.645$, we reject the null hypothesis.

**9-49. a.** 0.80

**b.** 0.20

**c.** The power increases, and beta decreases.

**d.** Since $\bar{x} = 1.23$ then $1.0398 < 1.23 < 1.3062$, do not reject $H_0$.

**9-51.** 0.8888

**9-53.** 0.3228

**9-55. a.** 0.0084

**b.** 0.2236

**c.** 0.9160

**9-57.** **a.** 0.1685
   **b.** 0.1446
   **c.** 0.1190
**9-59.** **a.** $H_0: \mu \geq 243$
   $H_A: \mu < 243$
   **b.** 0.0537.
**9-61.** **a.** $H_0: \mu \geq 15$
   $H_A: \mu < 15$
   **b.** 0.0606
**9-63.** **a.** $H_0 = \mu \geq \$47{,}413$
   $H_A = \mu < \$47{,}413$
   **b.** 0.1446
**9-65.** 0.0495
**9-67.** **a.** Since $t = -3.97 < -1.6991$, we reject $H_0$.
   **b.** 0.3557
**9-77.** **a.** If $\alpha$ is decreased, the rejection region is smaller making it easier to accept $H_0$, so $\beta$ is increased.
   **b.** If $n$ is increased, the test statistic is also increased, making it harder to accept $H_0$, so $\beta$ is decreased.
   **c.** If $n$ is increased, the test statistic is also increased, making it harder to accept $H_0$, so $\beta$ is decreased and power is increased.
   **d.** If $\alpha$ is decreased, the rejection region is smaller, making it easier to accept $H_0$, so $\beta$ is increased and power is decreased.

**9-79.** **a.** $z = \dfrac{\bar{x} - \mu}{\dfrac{\sigma}{\sqrt{n}}}$

   **b.** $t = \dfrac{\bar{x} - \mu}{\dfrac{s}{\sqrt{n}}}$

   **c.** $z = \dfrac{p - \pi}{\sqrt{\dfrac{\pi(1-\pi)}{n}}}$

**9-81.** **a.** $H_0: \mu \leq 4{,}000$
   $H_A: \mu > 4{,}000$
   **b.** Since $t = 1.2668 < 1.7959$, do not reject.
**9-83.** **a.** $H_0: \pi \geq 0.50$
   $H_A: \pi < 0.50$
   **b.** Since $z = -5.889 < -1.645$, reject the null hypothesis. Since $z = -5.889$, the $p$-value is approximately zero.
**9-85.** **a.** Since $z = -1.5275 > -1.645$, do not reject.
   **b.** Type II error
**9-87.** **a.** yes
   **b.** $p$-value $= 0.001$, reject
**9-89.** **a.** yes
   **b.** Since $z = -1.1547 > -1.96$, do not reject $H_0$.
**9-91.** **a.** $H_0: \mu = 6$ inches
   $H_A: \mu \neq 6$ inches
   **b.** Reject $H_0$ if $z > 2.58$ or $z < -2.58$; otherwise do not reject $H_0$.
   **c.** Since $\bar{x} = 6.03 > 6.0182$, reject the null hypothesis.
**9-93.** **a.** Because $z = 4.426 > 1.96$ we reject $H_0$.
   **b.** 50,650.33 ——— 51,419.67
**9-95.** $p$-value $= 0$, so reject $H_0$.
**9-97.** **a.** $H_0: \mu = 0.75$ inch
   $H_A: \mu \neq 0.75$ inch
   **b.** Since $t = 0.9496 < 2.6264$, do not reject $H_0$.

**9-99.** **a.** Since the $p$-value is less than $\alpha$, we reject $H_0$.
   **b.** 0.1170
**9-101.** **a.** Since the $p$-value is greater than $\alpha$, we do not reject $H_0$.
   **b.** 0.5476

## Chapter 10

**10-1.** $-6.54 \leq (\mu_1 - \mu_2) \leq 0.54$
**10-3.** $-13.34 \leq \mu_1 - \mu_2 \leq -6.2$
**10-5.** $0.07 \leq (\mu_1 - \mu_2) \leq 50.61$
**10-7.** $-19.47 \leq \mu_1 - \mu_2 \leq -7.93$
**10-9.** **a.** $-0.05$
   **b.** $-0.0974 \leq (\mu_1 - \mu_2) \leq -0.0026$
   **c.** The two lines do not fill bags with equal average amounts.
**10-11.** **a.** $-0.1043$ ——— $2.7043$; no
   **b.** no
**10-13.** **a.** highly unlikely
   **b.** (36.3551, 37.4449)
**10-15.** $-0.10 \leq \mu_1 - \mu_2 \leq 0.30$
**10-17.** **a.** 2.35%
   **b.** $-1{,}527.32$ ——— $4{,}926.82$
   **c.** plausible that there is no difference
   **d.** 3,227
**10-19.** Since $t = -4.80 < -2.1199$, we reject.
**10-21.** Since $z = 5.26 > 1.645$, reject the null hypothesis.
**10-23.** **a.** If $t > 1.9698$ or $t < -1.9698$, reject $H_0$.
   **b.** Since $5.652 > 1.9698$, reject $H_0$.
**10-25.** Because $t = 0.896$ is neither less than $t = -2.0167$, nor greater than $t = 2.0167$, do not reject.
**10-27.** **a.** Since $0.9785 > -1.677$, do not reject $H_0$.
   **b.** Type II error
**10-29.** Since $t = -4.30 < -1.6510$, we reject the null hypothesis.
**10-31.** **a.** $2{,}084/2{,}050 = 1.02$
   **b.** Because $p$-value $= P(t \leq 5.36) \cong 1.00$, the null hypothesis is not rejected.
**10-33.** **a.** The ratio of the two means is $9.60/1.40 = 6.857$.
   **b.** The ratio of the two standard deviations is $8.545/1.468 = 5.821$.
   **c.** Since $p$-value $= 0.966 > 0.25$, do not reject the null.
**10-35.** **a.** It is plausible to conjecture the goal has been met.
   **b.** Since the $p$-value is greater than 0.025, we do not reject the null hypothesis.
**10-37.** $-674.41 \leq \mu \leq -191.87$
**10-39.** **a.** $H_0: \mu_d \geq 0$
   $H_A: \mu_d < 0$
   **b.** Since $-3.64 < -1.3968$, reject $H_0$.
   **c.** $-2.1998$ ——— $-0.7122$
**10-41.** **a.** (7.6232, 13.4434)
   **b.** Because $t = 0.37 < 1.459$, the null hypothesis cannot be rejected.
**10-43.** **a.** The samples were matched pairs.
   **b.** Because $0.005 < p$-value $< 0.01 = \alpha$, the null hypothesis should be rejected.
**10-45.** **a.** Since $t = -7.35 < -1.98$, reject $H_0$.
   **b.** $-100.563$ ——— $-57.86$; yes.
**10-47.** **a.** Because $t = -9.24 < -2.3646$, reject.
   **b.** The ratio of the two standard errors is $3.84 \; (= 0.5118/0.13313)$.
**10-49.** Since $1.068 < 2.136$, do not reject the null hypothesis.
**10-51.** **a.** no
   **b.** no
   **c.** yes
   **d.** no

**10-53.** Because the $p$-value $= 0.367$ is greater than $\alpha = 0.05$, we do not reject the null hypothesis.

**10-55.** **a.** Since $z = 2.538 > 1.96$, reject $H_0$.
   **b.** Since $z = 2.538 > -1.645$, fail to reject $H_0$.
   **c.** Since $z = 2.538 > 1.96$, reject $H_0$.
   **d.** Since $z = 2.08 < 2.33$, fail to reject $H_0$.

**10-57.** Since the test statistic, $-0.4111 > -2.575$, do not reject the null hypothesis.

**10-59.** **a.** Since $p$-value $= 0.0244 < 0.05$ reject $H_0$.
   **b.** $0.00597$

**10-61.** **a.** yes
   **b.** Since the $p$-value $= 0.039 < 0.05$, the null hypothesis is rejected.

**10-63.** **a.** yes
   **b.** Since the $p$-value $= 0.095 > 0.01$, the null hypothesis is not rejected.
   **c.** Larger sample sizes would be required.

**10-67.** **a.** $(2.1064, 7.8936)$
   **b.** $t = -2.0687$
   **c.** $t = 2.0687$

**10-69.** $-120.8035$ —— $146.0761$

**10-71.** **a.** yes
   **b.** Since $0.7745 < 2.17$, do not reject $H_0$.

**10-73.** $-26.40 \le \mu_d \le -0.36$

**10-75.** **a.** paired samples experiment
   **b.** Since the $p$-value $= 0.000 < 0.05 = \alpha$, the null hypothesis is rejected.
   **c.** $(0.5625, 0.8775)$

**10-77.** **a.** Since $t = 5.25 > 2.3499$, reject.
   **b.** Type I error

## Chapter 11

**11-1.** $74,953.7 \le \sigma^2 \le 276,472.2$

**11-3.** Since $\chi^2 = 12.39 > 10.1170$, do not reject the null hypothesis.

**11-5.** **a.** Because $\chi^2 = 17.82 < \chi^2_{0.05} = 19.6752$ and because $\chi^2 = 17.82 > \chi^2_{0.95} = 4.5748$, do not reject.
   **b.** Because $\chi^2 = 12.96 < \chi^2_{0.025} = 31.5264$ and because $\chi^2 = 12.96 > \chi^2_{0.975} = 8.2307$, we do not reject the null hypothesis.

**11-7.** **a.** $0.01 < p$-value $< 0.05$; since $p$-value $< \alpha$, reject $H_0$.
   **b.** Since the test statistic $= 1.591 <$ the $\chi^2$ critical value $= 1.6899$, reject the null hypothesis.
   **c.** $p$-value $= 0.94$; do not reject.

**11-9.** $22.72 \le \sigma^2 \le 81.90$

**11-11.** $353.38 \le \sigma^2 \le 1,745.18$

**11-13.** **a.** $H_0$: $\mu \le 10$
   $H_A$: $\mu > 10$
   **b.** Since $1.2247 < 1.383$, do not reject $H_0$.
   **c.** Since $3.75 < 14.6837$, do not reject $H_0$.

**11-15.** **a.** $\sigma^2 = 4.884$
   **b.** Since the test statistic $= 10.47 <$ the $\chi^2$ critical value $= 13.8484$, do not reject. Since $t = -17.57 < -1.7109$, reject $H_0$.

**11-17.** **a.** $\sigma^2 = 0.000278$
   **b.** Since $p$-value $= 0.004 < 0.01$, we reject.

**11-19.** **a.** If the calculated $F > 2.278$, reject $H_0$, otherwise do not reject $H_0$.
   **b.** Since $1.0985 < 2.278$, do not reject $H_0$.

**11-21.** **a.** $F = 3.619$
   **b.** $F = 3.106$
   **c.** $F = 3.051$

**11-23.** Since $F = 1.154 < 6.388 = F_{0.05}$, fail to reject $H_0$.

**11-25.** Since $3.4807 > 1.984$, reject $H_0$.

**11-27.** **a.** Since $2.0818 < 2.534$, do not reject.
   **b.** Type I error. Decrease the alpha or increase the sample sizes.

**11-29.** Since $F = 3.035 > 2.526 = F_{0.05}$, reject $H_0$.

**11-31.** Since $1.4833 < 3.027$, do not reject $H_0$.

**11-33.** **a.** The $F$-test approach is the appropriate.
   **b.** $33.90$

**11-39.** $0.753 \le \sigma^2 \le 2.819$

**11-41.** Since $1.2129 < 2.231$, do not reject.

**11-43.** **a.** Since $\chi^2 = 37.24 > \chi^2_U = 30.1435$, reject $H_0$.
   **b.** $P(x \ge 3) = 0.0230 + 0.0026 + 0.0002 = 0.0256$

**11-45.** **a.** Since $F = 3.817 > 1.752 = F_{0.025}$, reject $H_0$.
   **b.** yes

**11-47.** Since $202.5424 < 224.9568$, do not reject.

**11-49.** Since $2.0609 > 1.4953$, reject the null hypothesis.

**11-51.** **a.** Since the $p$-value $= 0.496 > 0.05 = \alpha = 0.05$, do not reject.
   **b.** yes

## Chapter 12

**12-1.** **a.** $SSW = SST - SSB = 9,271,678,090 - 2,949,085,157 = 6,322,592,933$
   $MSB = 2,949,085,157/2 = 1,474,542,579$
   $MSW = 6,322,592,933/72 = 87,813,791$
   $F = 1,474,542,579/87,813,791 = 16.79$
   **b.** Because the $F$ test statistic $= 16.79 > F_\alpha = 2.3778$, we reject.

**12-3.** **a.** The appropriate null and alternative hypotheses are
   $H_0$: $\mu_1 = \mu_2 = \mu_3$
   $H_A$: Not all $\mu_j$ are equal.
   **b.** Because $F = 9.84 >$ critical $F = 3.35$, we reject. Because $p$-value $= 0.0006 < \alpha = 0.05$, we reject.
   **c.** Critical range $= 6.0$; $\mu_1 > \mu_2$ and $\mu_3 > \mu_2$

**12-5.** **a.** $df_B = 3$
   **b.** $F = 11.1309$
   **c.** $H_0$: $\mu_1 = \mu_2 = \mu_3 = \mu_4$
   $H_A$: At least two population means are different.
   **d.** Since $11.1309 > 2.9467$, reject $H_0$.

**12-7.** **a.** Because $2.729 < 15.5$, we conclude that the population variances could be equal; since $F = 5.03 > 3.885$, we reject $H_0$.
   **b.** Critical range $= 2.224$; pop 1 and 2 means differ — no other differences.

**12-9.** **a.** Since $F = 7.131 > F_{\alpha=0.01} = 5.488$, reject.
   **b.** $CR = 1,226.88$; Venetti mean is greater than Edison mean

**12-11.** **a.** Because $3.125 < 15.5$, we conclude that the population variances could be equal. Since $F = 1,459.78 > 3.885$, we reject $H_0$.
   **b.** Critical range $= 9.36$

**12-13.** **a.** Since $10.48326 > 5.9525$ reject $H_0$ and conclude that at least two populations means are different.
   **b.** Critical range $= 222.02$; eliminate Type D and A.

**12-15.** **a.** Since $0.01 < 0.05$, reject $H_0$ and conclude that at least two populations means are different.
   **b.**

|  | Absolute Differences | Critical Range | Significant? |
|---|---|---|---|
| Mini 1 − Mini 2 | 0.633 | 1.264 | no |
| Mini 1 − Mini 3 | 1.175 | 1.161 | yes |
| Mini 2 − Mini 3 | 1.808 | 1.322 | yes |

Student reports will vary, but they should recommend either 1 or 2 since there is no statistically significant difference between them.

**c.** 0.978 —— 2.678 cents per mile; $293.40 —— $803.40 annual savings

**12-17. a.** $p$-value $= 0.000 < \alpha = 0.05$

**b.** Average length of life differs between Delphi and Exide and also between Delphi and Johnson. There is not enough evidence to indicate that the average lifetime for Exide and Johnson differ.

**12-19. a.** $H_0: \mu_1 = \mu_2 = \mu_3 = \mu_4$
$H_A$: At least two population means are different.
$H_0: \mu_{b1} = \mu_{b2} = \mu_{b3} = \mu_{b4} = \mu_{b5} = \mu_{b6} = \mu_{b7} = \mu_{b8}$
$H_A$: Not all block means are equal.

**b.** $F$ Blocks $= 2.487$   $F$ Groups $= 3.072$

**c.** Since $46.876 > 2.487$, reject $H_0$.

**d.** Since $p$-value $0.0000326 < 0.05$, reject.

**e.** $LSD = 5.48$

**12-21.** Because $F = 14.3 >$ Critical $F = 3.326$, we reject and conclude that blocking is effective.
Because $F = 0.1515 <$ Critical $F = 4.103$, we do not reject.

**12-23. a.** Because $F = 32.12 > F_{\alpha=0.01} = 9.78$, reject the null hypothesis.

**b.** Because $F = 1.673 < F_{\alpha=0.01} = 10.925$, do not reject the null hypothesis.

**12-25. a.** Because $F = 22.32 > F_{\alpha=0.05} = 6.944$, reject the null hypothesis.

**b.** Because $F = 14.185 > F_{\alpha=0.05} = 6.944$, reject the null hypothesis.

**c.** $LSD = 8.957$

**12-27. a.** $p$-value $= 0.000 < \alpha = 0.05$

**b.** $p$-value $= 0.004 < \alpha = 0.05$

**c.** $LSD = 1.55$; $\mu_1 < \mu_3$ and $\mu_2 < \mu_3$

**12-29. a.** $p$-value $= 0.628 < \alpha = 0.05$

**b.** $p$-value $= 0.000 < \alpha = 0.05$

**c.** $LSD = 372.304$; $\mu_1 > \mu_2 > \mu_3$

**12-31. a.** $p$-value $= 0.854 > \alpha = 0.05$. Therefore, fail to reject $H_0$.

**b.** Since $F = 47.10 > F_{0.05} = 5.143$, reject $H_0$.

**c.** $p$-value $= 0.039 < \alpha = 0.05$. Therefore, reject $H_0$.

**12-33. a.** Since $0.4617 < 3.8853$, do not reject $H_0$.

**b.** Since $2.3766 < 3.8853$, do not reject $H_0$.

**c.** Since $5.7532 > 4.7472$, reject $H_0$.

**12-35. a.** Since $F = 39.63 > F_{0.05} = 3.633$, reject $H_0$.

**b.** Since $F = 2.90 < F_{0.05} = 9.552$, fail to reject $H_0$.

**c.** Since $F = 3.49 < F_{0.05} = 9.552$, fail to reject $H_0$.
Since $F = 57.73 > F_{0.05} = 9.552$, reject $H_0$.

**12-37. a.** Because $F = 1.016 < F_{\alpha=0.05} = 2.728$, do not reject.

**b.** Because $F = 1.157 < F_{\alpha=0.05} = 3.354$, do not reject.

**c.** Because $F = 102.213 > F_{\alpha=0.05} = 3.354$, reject.

**12-39. a.** Since $p$-value $= 0.0570 > 0.01$, do not reject.

**b.** Since $2.9945 < 6.0129$, do not reject.

**c.** Since $p$-value $= 0.4829 > 0.1$, do not reject

**12-41. a.** $\alpha = 0.025 < p$-value $= 0.849$. Therefore, fail to reject.

**b.** Since $F = 15.61 > F_{0.025} = 3.353$, reject.

**c.** Since $F = 3.18 < F_{0.025} = 3.353$, do not reject.

**d.** Since $-2.0595 < t = -0.69 < 2.0595$, fail to reject.

**12-49. a.** $\alpha = 0.05 < p$-value $= 0.797$. Therefore, fail to reject.

**b.** Since $F = 25.55 > F_{0.05} = 3.855$, reject.

**c.** Since $F = 0.82 < F_{0.05} = 3.940$, do not reject.

**12-51. a.** Since $F = 3.752 > 2.657$, we reject.

**b.** Critical range $= 9.5099$; $\mu_1 > \mu_B$, $\mu_1 > \mu_{1F}$, and $\mu_1 > \mu_G$

**12-53. a.** Since $(F_{1,200,0.05} = 3.888 < F_{1,998,0.05} < F_{1,100,0.05} = 3.936) < F = 89.53$, reject.

**b.** Since $t = -9.46 < (t_{250,0.05} = -1.9695 < t_{998,0.05} < t_{100,0.05} = -1.9840)$, reject.

**c.** Note that $(t\text{-value})^2 = (-9.46)^2 = 89.49 \approx 89.53$.

**12-55. a.** randomized block design

**b.** $H_0: \mu_1 = \mu_2 = \mu_3 = \mu_4$
$H_A$: At least two population means are different.

**c.** Since $3.3785 < 4.0150$, do not reject.

**d.** $H_0$: Since $20.39312 > 1.9358$, reject.

**e.** no difference

**12-57. a.** Since $F = 5.37 > F_{0.05} = 2.642$, reject.

**b.** Since $F = 142.97 > F_{0.05} = 5.192$, reject.

**c.** Since $F = 129.91 > F_{0.05} = 5.192$, reject; since $F = 523.33 > F_{0.05} = 5.192$, reject.

## Chapter 13

**13-1.** Because $\chi^2 = 6.4607 < 13.2767$, do not reject.

**13-3.** Because $\chi^2 = 218.62 > 18.3070$, we reject.

**13-5.** Because the calculated value of $595.657 > 13.2767$, we reject.

**13-7.** Because the calculated value of $4.48727$ is less than $12.8345$, do not reject.

**13-9. a.** Since chi-square statistic $= 3.379443 < 11.3449$, do not reject.

**b.** Based on the test, we have no reason to conclude that the company is not meeting its product specification.

**13-11.** Chi-square value $= 0.3647$; do not reject.

**13-13.** Since chi-square $= 3.6549 < 7.3778$, do not reject.

**13-15. a.** Because the calculated value of $1.97433$ is less than the critical value of $14.0671$, we do not reject.

**b.** Since $z = -16.12 < 1.645$, do not reject.

**13-17. a.** Since the calculated value of $27.9092 > 3.8415$, we reject.

**b.** $0.000000127$

**13-19. a.** $H_0$: Gender is independent of drink preference.
$H_A$: There is a relationship between gender and drink preference.

**b.** $12.331 > 3.8415$; reject.

**13-21. a.** $\chi^2 = 7.783 < 9.2104$, do not reject.

**b.** $0.0204$

**13-23. a.** $8.3584 > 6.6349$; reject.

**b.** $p$-value $= 0.00384$

**13-25.** The $p$-value $= 0.00003484$; reject.

**13-27. a.** Chi-square $= 0.932$; do not reject

**b.** A decision could be made for other reasons, like cost.

**13-29.** Because $\chi^2 = 24.439 > 12.5916$, reject the null hypothesis.

**13-31.** Collapse cells, chi-square $= 11.6 > 5.9915$, reject.

**13-33.** Since $0.308 < 5.991$, do not reject.

**13-41. a.** Chi-square $= 3{,}296.035$

**b.** $402.3279 > 4.6052$; reject.

**13-43.** Chi-square $= 0.172$; do not reject.

**13-45. a.** $H_0$: Airline usage pattern has not changed from a previous study.
$H_A$: Airline usage pattern has changed from a previous study.

**b.** Chi-square test statistic is $66.4083 > 15.08632$; reject.

**13-47. b.** $\chi^2 = 37.094 > 3.8415$; reject.

## Chapter 14

**14-1.** $H_0: \rho \le 0.0$
$H_A: \rho > 0.0$
$\alpha = 0.05$, $t = 2.50$, $2.50 > 1.7709$; reject.

**14-3. a.** $r = 0.206$

**b.** $H_0: \rho = 0$

$H_A: \rho \neq 0$

$\alpha = 0.10, -1.8595 < t = 0.59 < 1.8595$; do not reject $H_0$.

**14-5. a.** There appears to be a positive linear relationship.

**b.** $r = 0.9239$

**c.** $H_0: \rho \leq 0$

$H_A: \rho > 0$

$d.f. = 10 - 2 = 8$

Since $6.8295 > 2.8965$, reject $H_0$.

**14-7. a.** fairly strong positive correlation

**b.** $H_0: \rho \leq 0$

$H_A: \rho > 0$

$\alpha = 0.01, t = 7.856 > 2.4066$; reject the null hypothesis.

**14-9. a.** The dependent is the average credit card balance. The independent variable is the income variable.

**b.** does not appear to be a strong relationship

**c.** $H_0: \rho = 0.0$

$H_A: \rho \neq 0.0$

$\alpha = 0.05, t = -1.56 > -2.1604$; do not reject.

**14-11. a.** $r = 0.979$

**b.** $H_0: \rho \leq 0$

$H_A: \rho > 0$

$\alpha = 0.05, 6.791 > t = 2.9200$ as it was; we reject $H_0$.

**14-13. a.** positive linear relationship

**b.** using Excel, $r = 0.75644$.

**c.** $H_0: \rho \leq 0$

$H_A: \rho > 0$. If $t > 2.0096$, reject the null hypothesis; Because $t = 8.0957 > 2.0096$, reject the null hypothesis.

**14-15. a.** As 2001 revenue increases there is an increase in the 2004 revenue, which can be seen as the upward "tilt" of the scatter plot.

**b.** $r = 0.186$

**c.** $H_0: \rho \leq 0$

$H_A: \rho > 0$

$\alpha = 0.05, 1.325 < t = 1.67655$; do not reject $H_0$.

**14-17. a.** There appears to be a positive linear relationship between $x$ and $y$.

**b.** $\hat{y} = 15.31 + 4.92(x)$; $b_0$ of 15.31 would be the value of $y$ if $x$ were 0; $b_1$ of 4.92 means that for every one unit increase in $x$, $y$ will increase by 4.92.

**c.** $R^2 = 0.8702$

**d.** $H_0: \rho = 0$

$H_A: \rho \neq 0$

Because $t = 5.7923 > 4.0321$, reject $H_0$.

**e.** $H_0: \beta_1 = 0$

$H_A: \beta_1 \neq 0$

Because $t = 5.79 > 4.0321$, reject $H_0$.

**14-19. a.** $\hat{y} = 26.830 - 0.4923x$

**b.** when $x = 10, \hat{y} = 26.830 - 0.4923(10) = 21.907$

**c.** $10(-0.4923) = -4.923$

**d.** $H_0: \beta_1 \geq 0$

$H_A: \beta_1 < 0$

$\alpha = 0.025, -3.67 < -2.4469$; reject.

**14-21. a.** $-10.12$

**b.** $H_0: \beta_1 \geq 0$

$H_A: \beta_1 < 0$

Since $-3.2436 < -2.407$, reject $H_0$.

**14-23. a.** $t$ test statistic $= 10.86 > 2.1318$, reject

**b.** An increase of the average public college tuition of \$1 would accompany an increase in the average private college tuition of \$3.36.

**c.** $\hat{y} = 3,372 + 3.36(7,500) = \$28,572$

**14-25. a.** $R$-square $= 0.0395$

**b.** $S_\epsilon = 8,693.43$

**c.** $H_0: \beta_1 = 0.0$

$H_A: \beta_1 \neq 0.0$

$\alpha = 0.05, t = 1.11 < 2.0423$; do not reject.

**d.** insignificant

**14-27. b.** $\hat{y} = -1,995 + 1.25x$

**c.** $R^2 = 94.0\%$

$H_0: \beta_1 \geq 1.4$

$H_A: \beta_1 < 1.4$

$\alpha = 0.05$; $t$ test statistic $= -1.301$ is greater than the $t$-critical value of $-1.8595$. Do not reject.

**14-29. a.** $\hat{y} = 145,000,000 + 1.3220x$

**b.** The regression equation is $\hat{y} = 145,000,000 + 1.3220x$ and the coefficient of determination is $R^2 = 83.1\%$.

$H_0: \beta_1 = 0$

$H_A: \beta_1 \neq 0$

$\alpha = 0.05$; the $t$ test statistic of $7.02 > 2.2281$. Therefore, reject.

**c.** $\hat{y} = 1,000,000(1.322) = \$1,322,000$

**14-31. b.** $\hat{y} = 10.1 + (-0.7)(x)$

**c.** $-0.9594$ ——————— $-0.4406$

**d.** $2.98165$ ——— $7.41835$

**14-33.** $-0.0847$ ———————————————— $+0.2733$

**14-35. a.** $\hat{y} = \$58,766.11 + \$943.58(x)$

**b.** $H_0: \beta_1 = 0.0$

$H_0: \beta_1 \neq 0.0$

$\alpha = 0.05$

Because $t = 3.86 > 2.1315$, reject.

**c.** $\$422.58$ ——— $\$1,464.58$

**14-37. a.** $\hat{y} = 44.3207 + 0.9014x$

**b.** $H_0: \beta_1 = 0$

$H_A: \beta_1 \neq 0$

$\alpha = 0.05$

The $p$-value $< 0.05$ ($t = 6.717$ is greater than any value for 13 degrees of freedom shown in the table) and the null hypothesis is rejected.

**c.** $(0.6637, 1.1391)$

**14-39. a.** $\hat{y} = -6.2457 + (9.8731)(x)$

**b.** $\hat{y} = -6.2457 + (9.8731)(6) = 52.9929$ minutes

**c.** $78.123$ ——— $87.102$

**d.** $47.96866$ ——— $77.76391$

**14-41. b.** $\hat{y} = 11,991 - 5.92x$ and the coefficient of determination is $R^2 = 89.9\%$.

**c.** $(76.47 - 115.40)$

**14-43. b.** $(3.2426, 6.4325)$

**c.** $(3.78$ to $6.5)$

**14-45.** The value of 0.45 would indicate a relatively weak positive correlation.

**14-47.** no

**14-49. a.** no

**b.** cannot assume cause and effect

**14-51.** The answer will vary depending on the article the students select.

**14-53. a.** The regression equation is $\hat{y} = 3,372 + 3.36x$.

**b.** $H_0: \beta_1 \leq 0$

$H_A: \beta_1 > 0$

$\alpha = 0.05, t = 10.86$, $p$-value $= 0.000$

**c.** $(\$23,789, \$30,003)$

**d.** Since \$35,000 is larger than \$30,966, it does not seem to be a plausible value.

**14-55. a.** There appears to be a weak positive linear relationship.

**b.** 1. $r = 0.6239$

2. $H_0: \rho = 0$

$H_A: \rho \neq 0$

*d.f.* $= 10 - 2 = 8$

Since $2.2580 < 3.3554$, do not reject $H_0$.

**c.** 1. $\hat{y} = 0.9772 + 0.0034(x)$

2. The $y$-intercept has no interpretation in this case. The slope indicates that the average university GPA increases by 0.0034 for each increase of 1 unit in the SAT score.

**14-57. a.** There seems to be a random pattern in the relationship between the typing speed using the standard and ergonomic.

**b.** $H_0$: $\rho \leq 0$

$H_A$: $\rho > 0$

$\alpha = 0.05$, $r = 0.071$.

$t$ calc $= 0.2013 < t = 1.8595$; do not reject $H_0$.

**14-59. b.** $\hat{y} = 1,219.8035 + (-9.1196)(x)$

**c.** $-568.285 - 112.305$

**d.** Since $1.5 < 5.117$, do not reject $H_0$.

**14-61. a.** There appears to be a possible positive linear relationship between time (in hours) and rating.

**b.** $\hat{y} = 66.7111 + 10.6167(x)$

**14-63. a.** $\hat{y} = 3,786 + 1.35x$

**b.** $H_0$: $\beta_1 = 0$

$H_A$: $\beta_1 \neq 0$

$\alpha = 0.05$, $p$-value $= 0.000$. Since the $p$-value is less than $\alpha = 0.05$, we reject the null hypothesis.

**c.** ($265,597, $268,666)

**14-65. b.** $378.365 - 592.08$

**c.** no

**d.** $2,115.458 - 2,687.465$

**e.** $100 is outside of the range of the sample.

## Chapter 15

**15-1. a.** $\hat{y} = 87.7897 - 0.9705x_1 + 0.0023x_2 - 8.7233x_3$

**b.** $F = 5.3276 > F_{0.05} = 3.0725$; also, $p$-value $= 0.00689 <$ any reasonable alpha. Therefore, reject $H_0$: $\beta_1 = \beta_2 = \beta_3 = 0$.

**c.** $R^2 = \dfrac{SSR}{SST} = \dfrac{16,646.09124}{38,517.76} = 0.432$

**d.** $x_1$ ($p$-value $= 0.1126 > \alpha = 0.05$; fail to reject $H_0$: $\beta_1 = 0$) and $x_3$ ($p$-value $= 0.2576 > \alpha = 0.05$; fail to reject $H_0$: $\beta_3 = 0$) are not significant.

**e.** $b_2 = 0.0023$; $\hat{y}$ increases 0.0023 for each one-unit increase of $x_2$.

$b_3 = -8.7233$; $\hat{y}$ decreases 8.7233 for each one-unit increase of $x_3$.

**f.** The confidence intervals for $\beta_1$ and $\beta_3$ contain 0.

**15-3. a.** $b_1 = -412$; $b_2 = 818$; $b_3 = -93$; $b_4 = -71$

**b.** $\hat{y} = 22,167 - 412(5.7) + 818(61) - 93(14) - 71(1.39) = 68,315.91$

**15-5. a.** $y_i = 5.05 - 0.051x_1 + 0.888x_2$

**b.**

| | $y_i$ | $x_1$ |
|---|---|---|
| $x_1$ | 0.206 | |
| $x_2$ | 0.919 | 0.257 |

$H_0$: $\rho = 0$

$H_A$: $\rho \neq 0$

$\alpha = 0.05$, $t = 0.5954$, $-2.306 < t = 0.5954 < 2.306$; we fail to reject $H_0$.

**c.** $H_0$: $\beta_1 = \beta_2 = 0$

$H_A$: at least one $\beta_i \neq 0$

$\alpha = 0.05$, $F = 19.07$

Since $F = 19.07 > 4.737$, reject $H_0$.

**d.**

| Predictor | Coef | SE Coef | T | P | VIF |
|---|---|---|---|---|---|
| Constant | 5.045 | 8.698 | 0.58 | 0.580 | |
| $x_1$ | $-0.0513$ | 0.2413 | $-0.21$ | 0.838 | 1.1 |
| $x_2$ | 0.8880 | 0.1475 | 6.02 | 0.001 | 1.1 |

**15-7. a.** $\hat{y} = -977.1 + 11.252(\text{WK HI}) + 117.72(\text{P-E})$

**b.** $H_0$: $\beta_1 = \beta_2 = 0$

$H_A$: at least one $\beta_i \neq 0$

$\alpha = 0.05$, $F = 39.80 > 3.592$; we reject.

**c.** $\hat{y} = 1,607$

**15-9. a.** $\hat{y} = 503 - 10.5x_1 + 2.4x_2 + 0.165x_3 + 1.90x_4$

**b.** $H_0$: $\beta_1 = \beta_2 = \beta_3 = \beta_4 = 0$

$H_A$: at least one $\beta_i \neq 0$

$\alpha = 0.05$

Since $F = 2.44 < 3.056$, fail to reject $H_0$.

**c.** $H_0$: $\beta_3 = 0$

$H_A$: $\beta_3 \neq 0$

$\alpha = 0.05$, $p$-value $= 0.051 > 0.05$; fail to reject $H_0$.

**d.** $\hat{y} = 344 - 0.186x_1$.

The $p$-value $= 0.004$. Since the $p$-value $= 0.004 < 0.05$, reject.

**15-11. a.** There is a positive linear relationships between team win/loss percentage and game attendance, opponent win/loss percentage and game attendance, games played and game attendance. There is no relationship between temperature and game attendance.

**b.** There is a significant relationship between game attendance and team win/loss percentage and games played.

**c.** Attendance $= 14,122.24 + 63.15(\text{Win/loss\%})\ 10.10$ (Opponent win/loss) $+ 31.51(\text{Games played}) - 55.46$ (Temperature)

**d.** $R^2 = 0.7753$, so 77.53% is explained.

**e.** $H_0$: $\beta_1 = \beta_2 = \beta_3 = \beta_4 = 0$

$H_A$: at least one $\beta_i$ does not equal 0

significance $F = 0.00143$; reject $H_0$.

**f.** For team win/loss % the $p$-value $= 0.0014 < 0.08$

For opponent win/loss % the $p$-value $= 0.4953 > 0.08$

For games played the $p$-value $= 0.8621 > 0.08$

For temperature the $p$-value $= 0.3909 > 0.08$

**g.** 1,184.1274; interval of $\pm 2(1,184.1274)$

**h.**

| | VIF |
|---|---|
| Team win/loss percentage and all other $X$ | 1.569962033 |
| Temperature and all other $X$ | 1.963520336 |
| Games played and all other $X$ | 1.31428258 |
| Opponent win/loss percentage and all other $X$ | 1.50934547 |

Multicollinearity is not a problem since no VIF is greater than 5.

**15-15. a.** $x_2 = 1$, $\hat{y} = 145 + 1.2(1,500) + 300(1) = 2,245$

**b.** $x_2 = 0$, $\hat{y} = 145 + 1.2(1,500) + 300(0) = 1,945$

**c.** $b_2$ indicates the average premium paid for living in the city's town center.

**15-17. a.** As the vehicle weight increases by 1 pound, the average highway mileage rating would decrease by 0.003.

**b.** If the car has standard transmission the highway mileage rating will increase by 4.56, holding the weight constant.

**c.** $\hat{y} = 34.2 - 0.003x_1 + 4.56(1) = 38.76 - 0.003x_1$

**d.** $\hat{y} = 34.2 - 0.003(4,394) + 4.56(0) = 21.02$

**e.** Incorporating the dummy variable essentially gives two regression equations with the same slope but different intercepts depending on whether the automobile is an automatic or standard transmission.

**15-19. a.** $\hat{y} = 197 - 43.6x_1 - 51x_2$

**b.** $\beta_1 =$ The difference in the average PP100 between Domestic and Korean vehicles

$\beta_2 =$ The difference in the average PP100 between European and Korean vehicles

**c.** $H_0: \beta_1 = \beta_2 = 0$
$H_A:$ at least one $\beta_i \neq 0$
$\alpha = 0.05, F = 4.53 > 3.555$; reject $H_0$.

**15-21. a.** There appears to be a weak positive linear relationship between hours and net profit. There appears to be a weak negative linear relationship between client type and net profit.

**b.** $\hat{y} = -1,012.0542 + 69.1471(x_1)$

**c.** The $p$-value = 0.0531. The $R^2$ is only 0.3549.

**15-23. a.** $\hat{y} = 390 - 37.0x_1 + 0.263x_2$
$H_0: \beta_1 = 0$
$H_A: \beta_1 \neq 0$

**c.** $\alpha = 0.05$. Since $t = -20.45 < -1.9921$, we reject $H_0$.

**d.** $\hat{y} = 390 - 37.0x_1 + 0.263x_2 = 390 - 37.0(1) + 0.263(500) = 484.5 \approx 485$

**15-25. a.** A linear line is possible, nonlinear is more likely.

**c.** $\hat{y} = 4.937 + 1.2643x$; the $p$-value = $0.015 < \alpha = 0.05$, reject.
$\hat{y} = -25.155 + 18.983\ln x$

**15-27. b.** two quadratic models; interaction between $x_2$ and the quadratic relationship between $y$ and $x_2$
$\hat{y}_i = 4.9 - 3.58x_1 - 0.014x_1^2 + 1.42x_1x_2 + 0.528x_1^2x_2$

**c.** $\beta_3x_1x_2$ and $\beta_4x_1^2x_2$. So you must conduct two hypothesis tests:

i. $H_0: \beta_3 = 0$
$H_A: \beta_3 \neq 0$
$\alpha = 0.05$, $p$-value = 0.488; we fail to reject $H_0$.

ii. For $\beta_4 = 0$, the $p$-value = 0.001.

**d.** Conclude that there is interaction between $x_2$ and the quadratic relationship between $x_1$ and $y$.

**15-29. a.** The complete model is $y_i = \beta_0 + \beta_1x_1 + \beta_2x_2 + \beta_3x_3 + \beta_4x_4 + \varepsilon_i$. The reduced model is $y_i = \beta_0 + \beta_1x_1 + \beta_2x_2 + \varepsilon_i$. $H_0: \beta_3 = \beta_4 = 0$, $H_A:$ at least one $\beta_i \neq 0$. $SSE_C = 201.72$. So $MSE_C = SSE_C/(n - c - 1) = 201.72/(10 - 4 - 1) = 40.344$ and $SSE_R = 1,343$. $\alpha = 0.05$, $F = 14.144$; $14.144 > 5.786$; we reject $H_0$.

**b.** The complete model is $y_i = \beta_0 + \beta_1x_1 + \beta_2x_2 + \beta_3x_3 + \beta_4x_4 + \varepsilon_i$. The reduced model is $y_i = \beta_0 + \beta_1x_3 + \beta_2x_4 + \varepsilon_i$. $SSE_C = 201.72$. So $MSE_C = SSE_C/(n - c - 1) = 201.72/(10 - 4 - 1) = 40.344$ and $SSE_R = 494.6$. $H_0: \beta_1 = \beta_2 = 0$; $H_A:$ at least one $\beta_i \neq 0$; $\alpha = 0.05$, $F = 3.63$ The numerator degrees of freedom are $c - r = 4 - 2 = 2$ and the denominator degrees of freedom are $n - c - 1 = 10 - 4 - 1 = 5$. The $p$-value = $P(F \geq 3.630) = 0.1062$. Fail to reject.

**15-31. a.** two dummy variables
$x_2 = 1$ if manufacturing, 0 otherwise
$x_3 = 1$ if service, 0 otherwise
Net profit = $-586.256 + 22.862x_1 + 2,302.267x_2 + 1,869.813x_3$

**b.** Net profit = $5,828.692 - 334.406x_1 + 4.577x_1$ sq + $2,694.801x_2 + 12,874,953x_3$

**15-33. a.** Create scatter plot.

**b.** Second-order polynomial seems to be the correct model.
$\hat{y} = 8,083 - 0.273x + 0.000002x^2$.

**c.** $y = \beta_0 + \beta_1x_1 + \beta_2x_1^2 + \beta_3x_2 + \beta_4x_1x_2 + \beta_5x_1^2x_2 + \varepsilon$
The two interaction terms are $\beta_4x_1x_2$ and $\beta_5x_1^2x_2$. So you must conduct two hypothesis tests:

i. Test for $\beta_4 = 0$. Since the $p$-value = $0.252 > 0.05$, we fail to reject $H_0$.

ii. Test for $\beta_5 = 0$. Since the $p$-value for $\beta_5 = 0.273 > 0.05$, we fail to reject $H_0$.

**15-35. a.** Create scatter plot.

**b.** fourth order polynomial

**c.** The regression equation is
Admissions = $-30.0 + 24.5$(Average prices) $- 7.3(AP_2) + 0.98(AP_3) - 0.0499(AP_4)$.

**d.** Test the hypothesis $\beta_4 = 0$. Since $p$-value = $0.572 > 0.05$, we fail to reject $H_0$; there is sufficient evidence to remove the fourth order component. Similarly, there is evidence to remove the third order component.
$\hat{y}_i = -2.68 + 1.47x_1 - 0.129x_1^2$

**15-39. a.** $x_2$ and $x_4$ only; $x_1$ and $x_3$ did not have high enough coefficients of partial determination to add significantly to the model.

**b.** would be identical

**c.** Stepwise regression cannot have a larger $R^2$ than the full model.

**15-41. a.** None are significant.

**b.** Alpha-to-enter: 0.25; alpha-to-remove: 0.25
$\hat{y} = 26.19 + 0.42x_3, R^2 = 14.68$

**c.** $\hat{y} = 27.9 - 0.035x_1 - 0.002x_2 + 0.42x_3, R^2 = 14.8$
The adjusted $R^2$ is 0% for the full model and 7.57% for the standard selection model. Neither model offers a good approach to fitting this data.

**15-43. a.** $\hat{y} = 32.08 + 0.76x_1 - 5x_3 + 0.95x_4$

**b.** $\hat{y} = 32.08 + 0.76x_1 - 5x_3 + 0.95x_4$

**c.** $\hat{y} = 32.08 + 0.76x_1 - 5x_3 + 0.95x_4$

**d.** $\hat{y} = 32.08 + 0.76x_1 - 5x_3 + 0.95x_4$

**15-45. a.** $\hat{y} = -18.33 + 1.07x_2$

**b.** one independent variable ($x_2$) and one dependent variable ($y$)

**c.** $x_1$ was the first variable removed, $p$-value $(0.817) > 0.05$. $x_3$ was the last variable removed, $p$-value = $0.094 > 0.05$.

**15-47. b.** $\hat{y} = 1,110 + 1.60x_2^2$

**15-49. a.** Using Minitab you get an error message indicating there is multicollinearity among the predictor variables.

**b.** Either crude oil or diesel prices should be removed.

**c.** $\hat{y} = 0.8741 + 0.00089x_2 - 0.00023x_3$

**15-51. a.** $\hat{y} = -16.02 + 2.1277x$

**b.** $p$-value = $0.000 < 0.05$

**15-55. a.** Calls = $-269.838 + 4.953$(Ads previous week) $+ 0.834$(Calls previous week) $+ 0.089$(Airline bookings)
The overall model is not significant and none of the independent variables are significant.

**b.** The assumption of constant variance has not been violated.

**c.** It is inappropriate to test for randomness using a plot of the residuals over time since the weeks were randomly selected and are not in sequential, time-series order.

**d.** Model meets the assumption of normally distributed error terms.

**15-57. a.** $\hat{y} = 0.874 + 0.000887x_1 - 0.000235x_2$

**b.** The residual plot supports the choice of the linear model.

**c.** The residuals do not have constant variances.

**d.** The linear model appears to be insufficient.

**e.** The error terms are normally distributed.

**15-59. a.** $\hat{y} = -6.81 + 5.29x_1 + 1.51x_2 - 0.000033x_3$

**b.** Plot the residuals versus the independent variable ($x$) or the fitted value ($\hat{y}_i$).

**c.** $\hat{y} = 0.97 - 3.20x_1 + 0.285x_2 + 0.000029x_3 + 3.12x_1^2 + 0.103x_2^2 - 0.000000x_3^2$

**d.** The residual plot does not display any nonrandom pattern.

**e.** The error terms are normally distributed.

**15-63. a.** The relationship between the dependent and each independent variable is linear.

**b.** The residuals are independent.

**c.** The variances of the residuals are constant over the range of the independent variables.

**d.** The residuals are normally distributed.

**15-65. a.** The average $y$ increases by three units holding $x_2$ constant.

**b.** $x_2$, since $x_2$ only affects the $y$-intercept of this model.

**c.** The coefficient of $x_1$ indicates that the average $y$ increases by 7 units when $x_2 = 1$.

**d.** The coefficient of $x_1$ indicates that the average $y$ increases by 11 units when $x_2 = 1$.

**e.** Those coefficients affected by the interaction terms have conditional interpretations.

**15-69. a.** The critical $t$ for all pairs would be 2.1604, correlated pairs.
Volumes sold ($y$) − Production expenditures
Volumes sold ($y$) − Number of reviewers
Volumes sold ($y$) − Pages
Volumes sold ($y$) − Advertising budget

**b.** All $p$-values $> 0.05$

**c.** Critical $F = 3.581$; since $F = 9.1258 > 3.581$, conclude that the overall model is significant.

**e.** $\pm 2(24,165.9419) = \pm 48,331.8$

**f.** Constant variance assumption is satisfied.

**g.** The residuals appear to be approximately normally distributed.

**h.** The model satisfies the normal distribution assumption.

**15-71.** The $t$-critical for all pairs would be $\pm 2.0687$, correlated pairs are
For family size and age
For purchase volume and age
For purchase volume and family income

**15-73.** The significance $F = 0.0210$

**15-75.** Age entered the model.
The $R^2$ at step 1 was 0.2108 and the standard error at step 1 was 36.3553. The $R^2$ at step 2 is 0.3955 and the standard error at step 2 is 32.5313.

**15-77.** Other variables that enter into the model partially overlap with the other included variables in its ability to explain the variation in the dependent variable.

**15-79. a.** Normal distribution of the residuals.

**b.** The selected independent variables are not highly correlated with the dependent variable.

**15-81. a.** $\hat{y} = 2,857 - 26.4x_1 - 80.6x_2 + 0.115x_1^2 + 2.31x_2^2 + 0.542x_1x_2$

**b.** The residual plot supports the choice of the linear model.

**c.** The residuals do have constant variances.

**d.** The linear model appears to be insufficient. The addition of an independent variable representing time is indicated.

**e.** A transformation of the independent or dependent variables is required.

**15-83. a.** Quadratic relationship exists between cost and weight.

**b.** $r = 0.963$
$H_0: \rho = 0$

$H_A: \rho \neq 0$
$\alpha = 0.05$;
Since the $p$-value $= 0.000 > 0.05$, we reject $H_0$.

**c.** Cost $= -64.06 + 14.92$(Weight)

**d.** Cost $= 113.8 - 9.22$(Weight) $+ 1.44$(Weight$^2$)
Comparing the $R^2_{adj}$ for the quadratic equation (95.6%) and the $R^2$ for the simple linear equation (94.5%), the quadratic equation appears to fit the data better.

**15-85.** Vehicle year $= 73.18 - 9.1$(Gender) $+ 1.39$(Years education) $- 24$(Not seat belt)
$R$-squared $= 14.959\%$

## Chapter 16

**16-3.** Generally, quantitative forecasting techniques can be used whenever historical data related to the variable of interest exist and we believe that the historical patterns will continue into the future.

**16-7. a.** The forecasting horizon is 6 months.

**b.** a medium term forecast

**c.** a month

**d.** 12 months

**16-9. c.**

| Year | Radio | % radio | Newspaper | Laspeyres |
|------|-------|---------|-----------|-----------|
| 1 | 300 | 0.3 | 400 | 100 |
| 2 | 310 | 0.42 | 420 | 104.59 |
| 3 | 330 | 0.42 | 460 | 113.78 |
| 4 | 346 | 0.4 | 520 | 126.43 |
| 5 | 362 | 0.38 | 580 | 139.08 |
| 6 | 380 | 0.37 | 640 | 151.89 |
| 7 | 496 | 0.43 | 660 | 165.08 |

**d.**

| Year | Radio | % radio | Newspaper | Paasche |
|------|-------|---------|-----------|---------|
| 1 | 300 | 0.3 | 400 | 100 |
| 2 | 310 | 0.42 | 420 | 104.41 |
| 3 | 330 | 0.42 | 460 | 113.22 |
| 4 | 346 | 0.4 | 520 | 124.77 |
| 5 | 362 | 0.38 | 580 | 136.33 |
| 6 | 380 | 0.37 | 640 | 148.12 |
| 7 | 496 | 0.43 | 660 | 165.12 |

**16-13.**

| Year | Labor Costs | Material Costs | % Materials | % Labor | Laspeyres Index |
|------|-------------|----------------|-------------|---------|-----------------|
| 1999 | 44,333 | 66,500 | 60 | 40 | 100 |
| 2000 | 49,893 | 68,900 | 58 | 42 | 106.36 |
| 2001 | 57,764 | 70,600 | 55 | 45 | 113.59 |
| 2002 | 58,009 | 70,900 | 55 | 45 | 114.07 |
| 2003 | 55,943 | 71,200 | 56 | 44 | 112.95 |
| 2004 | 61,078 | 71,700 | 54 | 46 | 117.03 |
| 2005 | 67,015 | 72,500 | 52 | 48 | 122.09 |
| 2006 | 73,700 | 73,700 | 50 | 50 | 127.88 |
| 2007 | 67,754 | 73,400 | 52 | 48 | 123.44 |
| 2008 | 74,100 | 74,100 | 50 | 50 | 128.57 |
| 2009 | 83,447 | 74,000 | 47 | 53 | 134.95 |

**16-15. a.** The sum $\sum p_{1993} = 1.07 + 6.16 + 8.32 = 15.55$.
   **b.** 170.87
   **c.** 103.86; $\dfrac{170.87 - 103.86}{103.86} 100 = 64.52\%$

**16-17. a.** 102.31
   **b.** 15.41%
   **c.** 14.43%

**16-21.** January = 0.849; July = 0.966

**16-23. a.** upward linear trend with seasonal component as a slight drop in the 3rd quarter
   **b.** Normalize to get the following values:

| Quarter | Seasonal Index |
|---------|----------------|
| 1 | 1.035013 |
| 2 | 1.020898 |
| 3 | 0.959934 |
| 4 | 0.984154 |

   **c.** $MSE = 36.955$ and $MAD = 4.831$
   **d.** and **e.**

| Quarter | Period | Seasonally Unadjusted Forecast | Seasonal Index | Seasonally Adjusted Forecast |
|---------|--------|--------------------------------|----------------|------------------------------|
| Quarter 1 2010 | 17 | 250.15 | 1.0350 | 258.91 |
| Quarter 2 2010 | 18 | 256.17 | 1.0209 | 261.52 |
| Quarter 3 2010 | 19 | 262.18 | 0.9599 | 251.68 |
| Quarter 4 2010 | 20 | 268.20 | 0.9842 | 263.95 |

**16-27. b.** The seasonal indexes generated by Minitab are:

| Month | Index |
|-------|-------|
| 1 | 1.02349 |
| 2 | 1.07969 |
| 3 | 1.16502 |
| 4 | 1.12147 |
| 5 | 0.98695 |
| 6 | 0.83324 |
| 7 | 0.86807 |
| 8 | 0.91287 |
| 9 | 0.97699 |
| 10 | 1.07311 |
| 11 | 1.01382 |
| 12 | 0.94529 |

   **c.** $F = 1.98 + 0.0459(\text{Month})$
   **d.** $F_{25} = 1.98 + 0.0459(25) = 3.12$.
   Adjusted $F_{25} = (1.02349)(3.12) = 3.19$.
   $F_{73} = 1.98 + 0.0458589(73) = 5.32$.
   Adjusted $F_{73} = (1.02349)(5.32) = 5.44$.

**16-29. a.** seasonal component to the data
   **b.** $MSE = 976.34$ and $MAD = 29.887$
   **c.**

| Quarter | Index |
|---------|-------|
| 1 | 1.0290 |
| 2 | 0.9207 |
| 3 | 1.0789 |
| 4 | 0.9714 |

   **d.**

| 2009 | Period | Forecast |
|------|--------|----------|
| Qtr. 1 | 13 | 256.5620033 |
| Qtr. 2 | 14 | 260.0884382 |
| Qtr. 3 | 15 | 263.614873 |
| Qtr. 4 | 16 | 267.1413079 |

   **e.** $MSE = 926.1187$, $MAD = 29.5952$
   **f.** The adjusted model has a lower $MSE$ and $MAD$.

**16-31. a.** Forecast without transformation $= 36.0952 + 10.8714(16) = 210.0376$
   Forecast with transformation $= 65.2986 + 0.6988(16)^2 = 244.1914$
   Actual cash balance for Month 16 was 305. The transformed model had a smaller error than the model without the transformation.
   **b.** Model without transformation:

| For Individual Response y | |
|---------------------------|---|
| Interval Half Width | 48.27804189 |
| Prediction Interval Lower Limit | 161.7600534 |
| Prediction Interval Upper Limit | 258.3161371 |

   Model with transformation:

| For Individual Response y | |
|---------------------------|---|
| Interval Half Width | 23.89550188 |
| Prediction Interval Lower Limit | 220.29634337 |
| Prediction Interval Upper Limit | 268.08734713 |

   The model without the transformation has the wider interval.

**16-33. a.** Linear trend evidenced by the slope from small to large values. Randomness is exhibited since not all of the data points would lie on a straight line.
   **b.** $H_0: \beta_1 = 0$
   $H_A: \beta_1 \neq 0$
   $\alpha = 0.10$, Minitab lists the $p$-value as 0.000.
   **c.** The fitted values are $F_{38} = 36,051$, $F_{39} = 36,955$, $F_{40} = 37,858$, and $F_{41} = 38,761$.
   **d.** The forecast bias is $-1,343.5$. On average, the model over forecasts the e-commerce retail sales an average of $1,343.5 million.

**16-35. b.** A trend is present.
   **c.** Forecast $= 136.78$, $MAD = 23.278$
   **d.** Forecast $= 163.69$, $MAD = 7.655$
   **e.** The double exponential smoothing forecast has a lower $MAD$.

**16-37. a.** The time series contains a strong upward trend, so a double exponential smoothing model is selected.
   **b.** The equation is $\hat{y}_t = 19.364 + 0.7517t$. Since $C_0 = b_0$, $C_0 = 19.364$. $T_0 = b_1 = 0.7517$.
   **c.** Forecasts

| Period | Forecast | Lower | Upper |
|--------|----------|-------|-------|
| 13 | 29.1052 | 23.9872 | 34.2231 |

   **d.** $MAD$ as calculated by Minitab:

| Accuracy Measures | |
|-------------------|---|
| MAPE | 8.58150 |
| MAD | 2.08901 |
| MSE | 6.48044 |

**16-39. a.** The time series contains a strong upward trend, so a double exponential smoothing model is selected.
  **b.** $\hat{y}_t = 990 + 2,622.8t$. Since $C_0 = b_0$, $C_0 = 990$. $T_0 = b_1 = 2,622.8$.
  **c.** Forecast $= 58,852.1$
  **d.** $MAD = 3,384$

**16-41. a.** There does not appear to be any trend component in this time series.
  **c.** $MAD = 3.2652$
  **d.** $F_{14} = 0.25y_{13} + (1 - 0.25)F_{13} = 0.25(101.3) + 0.75(100.22) = 100.49$

**16-43. a.** Single exponential smoothing model is selected.
  **b.** The forecast is calculated as an example $F_1 = F_2 = 0.296$. Then $F_3 = 0.15y_2 + (1 - 0.15)F_2 = 0.15(0.413) + 0.85(0.296) = 0.3136$.
  **c.** $MAD = 15.765/71 = 0.222$
  **d.** $F_{73} = 0.15y_{72} + (1 - 0.15)F_{72} = 0.15(-0.051) + 0.85(0.259) = 0.212$

**16-45. a.** The double exponential smoothing model will incorporate the trend effect.
  **b.** From regression output, Initial constant $= 28,848$; Initial trend $= 2,488.96$. Forecast for period 17 $= 72,450.17$. $MAD = 5,836.06$.
  **c.** The $MAD$ produced by the double exponential smoothing model at the end of Month 16 is smaller than the $MAD$ produced by the single exponential smoothing model.
  **d. and e.** Of the combinations considered the minimum $MAD$ at the end of Month 16 occurs when alpha $= 0.05$ and beta $= 0.05$. The forecast for Month 17 with alpha $= 0.05$ and beta $= 0.05$ is $71,128.45$.

**16-47. a.** a seasonal component
  **b.** The pattern is linear with a positive slope.
  **c.** a cyclical component
  **d.** a random component
  **e.** a cyclical component

**16-49.** A seasonal component is one that is repeated throughout a time series and has a recurrence period of at most one year. A cyclical component is one that is represented by wavelike fluctuations that has a recurrence period of more than one year. Seasonal components are more predictable.

**16-51. a.** There does appear to be an upward linear trend.
  **b.** Forecast $= -682,238,010.3 + 342,385.3(\text{Year})$ Since $F = 123.9719 > 4.6001$, conclude that there is a significant relationship.
  **c.** $MAD = 461,216.7279$

  **d.**

| Year | Forecast |
|------|----------|
| 2010 | 4,929,275.00 |
| 2011 | 5,271,660.29 |
| 2012 | 5,614,045.59 |
| 2013 | 5,956,430.88 |
| 2014 | 6,298,816.18 |

  **e. For Individual Response y**

| | |
|---|---|
| Interval Half Width | 1,232,095.322 |
| Prediction Interval Lower Limit | 5,066,720.854 |
| Prediction Interval Upper Limit | 7,530,911.499 |

**16-55. a.** The time series contains a strong upward trend, so a double exponential smoothing model is selected.
  **b.** Since $C_0 = b_0$, $C_0 = -2,229.9$; $T_0 = b_1 = 1.12$.

  **c.** Forecast(2008) $= 740.073$
  **d.** $MAD = 89.975$

**16-57. a.** A cyclical component is evidenced by the wave form, which recurs approximately every 10 months.
  **b.** If recurrence period, as explained in part a, is 10 months, the seasonal indexes generated by Minitab are

| Period | Index |
|--------|-------|
| 1 | 0.98230 |
| 2 | 1.01378 |
| 3 | 1.00906 |
| 4 | 1.00979 |
| 5 | 0.99772 |
| 6 | 1.01583 |
| 7 | 0.99739 |
| 8 | 1.00241 |
| 9 | 0.98600 |
| 10 | 0.98572 |

  **c.** The nonlinear trend model (using $t$ and $t^2$) fitted to the deseasonalized data.
    $ARM = 3.28 + 0.114(\text{Month}) - 0.00177(\text{Monthsq})$
  **d.** The unadjusted forecast: $F_{61} = 3.28 + 0.114(61) - 0.00117(61)^2 = 5.8804$. The adjusted forecast is $F_{61} = (0.9823)(5.8804) = 5.7763$.
  **e.** The following values have been computed:
    $R^2 = 92.9\%$, $F$-statistic $= 374.70$, and standard error $= 0.226824$
    The model explains a significant amount of variation in the ARM.
    Durbin-Watson $d$ statistic $= 0.378224$.
    Because $d = 0.378224 < d_L = 1.35$, conclude that significant positive autocorrelation exists.

**16-59. a.** $MAD = 4,767.2$
  **c.**

| Alpha | MAD |
|-------|-----|
| 0.1 | 5,270.7 |
| 0.2 | 4,960.6 |
| 0.3 | 4,767.2 |
| 0.4 | 4,503.3 |
| 0.5 | 4,212.4 |

**16-61. a.** A strong trend component is evident in the data.
  **b.** Using 1980 = Year 1, the estimated regression equation is $\hat{y}_t = 490.249 + 1.09265t$, $R^2 = 95.7\%$
    $H_0: \beta_1 \leq 0$
    $H_A: \beta_1 > 0$
    $\alpha = 0.10$, $t = 23.19$, $n - 2 = 26 - 2 = 24$, critical value is $t_{0.10} = 1.3178$
  **c.** $\hat{y}_t = 490.249 + 1.09265(31) = 524.1212$

## Chapter 17

**17-1.** The hypotheses are $H_0: \tilde{\mu} \geq 14$
  $H_A: \tilde{\mu} < 14$
  $W = 36$
  $n = 11$, $\alpha = .05$; reject if $W < 13$.

**17-3.** The hypotheses are $H_0: \tilde{\mu} = 4$
$\qquad\qquad\qquad\qquad H_A: \tilde{\mu} \neq 4$

$W = 9, W = 19$:
Critical values for $n = 7$, assuming $\alpha = 0.1$ are 3 and 25.
Cannot reject.

**17-5. a.** The hypotheses are $H_0: \tilde{\mu} \leq 4$
$\qquad\qquad\qquad\qquad\quad H_A: \tilde{\mu} > 4$

    **b.** Using the Wilcoxon Signed Rank test, $W = 26$:
Upper tail test and $n = 12$, letting $\alpha = .05$, reject if
$W > 61$. So, cannot reject.

**17-7.** $H_0: \tilde{\mu} \geq 11$
$\qquad H_A: \tilde{\mu} < 11$
Using the Wilcoxon Signed Rank test, $W = 92$: Reject if
$W < 53$.

**17-9.** $H_0: \tilde{\mu} = 30$
$\qquad H_A: \tilde{\mu} \neq 30$
Using the Wilcoxon Signed Rank test, $W = 71.5, W = 81.5$:
Because some of the differences are 0, $n = 17$. The upper
and lower values for the Wilcoxon test are 34 and 119 for
$\alpha = 0.05$. Do not reject.

**17-11. a.** Using data classes one standard deviation wide, with
the data mean of 7.6306 and a standard deviation
of 0.2218:

| $e$ | $o$ | $(o-e)^2/e$ |
|---|---|---|
| 14.9440 | 21 | 2.45417 |
| 32.4278 | 31 | 0.06287 |
| 32.4278 | 27 | 0.90851 |
| 14.9440 | 16 | 0.07462  Sum = 3.5002 |

Testing at the $\alpha = 0.05$ level, $\chi^2_\alpha = 5.9915$.

    **b.** Since we concluded the data come from a normal distribu-
tion we test the following:
$H_0: \mu \geq 7.4$
$H_A: \mu < 7.4$
Decision rule: If $z < -1.645$, reject $H_0$; otherwise do not
reject. $Z = 10.13$

**17-13. a.** Putting the claim in the alternate hypothesis:
$H_0: \tilde{\mu}_1 - \tilde{\mu}_2 \geq 0$
$H_A: \tilde{\mu}_1 - \tilde{\mu}_2 < 0$

    **b.** Test using the Mann-Whitney $U$ Test.
$U_1 = 40, U_2 = 24$
Use $U_2$ as the test statistic. For $n_1 = 8$ and $n_2 = 8$ and
$U = 24$, $p$-value = 0.221.

**17-15. a.** $H_0: \tilde{\mu}_1 - \tilde{\mu}_2 \leq 0$
$\qquad\quad H_A: \tilde{\mu}_1 - \tilde{\mu}_2 > 0$

    **b.** Since the alternate hypothesis indicates Population 1
should have the larger median, $U_1 = 40$.
$n_1 = 12$ and $n_2 = 12$. Reject if $U \leq 31$.

**17-17.** $H_0: \tilde{\mu}_1 - \tilde{\mu}_2 = 0$
$\qquad\; H_A: \tilde{\mu}_1 - \tilde{\mu}_2 \neq 0$
Mann-Whitney Test and $CI: C_1, C_2$

| $C_1$ | $N = 40,$ | Median = 481.50 |
|---|---|---|
| $C_2$ | $N = 35,$ | Median = 505.00 |

Point estimate for $ETA_1 - ETA_2$ is $-25.00$
95.1% $CI$ for $ETA_1 - ETA_2$ is $(-62.00, 9.00)$
$W = 1,384.0$
Test of $ETA_1 = ETA_2$ vs. $ETA_1$ not $= ETA_2$ is significant at
0.1502.

**17-19. a.** $H_0: \tilde{\mu}_1 - \tilde{\mu}_2 = 0$
$\qquad\quad H_A: \tilde{\mu}_1 - \tilde{\mu}_2 \neq 0$

With $n = 8$, reject if $T \leq 4$.
Since $T = 11.5$, we do not reject the null hypothesis.

    **b.** Use the paired sample $t$ test. $p$-value = 0.699.

**17-21.** $H_0: \tilde{\mu}_1 - \tilde{\mu}_2 = 0$
$\qquad\; H_A: \tilde{\mu}_1 - \tilde{\mu}_2 \neq 0$
With $n = 7$, reject if $T \leq 2, T = 13$.

**17-23.** $H_0: \tilde{\mu}_2 = \tilde{\mu}_1$
$\qquad\; H_A: \tilde{\mu}_2 \neq \tilde{\mu}_1$
If $T \leq 0$ reject $H_0$; $T = 8$.

**17-25.** $H_0: \tilde{\mu}_W - \tilde{\mu}_{WO} \leq 0$
$\qquad\; H_A: \tilde{\mu}_W - \tilde{\mu}_{WO} > 0$
$U_1 = (7)(5) + (7)(7 + 1)/2 - 42 = 21$
$U_2 = (7)(5) + (5)(5 + 1)/2 - 36 = 14$
$U\text{test} = 21$
Since 21 is not in the table you cannot determine the exact
$p$-value, but you know that the $p$-value will be greater than
0.562.

**17-27. a.** $H_0: \tilde{\mu}_1 \leq \tilde{\mu}_2$
$\qquad\quad H_A: \tilde{\mu}_1 > \tilde{\mu}_2$

    **b.** Since $T = 51$ is greater than 16, do not reject $H_0$.

    **c.** Housing values are typically skewed.

**17-29.** $H_0: \tilde{\mu}_1 = \tilde{\mu}_2$
$\qquad\; H_A: \tilde{\mu}_1 \neq \tilde{\mu}_2$
$\mu = 40(40 + 1)/4 = 410$

$\sigma = \sqrt{40(40+1)(80+1)/24} = 74.3976$

$z = (480 - 410)/74.3976 = 0.94$
$p$-value = $(0.5 - 0.3264)2 = (0.1736)(2) = 0.3472$. Do not
reject $H_0$.

**17-31. a.** A paired-$t$ test.
$H_0: \mu_d \geq 0$
$H_A: \mu_d < 0$
$t = (-1.7)/(3.011091/\sqrt{10}) = -1.785$

Since $-1.785 > t$ critical $= -2.2622$, do not reject $H_0$.

    **b.** $H_0: \tilde{\mu}_O \geq \tilde{\mu}_N$
$\qquad H_A: \tilde{\mu}_O < \tilde{\mu}_N$
$T = 5.5$. Since $5.5 < 6$, reject $H_0$ and conclude that the
medians are not the same.

    **c.** Because you cannot assume the underlying populations are
normal you must use the technique from part b.

**17-33. a.** $H_0: \tilde{\mu}_N \geq \tilde{\mu}_C$
$\qquad\quad H_A: \tilde{\mu}_N < \tilde{\mu}_C$
$U_1 = 4,297, U_2 = 6,203, \mu = 5,250, \sigma = 434.7413$
$z = -2.19$
$p$-value = 0.0143

    **b.** a Type I error

**17-35. a.** The data are ordinal.

    **b.** The median would be the best measure.

    **c.** $H_0: \tilde{\mu}_1 = \tilde{\mu}_2$
$\qquad H_A: \tilde{\mu}_1 \neq \tilde{\mu}_2$
Using $\alpha = 0.01$, if $T \leq 2$, reject $H_0$. Since $12.5 > 2$, do not
reject $H_0$.

    **d.** The decision could be made based on some other factor,
such as cost.

**17-37. a.** $H_0: \tilde{\mu}_1 = \tilde{\mu}_2 = \tilde{\mu}_3$
$\qquad H_A:$ Not all population medians are equal.
$H = 10.98$. Since, with $\alpha = 0.05$, $\chi^2_\alpha = 5.9915$, and
$H = 10.98$, we reject.

**17-39. a.** $H_0: \tilde{\mu}_1 = \tilde{\mu}_2 = \tilde{\mu}_3 = \tilde{\mu}_4$
$\qquad H_A:$ Not all population medians are equal.

    **b.** Use Equation 17-10.
Selecting $\alpha = 0.05$, $\chi^2_\alpha = 7.8147$, since $H = 42.11$, we
reject the null hypothesis of equal medians.

**17-41. a.** Salaries in general are usually thought to be skewed.
   **b.** The top-salaried players get extremely high salaries compared to the other players.
   **c.** $H_0: \tilde{\mu}_1 = \tilde{\mu}_2 = \tilde{\mu}_3$
   $H_A$: Not all population medians are equal.
   $H = 52.531$. If $\alpha = 0.05$, $\chi_\alpha^2 = 5.9915$. Reject

**17-43.** $H_0: \tilde{\mu}_1 = \tilde{\mu}_2 = \tilde{\mu}_3 = \tilde{\mu}_4$
   $H_A$: Not all population medians are equal.
   Using PHStat, $H$ test statistic = 11.13971. Adjusting for ties, the test statistic is 11.21, which is smaller than the critical value (11.34488).

**17-45.** $H_0: \tilde{\mu}_1 = \tilde{\mu}_2 = \tilde{\mu}_3$
   $H_A$: Not all population medians are equal.
   $H = 13.9818$, testing at $\alpha = 0.05$, $\chi_\alpha^2 = 5.9915$
   Since $13.9818 > 5.9915$, reject $H_0$.

**17-53.** $H_0: \tilde{\mu}_1 - \tilde{\mu}_2 = 0$
   $H_A: \tilde{\mu}_1 - \tilde{\mu}_2 \neq 0$
   $U_1 = 107$, $U_2 = 14$; $U$ test = 14
   with $\alpha = 0.05$, $U_\alpha = 30$.
   Since $14 < 30$, reject $H_0$.

**17-55. a.** A nonparametric test.
   **b.** $H_0: \tilde{\mu}_O - \tilde{\mu}_N \geq 0$
   $H_A: \tilde{\mu}_O - \tilde{\mu}_N < 0$
   $U_1 = 71$, $U_2 = 29$; $U$ test = 29
   If $\alpha = 0.05$, $U_\alpha = 27$.
   Since $29 > 27$, do not reject $H_0$.

**17-57.** The hypotheses being tested are
   $H_0: \tilde{\mu} = 1,989.32$
   $H_A: \tilde{\mu} \neq 1,989.32$
   Find $W = 103$, $W = 68$.
   With $\alpha = 0.05$, reject if $W \leq 40$ or $W > 131$.

**17-59. a.** $H_0: \tilde{\mu} = 8.03$
   $H_A: \tilde{\mu} \neq 8.03$
   **b.** $W = 62.5$, $W = 57.5$
   This is a two-tailed test with $n = 15$. If $\alpha = 0.05$, reject if $W \leq 25$ or $W > 95$.

**17-61.** $H_0: \tilde{\mu}_1 = \tilde{\mu}_2$
   $H_A: \tilde{\mu}_1 \neq \tilde{\mu}_2$
   Constructing the paired difference table, $T = 44.5$. With $\alpha = 0.05$, reject if $T \leq 21$ or if $T \geq 84$.
   **b.** a Type II error

**17-63. a.** They should use the Wilcoxon Matched-Pairs Signed Rank.
   **b.** $H_0: \tilde{\mu}_{w/oA} \geq \tilde{\mu}_A$
   $H_A: \tilde{\mu}_{w/oA} < \tilde{\mu}_A$
   $T = 6$
   Using $\alpha = 0.025$, $T_\alpha = 4$.
   **c.** Do not reject $H_0$.

## Chapter 18

**18-9.** Some possible causes by category are:
   People: Too Few Drivers, High Driver Turnover
   Methods: Poor Scheduling, Improper Route Assignments
   Equipment: Buses Too Small, Bus Reliability, Too Few Buses
   Environment: Weather, Traffic Congestion, Road Construction

**18-11. a.** $A_2 = 0.577$; $D_3 = 0$ and $D_4 = 2.114$
   **b.** The $R$-chart upper control limit is $2.114 \times 5.6 = 11.838$.
   The $R$-chart lower control limit is $0 \times 5.6 = 0$.
   **c.** $X$-bar chart upper control limit = $44.52 + (0.577 \times 5.6) = 47.751$; Lower control limit = $44.52 - (0.577 \times 5.6) = 41.289$

**18-15. a.** $x$-bar chart centerline = 0.753
   $UCL = 0.753 + (0.577 \times 0.074) = 0.7957$
   $LCL = 0.753 - (0.577 \times 0.074) = 0.7103$

   **b.** $R$-chart centerline = 0.074
   $UCL = 2.114 \times 0.074 = 0.1564$
   $LCL = 0 \times 0.074 = 0.000$
   **c.** There are no subgroup means outside of the upper or lower control limits on the $x$-bar chart. For the $R$-chart, there are no subgroup ranges outside the control limits.

**18-17. a.** The process has gone out of control since all but two observations and the 1st eight in sequence are below the LCL.

**18-19. a.** $c$-chart
   **b.** $\bar{c} = 3.2841$
   $UCL = 6.5682 + 3(\sqrt{6.5682}) = 14.2568$
   $LCL = 6.5682 - 3(\sqrt{6.5682}) = -1.1204$, so set to 0
   **c.** in statistical control

**18-21. a.** For $R$-chart
   $UCL = 2.282 \times 100.375 = 229.056$
   $CL = 100.375$
   $LCL = 0 \times 100.375 = 0$
   **b.** For $x$-bar chart
   $UCL = 415.3 + 0.729(100.375) = 488.473$
   $CL = 415.3$
   $LCL = 415.3 - 0.729(100.375) = 342.127$
   **c.** out of control

**18-23. b.** 82.46
   **c.** 12.33
   **d.** $UCL = 2.114 \times 12.33 = 26.07$ and $LCL = 0 \times 12.33 = 0$
   **e.** $UCL = 82.46 + (0.577 \times 12.33) = 89.57$
   $LCL = 82.46 - (0.577 \times 12.33) = 75.35$
   **f.** There is a run of nine values above the centerline.

**18-25. b.** $\bar{P} = 441/(300 \times 50) = 0.0294$
   $s = \sqrt{(0.0294)(1 - 0.0294)/50} = 0.0239$
   $UCL = 0.0294 + 3(0.0239) = 0.1011$
   $LCL = 0.0294 - 3(0.0239) = -0.0423$, so set to 0
   **c.**

| Sample Number | 301 | 302 | 303 |
|---|---|---|---|
| $p$-bar | 0.12 | 0.18 | 0.14 |

   The process has gone out of control.
   **b.** 0.28, which is again above the UCL

**18-27. a.** $\bar{c} = 29.3333$
   $UCL = 29.3333 + 3(\sqrt{29.3333}) = 45.5814$
   $LCL = 29.3333 - 3(\sqrt{29.3333}) = 13.0852$
   **b.** The process seems to be out of control.
   **c.** Need to convert the data to bags per passenger by dividing bags by 40 and then developing a $u$-chart based on the explanation in optional topics.
   $CL = 29.333/40 = 0.7333$
   $UCL = 0.7333 + 3 \times \sqrt{0.7333/40} = 1.1395$
   $LCL = 0.7333 - 3 \times \sqrt{0.7333/40} = 0.3271$
   **d.** Process is out of control.

**18-29. a.** $A_2 = 1.023$
   $D_3 = 0.0$ and $D_4 = 2.575$
   **b.** $UCL = 2.575 \times 0.80 = 2.06$
   $LCL = 0 \times 0.80 = 0$
   **c.** $UCL = 2.33 + (1.023 \times 0.80) = 3.1468$
   $LCL = 2.33 - (1.023 \times 0.80) = 1.512$

**18-31.** The centerline of the control chart is the average proportion of defective $= 720/(20 \times 150) = 0.240$. For 3-sigma control chart limits we find

$$UCL = 0.240 + 3 \times \sqrt{\frac{0.240 \times (1 - 0.240)}{150}} = 0.345$$

$$LCL = 0.240 - 3 \times \sqrt{\frac{0.240 \times (1 - 0.240)}{150}} = 0.135$$

**18-33.** $p$-chart; $\overline{p} = 0.0524$

$$S_{\overline{p}} = \sqrt{\frac{0.0524 \times (1 - 0.0524)}{100}} = 0.0223$$

Lower Control Limit $= 0.0524 - 3 \times 0.0223 = -0.0145$, so set to 0
Centerline $= 0.0524$
Upper Control Limit $= 0.0524 + 3 \times 0.0223 = 0.1193$
in control

**18-35.** The appropriate control chart for monitoring this process is a $c$-chart.
The 3-sigma upper control limit is $23.00 + (3 \times 4.7958) = 37.3875$.
The 3-sigma lower control limit is $23.00 - (3 \times 4.7958) = 8.6125$.
Note that sample number 5 with 38 defects is above the upper control limit.

**18-37. a.** $x$-bar chart: CL $= 0.7499$
UCL $= 0.7499 + (0.577)(0.0115) = 0.7565$
LCL $= 0.7499 - (0.577)(0.0115) = 0.7433$
$R$-chart: CL $= 0.0115$
UCL $= (0.0115)(2.114) = 0.0243$
LCL $= (0.0115)(0) = 0$

**b.** It now appears that the process is out of control.

# Glossary

**Adjusted *R*-squared** A measure of the percentage of explained variation in the dependent variable in a multiple regression model that takes into account the relationship between the sample size and the number of independent variables in the regression model.

**Aggregate Price Index** An index that is used to measure the rate of change from a base period for a group of two or more items.

**All-Inclusive Classes** A set of classes that contains all the possible data values.

**Alternative Hypothesis** The hypothesis that includes all population values not included in the null hypothesis. The alternative hypothesis will be selected only if there is strong enough sample evidence to support it. The alternative hypothesis is deemed to be true if the null hypothesis is rejected.

**Arithmetic Average or Mean** The sum of all values divided by the number of values.

**Autocorrelation** Correlation of the error terms (residuals) occurs when the residuals at points in time are related.

**Balanced Design** An experiment has a balanced design if the factor levels have equal sample sizes.

**Bar Chart** A graphical representation of a categorical data set in which a rectangle or bar is drawn over each category or class. The length or height of each bar represents the frequency or percentage of observations or some other measure associated with the category. The bars may be vertical or horizontal. The bars may all be the same color or they may be different colors depicting different categories. Additionally, multiple variables can be graphed on the same bar chart.

**Base Period Index** The time-series value to which all other values in the time series are compared. The index number for the base period is defined as 100.

**Between-Sample Variation** Dispersion among the factor sample means is called the *between-sample variation*.

**Bias** An effect which alters a statistical result by systematically distorting it; different from a random error which may distort on any one occasion but balances out on the average.

**Binomial Probability Distribution Characteristics** A distribution that gives the probability of $x$ successes in $n$ trials in a process that meets the following conditions:

1. A trial has only two possible outcomes: a success or a failure.
2. There is a fixed number, $n$, of identical trials.
3. The trials of the experiment are independent of each other. This means that if one outcome is a success, this does not influence the chance of another outcome being a success.
4. The process must be consistent in generating successes and failures. That is, the probability, $p$, associated with a success remains constant from trial to trial.
5. If $p$ represents the probability of a success, then $1 - p = q$ is the probability of a failure.

**Box and Whisker Plot** A graph that is composed of two parts: a box and the whiskers. The box has a width that ranges from the first quartile ($Q_1$) to the third quartile ($Q_3$). A vertical line through the box is placed at the median. Limits are located at a value that is 1.5 times the difference between $Q_1$ and $Q_3$ below $Q_1$ and above $Q_3$. The whiskers extend to the left to the lowest value within the limits and to the right to the highest value within the limits.

**Business Statistics** A collection of procedures and techniques that are used to convert data into meaningful information in a business environment.

**Census** An enumeration of the entire set of measurements taken from the whole population.

**Central Limit Theorem** For simple random samples of $n$ observations taken from a population with mean $\mu$ and standard deviation $\sigma$, regardless of the population's distribution, provided the sample size is sufficiently large, the distribution of the sample means, $\bar{x}$, will be approximately normal with a mean equal to the population mean ($\mu_{\bar{x}} = \mu_x$) and a standard deviation equal to the population standard deviation divided by the square root of the sample size $\sigma_{\bar{x}} = \sigma / \sqrt{n}$. The larger the sample size, the better the approximation to the normal distribution.

**Class Boundaries** The upper and lower values of each class.

**Class Width** The distance between the lowest possible value and the highest possible value for a frequency class.

**Classical Probability Assessment** The method of determining probability based on the ratio of the number of ways an outcome or event of interest can occur to the number of ways *any* outcome or event can occur when the individual outcomes are equally likely.

**Closed-End Questions** Questions that require the respondent to select from a short list of defined choices.

**Cluster Sampling** A method by which the population is divided into groups, or clusters, that are each intended to be mini-populations. A simple random sample of $m$ clusters is selected. The items chosen from a cluster can be selected using any probability sampling technique.

**Coefficient of Determination** The portion of the total variation in the dependent variable that is explained by its relationship with the independent variable. The coefficient of determination is also called *R*-squared and is denoted as $R^2$.

**Coefficient of Partial Determination** The measure of the marginal contribution of each independent variable, given that other independent variables are in the model.

**Coefficient of Variation** The ratio of the standard deviation to the mean expressed as a percentage. The coefficient of variation is used to measure variation relative to the mean.

**Complement** The complement of an event $E$ is the collection of all possible outcomes not contained in event $E$.

**Completely Randomized Design** An experiment is completely randomized if it consists of the independent random selection of observations representing each level of one factor.

**Composite Model** The model that contains both the basic terms and the interaction terms.

**Conditional Probability** The probability that an event will occur *given* that some other event has already happened.

**Confidence Interval** An interval developed from sample values such that if all possible intervals of a given width were constructed, a percentage of these intervals, known as the confidence level, would include the true population parameter.

**Confidence Level** The percentage of all possible confidence intervals that will contain the true population parameter.

**Consistent Estimator** An unbiased estimator is said to be a consistent estimator if the difference between the estimator and the parameter tends to become smaller as the sample size becomes larger.

**Contingency Table** A table used to classify sample observations according to two or more identifiable characteristics. It is also called a *crosstabulation table*.

**Continuous Data** Data whose possible values are uncountable and which may assume any value in an interval.

**Continuous Random Variables** Random variables that can assume an uncountably infinite number of values.

**Convenience Sampling** A sampling technique that selects the items from the population based on accessibility and ease of selection.

**Correlation Coefficient** A quantitative measure of the strength of the linear relationship between two variables. The correlation ranges from $-1.0$ to $+1.0$. A correlation of $\pm 1.0$ indicates a perfect linear relationship, whereas a correlation of 0 indicates no linear relationship.

**Correlation Matrix** A table showing the pairwise correlations between all variables (dependent and independent).

**Critical Value** The value corresponding to a significance level that determines those test statistics that lead to rejecting the null hypothesis and those that lead to a decision not to reject the null hypothesis.

**Cross-Sectional Data** A set of data values observed at a fixed point in time.

**Cumulative Frequency Distribution** A summary of a set of data that displays the number of observations with values less than or equal to the upper limit of each of its classes.

**Cumulative Relative Frequency Distribution** A summary of a set of data that displays the proportion of observations with values less than or equal to the upper limit of each of its classes.

**Cyclical Component** A wavelike pattern within the time series that repeats itself throughout the time series and has a recurrence period of more than one year.

**Data Array** Data that have been arranged in numerical order.

**Degrees of Freedom** The number of independent data values available to estimate the population's standard deviation. If $k$ parameters must be estimated before the population's standard deviation can be calculated from a sample of size $n$, the degrees of freedom are equal to $n - k$.

**Demographic Questions** Questions relating to the respondents' characteristics, backgrounds, and attributes.

**Dependent Events** Two events are dependent if the occurrence of one event impacts the probability of the other event occurring.

**Dependent Variable** A variable whose values are thought to be a function of, or dependent on, the values of another variable called the *independent variable*. On a scatter plot, the dependent variable is placed on the $y$ axis and is often called the response variable.

**Discrete Data** Data that can take on a countable number of possible values.

**Discrete Random Variable** A random variable that can only assume a finite number of values or an infinite sequence of values such as $0, 1, 2. \ldots$

**Dummy Variable** A variable that is assigned a value equal to either 0 or 1, depending on whether the observation possesses a given characteristic.

**Empirical Rule** If the data distribution is bell-shaped, then the interval

$\mu \pm 1\sigma$ contains approximately 68% of the values

$\mu \pm 2\sigma$ contains approximately 95% of the values

$\mu \pm 3\sigma$ contains virtually all of the data values

**Equal-Width Classes** The distance between the lowest possible value and the highest possible value in each class is equal for all classes.

**Event** A collection of experimental outcomes.

**Expected Value** The mean of a probability distribution. The average value when the experiment that generates values for the random variable is repeated over the long run.

**Experiment** A process that produces a single outcome whose result cannot be predicted with certainty.

**Experimental Design** A plan for performing an experiment in which the variable of interest is defined. One or more factors are identified to be manipulated, changed, or observed so that the impact (or influence) on the variable of interest can be measured or observed.

**Experiment-Wide Error Rate** The proportion of experiments in which at least one of the set of confidence intervals constructed does not contain the true value of the population parameter being estimated.

**Exponential Smoothing** A time-series and forecasting technique that produces an exponentially weighted moving average in which each smoothing calculation or forecast is dependent on all previous observed values.

**External Validity** A characteristic of an experiment whose results can be generalized beyond the test environment so that the outcomes can be replicated when the experiment is repeated.

**Factor** A quantity under examination in an experiment as a possible cause of variation in the response variable.

**Forecasting Horizon** The number of future periods covered by a forecast. It is sometimes referred to as *forecast lead time*.

**Forecasting Interval** The frequency with which new forecasts are prepared.

**Forecasting Period** The unit of time for which forecasts are to be made.

**Frequency Distribution** A summary of a set of data that displays the number of observations in each of the distribution's distinct categories or classes.

**Frequency Histogram** A graph of a frequency distribution with the horizontal axis showing the classes, the vertical axis showing the frequency count, and (for equal class widths) the rectangles having a height equal to the frequency in each class.

**Hypergeometric Distribution** The hypergeometric distribution is formed by the ratio of the number of ways an event of interest can occur over the total number of ways any event can occur.

**Independent Events** Two events are independent if the occurrence of one event in no way influences the probability of the occurrence of the other event.

**Independent Samples** Samples selected from two or more populations in such a way that the occurrence of values in one sample has no influence on the probability of the occurrence of values in the other sample(s).

**Independent Variable** A variable whose values are thought to impact the values of the *dependent variable*. The independent variable, or explanatory variable, is often within the direct control of the decision maker. On a scatter plot, the independent variable, or explanatory variable, is graphed on the x axis.

**Interaction** The case in which one independent variable (such as $x_2$) affects the relationship between another independent variable ($x_1$) and a dependent variable ($y$).

**Internal Validity** A characteristic of an experiment in which data are collected in such a way as to eliminate the effects of variables within the experimental environment that are not of interest to the researcher.

**Interquartile Range** The interquartile range is a measure of variation that is determined by computing the difference between the third and first quartiles.

**Least Squares Criterion** The criterion for determining a regression line that minimizes the sum of squared prediction errors.

**Left-Skewed Data** A data distribution is left skewed if the mean for the data is smaller than the median.

**Levels** The categories, measurements, or strata of a factor of interest in the current experiment.

**Line Chart** A two-dimensional chart showing time on the horizontal axis and the variable of interest on the vertical axis.

**Linear Trend** A long-term increase or decrease in a time series in which the rate of change is relatively constant.

**Margin of Error** The amount that is added and subtracted to the point estimate to determine the endpoints of the confidence interval. Also, a measure of how close we expect the point estimate to be to the population parameter with the specified level of confidence.

**Mean** A numerical measure of the center of a set of quantitative measures computed by dividing the sum of the values by the number of values in the data.

**Median** The median is a center value that divides a data array into two halves. We use $\tilde{\mu}$ to denote the population median and $M_d$ to denote the sample median.

**Mode** The mode is the value in a data set that occurs most frequently.

**Model** A representation of an actual system using either a physical or a mathematical portrayal.

**Model Diagnosis** The process of determining how well a model fits past data and how well the model's assumptions appear to be satisfied.

**Model Fitting** The process of estimating the specified model's parameters to achieve an adequate fit of the historical data.

**Model Specification** The process of selecting the forecasting technique to be used in a particular situation.

**Moving Average** The successive averages of $n$ consecutive values in a time series.

**Multicollinearity** A high correlation between two independent variables such that the two variables contribute redundant information to the model. When highly correlated independent variables are included in the regression model, they can adversely affect the regression results.

**Multiple Coefficient of Determination** The proportion of the total variation of the dependent variable in a multiple regression model that is explained by its relationship to the independent variables. It is, as is the case in the simple linear model, called $R$-squared and is denoted as $R^2$.

**Mutually Exclusive Classes** Classes that do not overlap so that a data value can be placed in only one class.

**Mutually Exclusive Events** Two events are mutually exclusive if the occurrence of one event precludes the occurrence of the other event.

**Nonstatistical Sampling Techniques** Those methods of selecting samples using convenience, judgment, or other nonchance processes.

**Normal Distribution** The normal distribution is a bell-shaped distribution with the following properties:

1. It is *unimodal*; that is, the normal distribution peaks at a single value.
2. It is *symmetrical*; this means that the two areas under the curve between the mean and any two points equidistant on either side of the mean are identical. One side of the distribution is the mirror image of the other side.
3. The mean, median, and mode are equal.
4. The normal approaches the horizontal axis on either side of the mean toward plus and minus infinity ($\infty$). In more formal terms, the normal distribution is *asymptotic* to the x axis.
5. The amount of variation in the random variable determines the height and spread of the normal distribution.

**Null Hypothesis** The statement about the population parameter that will be assumed to be true during the conduct of the hypothesis test. The null hypothesis will be rejected only if the sample data provide substantial contradictory evidence.

**Ogive** The graphical representation of the cumulative relative frequency. A line is connected to points plotted above the upper limit of each class at a height corresponding to the cumulative relative frequency.

**One-Tailed Test** A hypothesis test in which the entire rejection region is located in one tail of the sampling distribution. In a one-tailed test, the entire alpha level is located in one tail of the distribution.

**One-Way Analysis of Variance** An analysis of variance design in which independent samples are obtained from two or more levels of a single factor for the purpose of testing whether the levels have equal means.

**Open-End Questions** Questions that allow respondents the freedom to respond with any value, words, or statements of their own choosing.

**Paired Samples** Samples that are selected in such a way that values in one sample are matched with the values in the second sample for the purpose of controlling for extraneous factors. Another term for paired samples is *dependent samples*.

**Parameter** A measure computed from the entire population. As long as the population does not change, the value of the parameter will not change.

**Pareto Principle** 80% of the problems come from 20% of the causes.

**Percentiles** The $p$th percentile in a data array is a value that divides the data set into two parts. The lower segment contains at least $p\%$ and the upper segment contains at least $(100 - p)\%$ of the data. The 50th percentile is the median.

**Pie Chart** A graph in the shape of a circle. The circle is divided into "slices" corresponding to the categories or classes to be displayed. The size of each slice is proportional to the magnitude of the displayed variable associated with each category or class.

**Pilot Sample** A sample taken from the population of interest of a size smaller than the anticipated sample size that is used to provide an estimate for the population standard deviation.

**Point Estimate** A single statistic, determined from a sample, that is used to estimate the corresponding population parameter.

**Population Mean** The average for all values in the population computed by dividing the sum of all values by the population size.

**Population Proportion** The fraction of values in a population that have a specific attribute.

**Population** The set of all objects or individuals of interest or the measurements obtained from all objects or individuals of interest.

**Power** The probability that the hypothesis test will correctly reject the null hypothesis when the null hypothesis is false.

**Power Curve** A graph showing the probability that the hypothesis test will correctly reject a false null hypothesis for a range of possible "true" values for the population parameter.

**Probability** The chance that a particular event will occur. The probability value will be in the range 0 to 1. A value of 0 means the event will not occur. A probability of 1 means the event will occur. Anything between 0 and 1 reflects the uncertainty

of the event occurring. The definition given is for a countable number of events.

*p*-**Value** The probability (assuming the null hypothesis is true) of obtaining a test statistic at least as extreme as the test statistic we calculated from the sample. The *p*-value is also known as the *observed significance level*.

**Qualitative Data** Data whose measurement scale is inherently categorical.

**Quantitative Data** Measurements whose values are inherently numerical.

**Quartiles** Quartiles in a data array are those values that divide the data set into four equal-sized groups. The median corresponds to the second quartile.

**Random Component** Changes in time-series data that are unpredictable and cannot be associated with a trend, seasonal, or cyclical component.

**Random Variable** A variable that takes on different numerical values based on chance.

**Range** The range is a measure of variation that is computed by finding the difference between the maximum and minimum values in a data set.

**Regression Hyperplane** The multiple regression equivalent of the simple regression line. The plane typically has a different slope for each independent variable.

**Regression Slope Coefficient** The average change in the dependent variable for a unit change in the independent variable. The slope coefficient may be positive or negative, depending on the relationship between the two variables.

**Relative Frequency** The proportion of total observations that are in a given category. Relative frequency is computed by dividing the frequency in a category by the total number of observations. The relative frequencies can be converted to percentages by multiplying by 100.

**Relative Frequency Assessment** The method that defines probability as the number of times an event occurs divided by the total number of times an experiment is performed in a large number of trials.

**Research Hypothesis** The hypothesis the decision maker attempts to demonstrate to be true. Because this is the hypothesis deemed to be the most important to the decision maker, it will be declared true only if the sample data strongly indicates that it is true.

**Residual** The difference between the actual value of the dependent variable and the value predicted by the regression model.

**Right-Skewed Data** A data distribution is right skewed if the mean for the data is larger than the median.

**Sample** A subset of the population.

**Sample Mean** The average for all values in the sample computed by dividing the sum of all sample values by the sample size.

**Sample Proportion** The fraction of items in a sample that have the attribute of interest.

**Sample Space** The collection of all outcomes that can result from a selection, decision, or experiment.

**Sampling Distribution** The distribution of all possible values of a statistic for a given sample size that has been randomly selected from a population.

**Sampling Error** The difference between a measure computed from a sample (a statistic) and the corresponding measure computed from the population (a parameter).

**Scatter Diagram, or Scatter Plot** A two-dimensional graph of plotted points in which the vertical axis represents values of one quantitative variable and the horizontal axis represents values of the other quantitative variable. Each plotted point has coordinates whose values are obtained from the respective variables.

**Scatter Plot** A two-dimensional plot showing the values for the joint occurrence of two quantitative variables. The scatter plot may be used to graphically represent the relationship between two variables. It is also known as a scatter diagram.

**Seasonal Component** A wavelike pattern that is repeated throughout a time series and has a recurrence period of at most one year.

**Seasonal Index** A number used to quantify the effect of seasonality in time-series data.

**Seasonally Unadjusted Forecast** A forecast made for seasonal data that does not include an adjustment for the seasonal component in the time series.

**Significance Level** The maximum allowable probability of committing a Type I statistical error. The probability is denoted by the symbol $\alpha$.

**Simple Linear Regression** The method of regression analysis in which a single independent variable is used to predict the dependent variable.

**Simple Random Sample** A sample selected in such a manner that each possible sample of a given size has an equal chance of being selected.

**Simple Random Sampling** A method of selecting items from a population such that every possible sample of a specified size has an equal chance of being selected.

**Skewed Data** Data sets that are not symmetric. For skewed data, the mean will be larger or smaller than the median.

**Standard Deviation** The standard deviation is the positive square root of the variance.

**Standard Error** A value that measures the spread of the sample means around the population mean. The standard error is reduced when the sample size is increased.

**Standard Normal Distribution** A normal distribution that has a mean = 0.0 and a standard deviation = 1.0. The horizontal axis is scaled in $z$-values that measure the number of standard deviations a point is from the mean. Values above the mean have positive $z$-values. Values below the mean have negative $z$-values.

**Standardized Data Values** The number of standard deviations a value is from the mean. Standardized data values are sometimes referred to as $z$ scores.

**Statistic** A measure computed from a sample that has been selected from a population. The value of the statistic will depend on which sample is selected.

**Statistical Inference Procedures** Procedures that allow a decision maker to reach a conclusion about a set of data based on a subset of that data.

**Statistical Sampling Techniques** Those sampling methods that use selection techniques based on chance selection.

**Stratified Random Sampling** A statistical sampling method in which the population is divided into subgroups called *strata* so that each population item belongs to only one stratum. The objective is to form strata such that the population values of interest within each stratum are as much alike as possible. Sample items are selected from each stratum using the simple random sampling method.

**Structured Interview** Interviews in which the questions are scripted.

**Student's *t*-Distributions** A family of distributions that is bell-shaped and symmetric like the standard normal distribution but with greater area in the tails. Each distribution in the *t*-family is defined by its degrees of freedom. As the degrees of freedom increase, the *t*-distribution approaches the normal distribution.

**Subjective Probability Assessment** The method that defines probability of an event as reflecting a decision maker's state of mind regarding the chances that the particular event will occur.

**Symmetric Data** Data sets whose values are evenly spread around the center. For symmetric data, the mean and median are equal.

**Systematic Random Sampling** A statistical sampling technique that involves selecting every $k$th item in the population after a randomly selected starting point between 1 and $k$. The value of $k$ is determined as the ratio of the population size over the desired sample size.

**Tchebysheff's Theorem** Regardless of how data are distributed, *at least* $(1-1/k^2)$ of the values will fall within $k$ standard deviations of the mean. For example:

At least $\left(1 - \dfrac{1}{1^2}\right) = 0 = 0\%$ of the values will fall within $k = 1$ standard deviation of the mean.

At least $\left(1 - \dfrac{1}{2^2}\right) = \dfrac{3}{4} = 75\%$ of the values will lie within $k = 2$ standard deviations of the mean.

At least $\left(1 - \dfrac{1}{3^2}\right) = \dfrac{8}{9} = 89\%$ of the values will lie within $k = 3$ standard deviations of the mean.

**Test Statistic** A function of the sampled observations that provides a basis for testing a statistical hypothesis.

**Time-Series Data** A set of consecutive data values observed at successive points in time.

**Total Quality Management** A journey to excellence in which everyone in the organization is focused on continuous process improvement directed toward increased customer satisfaction.

**Total Variation** The aggregate dispersion of the individual data values across the various factor levels is called the *total variation* in the data.

**Two-Tailed Test** A hypothesis test in which the entire rejection region is split into the two tails of the sampling distribution. In a two-tailed test, the alpha level is split evenly between the two tails.

**Type I Error** *Rejecting* the null hypothesis when it is, in fact, true.

**Type II Error** *Failing to reject* the null hypothesis when it is, in fact, false.

**Unbiased Estimator** A characteristic of certain statistics in which the average of all possible values of the sample statistic equals a parameter, no matter the value of the parameter.

**Unstructured Interview** Interviews that begin with one or more broadly stated questions, with further questions being based on the responses.

**Variance** The population variance is the average of the squared distances of the data values from the mean.

**Variance Inflation Factor** A measure of how much the variance of an estimated regression coefficient increases if the independent variables are correlated. A *VIF* equal to 1.0 for a given independent variable indicates that this independent variable is not correlated with the remaining independent variables in the model. The greater the multicollinearity, the larger the *VIF*.

**Variation** A set of data exhibits variation if all the data are not the same value.

**Weighted Mean** The mean value of data values that have been weighted according to their relative importance.

**Within-Sample Variation** The dispersion that exists among the data values within a particular factor level is called the *within-sample variation*.

# Index

# Photo Credits